JURAN'S
QUALITY CONTROL
HANDBOOK

Other McGraw-Hill Reference Books of Interest

Handbooks

Avallone and Baumeister · MARKS' STANDARD HANDBOOK FOR MECHANICAL ENGINEERS

Brady and Clauser · MATERIALS HANDBOOK

Carrubba and Gordon · PRODUCT ASSURANCE PRINCIPLES

Considine · PROCESS INSTRUMENTS AND CONTROLS HANDBOOK

Crosby · QUALITY IS FREE

Crosby · QUALITY WITHOUT TEARS

Feigenbaum · TOTAL QUALITY CONTROL

Fink and Beaty · STANDARD HANDBOOK FOR ELECTRICAL ENGINEERS

Fink and Christiansen · ELECTRONICS ENGINEER'S HANDBOOK

Gerelle and Stark · INTEGRATED MANUFACTURING

Harrington · THE IMPROVEMENT PROCESS

Higgins and Morrow · MAINTENANCE ENGINEERING HANDBOOK

Hradesky · PRODUCTIVITY AND QUALITY IMPROVEMENT

Ireson and Coombs · HANDBOOK OF RELIABILITY ENGINEERING AND MANAGEMENT

Juran · MANAGERIAL BREAKTHROUGH

Juran and Gryna · QUALITY PLANNING AND ANALYSIS

Lubben · JUST-IN-TIME MANUFACTURING

Maynard · INDUSTRIAL ENGINEERING HANDBOOK

Ott · PROCESS QUALITY CONTROL

Perry and Green · PERRY'S CHEMICAL ENGINEERS' HANDBOOK

Ross · TAGUCHI TECHNIQUES FOR QUALITY ENGINEERING

Shinskey · PROCESS CONTROL SYSTEMS

Taylor · QUALITY CONTROL SYSTEMS

Woodson · HANDBOOK OF HUMAN FACTORS ENGINEERING DATA

Encyclopedias

CONCISE ENCYCLOPEDIA OR SCIENCE AND TECHNOLOGY
ENCYCLOPEDIA OF ELECTRONICS AND COMPUTERS
ENCYCLOPEDIA OF ENERGY
ENCYCLOPEDIA OF ENGINEERING
ENCYCLOPEDIA OF PHYSICS

Dictionaries

DICTIONARY OF SCIENTIFIC AND TECHNICAL TERMS
DICTIONARY OF MECHANICAL AND DESIGN ENGINEERING
DICTIONARY OF ELECTRONICS AND COMPUTER TECHNOLOGY
DICTIONARY OF ENGINEERING

For more information about other McGraw-Hill materials, call 1–800–2–MCGRAW in the United States. In other countries, call your nearest McGraw-Hill office.

JURAN'S QUALITY CONTROL HANDBOOK

J. M. Juran Editor-in-Chief
Founder and Chairman Emeritus, Juran Institute, Inc.
Wilton, Connecticut

Frank M. Gryna Associate Editor
Vice President, Juran Institute, Inc.
Wilton, Connecticut
Distinguished Professor of Industrial Engineering
Emeritus, Bradley University

FOURTH EDITION

McGRAW-HILL BOOK COMPANY
New York   St. Louis   San Francisco   Auckland   Bogotá
Hamburg   London   Madrid   Mexico   Milan
Montreal   New Delhi   Panama
Paris   São Paulo   Singapore
Sydney   Tokyo   Toronto

Library of Congress Cataloging-in-Publication Data

Juran's quality control handbook / J. M. Juran, editor-in-chief, Frank
  M. Gryna, associate editor. — 4th ed.
        p.   cm.
      Rev. ed. of: Quality control handbook. 3rd ed. 1974.
      Includes bibliographies and indexes.
      ISBN 0-07-033176-6
        1. Quality control—Handbooks, manuals, etc.   I. Juran, J. M.
  (Joseph M.), 1904-   . II. Gryna, Frank M.   III. Quality control
  handbook.   IV. Title: Quality control handbook.
  TS156.J87   1988
  658.5′62—dc19
                                                            88-4002
                                                            CIP

1234567890   DOC/DOC   89321098

ISBN 0-07-033176-6

*The editors for this book were Betty Sun and Lester Strong and the
production supervisor was Richard Ausburn. It was set in Times Roman
by University Graphics, Inc.*

Printed and bound by R. R. Donnelley & Sons Company.

*For more information about other McGraw-Hill materials,
call 1–800–2–MCGRAW in the United States. In other
countries, call your nearest McGraw-Hill office.*

CONTENTS

CONTENTS

CONTRIBUTORS

Dr. Edward M. Baker
*Director, Total Quality Planning,
Consulting, and Statistical Methods, Ford
Motor Company, World Headquarters,
Dearborn, MI*
SECTION 10, MANAGING HUMAN
PERFORMANCE

E. Harvey Barnett
*Research Associate, Statistics, Corning
Glass Works Corning, NY*
SECTION 26, DESIGN AND ANALYSIS OF
EXPERIMENTS

Richard S. Bingham, Jr.
Consultant, Wisconsin Rapids, WI
SECTION 28, PROCESS INDUSTRIES

Dr. Edward J. Dudewicz
*Professor, Department of Mathematics, and
Chairman, University Statistical Council,
Syracuse University, Syracuse, NY*
SECTION 23, BASIC STATISTICAL METHODS

Professor F. Egermayer, RN Dr., Dr. Sc.
*Department of Industrial Engineering,
Faculty of Mechanical Engineering, Czech
Technical College, Prague, Czechoslovakia*
SECTION 35H, QUALITY IN SOCIALIST
COUNTRIES

J. Douglas Ekings
*Manager, Customer Satisfaction, Xerox
Corporation, Stamford, CT*
SECTION 30, ASSEMBLY INDUSTRIES

John W. Enell, Eng.Sc.D.
*Vice President, Research, Juran Institute,
Inc., Wilton, CT*
SECTION 33, SERVICE INDUSTRIES

Dr. Patrick Fortune
*President, Parenteral Products Division,
Baxter Healthcare Corporation, Deerfield,
IL*
SECTION 14, SOFTWARE DEVELOPMENT

A. Blanton Godfrey, Ph.D.
*Chairman and CEO, Juran Institute, Inc.,
Wilton, CT*
SECTION 29, ELECTRONIC COMPONENTS
INDUSTRIES

Jean-Marie Gogue
President, Mast, Inc., Paris, France
SECTION 35C, QUALITY IN FRANCE

Dr. Frank M. Gryna
*Vice President, Juran Institute, Inc.,
Wilton, CT*
SECTION 4, QUALITY COSTS; SECTION 9,
QUALITY ASSURANCE; SECTION 11, TRAINING
FOR QUALITY; SECTION 12, FIELD
INTELLIGENCE; SECTION 13, PRODUCT
DEVELOPMENT; SECTION 15, SUPPLIER
RELATIONS; SECTION 16, MANUFACTURING
PLANNING; SECTION 17, PRODUCTION;
SECTION 19, MARKETING; SECTION 20,
CUSTOMER SERVICE; SECTION 21,
ADMINISTRATIVE AND SUPPORT OPERATIONS;
SECTION 22, QUALITY IMPROVEMENT

Dr. J. Stuart Hunter
Consultant, Princeton, NJ
SECTION 26, DESIGN AND ANALYSIS OF
EXPERIMENTS

William G. Hunter
*Director, Center for Quality and
Productivity Improvement; Professor,
Statistics and Engineering, University of
Wisconsin, Madison, WI*
SECTION 26, DESIGN AND ANALYSIS OF
EXPERIMENTS

Dr. J. M. Juran
*Founder and Chairman Emeritus, Juran
Institute, Inc., Wilton, CT*
SECTION 1, HOW TO USE THE HANDBOOK;
SECTION 2, QUALITY FUNCTION; SECTION 3,
QUALITY AND INCOME; SECTION 5, QUALITY
POLICIES AND OBJECTIVES; SECTION 6,
COMPANYWIDE PLANNING FOR QUALITY;
SECTION 7, ORGANIZATION FOR QUALITY;
SECTION 8, UPPER MANAGEMENT AND
QUALITY; SECTION 34, QUALITY AND
SOCIETY; SECTION 35A, QUALITY AND THE
NATIONAL CULTURE; SECTION 35G, QUALITY
IN THE UNITED STATES OF AMERICA

Dr. Robert Kerwin
*Technology Management Director, AT&T,
Berkeley Heights, NJ*
SECTION 29, ELECTRONIC COMPONENTS
INDUSTRIES

Truman L. Koehler
Vice President, Sandoz Corporation, East Hanover, NJ
SECTION 26, DESIGN AND ANALYSIS OF EXPERIMENTS

Dr. Yoshio Kondo
Professor Emeritus, Kyoto University, Kyoto, Japan
SECTION 35F, QUALITY IN JAPAN

Mary G. Natrella
Guest Worker, National Bureau of Standards, Gaithersburg, MD
SECTION 26, DESIGN AND ANALYSIS OF EXPERIMENTS

Fredric I. Orkin
Vice President, General Manager, Multiplex Systems Division of Baxter Healthcare Corporation, Round Lake, IL
SECTION 27, COMPUTERS AND QUALITY

Dr. Lennart Sandholm
Management Consultant, Bjorklund and Sandholm, Djursholm, Sweden
SECTION 35B, QUALITY IN DEVELOPING COUNTRIES

Dr. Edward G. Schilling
Paul A. Miller Distinguished Professor and Chairman of the Graduate Statistics Department, Rochester Institute of Technology Center for Quality and Applied Statistics, Rochester, NY
SECTION 25, ACCEPTANCE SAMPLING

Dipl.-Ing. Ernst Schlötel
Lecturer & Consultant in Quality Matters, Bad Homburg, Federal Republic of Germany
SECTION 35D, QUALITY IN THE FEDERAL REPUBLIC OF GERMANY

Leonard A. Seder
Leonard A. Seder and Associates, Lexington, MA
SECTION 32, JOB SHOP INDUSTRIES

Dorian Shainin, CMC
Shainin Consultants, Inc., Manchester, CT
SECTION 24, STATISTICAL PROCESS CONTROL

Peter D. Shainin, PE
Shainin Consultants, Inc., Burlington, WA
SECTION 24, STATISTICAL PROCESS CONTROL

Dan J. Sommers
Manager, New Product Quality, General Electric Company, Cleveland, OH
SECTION 25, ACCEPTANCE SAMPLING

Wilfred R. Thoday, Ph.D.
Vice President, Institute of Quality Assurance, London, England
SECTION 35E, QUALITY IN GREAT BRITAIN

H. Dean Voegtlen
Consultant, Inglewood, CA, Formerly Director, Product Cost Effectiveness, Hughes Aircraft Company
SECTION 31, COMPLEX INDUSTRIES

Clyde H. Walden, Ph.D.
Consultant, Piedmont, CA
SECTION 28, PROCESS INDUSTRIES

Joseph J. Zeccardi
Vice President, Customer Service Logistics, Unisys Corporation, Blue Bell, PA
SECTION 18, INSPECTION AND TEST

Charles D. Zimmerman, III
Vice President, Human Resources, United States Fidelity & Guaranty Co., Baltimore, MD
SECTION 33, SERVICE INDUSTRIES

PREFACE TO THE FOURTH EDITION

Over four decades have passed since *Quality Control Handbook* (now *Juran's Quality Control Handbook*) was first in gestation. (The contract to produce it was signed in 1945; the First Edition was published in 1951.) In the intervening years it has attained the status of the leading international reference work on the subject. Including its various translations, the first three editions have exceeded 350,000 copies, cumulatively.

A parallel development has been a remarkable growth in the importance of quality to society generally. Much of this growth is due to the phenomenon of "Life behind the Quality Dikes." The industrial society provides its citizenry with the marvelous benefits of technology. However it also makes the continuity of that life style depend absolutely on the quality of the goods and services which are the base of an industrial society.

In addition there has been a growth of competition in quality. This has become especially intense on the international level. Quality is now a critical element in international trade, in defense capability, in human safety and health, in maintaining the environment.

Industrial companies have been responding to this growth in importance of the quality function. This response is evident in a number of ways:

1. The scope of "quality" has increasingly been broadened to include:

   Manufacturing support activities

   Business processes

   The needs of internal customers

2. Planning for quality has increasingly been evolving into a formalized, structured approach involving extensive internal participation as well as joint planning with clients and suppliers.

3. Upper managers are increasingly taking charge of managing for quality. This trend is evident from such movements as:

   Evolution of the concept of companywide quality management (total quality control, etc.)

   Creation of high-level quality councils

   Enlargement of the business plan to include annual quality improvement

   Establishment of corporate quality goals, measures of performance, and upper management reviews

4. Training in managing for quality has increasingly been extended into all functions, including general management.

In addition various organs of society—government, academia, professional societies, etc.—have increasingly become involved with managing for quality in ways such as:

   Government sponsorship of national quality motivation programs

   Creation of national awards for quality

Promulgation of laws to protect safety, health, and the environment

Proliferation of training courses and consultancies oriented to various aspects of managing for quality

The Fourth Edition has recognized the emerging massive changes through extensive revisions in structure as well as through updating. A major change has been the construction of a new conceptual approach to managing for quality—the Trilogy of processes through which quality is managed: quality planning; quality control; quality improvement. This Trilogy has established itself as a tested framework on which to build a cohesive, unified approach to managing for quality.

The organizational structure of the Third Edition met with a distinctly favorable reception from users. In consequence I have retained much of that structure. It consists mainly of:

1. A series of 12 sections setting out the various managerial concepts and tools associated with achieving quality
2. Another series of 10 sections which follow the product through its life cycle
3. Four sections devoted to the statistical tools associated with attaining quality
4. Six sections which exemplify application of concepts, methods, and tools in important industries
5. Nine sections which examine the ways of managing quality in various national cultures

Many of the sections retain the same titles they had in the Third Edition, but the user should not be deceived. No section has escaped extensive revision. It is doubtful that as much as 20 percent of the Third Edition was incorporated into the Fourth Edition.

All this growth and change have enlarged the editorial burdens as well. As a result I am most grateful to those whose collaboration has made this Fourth Edition possible.

Dr. F. M. Gryna has for the third time served as associate editor while enlarging his role as author. He collaborated fully in planning the revision, and he carried the major burden of enlisting the contributing authors and critiquing their outlines and manuscripts. Collectively all this was an extensive undertaking.

Another debt is owed to the authors—managers, educators, and specialists—who took time from full schedules to share their knowledge and experience with their international counterparts. These contributions are the very heart of the handbook. Supporting these authors are the numerous secretaries, staff members, and librarians (as well as family members) who assisted in the exacting preparation of the technical manuscripts. All of us deeply appreciate the dedication behind this essential support.

I am indebted to the Literary Executor of the late Sir Ronald A. Fisher, F.R.S., to Dr. Frank Yates, F.R.S., and to Oliver and Boyd, Edinburgh, for permission to reprint Table III from their book *Statistical Tables for Biological, Agricultural and Medical Research.*

In the planning stages of this edition, the editors were fortunate to receive advice from a number of highly experienced professionals. These included W. Edwards Deming, J. Douglas Ekings, Ralph A. Evans, H. James Harrington, Lloyd S. Nelson, Naomi J. McAfee, Arnold O. Putnam, John S. Ramberg, and Edward A. Reynolds.

Many practitioners contributed examples and advice in specific areas. Particularly helpful were Roger W. Berger, Roger L. Bollenbacher, J. Douglas Ekings, Donald N. Ekvall, Ronald Follett, Richard A. Freund, Derek S. Gryna, Gerald J. Hahn, John A. Keane, James F. Leonard, Dana B. Loson, Joseph M. Mazzeo, David A. McGaughy, Fredric I. Orkin, Joseph J. Pignatiello, Jr., Lawrence J. Schrader, R. M. Smith, Ronald D. Snee, James L. Thresh, Joseph J. Tsiakals, H. DeanVoegtlen, and Harrison M. Wadsworth.

John W. Enell, Al C. Endres, and Harris M. Brokke contributed significantly to the review and editing of manuscripts. In the final preparation of all sections, Randolph Warren provided editorial assistance while acting as liason with the publisher's Production Department.

Our administrative assistants at the Juran Institute, Inc., particularly Judith A. Schalick, Marilyn M. Schmid, and Sharon Davis, were most helpful in preparing the manuscripts and conducting related researches, as well as maintaining correspondence with authors and others. Additional participants included Laura A. Sutherland and Margaret Cutrona at Juran Institute and Willie Luscher and Rita Borwick at Bradley University.

Dr. Gryna continues to be amazed by the support from his wife Dee, and her infinite patience and understanding.

Finally, I acknowledge the moral support provided by my wife of 62 years standing. This Fourth Edition is the only edition for which she did not personally prepare the bulk of the manuscript. As befits a gallant lady, her patience and encouragement have not wavered. I am once more deeply grateful to her.

One last note: Recognizing as we do the important and growing role of women in business and industry, every effort has been made to use gender-neutral language in this book. However, we have retained terms such as "ombudsman," "workmanship," and "craftsmanship," for which no generally agreed-upon gender-neutral equivalents exist; likewise in historical discussions we have not changed the terms "master" and "journeyman," which had technical meanings within the guild systems of the medieval era; and we have not altered terminology used in direct quotations from other sources. In all those instances, the words should be taken in a purely generic sense, intended to apply to women as well as to men.

J. M. JURAN

SECTION 1

HOW TO USE THE HANDBOOK

J. M. Juran

INTRODUCTION

This is a reference book for all who are involved with "fitness for use" of products and services. "All who are involved" includes:

The various departmental functions, e.g., product development, purchasing, manufacture, inspection, sales, customer service, and various support functions

The various levels of management, from top executives through supervisors

The various staff specialties associated with policies, objectives, planning, organizing, and improving and controlling quality

Practitioners in a variety of industries and processes, e.g., chemical, metallurgical, mechanical, electronic, job shop, service, etc.

It is a mistake to assume that the sole purpose of the book is to serve the needs of quality managers and quality specialists. The purpose of the book is to serve the entire quality function, and this includes participation from every major department of the organization.

While there is a great deal of know-how in this book, it takes skill and a bit of determination to learn how to find and make use of it. This first section of the book has therefore been designed to help the reader to find and apply those contents of the handbook which relate to the problem at hand.

USES OF THE HANDBOOK

Practitioners make a wide variety of uses of the *Quality Control Handbook.* A survey conducted as part of the planning for the Fourth Edition showed that usage is dominated by the following principal motives:

1. To study the narrative material as an aid to solving problems
2. To find structured answers in tables, charts, formulas, etc.
3. To review for specific self-training
4. To secure material for the teaching or training of others

Beyond these four most frequent uses, there is a longer list of less frequent uses:

To review for personal briefing prior to attending a meeting

To cross-check one's approach to tackling a problem

As references for instructors and students during training courses

To indoctrinate the boss

To train new employees

To help sell ideas to others, based on (1) the information in the handbook and (2) the authoritative status of the handbook

Usage appears to be more frequent during times of change, e.g., while developing new programs, working on new contracts and projects, reassigning functions, or trying out new ideas.

Irrespective of intended use, the information is very likely there. The problem for the practitioner becomes one of (1) knowing where to find it and (2) adapting the information to his or her specific needs.

ORGANIZATION OF THE HANDBOOK

Knowing "where to find it" starts with understanding how the handbook is structured. The handbook consists of several broad groupings, outlined below, of quality control know-how.

Managing the Quality Function.   This Management Group of handbook sections (i.e., chapters) is devoted to the attainment of quality in *any* industry, product, or process. Some of the sections in this group follow the "management sequence" as applied to the quality function: policy formation, goal setting, planning, organizing, training, etc. Other sections of this Management Group follow the "product progression sequence": new-product development, purchasing, manufacture, test, marketing, customer service, etc. Still other sections deal with broad problems of a coordinating nature, e.g., quality costs and quality improvement. Collectively, the Management Group consists of 33 sections and subsections (Sections 2 through 22, 27, 34 through 35H, and Appendices III and IV), and constitutes about 60 percent of the contents of the handbook.

Statistical Methods.   This Statistical Group shows how to make use of most of the statistical tools which are available for controlling and improving quality. This group is made up of the following:

1. Sections 23 through 26, each of which deals with one or more of these statistical tools
2. The Glossary of Symbols (Appendix I)
3. The supplemental statistical tables and charts (Appendix II)

Collectively, the Statistical Group makes up about 20 percent of the handbook.

Industries.   This Industry Group summarizes how quality is attained and maintained in each of a number of leading industries. These may be product-based (e.g., Assembly Industries) or process-based (e.g., Process Industries). This group (Sections 28 through 32) constitutes about 20 percent of the handbook. The growing service sector is represented by its own section, 33.

HOW TO FIND IT

There are three main roads for locating information in the handbook:

1. Tables of Contents
2. The Index
3. Cross-references

In addition, there are supplemental devices to aid in securing elaboration.

Note that the handbook follows a *dual system of numbering,* consisting of the section number followed by page number, figure number, or table number. For example, page number 16.7 is the seventh page in Section 16. Figure or table number 12.4 is in Section 12, and it is the fourth figure or table in that section.

Tables of Contents.   There is a hierarchy of these. At the top is the list of 42 *section and subsection headings,* each of which describes, in the broadest terms, the contents of that section.

Next there is the *list of contents* that appears on the first page of each section. Each item in any section's list of contents becomes a *major heading* within that section.

Next, under each of these major headings, there may be one or more *minor headings,* each descriptive of its bundle of contents. Some of these bundles may be broken down still further by alphabetic or numeric lists of subtopics.

In a good many cases, it will suffice merely to follow the hierarchy of tables of contents to find the information sought. In many other cases it will not. For such cases, an alternative approach is to use the Index.

Use of the Index.   A great deal of effort has gone into preparing the Index so that, through it, the reader can locate *all* the handbook material bearing on a subject. For example, the topic "self-control" is found in several sections (e.g., 16, Manufacturing Planning; 17, Production, etc.). The Index entry for "self-control" assembles *all* uses of the self-control concept and shows the numbers of the pages on which they may be found.

The fact that information about a single topic is found in more than one section (and even in many sections) gives rise to criticisms of the organization of the handbook, i.e., Why can't all the information on one subject be brought together in one place? The answer is that we require multiple and interconnected uses of knowledge, and hence these multiple appearances cannot be avoided. In fact, what must be done to minimize duplication is to make one and only one exhaustive explanation at some logical place and then to use cross-referencing elsewhere. In a sense, all the information on one subject *is* brought together—in the Index.

Some key words and phrases may be explained in several places in the handbook. However, there is always one passage which constitutes the major explanation or definition. In the Index, the word "defined" is used to identify this major definition, for example, "Evolutionary Operation, defined."

The Index also serves to assemble all case examples or applications under one heading for easy reference. For example, Section 22 deals with the general approach to quality improvement and includes numerous examples of the application of this approach. However, additional examples are found in other sections, notably Sections 21, and 28 through 33. The Index enables the reader to find these additional examples readily, since the page numbers are given.

Cross-References. The handbook makes extensive use of cross-references in the text in order to (1) guide the reader to further information on a subject and (2) avoid duplicate explanations of the same subject matter. The reader should regard these cross-references, wherever they occur, as extensions of the text.

Cross-referencing is to either (1) specific major headings in various sections or (2) specific figure numbers or table numbers. Study of the referenced material will provide further illumination.

A Note on Abbreviations. Abbreviations of names or organizations are usually used only after the full name has previously been spelled out, e.g., American Society for Quality Control (ASQC). In any case, all such abbreviations are listed and defined in the Index.

Main Road and Side Roads. The text of the handbook emphasizes the "main road" of quality control know-how, i.e., the comparatively limited number of usual situations which nevertheless occupy the bulk of the time and attention of practitioners. Beyond the main road are numerous "side roads," i.e., less usual situations which are quite diverse and which require special solutions.

(The term "side road" is not used in any derogatory sense. The practitioner who faces an unusual problem must nevertheless find a solution for it.)

As to these side roads, the handbook text, while not complete, nevertheless points the reader to available solutions. This is done in several ways:

Citations. The handbook cites numerous papers, books, and other bibliographic references. In most cases these citations also indicate the nature of the special contribution made by the work cited in order to help the reader to decide whether to go to the original source for elaboration.

Special Bibliographies. Some sections provide supplemental lists of bibliographical material for further reference. The editors have attempted to restrict the contents of these lists to items which (1) bear directly on the subject matter discussed in the text or (2) are of uncommon interest to the practitioner. A special bibliography in Appendix III lists quality standards and specifications.

Literature Search. Papers, books, and other references cited in the handbook contain further references which can be hunted up for further study. Use can be made of available abstracting and indexing services. A broad abstracting service in the engineering field is Engineering Index, Inc., 345 E. 47 St., New York, NY

10017. A specialized abstracting service in quality control and applied statistics is Executive Sciences Institute, Inc., 1005 Mississippi Ave., Davenport, IA 52803. In addition, various other specialized abstracting services are available on such subjects as reliability, statistical methods, research and development, etc.

In searching the literature, the practitioner is well advised to make use of librarians. To an astonishing degree, library specialists have devised tools for locating literature on any designated subject: special bibliographies, abstracting services, indexes by subject and author, etc. Librarians are trained in the use of these tools, and they maintain an effective communication network among themselves.

Author Contact.   The written book or paper is usually a condensation of the author's knowledge; i.e., what he or she wrote is derived from material which is one or two orders of magnitude more voluminous than the published work. In some cases it is worthwhile to contact the author for further elaboration. Most authors have no objection to being contacted, and some of these contacts lead not only to more information but also to visits and enduring collaboration.

Other Sources.   Resourceful people are able to find still other sources of information relating to the problem at hand. They contact the editors of journals to discover which companies have faced similar problems, so that they may contact these companies. They contact suppliers and customers to learn if competitors have found solutions. They attend meetings—such as courses, seminars, and conferences of professional societies—at which there is discussion of the problem. There is hardly a problem faced by any practitioner which has not already been actively studied by others.

ADAPTING TO USE

In many cases a practitioner is faced with adapting, to a special situation, knowledge derived from a totally different technology, i.e., industry, product, process. Making this transition requires that he or she identify the commonality, i.e., the common principle to which both the special situation and the derived knowledge correspond.

Often the commonality is managerial in nature and is comparatively easy to grasp. For example, the concept of self-control is a management universal and is applicable to any person in the company.

Commonality of a statistical nature is even easier to grasp, since so much information is reduced to formulas which are indifferent to the nature of the technology involved.

Even in technological matters, it is possible to identify commonalities despite great outward differences. For example, concepts such as process capability apply not only to manufacturing processes, but to administrative and support processes as well. (See Section 21 under Process Development.) In like manner, the approaches used to make quality improvements by discovering the causes of defects have been classified into specific categories which exhibit a great deal of commonality despite wide differences in technology. (See Section 22 under Diagnosis.)

In all these situations, the challenge to practitioners is to establish a linkage between their own situations and those from which the know-how was derived. This linkage is established by discovering the commonality which makes them both members of one species.

SECTION 2
THE QUALITY FUNCTION

J. M. Juran

This section is devoted to some fundamental concepts which underlie the subject of quality: what is meant by the word "quality"; how to think about quality, i.e., the organization of the subject. To explain these concepts requires definition of what is meant by the associated key words, e.g., "product," "customer." Those definitions will be provided at the first use of such key words.

"QUALITY" DEFINED

The word quality has multiple meanings. Two of those meanings dominate the use of the word:

1. Quality consists of those product features which meet the needs of customers and thereby provide product satisfaction.
2. Quality consists of freedom from deficiencies.

To explain these dominant meanings it is first necessary to define the key words.

Product.   "Product" is the output of any process. It consists mainly of goods, software, and services. "Goods" are physical things: pencils, color television sets, office buildings. "Software" has more than one meaning. A major meaning is instruction programs for computers. Another major meaning is information generally: reports, plans, instructions, advice, commands. "Service" is work performed for someone else. Entire industries are established to provide services in such forms as central energy, transportation, communication, entertainment, etc.

Product Feature.   A "product feature" is a property which is possessed by a product and which is intended to meet certain customers' needs. Product features may be technological in nature, e.g., fuel consumption of a vehicle, dimension of a mechanical component, viscosity of a chemical, uniformity of the voltage of an electric power supply. Product features may also take other forms, e.g., promptness of delivery, ease of maintenance, courtesy of service.

Hierarchy of Product Features.   Products exist in a sort of hierarchical or pyramidal organization. At the apex is the overall product or system. Below the apex are multiple layers made up of subsystems, components, etc. At each layer the products have features which must be defined by specifications and procedures. In the bottom layer are numerous bits of the whole, e.g., tasks in a procedure, properties of materials or piece parts. For such tasks or properties, the product features consist of elemental definitions, e.g., the temperature of the oven, the diameter of the shaft. Such product features are often referred to as "quality characteristics."

Customer.   A customer is someone who is impacted by the product. Customers may be external or internal.

External Customers.   These are impacted by the product but are not members of the company (or other institution) which produces the product. External customers include clients who buy the product, government regulatory bodies, the public (which may be impacted because of unsafe products or damage to the environment), etc.

Internal Customers.   Within any company there are numerous situations in which departments and persons supply products to each other. The recipients are often called "customers" despite the fact that they are not customers in the dictionary sense, i.e., they are not clients.

Users. Users are customers who carry out positive actions with respect to the product. Users include processors who buy the product as an input to their process, merchants who resell the product, and consumers who carry out the ultimate use of the product.

Customer Needs. All customers have needs to be met, and the product features should be responsive to those needs. This applies to both external and internal customers. In the case of external customers, the response determines product satisfaction, and in consequence, product salability. In the case of internal customers, the response determines the company's competitiveness in productivity, quality, etc., as well as the state of morale among internal departments.

Product Satisfaction. Product features which do respond to customer needs are said to provide "product satisfaction," a state of affairs which is decisive as to salability of the product. In competitive markets there are multiple suppliers of product features. The resulting variation leads to degrees of product satisfaction, and to associated differences in market share for the respective suppliers.

Grade. A popular name for degrees of product satisfaction is "grade," sometimes called "quality of design." Products whose features are perceived as meeting customer needs to a superior degree are called "higher-grade" products. Sometimes these grades are established formally, as in hotel services or cuts of meat.

Conformance to Specification; also, Conformance to Requirements. Some people define quality as consisting of conformance to some standard, e.g., conformance to specifications, procedures, or requirements. Such definitions can be helpful in clarifying the quality responsibilities of workers and supervisors. At those levels the personnel may lack full knowledge of what are the needs of the numerous external and internal customers. Yet these same workers and supervisors need clear definitions of their responsibilities with respect to quality. Such needs can be met through stating the responsibilities in terms of conformance. However, none of these conformance definitions adequately defines the quality responsibility of the company. For the company, the definition should be stated in terms of (1) meeting customer needs, and (2) freedom from deficiencies.

Product Deficiency. The second major definition of quality is "freedom from deficiencies." Product deficiencies take such forms as late deliveries, field failures of goods, errors in invoices, factory scrap or rework, and design changes. Each of such events is the result of some deficiency in a product or process. Each makes trouble for customers.

Product Dissatisfaction. A consequence of product deficiencies is that customers are dissatisfied. External customers express their dissatisfaction in such forms as field complaints, returns, and claims. If the response to these dissatisfactions is inadequate, or if the extent of dissatisfaction is too high, the external customers may stop buying the product. These reactions by external customers impact the supplier through a combination of lower sales, higher costs, fewer on-time deliveries, lower productivity, etc.

 Product deficiencies can also impact internal customers. These internal customers then express their dissatisfaction in the form of internal complaints. If the response is inadequate, or if the level of dissatisfaction is too high, the consequences are a deterioration in the cooperation between departments, mutual blame, poor morale, etc. Such consequences likewise contribute to lower sales, high cost, fewer on-time deliveries, lower productivity, etc.

Product Satisfaction and Product Dissatisfaction Are Not Opposites.   For the most part, the two concepts are unrelated. Product satisfaction has its origin in product features, and is why clients buy the product. Product dissatisfaction has its origin in nonconformances, and is why customers complain. There are many products which give little or no dissatisfaction; the products do what the supplier said they would do. Yet the products are not salable because some competing product provides greater product satisfaction.

Definitions in the Literature.   ANSI/ASQC Standard A3-1987 (draft) recognizes that the word "quality" has multiple meanings. The meaning adopted in the standard is: "The totality of features and characteristics of a product or service that bear on its ability to satisfy stated or implied needs."

The European Organization for Quality Control Glossary (1981) has the following definition for quality: "The totality of features and characteristics of a product or service that bear on its ability to satisfy a given need. N.B. with manufactured products quality is mainly determined by quality of design and quality of manufacture."

The Soviet encyclopedia defines quality as follows: "Quality of Products, the aggregate of properties of a product determining its ability to satisfy the needs it was built to satisfy."

For some detailed views on whether quality is conformance to standard or fitness for use, see Groocock (1980), Zaludova (1981), Thoday (1981), Seghezzi (1981), and Groocock (1981).

THE QUALITY FUNCTION

Any organization produces and distributes its products through a series of specialized activities carried out by specialized departments. In industrial companies these specialized departments include product development, process development, production, marketing, etc. Figure 2.1, the Spiral of progress in quality, depicts a typical progression of activities as carried out in industrial companies. This figure will be referred to as the "Spiral."

Each specialized department is given the responsibility to carry out its assigned special function. In addition, each specialized department is also assigned a share of the responsibility of carrying out certain companywide functions such as human relations, finance, and *quality.*

A companywide quality function arises from the fact that product quality is the resultant of the work of all departments around the Spiral. Each of those specialized departments has not only the responsibility to carry out its special function; it also has the responsibility to do its work correctly—to make its products fit for use. In this way, each department has a quality-oriented activity to carry out along with its main function. (These departmental quality-oriented activities are supplemented by other quality-oriented activities carried out by staff departments and by upper management.)

It is convenient to have some short name to represent the activities, departmental and companywide, which collectively result in product quality. In this handbook that short name is the "quality function."

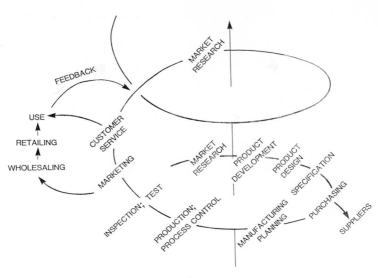

FIG. 2.1   The Spiral of progress in quality.

The quality function is the entire collection of activities through which we achieve fitness for use, no matter where these activities are performed.

HOW TO THINK ABOUT QUALITY

Individuals performing any important function have a need to think through and define the universal concepts which underlie the activity's very existence as a function. In addition the language describing the function needs to evolve and be standardized so that the key concepts can be communicated and understood.

In the case of the quality function, identification of the universal concepts has followed an erratic course. The concept of inspection and test is thousands of years old, as is the concept of measurement. Application of statistical methodology to the quality function is largely a twentieth century phenomenon. Significant efforts to identify the managerial processes inherent in the quality function did not get under way until the second half of the twentieth century.

There are a number of alternative ways for organizing the subject of how to think about quality. A major criterion for choosing from these alternatives is the ease of explaining the quality function to nonexperts, and especially to upper managers. In the author's experience, these upper managers have most readily understood the subject when it is presented to them in the form of a trilogy of managerial processes—the same managerial processes which have long served as the basis for organizing the subject of finance.

The Financial Analogy.   The finance function has been under intense study for centuries. That study has evolved various alternative ways for organizing the subject—how to think about finance. The dominant alternative is now to think of attaining good financial results through three managerial processes: planning, control, and improvement.

Financial Planning.   This planning is centered on preparation of the annual financial budget. In turn, this preparation involves a companywide process which starts by defining the deeds to be done in the year ahead. These deeds are then translated into money equivalents. Such translation permits summary and analysis to determine the financial consequences of doing all those deeds. After revisions, the final result sets the financial goals for the company and its various divisions and departments.

Financial Control.   This well-known process is used to aid managers in reaching the established financial goals. The process consists of evaluating actual financial performance, comparing this with financial goals, and taking action on the difference—the "variance." There are numerous subprocesses for financial control: cost control, expense control, inventory control, etc.

Financial Improvement.   This process takes many forms: cost reduction projects, purchase of new facilities to improve productivity, development of new products to increase sales, acquisition of other companies, etc.

The Quality Trilogy.   Managing for quality is done by use of the same three managerial processes of planning, control, and improvement. The conceptual approaches are identical with those used to manage for finance. However, the procedural steps are special, and the tools used are also special.

Quality Planning.   This is the activity of developing the products and processes required to meet customers' needs. It involves a series of universal steps:

1. Determine who are the customers.
2. Determine the needs of the customers.
3. Develop product features which respond to customers' needs.
4. Develop processes which are able to produce those product features.
5. Transfer the resulting plans to the operating forces.

For an elaboration of the quality planning process, see Section 6, Companywide Planning for Quality. See also Juran (1988).

Quality Control.   This process is used by the operating forces as an aid to meeting the product and process goals. It is based on the feedback loop, and consists of the following steps:

1. Evaluate actual operating performance
2. Compare actual performance to goals
3. Act on the difference

Section 6, Companywide Planning for Quality, elaborates on the use of the feedback loop for quality control. Many sections of this handbook provide examples of use of the control process. Section 24 discusses use of statistical tools as part of the control process; Section 9 elaborates on the use of the control process for quality assurance.

Quality Improvement.   This third member of the quality trilogy aims to attain levels of performance which are unprecedented—levels which are significantly better than any past level. The methodology consists of a process—an unvarying series of steps. These are set out in detail in Section 22, Quality Improvement.

The Juran Trilogy.   The three processes of the quality trilogy are interrelated. Figure 2.2, the Juran Trilogy, shows this interrelationship.

The Juran Trilogy is a graph with time on the horizontal axis and cost of poor quality (quality deficiencies) on the vertical axis. The initial activity is quality planning. The planners determine who are the customers and what their needs are. The planners then develop product and process designs which are able to respond to those needs. Finally, the planners turn the plans over to the operating forces.

The job of the operating forces is to run the processes and produce the products. As operations get under way, it becomes evident that product deficiencies abound. In the company represented in Figure 2.2, the products produced are deficient in various ways, resulting in a total of 20 percent deficiency. Why are the products deficient? Most usually, the deficiencies are traceable to the planning process. That planning process, for whatever reasons, has resulted in that high level of product deficiencies. This waste then becomes chronic because *the operating process was planned that way.*

Under conventional responsibility patterns the operating forces are unable to get rid of that planned chronic waste. What they do instead is to carry out *quality control*—to prevent things from getting worse. Control includes putting out the fires, such as that sporadic spike in Figure 2.2.

But the chart also shows that in due course the chronic waste was driven down to a level far below that planned originally. That gain was achieved by the third process in the trilogy—*quality improvement.* In effect, it was realized that the chronic waste was also an opportunity for improvement. So steps were taken to seize that opportunity.

In most companies there exists a widespread situation in which:

1. Numerous operating processes are deficient. Each is an opportunity for quality improvement through the project by project approach, as described in Section 22, Quality Improvement.

2. The approach to quality planning is also deficient. This deficiency is the root cause of most of those deficient operating processes. That same deficient planning process continues to create new wasteful operating processes. The remedy is to improve the planning process.

FIG. 2.2   The Juran Trilogy.

To improve the quality planning process requires several major changes:

1. A revision in priorities so that the planners are given enough time and resources to do a more thorough job of quality planning.
2. A more structured approach to quality planning, as set out in Section 6, Companywide Planning for Quality.
3. A broader data base for quality planners, derived from "lessons learned," i.e., feedback from problems encountered and solved during the control process, and especially during the improvement process. The concept of "lessons learned" is discussed in Section 6.

FITNESS FOR USE

It would be most convenient to have some short phrase which is universally accepted as a comprehensive definition of quality, i.e., so that it includes the product features which lead to product satisfaction, and in addition includes freedom from deficiencies. Various such phrases have been proposed by practitioners but none has achieved universal acceptance.

Nevertheless, in a handbook such as this it is most convenient to standardize on a short definition of the word "quality." In the preceding Third Edition, quality was defined as "fitness for use." This definition has in fact attained wide acceptance. In view of this, this Fourth Edition will also adopt the definition "quality is fitness for use," realizing that the definition has not achieved universal acceptance.

Product Features and Quality Characteristics. Human needs are extremely diverse, and this has led to a corresponding proliferation of product features and quality characteristics. This proliferation extends to multiple human disciplines, as in the following examples:

Technological: Hardness, inductance, acidity, etc.

Psychological: Taste, beauty, status, etc.

Time-oriented: Reliability, maintainability, etc.

Contractual: Guarantee provisions, etc.

Ethical: Courtesy of sales personnel, honesty of service shops, etc.

The concept of "quality characteristics" is as old as the human species (the entire biological world is responsive to the concept). Moreover, there has been a long-range trend to quantify these characteristics. Technological characteristics, notably properties of materials, were extensively quantified beginning several centuries ago with the accelerated growth of instrumentation. The twentieth century has seen a similar movement to quantify the remaining types of characteristics.

Service industry quality characteristics, while including all of the above subspecies, are dominated by the psychological and ethical. In addition, the service industries generally regard promptness of service as a quality characteristic, whereas the manufacturing industries generally do not. Instead, manufacturing companies regard promptness (i.e., timely delivery of products to customers in accordance with promised date) as a parameter very different from "quality." The distinction is so sharp that there is a separate organization (Materials Management) to set standards for delivery time (schedules), measure performance, and stimulate compliance.

Parameters of Fitness for Use.   Beyond those product features which bear directly on product satisfaction there are additional aspects of the product which also contribute to fitness for use. These additional aspects are often called "parameters" of quality. An example is the time-related "abilities."

For products which are consumed promptly (food, fuel, many services) fitness for use is determined by (1) the adequacy of the product design and (2) the extent to which the product originally conforms to that design. For long lived products, some new time-oriented factors come into play: availability, reliability, and maintainability. These abilities are closely interrelated and are vital to fitness for use.

Total is the product of subsystem avability

Availability.   Continuity of life in the industrial society depends absolutely on the continuity of service from sources of energy, communication, transport, water, etc. To provide this continuity, much effort has been devoted to discovering how to minimize the failure rates of products and how to restore service promptly in case of failure. One element of this effort has been to recognize continuity of service as a parameter of fitness for use and to set up to measure it. The name given to this parameter is "availability." It is time-related and is measured by the extent to which the user can secure service when he or she wants it.

A product is said to be available when it is in an operative state. The total time in the operative state (also called uptime) is the sum of the time spent (1) in active use and (2) in standby state.

The total time in the nonoperative state (also called downtime) is the sum of the time spent (3) under active repair (i.e., diagnosis and remedy), and (4) waiting for spare parts, paperwork, etc.

Availability is expressed mathematically by the ratio:

$$\frac{\text{Uptime}}{\text{Uptime} + \text{downtime}}$$

In equivalent terminology, availability is also expressed by the ratio:

$$\frac{\text{Mean time between failures (MTBF)}}{\text{MTBF} + \text{mean time to repair (MTTR)}}$$

Other terms used as equivalents of availability are "operational readiness" and "percent uptime."

Reliability.   If products never failed, availability would be 100 percent. However, products do fail, so that an essential subparameter of availability is freedom from failure, for which the accepted technical term is "reliability." The classic definition is "the probability of a product performing without failure under given conditions for a specified period of time" (AGREE, 1957).

Architects and designers have for millennia tried to design structures and products for long life. What is now new is the movement to quantify reliability. It is a movement similar to, and probably as important as, the movement several centuries ago to quantify properties of materials. Once we are able to quantify reliability, we can more scientifically do many other things about reliability: predict, apportion, plan, achieve, test, control, improve, etc.

The probability of performing without failure can be converted readily to other measures, such as mean time between failures, failure rate, etc. For simple systems the calculations are comparatively simple. However, for complex systems they become extremely complex. This has given rise to a huge literature on the methods for quantifying reliability.

Reliability is determined largely by the quality of design. The attainable reliability inherent in the design is called "intrinsic reliability." However, the achieved reliability is usually less than this because of unanticipated environments during use, lapses in quality of conformance, inadequacies in maintenance, etc.

The term "operational reliability" is sometimes used to distinguish attained reliability from intrinsic reliability.

Reliability is not to be confused with conformance to product specification (as evidenced by test of conformance) or even with reliability estimates based on life tests in the laboratory. The evaluation of achieved reliability requires actual use of product over a period of time plus collection and interpretation of data on performance and failures during that time.

For a discussion of quantifying reliability, see Section 13 under Planning for Time-Oriented Performance.

Maintainability.   The need for continuity of service has also stimulated much effort to improve the maintenance of long-life products. This maintenance takes place in two major ways:

1. Preventive or scheduled maintenance consisting of tests and checkouts to detect potential failures, scheduled servicing (e.g., lubrication), and planned overhauls plus replacement of worn or failure-prone parts
2. Unscheduled maintenance consisting of restoring service in the event of failure

The term "maintainability" has been adopted as an expression of the ease with which maintenance can be conducted.

Attempts to quantify maintainability soon encounter the fact that multiple measures are involved. Maintenance requires the time of technicians, spare parts, expendable supplies, and other costs. Hence multiple measures of maintenance have been developed to correspond to these multiple factors. Of these measures, those that are time-oriented are regarded as most important, because so much human activity remains disturbed until service is restored.

The measures of maintainability actually in use include:

Mean time to repair

Probability of restoring service in the time period specified

Mean time for scheduled maintenance (this is often subdivided between the inspecting and the servicing)

An emerging practice is to establish standards for the various repetitive time-consuming elements of maintenance.

Effectiveness of maintenance is strongly influenced by the supporting technology: design for easy access and modular replacement at the users' premises, special instruments for easy diagnosis of causes of failure, special repair tools, and technical information about the product and its use. Providing this supporting technology is generally regarded as a part of the subject matter of maintainability.

Effectiveness of maintenance is also strongly influenced by the availability of spare parts, sometimes called "logistical support." Providing this logistical support is regarded by some practitioners as part of the subject matter of maintainability.

Terminology associated with maintainability is still in a state of evolution. Some practitioners separate maintainability into two categories: (1) the ease of conducting scheduled inspections and servicing, called "serviceability," and (2) the ease of restoring service after failure, called "repairability."

In the case of maintenance of aircraft, recent studies have led to extensive revisions in the concept of maintenance. From the earliest days of flying, maintenance of aircraft engines was done under the concept of "overhaul"—a scheduled complete disassembly of the engine, followed by inspection of all parts, repair or replacement as needed, and finally reassembly. During the last several decades the airlines enlarged their data systems so that they could go beyond the needs of restoring service, and could reexamine long standing practices. One stunning finding was that of the items in the product, *89 percent exhibited failure patterns which were not age-related.* Hence such items could not benefit from the overhaul concept. The findings have led to new concepts, e.g., "on-condition" maintenance. They have also led to fundamental improvements in engine performance and availability through feedback to engine design, manufacture, and test. (For an extensive discussion, see Nowlan and Heap, 1978).

Producibility (or Manufacturability). This parameter measures the extent to which the product design can be readily produced with the facilities and process available to the operating forces. Producibility has no direct relation to fitness for use of external customers, but is obviously of great importance to internal customers.

Additional Terminology. The search for a short phrase to describe "everything"—product features and freedom from deficiencies—has stimulated a variety of local dialects. For example, in certain complex systems industries (military, aerospace), terms such as "system effectiveness," "product performance," or "product effectiveness" have been tested out. Sometimes such special terminology finds acceptance in specific industries, and may endure for some years before being revised. However, the special nature of the industry makes the terms not acceptable to other industries, e.g., the word "system" is too elaborate to be applied to production of simple products.

BUSINESS, MANAGEMENT, AND TECHNOLOGY

The activities needed to achieve fitness for use (Figure 2.1) can also be classified in terms of the basic disciplines employed. Three of these are of major concern:

1. *Business or entrepreneurship:* This is concerned with taking the risks associated with doing business at all and with the circumstances under which risks are taken. It includes judging the economic climate, choosing which markets to enter, financing the enterprise, taking specific investment risks, etc.

2. *Management:* This is the process through which people are mobilized to achieve designated goals. When applied to the quality function, management consists of the three elements of the quality trilogy: quality planning, quality control, and quality improvement. The leaders who preside over these managerial processes are generally called "managers." What distinguishes managers from other individuals is that the managers must secure results through the efforts of other people.

3. *Technology:* This is concerned with harnessing the forces and materials of nature for the benefit of human beings. Technological quality matters include designs, specifications, processes, instruments, tests, and failure analysis.

Many quality problems are traceable to the fact that top managers live in the world of business and management, whereas the quality specialists live in the world of technology. The higher that people climb the managerial hierarchy, the more time they devote to business and managerial problems. Top management's attention to quality activities is almost exclusively devoted to managerial matters. When we ask company presidents "What does the word 'quality' mean to you?" they usually answer in business terminology, e.g., "Quality is what we sell. It's what our customers want. Our reputation is built on quality." Seldom is the answer in technological terms, e.g., tolerances, control charts, gage laboratories, etc.

These same differences are evident in the setting of quality goals and in planning to meet those goals. Company goals and plans are usually in business and managerial terms, whereas departmental goals and plans are usually in technological terms. In this handbook, the sections dealing with business and management make little distinction as to industry involved, since these two disciplines apply to all industries with little variation in application.

STANDARDIZATION OF TERMINOLOGY IN THE QUALITY FUNCTION

The search for universal concepts and principles in the quality function is a relatively recent phenomenon. In consequence, standardization of terminology is still in the formative stages. Many words and phrases are used in special meanings which differ from the dictionary meanings. In view of this state of affairs, this handbook attempts to define key words and phrases as they appear (or define them through cross-referencing). In addition, the Index identifies, for each key word or phrase, the location of the principal definition.

Despite these efforts, the reader is urged to keep in mind that there remains much confusion in the language of quality. Some words or phrases are used in special meanings which have not yet found their way into the dictionaries. Other words have multiple meanings, e.g., "quality." It is quite common for participants in meetings to be forced to ask each other: In what sense are you using that word? To illustrate, in a meeting of managers the question arises: Does higher quality cost more or does it cost less? The resulting discussion may well yield no agreement. The reason is that some participants have in mind quality in the sense of grade, in which case higher quality usually does cost more. Other participants have in mind quality in the sense of freedom from deficiencies, in which case higher quality usually does cost less. So each is right, but there is no meeting of the minds.

Much has been done within specific organizations to establish local glossaries. In addition, some professional societies have evolved glossaries of quality-related terms. A major glossary of terms is the European Organization for Quality Control (EOQC) *Glossary of Terms Used in Quality Control* (1981). This compilation lists 398 terms and defines them in English. In addition, the compilation shows, for 14 other languages (13 European plus Arabic), the equivalents of these 398 terms (but not equivalent definitions). This glossary was prepared by the Glossary Committee of EOQC. It is available from the European Organization for Quality Control, Secretariat, P.O. Box 2613, CH-3001, Berne, Switzerland.

Additional glossaries are available in several American National Standards, as follows:

ANSI/ASQC A1-1987, *Definitions, Symbols, Formulas and Tables for Control Charts*

ANSI/ASQC A2-1987, *Terms, Symbols and Definitions for Acceptance Sampling*

ANSI/ASQC A3-1987 (draft), *Quality Systems Terminology*

All of these are available from the American Society for Quality Control, 310 West Wisconsin Ave., Milwaukee.

A Wistful Postscript. It would be wonderful if all managers and practitioners were to standardize on the terminology used to describe concepts, deeds, and meanings. Such a paradise is far away, since there are some very active obstacles to standardization. These obstacles are mainly the following:

The differences in the technology, dialect, and cultural history of the various industries

The rapidly changing ingredients of fitness for use

The deliberate efforts of human beings to create and use terminology to secure benefits for their organizations and for themselves

The prime need is to discover the realities under the labels, i.e., the deeds, activities, or things which the other person is talking about. Once these are understood, accurate communication can take place whether the labels are agreed on or not. In contrast, if communication is purely through labels, it is easy to be deluded into believing there is an understanding despite the fact that each of the parties literally does not know what the other is talking about.

REFERENCES

AGREE (1957). This is the historic report, *Reliability of Military Electronic Equipment*, by the Advisory Group on Reliability of Electronic Equipment, Office of the Assistant Secretary of Defense (R&D), June 1957.

European Organization for Quality Control (1981). *Glossary of Terms Used in Quality Control*, 5th ed. Berne, Switzerland.

Groocock, J. M. (1980). "Conformance or Fitness for Use?" *EOQC Quality*, vol. 2, pp. 3–6.

Groocock, J. M. (1981). "Conformance or Fitness for Use? (II)." *EOQC Quality*, vol. 4. pp. 5–7.

Juran, J. M. (1988). *Juran on Planning for Quality.* The Free Press, New York.

Nowlan, F. Stanley and Heap, Howard F. (1978). *Reliability-Centered Maintenance.* Available from National Technical Information Service, Springfield, VA 22161. (Catalog no. ADA 066579.)

Seghezzi, H. D. (1981). "What is Quality? Conformance with Requirements or Fitness for the Intended Use?" *EOQC Quality*, vol. 4, pp. 3–4.

Thoday, W. R. (1981). "Additional Reflections on Quality Terminology." *EOQC Quality*, vol. 1, p. 11.

Zaludova, A. H. (1981). "Some Reflections on Quality Terminology." *EOQC Quality*, vol. 1, pp. 3–10.

SECTION 3

QUALITY AND INCOME

J. M. Juran

QUALITY AND ECONOMICS

Quality affects a supplier's economics in two principal ways:

1. *The effect on costs:* With respect to its effect on costs, the word "quality" is used in the sense of freedom from deficiencies, or the degree of conformance to standards, goals, specifications, etc. In this sense "higher quality" means greater freedom from deficiencies, and hence also lower costs. That subject of the effect of quality on costs is discussed in Section 5, Quality Costs.

2. *The effect on income:* As used here, "income" refers to such things as the sales of an industrial company; the appropriations received by a government agency; the tuition, grants, etc., received by an educational institution. Income also refers to the gross receipts, not to the surplus or profit. With respect to its effect on income, the word "quality" is used here in the sense of the features of the product which respond to customer needs. Those features make the product salable and provide "product satisfaction" to customers. The subject of the effect of quality on income is discussed in this section. The section discusses the forces through which quality affects income and the methods in use for studying the cause-effect relationships.

Closely related to this subject of quality and income are several other sections of the handbook:

Section 12—Field Intelligence

Section 19—Marketing

Section 20—Customer Service

The above two effects of quality—on costs and on income—interact with each other. Product deficiencies which directly affect a company's clients will often result in higher costs in such forms as complaints, claims, etc. In addition, news of those deficiencies reaches the ears of those who make the purchase decisions. The result may be lower sales income for the guilty supplier.

Product deficiencies found internally by the manufacturer can also have an effect on income. There is always a high correlation between the level of these product deficiencies and the level of product deficiencies reported by customers. In addition, success in reducing deficiencies through quality improvement is a form of cost reduction. The resulting improvement in cost competitiveness is an aid to securing higher share of market.

In recent decades there has been much study of the effect of quality on costs, especially on the costs of poor quality. (See generally, Section 5, Quality Costs). In contrast, study of the effect of quality on income has lagged. This imbalance is all the more surprising since in the view of upper managers the effect of quality on income is the more important of the two effects. This same imbalance presents an opportunity for creative and imaginative invention of new ways to study the effect of quality on income.

MAJOR ECONOMIC INFLUENCES

The ability of an industrial company to secure income is strongly influenced by the economic climate and by the cultural habits which the various economies have evolved. These overriding influences affect product quality as well as other elements of commerce.

National Affluence and Organization. The form of a nation's economy and its degree of affluence strongly influence the approach to its quality problems.

Subsistence Economies. In such economies the numerous impoverished users have little choice but to devote their income to basic human needs. Their protection against poor quality is derived more from collective political power than from their collective economic power. Most of the world's population remains in a state of subsistence economy.

Planned Economies. In all countries there are some socialized industries, i.e., government monopolies for specific products or services. In some countries the entire economy is so organized. These monopolies limit the choice of the user to those qualities which result from the national planning and its execution. For elaboration, see Section 35A, Quality and National Culture.

Shortages and Surpluses. In all economies, a shortage of goods (a "sellers' market") results in a relaxing of quality standards. Because the demand for goods exceeds the supply, users take what they can get (and bid up the price to boot). In contrast, a buyers' market results in a tightening of quality standards.

Life Behind the Quality Dikes. As societies industrialize they revise their life-style in order to secure the benefits of technology. These benefits consist of numerous varieties of goods and services. Collectively these goods and services have greatly improved the quality of life, but they have also created a new dependence. In the industrial societies, great masses of human beings place their safety, health, and even their daily well-being behind numerous protective dikes of quality control.

For example, the daily safety and health of the citizenry now depend absolutely on the quality of manufactured products: drugs, food, aircraft, automobiles, elevators, tunnels, bridges, etc.

The very continuity of our daily lives is built around the continuity of numerous vital services: power, transport, communication, water, waste removal, and many others. We have structured our society on the premise that these services will continue without interruption. A major power failure paralyzes the lives of millions of people.

Not only individuals but also nations and their economies live dangerously behind the dikes of quality control. National productivity relies on automated processes. National defense relies on complex weaponry. The national income depends on the marketability of products. The growth of the national economy is keyed to the reliability of its systems for energy, communication, transport, etc.

In such situations, users (whether individuals or nations) are willing to pay for good dikes. (For elaboration of this theme, see Juran, 1969.)

Voluntary Obsolescence.   As customers acquire affluence, the industrial companies increasingly bring out new products (and new models of old products) which they urge prospective users to buy. Many of the users who buy these new models do so while possessing older models which are still in working order. This practice is regarded by some economists and reformers as a reprehensible economic waste.

In their efforts to put an end to this waste, the reformers have attacked the industrial companies who bring out these new models and who promote their sale. Using the term "planned obsolescence," the reformers imply (and state outright) that the large companies, by their clever new models and their powerful sales promotion, break down the resistance of the users. Under this theory, the responsibility for the waste lies with the industrial companies who create the new models.

In the experience and judgment of the author, this theory of planned obsolescence is mostly nonsense. The simple fact, obvious both to manufacturers and consumers, is that *the consumer makes the decision* (of whether to discard the old product and buy the new). Periodically this fact is dramatized by some massive marketing failure.

For example, in March 1971, E. I. Du Pont de Nemours & Co., Inc. (Du Pont) announced its plans to discontinue the manufacture and sale of "Corfam," a synthetic material invented to compete with leather for shoe uppers (and other applications). Corfam, though costly, possessed excellent properties for shoe uppers: durability, ease of care, shape retention, scuff resistance, water repellency, and ability to "breathe." Although Du Pont became a major supplier of shoe uppers materials, it withdrew from the business because Corfam "never attained sufficient sales volume to show a profit."

Industry observers felt that the high durability of Corfam was an irrelevant property because of rapid style obsolescence; i.e., the life of the shoes was determined not by the inherent technological properties but by style obsolescence. Du Pont's investment in Corfam may have exceeded $100 million.

In the Corfam case, a large corporation undertook a program which was antagonistic to obsolescence, but the users decided against it. In a miscalculation involving an even larger investment, the Ford Motor Company's Edsel automobile failed to gain consumer acceptance despite possessing numerous innovations and being promoted by an extensive marketing campaign.

Involuntary Obsolescence.   Quite a different situation is the case in which long-life products contain components which will not last for the life of the product. The life of these components is determined by the manufacturer. As a result, even though the user decides to have the failed component replaced (to keep the product in service), *the manufacturer makes the real decision* because the design determines the life of the component.

This situation is at its worst when the original manufacturer had designed the product in such a way that the supplies, spare parts, etc., are nonstandard, so that, in effect, the sole source for these needs is the original manufacturer. In such a situation, the user is locked in to a single source of supply. Collectively, these cases have lent themselves to a good deal of abuse and have contributed to the consumerism movement.

For elaboration, see Juran, 1970.

CONTRAST IN VIEWS: CUSTOMER AND SUPPLIER

Industrial companies derive their income from the sale of their products. These sales are made to "customers," but customers vary as to their function. Customers may be merchants, processors, ultimate users, etc. These variations in function result in variations in customer needs. Such a response must be preceded by an understanding of what are the needs of customers.

Human needs cover a wide spectrum. To meet these needs suppliers evolve a correspondingly wide spectrum of products and product features. Moreover, human needs are complex. They extend beyond technological matters into social, artistic, status, and other seemingly intangible areas. Suppliers are nevertheless obliged to understand these seeming intangibles in order to be able to provide product responses.

The Spectrum of Affluence.   In all economies the affluence of the population varies across a wide spectrum. Suppliers respond to this spectrum by developing variations in product features. These variations are often called "grades." For example, hotels all offer the basic service of overnight sleeping accommodations. Beyond this basic function hotels vary remarkably in the range of services offered, and the grades (deluxe, etc.) reflect this variation. In like manner any model of automobile provides the basic function of point-to-point transportation. However, there are multiple grades of automobiles. The higher grades supply services beyond pure transportation, including higher levels of appearance, comfort, status, etc.

Stated Needs and Real Needs.   Customers state their needs as seen by them, and in their language. Suppliers are then faced with understanding the real needs and also translating those needs into suppliers' language. For example, travelers need transportation. They may state their needs in such forms as:

> I wish to buy a bicycle.
>
> I wish to rent a bicycle.
>
> I wish to buy a bus ticket.

It is quite common for customers to state their needs in the form of goods when their real needs are for the services provided by these goods. Some manufacturers are careful to make this distinction in their sales promotion. They emphasize the service provided by the goods. For example:

Manufacturer's goods	Emphasis of the sales promotion
Grinding wheels	Metal removal
Nuts and bolts	Fastening systems
Toothpaste	Clean teeth, sweet breath, improved social life
Aluminum siding	Maintenance-free exteriors

In contrast, preoccupation with the concept of selling goods can divert attention from the real needs of customers. For example, two hairnet manufacturers were in competition. They devoted much energy to improving the qualities of the product and to strengthening their marketing techniques. They were both made extinct when someone developed a hair spray which gave the user a better way of holding hair in place. (Private communication to J. M. Juran.)

(For elaboration, see the classic, widely read paper "Marketing Myopia" by Theodore Levitt, 1960.)

Reasons behind the Stated Needs.   These reasons may become evident through in-depth discussions with users. An interesting example is narrated by Charles A. Lindbergh (Lindbergh, 1970, pp. 517–620). He was interviewing combat fliers to secure inputs for aircraft design. He found it quite important to understand the reasons behind the pilots' recommendations.

Differences in Language.   Often the stated needs are real needs but stated in the language of the buyer. In such cases it is necessary to translate those needs into the language of the supplier. For a case example involving paper towels, see Mottle and Shiah (1974).

Nonfunctional Needs.   For many products, customer needs extend beyond the pure function of the product; the needs include matters of a psychological nature. Such intangible needs apply to both goods and services.

To illustrate: A man in need of a haircut has the option of going to (1) a barbershop inhabited by barbers or (2) a "salon" inhabited by "hair stylists." The end result is the same. Either way he is shorn by a skilled artisan. Either way he emerges with the same outward appearance. What differs is (a) his remaining assets and (b) his sense of well-being.

What applies to services also applies to physical goods.

There are factories in which chocolate-coated candies are carried by a belt to the packaging department. At the end of the belt are two teams of packagers. One of these teams packs the chocolates into modest cardboard boxes destined for budget-priced merchant shops. The other team packs the chocolates into satin-lined wooden boxes destined to be sold in deluxe shops. The resulting price for a like amount of chocolate can differ by several fold. The respective purchasers encounter other differences as well: the decor, the extent of service, the box. However, the chocolates are identical. In fact, when any chocolate reaches the packers it has no way of predicting whether it will end up in the budget shops or in the deluxe shop.

Nonfunctional needs take such forms as securing attention, courteous treatment, prompt service, pleasant surroundings, and sense of importance. Despite their detachment from the technological functions of the product, these needs are very real to the customers and hence to the income of the suppliers.

Definition of Quality.   The differences in viewpoints (of customers and suppliers) can readily extend to a difference in the definition of what is quality. Any such difference is an invitation to trouble.

To most customers, quality means those features of the product which respond to customer needs. In addition, quality means freedom from deficiencies, as well as good customer service if deficiencies do occur. One comprehensive definition for the above is "fitness for use." (There are of course some exceptions. In the nuclear energy industry the regulatory bodies tend to reserve to themselves the determination of fitness for use, leaving to the manufacturers the more limited function of conformance to specification.)

In contrast, many manufacturers of goods had for years tended to equate quality with conformance to specification at the time of final product test. This form of definition of quality gave inadequate attention to numerous factors which influenced quality as defined by customers: packaging, storage, transport, installation, reliability, maintainability, customer service, etc.

Table 3.1 tabulates some of the differences in viewpoint as applied to long-life goods.

TABLE 3.1   Contrasting Views: Customers and Suppliers

Aspects	Principal views	
	Of customers	Of manufacturers
What is bought	A service needed by the customer	Goods made by the manufacturer
Definition of quality	Fitness for use during the life of the product	Conformance to specification on final test
Cost	Cost of use, including Purchase price Operating costs Maintenance Downtime Depreciation Loss on resale	Cost of manufacture
Responsibility for keeping in service	Over the entire useful life	During the warranty period
Spare parts	A necessary evil	A profitable business

The ongoing revolution in quality has consisted in part of revising the manufacturers' definition of quality to be more nearly in accord with the customers' definition.

Cost of Use.   For consumable products the purchase price paid by the customer is quite close to the total cost of using (consuming) the product. However, for long-lived products the cost of use can diverge considerably from the purchase price because of added factors such as operating costs, maintenance costs, downtime, depreciation, etc.

The centuries-old emphasis on purchase price has tended to obscure the subsequent costs of use. One consequence has been a practice of suboptimization, i.e., manufacturers optimize their costs rather than the combined costs of manufacturers and customers.

The concept of life cycle costing offers a solution to this problem, and progress is being made in adopting this concept. (See Life Cycle Costing, below.)

DEGREES OF USER KNOWLEDGE

In a competitive market, customers for products have multiple sources of supply. In choosing from these alternatives, product quality is an obvious consideration. However, prospective customers vary considerably as to their ability to evaluate quality, especially prior to purchase. Table 3.2 summarizes the extent of customer knowledge and strength in the market place as related to quality matters.

TABLE 3.2 Customer Influences on Quality

Aspects of the problem	Original equipment manufacturers (OEM)	Dealers and repair shops	Consumers
Makeup of the market	A few very large customers	Some large customers plus many smaller ones	Very many very small customers
Economic strength of any one customer	Very large, cannot be ignored	Modest or low	Negligible
Technological strength of customer	Very high; has engineers and laboratories	Low or nil	Nil; requires technical assistance
Political strength of customer	Modest or low	Low to nil	Variable, but can be very great collectively
Fitness for use is judged mainly by	Qualification testing	Absence of consumer complaints	Successful usage
Quality specifications dominated by	Customers	Manufacturer	Manufacturer
Use of incoming inspection	Extensive test for conformance to specification	Low or nil for dealers; in-use tests by repair shops	In-use test
Collection and analysis of failure data	Good to fair	Poor to nil	Poor to nil

The broad conclusions which can be drawn from Table 3.2 are as follows:

1. Original equipment manufacturers (OEMs) can protect themselves through their technological and/or economic power as much as through contract provisions.

2. Merchants and repair shops must rely mainly on contract provisions supplemented by some economic power.

3. Small users have very limited knowledge and protection. The situation of the small user requires some elaboration.

Fitness for Use. With few exceptions, small users are devoid of understanding of the technological nature of the product. The user does have sensory recognition of some aspects of fitness for use: the bread smells fresh-baked; the radio set has clear reception; the shoes are good-looking. Beyond such sensory judgments, and especially concerning the long-life performance of the product, the small user must rely mainly on prior personal experience with the manufacturer or merchant. Lacking such prior experience, the small user must choose from the propaganda of competing manufacturers plus other available inputs (neighbors, merchants, independent laboratories, etc.).

To the extent that the user does understand fitness for use, the effect on the manufacturer's income is somewhat as follows:

As seen by the user, product or service is	*Resulting income to the producer is*
Not fit for use	None, or in immediate jeopardy
Fit for use but noticeably inferior to competitive products	Low because of need for lowering prices
Fit for use and competitive	At market prices
Noticeably superior to competitive products	High because of premium prices or greater share of market

In the foregoing, the terms "fitness for use," "inferior," "competitive," and "superior" all relate to the situation *as seen by the user.* (The foregoing table is valid as applied to both large customers and small users.)

QUALITY AND PRICE

There is general awareness that product price bears some rational relationship to product quality. However, researches on the subject have often reported confused relationships, some of which appear to run contrary to logical reasoning. To interpret these researches it is useful to separate the subject as between consumer products and industrial products.

Consumer Products. Numerous researches have tried to quantify the correlation between product quality and product price. See, for example, Reisz (1979); also Morris and Bronson (1969). A major data base for these researches has been the journal *Consumer Reports,* a publication of Consumer Union, a nonprofit supplier of information and advice to consumers. The specific information used in the researches consisted of *Consumer Reports'* published quality ratings of products, along with the associated prevailing market prices.

The researches generally concluded that there is little positive correlation between quality ratings and market prices. For a significant minority of products the correlation was negative. Such conclusions were reached as to foods, both convenience and nonconvenience (Reisz, 1979). Similar conclusions were reached as to other consumable products, household appliances, tools, and other long-life products (Morris and Bronson, 1969).

Researchers offer various theories to explain why so many consumers seem to be acting contrary to their own best interests:

1. The quality ratings are based solely on evaluations of the functional features of the products—the inherent quality of design. The ratings do not evaluate various factors which are known to influence consumer behavior. These factors include *service* in such forms as attention, courtesy, and promptness; also *decor* in such forms as pleasant surroundings and attractive packaging.
2. Consumers generally possess only limited technological literacy, and most are unaware of the quality ratings.

3. Lacking objective quality information, consumers give weight to the image projected by manufacturers and merchants through their promotion and advertising.

4. The price itself is perceived by many consumers as a quality rating. There appears to be a widespread belief that a higher-priced product is also a higher-quality product. Some companies have exploited this belief as a part of their marketing and pricing strategy ("Pricing of Products Is Still an Art," 1981).

Price Differences.   Premium priced products most usually run about 10 to 20 percent higher than other products. For example, branded products often are priced in this range relative to generic products. However, there are many instances of much greater price differences.

Haircuts given in some "salons" sell at several times the price prevailing in "barbershops."

Chocolates packaged in elegant boxes and sold in deluxe shops may sell for several times the price of the identical chocolates packaged in simple boxes and sold in budget shops.

Restaurant meal prices can vary by an order of magnitude.

Many branded drugs regularly sell for several times the price of generic drugs asserted to be therapeutically equivalent.

A price premium based on perceived quality differences is constantly under threat from competitors who look for ways to wipe out those quality differences. For a case example (washing machines), see "The Problem of Being Premium" (1978).

Quality and Value.   What emerges is that for many consumers, perception of the quality-price relationship is derived from unique interpretations of the terms used:

Quality is interpreted as including factors which go beyond the inherent functional features of the product.

Price is interpreted as relating to "value" and is paid for those added factors, along with the inherent functional features.

Efforts to Quantify Value.   These efforts are generally restricted to inherent functional properties of products. For example, the U.S. Department of Transportation evaluated and published the performance of automobile tires for several qualities, notably tread wear. Quantifying the amount of tread wear under standard test conditions made it possible to estimate the cost per unit of distance traveled ("Consumer Guide on Tires," 1980). Consumers Union periodically undertakes such evaluations for consumer products. For an example, see "Dishwashing Liquids" (1984).

Such evaluations clearly can be useful to consumers. However, the impact of such information is limited because of consumer unawareness and because consumer perceptions are based on broader concepts of what constitutes quality and value.

Industrial Products.   These products employ the concepts of quality, price, and value in much the same way as consumer products. However, industrial buyers are generally much better informed as to the significance of these concepts. In addition, industrial buyers are better provided with the technological and economic information needed to make rational decisions.

Product Differences. In the competitive marketplace product differences abound. These differences create problems in applying the principle of "standard product, market price."

For example, a company making standard power tools improved the reliability of the tools, but the marketing manager resisted increasing the prices on the ground that they were standard tools and market share would be lost if prices were raised. A field study disclosed that the high-reliability tools greatly reduced the costs of the (industrial) users in maintenance and especially in downtime. This information then became the means of convincing users to accept a price increase (of $500,000 per year).

When product differences are obvious (e.g., additional features or functions) both suppliers and buyers are open to establishing price differences. Now the problem becomes: How much difference? Suppliers and buyers both are faced with (1) making product comparisons to identify the differences and (2) establishing price differences in accordance with the product differences. In some markets a great many different products may be involved.

An early approach, involving several thousands of products, made use of two concepts:

1. A "percentage of desirability" determined by comparing the quality of design of company products to those of competitors
2. A "competitive price index" determined by dividing the price ratio by the percentage of desirability

For details, see MacGowan (1957).

Commodity versus Specialty or System. An important question in much industrial buying is whether the product being bought is a commodity or something broader. The greater breadth may involve a specialty or a system of which the commodity is a part, but which includes other attributes of special value to the buyer.

Commodities are typically bought at market prices, and the price tends to dominate the purchasing decisions. Any perceived quality superiority tends to be translated into higher share of market rather than into a price differential. In contrast, specialties are not standard. What is being bought includes additional attributes which result in premium prices, the premium being paid for the additional attributes.

The additional attributes which make premium prices possible are numerous. Some of these attributes are widely prevalent: predictable uniformity of product, promptness of delivery, technological advice and service, assistance in training buyers' personnel, prompt assistance in trouble shooting, and product innovation. Still other influences in the pricing decision include prestige of the supplier, mutual confidences established, sharing of inspection and test data, personal relationships established, joint quality planning, and joint projects for quality improvement. For a case example of a joint quality improvement project involving Aluminum Company of America and Eastman Kodak, see Kegarise and Miller (1986) and Kegarise et al. (1987) in *The Juran Report,* no. 6 and no. 8, respectively.

There is no known, agreed method for quantifying the extent to which those additional attributes contribute to the pricing decision. What can be done is to secure buyers' subjective estimates of the relative importance of the respective attributes. These estimates can then be used as inputs to marketing strategy and as a basis for allocating resources.

For an interesting research on pricing in the chemicals industry, along with an approach to evaluation of the "additional attributes," see Gross (1978). See also Section 12, under Examples of Field Studies.

The Bundled Price.   When products are sold as specialties or as part of a system, the price is often "bundled." Bundled prices provide no breakdown of price as between the goods (commodities) and the associated services.

Bundled prices are an advantage to the manufacturer as long as the product remains a specialty and requires the associate technical services. However, if wide use of the specialty products results in standardization, the need for the technical services diminishes. In such cases it is common for competitors to offer the standard product at lower prices but without the technical services. This is a form of "unbundling" the price.

The Macroeffect of Pricing Strategy.   Companies whose products are in the high-quality category have the option of seeking their reward through either higher price, or higher share of market (or both). Generally companies' strategy has been to opt for higher price.

A report, *Pricing High Quality Products* (PIMS, 1978), raises questions concerning this strategy. According to the report the market is willing to pay premium prices for high quality products. However, if the premium price is not demanded, the market responds by awarding so high an increase in market share that the supplier ends up with a return on investment greater than that resulting solely from premium pricing.

QUALITY AND SHARE OF MARKET

Once a product is actively on the market it attains some "share of market," i.e., a proportion of all sales by all suppliers of that type of product. The size of the attained market share is of great economic importance. Greater market share means higher sales volume. In turn, higher sales volume results in disproportionately higher return on investment due to the nature of the breakeven chart (Figure 3.1).

In Figure 3.1, an increase of 20 percent in sales creates an increase of 50 percent in profit, since no increase in "constant" costs is involved. (Actually, constant costs do vary with volume, but not at all in proportion.) There is little risk involved in such an increase, since the technology, production facilities, market, etc., are already in existence and of proved effectiveness. In contrast, to increase sales by creating a new product line involves much investment in market research, technology, facilities, and personnel. In addition, the venture is far more risky than greater share of market in an existing product line. In this way, a dollar of sales gained through quality superiority is commonly much more valuable than a dollar of sales gained through investment in a new venture.

Effect of Quality Superiority.   Quality superiority can usually be translated into higher share of market but it may require special effort to do so. Much depends on the degree of superiority and on the ability of the buyer to perceive the difference and its significance.

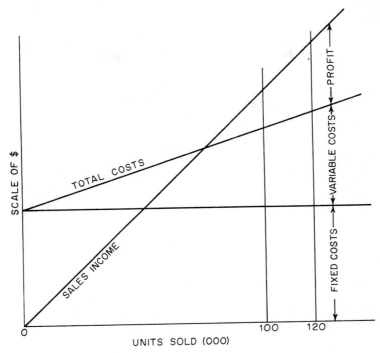

FIG. 3.1 Break-even chart.

Quality Superiority Obvious to the Buyer. In such cases the obvious superiority can be translated into higher share of market. This concept is fully understood by marketers, and they have from time immemorial urged product developers to come up with product features which can then be used to secure higher share of market. Examples of such cases are legion.

Quality Superiority Translatable into Users' Economics. Some products are outwardly "alike" but have unlike performances. Obvious examples are the electric power consumption of an appliance or the fuel consumption of an automobile. In these and similar examples it is feasible to translate the technological superiority into the language of money. Such a translation makes it easier for those who lack technological expertise to understand the significance of the quality superiority.

The power tool case (p. 3.11) is to the same effect. In that case the superior reliability was translated into the language of money to secure a price premium. It could instead have been used to secure higher share of market. Cases such as tire wear (p. 3.10) can similarly be translated into the language of money.

The initiative to translate may also be taken by the buyer. For example, some users of abrasive grinding wheels keep records on wheel life. This is then translated into money—grinding wheel cost per 1000 pieces processed. Such a measure makes it unnecessary for the buyer to become expert in the technology of abrasives.

Collectively, cases such as the above can be generalized as follows:

There is in fact a quality difference among competing products.

This difference is technological in nature so that its significance is not understood by many users.

It is possible, by appropriate data collection in the field, to translate the technological difference into the language of money or into other meaningful forms.

To stimulate action by users the results must be presented in terms of the users' system of values, not the manufacturers'.

Quality Superiority Minor but Demonstrable. In some cases product superiority can be used to secure addded share of market even though the "inferior" product meets customer needs. For example, a manufacturer of antifriction bearings had refined his processes to such an extent that his products were more precise than those of his competitors. As it happened, the competitors' products were entirely fit for use, so no price differential was feasible. Nevertheless, the fact of greater precision was a forceful selling tool and resulted in increased share of market.

In the case of consumer products, even a small product difference can be translated into an increased share of market if the consumers are adequately sensitized. For example, a manufacturer of candy-coated chocolates seized on the fact that its product did not create chocolate smudge marks on consumers' hands. The company dramatized this in television advertisements by contrasting the appearance of children's hands after eating its own and competitors' (uncoated) chocolate. The company's share of market rose dramatically.

Quality Superiority Accepted on Faith. It has been amply demonstrated that buyers can be persuaded to accept on faith, assertions of product superiority which the buyers themselves are unable to verify. A dramatic example involved an ingenious market research on electric razors. The sponsoring company (Schick) employed an independent test laboratory to conduct the tests. During the research, consumer panelists shaved themselves twice, using two electric razors one after the other. On one day the Schick razor was used first and a competing razor immediately after. On the next day the sequence was reversed. In all tests the contents of the second razor were weighed precisely. The data assertedly showed that when the Schick was second, its weighed contents were more than those of competitors. The implication was that Schick razors gave a cleaner shave. Within a few months the Schick share of market rose as follows:

September	8.3 percent
December	16.4 percent

The most striking feature of the above case is the fact that the consumer had *no way to verify* the validity of the published account. They had the choice of accepting it on faith, or not. Many accepted it on faith.

No Quality Superiority. Where there is no demonstrable quality superiority, share of market is determined by the marketing skills. These take such forms as persuasive propaganda, attractive packaging, etc. (See Section 19, Marketing, under Emotional Stimuli.) Price reductions in various forms provide only temporary increases in share of market, since competitors usually move promptly to take similar action.

Consumer Preference and Share of Market.   The willingness of consumers to respond to qualities and to differences they can sense has resulted in much study to:

1. Develop objective methods for measuring consumer preference and other forms of consumer response. A large body of literature is now available setting out the types of sensory tests, the methods for conducting them, and the interpretation of the resulting data. (See Section 18, under Sensory Testing.)
2. Use these methods to aid in making decisions. While much of this application has been for process control and product acceptance decisions (see Section 18), there is a growing use of these methods for market testing, product development, advertising, and marketing of products.

For some products it is easy to secure a measure of consumer preference through "forced choice" tests. For example, a table is set up in a department store and passersby are invited to taste two cups of coffee, A and B, and to express their preference. Or pairs of swatches of carpet may be shown to panels of potential buyers with the request that they indicate their preferences. For comparatively simple consumer products, these preference tests can secure good data on consumer preference. In turn, these data can be used to make sound marketing decisions.

The value of consumer preference data is greatly multiplied through correlation with data on share of market. Figure 3.2 shows such a correlation for 41 different packaged consumer products. This was an uncommonly important analysis and deserves careful study.

FIG. 3.2   Consumer preference versus share of market.

Each dot on Figure 3.2 represents a food product sold on supermarket shelves. It competes these with other products for shelf space. The competing products sell for identical prices and are packaged in identically sized boxes containing identical amounts of product. What may influence the buyer are:

1. The marketing skills, i.e., attractiveness of the package, the appeal of the prior advertising, the reputation of the manufacturer, etc.
2. The contents of the package as judged by the buyer's senses and usage, which may cause her or him to prefer A to B

On Figure 3.2 the horizontal scale shows consumer preference over the leading competitor as determined by statistically sound preference testing. The vertical scale shows the share of market versus the leading competitor, considering the two as constituting 100 percent.

It is evident that in no instance did any product exhibit a consumer preference below 25 percent (or above 75 percent). This phenomenon is undoubtedly related to the fact that a consumer quality preference above 75 percent means that the product is so superior that three out of four users can detect that superiority. Since all other factors are essentially equal, the product which is so overwhelmingly preferred takes over the entire market while its competition disappears.

In contrast to the vacant areas on the horizontal scale of consumer preference, the vertical scale of share of market has data along the entire spectrum. One product (marked A on Figure 3.2) lies squarely on the 50 percent consumer preference line, which probably means (under forced choice testing) that the users are guessing as to whether they prefer that product or its competition. Yet this product has only 10 percent share of market and its competitor 90 percent. Not only that, this inequality in share of market has persisted for years. The reason is that the 90 percent company had pioneered in that product, acquired a "prior franchise," and retained its position through good promotion thereafter.

The conclusion is that when competing products are quite similar in consumer preference, any effect of such small quality differentials is obscured by the effect of the marketing skills. In consequence, it is logical to conclude that when quality preferences are clearly evident to the user, such quality differences are decisive in share of market, all other things being equal. When quality preferences are slight, the decisive factor in share of market is the marketing skills.

As a corollary, it appears that companies are well advised to undertake quality improvements which will result in either (1) bringing them from a clearly weak to an acceptable preference or (2) bringing them from an acceptable preference to a clearly dominant preference. However, companies are not well advised to undertake quality improvements which will merely move them from one acceptable level to another, since the dominant role in share of market in such cases is played by the marketing skills. For elaboration, see Juran (1959).

It is easy for technologists to conclude that what they regard as important in the product is also of prime concern to the user. In the carpet industry, the engineers devote much effort to improving wear qualities and other technological aspects of fitness for use. However, a market survey established that consumers' reasons for selecting carpets were primarily sensory, i.e.,

Color	56 percent
Pattern	20 percent
Other sensory	6 percent
Nonsensory	18 percent

For more complex consumer products it would seem feasible, in theory, to study the relation of quality to share of market by securing quantitative data on (1) actual changes in buying patterns of consumers and (2) states of quality which may have brought about these changes.

In practice, it is soon discovered that such data are difficult to acquire and that it is also very difficult to conclude, in any one instance, why the purchase was of model A rather than B. What does emerge are some "demographic" patterns, i.e., age of buyers, size of family, etc., which favor model A rather than B. In addition, there emerge some "negatives," i.e., what not to do.

Industrial Products and Share of Market.   Industrial products are sold much more on technological performance than on sensory qualities. However, the principle of preference is still present, and there is need to find ways of relating quality to customer preference and to share of market.

One approach is that of sales analysis, as described in Section 12, under Analysis of Available Field Intelligence: Decline in Sales. For the vital few large accounts, such analyses can be made individually. For the numerous small accounts, sampling is adequate.

Another approach is to analyze the company's performance during its bidding for contracts. The practice of competitive bidding is widespread. Most government agencies are required by law to secure competitive bids before awarding large contracts. Industrial companies require their purchasing managers to do the same. The usual factors of price, delivery date, and quality enter the bidding process, as do the marketing skills. Quality includes the usual parameters of fitness for use plus the important factor of quality reputation of the manufacturer.

The ratio of awards received to bids made is of great significance. The volume of sales and profit depends importantly on this ratio. In addition, the cost of preparing bids is substantial; for large systems the cost of bid preparation is itself large. Finally, the ratio affects the morale of the people involved. (Members of a winning team fight their competitors; members of a losing team fight with each other.)

It is feasible to analyze the record of prior bids in an effort to improve the award percentage. Table 3.3 shows such an analysis involving 20 unsuccessful bids. The installation price turned out to be the biggest influencing factor. This led to a revision of the process for estimating the installation price, and an improvement in the bidding success ratio.

QUALITY LEADERSHIP AND BUSINESS STRATEGY

Among marketers there has always been a school of thought which gave quality the highest weight among the factors which determine marketability. A survey (Hopkins and Bailey, 1971) of 125 senior marketing executives as to their first preference for their own product superiority showed the following:

Form of product superiority	*Percent of marketing executives giving first preference to this form*
Superior quality	40
Lower price (or better value)	17
More features, options, or uses	12
All others	31

TABLE 3.3   Analysis of Unsuccessful Bids*

Contract proposal	Bid not accepted due to				
	Quality of design	Product price	Installation price†	Reciprocal buying	Other
A 1	⋯	✕	✕	⋯	✕
A 2	⋯		✕✕		
A 3	✕✕	✕			
A 4	✕✕	⋯	✕		
A 5	✕✕				
A 6	✕✕				
A 7	⋯	✕✕			
A 8	⋯	✕✕			
A 9	⋯	⋯	✕✕		
A 10	⋯	⋯	✕✕		
B 1	✕	⋯	✕		
B 2	⋯	⋯	⋯	✕✕	
B 3	⋯	⋯	⋯	✕✕	
B 4	⋯	⋯	⋯	✕✕	
B 5	⋯	✕	✕		
B 6	⋯	✕	✕✕		
B 7	✕✕				
B 8	⋯	✕	✕		
B 9	⋯	⋯	⋯	✕	
B 10	✕	✕	✕		
Totals	7	8	10 (of 14)	4	1

*✕ = Contributing reason; ✕✕ = main reason.
†Only 14 bids were made for installation.

Such opinions are supported by the PIMS study (Schoeffler, Buzzell, and Heany, 1974). That study, involving 521 businesses, undertook (among other things) to relate (1) competitiveness in quality with (2) share of market. The findings can be expressed as follows:

Quality vs. competitors	Number of businesses in these zones of share of market		
	Under 12%	12–26%	Over 26%
Inferior	79	58	35
Average	51	63	53
Superior	39	55	88
Total	169	176	176

Building Quality Leadership.   Quality leadership is usually the result of an original quality superiority which gains what the marketers call a "prior franchise." Once gained, this franchise can be maintained through continuing product improvement and effective market promotion.

Companies which have attained quality leadership have usually done so based on one of two principal strategies:

1. Let nature take its course. In this approach, companies apply their best efforts, confident that in time these efforts will be recognized.
2. Help nature out by adopting a positive policy, i.e., establish leadership as a formal goal and then set out to reach that goal.

Those who decide to make quality leadership a formal goal soon find that they must answer also the question, "Leadership in what?" Quality leadership can exist in any of the multiple aspects of fitness for use, but the structure of the company will differ significantly depending on which aspect is chosen.

If quality leadership is to consist of	*The company must emphasize*
Superior quality of design	Product development, systems development
Superior quality of conformance	Manufacturing quality controls
Availability	Reliability and maintainability programs
Guarantees, field service	Field service capability

Once attained, quality leadership endures until there is significant cumulative evidence that some competitor has overtaken the leader. Lacking such evidence, the leadership can endure for decades and even centuries.

However, quality leadership can also be lost through some catastrophic change. For example a leading brewing company was reported to have changed its beer brewing formulation in an effort to reduce costs. Within several years its share of market had declined dramatically. The original formula was subsequently restored but the market share did not recover. (See "The Perils of Cutting Quality," 1982.)

In some cases the quality reputation is built not around a specific company but around an association of companies. In that event this association adopts and publicizes some mark or symbol. The quality reputation becomes identified with this symbol, and the association goes to great lengths to protect this reputation.

The medieval guilds imposed strict specifications and quality controls on their members, including "export" (i.e., beyond the city) controls on the finished goods. Such export controls are common in some industrial countries today.

The growth in competition in quality has stimulated the expansion of strategic business planning to include planning for quality and quality leadership. See Section 6, under Companywide Quality Management.

The "Market Leader" Concept.   One approach to quality leadership is through development of product in collaboration with the leading user (or users) of such products. The term "leading user" here has a meaning of influential in the market, and hence likely to be followed. For example, in the medical field, a leading user might be one who is "internationally renowned; a chairman of several scientific societies; is invited to congresses as speaker or chairman; writes numerous scientific papers" (Ollson, 1986, pp. 62, 63).

Determining who is the leading user requires some analysis. (In some respects the situation is similar to the marketer's problem of discovering who within the client company is the most influential in the decision to buy.) Ollson lists ten leader types, each serving a different function.

Carryover of Failure-Prone Features. A widespread form of loss of quality leadership is through perpetuating failure-prone features of predecessor products. The guilty features are well known; the field service force is busy restoring service because of the product failures resulting from these features. Nevertheless there has been an extensive practice of carryover of those same features into new models. At the least, this practice of carryover perpetuates a sales detriment and a cost burden. At its worst it is a cancer which can destroy market share leadership of seemingly healthy product lines.

A widely publicized example was the small "tabletop" copier machine. In that case the "top ten" list of field failure modes remained essentially identical, model after model. A similar phenomenon prevailed for years in the automobile industry.

The reasons behind this carryover have much in common with the chronic internal wastes which abound in so many companies:

1. The alarm signals are disconnected. The wastes get incorporated into the budgets, and the departments are meeting their budgets.

2. It is no one's responsibility to take the initiative to get rid of the wastes.

There are also other factors. The product and process developers of course have the technological capability to eliminate much of the carryover. However, those developers are usually occupied with bringing new models to market, i.e., developing new product and process features. In addition, they share a distaste for spending their time on cleaning up old problems. In their culture there is greater social prestige in developing the new.

The surprising result can be that each department is carrying out its assigned responsibilities and yet the product line is dying. Seemingly nothing short of upper management intervention can break up the impasse.

LIFE CYCLE COSTING

In its simplest form, a sales contract is based on a purchase price for a specific product (goods or services), e.g., X cents for a glass of milk; Y dollars for a bus ticket. For simple consumable products, the purchase price is also the cost of using the product. Consuming the milk or taking the bus ride normally involves no cost for the user, beyond the original purchase price. Expressed in simple terms,

$$\text{Purchase price} = \text{cost of use}$$

As products grow in complexity and especially as they are used over long periods of time, this simple equation is no longer valid. Purchase price expands to include such factors as cost of capital invested, installation cost, deductions for resale value, etc. Cost of use expands to include costs of operation and maintenance. Even "simple" consumer products are impacted. For some articles of clothing the cumulative costs of cleaning and maintenance can easily exceed the original purchase price. (The famous comedian Ed Wynn is said to have worn the same $3.50 shoes throughout his long career in vaudeville, radio, and television. They cost him $3000 in repairs.)

The basic concept of life cycle costing is one of finding the optimum—finding that set of conditions which (1) meets the needs of both supplier and customer, and (2) minimizes their combined costs.

Life cycle cost is only one of many names given to this concept of an optimum. Other names include:

Cost of ownership

Cost of use (or usage)

Mission cost

Lifetime cost

Cost effectiveness

The life cycle cost concept can be applied to any product. The concept can be defined in models which identify the factors to be considered, the data to be acquired, and the equations to be used in arriving at life cycle costs. The slow pace to date in adopting the concept is not due to difficulty in setting up the models. Instead, the slow pace is due mainly to inadequacies in the needed data and especially to cultural resistance to adopting the life cycle cost concept.

Steps in Life Cycle Cost Analysis.   The literature has gone far to organize the subject of conducting life cycle cost analyses. The steps set out below represent a typical organized approach. For elaboration on various organized approaches, see Brook and Barasia (1977), Ebenfelt and Ogren (1974), Stokes and Stehle (1968), Toohey and Calvo (1980), and Wynholds and Skratt (1977).

Identify the Life Cycle Phases.   Optimizing life cycle cost requires striking a balance among numerous costs, some of which are antagonistic to others. The starting point is to identify the phases or activities through which the product goes during its life cycle. These activities are usually mapped out in a flow diagram as an aid to group understanding. Typical sequences of such activities include:

Product research.

Product development. (In some complex systems there may be several subphases of product development.)

Product design.

Manufacturing planning.

Production.

Installation.

Provision of spares.

Operation.

Maintenance.

Support services.

Modifications.

Disposal.

Identify the Cost Structure.   Once the phases of activity are defined the next step is to identify the cost structure associated with each phase. For example, operating costs for civilian aircraft include (Rose and Phelps, 1979):

Maintenance labor and material

Delay/flight interruptions

Administrative

Insurance

Spares holding

Training

Flight operation (crew, aircraft and traffic servicing, fuel and oil)

For an example from the Tennessee Valley Authority, see Duhan and Catlin (1973).

Acquire the Cost Data.   This step can be a formidable obstacle. At best, the prevailing accounting systems provide only part of the essential cost information. The rest must be acquired by special study, by estimate, or by restructuring the accounting system. The work involved can be reduced by concentrating the detailed efforts on the vital few cost categories. These are normally the largest in amount. However close attention must also be given to those categories which are highly sensitive, i.e., they are leveraged to respond to small changes in other factors—the "cost drivers."

Analyze Relationships.   This step undertakes to quantify the interrelationship among the cost factors. Such analysis goes far beyond organizing the figures in various ways. The main part of the analysis is to quantify the interrelationships of the activities which generate costs. For example, a comparatively simple analysis establishes that for automotive vehicles, tire wear correlates mainly with distance traveled and speed of travel. For aircraft, the tire wear correlates mainly with number of landings and takeoffs.

However, many analyses are far more complex. A common example is the relationship of designed mean time between failures (MTBF) and mean time to repair (MTTR) to the subsequent costs of operation and maintenance. For some products (e.g., certain military categories) repair and maintenance (R&M) costs over the life of the product run to many multiples of the original purchase price. These R&M costs are highly sensitive to the designed MTBF and MTTR. However, efforts to quantify the interrelationship run into complex estimates bounded by a wide range of error. For a case example involving military avionics, see Toohey and Calvo (1980).

Formulate Aids to Decision Making.   The purpose of these analyses is to aid decision making. Typically the decision maker first establishes what categories of cost are to be included in the decison-making process. Then, based on the analysis, equations are set up to arrive at the life cycle cost in terms of those same established cost categories. For example, the State of Virginia arrived at the following equation for estimating cost per hour for a certain class of highway machinery:

> Cost per hour equals initial price, plus repair parts, plus foregone interest, less resale value, all divided by operating hours (Doom, 1969, p. 25).

Breadth of Application.   Ideally the life cycle cost analysis should provide aid to sweeping decisions on grand strategy of optimizing costs. In practice this is feasible only for rather simple products. For the most part, life cycle cost analyses are being used as aids to decision making on a more limited scope; for example, see state government purchase of room air-conditioners (Doom, 1969); optimum

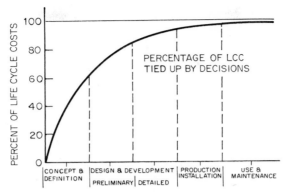

FIG. 3.3 Phases affecting life cycle cost. *(Adapted from Björklund, 1981, p. 3.)*

inventory levels (Dushman, 1970); repair level strategy, i.e., discard, base repair, or depot repair (Henderson, 1979); effect of test system requirements of operation and support costs (Gleason, 1981); optimization of number of thermal cycles (Shumaker and DuBuisson, 1976).

Probably the widest application has been in the area of industrial products. (See below under Application to Industrial Products.)

Irrespective of area of application, most investigators have concluded that the decisions which determine life cycle cost are concentrated in the early stages of the product life cycle. Figure 3.3 is a typical model. It shows that life cycle cost is determined mainly by decisions made during the very early phases of the life cycle. Such a concentration makes clear the need for providing the product researchers, developers, and designers with a good data base on the subsequent costs of production, installation, operation, and maintenance.

Application to Consumer Products. In a classic study, Gryna (1970) found that for various household appliances and television sets the ratio of life cycle costs to original price ranged from 1.9 to 4.8. (See Table 3.4.)

TABLE 3.4 Life Cycle Costing: Consumer Products

Product	Original price, $	Cost of operation plus maintenance, $	Total cost, $	Ratio, life cycle cost to original price
Room air conditioner	200	465	665	3.3
Dishwasher	245	372	617	2.5
Freezer	165	628	793	4.8
Range, electric	175	591	766	4.4
Range, gas	180	150	330	1.9
Refrigerator	230	561	791	3.5
TV (black and white)	200	305	505	2.5
TV (color)	560	526	1086	1.9
Washing machine	235	617	852	3.6

Source: Gryna, 1970.

A study, *Consumer Appliances: The Real Cost* (MIT, 1974), found the following proportions of life cycle costs to prevail during the year 1972 for color TV sets and household refrigerators:

Elements of life cycle cost	Color TV sets	Household refrigerators
Purchase price	53	36
Power	12	58
Service	35	6
Total	100	100

Lund (1978) provides some supplemental information based on a followup study.

Fody (1977) reported on how a U.S. government agency made its first application of the life cycle cost concept to the procurement of room air conditioners. The suppliers made their bids based on original price. However, the agency considered in addition the expected electric power cost based on certified energy efficiency rates. The basis for awarding the contracts then became the lowest life cycle costs rather than the lowest bid price.

Life cycle costs for automobiles have been studied in depth. Table 3.5 shows life cycle costs for intermediate size cars driven 120,000 mi (192,000 km) in 12 years.

TABLE 3.5   Life Cycle Costs, Automobiles

Original price	$10,320
Additional "ownership" costs	
Accessories	198
Registration	240
Titling	516
Insurance	6,691
Scheduled maintenance	1,169
Nonoperating taxes	33
Subtotal	$ 8,847
Operation and maintenance costs	
Gasoline	$ 6,651
Unscheduled maintenance	4,254
Tires	638
Oil	161
Gasoline tax, federal	514
Gasoline tax, other	771
Sales taxes	130
Parking, tolls	1,129
Subtotal	$14,248
Grand total	$33,415

Source: Federal Highway Administration, 1984.

Although data on life cycle cost of consumer products have become increasingly available, consumer use of such data has lagged. The major reasons include:

1. Cultural resistance (see below)
2. The economics of administering numerous small long-life contracts
3. The complexities created by multiple ownership

The most notable example of the last problem is passenger automobiles, which, in the United States, usually go through multiple ownership before being scrapped. Even under short-term guarantees, the transfer of ownership creates severe problems of administering guarantee contracts. Existing practice usually imposes a charge for transfer of short-term guarantees between successive owners. For contracts over the useful life of the product, this problem would become considerably more complicated.

Application to Industrial Products.   In terms of broad decision making, this is probably the area of greatest progress. A major example is seen in the airlines' evolution of life cycle costing strategy for aircraft engine maintenance. A critical element has been establishment of an adequate data system relative to field operation and maintenance. Data analysis then resulted in a change in grand strategy for maintenance, from the overhaul concept to the concept of on-condition maintenance. In addition, the data analysis resulted in a superior feedback to product designers and manufacturers. For a well-documented explanation, see Nowlan and Heap (1978).

Part of the competition to sell industrial equipment consists of convincing prospective buyers that their operation and maintenance costs will be low. In some cases this conviction is created by guaranteeing the operating costs, or by offering low-cost maintenance contracts. Some manufacturers provide record-keeping aids to enable users to accumulate data on competitive products as an aid to future purchasing decisions. Some industrial users build up data banks on cost of downtime for various types of industrial equipment as an input to future decision making.

The approach to making decisions to acquire capital equipment follows generally the steps set out above under the heading Steps in Life Cycle Cost Analysis. Kaufman (1969) gives an explanation of methodology along with case examples of application.

Application to Defense Industries.   During the twentieth century many governments greatly expanded their acquisition of military weaponry, both in volume and in complexity. Mostly the governments acquired these weapons by purchase rather than by expansion of government arsenals and shipyards. It was most desirable that the life cycle cost concept be applied to such weapons. However a major obstacle was the deeply rooted practice of buying based on the lowest bid price.

Starting in about the 1960s the U.S. Department of Defense organizations stepped up their efforts to make the life cycle cost concept effective in procurement contracts. Directives were issued to define the new emphasis and to clear away old obstacles. However, as events unfolded it became evident that to apply the concept to government procurement was more difficult than for comparable situations in civilian procurement. The differences have their origin in such factors as the nature of the respective missions, the system of priorities, the organization for decision making and the extent of public scrutiny. For a more detailed discussion of these differences, see Gansler (1974); also Pedrick (1968); also Bryan (1981).

The urge for applying the life cycle concept to military products has stimulated an extensive literature. Most of the published papers relate to division of the subject and to the structure of models. See, for example, Barasia and Kiang (1978), Peratino (1968), and Ryan (1968).

There are also numerous papers on application. These are mainly directed at subsystems, e.g., optimizing inventory levels. Alternatively, the applications are directed at lower level components. A published example relates to standardization of electronic modules (Laskin and Smithhisler, 1979). Another example deals with standardization of test equipment (Rosenberg and Witt, 1976). See also Eustis (1977); also Gallagher and Knobloch (1971). Application to subsystems or lower level components obviously runs the risk of suboptimizing unless care is taken to examine the impact of any proposed change on related subsystems or components.

Cultural Resistance.   This is a major force holding back the application of the life cycle cost concept. Purchase based on original price has dominated commercial practice for thousands of years. The skills, habit patterns and status of many persons—product designers, purchasing managers, marketers—have long been built around the original purchase price concept. To change over to a life cycle cost concept demands a considerable change in habit patterns with associated risks of damage to long-standing skills and status.

The most deeply rooted habits are probably those of consumers—small buyers for personal use. They keep few records on costs of operation and maintenance, and tend to underestimate the amounts. For less-than-affluent consumers the purchase of a costly product is obscured by the fact that they may lack the capital needed even for the original price and hence must borrow part of it. In addition, the laws of sales are well worked out as applied to original price contracts but are still in evolution as applied to life cycle cost contracts.

Obviously, makers of consumer goods cannot abandon marketing on original price when such is the cultural pattern. What they can do is to experiment by offering some optional models designed for lower cost of usage as a means of gaining experience and time for the day when life cycle costing comes into wide use.

Makers of industrial products also face cultural resistance in trying to use life cycle costing as a business opportunity. However, with good data they can make out a persuasive case and strike responsive chords in buyers who see in these data a way to further the interests of their company and themselves.

Contracts Based on Amount of Use.   An alternative approach to life cycle costing is through sales contracts which are based on the amount of use. Such contracts shift all the life cycle costs to the supplier, who then tends to redesign the system in a way which optimizes the cost of providing service.

The public utilities—e.g., telephone, power—are long-standing examples. These utilities do not sell a product nor do they often even lease a product; they sell only the service (e.g., watthours of electricity, message units of telephone service). In such cases the ownership of the equipment remains with the utility, which also has the responsibility of keeping the equipment maintained and repaired. The consequence is that the income of the utility is directly bound up with keeping the equipment in service. There are numerous other instances; e.g., the "U-drive" car is rented based on the actual mileage driven; laundromat machines are rented based on minutes of use.

Sale of goods can sometimes be converted into a sale of use. It is common practice for vehicle fleets to buy tires based on mileage. Airlines buy engines based on hours of use. There is much opportunity for innovation in the use of this concept.

For consumer products, the metering of actual use adds many complications. Common practice is therefore to use elapsed time as an approximation of amount of use.

PERFECTIONISM

The human being exhibits an instinctive drive for precision, beauty, and perfection. When unrestrained by economics, this drive has created the art treasures of the ages. In the arts and in esthetics, this timeless human instinct still prevails.

In the industrial society there are many situations in which this urge for perfection coincides with technological needs. In food and drug preparation, certain organisms must be completely eliminated or they will multiply and create health hazards. Nuclear reactors, underground mines, aircraft, and other structures susceptible to catastrophic destruction of life require a determined pursuit of perfection to minimize dangers to human safety. So does the mass production of hazardous products.

However, there are numerous other situations in which the pursuit of perfection is antagonistic to society, since it consumes materials and energy without adding to fitness for use, either technologically or esthetically. This wasteful activity is termed "perfectionism" because it adds cost without adding value.

Perfectionism in Quality of Design. This is often called "overdesign." Common examples are:

Long life for products which will become obsolete before they wear out.

Costly finishes on nonvisible surfaces.

Tolerances or features added beyond the needs of fitness for use. (The military budget reviewers call this "gold-plating.")

Some cases of overdesign are not simple matters of yes or no. For example, in television reception there are "fringe areas" which give poor reception with conventional circuit design. For such areas, supplemental circuitry is needed to attain good quality of image. However, this extra circuitry is for most areas an overdesign and a waste. The alternative of designing an attachment to be used only in fringe areas creates other problems, since these attachments must be installed under nonfactory conditions.

It is best to prevent overdesign during design review, while the design is still fluid. Those who understand the economics of manufacture, marketing, use, and maintenance can then challenge any design features which do not contribute to fitness for use and which therefore will add to costs without adding to income. Some systems of design review provide for classification of characteristics, e.g., essential, desirable, unessential. The unessential then become candidates for removal on the ground of perfectionism.

Overdesign is one of the targets of value analysis. See Section 13, Product Development, under Value Engineering.

Perfectionism in Quality of Conformance. Typical examples are:

Insistence on conformance to specification despite long-standing successful use of nonconforming product

Setting of appearance standards to levels beyond those sensed by users

Generally, perfectionism in quality of conformance can be held in check by separating two decisions which are all too often confounded: (1) the decision on whether product conforms to specification and (2) the decision on whether nonconforming product is fit for use. Decision (1) may be delegated to the bottom of the hierarchy. Decision (2) should be made only by people who have knowledge of fitness for use.

Perfectionism in the "Abilities." Some of the examples encountered are these:

"Worst case" designs in which provision is made to anticipate the worst combination of adverse conditions which might converge to cause a failure, even when the odds against such a combination are fantastically high. Such designs can be justified in critical situations but not necessarily in noncritical situations.

Use of unduly large factors of safety.

Use of high-duty or high-precision components for products which will be subjected to conventional usage.

Because such instances have their origin in design, the remedies are through design reviews such as are discussed above under Perfectionism in Quality of Design.

Perfectionism in Field Service. To date there has been little of this; more commonly the service has been inadequate.

Perfectionism by Government Regulators. There is an uncomfortable degree of this, though with more experience the practice tends to moderate.

Some of this perfectionism is undoubtedly influenced by the pressures to which regulators are subjected from reformers, special pleaders, and zealots. Public officials cannot readily defend themselves against all such pressures.

The Perfectionists. It is possible to categorize the people most often contributing to perfectionism, and the more usual forms in which their proposals are presented. Table 3.6 shows this relationship.

Those who advocate perfectionism often do so with the best intentions and always for reasons which seem logical to them. The resulting proposals are nevertheless of no benefit to users for one of several common reasons:

The added perfection has no value to the user. (The advocate is not aware of this.)

TABLE 3.6 Perfectionists

Basis for perfectionism	Usual guilty parties
"Superiority" which does not add to fitness for use	Top management, marketing managers
Urge to comply with the specification despite clear evidence of fitness for use	Government regulators, industrial quality managers
Belief that tighter specifications assure greater fitness for use	Researchers; designers; theoreticians
Belief that humans can be motivated to make no errors	Enthusiasts and fanatics behind misguided motivational programs
Contention that failure to conform is proof of unfitness for use	Reformers, politicians, journalists, publicity seekers
Adverse publicity given to isolated failures	Muckrakers, publicity seekers

The added perfection has value to the user, but not enough to make up for the added cost. (The advocate is unaware of the extent of the costs involved.)

The added perfection is proposed not to benefit the user but to protect the personal position of the advocate (e.g., he or she has responsibility for conformance but not for cost), or to make a hero of the advocate in the eyes of some bloc.

The weaknesses of these proposals are all related back to costs: e.g., ignorance of the costs, no responsibility for costs, indifference to costs due to preoccupation with something else. Those who do have responsibility for the costs should quantify them and then dramatize the results in order to provide the best challenge.

Defenses against Perfectionism. There are several of these: quantifying the economics; dramatizing the feedback of fitness for use; use of the concept that "the customer is right."

Quantifying the Economics. A major defense against perfectionism is to quantify and dramatize the costs. Precision, reliability, or conformance can always be improved, but the cost of improvement can rise spectacularly as we approach perfection.

Dramatizing Fitness for Use. Originally, evidence of fitness for use is derived from product development and test information. Then, as the product is marketed, new evidence comes from the marketplace in the form of repeat orders, absence of complaints, absence of orders for spare parts, etc. This growing feedback should be embodied into the decision-making process, e.g., material review board decisions, deviation practices, design changes.

"The Customer Is Right." Use can also be made of the concept that "the customer is right," not only as to things customers can sense but also as to things customers cannot sense.

REFERENCES

Barasia, R. K. and Kiang, T. D. (1978). "Development of a Life Cycle Management Cost Model." *Proceedings, Annual Reliability and Maintainability Symposium.* IEEE, New York, pp. 254–260.

Björklund, O. (1981). "Life Cycle Costs; An Analysis Tool for Design, Marketing, and Service." *Q-Bulletin* of Alfa-Laval, no. 2, pp. 1–4.

Brook, Cyril and Barasia, Ramesh (1977). "A Support System Life Cycle Cost Model." *Proceedings, Annual Reliability and Maintainability Symposium.* IEEE, New York, pp. 297–302.

Bryan, N. S. (1981). "Contracting for Life Cycle Cost to Improve System Affordability." *Proceedings, Annual Reliability and Maintainability Symposium.* IEEE, New York, pp. 342–345.

"Consumer Guide on Tires Is Issued by U.S. Agency" (1980). *New York Times,* Dec. 31, p. 6.

"Dishwashing Liquids" (1984). *Consumer Reports,* July, pp. 412–414.

Doom, I. F. (1969). *Total Cost Purchasing Applied to Heavy Equipment Procurement.* Virginia Highway Research Council, Charlottesville.

Duhan, Stanley and Catlin, John C., Sr. (1973). "Total Life Cost and the 'Ilities'." *Proceedings, Annual Reliability and Maintainability Symposium.* IEEE, New York, pp. 491–495.

Dushman, Allan (1970). "Effect of Reliability on Life Cycle Inventory Cost." *Proceedings, Annual Reliability and Maintainability Symposium.* IEEE, New York, pp. 549–561.

Ebenfelt, Hans and Ogren, Stig (1974). "Some Experiences from the Use of an LCC Approach." *Proceedings, Annual Reliability and Maintainability Symposium.* IEEE, New York, pp. 142–146.

Eustis, G. E. (1977). "Reduced Support Costs for Shipboard Electronic Systems." *Proceedings, Annual Reliability and Maintainability Symposium.* IEEE, New York, pp. 316–319.

Fody, Theodore, J. (1977). "The Procurement of Window Air Conditioners Using Life Cycle Costing." *Proceedings, Annual Reliability and Maintainability Symposium.* IEEE, New York, pp. 81–88.

Gallagher, B. M. and Knobloch, W. H. (1971). "Helicopter Auxiliary Power Unit Cost of Ownership." *Proceedings, Annual Symposium on Reliability.* IEEE, New York, pp. 285–291.

Gansler, J. S. (1974). "Application of Life Cycle Costing to the DOD System Acquisition Decision Process." *Proceedings, Annual Reliability and Maintainability Symposium,* IEEE, New York, pp. 147–148.

Gleason, Daniel (1981). "The Cost of Test System Requirements." *Proceedings, Annual Reliability and Maintainability Symposium.* IEEE, New York, pp. 108–113.

Gross, Irwin (1978). "Insights from Pricing Research." In *Pricing Practices and Strategies,* ed. E. L. Bailey. The Conference Board, New York, pp. 34–39.

Gryna, F. M., Jr. (1970). "User Costs of Poor Product Quality." Doctoral dissertation, University of Iowa, Iowa City. For additional data and discussion, see Gryna, F. M., Jr. (1970). "Quality Costs: User vs. Manufacturer." *Quality Progress,* June, pp. 10–13.

Henderson, J. T. (1979). "A Computerized LCC/ORLA Methodology." *Proceedings, Annual Reliability and Maintainability Symposium.* IEEE, New York, pp. 51–55.

Hopkins, David S. and Bailey, Earl (1971). "New Product Pressures." *The Conference Record,* June. pp. 16–24.

Juran, J. M. (1959). "A Note on Economics of Quality." *Industrial Quality Control,* February, pp. 20–23.

Juran, J. M. (1969). "Mobilizing for the 1970s." *Quality Progress,* August, pp. 8–17.

Juran, J. M. (1970). "Consumerism and Product Quality." *Quality Progress,* July, pp. 18–27.

Kaufman, R. J. (1969). "Life Cycle Costing: Decision-Making Tool for Capital Equipment Acquisitions." *Journal of Purchasing,* August, pp. 16–31.

Kegarise, R. J. and Miller, G. D. (1986). "An Alcoa-Kodak Joint Team." *The Juran Report,* no. 6, pp. 29–34.

Kegarise, R. J., Heil, M., Miller, G. D., and Miller, G. (1987). "A Supplier/Purchaser Project: From Fear to Trust." *The Juran Report,* no. 8, pp. 284–252.

Laskin, R. and Smithhisler, W. L. (1979). "The Economics of Standard Electronic Packaging." *Proceedings, Annual Reliability and Maintainability Symposium.* IEEE, New York, pp. 67–72.

Levitt, Theodore (1960). "Marketing Myopia." *Harvard Business Review,* July–August, pp. 26–28ff.

Lindbergh, Charles A. (1970). *The Wartime Journals of Charles A. Lindbergh.* Harcourt Brace Jovanovich, New York.

Lund, Robert T. (1978). "Life Cycle Costing: A Business and Societal Instrument." *Management Review,* April, pp. 17–23.

MacGowan, T. G. (1957). *Competitive Pricing.* National Industrial Conference Board Studies in Business Policies, no. 84, New York, pp. 116–119.

MIT (1974). *Consumer Appliances: The Real Cost.* Prepared jointly by the Massachusetts Institute of Technology Center for Policy Alternatives with the Charles Stark Draper Laboratory, Inc. Sponsored by the National Science Foundation. Available from RANN Document Center, National Science Foundation, Washington, DC 20550.

Morris, Ruby Turner and Bronson, Claire Sekulski (1969). "The Chaos of Competition Indicated by Consumer Reports." *Journal of Marketing,* July, pp. 26–34.

Mottl, N. J. and Shiah, P. M. (1974). "Prepared Consumer Standards." *ASQC Technical Conference Transactions,* Milwaukee, pp. 218–222.

Nowlan, F. S. and Heap, H. F. (1978). *Reliability Centered Maintenance.* Document ADA066579, Defense Documentation Center, Alexandria, VA.

Ollson, John Ryding (1986). "The Market-Leader Method; User-Oriented Development." *Proceedings, 30th EOQC Annual Conference,* pp. 59–68.

Pedrick, P. C. (1968). "Survey of Life Cycle Costing Practices of Non-Defense Industry." *Proceedings, Annual Symposium on Reliability.* IEEE, New York, pp. 188–192.

Peratino, G. S. (1968). "Air Force Approach to Life Cycle Costing." *Proceedings, Annual Symposium on Reliability.* IEEE, New York, pp. 184–187.

"The Perils of Cutting Quality" (1982). *New York Times,* Aug. 22.

PIMS (1978). "Pricing High-Quality Products." *The PIMSletter.* The Strategic Planning Institute, Cambridge, MA.

"Pricing of Products Is Still an Art." (1981). *Wall Street Journal,* Nov. 25, pp. 25, 33.

"The Problem of Being Premium" (1978). *Forbes,* pp. 56, 57.

Riesz, Peter C. (1979). "Price-Quality Correlations for Packaged Food Products," *Journal of Consumer Affairs.*

Rose, John and Phelps, E. L. (1979). "Cost of Ownership Application to Airplane Design." *Proceedings, Annual Reliability and Maintainability Symposium.* IEEE, New York, pp. 47–50.

Rosenberg, H. and Witt, J. H. (1976). "Effects on LCC of Test Equipment Standardization." *Proceedings, Annual Reliability and Maintainability Symposium.* IEEE, New York, pp. 287–292.

Ryan, W. J. (1968). "Procurement Views of Life Cycle Costing." *Proceedings, Annual Symposium on Reliability.* IEEE, New York, pp. 164–168.

Schoeffler, Sidney, Buzzell, Robert D., and Heany, Donald F. (1974). "Impact of Strategic Planning on Profit Performance." *Harvard Business Review,* March–April, pp. 137–145.

Shumaker, M. J. and DuBuisson, J. C. (1976). "Tradeoff of Thermal Cycling vs Life Cycle Costs." *Proceedings, Annual Reliability and Maintainability Symposium.* IEEE, New York, pp. 300–305.

Stokes, R. G. and Stehle, F. N. (1968). "Some Life-Cycle Cost Estimates for Electronic Equipment: Methods and Results." *Proceedings, Annual Reliability and Maintainability Symposium.* IEEE, New York, pp. 169–183.

Toohey, Edward F. and Calvo, Alberto B. (1980). "Cost Analyses for Avionics Acquisition." *Proceedings, Annual Reliability and Maintainability Symposium.* IEEE, New York, pp. 85–90.

Wynholds, Hans W. and Skratt, John P. (1977). "Weapon System Parametric Life Cycle Cost Analysis." *Proceedings, Annual Reliability and Maintainability Symposium.* IEEE, New York, pp. 303–309.

SECTION 4
QUALITY COSTS[1]

Frank M. Gryna

[1]In the Third Edition, the section on Quality Costs was prepared by Daniel M. Lundvall and J. M. Juran.

EVOLUTION OF THE QUALITY COST CONCEPT

All organizations make use of the concept of identifying the costs needed to carry out the various functions—product development, marketing, personnel, production, etc. Until the 1950s this concept had not been extended to the quality function, except for the departmental activities of inspection and test. There were, of course, many other quality-related costs, but they were scattered among various accounts, especially "overhead" accounts.

During the 1950s there evolved numerous quality-oriented staff departments. The heads of these new departments were faced with "selling" their activities to the company managers. Because the main language of those managers was money, there emerged the concept of studying quality-related costs as a means of communication between the quality staff departments and the company managers.

Over the decades as the staff quality specialists extended their studies, some surprises emerged:

The quality-related costs were much larger than had been shown in the accounting reports. For most companies these costs ran in the range of 20 to 40 percent of sales.

The quality costs were not simply the result of factory operation; the support operations were also major contributors.

The bulk of the costs were the result of poor quality. Such costs had been buried in the standards, but they were in fact avoidable.

While the costs of poor quality were avoidable, there was no clear responsibility for action to reduce them. Neither was there any structured approach for doing so.

These findings emerged slowly, amid a good deal of confusion. At the outset many quality specialists took their companies into vague quality cost "programs" without being clear on the objectives. Gradually the objectives emerged in two main forms:

1. Estimate the costs of poor quality as a "one-shot" study, and then use the findings to identify specific projects for improvement.
2. Expand the accounting system to quantify quality costs, and then publish the results as a continuing scoreboard. The expectation was that the published figures would stimulate managers to take action to reduce the costs.

It has turned out that these two objectives are interrelated. Some companies which opted for objective 1 did use the estimates to identify improvement projects, after which they actually made improvements. Having done so, they found that to hold the gains they needed controls, including financial controls. Those financial controls were then established based on quantifying the pertinent quality costs. While there is a logic behind both objectives 1 and 2, getting actual cost reductions solely through publication has turned out to be illusory. By themselves, the published figures do *not* stimulate action unless the company sets up a structured process for quality improvement. (See generally, Section 22 on Quality Improvement.) Identifying the specific projects is a necessary step in that structured approach, but it is not sufficient. The full structure must be set up.

Lessons Learned.   Since those early decades a great deal of experience has been accumulated, leading to some useful lessons learned.

The Meaning of "Quality Costs."   The term "quality costs" had different meanings to different people. Some equated "quality costs" with the costs of attaining quality. Others equated the term with the costs of running the Quality Department. The emerging interpretation of the quality specialists has been to equate "quality costs" with the cost of poor quality (mainly the costs of finding and correcting defective work).

The trend has been to adopt the interpretation of the quality specialists. Increasingly, when managers use the term "quality costs" they mean the cost of poor quality. In this handbook, the term "quality costs" means the *cost of poor quality*.

Objectives of Evaluation.   The accumulated experience has also identified the main objectives which lead companies to go into programs of evaluating quality costs. The primary objectives are:

1. *Quantify the size of the quality problem in language that will have impact on upper management:*   The language of money improves communication between middle managers and upper managers. In some companies the need to improve communications on quality-related matters has been so acute as to become a major objective for embarking on a study of the costs of poor quality.

Some managers say: "We don't need to spend time to translate the defects into dollars. We realize that quality is important and we already know what the major problems are." Typically when the study is made, these managers are surprised by two results. First, the quality costs turn out to be much higher than had been realized. In many industries they are in excess of 20 percent of sales. Second, while the distribution of the quality costs confirms some of the known problem areas, it also reveals other problem areas that had not previously been recognized.

2. *Identify major opportunities for cost reduction:*   Costs of poor quality do not exist as a homogeneous mass. Instead, they are the result of some specific segments, each traceable to some specific cause. These segments are unequal in size, and a relative few of the segments account for the bulk of the costs. A major byproduct of evaluation of costs of poor quality is identification of these vital few segments.

3. *Identify opportunities for reducing customer dissatisfaction and associated threats to produce salability:*   Some costs of poor quality are the result of product failures which take place after sale. In part, these costs are paid by the manufacturer in the form of warranty charges, claims, etc. But whether the costs are paid by the manufacturer or not, the failures add to customers' costs due to downtime and other forms of disturbance. Analysis of the manufacturer's costs, supplemented by marketing research into customers' costs of poor quality, can identify the vital few areas of high costs. These areas then lead to problem identification.

While the above have turned out to be the primary objectives of evaluation, there have been secondary objectives as well:

4. *Expand budgetary and cost controls:*   Most companies establish financial controls on a basis which parallels the departmental organization. The resulting budgets and cost controls have included the costs of inspection and test since these costs are incurred by a recognized department—Inspection and Test. However, most companies have not established financial controls on such costs as scrap, rework, and field failures which cut across departmental lines. As a result, one objective of evaluating quality costs is to expand budgetary and cost controls to cover the nondepartmental costs of poor quality.

5. *Stimulate improvement through publication:*   Some companies have undertaken to evaluate costs of poor quality in the belief that publication of the cost data will stimulate the responsible managers to take action to reduce the costs. The realities are that publication alone is not enough. As noted above, this seemingly logical objective has not been borne out in practice. Publication alone makes no provision for identifying projects, establishing clear responsibilities, providing resources, and taking other essential steps. (See generally, Section 22 on Quality Improvement.)

Scoreboards, if properly designed, can be a healthy stimulus to competition among departments, plants, and divisions. To work effectively, the scoreboard must be supplemented by a structured improvement program. In addition, scoreboards must be designed to take into account inherent differences in operations among various organizational units. Otherwise, comparisons made will become a source of friction.

The Language of Money Is Essential.   Another lesson learned is the soundness of the concept of using money as a language. Money *is* the basic language of upper management. Despite the prevalence of estimates, the figures have provided upper managers with information showing:

The overall size of the quality costs

Their prevalence in areas beyond manufacture

The major areas for potential improvement

Without the estimated quality cost figures, the communication of such information to upper managers would have been slower and less effective.

Why High Quality Costs Have Persisted.   Most companies have for years made various forms of cost reduction: e.g., improvement budgets, management by objectives, and structured annual improvement programs. For the most part, these efforts have addressed "conventional" areas of cost reduction: product redesign to reduce cost of materials and manufacture; methods improvement to reduce labor costs; automation; new facilities to increase productivity; and improved materials management to reduce costs of material handling, warehousing, distribution, and inventories. These same efforts did not address the "unconventional" quality-related costs which were largely buried in the overheads. The fact that these costs could not readily be allocated to specific departments was a further and serious limitation.

A related lesson learned has been that new organization machinery is needed to attack and reduce the high costs of poor quality. The nature of this organization machinery is discussed in Section 22, Quality Improvement.

Some Quality Cost "Programs" Have Failed.   There have been numerous efforts by companies to use quality cost information as a basis for making improvements. Many of these efforts have failed. The reasons are mostly those discussed later in this section, under the heading Why Quality Cost Programs Fail.

CATEGORIES OF COST OF POOR QUALITY

Many companies summarize these costs into four broad categories. These categories and examples of typical subcategories are discussed below. (A useful reference that includes details of these four categories is ASQC, 1986. A reference that applies these same categories to a service industry, banking, is Aubrey and Zimbler, 1982.)

Internal Failure Costs. These are costs associated with defects that are found prior to transfer of the product to the customer. They are costs that would disappear if no defects existed in the product prior to shipment. Examples of subcategories are:

Scrap: The labor, material, and (usually) overhead on defective product that cannot economically be repaired. The titles are numerous—scrap, spoilage, defectives, etc.

Rework: The costs of correcting defectives to make them fit for use.

Failure analysis: The costs of analyzing nonconforming product to determine causes.

Scrap and rework—supplier: The costs of scrap and rework due to nonconforming product received from suppliers.

One hundred percent sorting inspection: The costs of finding defective units in product lots which contain unacceptably high levels of defectives.

Reinspection, retest: The costs of reinspection and retest of products that have undergone rework or other revision.

Avoidable process losses: The cost of losses that occur even with conforming product. For example, "overfill" of containers (going to customers) due to excessive variability in filling and measuring equipment.

Downgrading: The difference between the normal selling price and the reduced price due to quality reasons.

External Failure Costs. These are costs associated with defects that are found after product is shipped to the customer. These costs also would disappear if there were no defects. Examples are:

Warranty charges: The costs involved in replacing or making repairs to products that are still within the warranty period

Complaint adjustment: The costs of investigation and adjustment of justified complaints attributable to defective product or installation

Returned material: The costs associated with receipt and replacement of defective product received from the field

Allowances: The costs of concessions made to customers due to substandard products accepted by the customer as is or to conforming product that does not meet fitness-for-use needs.

Appraisal Costs. These are the costs incurred to determine the degree of conformance to quality requirements. Examples are:

Incoming inspection and test: The costs of determining the quality of purchased product, whether by inspection on receipt, by inspection at the source, or by surveillance

In-process inspection and test: The costs of in-process evaluation of conformance to requirements

Final inspection and test: The costs of evaluation of conformance to requirements for product acceptance

Product quality audits: The costs of performing quality audits on in-process or finished products

Maintaining accuracy of test equipment: The costs of keeping measuring instruments and equipment in calibration

Inspection and test materials and services: The costs of materials and supplies in inspection and test work (e.g., x-ray film) and services (e.g., electric power) where significant

Evaluation of stocks: The costs of testing products in field storage or in stock to evaluate degradation

In collecting appraisal costs, what is decisive is the kind of work done and not the department name (the work may be done by chemists in the laboratory, by sorters in Production, by testers in Inspection, or by an external firm engaged for the purpose of testing).

Prevention Costs.   These are costs incurred to keep failure and appraisal costs to a minimum. Examples are:

Quality planning: This includes the broad array of activities which collectively create the overall quality plan and the numerous specialized plans. It includes also the preparation of procedures needed to communicate these plans to all concerned.

New-products review: The costs of reliability engineering and other quality-related activities associated with the launching of new designs.

Process planning: The costs of process capability studies, inspection planning, and other activities associated with the manufacturing process.

Process control: The costs of in-process inspection and test to determine the status of the process (rather than for product acceptance).

Quality audits: The costs of evaluating the execution of activities in the overall quality plan.

Supplier quality evaluation: The costs of evaluating supplier quality activities prior to supplier selection, auditing the activities during the contract, and associated effort with suppliers.

Training: The cost of preparing and conducting quality-related training programs. As in the case of appraisal costs, some of this work may be done by personnel who are not on the payroll of the Quality Department. The decisive criterion is again the type of work, not the name of the department performing the work.

The costs of poor quality are a collection of costs that are incurred by many departments in a company. An example ("Quality Costs," 1975) for one company is shown in Table 4.1.

Although many organizations have found it useful to divide the overall cost into the internal failure, external failure, appraisal, and prevention categories, the structure is not a panacea. In defining the costs of poor quality for a given organization, the following points should be kept in mind:

1. The definitions should be tailor-made for each organization. The usual approach is to review the literature and select those detailed categories which apply to the organization. The titles used should be those of the organization, not the literature. This selected list is then discussed with the various functions to

TABLE 4.1 Quality Cost Matrix

	Prevention	Appraisal	Failure
Design	1. Design reviews 2. Design checking	1. Prototype inspection 2. Design evaluation tests 3. Qualification tests	1. Redesign efforts 2. Scrap, rework, warranty, unplanned purchases, and lost-time costs due to design deficiencies
Purchasing	1. Supplier capability surveys 2. Purchase order tech data review and control 3. Supplier product inspection and test planning	1. Source surveillance 2. Incoming inspection and test 3. First article inspection and test 4. Qualification test	1. Evaluation, disposition, corrective action, and repurchasing efforts for supplier product rejects. 2. Scrap, rework, lost time, and warranty costs due to defective purchased material
Production	1. Machine and process capability studies 2. Tool inspection and control 3. Preventive maintenance 4. Process control and inspection and test planning 5. Inspection and test equipment design 6. Prevention training programs 7. Quality audits and administration 8. Customer inspection liaison	1. Product inspection and test 2. Process control measurements 3. Pack and ship inspection 4. Stock room audits 5. Calibration and maintenance of measurement equipment 6. Production environmental tests	1. Review, disposition, and corrective action efforts for nonconforming material 2. Scrap, rework, lost time, and warranty costs due to deficient workmanship, tooling, maintenance, and operator instructions 3. Rework or redesign costs for deficient manufacturing plans, procedures, and tooling

Source: "Quality Costs," 1975.

4.7

identify additional categories, refine the wording, and decide on broad groupings, if any, for the costs. The resulting definitions are "right" for the organization. Whether they conform to the literature is not critical. It is far more important that the definition within an organization be based on local needs.

(It would be useful if all organizations defined the cost of poor quality in the same way. This would then permit comparisons among organizations and eventually lead to the development of typical values by type of industry. The difficulties of accomplishing such standardization are so formidable that all attempts have been unsuccessful.)

2. The key categories are the failure cost elements because these provide the major opportunity for reduction in costs and for removal of the causes of customer dissatisfaction. These are the costs that should be attacked first. Appraisal costs are also an area for reduction, especially if the causes of the failures are identified and removed so as to reduce the need for appraisal. The compilation of prevention costs can be initially important because it highlights the small investment made in prevention activities and suggests the potential for an increase in prevention costs with the aim of reducing failure costs.

Experience suggests, however, that continuing measurement of prevention costs can often be excluded in order to (a) focus on the major opportunity, i.e., failure costs and (b) avoid the time spent discussing what should be counted as prevention costs.

(Strictly defined, the "cost of poor quality" is the sum of the internal and external failure cost categories. This assumes that those elements of appraisal costs— e.g., 100 percent sorting inspection—necessitated by inadequate processes are classified under internal failures. Some practitioners use the four broad categories but refer to the failure categories as resultant costs and the appraisal and prevention categories as controllable costs.)

3. Agreement should be reached on the categories of cost to be included before any data are collected. Upper management should be a party to this agreement. Initially, summarized data on scrap and rework can gain management's attention and stimulate the need for a full study. Such summaries can be an impetus for management to become personally involved by calling and chairing the meetings to discuss a draft definition of the costs of poor quality. The draft should be prepared jointly by the quality specialist and the accountant with inputs from all areas.

4. The costs of poor quality have in the past been associated with costs that directly involve the product, e.g., scrap, inspection, etc. However, the trend is to broaden the concept; i.e., poor quality is increasingly being viewed as applying to any activity in the company. Thus, any work that must be discarded or repeated is viewed as a cost of poor quality. Some of these costs can be readily identified and should be included in an overall study. An example is the cost incurred when a customer receives an incorrect shipment.

5. Certain costs routinely incurred in a company may have been accepted as inevitable but are really part of the costs of poor quality. Examples are the costs of redesigning the product due to deficiencies in fitness for use and the costs of changing manufacturing processes because of an inability to meet product specifications. If the original design and original manufacturing plans had been adequate, these costs would not have occurred. Typically, these costs have been accepted as normal operating costs, but should be viewed as opportunities for improvement and subsequent cost reduction.

Ten "scenarios" describing issues in defining and using quality costs are given by Gryna (1978).

Example. An example of a study for a tire manufacturer is shown in Table 4.2. This example resulted in some conclusions that are typical in these studies:

1. The total of almost $900,000 per year is large.
2. Most (79.1 percent) of the total is concentrated in failure costs, specifically in "waste-scrap" and consumer adjustments.
3. Failure costs are about five times the appraisal costs. Failure costs must be attacked first.
4. A small amount (4.3 percent) is spent on prevention.
5. There are some consequences of poor quality that could not be conveniently quantified, e.g., "customer ill will" and "customer policy adjustment." Here, the factors were listed as a reminder of their existence.

As a result of this study, management decided to increase the budget for prevention activities. Three engineers were assigned to identify and pursue specific quality improvement projects.

CONTROVERSIAL COST CATEGORIES

As the detailed categories of the cost of poor quality are identified, there are some that will be controversial. Much of the controversy centers around the point:

TABLE 4.2 Annual Quality Cost—Tire Manufacturer

1. Cost of quality failures—losses		
a. Defective stock	$ 3,276	0.37
b. Repairs to product	$ 73,229	8.31
c. Collect scrap	$ 2,288	0.26
d. Waste-scrap	$187,428	21.26
e. Consumer adjustments	$408,200	46.31
f. Downgrading products	$ 22,838	2.59
g. Customer ill will	Not counted	
h. Customer policy adj.	Not counted	
Total	$697,259	79.10%
2. Cost of appraisal		
a. Incoming inspection	$ 32,655	2.68
b. Inspection 1	$ 32,582	3.70
c. Inspection 2	$ 25,200	2.86
d. Spot-check inspection	$ 65,910	7.37
Total	$147,347	16.61%
3. Cost of prevention		
a. Local plant Quality control engineering	$ 7,848	0.89
b. Corporate Quality control engineering	$ 30,000	3.40
Total	$ 37,848	4.29%
Grand total	$882,454	100.00%

"These are not quality-related costs but costs that are part of normal operating expenses and therefore should not be included." Examples are:

1. Inclusion of overhead on top of direct labor and direct material costs of scrap and rework. (One approach is to include variable overhead but exclude fixed overhead costs.)

2. Unavoidable manufacturing waste. These are not defective parts, but trim removed from the beginning of a coil of wire, excess material surrounding a molded plastic part, spillage of a chemical loaded into a process. It is argued that this is a normal part of operating a process.

3. Profit lost on scrapped product.

4. Product liability costs.

5. Depreciation on measuring equipment.

6. Preventive maintenance. (Many of the controversial categories are classified as prevention costs. Ironically, prevention usually accounts for less than 5 percent of the total quality cost.)

7. Tool maintenance.

8. Production delays due to a high scrap rate.

9. Loss in customer good will and sales.

10. Loss in morale.

Arguments about including such categories can result in the downfall of the entire study. If the numbers are included without prior agreement, then doubt is cast on the entire study because it is claimed that the controversial costs were included in order to increase the total.

In most companies, the cost of poor quality is a large sum, frequently larger than the company's profits. This is true even when the controversial categories are not included, so it seems prudent to omit these categories and avoid the controversy in order to focus attention on the major areas of potential cost reduction. Numerous efforts to quantify quality costs have failed because of tenacious insistence by some specialists that certain controversial categories be included. A useful guide is to ask: "Suppose all defects disappeared. Would the cost in question also disappear?" A "yes" answer means that the cost is associated with quality problems and therefore should be included. A "no" answer means that the category should not be included in the cost of poor quality.

At the minimum, controversial categories should be separated out of the totals so that attention will be directed to the main issues.

Another controversy concerns the categorization of cost items. Some examples are:

1. Should 100 percent inspection costs be included as part of appraisal costs or internal failure costs? If the 100 percent inspection was performed in order to improve an unsatisfactory quality level, then it is part of an internal failure cost. If the quality level is satisfactory but 100 percent inspection is performed because of a requirement by the customer or management, then the cost is an appraisal cost.

2. Should the costs of investigating and correcting the causes of failures be included as part of prevention costs or failure costs? The point is made that the investigations will prevent future defects. As the investigations were initiated because of actual failures, we believe that such efforts should be included

as failure costs. Design reviews and other activities connected with the evaluation of new designs would be classified as prevention.

Such controversies should be settled quickly (even if arbitrarily) and not permitted to divert attention from the main target—the failure costs.

There are also costs incurred that may result in understating the costs of poor quality. These "hidden" costs include:

1. Potential lost sales.

2. Costs of redesign due to quality reasons.

3. Costs of changing manufacturing processes due to inability to meet quality requirements.

4. Costs of software changes due to quality reasons.

5. Costs included in standards because history shows that a certain level of defects is inevitable and allowances should be included in standards:

   a. *Extra material purchased:* The purchasing agent orders 5 percent more than the production quantity needed.

   b. *Allowances for scrap and rework during production:* History shows that 3 percent is "normal" and accountants have built this into the cost standards. One accountant said, "Our scrap cost is zero. We make about 3 percent defective and have built this into our standard cost system. The production departments are able to stay within this 3 percent and therefore the scrap cost is zero."

   c. *Allowances in time standards for scrap and rework:* One manufacturer allows 9.6 percent in the time standard for certain operations to cover scrap and rework.

In such cases, the alarm signals ring only when the standard value is exceeded. However, even when operating within those standards, the costs should be a part of the cost of poor quality. They represent opportunities for improvement.

6. Extra manufacturing costs due to defects. These include additional costs for space, inventory charges, and overtime.

7. Scrap not reported. This may mean scrap that is never reported because of fear of reprisals, or scrap that is charged to a general ledger account without an identification as scrap.

8. Excess process costs for acceptable product. For example, a process for filling packages with a dry soap mix meets requirements for label weight on the contents. However, the process aim is set above label weight to account for the variability in the filling process. If the variability is "large" then the aim must be set far enough above the minimum to accomodate the variability. A reduction in variability could mean setting the aim closer to the minimum and thus reduce the average amount of overfill.

9. Cost of errors made in support operations such as order filling, production control, etc.

10. Costs of poor quality within a supplier's plant. These costs are included in the selling price.

These hidden costs can accumulate to a large amount. (Brown and Kane, 1978, report a multiplier effect of 3 or 4 times the reported failure cost.) Where agreement can be reached to include some of these costs, and where credible data or estimates are available, then they should be included in the initial study on the cost of poor quality. Otherwise, they should be left for future exploration.

The results of research on difficulties in complementation of quality cost concepts are summarized by Dale and Plunkett (1986). Hagan (1985) traces some evolution of quality costs and proposes certain changes in the definition and use.

MAKING THE INITIAL COST STUDY

It would seem logical that a study on the cost of poor quality would be made by the accountant, but the usual approach follows a different scenario. A quality manager learns about the quality cost concept and speaks with the accountant about making a study. The accountant responds that "the books are not kept that way." The accountant does provide numbers on scrap, rework, or certain other categories, but is not convinced to take the initiative to prepare and define a complete list of categories and collect the data. The quality manager decides that the study should be made and follows one of two routes: (1) unilaterally prepares a definition of the categories and collects data or (2) presents the limited data provided by the accountant to upper management with a recommendation that a full study be made using the resources of Accounting, Quality, and other functions. To assure acceptance of the results of the study, the second approach is preferred.

A recommended approach is this:

1. Present to management whatever information is readily available to show that the quality problem is potentially big. This information has maximum impact if it is in the language of money.

2. Recommend that someone in management chair a task force to determine the costs of poor quality. The task force should include personnel from Accounting and major line functions. More simply, the operating committee of the plant can act as the task force, the study being regarded as an agenda item for their meetings.

3. Propose a list of categories comprising the costs of poor quality. The list can be prepared in a short time by the quality manager using the literature plus inputs from Accounting and other functions.

4. Recommend that upper management finalize the definitions and assign responsibilities, with a schedule for data collection.

This approach provides an opportunity for upper management to demonstrate leadership on quality, and it also assures the involvement of functions so that the study receives priority and the results are recognized as credible. Without leadership by upper management, the study will likely be made by the Quality manager with minimum input from others. The risk is that the results will be viewed with skepticism because they were prepared by someone with a biased viewpoint.

Next comes the problem of obtaining the figures. There are two main approaches:

1. *By estimate:* This is the practical approach. It involves only a modest amount of effort. It can, in a few days or weeks, find out enough about quality related costs to tell:

   Whether there is a major cost reduction opportunity or not

   Where this opportunity is concentrated

2. *By enlarging the accounting system:* This is a more elaborate approach. It requires a lot of effort from various departments, especially Accounting and Quality. It also takes a lot of time, running into months and even years.

In the early stages of quality improvement, the estimates are good enough. They involve less work and they provide answers in far less time. The study in Table 4.2 required only 3 weeks and it was conducted in an Industrial Engineering Department by personnel who had no prior knowledge of quality costs.

Many companies have chosen to embark on programs of enlarging the accounting system—setting up to compute and publish "quality costs." All too often these programs have run into maddening delay due to the time required to define the accounting categories, argue out the classifications, set up the data systems, etc. Still more delay has resulted from preoccupation with a level of accuracy not needed for managerial decision making.

To illustrate, the cost of defect X in an electronics company was $3 million per year. That figure was an estimate. The real figure might have been as high as $3.5 million or as low as $2.5 million. Had the accuracy of the estimates been challenged, the managers' response would have been: "All three figures are too high, so let's go after the cost reduction." Over a wide range of estimate, managerial decisions are identical. In the initial study, estimates within 20 percent are sufficient for taking action.

The initial study collects cost data from different sources:

1. *Established accounts:* Examples are appraisal activities conducted by an Inspection Department and warranty expenses to respond to customer problems.
2. *Analysis of ingredients of established accounts:* For example, an account called "customer returns" may report the cost of all goods returned. However, returns are made to reduce inventories as well as to send back defective product. Hence, it may be necessary to go back to the basic return documents to separate the quality costs from the rest.
3. *Basic accounting documents:* For example, some product inspection is done by Production Department employees. By securing their names and the associated payroll data, it is feasible to quantify these quality costs.
4. *Estimates:* Several approaches may be needed.
    a. *Temporary records:* For example, some production workers spend part of their time repairing defective product. It may be feasible to arrange with their supervisor to create a temporary record so as to evaluate the repair time and thereby the repair cost. This cost can then be extrapolated for the time period to be covered by the study.
    b. *Work sampling:* In another approach, random observations of activities are taken and the percent of time spent in each of a number of predefined categories can then be estimated. (See Salvendy, 1982, chapter 4.6.)
    c. *Allocation:* For example, in one of the engineering departments, some of the engineers are engaged part time in making product failure analyses. However, the department makes no provision for charging engineering time to multiple accounts. Ask each engineer to make an estimate of time spent on product failure analysis.
    d. *Standard costs data:* Examples include scrap, rework, and replacement of field samples. Note that such data may be based on history that is obsolete.
    e. *Opinions of knowledgeable personnel:* Examples are design review, training, etc.

Special Problems Encountered in Data Collection. A special problem is whether all of the defective product is reported. This problem can occur if there is no procedure for recording the defectives. It can also occur for an ominous reason. Organizations that have "drives" on quality may create a fear that results in people hiding the scrap:

> The defective valves under a pile of snow in the far corner of the parking lot
>
> The poor grade paint buried in the ground
>
> The defective rubber product kept in transit between plants

An approach that can be used to estimate the total amount of scrap follows an "input-output" analysis of material. A manufacturer of molded plastic parts followed this approach:

1. Determine (from inventory records) the pounds of raw material placed in the manufacturing process.
2. Determine the pounds of finished goods shipped. If necessary, convert shipments from units to pounds.
3. Calculate the overall loss as step 1 minus step 2.
4. Make subtractions for work in process and finished goods inventory.

The result is the amount of raw material unaccounted for and is presumably due to defective product (or other unknown reasons). A comparison of this result and the recorded amount of defectives provides a practical check on the recorded number of defectives.

Another special problem is the rare but large cost. Examples are liability costs, or a sales order lost because of customer dissatisfaction with previous quality. When they occur, these can be significant costs, but including them in a study may present a distorted picture. Such costs can be handled in two ways:

1. Report the cost in a special category separating it from the total for the other categories. (Financial reports use this approach to handle unusual transactions such as the sale of a portion of a company.)
2. Use an average of the cost over, say, a 5-year period of history. As a refinement of this approach, calculate an expected cost as the product of the probability of occurrence of the unlikely event and the cost if the event does occur. (See Vaughn, 1975.)

In most cases, the first approach is preferable.

PRESENTATION OF INITIAL FINDINGS TO MANAGEMENT

The results can have a striking impact on management if the presentation shows the size of the total cost and identifies areas for improvement.

Use of the Grand Total to Demonstrate Need for Quality Improvement. The most significant figure in a quality cost study is the total of the quality costs. The total may be so small as to fail to compete for managerial priority. For example, in a confectionery company the avoidable quality costs totaled

$44,500 per year. The managers decided that any program to reduce these costs would have to wait, since numerous other problems had higher priority.

More usually, managers are stunned by the size of the total—they had no idea the amount was so big. One memorable example was a leading manufacturer of aircraft engines. When the total quality costs were made known to the managing director, he promptly convened his senior executives to discuss a broad plan of action.

Those presenting the report should be prepared for the report to be greeted with skepticism. The cost may be such that it will not be believed. This can be avoided if management has previously agreed to the definitions of the cost categories and if the accounting function has either collected the data or has been a party to the data collection process.

Relating the Grand Total to Business Measures. Interpretation of the total is aided by relating total quality costs to other figures with which managers are familiar. The relationships which have the greatest impact on upper management are:

1. *Quality costs as a percent of sales:* The financial reports to upper managers and even to shareholders make extensive use of sales as a basis for comparison. When quality costs are similarly related to sales, it becomes easier for upper management to grasp the significance of the numbers.

2. *Quality costs compared to profit:* It comes as a shock to managers to learn that quality costs exceed the company's profit (which often they do). A component manufacturer with a strong reputation for quality reported direct costs of scrap and rework of $7.5 million versus a profit of $1.5 million.

3. *Quality costs compared to the magnitude of current problems:* While money is the universal language of upper management, there are additional ways of conveying significance to these managers.

(Two universal languages are spoken in the company. At the "bottom" the language is that of things and deeds: square meters of floor space, schedules of 400 tons per week, rejection rates of 3.6 percent. At the "top" the language is that of money: sales, profit, taxes, investment. The middle managers and the technical specialists must be *bilingual.* They must be able to talk to the "bottom" in the language of things and to the "top" in the language of money.)

In one company which was preoccupied with meeting delivery schedules, the quality costs were translated into equivalent added production. Since this coincided with the chief current goals of the managers, their interest was aroused. In another company, the total quality costs of $76 million per year for the company were shown to be equivalent to one of the company plants employing 2900 people, occupying 1.1 million ft² of space and requiring $6 million of in-process inventory. These latter three figures in turn meant the equivalent of one of their major plants making 100 percent defective work every working day of the year. This company is the quality leader in its industry.

Other relationships include:

4. *Dollars per share of common stock outstanding*

5. *Dollars as a percent of cost of goods sold*

6. *Dollars as a percent of total manufacturing cost*

7. *Effect of quality costs on the breakeven point*

(See Grimm, 1974; see also below under Scoreboard on the Cost of Poor Quality.)

Interrelation of Categories.   Additional useful comparisons are available from the interrelationship among the subtotals of the quality costs for the major categories. In many companies the appraisal costs have been budgeted and hence have long been a subject for discussion. However, the typical quality cost study will show that the previously underemphasized failure costs are several times the appraisal costs. This comes as a surprise to most managers and forces them to reconsider their emphasis.

In like manner, when managers discover that prevention costs are pitifully low in relation to the total, their instinctive reaction is to look more attentively at the possibilities of increasing preventive efforts. The relationship between internal failure costs and external failure costs likewise has significance. The former generally point to the need for programs involving manufacturing planning and production, whereas the latter generally point to programs involving product design and field service.

An example, using data for 8 months, is shown in Table 4.3. Here, for each product, the failure costs are over 80 percent of the total, failure costs are at least six times the appraisal costs, and prevention costs are less than 2 percent of the total. The implications are clear:

1. To achieve any significant cost reduction, the failure costs must be attacked first. This will have more impact than reducing the inspection (appraisal) costs.
2. An increase in prevention costs could reap a return in terms of lower failure costs.
3. The largest opportunity for cost reduction is with product A. Note that using "quality cost to shipments" and "total quality cost per machine" results in highlighting product C. This is because of the product mix.
4. Product A is generating scrap and rework internally but there are also field (external) problems. For products B and C, the problem centers more on internal scrap and rework.

A simulation model is useful in studying the interrelation of categories of quality costs. Krishnamoorthi (1986) supplies a computer program and presents results of simulations.

TABLE 4.3   Quality Cost Statement by Product Line

	Product A	Product B	Product C
Prevention, $	5,698	1,569	1,908
Appraisal, $	37,676	10,384	9,206
Internal failures, $	119,107	60,876	63,523
External failures, $	133,168	12,625	15,755
Grand total, $	295,649	85,454	90,392
Shipments, $	8,165,000	1,750,000	840,000
Ratio—quality to shipments, %	3.62	4.88	10.76
Machines, number of	71	14	14
Total quality cost per machine, $	4,165	6,104	6,456

GAINING APPROVAL FOR THE QUALITY IMPROVEMENT PROGRAM

Those presenting the results of the cost study should be prepared to answer this question from management: "What action must we take to reduce the cost of poor quality?"

The control of quality in many companies has followed a recognizable pattern—as defects increase take action in the form of more inspection. This approach has failed because it usually does not remove the causes of defects, i.e., it is detection but not prevention. To achieve a significant and lasting reduction in costs requires a structured process for attacking the main sources of loss—the failure costs. Such an attack requires proceeding on a project-by-project basis. These projects in turn will require resources of various types (see Section 22 under Organizing for Projects).

To launch such an attack requires resources, and these must be justified by the expected benefits. Several justifications are possible.

1. Establish that the costs are large enough to justify action (see, for example, Table 4.2).

2. Use a successful case history (a "bellwether" project) of quality improvement in the company to justify a broader program.

3. Show the opportunities presented by a reasonable goal for cost reduction coupled with identification of projects. A typical goal for a structural program on quality improvement is to cut the cost of poor quality in half within 5 years. An important tool in identifying projects is the Pareto analysis which distinguishes between the "vital few" and the "useful many" elements of quality cost. This concept and other aids in identifying projects is covered in Section 22 under The Project Concept.

4. Compare the return on investment from reducing cost of poor quality with the return from investment in added sales.

5. Calculate the improvement in return on investment resulting from improvement in quality.

6. Show the effect of quality improvement on sales income. Although an increase in sales income may be difficult to estimate, it is an intangible factor that can help to justify a quality improvement program.

Justification is essential for an effective program of quality improvement. The approaches listed above are discussed in more detail in Section 22 under Proof of the Need.

DISCOVERING THE OPTIMUM

When cost summaries on quality are first presented to managers, one of the usual questions is: "What are the right costs?" The managers are looking for a standard ("par") against which to compare their actual costs so that they can make a judgment on whether there is a need for action.

Unfortunately, few credible data are available. Companies almost never publish such data. Attempts to conduct research on these costs have encountered several obstacles. (See "Quality Cost Survey," 1980, and Gilmore, 1983.) First, the cost data are confidential and most companies will not release the information. Second, the definition of quality costs varies by company. For example, some companies include unavoidable manufacturing waste as a part of the cost of poor quality, while other companies do not; some companies add overhead to the direct cost of labor and material on scrap and rework, while other companies do not. The wide ranges in published examples are a grim reminder of the risk in comparing quality cost in one company with so-called industry averages. Three conclusions do stand out: The total costs are higher for complex industries, failure costs are the largest percent of the total, and prevention costs are a small percent of the total.

Analyzing the Categories of Costs of Poor Quality.   Analysis of how quality costs are distributed among the various categories can shed further light on the significance of the cost of poor quality. When such analysis is carried out over a period of time it can help to guide the direction of the overall improvement program. An example showing how the costs are distributed over a period of time is shown in Table 4.4. This table shows that the distribution of the total cost changed as the improvement program evolved. At the start of the program, 82 percent of the total cost was in the failure categories. As the program proceeded, the costs shifted from the failure categories into prevention and appraisal. The improvement efforts were successful, since the overall cost (quality cost as percent of sales) dropped from 4.5 percent of sales to 1.5 percent. In this case, the strong initial concentration of costs in the failure categories highlighted the opportunity to reduce the cost of internal and external failures. The shifting of the costs showed the progress of the improvement program.

TABLE 4.4   History of Quality Costs at an Allis-Chalmers Plant

	1967	1968	1969	1970	1971	1972	1973	1974
Prevention, %	5	9	18	20	24	27	27	26
Appraisal, %	13	20	30	30	31	32	33	35
Internal failure, %	36	34	32	35	35	25	29	33
External failure, %	46	37	20	15	10	16	11	6
Quality cost as % of sales	4.5	3.9	2.0	1.9	1.7	1.8	1.7	1.5

Source: Kolacek, O. G. (1976). "Quality Cost—A Place for Financial Impact." *Transactions of the 1976 Annual Conference of ASQC,* Milwaukee, p. 131.

Noz, Redding, and Ware (1983) explain a technique in which knowledge of the phase of an improvement program can be combined with "opportunity dollars" to establish a priority matrix for optimizing quality costs.

Economic Models of Quality of Conformance.   The study of the distribution of quality costs over the major categories can be further explored using models as shown in Figure 4.1 *a* and *b*.
Each model shows three curves:

1. *The failure costs:*   These equal zero when the product is 100 percent good, and rise to infinity when the product is 100 percent defective. (Note that the vertical scale is *cost per good unit* of product. At 100 percent defective, the number of good units is zero, and hence the cost per good unit is infinity.)

FIG. 4.1   Model for optimum quality costs: (*a*) traditional processes, (*b*) emerging processes.

2. *The costs of appraisal plus prevention:*   These costs are zero at 100 percent defective, and rise as perfection is approached. However, the amount of rise differs for the two models.

3. *The sum of curves 1 and 2:*   This third curve is marked "total," and represents the total cost of quality per good unit of product.

The model in part *a* of Figure 4.1 represents the conditions which prevailed widely during much of the twentieth century. "Appraisal plus prevention" consisted of much appraisal and little prevention. Moreover, most appraisal was carried out by fallible human beings who are unable to maintain attention 100 percent of the time, are unable to exert muscular energy 100 percent of the time, etc. This human fallibility effectively limits the efforts to attain perfection at finite costs. Hence the model shows the curve "costs of appraisal plus prevention" rising to infinity as perfection is approached. In consequence the "total cost" curve also rises to infinity.

The model in part *b* of Figure 4.1 represents conditions as they evolved in the late twentieth century. Priorities on prevention became higher. New technology reduced the inherent failure rates of materials and products. Robotics and other forms of automation reduced human error during production. Automated inspection and testing reduced the human error of appraisal. (Automated processes do not have lapses in attention, do not get tired, etc.) Collectively these developments have resulted in an ability to achieve perfection at finite costs.

While perfection is obviously the goal for the long run, it does not follow that perfection is the most economic goal for the short run, or for every situation. In the left-hand model (Figure 4.1*a*) the total cost curve reaches a minimum at a level short of perfection. That minimum has had practical meaning and application, as shown in Figure 4.2.

Figure 4.2 divides the total quality cost curve of Figure 4.1*a* into three zones. The zone a company is in can usually be identified from the prevailing ratios of the quality costs in the principal categories, as follows:

Quality Improvement Zone.   This is the left-hand portion of Figure 4.2. The usual distinguishing features are that failure costs constitute over 70 percent of the total quality costs, while prevention costs are under 10 percent of the total. In such cases, there are opportunities to reduce total quality costs by improving the quality of conformance. The approach is to identify specific improvement projects and pursue them to improve the quality of conformance and thereby reduce the costs of poor quality, especially the failure costs.

FIG. 4.2   Optimum segment of quality cost model.

High Appraisal Cost Zone.   This is the right-hand zone of Figure 4.2 and is usually characterized by the fact that appraisal costs exceed failure costs. In such cases there are also opportunities to reduce costs. This may be done in ways such as:

1. Compare the cost of detecting defects to the damage done if they are not detected. For example, a company had long engaged in detailed inspection for quality characteristic X. The detailed inspection had been started at a time when defect X was widespread. Meanwhile over the years, the process had been improved to a point where defect X was now a rare occurrence—only 15 defects per million parts. However, the detailed inspection went on and on. A study showed that it was costing the company about $2.80 to find each of the defects, yet the sales price of the product was about 5 cents each.

2. Review the quality standards to see if they are realistic in relation to fitness for use.

3. See if it is feasible to reduce the amount of inspection through sampling based on knowledge of process capability and order of manufacture.

4. See if it is feasible to avoid duplication of inspection through use of audit of decisions.

Indifference Zone.   This is the central zone of Figure 4.2. In this zone the failure costs are usually about half of the quality costs while prevention costs are about 10 percent of the quality costs. In the indifference zone the optimum has been reached in terms of worthwhile quality improvement projects to pursue. Further improvement may be possible, but the projects are competing against other worthwhile projects, projects which are not yet at optimum levels.

Several concepts need to be stressed in relation to Figures 4.1 and 4.2.

1. The models are conceptual and illustrate the importance of an optimum value of quality of conformance for many industries. In practice, data are not available to construct the curves shown.

2. Improving the quality of conformance results in a reduction of total costs over

most of the horizontal spectrum. This is contrary to the belief that higher "quality" results in higher costs.

3. A reduction in cost can be achieved by moving toward the optimum from either the zone of improvement or the zone of high appraisal costs.

4. Companies which have not yet engaged extensively in quality improvement are likely to find their processes mainly in the improvement zone. For such companies, the main opportunities for cost reduction are through projects for improving conformance.

5. The hidden costs of poor quality (see above under Controversial Cost Categories) are not included in the model. If the data were available, the effect would be to move the optimum toward 100 percent conformance.

The most important criterion for evaluating whether quality improvement has reached the economic limit is to compare the benefits possible from specific projects with the costs involved in achieving these benefits. When no justifiable projects can be found, the optimum has been reached.

Cost Balance Different in Certain Circumstances.   The models shown in Figures 4.1 and 4.2 apply to a wide variety of industries. However, there are exceptions:

1. *Industries producing goods that have a critical impact on human safety:*   Examples include generation of nuclear power, or manufacture of pharmaceuticals. Such industries are subject to societal pressures to achieve perfect quality at almost any cost.

2. *Highly automated industries:*   Here, it is often possible to achieve a low level of defects by proper planning of the manufacturing process to assure that processes are capable of meeting specifications. In addition, automated inspection often makes it economically feasible to perform 100 percent inspection to find all the defects.

3. *Companies selling to affluent clients:*   These customers are often willing to pay a premium price for perfect quality to avoid even a small risk of a defect.

4. *Companies striving to optimize the user's cost:*   The models depicted in Figure 4.1*a* and *b* show the concept of an optimum from the viewpoint of the producer. When the user's costs due to product failure are added to such models, the optimum point moves toward perfection. The same result occurs if lost sales income to the manufacturer is included in the failure cost. (See below for a discussion of the contrast between company costs and user costs.)

Such exceptions to the models of Figures 4.1 and 4.2 can make it economic to produce at 100 percent conformance. The reason is that the added sales value of perfect product more than offsets the added cost of attaining 100 percent conformance. This has already approached realization in products such as electrical refrigerators and color television sets. The prospect is that the trend to 100 percent conformance will extend to more and more products of greater and greater complexity.

For additional discussion relative to the models (Figures 4.1*a*, *b* and 4.2), see:

Kume (1985): This paper discusses quality economics and makes the point (among others) that "From a management perspective quality economics is more important than quality cost."

Letters to the editor of *Quality Progress* relative to the Kume paper, by Caplan,

Johnson, Ortwein, and Kume, all in *Quality Progress,* February 1986, pp. 6, 8; also by Juran, in *Quality Progress,* April 1986, p. 10.

Schneiderman (1986); also Juran (1987), relative to Schneiderman's paper.

SCOREBOARD ON THE COST OF POOR QUALITY

Some companies use periodic reporting on the cost of poor quality in the form of a scoreboard. Such a scoreboard can be put to certain constructive uses. However, creating and maintaining the scoreboard requires a considerable expenditure of time and effort. Before undertaking such an expenditure the company should look beyond the assertions of the advocates; it should look also at the realities derived from experience. (Many companies have constructed quality cost scoreboards and have then abandoned them as not achieving the results promised by the advocates.) Whether or not to have such a scoreboard involves a number of issues, which are summarized in Table 4.5.

TABLE 4.5   Issues Concerning Scoreboard on Costs of Poor Quality

Assertions	Realities
1. Publication of the cost figures will stimulate cost reduction.	Publication alone will not result in cost reduction unless the company is well set up to identify projects, organize for improvement, etc.
2. Knowledge of these costs enables us to transfer charges to the guilty departments, thereby stimulating improvement.	True, provided (*a*) we really know who is guilty and (*b*) the company is well organized to identify and carry out improvement projects.
3. We need a financial scoreboard for these costs just as we do for any other kind of costs.	A valid reason, but the choice of standards is critical. The standards for these costs should be the levels reached *after* a quality improvement program has brought the costs down. Otherwise the cost controls will help perpetuate the high level of costs.
4. A financial scoreboard is needed to help hold the gains resulting from the quality improvement program.	Usually correct. Of course, such a scoreboard is created after the costs have been reduced. In this way, control is applied to the improved level.
5. The figures are needed to identify the smaller projects which cannot be identified through broad estimates.	A valid reason if we have already made some of the big gains.
6. The figures are needed for contract reasons, e.g., to bid for business, or because a major client asks to see them.	These are persuasive reasons.
7. The conferences and published papers report how other companies have gotten good results from quantifying these costs.	Seldom an adequate reason. Published reports are biased. (People do not report their failure stories.)

Once there has been a decision to go forward with such a cost scoreboard, the planning must include:

Finalizing the cost categories
Collecting and summarizing the data
Establishing bases for comparison
Reporting the results

Defining the Cost of Poor Quality.   For the scoreboard to be useful, the line departments must agree with the choice of categories of costs of poor quality. The categories used in the literature can serve as a starting point. For example, many companies include the four broad categories in their initial study but restrict the scoreboard to those categories of failure costs which represent the opportunities for improvement.

Collecting and Summarizing the Data.   The data collection system must provide for accumulating basic data in various units of measure, converting these to monetary units, and charging the proper accounts. A basic step is to provide code numbers to facilitate data recording on the source documents and also to simplify the subsequent data processing. Code numbers are assigned to the accounts, departments, products, components, operations, dates, machine classes, types of defects, job orders, suppliers, customers, workers, etc. The many types of source records include a time card, material requisition, inspection report, scrap ticket, repair ticket, field service report, complaint report, and Material Review Board report. Increasing use is being made of automated data collection system (for example, see Adamek, 1979).

There are multiple ways of summarizing the cost data. The most basic ways are:

1. *By product, process, component, defect type, or other likely defect concentration pattern:*   Such summaries make it easy to prepare a Pareto analysis to identify the vital few contributors to the cost.

2. *By organizational unit:*   Such summaries are by division, department, or other convenient organizational unit. These summaries not only evaluate the performance of specific organization units; they tend to be regarded as a form of personal scoreboard by the managers of the respective organization units.

Many companies also prepare such summaries for outside suppliers. The results are then used as a basis for action, whether relative to specific suppliers or to suppliers generally.

3. *By category of cost of poor quality:*   These summaries are useful for study of the cost relationships among categories. For example, to apply the model of Figure 4.2 requires information on the makeup of quality costs by category. In addition, the trends of the respective costs by category are informative as to the progress of efforts to reduce costs.

4. *By time:*   Summaries of cost data by calendar periods provide information on trends and progress in improvement efforts. To help spotlight trends, it is useful to plot the current data and also a moving average. An example of this is shown in Figure 4.3 where monthly data on internal failure costs are plotted along with a 6-month moving average. Each average is based on 6 months of data. (As the data become available for a new month, data for the oldest month are discarded and then the "moving average" is recalculated for the most recent six values.)

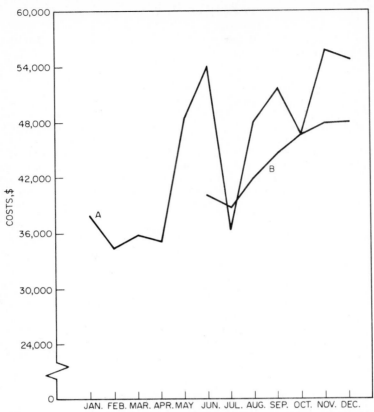

FIG. 4.3 Internal failures costs. *A*, monthly costs curve; *B*, moving averages curve.

TABLE 4.6 Measurement Bases for Quality Costs

Base	Advantages	Disadvantages
Direct labor hour	Readily available and understood	Can be drastically influenced by automation
Direct labor dollars	Available and understood; tends to balance any inflation effect	Can be drastically influenced by automation
Standard manufacturing cost dollars	More stability than above	Includes overhead costs both fixed and variable
Value-added dollars	Useful when processing costs are important	Not useful for comparing different types of manufacturing departments
Sales dollars	Appeals to higher management	Sales dollars can be influenced by changes in prices, marketing costs, demand, etc.
Product units	Simplicity	Not appropriate when different products are made unless "equivalent" item can be defined

Often, the published summaries involve combinations of these different ways. Table 4.3 summarizes data by product and by category of quality cost along with several indices based on the amount of production.

Bases for Comparison.   When managers use a scoreboard on the cost of poor quality, they are not content to look at the gross dollar figures. They want, in addition, to compare the costs with some base which is an index of the opportunity for creating these costs. A summary of some widely used bases, along with the advantages and disadvantages of each, is presented in Table 4.6. The base used can greatly influence the interpretation of the cost data.

It is best to start with several bases and then, as managers gain experience with the reports, retain only the most meaningful. The literature stresses that quality costs be stated as percent of sales income. This is a useful base for some, but not all, purposes (see Table 4.6).

Reporting the Results.   The specific matters requiring decision include:

1. *Format:*   The most widely used formats are tabular, graphic, and narrative. An example of a graphical report is given in Figure 4.4. Note that (*a*) the

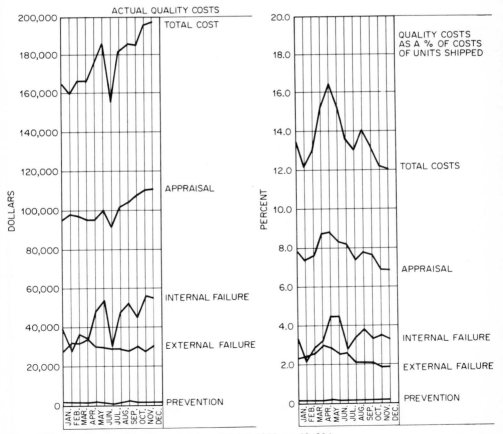

FIG. 4.4   Graphs of quality cost data.   *(ASQC, 1977, pp. 18, 20.)*

interpretation of the data is influenced by the base chosen and (b) prevention costs are essentially constant during the period studied.

Another means of "publication" involves the display of information at a computer terminal (see Tsiakals, 1983). The data are presented on a color graphic screen in the form of graphs which can be selected by the manager from a "menu" offered on the screen. (Paper copy output is also available.) The cost data for the entire plant can be viewed and then, if desired, the manager can examine layers of intermediate information providing greater detail. In a 1-h session, about 20 graphs can be generated and examined from many thousands of combinations available. The graphs have a time base so that all data are presented in trend chart form. Users may select monthly or year-to-date data; dollars, dollars divided by the value of production, or dollars divided by machine hour. Summaries can also be presented in ratio form such as prevention cost/internal failure cost, product A/product B.

2. *Frequency:* Here again, the regular cost control reporting system will provide guidelines. Reports to upper management are quarterly and monthly. Reports to middle and lower management are typically more frequent.

Reports on improvement projects are normally quarterly, since change proceeds slowly. Of course, the minutes of the team meetings provide more detail of what is happening, and with greater frequency.

3. *Distribution:* All levels of management receive quality cost reports, but they do not all receive the same data. The basic quality data are common to all reports. To provide the assorted summaries from common data sources requires a well organized data network and a modular concept of report preparation.

4. *Responsibility for publication:* This responsibility is best carried out as a joint venture between Accounting and Quality. The planning has, of course, been done jointly to assure that the end result meets the needs of the line managers. Carrying out the plan is commonly done by giving Accounting the responsibility for basic cost data collection, data processing, and preparation of the summaries. Such an approach utilizes Accounting's extensive experience in such matters while reducing jurisdictional disputes. This same approach adds credibility to the figures, since upper management looks to Accounting for unbiased financial reporting.

OTHER APPLICATIONS OF THE QUALITY COST CONCEPT

The costs of poor quality are present not only in production operations, but also in many other company operations. For example, Schrader (1986) describes the measurement of quality costs in a product development organization. The application to finance, personnel, and other "white-collar" areas is discussed by Harrington (1986). Nickell (1985) describes how a marketing organization identified opportunities including one to reduce the percent of cancelled sales orders. Juran and Gryna (1980, pp. 18, 349) present examples from gage control and auditing activities.

In selected activities of an organization, quantifying the costs of errors can draw attention to the seriousness of a problem and identify specific problem areas (Groocock, 1977).

WHY QUALITY COST PROGRAMS FAIL

A number of "Quality Cost Systems" have failed to get useful results. The major reasons for failure are summarized in Table 4.7.

TABLE 4.7 Reasons Why Quality Cost Systems Fail

Reason	Preferred approach
1. Accounting Department is ignored because of its lack of cooperation.	Work with Accounting to whatever degree it is willing to participate.
2. Quality Department insists that certain controversial costs be included.	Agree to exclude or at least separately identify any such costs.
3. Corporate Quality Department issues one quality cost procedure without giving each plant the opportunity to review before issuance.	Provide time for plants to comment. Allow enough flexibility to care for plant differences.
4. Reports fail to talk the different languages needed at various management levels.	Use different units of measure for various levels. Try out a sample report before finalizing the system.
5. No provision is made for investing additional funds in prevention activities.	Tell management the amount and type of resources needed to achieve a defined saving.
6. Role of top management in quality improvement.	Propose numerical goals and identify specific projects. Ask management to provide necessary resources and assign responsibility to line departments.
7. No provision is made to obtain the facts needed to diagnose causes of problems.	Propose some organizational mechanism that will be responsible for diagnosis of causes.
8. Cost data are presented in categories that are too broad to be useful.	Provide detail to the level needed.
9. System is instituted for all products and departments at one time.	Try it out for one product to obtain a successful case history.
10. Divisiveness caused by unfair comparisons of results among plants.	Recognize that plants are different. Make comparisons of planned action programs.
11. Assumption that publication alone will achieve an improvement in quality.	Structured program of improvement with responsibility and resources assigned.
12. Arguments occur about "transfer of charges."	Agree on some arbitrary way to settle the assignment of charges.
13. Undue emphasis is placed on precision in the figures.	Emphasis should be on identification of problem areas. This does not require extreme precision.
14. System is personalized. It is associated with an individual who is a strong advocate and sponsor.	Quality cost system should be depersonalized. Tie it in with a structured program of quality improvement that has the support of middle and upper management.
15. Quality Department regards the system as "its own" to maintain.	Turn over data collection and issuance of reports to Accounting. Quality Department should concentrate on analysis of the data.

The failures have been primarily due to losing sight of the key objective: show the size of the quality problem and identify the projects for improvement.

COMPANY COSTS AND USER COSTS

The costs of poor quality affect two parties—the manufacturer and the user. This section discusses the impact on the manufacturer. Poor quality also increases the costs of the user of the product in the form of repair costs after the warranty period, various losses due to downtime, etc. Gryna (1977) presents a methodology with case examples of user costs of poor quality. The extent of these user costs clearly affects future purchasing decisions of the user. This in turn influences the sales income of the manufacturer. This section stresses the potential for profit improvement by reducing manufacturer costs. The effects of quality on sales income is even more important. See Section 3, under Quality and Sales Income.

ROAD MAP FOR INTRODUCING A SYSTEM FOR REPORTING THE COST OF POOR QUALITY

The sequence of events needs to be tailored for each company. However, the following have application to most companies:

1. Review the literature on quality costs. Consult others in similar industries who have had experience with installing a program.
2. Select one organizational unit of the company to serve as a pilot run. This unit may be one plant, one large department, one product line, etc.
3. Discuss the objectives of the study with the controller in the organization. The objectives should stress determining the size of the quality problem and identification of specific projects for improvement.
4. Collect whatever cost data are conveniently available from the accounting system and use this information to gain the support of management in making a full cost study.
5. Make a proposal to management for a full study. The proposal should provide for participation of all concerned parties to develop the list of categories. The proposal should include setting up a task force to gain agreement on the definition of the costs of poor quality.
6. Publish a draft of the categories defining the cost of poor quality. Secure comments and revise as needed.
7. Finalize the definitions and secure management approval.
8. Secure agreement on responsibility for data collection and report preparation.
9. Collect and summarize the data. Ideally, this should be done by Accounting.
10. Present the cost results to management along with a report of a successful "bellwether" quality improvement project (if available). Request authorization to proceed with a broader companywide program of measuring the costs and pursuing projects.
11. If needed, first conduct the several trial projects and then propose a companywide program.

12. Based on the initial experiences, review the need for simplification or other revision of the cost categories.

13. Extend the program of cost measurement and project improvement to other departments.

14. Consider the need for a corporate scoreboard on the costs of poor quality.

Harrington (1986) provides further elaboration on the steps involved in implementation of a "poor-quality cost system."

REFERENCES

Adamek, Kenneth C. (1979). "Automated Collective Analysis of Scrap and Rework." *ASQC Technical Conference Transactions,* Milwaukee, pp. 190–199.

ASQC (1977). *Guide for Reducing Quality Costs,* American Society for Quality Control, Milwaukee, pp. 18, 20.

ASQC (1986). *Principles of Quality Costs,* American Society for Quality Control, Milwaukee.

Aubrey, C. A., III and Zimbler, D. A. (1982). "A Banking Quality Cost Model: Its Uses and Results." *ASQC Quality Congress Transactions,* Milwaukee, pp. 195–201.

Brown, F. X. and Kane, R. W. (1978). "Quality Cost and Profit Performance." *ASQC Technical Conference Transactions,* Milwaukee, pp. 505–514.

Caplan, Frank (1986). Letter to editors. *Quality Progress,* February, p. 6.

Dale, B. G. and Plunkett, J. J. (1986). "The Determination and Use of Quality Related Costs in Manufacturing Industry." *EOQC Quality,* March, pp. 3–6.

Gilmore, Harold L. (1983). "Consumer Product Quality Control Costs Revisited." *Quality Progress,* April, pp. 28–32.

Grimm, A. F. (1974). "Quality Costs: Where Are They in the Accounting Process?" *ASQC Technical Conference Transactions,* Milwaukee, pp. 190–200.

Groocock, J. M. (1977). "Quality Costs and No Failure Costs." *Quality,* vol. 2, p. 9.

Gryna, Frank M. (1977). "Quality Costs: User vs. Manufacturer." *Quality Progress,* June, pp. 10–15.

Gryna, Frank M. (1978). "Quality Costs—What Does Management Expect?" *ASQC Technical Conference Transactions,* Milwaukee, pp. 210–217.

Hagan, John T. (1985). "Quality Cost II—The Economics of Quality Improvement." *Quality Progress,* October, pp. 48–51.

Harrington, H. James (1986). *Poor-Quality Cost.* ASQC Quality Press, Milwaukee, and Marcel Dekker, New York.

Johnson, Michael (1986). Letter to editors. *Quality Progress,* February, p. 6.

Juran, J. M. and Gryna, Frank M. (1980). *Quality Planning and Analysis.* McGraw-Hill, New York.

Juran, J. M. (1986). Letter to editors. *Quality Progress,* April, p. 10.

Juran, J. M. (1987). Letter to editors. *Quality Progress,* April, pp. 7, 9.

Krishnamoorthi, K. S. (1986). "Predicting Quality Cost Changes Using Regression." *ASQC Quality Congress Transactions,* Milwaukee, pp. 406–410.

Kume, Hitoshi (1985). "Business Management and Quality Cost: The Japanese View." *Quality Progress,* May, pp. 13–18.

Kume, Hitoshi (1986). Reply to letters to editors. *Quality Progress,* February, p. 8.

Nickell, Warren L. (1985). "Quality Improvement in Marketing," *The Juran Report,* no. 4 (winter), pp. 29–35.

Noz, William C., Jr., Redding, Bradley F., and Ware, Paul A. (1983). "The Quality Manager's Job: Optimize Costs." *ASQC Quality Congress Transactions,* Milwaukee, pp. 301–306.

Ortwein, W. J. (1986). Letter to editors. *Quality Progress,* February, pp. 6, 8.

"Quality Costs: The Real Measurement of Performance." (1975). *Quality Management and Engineering,* January, Hitchcock Publishing Company.

"Quality Cost Survey." (1980). *Quality,* July, pp. 16–17.

Salvendy, Gavriel (1982). *Handbook of Industrial Engineering.* John Wiley & Sons, New York.

Schneiderman, Arthur M. (1986). "Optimum Quality Costs and Zero Defects: Are they Contradictory Concepts?" *Quality Progress,* November, pp. 28–31.

Schrader, Lawrence J. (1986). "An Engineering Organization's Cost of Quality Program." *Quality Progress,* January, pp. 29–34.

Tsiakals, Joseph J. (1983). "Management Team Seeks Quality Improvement from Quality Costs." *Quality Progress,* April, pp. 26–27.

Vaughn, T. C. (1975). "Zubits: Regular $18.50-Liability Extra." *Quality Progress,* February, p. 16.

SECTION 5

QUALITY POLICIES AND OBJECTIVES[1]

J. M. Juran

---

[1]*Note:* This section contains many extracts from company manuals on quality, but the identities of the companies are not always disclosed. Companies are well advised to secure, where feasible, copies of the quality manuals of other companies.

THE NEED FOR QUALITY POLICIES

All organizations have in mind (or in writing) some principles, creeds, beliefs, etc., which are their broad guides to managerial conduct. These guides rest on a philosophical and ethical base. They concern important issues, are the result of much reflection, and are intended to have long life, i.e., to act as a stabilizer. In this handbook such principles, etc., are designated as "policies."

(Note that the word "policy" is not standardized as to meaning. In many companies the organization charts and the procedures for control are assembled into a manual which is called the "policy manual" or "policy and procedures manual.")

In tiny organizations where one person makes all the decisions, these guides to conduct are literally "in mind." The one person operates in accordance with an unwritten code of conduct. Anyone who wants to discover that code must deduce it from the observed deeds.

For example, the master of a small shop adheres to the (unwritten) policy of making good on any defects in shop products. The townspeople discover this policy from the shop owner's deeds and "publish" the policy by word-of-mouth.

As organizations grow, more and more managers are engaged in making significant decisions. These decisions affect numerous people inside and out of the organization, including the managers themselves. Unless there is consistency in these decisions, there is no predictability; neither insiders nor outsiders know what to expect. An impersonal way of creating this predictability is to think through, write down, and publish the policies which then become the basis for consistent conduct.

The Urge for Written Quality Policies. Behavior of large organizations is not determined by the decisions and actions of some one individual. Many individuals take actions on behalf of the organization, and it becomes easy for the organization to present multiple and inconsistent faces to outsiders. Within the organizations, behavior in some functional areas can be antagonistic to the long-range goals of the organization. As the unwelcome incidents accumulate, there arises a growing urge to think through, write out, and publish quality policies to serve as guides to managerial action.

Recent Massive Forces. Until the 1950s, published quality policy statements were rare. The exceptions were usually the result of requirements by government agencies that their contractors prepare written manuals for review and approval.

During the last half of the twentieth century some massive new forces came over the horizon:

A "population explosion" of consumer products with a resulting spectacle of millions of consumers depending for day-to-day health and convenience on products they own but are unable to repair or even understand ("Life behind the quality dikes")

A public awakening to the problems of pollution, many of which have their origin in the operation of manufactured products

An erosion of traditional manufacturers' defenses in matters of safety and product liability

The emergence of very complex apparatus—aerospace systems, automated factories, defense systems, and computers

A consumerism movement directed at protecting the small user from misleading advertising and from failures without recourse

A growing invasion by government regulation not only into the traditional fields of human health and safety but also into consumer economics, i.e., integrity of guarantee, product labeling, etc.

A new, intense level of international competition in quality, resulting in large scale shifts of shares of market and trade balances, with associated severe impacts on employment in the impacted industries.

Each of the above forces was in the nature of a revolutionary change in the existing order, and has required a revolutionary response. A part of that response has consisted of communicating to all concerned the nature of the new changes and the associated guides to company action. In part, this communication has been through published quality policies. For elaboration, see Juran (1969 and 1970).

That same list of massive forces also sheds light on the stability of quality policies. If well thought through, policies are quite stable. They seldom require change from year to year. However, in our industrial societies, quality policies do require changes from decade to decade.

Advantages of Written Policies. Organizations which have undertaken to prepare written quality policies generally report that the benefits have been worth the effort. They point to certain specific advantages of the undertaking:

1. It provides insiders and outsiders with a new, superior form of predictability, i.e., a *written* guide to managerial action.
2. It forces the organization to think about quality problems to a depth never before achieved. "Before you can write it down, you must first think it out."
3. It establishes legitimacy and can be communicated in an authoritative, uniform manner. Policies which are not established at high levels may, by default, be established at low levels.
4. It provides a basis for management by agreed policies agreed upon rather than by crisis or opportunism.
5. It permits practice to be audited against that policy.

Disadvantages of Written Policies. The major disadvantage is the work involved. In the great majority of organizations, quality policies must be approved at the very highest levels of organization. These top officials understandably want to avoid being drawn into the detailed work of sitting in meetings to evolve and refine the drafts. One way of avoiding this work is to insist that the final draft bear the approval of all subordinate organizations. Since many diverse interests are involved, it takes many meetings and a great deal of time to reach full agreement on the drafts.

Beyond the work involved, there is a feeling among some managers that written policies tend to restrict innovation and to narrow the range of action available to adapt to changing conditions. There is merit in this contention. Policies are intended to be a guide as to what *not* to do, as well as what to do. However, in most organizations the policies are regarded as guides, and there is awareness that conditions may arise requiring departure from established policies.

CORPORATE QUALITY POLICIES

As a company grows to an extent which involves it in multiple markets and products, it becomes evident that no one set of quality policies can fit all company activities. This problem is solved by creating several levels of quality policy. One of these levels is corporate quality policy, which consists of the following:

1. A statement of those policies which are companywide in their effect and hence binding on all company organization units. This corporate policy statement usually sets out:
   a. The purpose of writing and publishing quality policies
   b. A brief statement of corporate intent as to quality (the "motherhood" statement)
   c. The minimal actions to be taken by company divisions with respect to quality (see below)
   d. Interdivisional relationships concerning quality
   e. Quality standards policies for overlapping markets
   f. Provision for corporate audit of compliance with quality policies
   g. Relationship of quality policies to other company policies
2. A delegation of authority to subordinate company organization units (usually the "profit centers" known as "divisions") to establish subsidiary quality policies appropriate to their needs. This delegation is needed because the divisions are commonly engaged in different businesses—each involving different markets, laws, traditions, technology, etc.—which require different policies.

Summary Statement. Virtually all published statements of corporate quality policy contain a brief declaration which summarizes the company's position. For example:

It is the policy of the company to provide products and services of a quality that meet the initial and continuing needs and expectations of customers in relation to the price paid and to the nature of competitive offerings, and in doing so, to be the leader in product quality reputation.

To achieve and sustain a reputation for quality at competitive prices in the National and International markets for our entire product range.

To provide a product which satisfies the performance, quality, reliability, and safety requirements of our customers at a fair market price.

To provide products and services which consistently meet the needs and expectations of our customers and of users within the company.

No one quarrels with such statements. However, they are regarded by most managers as too vague to provide guides for conduct. (Hence the name "motherhood" policies; i.e. everyone is in favor of motherhood.) To be useful, quality policies should provide specific guides to action for specific, important matters. Such guides help the insiders to understand what is expected of them and the outsiders to understand what to expect from the company managers.

Increasingly the emerging policy statements do provide such specifics. Usually these specifics are contained in the functional level policies. (See below.) However, some specifics are elaborations of corporate quality policy.

Definition of Quality. Usually these definitions are built around quality parameters such as safety, performance, reliability, economy, appearance, "user friendliness," etc. Alternatively the definitions relate to such aspects as quality of market research, quality of design, quality of conformance, etc.

Other Elaborations. The subject matter of elaboration varies from company to company. The choice is no doubt influenced by the specific pressures present at the time the policy drafts are in preparation. The subjects most frequently elaborated include those discussed below.

Importance of Quality. In many companies, the top priority prior to the 1980s was *not* on quality. The top priority was on delivery dates, cost, or other parameters. The emerging forces then required raising the priority given to quality. This new need then gave rise to quality statements such as:

Leadership in quality has top priority.

Quality shall be given equal priority to costs and delivery.

Managerial decisions must give equal consideration to quality as well as to aspects of cost and schedule.

Quality Competitiveness. Quality policy statements usually refer to competitiveness, whether in the short summary or in elaborations. The various wordings in general state that the company's products shall:

Equal or exceed competitive quality

Be of the highest quality

Have quality excellence

Be best in class

Provide unmatched value

Attain world leadership

Customer Relations. Here the elaboration often identifies specific customer needs to be met; e.g., the company's products should:

Provide customer satisfaction

Meet customer perceptions of good quality

Be useful, reliable, maintainable

Provide value

A typical comprehensive statement reads:

> Assure that customer needs are identified and that our products meet these needs.

Internal Customers. There has been a growing trend to widen the meaning of the word "customers" to include internal persons and organizations who are impacted by the product. This trend is reflected in quality policy statements such as:

> We regard the receivers of our work results as "customers" whose needs are important to understand and satisfy.

> Quality should extend to all phases of the business.

> Processes should be established at high yields and process capability.

> Product designs should be producible.

Work Force Involvement. A special case of internal customers is the work force—the nonsupervisors in factories, offices, warehouses, etc. Some quality policy elaborations aim to emphasize the role of the work force, along with related aspects of work force involvement. Typical statements include:

> Our policy is to foster a spirit of pride among employees regarding the company's quality performance.

> Our policy is to stimulate our co-workers' creativity, initiative, and sense of responsibility.

> Our policy is to provide current skills training and promote open communications to maximize employee contributions.

> No employee of this company will ever be called upon to do anything in the line of duty that is morally, ethically, or legally wrong.

Quality Improvement. This activity has expanded enormously starting in the early 1980s. This expansion is reflected in quality policy elaborations such as:

> Resources will be allocated primarily to the prevention of defects, and corrective action will be focused on root-cause identification and elimination.

> Preventive quality actions and correction of quality deficiencies shall be given priority.

> The quality assurance program should be designed to emphasize preventive techniques coupled with aggressive investigation and corrective action programs.

Planning and Organization. Many published statements of quality policy include declarations which actually relate to other managerial matters, e.g., planning and organization. In this handbook such matters are discussed in their respective sections.

Additional Subject Matter. The above examples of subject matter for corporate quality policies are widely applicable. However, some organizations face special quality questions which may require formulation of quality policy. Examples of such questions include:

Is the aim to sell standard goods (commodities) or to sell a broad service in which the goods are only one element?

Is the aim to sell on the basis of life cycle costing or on the basis of initial price?

Which part of the spectrum of affluence is to be the target for the company's products?

Questions such as these have an impact on all major functions of the organization, including the quality function. It can be useful to the managers to have answers in the form of written policy. Whether the resulting declarations are included among the quality policy statements or elsewhere is not critical.

DIVISIONAL QUALITY POLICIES

In large companies it is common for the corporation to require that the divisions establish divisional quality policies as needed, and within the framework of corporate policies. It is also common to require the divisions to:

Prepare a formal plan for quality assurance, including minimal contents such as formal systems for design reviews, supplier qualification, process control, inspection and test, and field feedback.

Publish a quality manual which includes the formal plans, the definitions of responsibility, the organization charts, the procedures, etc.

Conduct audits to determine the extent to which the plans are adequate and are being carried out. (Copies of the audit reports are sometimes required to be submitted to the corporate offices.)

The delegation to divisions may also impose limitations. For example, some multinational companies conduct manufacturing operations in multiple facilities, and then market the resulting goods in multiple countries. In such situations the corporation may mandate product uniformity. One such mandate is worded as follows:

The same design shall be used in all factories making a specific product.
Quality of design and quality of conformance for a specific product shall be the same in all markets.

In certain industries the company divisions are organized around specific "programs" such as major government defense contracts or major construction projects. In such cases the customers typically make extensive use of mandated quality policies and regulations. These mandates then apply to all contractors who, in turn, must apply them to subcontractors.

Policies on Improvement. The acute need for quality improvement has also been reflected in quality policy formation. Increasingly the corporate policies emphasize allocating efforts to eliminate quality problems at their source rather than detecting and correcting them afterward. An example of such a policy declaration is as follows:

> Resources will be allocated primarily to the prevention of defects, and corrective action will be focused on root-cause identification and elimination.

QUALITY POLICIES FOR FUNCTIONS

Many of these policies are prepared to provide guidance to managers in specific functional departments such as product development, manufacture, and marketing. Additional policies relate to activities of an interdepartmental nature such as the process for developing, making, and marketing new products. Still other functional policies focus on specific quality parameters and their impact, whether departmental or interdepartmental. Examples are product safety and product reliability.

The written functional policy statements may be assembled into a comprehensive policy manual which includes corporate quality policies as well. Alternatively, the functional policy statements are published as part of a departmental manual which includes other departmental information, e.g., planning and organization.

New Product Introduction.   Quality policies in this vital area often mandate the use of specified managerial processes. A common example is the phase system. Under this system a sequence of milestones is established. As each milestone is reached, a business decision must be made to determine whether work should proceed on the next phase in the sequence. A simple example of a sequence of milestones is design completion, prototype release, release for production, and release for shipment.

Within the phase system there may be further mandated processes such as engineering change control and design reviews and audits. For example, the following is a policy statement mandating design reviews:

> Design reviews shall be conducted that cover the compliance of the design with customer market and regulatory body requirements for function, quality, reliability, and safety.

For additional discussion, see Section 13, Product Development, under Basic Concepts: Design Review.

Supplier Relations.   Quality policy formation in this area has been active due to an emerging change from an adversary relationship to a teamwork relationship. An early example of this trend is seen in extracts from the Johnson & Johnson policy on supplier relations:

> To place, whenever possible, the facilities of our research, development, and technical services at the disposal of our suppliers in order to help them with any problems they may encounter in supplying materials to our specifications and to aid them in developing better means for production and quality improvement
>
> To encourage exchange visiting by our suppliers' technical personnel and our technical personnel to observe our respective plant operations, thereby promoting a better understanding of mutual problems and objectives

Some recent policy statements exemplify the trend to a teamwork relationship:

> We will work cooperatively with our suppliers to assure that their materials meet the same standards as our products.
>
> We will assure that our requirements are accurately specified and communicated to suppliers.
>
> We seek to establish long-term, open relations with our suppliers.

See Section 15, Supplier Relations, for further discussion.

Manufacturing Planning.   This function (also called "process engineering") has recently been heavily impacted by the concept of process capability and the associated statistical methodology. One result of this impact has been the emergence of quality policy declarations relative to manufacturing process capability. Here are some examples:

> Manufacturing process capability must be verified during the product development cycle.
>
> Manufacturing equipment shall be able to meet quality requirements with sufficient margin and at the lowest cost.
>
> Process variability and capability must be understood, and operating procedures clearly specified.

The increased emphasis on quality-oriented parameters has intensified some earlier policy questions relative to manufacturing planning. Examples include:

> Should the quality-oriented portion of manufacturing planning be done by quality specialists, or should the manufacturing planners be trained in the necessary skills and techniques?
>
> Should design reviews for producibility be mandated?
>
> Should formal planning for safety, reliability, maintainability, etc., be applied to the manufacturing process as well as to the product?

For additional discussion, see Section 16, Manufacturing Planning.

Production.   This function has also been impacted by the increased use of statistical methodology. In addition, there has been a trend to enlarge worker participation in the affairs of the company and of their own jobs. The two principal forms of such participation have been:

1. Increasing the role of workers in data collection, analysis, and feedback.
2. Use of Quality Circles for making improvements in performance. (See Section 10, Managing Human Performance, under Team Performance: Quality Circles.)

The above two trends of increased use of statistical methodology and enlarged worker participation have been especially strong in the production function and have stimulated much development of relevant policy. Here are some policy examples:

> It is the policy to foster involvement and a spirit of pride among employees by encouraging ideas and resolutions regarding the company's quality performance.

Each employee must accept responsibility for maintaining, and where possible, improving product quality within the scope of the employee's job assignment.

All managers are responsible for providing an environment reflecting quality as the top priority objective, including clearly defined expectations which provide each employee the maximum opportunity to contribute.

Looming behind such policy statements is the broader question of whether to retain the Taylor system of separating planning from execution. The major premise of the Taylor system was that the work force lacked the technological literacy needed to do planning. (That same premise applied to many of the first-line supervisors of that day.) Since then a remarkable growth in education levels has made Taylor's premise obsolete and hence has brought the current validity of the system into question.

Once a consensus emerges on what is to replace the Taylor system, it will be necessary to formulate new policy statements to guide the changeover process. Some sensitive issues will need to be addressed. Increased worker participation in planning can affect long-standing "management prerogatives" such as the right to "stop the line," the right to decide which topics are to have priority on the management agenda, and the right of workers to take over work formerly performed by engineers or supervisors.

For additional discussion, see Section 17, Production.

Marketing; Customer Service.   These functions have been impacted by recent major forces which include:

Growing dependence of continuity of customers' operations on the reliability of processes, goods, and services provided by suppliers

Growth of life cycle costing with its need for information on product performance and user costs over the life of the product

Growth of competition in quality, requiring continuing improvement to remain competitive

Response to such forces has required increased emphasis on information from the field, especially with respect to:

1. Market research to determine customers' needs and competitive performance
2. Feedback of field information on product performance and users' costs over the life of the product

In part this response is reflected in policy statements. Such statements are usually included in the marketing/customer service sections of the policy manual, since in many companies these functions have major responsibilities for interface with clients and users.

Examples of pertinent policy statements include:

Marketing shall create only such customer expectations as can realistically be met. Systems must be developed and maintained to provide accurate and current information on product quality performance and customer acceptance.

When specified, data on products shipped to customers will be transmitted to them for their assistance in determining the usability of the product.

Service operations shall be conducted so as to minimize customers' shutdowns.

Managers involved in customer interface must assure that performance expectations are clearly defined and that their employees are qualified to meet those expectations.

Quality Assurance.   It is common for corporate policy statements to mandate the creation and "independence" of a quality assurance function. For example:

Each division is to maintain a Quality Assurance department which:

1. Will report to divisional top management
2. Will not be subordinate to the production function

There shall be a clearly defined Quality organization with sufficient, well-defined responsibility and organization freedom to identify and evaluate quality problems and to initiate, recommend, or provide solutions.

Until the 1980s the Quality Assurance departments played major roles in managing the quality affairs of the companies. Those roles are bound to undergo extensive change due to the recent growth of emphasis on quality. This change of emphasis will require development of new policies relative to the quality assurance function, but this development has been proceeding slowly.

The earliest expressions of the new policies have been in such broad forms as:

Quality has top priority.

Quality is everyone's job.

Prevention, not detection.

These are well-meaning expressions of intent but they generally have not been accepted by subordinates as guides to action. The statements are very general, whereas the prior responsibilities have been very specific, and there has been no discernible change in responsibilities, or in evaluation of performance, or in the nature of the reward system.

To put those broad expressions into effect requires extensive changes such as:

Revisions in the planning process so that quality-oriented planning will be largely carried out by line managers and specialists rather than by quality specialists

A revolutionary growth in the effort allocated by line organizations to quality improvement

Massive training of line managers and specialists to be able to carry out their new quality-oriented responsibilities

There is much need here for policy formulation. However, the resulting statements must be much more specific than the vague declarations which dominated the scene during the early 1980s.

Administrative and Support Functions.   This is usually shortened to A&S functions. A basic policy question is whether the company's formal approach to managing for quality should include the quality of A&S operations. To illustrate, should the concept of "quality" include such matters as:

The extent to which the invoicing process produces correct invoices

The promptness of service provided to internal customers, e.g., recruitment done by the employment department

The accuracy of the sales forecast relative to subsequent realities

Historically such matters were *not* regarded as related to "quality" since they did not directly impact the goods or services sold. However, the emerging trends are clear and in the direction of enlarging the concept of quality to include A&S operations. Upper managers, in particular, have readily accepted this enlarged concept.

As of the early 1980s the needed policy formulations had not kept pace with this trend. This deficiency remains to be remedied. Otherwise there will be delays in establishing the infrastructure needed to improve the quality of A&S operations—infrastructure such as means for setting quality objectives and processes for planning, controlling, and improving quality.

QUALITY POLICIES FOR SPECIFIC PARAMETERS

This has been a growth area for quality policy formation. The most active parts of this area have related to product safety and reliability.

Product Safety.   Starting in the 1960s there emerged a great expansion of government regulation relative to the impact of products on safety, health, and the environment. In addition there has been an explosive growth in lawsuits and the associated awards for product liability. All this has had its effect on quality policy, leading to statements such as:

> Our products shall be free from unacceptable properties that cause damage, and shall meet applicable standards and regulations.

> All products must comply with applicable health, safety, and environmental laws and regulations, and with Corporate policy relating to health, safety, and the environment.

All available evidence indicates that this emphasis will continue, even to the extent of spending huge sums of money to undo the accumulated damage of the past.

For additional discussion, see Section 35, Impact of Quality on Society.

Reliability.   This is widely recognized as a parameter of the highest importance. It is already a major basis for marketplace competition and is destined to remain so. This importance is reflected in some company policy statements:

> Reliability goals shall be established in the early stages of product design.

> The reliability of any new product must be at least equal to that of the product it replaces, and at least equal to that of leading competitive models.

> Each division shall identify the organization responsible for reliability functions

applicable to the products and services of the division. The Reliability organization shall have sufficient, well-defined responsibility, authority, and organizational freedom to identify and evaluate Reliability problems and to initiate, recommend, or provide solutions.

For additional discusssion, see Section 13, Product Development, under Planning for Time-Oriented Performance (Reliability).

FORMULATION OF QUALITY POLICIES

Policies are approved at the highest levels of organization. The chief executives logically require, prior to this approval, that their subordinate executives review the drafts. In this way the key managers all participate in the formulation of quality policies.

The "Right" Policies.   Managers often wonder whether the "right" policies can be found somewhere in the literature. The answer is that there are no "right" policies other than for a few rather obvious questions. Instead, policy decisions must be made to measure. Each company is unique in its history, management, and state of development. The deliberating managers must identify that uniqueness and structure their policies to fit it.

The Policy Formulation Process.   The process of formulating policies requires that the key managers have the opportunity for participation but without the burden of performing the detailed staff work. One way to do this is to assign to a specialist the job of securing from these key managers:

1. Their nominations for what should be the subject matter contained in quality policies
2. Their judgments as to what should be the direction of the company with respect to these subjects

Through this method it is possible to discover the consensus among these key managers for the various subjects. A draft prepared in the light of this consensus then contains the basis for a meeting of the minds, even on abstract matters.

For example, in one company it became important to establish a policy on a number of quality matters including the elusive question of quality leadership. The individual assigned to interview the key managers included in the questions a choice of quality leadership levels, i.e., should the company aim to be:

1. The recognized quality leader of the industry ("sole leadership")?
2. One of the top group of companies ("shared leadership")?
3. Competitive with the average of the industry ("respectability")?
4. Adequate as to quality so as to secure minimal costs and charge minimal prices ("adequacy")?

The 26 managers interviewed opted as follows:

Sole leadership	3
Shared leadership	22

Respectability	1
Adequacy	0

This consensus resolved a long-standing debate.

Policies: Holy Ground?   In many companies there is little initiative from lower or middle management to propose policies. In some cases this is the result of an unfavorable climate created by previous or present top managements. In other cases there is lack of awareness by middle management that their proposals are an expected and useful contribution. Some of this lack of awareness is the result of a mistaken belief that company policies are "holy ground." The belief stems from reasoning as follows: since only top management can approve company policies, only top management can venture on such ground.

In most companies this reasoning is not well founded. The road to final approval of policies is somewhat as follows:

	Usual roles	
Activities in formulating policies	Middle management	Upper management
Identify need and nominate	X	X
Draft proposal	X	
Review		X
Redraft	X	
Review		X
Approve		X

It is evident that middle management has a very real role to play.

Publication of Quality Policies.   Until the 1960s, examples of written quality policy were rare. Such publication as took place was for internal use and usually restricted to the upper levels of the hierarchy.

All this has changed radically. Many companies have written out comprehensive quality policies. Publication to insiders is now extensive. The short declarations are widely publicized down to the work force.

Publication now also extends to outsiders, on a selective basis. Appropriate portions of the policy are made available to customers, suppliers, the media, government regulators, etc. In some cases quality policy statements have been included in the annual report to stockholders.

ADHERENCE TO POLICIES

Before a policy is published, it is well to face realistically the question, "Do we intend to adhere to this policy?" If there is doubt about this, the policy should not be published.

In the long run, insiders and outsiders alike draw their conclusions about company policy from the deeds. If the company's products continue to show innovation, observers conclude that the company has a policy of design leadership. If the company adjusts quality complaints promptly and fairly, the observers conclude that the company has a policy of ethical dealing on quality.

If, in addition, there is a written policy and it conforms to the deeds, the written policy gains credibility. If, however, the written policy says one thing and the deeds say something else, what is believed is the deeds. Not only does the written policy lose its credibility, but other pronouncements of the company become suspect as well.

So important is the need for adherence to published policy that most companies establish audits to provide a feedback on how well the policies are being followed.

QUALITY OBJECTIVES

An objective is an aimed-at target—an achievement toward which effort is expended. A quality objective is an aimed-at quality target. The word "goal" is a synonym for "objective."

The concept of objectives is in wide use, and this use extends broadly into managing for quality. Under this concept, managers establish objectives which then are reduced to writing and become the basis of planning for results. The concept is effective because well-defined objectives:

Help to unify the thinking of all concerned

Have the power within themselves to stimulate action

Are a necessary prerequisite for operating on a planned basis rather than on a crisis to crisis basis

Permit a subsequent comparison of performance against objectives

Objectives Compared to Policies. The two concepts differ widely. Table 5.1 sets out the major differences.

Objectives Compared to Standards. As used in this handbook, a standard is a model to be followed. It is often mandated by external sources.

Standards differ from objectives in ways which are set out in Table 5.2. However, the distinction is often blurred in practice. There is no confusion when the standard is mandated by outside forces, e.g., government regulations or industry codes. However, some mandates originate with internal sources, e.g., product tolerances published by the Design Department. In such cases it is common for the operating departments to look upon them as continuing objectives.

Subject Matter of Quality Objectives. Quality objectives are in use throughout the entire organization hierarchy.

At the worker level the objectives usually take such forms as conformance to specific product features or to specific process features.

Above the worker levels it becomes necessary to widen the objectives. Much of this is done by creating groupings such as multiple product features and multiple process features. The groupings become progressively broader at progressively higher levels of organization.

In the supervisory levels the groupings of quality features may be based on product families. The resulting quality objectives are expressed in such terms as

TABLE 5.1   Objectives Compared to Policies

Features	Objectives	Policies
Subject matter	Wide range of activities	Broad, managerial
Formulation by	Many levels of organization	Middle managers, specialists
Language	Usually in numbers; often with associated schedule	Narrative
Approval at	Many levels	Highest levels
Duration	Limited; often revised annually	Lengthy; extends for years, even decades

error rates in type X insurance policies, or assembly repair rates for type Y color television sets.

At middle management levels the objectives are stated in terms such as:

To reduce the cost of poor quality for the X product line by 50 percent over the next 5 years

To reduce the cancellation rate of sales contracts by 50 percent over the next 2 years

In many cases the functions and the organization units which perform the functions are coextensive. For example, the function of filling customer orders may be carried out by a Customer Order Department which has no other function. In such cases the quality objective for the function can also serve as a goal for the organization unit and thereby as an objective for the manager of that unit.

In other cases function and organization unit are not coextensive. Some organization units carry out multiple functions; some functions are carried out by

TABLE 5.2   Objectives Compared to Standards

Features	Objectives	Standards
Usual origin	Internal decisions	Outside forces
Usual range of application	Local, to originating organizations	Wide, to many organizations
Voluntariness	Often preceded by internal participation, negotiation	Often mandated by law or powerful economic forces
Purpose: improvement versus control	Often requires improvement	Largely limited to control
Effort demanded	Often requires extra effort	Usually requires only holding status quo
Attainability	Often unproven	Usually proven
Stability	Often revised annually	Stable over long periods

multiple organization units. Where function and organization are not coextensive, it is common to evolve objectives for the organization units as well as for the functions.

At the highest level are the strategic corporate goals for quality. These goals are properly an extension of the business goals of the corporation. Here are some examples:

On-time arrivals must attain a level of 80 percent by the end of the next year [an airline].

Our product performance must at least be equal to that of our three principal competitors.

During the next 5 years our objective is to bring the cost of poor quality down to 6 percent of sales.

During the next 5 years we should cut by a third the time required to bring new products to market.

AN OBJECTIVE SHOULD BE—

From long experience we have evolved a list of criteria to be met by those who establish quality objectives.

An objective should be:

Measurable: Objectives which are stated in numbers can be communicated with precision.

Optimal as to overall results: Objectives which "suboptimize" performance of various activities can easily damage overall performance.

All-inclusive: Activities for which objectives have been set tend to have high priority but at the expense of the remaining activities.

Maintainable: Objectives should be designed in modular fashion so that elements can be revised without extensive teardown.

Economic: The value of meeting the objectives should be clearly greater than the cost of setting and administering them.

No less important is the list of criteria as perceived by those who are faced with meeting the objectives. To these operating forces, objectives should be:

Legitimate: Objectives should have undoubted official status.

Understandable: They should be stated in clear, simple language—ideally in the language of those who are faced with meeting the objectives.

Applicable: The objectives should fit the conditions of use or should include the flexibility to adapt to conditions of use.

Worthwhile: Meeting the objective should be regarded as benefiting those who do the added work as well as benefiting the organization which established the objective.

Attainable: It should be possible for "ordinary" people to meet the objectives by applying reasonable effort.

Equitable: Since performance against objectives is frequently used for merit rating of individuals, the objectives should be reasonably alike as to difficulty of attainment.

THE BASES FOR ESTABLISHING QUALITY OBJECTIVES

There are various bases for setting quality objectives, for example, history, engineering study, the market, and mandates. Each of these (and others) has its merits and deficiencies.

History as a Basis. Historical performance is widely used as a basis for quality objectives. In manufacturing areas we make use of historical data (on scrap, rework, etc.) for planning the amount of material to order, how much machinery to provide, how many workers, etc. In the field service department we make similar use of historical field failure data for planning the size of the field service force and the inventories of spare parts. In the functional departments we use historical data on error rates as an input to next year's planning. In preparing the annual budget we take notice of historical levels of performance such as cost of poor quality.

The historical basis for an objective has much appeal for the operating forces who face the problem of meeting that objective in the future. A major reason is that such an objective meets the criterion of attainability. It has already been attained; hence it is attainable. Historical bases are also a source of stability and predictability since they demand no departure from established practice. In addition they are also economic—the data base is largely in existence.

All those benefits of historical bases can easily hide a serious weakness—we may be perpetuating a poor level of performance. This has in fact taken place on a huge scale. Many companies have lost their quality leadership by perpetuating failure-prone product designs, incapable manufacturing processes, error-prone clerical processes, or high costs of poor quality. The quality leadership was taken over by companies which moved aggressively into planning to improve on historical performance.

Engineering Study as a Basis. By engineering study we mean scientific collection and analysis of data. This approach has long been used for activities such as design of technological goods and processes. The resulting quality objectives (often called standards) are expressed in technological units of measure and take the form of limiting tolerances: maxima, minima, ranges. Products and processes based on such engineering studies have in general greatly outperformed those which are empirically based.

Despite the inherent superiority of the scientific approach, we continue to encounter severe problems when we try to meet the quality objectives established by engineering study. Some of these problems are traceable to weaknesses in our use of the scientific approach. However, the bulk of them seem to be traceable to weaknesses in our organizational and managerial structure.

These organizational and managerial weaknesses usually arise from the fact that two categories of people are often involved ("two worlds"):

Those who establish the quality objectives: systems analysts, researchers, product developers, designers, etc.

Those who are impacted by the resulting quality objectives: the end users, the intermediate users, the operating forces who have the responsibility of meeting the objectives

Where there is a strict organizational separation between these categories it is easy to end up with quality objectives which are:

Not applicable: The objectives were evolved under "laboratory" conditions, not under operating conditions.

Not attainable: For the same reason.

The "laboratory" world is characterized by distinct features:

Conditions of use are simulated, not real.

Many environmental conditions are deliberately controlled in order to keep out extraneous variables.

The personnel are trained in the associated technology.

The basic mission is to attain "structural integrity."

Major emphasis is on external customers and end use. Other customers, including "those faced with meeting the quality objectives," receive lower priority.

In contrast, the "real" world of the customers and operating forces exhibits a different set of features:

The conditions of use are "actual," including misuse.

The environment is subject to entry of extraneous variations.

The personnel are not necessarily trained in the associated technology. (In the case of consumers there is extensive ignorance of the technology.)

There are multiple users, many of whom are not end users.

The basic mission is to meet operating objectives and/or fitness for end use.

Many of our quality problems have their origin in the separation between these two worlds. To minimize these problems we must provide connecting bridges. Chief of these is the participation concept. Under that concept the operating forces and other customers are brought into the process of establishing the quality objectives.

The Market as a Basis.   Another major basis for setting quality objectives is "the market." We define the market as the composite of performances in a competitive society.

There are some persuasive reasons for using the market as one of the bases for setting quality objectives:

The market objective is *attainable under operating conditions.* The proof is that others are already attaining it.

It we are not meeting the market level of quality our clients will in due course discover this. (We may already be in trouble.)

We should have early warning of lack of competitiveness so we have time to take remedial action.

It can be a lot of work to discover what is the level of market quality. We must acquire information on competitive products, in a variety of ways. The more usual ways include:

Physical inspection and test: This may require that we buy or borrow competitors' products and conduct the necessary programs of inspection and test.

Acquisition of field performance data: We may need to put competing products into service to secure such data. Alternatively we can buy the data from ultimate users, maintenance shops, etc. We can even contract to do maintenance service for ultimate users with a view of securing the performance data as a major byproduct.

Marketing research to discover customers' perceptions: For the methods used, see Section 12, Field Intelligence, under Analysis of Available Field Intelligence: Data from Customers.

The concept of market-based quality objectives applies to all levels in the company, from the general manager to the nonsupervisors.

OBJECTIVES FOR BREAKTHROUGH OR CONTROL

A major decision in setting objectives is whether to go for a breakthrough (an improvement to unprecedented levels of performance) or to hold the status quo. In popular terminology, control aims to do things right whereas improvement aims to do the right things.

Objectives for Breakthrough.   There are many reasons why managers create objectives for breakthrough. Among the more usual are:

1. The managers wish to attain or hold quality leadership. (Even to hold quality leadership requires continuing breakthrough because competitors are ever closing the gap.) They may launch innovative product designs, offer superior service, provide more complete technical assistance, etc.

2. They have identified some opportunities to improve income through superior fitness for use. For example, one company improved the reliability of its products and found from field studies that the users' costs of maintenance, and especially of downtime, were sharply reduced thereby. In consequence, the company was able to increase its prices without losing customers.

3. They are losing share of market through lack of competitiveness. For example, a company making abrasive cloth found that although its products met specification, the users' "cost per hundred pieces polished" was greater than when using competitive cloth.

4. They have too many field troubles—failures, complaints, returns—and wish to reduce these as well as cutting the external costs resulting from guarantee charges, investigation expense, product discounts, etc. Solution may require new test programs, product redesign, training manuals for users, etc.

5. They have identified some projects which offer internal cost-reduction opportunities, e.g., improvement of process yields or reduction of scrap, rework inspection, or testing.

6. They have a poor image with customers, suppliers, the public, or other groups of outsiders.

7. There is internal dissension and a need to improve motivation and morale.

Objectives for breakthrough are not limited to "hardware," or to things which can be counted, e.g., income, cost. Objectives for breakthrough can include projects such as a reliability training program for designers, a supplier rating plan, a complaint investigation manual, a reorganization for the quality control staff, or a new executive report on quality.

Objectives for Control. Managers have many reasons for avoiding breakthrough. In such cases the objectives are to hold the status quo, i.e., maintain control at present levels. The more usual reasons for choosing control in specific situations are:

1. The managers believe that improvement is uneconomic; i.e., the cost of trying for breakthrough would not be recovered.
2. Present performance is competitive. Many managers regard "the market" as a sound standard since it embodies the breakthrough efforts of competitors.
3. There are few alarm signals—e.g., few complaints or internal flareups—to suggest the need for breakthrough.
4. There is need for breakthrough, but it is not timely to undertake breakthrough because (a) there has been no agreement on the specific projects to be tackled or (b) the climate for quality breakthrough is unfavorable (e.g., too many other programs going; some key manager is not convinced; the breakthrough would require risky technological research).

The more usual objectives for control include holding the materials, processes, and products to specification; holding the field failures, complaints, returns, and other external performance measures to current levels; holding costs of inspection, test, scrap, rework, and other internal costs to current levels; and holding the gains achieved by recent breakthrough projects.

ZERO DEFECTS AS AN OBJECTIVE

This topic is awash in confusion arising from the two major meanings of the term "zero defects":

1. Defect-free product, which is the literal meaning
2. A slogan to be used during "drives" to improve quality

Defect-Free Product. This concept has value as a long-range objective, since it implies the need for never-ending improvement. The concept rejects the idea that we can relax our efforts short of perfection.

In contrast, if we decree defect-free product as a short-range objective, such a goal is in the great majority of cases not attainable. In such cases the risk is that the decree will be counterproductive by shutting off efforts to reach attainable goals.

Zero Defects as a Slogan. In this meaning the term is adopted as a kind of banner to fly during a company "drive" to improve quality. In its best usage this is comparable to adopting an appealing brand name to help sell a product. In such cases much depends on the substance behind the drive. If the drive is well conceived (i.e., a "good" product), then a good brand name is an aid to selling it to the internal customers. If the drive is ill-conceived (e.g., an attempt to solve the company's quality problems by exhorting the work force), then it will fail no matter how clever is the slogan.

ESTABLISHING QUALITY OBJECTIVES

Objectives for control are usually self-evident from the mandates, specification, procedures, etc., issued by the various sources. Objectives for improvement are not so self-evident. Even where the need is evident, it takes some effort to translate that need into an official, legitimate quality objective.

Until the 1980s objectives for control were dominant. Under the prevailing priorities, neither quality nor quality improvement had top priority. The urge for quality improvement usually came from two main sources:

1. Specific quality crises, either external or internal

2. Specific projects urged by conscientious middle managers, often quality managers

The 1980s ushered in a climate much more favorable to establishment of objectives for quality improvement. This same climate stimulated ways to identify what were the needed improvements and to list them as official quality objectives. The methods for identifying potential quality improvement projects are quite similar to those used in broad undertakings to improve quality. (See Section 22, Quality Improvement, under The Project Concept: Nominations for Projects. That same section also discusses approaches used for establishing priorities for improvement projects, and for quantifying proposals for improvement into the language of money—the major language of upper managers.)

Experience has shown that upper managers' approval of proposals for quality objectives is strongly influenced by three vital criteria:

1. Objectives for improvement are preferred over objectives for control.

2. Objectives which have a clear orientation to business or managerial matters (e.g., sales, growth, manager development) are preferred over objectives which are oriented to technology or technique.

3. Objectives which are quantified in money are preferred over objectives which are not.

STRATEGIC QUALITY OBJECTIVES

As companies acquire experience in companywide quality management (See Section 6, under Companywide Quality Management), there arises the concept of enlarging the strategic business plan to include *strategic quality planning.* Under that concept, broad quality objectives are established at corporate and division levels. These broad objectives are then "deployed" to lower levels of management. The middle managers then have the responsibility to do the quality planning—to identify what actions need to be taken to meet the objectives and what resources will be required. The approach is entirely analogous to the approach long used for carrying out other types of strategic objectives.

The methodology behind strategic quality planning is described in Section 6. However it is well to note here that before a company embarks on strategic quality planning, *all* levels of management should have acquired substantial training and experience in managing for quality. This training and experience should extend to all the processes of the quality trilogy: quality planning, quality control, and quality improvement.

REFERENCES

Juran, J. M. (1969). "Mobilizing for the 1970s." *Quality Progress,* August, pp. 8–17.

Juran, J. M. (1970). "Consumerism and Product Quality." *Quality Progress,* July, pp. 18–27.

SECTION 6

COMPANYWIDE PLANNING FOR QUALITY[1]

J. M. Juran

---

[1]In the Third Edition, the section on quality planning was prepared by Richard J. Pierce.

DIVISION OF THE SUBJECT

The subject of quality planning can be divided in a variety of ways, such as by subsystems, functions, hierarchical levels, and tools used. Any extensive treatment of the subject inevitably requires discussion of every one of those ways, but not necessarily in the same sequence. The choice of sequence involves making some judgmental decisions.

A popular method has been to divide the subject on the basis of subsystems product development, supplier relations, measurement, human relations). This method has been followed by Caplan (1980, 1984), Cound (1965), Kolacek (1978), Lewis (1964), and Wilhelm (1980). Other methods have been followed by Kofoed (1982), Olsbro (1970), Scanlon and Hagan (1982), and Taguchi (1978).

In this section the first division of the subject has been based on the universal sequence of steps taken during planning for quality. Thereafter the remaining topics are treated, the sequence being generally that which is encountered by planners as their work impacts operations.

THE QUALITY PLANNING CONCEPT

Quality planning is one of the three basic processes used in managing for quality. (See Section 2, under The Quality Trilogy, for a discussion of the three processes.) In its broadest sense quality planning is the process of establishing quality objectives and developing the means (plans) for meeting those objectives.

The terminology associated with quality planning is not well standardized. Objectives are all aimed-at targets, but they may be called "goals," "requirements," "missions," "visions," and so on. Plans may be called "systems," "procedures," "processes," "programs," and so forth. In specific applications the terminology may also become specific. For example, in manufacture of goods, the objective may be called the "specification" or "tolerance." The plan may be called a "production process."

Section 5, under Quality Objectives and the headings that follow, sets out certain fundamentals relative to quality objectives. It is shown there that quality objectives exhibit wide variation in nature and scope. They may be intended for breakthrough or for control. They can be departmental, companywide, or intercompany in scope. They can deal with matters of great importance or with numerous matters of limited importance. The resulting permutations of kind and scope of quality objectives call for a corresponding assortment of quality plans. Table 6.1 lists the more usual quality objectives and the types of quality plan which have been evolved in response to the various objectives.

THE QUALITY PLANNING ROAD MAP

Within any organization the quality plans are closely interrelated. At the top of the organization, the broad quality objectives require broad-based plans. Such broad-based plans then require establishment of subobjectives, each of which requires a subplan. In large organizations this subdivision can involve many layers of objectives and plans.

Irrespective of level in the hierarchy, quality planning involves meeting the quality needs of customers. To meet these quality needs, a universal series of actions must be taken. This series is shown graphically in Figure 6.1 as the quality planning road map. It consists of a structured, coherent sequence of steps. Each step is an activity whose output becomes an input to the next step in the sequence. The quality planning road map is described in detail in the training manual *Planning for Quality* (Juran, 1986), published in hardback under the title Juran on Planning for Quality (Juran, 1988), and in the videocassette series *Juran on Quality Planning* (Juran Institute, 1988).

TABLE 6.1 Types of Quality Plan

Objectives	Associated forms of quality planning	Discussed under
Establish self-control	Triple-role concept; feedback loop	Self-control; The Triple-Role concept; The Feedback Loop
Maintain quality for repetitive activities	Quality manual; feedback loop	The Quality Manual; The Feedback Loop
Launch numerous small changes	Multiuse procedures; quality manual	The Quality Manual
Launch major changes, programs	Central quality planning; program management; quality planning road map	Application to Multifunctional Systems; Application to Major Programs; The Quality Planning Road Map
Review execution versus plans	Quality reports; quality audits	Control Reports; Quality Assurance (see Section 9)
Eliminate existing chronic quality problems	Project-by-project improvement	Quality Improvement (see Section 22)
Avoid creation of new chronic quality programs	Quality planning road map	The Quality Planning Road Map
Attain quality for new major products, programs	Central quality planning; program management; quality planning road map	Application to Multifunctional Systems; Application to Major Programs; The Quality Planning Road Map
Establish and meet broad corporate quality goals	CWQM; strategic quality planning as part of business plan	Companywide Quality Management (CWQM)

Identification of Customers.   The first step is to identify the "customers." The word "customer" is used here in the sense of anyone who is impacted by the product or process. Customers can be "external" or "internal" (see Section 2, under Customer).

A fundamental planning tool for identifying customers is the flow diagram (Figure 6.2). The flow diagram is a graphic means for depicting the steps or activities which constitute a process. The flow diagram is constructed from standardized symbols (Figure 6.3).

In many cases the customers are numerous. In addition, what appears to be one customer may actually be an entire cast of characters. For example, a hospital supply company has customers in the form of hospitals. However, the supplies sold to the hospital impact a large number of persons in a large number of departments: purchasing managers; pharmacists; heads of test laboratories; physicians; nurses; and of course, patients.

Where customers are numerous, it is useful to apply the Pareto principle and to classify the customers between the two categories of the vital few and the useful many. Such classification helps to assure that the allocation of planning resources is concentrated in the areas of major importance.

Some classes of useful many customers are so numerous that the class is treated as one of the vital few. Examples are consumers and the internal work force.

FIG. 6.1 The quality planning road map.

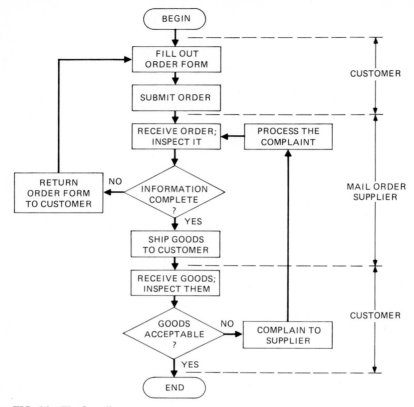

FIG. 6.2 The flow diagram.

Discovery of Customer Needs. Customers state their needs from their own viewpoints and (often) in their own language. However, much may lie below the surface.

Real needs may differ from stated needs. Stated needs for goods are often a popular way of expressing needs for services. For instance, the stated need may be a color television set, whereas the real need may be entertainment.

Customers' perceptions of needs often differ from those of suppliers. Industrial buyers may mandate that suppliers provide extensive documentation or keep statistical control charts which the suppliers feel are merely adding cost without adding value. Consumers may pay a premium price for identical products in order to shop amid handsome decor and attentive service. Customers' use (and misuse) of products can differ from suppliers' intended use.

Customers (especially internal customers) may resist introduction of some new product or process because it carries some unwelcome social consequence or threat.

Proliferation of Customer Needs. Customer needs tend to proliferate into very large numbers. A basic need such as transportation breaks down into primary needs such as safety, economy, dependability, and comfort. The primary need of

BASIC SYMBOLS

Most flow diagrams are built up out of a few basic symbols:

The activity symbol is a rectangle which designates an activity. Within the rectangle is a brief description of that activity.

The decision symbol is a diamond which designates a decision point from which the process branches into two or more paths. The path taken depends on the answer to the question which appears within the diamond. Each path is labeled to correspond to an answer to the question.

The terminal symbol is a rounded rectangle which unambiguously identifies the beginning or end of a process, according to the word within the terminal. "Start" or "begin" is used to designate the starting point of process flow; "stop" or "end" is used to designate the end of process flow.

The document symbol represents a document pertinent to the process.

The flow line represents a process path which connects process elements, e.g., activities, decisions, etc.; the arrowhead on a flow line indicates direction of process flow.

The connector is a circle which is used to indicate a continuation of the flow diagram.

FIG. 6.3   Standard symbols for flow diagrams.

economy (for a consumer-owned vehicle) then breaks down into secondary needs such as low purchase price, low financing cost, low operating and maintenance cost, high resale value, and high trade-in value. In turn, low operating and maintenance cost breaks down into tertiary needs such as warranty coverage, fuel efficiency, dependability, and adequacy of service. This proliferation continues on down the hierarchy of products to the properties of bits and pieces of goods, and to the basic tasks inherent in services.

To deal with this proliferation, in an organized, orderly way, quality planners make use of quality planning spreadsheets (Figures 6.4, 6.5, and 6.6). These spreadsheets are discussed below. See also Section 13 under Planning for Basic Functional Requirements.

Spreadsheets do not provide the planners with answers. However, spreadsheets do serve to organize the planning information in ways which permit easy reference and self-checking. Such organization is an obvious aid to the planners and to the other participants in the planning process.

Methods for Discovering Customer Needs.   The major methods consist of:

Being a customer

Communicating with customers

Simulating customers' needs

Planners who acquire experience in use of products thereby learn much about the needs of external customers for those products. Similarly, planners who undergo training in various phases of product progression learn much about the

CUSTOMER'S NEED	SENSOR	PRODUCT FEATURE A	PRODUCT FEATURE B	. . .	COMPONENT PACKAGING	SOLDERED JOINTS	. . .
⋮							
MECHANICALLY STRONG CONNECTIONS	VIBRATION TEST					**	
ELECTRICAL CONTINUITY	CONTINUITY TEST					**	
EASY COMPONENT INSERTION	INSERTION PROCESS				**		
⋮							

KEY: **STRONG RELATIONSHIP

FIG. 6.4 Quality planning spreadsheet: customer needs and product features. (The product is an electronic circuit board.)

PRODUCT FEATURE	GOAL	PROCESS FEATURE 1	PROCESS FEATURE 2	• • •	WAVE SOLDER	AUTOMATED INSERTION	• • •
PRODUCT FEATURE A							
PRODUCT FEATURE B							
⋮							
COMPONENT PACKAGING	100% AUTOMATED INSERTION					**	
SOLDERED JOINTS	100% ELECTRICAL CONTINUITY				**		
⋮							

KEY: ** STRONG RELATIONSHIP

FIG. 6.5 Quality planning spreadsheet: product features and process features. (The product is an electronic circuit board.)

6.8

PROCESS CONTROLS

PROCESS FEATURE	CONTROL SUBJECT	SENSOR	GOAL	MEASURE-MENT FREQUENCY	SAMPLE SIZE	CRITERION	RESPONS-IBILITY
PROCESS FEATURE 1							
PROCESS FEATURE 2							
. . .							
WAVE SOLDER	SOLDER TEMPER-ATURE	THERMO-COUPLE	505°F	CONTIN-UOUS	N/A	≥510°F, DECREASE HEAT; 500°F, INCREASE HEAT	OPERATOR
	CONVEYOR SPEED	FT/MIN METER	4.5 FT/MIN	1/HOUR	N/A	≥5 FT/MIN, REDUCE SPEED; ≤4 FT/MIN, INCREASE SPEED	OPERATOR
	ALLOY PURITY	LAB. CHEM. ANALYSIS	1.5% MAX TOTAL CONTAMIN-ANTS	1/MONTH	15 GRAMS	≥1.5%, DRAIN BATH, REPLACE SOLDER	PROCESS ENGINEER

FIG. 6.6 Quality planning spreadsheet: process features and process control features. (The product is an electronic circuit board.)

6.9

needs of internal customers as well as those of external customers. Some companies establish training courses in order to expose planners to customer needs. During this training the planners *make* the product in factory departments; they *sell* the product in merchant shops; they *service* the product in repair shops.

Communication with customers is the most widely used method of discovering customer needs. Some of this communication is initiated by customers through complaints, claims, returns, and other manifestations of dissatisfaction. Other communication is at the initiative of suppliers and usually relates to product satisfaction and salability of the product. Such supplier-initiated communication makes extensive use of the tools of marketing research. (See generally, Section 12, under Summary of Marketing Research Tools and Techniques.)

A third method for discovering customer needs is simulation. Customer needs can, in part, be simulated in the laboratory. In the laboratory it is possible to exclude unwanted variables, to measure with precision, and otherwise to secure pertinent technological information. However, simulation does not fully reproduce operating conditions and hence cannot by itself provide complete answers relative to customer needs.

Translation into Suppliers' Language.   Customers' needs may be stated in any of several languages: customers' language, suppliers' language, and a common language. If the needs are stated in customers' language, it becomes necessary to translate those needs into suppliers' language.

The translation process is handicapped because of vague terminology and multiple dialects, even within the same company. These differences become magnified when the relationships involve multiple companies, industries, and countries.

Tools for Translation.   A number of tools have been evolved to aid in translation and communication of customer needs.

The "glossary" is a sort of dictionary—a list of key terms along with agreed definitions for each.

"Samples" take such forms as textile swatches, colored chips, and audiocassettes. They are often used as specifications for sensory product features (e.g., feel, color, sound).

"Standardization" is a tool widely used to improve communication at various levels: intracompany, intraindustry, interindustry, and international. Official standards organizations are available to coordinate the efforts. The pace is painfully slow, but without standardization the modern industrial societies would be seriously handicapped.

"Measurement systems" are the means of "saying it in numbers"—the most effective means known for precise communication. These systems require agreement on (1) units of measure and (2) means (sensors) to carry out the measurement.

"Special organization" to translate is used when other tools are unavailable or inadequate. An example of such an organization is "order editing." It receives purchase orders from clients and then produces a translated version for use within the supplier company.

Translation for Managerial Products.   A critical problem in translation is "products" of a managerial nature. These include policies, objectives, reviews, incentives, and audits. The customers are mainly internal, across all functions and all levels. The problem is to assure that these internal customers interpret these products in ways intended by the internal suppliers. In turn, there is the problem of assuring that the responses are made in ways which minimize misunderstanding.

Tools for translation of managerial products consist mainly of the glossary, standardization, and measurement systems. Often these are assembled and published in the quality manual (see below, under Quality Manual).

Product Development.   This step on the quality planning road map determines the product features required to meet customer needs. In competitive situations, product development is subject to constraints—the product features should comply with the following criteria:

Meet the needs of the customers

Meet the needs of the suppliers

Be competitive

Optimize the combined costs of the customers and suppliers

Quality planning is a part of the product development activity. The quality planning may be done by product designers, quality specialists, operating personnel, or some combination of personnel in all these categories. Irrespective of who does the quality planning, the preceding criteria should all be met.

The activity of product development faces squarely the proliferation of needs as the development proceeds down the product hierarchy. The numerous customer needs demand numerous responses in the form of numerous product features. To deal with all those numbers, it is necessary to employ a structured, systematic approach in which the spreadsheet (Figure 6.4) plays a central role.

In Figure 6.4, the first of three key spreadsheets used in planning for quality, each horizontal row relates to a particular customer need. The vertical columns are used to accumulate information pertinent to the product features which will provide the means of meeting those customer needs. The remaining two key spreadsheets are Figures 6.5 and 6.6.

The Role of Measurement.   Measurement plays an extensive role throughout the entire quality planning process; thus Figure 6.1 shows measurement as applying to all steps of the quality planning road map.

The most obvious use of measurement is seen during product development for physical goods, since this so often demands journeys into technology. However, measurement and other, less precise forms of evaluation all play important roles in product development for nontechnological features as well. Objectives of all sorts are quantified, and this requires that the associated planning also make use of measurement and evaluation.

Tools for Product Developers.   Numerous tools have been evolved to assist quality planning during product development. These tools are described in the following paragraphs.

The Spreadsheet.   The spreadsheet can assemble a great deal of information into condensed, convenient form (see Figure 6.4).

The Phase System.   Under this concept (also called the "stage system"), the product development cycle is divided into phases. Each phase is defined in terms of the activities to be carried out and the results to be achieved. The definitions include criteria to be satisfied for completion of the phase.

Criticality Analysis.   This analysis is used to identify the "vital few" product features so that they will receive priority of attention and resources. Product features may be classified as critical for reasons such as: essential to human safety, legislated mandates, essential to salability, demanding as to investment, demanding as to continuity of performance (reliability, failure rate, uptime, maintain-ability, etc.), and long lead time.

Some of these reasons for criticality (e.g., continuity of performance) can be so demanding that they require as much product development effort as the conventional technological product features. The extent of criticality analysis may require construction of a separate spreadsheet as an aid.

Competitive Analysis.   This analysis compares product features with those offered by competitors. The obvious reason is that customers make such comparisons. An example on a major scale was that undertaken by Ford Motor Company during the quality planning for the Taurus/Sable line of motor vehicles. The analysis involved 400 key product features, and the objective was to be "best in class" throughout (Veraldi, 1985).

Salability Analysis.   This analysis attempts to establish relationships between product quality and product salability. Customer *behavior* can be studied to determine which products customers buy, which they do not buy, and why. Demand for nonstandard product features—options, or "specials"—can also be studied. The analysis can be extended to the process of bidding for business, i.e., why bids are successful or unsuccessful. (See Section 3, under Industrial Products and Share of Market.)

Customer *perceptions and opinions* can also be analyzed, using the methods of marketing research. See Section 12, under Summary of Marketing Research Tools and Techniques, for discussion of the methods used.

Yet another approach is to study competitive product differences and their impact on share of market. See Section 3, under Quality and Share of Market, for an extended discussion, with examples.

Value Analysis.   This tool is an aid to identifying the functions to be performed by the product and to providing those functions at minimum cost. See Section 13, under Planning to Minimize Cost; Value Engineering.

Systematic Obstacles.   These abound in the product development area. A widespread example is failure-prone features which are carried over from prior models to new models. In such cases the vulnerability for failure is usually well known and even notorious. However, the "solution" has been to make customer service available in the event of failure. Such a solution perpetuates the problem by disconnecting the alarm signals. Of course, customers do not regard the problem as solved. The real solution is to bring these failure-prone features to the surface and place them on the product development agenda along with the new features required to meet customer needs.

A second widespread systematic obstacle is inadequacy of early warning to product designers, resulting in future problems for customers, especially internal customers. The remedy is through systems of participation and design review (see below, under Optimizing Product Design).

Optimizing Product Design.   This step on the quality planning road map is intended to "optimize" the product design. The optimum is defined as the result which meets the needs of customer and supplier alike and minimizes their combined costs. The resulting product features become the objectives or goals to be met.

Between customers and external suppliers, the ideal approach for optimization is joint quality planning. Lacking this, the need is for open communication and mutual trust. Failing these the result is pursuit of local goals. This pursuit of local goals is known as suboptimizing. The result of suboptimization is usually a detriment to one of the parties, or more usually, to both parties.

Suboptimization also takes place within companies, that is, between internal customers and internal suppliers. The major causes of internal suboptimization are (1) monopolies on issuance of documents and (2) merit rating systems which encourage strict adherence to local goals.

Monopolies on Issuance of Documents.   For certain critical documents (e.g., product specifications, purchase orders, sales contracts), it is necessary to provide all concerned with the means of knowing whether such documents have official status. To this end there is widespread use of internal monopolies. Under the monopoly concept the documents are valid only if they have been signed by certain designated persons in designated departments.

These internal monopolies are very useful for establishing clear responsibility as to whose signature renders a document legitimate. In addition, the monopolies help to minimize any confusion as to whether a specific document is official. However, in many cases these monopolies spread into other areas, notably:

A monopoly on the choice of the inputs and criteria which then become the basis for decision making

A monopoly on decision making, i.e., to have the last word in the event of a difference of opinion

For instance, virtually all companies give their product design departments a clear monopoly on approval of product designs. No product design has official status until it is approved by that department. However, in many of these same companies the product design department has over the years acquired a monopoly on choice of inputs and criteria, and on decision making. The latter two monopolies have been a source of much discord and damage. They have often resulted in designs of products which are uneconomic to produce, difficult to test, unreliable in service, difficult to maintain, and so on. In effect, one activity (product development) has used its monopoly to unilaterally create problems for other activities. They key to avoidance of such damage and discord is *participation* in such forms as design review.

Emphasis on Departmental Goals.   A further source of internal suboptimization is the merit rating system. Many companies establish departmental goals and then use the merit rating system to stimulate department managers to meet the goals. These systems generally do stimulate attainment of goals. However, they also invite the risk that high attainment in one department will unilaterally reduce attainment in other departments. A major tool for reducing this risk is again participation among departments.

Participation.   The participation concept is inherently a team approach. The team membership includes customers and suppliers, whether between companies or within companies. The team members use their experience and expertise to make contributions such as those described in the following paragraphs.

Early Warning of Upcoming Problems.   "If you plan it this way, here is the problem I will face."

Data to Aid in Finding the Optimum.   The various customers are frequently in a position to provide data in the form of costs which will be incurred, process capability of facilities, and so on. Such data are of obvious value for optimizing overall performance.

Challenge to Theories.   Specialist departments are typically masters of their own specialty but seldom masters of the specialties of other departments. In the absence of participation by those other departments the risk is that unproven theories or unwarranted beliefs will prevail. Participation by the customers provides an informed challenge.

Resolving Differences.   Securing participation requires a detailed understanding of the forces which favor suboptimization. In the case of external customers these forces are mainly of a technological and economic nature. In the case of internal customers, some additional forces of a behavioral nature are present.

Essential Inputs.   Discovery of the optimum requires certain inputs which are not needed by the forces of suboptimization. Examples in the area of product design include competitive analysis, salability analysis, value analysis, and life cycle costing.

Technological Analysis.   Many problems in product design involve the convergence of numerous variables. Discovery of the optimum combination of these variables can require sophisticated design of experiments and equally sophisticated analysis of the resulting data. The major forms of such designs are discussed in Section 26, Design and Analysis of Experiments.

Behavioral Obstacles.   These obstacles prevail widely within companies. Often they arise from a departmental claim of exclusive jurisdiction over some area of broad subject matter. The claim may be stated in such forms as: "We are responsible for quality" (or for cost, schedule, etc). Actually, any broad subject matter has broad impacts, so that numerous departments are "responsible." The real purpose of the claim is often to guard a status (real or imagined) which is derived from exclusive jurisdiction over an essential area of subject matter.

To deal with claims of exclusive jurisdiction, it is necessary to identify the specific decisions and actions which are at issue. Managers can usually agree as to who should be responsible for making specific decisions or taking specific actions. Managers can seldom agree as to who should have responsibility for broad abstractions. For an example of such an analysis as applied to who is responsible for quality on the factory floor, see Section 17, under Quality Responsibilities on the Factory Floor.

Authority of Expertise.   With respect to some critical matters, it is necessary to rely on the judgment of acknowledged experts, or even to give the experts a monopoly on making such judgments (e.g., a license to practice). For example, regarding matters of potential safety hazards, reliance is placed on the design engineer to determine the safety factor needed for structural integrity. Regarding structural integrity, the engineer is given the benefit of the doubt and the last word.

In applying this principle of authority of expertise, it is necessary to distinguish carefully between the areas of expertise and the broad planning of which they are a part. Companies do look to the product designer to provide the expertise needed to attain structural integrity. They do not give the product designer the last word on whether to go to market with the product—that is a business decision.

Methodologies.   Practicing managers and behavioral scientists have given much thought to ways to resolve differences. One of these ways was described in a classic paper (Coonley and Agnew, 1941). Relative to the problem at hand (a national standard for cast-iron pipe), the method was as follows:

1. They must identify their areas of agreement and their areas of disagreement: "That is, they must first agree upon the exact point at which the road began to fork." When this was done, it was found that a major point of disagreement concerned the validity of a certain formula.

2. "They must agree on *why* they disagreed. . . . " They concluded that the known facts were inadequate to decide whether the formula was valid.

3. "They must decide *what* they were going to do about it." The decision was to raise a fund to conduct the research needed to establish the necessary facts. "With the facts at hand, the controversies disappeared."

A second method for resolving differences is proposed by Follett (1941). This is the method of "constructive conflict." Under this concept, the parties, working together, use their ingenuity to devise unprecedented ways to arrive at an optimum. This approach contrasts with "dominance" and "compromise"—methods which arrive at decisions but leave some parties dissatisfied.

Section 22, under Resistance to Change, describes another method for resolving differences.

Process Development.   Once the product goals have been established the next planning step is process development or process planning. (The terminology is not well standardized.) In this handbook, process planning is the activity of providing the operating forces with the means of producing products which can meet customers' needs. The end result of process planning includes:

1. The process design, which defines the specific means to be used. This definition covers (*a*) the necessary physical facilities; (*b*) the associated software (the brain and the nervous system of the equipment; and (*c*) information on how to operate, control, and maintain the facilities.

2. Provision of the facilities.

Review of Product Goals.   Ideally, the product goals should have been established with the participation of the process planners and the operating forces. Where this prior participation has been deficient, it is useful for the process planners to review the product goals with the product planners. The purpose of the review is to identify such obstacles to process planning as unrealistic goals or incomplete product information. The earlier these obstacles are identified, the wider is the range of potential solutions.

Operating Realities.   A critical consideration in process planning is what the operating realities will be. These realities include:

The training and skills of those who will use the process.

The environments of use—these can differ radically from the "laboratory" environment in which process development takes place.

The manner of actual use (and misuse)—this can differ from intended use.

Process planners learn about these operating realities from various sources: prior experience in operations, study of operating conditions, and participative meetings with operating personnel. The more complete the planners' knowledge, the less the risk that the resulting process plan will be unrealistic under operating conditions.

Carryover of Prior Process Designs.   A good deal of process design consists of carryover of prior designs. Such carryover may unwittingly include unwelcome, uninvited guests—chronic quality problems which have never been solved. Process designers should inform themselves as to the prior performance of the potential carryover. Once informed, they are faced with alternatives: reject, revise, or adopt as is.

Optimizing Process Designs. As in the case of product design, there is need to optimize the process design. The methods are quite similar to those described above for product design—joint planning, participation, and so on.

Tools for Process Planners. These tools are numerous. Those which are strongly quality-oriented include the concept of dominance, the concept of anatomy of the process, process capability quantification, and the spreadsheet.

Concept of Dominance. Operating processes harbor numerous variables, but these follow the Pareto principle of the vital few and useful many. Often one variable is more important than all the rest collectively—it is the dominant variable. If quality planners are able to identify which is the dominant variable, they can, with confidence, assign top priority to acquiring mastery over that variable.

In the case of manufacturing processes, the more usual forms of dominance include setup-dominant, time-dominant, component-dominant, worker-dominant, and information-dominant. (See Section 17, under Process Control Tools, for extended discussion.)

Concept of Anatomy of the Process. Processes assume various forms: autonomous, assembly tree, procession, and still others. The *autonomous* department, such as in manufacturing, receives basic materials and fabricates them into finished products, all within a self-contained department. In the *assembly tree* form, numerous suppliers or in-house departments make parts or components, and these then converge to be assembled in other departments. In the *procession* form, products progress sequentially through numerous in-house departments (with occasional supplier departments), each performing some operation which contributes to the final result. See Juran (1988) for further discussion of the anatomy of the process. See also Section 16 under Responsibility for Manufacturing Planning.

Choice of anatomy of the process can strongly influence the level of attained quality. For example, an assembly line (a procession) is converted to an autonomous process in which one worker assembles a unit of product complete from bits and pieces. The effect on quality is almost always to improve it. A major reason is that workers now have a much clearer understanding of the quality needs of the various steps in the assembly process; thus, over and over again, workers are their own customers.

Process Capability Quantification. This is one of the most useful of all process planning tools. For a detailed discussion, see Section 16 under Process Capability: The Concept.

The potential benefits of process capability quantification are impressive. They include:

An ability to evaluate process capability in numbers and in standardized form (usually six standard deviations of the frequency distribution)

An aid to early warning during design review

A means of specifying what is an acceptable process capability (usually in the form of a ratio of six standard deviations to the product tolerance)

An aid to comparing the capability of alternative processes

The Spreadsheet. This tool helps planners to organize their work in a systematic manner. Applied to process planning, the spreadsheet (Figure 6.5) shows the product features in the horizontal rows. It then accumulates in the vertical columns the process features needed to produce the product features and meet the product goals.

Process Control.   Quality planning includes the activity of establishing process control—the means of maintaining the process in its planned state. All control is based on the feedback loop. The general approach to control is described later in this section under the heading Planning for Control. What follows now relates to the application of the control principle to planning for process control.

Who Plans for Process Control?   Generally the responsibility is related to criticality of the process. For processes which present potential serious dangers to human safety or to the environment, it is common to assign the responsibility to the process planners. For other processes, it is usual to assign the responsibility to the operating managers.

Critical Processes.   Processes are "critical" if they involve serious risks to human safety, to the environment, to large sums of money, and so on. To reduce these risks, special features are built into the process control system, features such as:

Criteria for selection, training and qualification of control personnel

Redundancy in the various elements of the feedback loop

Independent audits to assure compliance with specified procedures

Followup of critical incidents to determine and eliminate root causes

These and other special provisions are vital parts of the control system for critical processes. Experience with such processes suggests that disasters and near disasters are often attributable to failures in the operating controls rather than to the failures of the physical facilities.

The Feedback Loop.   In process control, this follows closely the general approach described below, under Planning for Control. The control subjects (features to be controlled) include process features as well as product features. For each control subject it is necessary to provide means to measure or evaluate actual performance. Actual performance is then compared to goals, whether by technological or by human methods. Means must also be provided to close the loop—to take remedial action in the event performance does not conform to goals.

The Spreadsheet.   The third spreadsheet (Figure 6.6) is organized with process features in the horizontal rows. Then as planning for control progresses, the vertical columns accumulate the process control features required to run the process and meet the operating goals.

Transfer to Operations.   This transfer is the final step in the quality planning process. It usually involves a complete shift of responsibility, since the planners soon become fully occupied with the next planning project.

Proof of Process Capability.   The ideal proof is a demonstration of capability under operating conditions. For established processes, such proof may be available from previous performance. In the absence of such proof, other forms of demonstration are needed. One such form is the "dry run," in which a small-scale operation is conducted solely to demonstrate process capability. Another form is the "pilot run"—the first full-scale operation, during which special arrangements are made to evaluate the process capability.

In some industries proof of process capability is mandated under the name "process validation." A guideline drafted by the Food and Drug Administration defines the term as follows:

> Process validation is a documented program which provides a high degree of assurance that a specific process will consistently produce a product meeting its predetermined specifications and quality attributes.

In some cases, proof of process capability must be based on simulation in the "laboratory" or on mathematical models. Such forms of proof require extrapolation from the world of the laboratory to the world of operations. These two worlds differ in several important respects: the respective missions, the technology, the scale of operations, and the training and motivation of the personnel. Such differences require that extrapolation from laboratory findings be based on input from both worlds. The technologists are quite competent to interpret what happened in the laboratory. However, they are not necessarily able to extrapolate—to predict what will happen in the world of operations—unless they have adequate knowledge of how life is lived in that world. Lacking such knowledge, they must acquire it from inhabitants of the world of operations through such team efforts as joint planning, design review, and by other means.

Proof of Process Controllability.   This is the proof that means have been provided to enable the operating forces to carry out the activities within the feedback loop. These means include such process features as measurement reproducibility, information on the relationship between process variables and product results, process stability, and maintainability. Providing these means should not be left for the last (on the theory that planning for control will then be done by the operating forces). Instead, planning to provide these means should be done concurrently with process planning, and done jointly with the operating forces.

Transfer of Know-How.   This transfer always includes the process specifications which set out the process goals to be met. Ideally, the transfer should also include a database in the form of procedures, cautions, and lessons learned during the planning. Such a database has value for training operating personnel and for reference.

Some companies make a practice of organizing briefing meetings to facilitate the transfer. These may include training sessions in which planners participate as instructors. Such training is vital in the case of radically new processes. These briefing meetings also establish a reverse flow of information—the planners learn from the feedback.

For additional discussion relative to transfer to operations, see Bemesderfer (1979) relative to manufacturing processes and Norton and Mason (1987) relative to nuclear projects.

APPLICATION OF THE QUALITY PLANNING ROAD MAP

This road map (Figure 6.1) is universal in nature. It is applicable to quality planning throughout the economy. It is applicable to all industries (e.g., service, manufacture, defense), at all levels (e.g., corporate, division, department, job), to all functions (e.g., product development, production, marketing, finance), and to all organization forms (e.g., functional, matrix, project-oriented). Some of these applications are elaborated below.

Application to Supervisory and Worker Levels.   At the bottom of the hierarchy, work consists of operations or tasks—definable types of activity. Obvious examples are edit, assemble, and transport. Each employee is given responsibility to perform one or more tasks. When the assigned responsibility occupies any person on a full-time basis, it is usually called a "job."

A great many tasks and jobs in the lower levels of organization require quality planning. These jobs do not remain static—they continue to change and hence require replanning. The resulting volume of needed quality planning has stimulated interest in training the lower levels of supervision so that they can do the quality planning or replanning for their departments. In some cases this training is extended to selected nonsupervisors to enable them to plan their own jobs.

Quality planning at these levels makes use of a few helpful concepts and tools, as described in the following paragraphs.

The Concept of Self-Control.   Ideally, the quality planning for any job should put the employee into a state of self-control. When work is organized in a way which enables a person to have full mastery over the attainment of planned results, that person is said to be in a state of self-control and can therefore properly be held responsible for the results. Self-control is a universal concept, applicable to the general manager responsible for running a company division at a profit, the plant manager responsible for meeting the various goals set for that plant, the machinist running a lathe, and others. (Closely related to the concept of self-control is the triple role concept; see the Triple-Role Concept below.)

To put people into a state of self-control, several fundamental criteria must be met. People must be provided with:

1. Knowledge of what they are supposed to do, e.g., the budgeted profit, the schedule, and the specification.
2. Knowledge of what they are doing, e.g., the actual profit, the delivery rate, the extent of conformance to specification.
3. Means for regulating what they are doing in the event that they are failing to meet the goals. These means must always include the authority to regulate and the ability to regulate by varying either (*a*) the process under the person's authority or (*b*) the person's own conduct.

If all the foregoing parameters have been met, the person is said to be in a state of self-control and can properly be held responsible for any deficiencies in performance. If any parameter has not been met, the person is not in a state of self-control and, to the extent of the deficiency, cannot properly be held responsible.

The application of the concept of self-control can be seen in detail in Section 17, under Concept of Controllability.

The Triple-Role Concept.   This concept is shown graphically in Figure 6.7. Under this concept any job requires the job holder to carry out three roles:

As a *customer* who receives inputs from suppliers

As a *processor* who converts these inputs into products

As a *supplier* who delivers the resulting products to customers

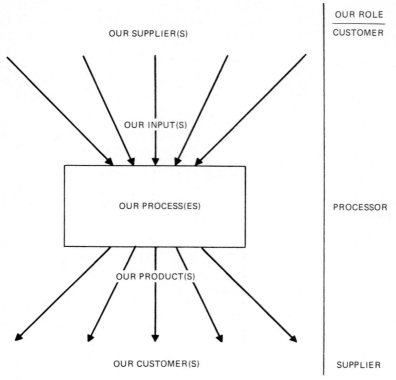

FIG. 6.7   The triple role.

(Actually, the concept operates in reverse as well, since each customer provides feedback to suppliers.)

The triple-role concept helps the quality planning to proceed in its natural progression. It starts at the base of Figure 6.7 by analysis of who the customers are and what their needs are. The analysis then proceeds on to the product, the process, and the inputs to the process.

The Tools of Analysis.   These are general-use tools—they are not unique to quality planning at the supervisory and worker levels. The tools include:

The flow diagram: This diagram maps out the process flow in detail and helps to make clear who is impacted. For examples, see Figures 16.3, 28.6, 28.9, 28.13, 28.14, 29.7, 30.9, and 30.21 in their respective sections of this handbook.

The Pareto principle: This principle is employed to identify the "vital few," whether customers, customer needs, product features, process features, or inputs. Identification of the vital few helps to assure that resources and attention are concentrated where they will do the most good.

Process capability analysis: This analysis quantifies the inherent ability of a process to meet the demands of quality objectives.

Basic statistical tools: These include tally sheets, frequency distributions, control charts, and sampling. These simple tools go far to solve many problems. The mid-1980s witnessed a resurgence of interest in these tools, with a corresponding growth in statistical literacy.

The need for job planning goes beyond quality planning. It extends to planning for productivity, costs, human relations, and still other parameters. Each of these areas has a degree of uniqueness which demands "professional" planning, that is, use of special planning tools and skills, as well as special application of general-use tools. If supervisors or workers are to carry out quality planning in a professional way they must be trained in use of the associated concepts and tools.

Application to Functional Levels. These levels relate to broad functions such as product development, purchasing, and manufacture. Planning for such functions is often done by the functional managers in collaboration with full-time planners. The planning is normally done for multiple parameters, but with major emphasis on the core responsibility of the function. For example, planning for the purchasing function places major emphasis on the defined role of the purchasing department.

For such functions the managers and planners tend to be "professionals" with respect to the core responsibility, but not with respect to the quality parameter. Regarding the quality parameter, they are usually experienced amateurs who lack expertise in the special skills and tools of planning for quality.

The major alternative (to use of experienced amateurs) has been to assign planning for quality to quality specialists (e.g., quality engineers, reliability engineers). This has been the major alternative in the United States.

A second alternative is to help the experienced amateurs to become professional through training in the skills and tools of planning for quality. This has been the trend in Japan for some years. More recently such a trend has become evident in the United States.

As a further aid to functional planners, the emerging literature is identifying the key element of quality planning for various functions. Some examples are:

Writing technical specifications (Livni, 1985)

Manufacturing engineering (Müller, 1971)

Information systems (Hill and Sorrell, 1985)

For additional discussion as applied to support operations, see Section 21, Administrative and Support Operations.

Application to Multifunctional Systems. Examples of such systems include new-product development and launch, the system of human relations, and the management information system. Such systems are all-pervasive. They demand inputs from all major functions. The quality of the systems depends importantly on the quality of those inputs. The systems represent large commitments which can be jeopardized by inadequate quality planning. In the discussion which follows, the system for new product development will be used to illustrate the approach to multifunctional quality planning.

Central Quality Planning. For any new product, there is need for some degree of central planning. This central planning establishes the overall objectives for such parameters as:

The performance features of the finished product

The cost target for the finished product

The overall schedule

The budget for the work of product development and launch

To meet these overall objectives, considerable planning, including quality planning, is necessary. Some of this planning must be done with central coordination, since the final result is a composite of many elements. This central planning may be carried out by various methods:

A team (or committee) of functional managers

A similar team, with the assistance of quality specialists

A Project Management Department

The Quality Assurance Department

A complicating factor is that the needed planning involves not only quality planning but also planning for other parameters. If the planners lack expertise in quality planning, the quality planning will be done by "experienced amateurs."

Functional Quality Planning.   Beyond the central quality planning there is need for functional quality planning. Here again there is a range of choice. Functional quality planning may be done by:

The same organization form which does the central planning

The respective functional department managers

Quality specialists, e.g., quality engineers, reliability engineers

No matter which organization form is chosen, the responsibility should be made clear. The quality planning tasks should be defined, and there should be clear assignment of who is to perform which tasks. (The quality planning tasks associated with various functions are generally described in Sections 12 through 21 of this handbook.)

Allocation of the quality planning tasks is often linked to the phased system of product development. Under that system, the progression of events is divided into logical stages or phases, such as market evaluation, research and development, product design, process design, materials acquisition, production, test, marketing, and field service. (For elaboration, see Section 13, Product Development.) The quality planning tasks are then identified and assigned to the appropriate planners. Where these assignments are made to various functional departments, it is feasible to publish a matrix showing which planning tasks are assigned to which department (see, e.g., George, 1977).

Coordination of Functional Quality Planning.   This coordination may be supplied through centralized forms such as a project management department or a multifunctional committee of managers. If no specific provision is made for coordination, the risk is that every function will be on its own. For example, one approach to product development has been the "procession." According to that approach, product development progresses sequentially from one functional department to the next, each then carrying out its assigned functional responsibility. This arrangement then makes it tempting for the functional departments to meet their schedules and budgets by shortcutting the needed coordination with their internal customers. In some industries there has been considerable damage done by this shortcutting.

Application to Major Programs.   The term "major program" is used here in the sense of a costly undertaking such as a military weapon system, a nuclear power plant, or an ocean oil-drilling platform. Each such program has so great a degree of complexity and uniqueness as to require the quality planning to be specially designed for the program.

Quality planning for major programs is nearly always subject to some extensive restraints:

The clients (Department of Defense, electric utilities, etc.) impose mandated quality plans which are extensive in scope

The organization for planning is usually in the form of a Program Management Department

The organization for quality planning is often closely linked to the Program Management Department

In these major programs it is common for clients to incorporate, in the purchase contract, the mandated quality plans as well as the product performance specification and numerous auxiliary specifications. The contractor then supplements these as needed or required. However, on critical performance matters the role of the contractor is one of conformance to mandated plans and specifications, since the critical decisions on product performance are reserved by the client.

The principle underlying the preceding approach is that the contractor must not only deliver the product under contract but also *provide the assurance* that the quality is according to contract. In this way, the client is not forced to create a large organization to duplicate much of the work done by the contractor, with resulting added cost and delay.

The contractor provides assurance to the client in a number of ways, such as:

Submitting the quality plans for review by the client

Providing the client with access to information of all sorts: logs of actions taken, test reports, essential correspondence, etc.

Conducting independent quality audits and providing the client with access to the audit reports

The amount of this documentation can be extensive, and this is often a source of contention between contractors and clients. Many contractors sincerely believe that much of the documentation could be eliminated without any detriment to quality. However, many clients are equally sincere in feeling that the documentation is essential to providing assurance of quality as well as serving other purposes within the client organizations and the regulatory bodies (e.g., traceability, defense against lawsuits).

For elaboration on the documentation problem, see Juran, "Quality and Its Assurance—an Overview" (1977).

COMPANYWIDE QUALITY MANAGEMENT (CWQM)

A major application of the quality planning concept is "strategic quality planning," sometimes called "companywide quality management" (CWQM). CWQM is, in effect, an extension of the company's business planning to include planning for quality. The nature of CWQM is readily understood by looking at the makeup of strategic business planning. Strategic business planning consists of a sequence of activities somewhat as follows:

Establish broad business goals

Determine the deeds needed to meet the goals

Organize—assign clear responsibility for doing those deeds

Provide the resources needed to meet those responsibilities

Provide the needed training

Establish the means to evaluate actual performance against goals

Establish a process for periodic review of performance against goals

Establish a reward system which relates rewards to performance

CWQM applies this same sequence to managing for quality. While the sequence is the same, the application to quality requires special organization design, skills, tools, training, and so on. In addition, CWQM requires the upper managers to become personally involved in the setting and meeting of broad quality goals.

Purposes of CWQM.   Traditionally, planning for quality has been delegated to the functional departments. Each department has been responsible for establishing and meeting quality goals for its function. Despite the presence of various means for coordination, in many companies this approach has failed to optimize company performance relative to quality. In addition, there are indications that adoption of CWQM (notably by some major Japanese companies) has contributed to quality superiority.

The advocates of CWQM point out that adoption of the concept makes it easier to broaden the concept of quality to include all company processes—not just manufacture. The advocates also point out that optimizing company performance demands increased teamwork between upper management and the functional departments, as well as among the functional departments. This teamwork then persists beyond the planning stages and into the subsequent operations. [For additional discussion, see Juran (1988), *Juran on Planning for Quality*, chapters 11 and 13; see also Bhote (1985).]

Disadvantages of CWQM.   For a company to adopt CWQM requires establishing a high-level organization (e.g., a Quality Council) to coordinate quality at the highest level. CWQM also requires establishing the organization structure needed to prepare the quality equivalent of the financial budget and the financial reports. (See below, under Organization for CWQM.)

Adoption of CWQM invariably adds to the workload of the uppper managers—people who usually are already quite busy. Introduction of CWQM also invades some of the prior autonomy of the company divisions and departments. Those organizations resist such invasion. Finally, there is no proof that CWQM will, in fact, improve results in a specific company until it has been tried out. In some companies these disadvantages have impeded the adoption of CWQM until the concept has been tested out in some division of the company.

Establishing Strategic Quality Goals.   The general nature of quality goals is discussed in Section 5, under Quality Objectives, and subsequent headings. Establishment of specific quality objectives (or goals) starts with focus on the "driving forces" which significantly impact quality. Some of these forces are of a broad political, social, and economic nature. Other forces are very specific with respect to the company's operations: activities of competitors, trends in technology, relations with suppliers, and internal cooperation. [For further discussion, see Kohoutek (1983).]

It is relatively easy to list the "driving forces." However, such a list is of little help to managers unless action is taken to evaluate those forces and their impact on quality. Such evaluation requires data and data analysis.

Some essential data are readily available as a byproduct of operations. Examples of such data are presented in a number of sections of this handbook. (See, for example, Section 12, Field Intelligence, under Organization for Field Intelligence; Data Sources; also Section 8, Upper Management and Quality, under Executive Reports on Quality.) However, CWQM also requires the creation and analysis of additional data sources. Generally these additional sources require a review of history in order to develop "lessons learned."

Deployment of Corporate Quality Goals. Broad objectives do not lead directly to results; they must first be "deployed." Such deployment consists of:

Division and subdivision of the objectives until they identify specific deeds to be done

Allocation of responsibility for doing the deeds

Provision of the needed resources

Such deployment involves communication both up and down the hierarchy. Corporate quality goals may be proposed at the top. The lower levels then identify the deeds which, if done, will collectively meet the goals. The lower levels also submit the bill: To perform these deeds, we need the following resources. The subsequent negotiations then arrive at an optimum which balances the value of meeting the goals against the cost of doing so. [For a case example, see Brunetti (1986).]

While deployment usually follows the hierarchical organization (corporation to division to functional department) there are many goals which are inherently multidivisional or multifunctional in nature. For such goals, deployment generally must go down to project *teams.*

Corporate goals often originate through nomination from below. Managers at lower levels may identify needs which should be met but which require corporate participation owing to such features as extensive resources required, multidivisional impact, and major precedents to be set. As experience is acquired in setting and deploying corporate quality goals, the organization becomes progressively more comfortable in upward communication as well.

Once responsibility has been assigned, quality planning to carry out the deeds then follows the planning processes described earlier in this section.

Providing Resources. Many well-meaning efforts to attain and improve quality have been defeated by failure to provide the needed resources. This failure has been notorious in the case of efforts applied to quality improvement projects. To bring such projects to completion, various resources are required: time for project team members to guide the projects, support from technicians and specialists, and training in several directions. With the exception of some aspects of training, these resources seldom have been provided adequately. In turn, lack of the resources has thwarted many efforts to improve quality on a scale which offered major benefits.

The CWQM approach, which is tied into companywide business planning, offers a way to overcome this deficiency. Companywide business planning has long included a positive approach to bring out into the open the resources required to meet the corporate business goals. Those who are apprehensive about "corporate interference" (see below) should note that CWQM provides a channel for dealing with the problem of securing resources.

Organization for CWQM. To adopt CWQM requires setting up special organizational machinery similar to that widely used for companywide business planning. The major components of this special organization consist of:

1. *A companywide quality committee (CWQC):* Committee members are high-level upper managers, and membership is a part-time assignment. This committee proposes the broad quality objectives. It also approves the final objectives and the associated resources. In addition, the committee carries out a broad control through review of performance against objectives and through high-level quality audits. The committee responsibilities generally parallel those of the Finance Committee with respect to finance. See also Section 8, under Quality Audits by Upper Managers.

2. *A full-time, quality management department:* This department has a coordination responsibility relative to deployment of objectives, preparation of the final list of objectives, and provision of the associated resources. The department also has the responsibility to prepare reports of performance against objectives and to assist in the conduct of high-level quality audits. These responsibilities relative to quality parallel those of the financial controller relative to finance.

Assurance of Performance against Objectives. This assurance is carried out mainly through review of reports of performance against objectives (see Section 8, under Executive Reports on Quality) and quality audits (see Section 9, under Quality Audits.)

APPLICATION TO SMALL COMPANIES

Many elements of quality planning are applicable to small companies as well as large ones. However, a significant difference in size tends to become difference in kind and hence results in differences in behavior, including approaches to quality planning. Small companies operate with less formality and system than do large companies. The reasons proceed logically from the difference in size.

How Small Is Small? The dividing line is quite arbitrary. In the United States the Small Business Administration defines small business as companies which are profit-seeking, have 500 or fewer employees, and are not dominant in their field. In a study in Ireland, the boundary was drawn at 100 (Roche and Sheil, 1984). Regardless of the boundary, small companies abound. Even at a boundary of 500, over 95 percent of all companies are "small."

Many large companies include autonomous divisions which, if independent, would be classified as small companies. Such autonomous divisions tend to follow practices in quality planning similar to those used by independent small companies.

Inherent Features. Small companies possess certain features which tend to shape the approach to quality planning:

The business scope is limited to a niche involving a relatively narrow product line. The actions of any manager thereby impact fewer customers.

The organization has fewer functional departments. Much multifunctional planning takes place within the minds of individuals.

The organization has fewer layers in the hierarchy. The upper managers are closer to the actions which take place at the work level.

The total number of managers is fewer, thus simplifying the work of communication and coordination.

Separation of Planning from Execution. Those same inherent features of small companies require a close linkage between planning and execution. Quality planning is, therefore, carried out largely by operating personnel, and this includes the work force. The craft workers concept is widely retained. Workers undergo a form of apprenticeship under the guidance of supervisors or of experienced workers. For example, at Steinway and Sons Piano Company, workers progress upward within three crafts: woodworker, machinist, and tuner (Karabatsos, 1983). Anchor Brewing Company employs 14 full-time and 7 part-time employees. The management system involves extensive delegation to the work force. In turn, the work force is able to accept extensive delegation because of prior indoctrination and training (Maytag, 1986.)

In small companies the concept of quality planning by operating personnel applies also to multifunctional projects such as new product launching. Hartz (1982) describes such an approach using multifunctional "working groups."

For small projects within large companies, the quality planning may assume hybrid forms. Lange (1978) gives examples in which multifunctional teams are aided by specialized quality planners and by adapting the company's standard practices as needed.

Extent of Formality in Quality Planning. This topic was researched by Roche and Sheil (1984). The study extended to 591 small companies and 380 large companies; the size criterion was 100 employees. Both groups made wide use of product inspection and test. However, there were significant differences in use of such planned control methods as formal supplier evaluation and such tools as statistical methodology.

Such differences in formality are generally known to large buyers whose suppliers include small companies. Some of those large buyers recognize the differences when buying from small companies. The approach is usually to classify purchase contracts according to importance. Contracts of high levels of importance require the supplier to establish a full array of formal quality systems and procedures. Contracts of lower levels of importance require fewer and less formal systems and procedures.

Military buyers formalize these distinctions by publishing several levels of military or defense standards defining quality assurance systems [for further details, see Heslop (1981) and below, under Generic Standards].

Advantages and Limitations of Informality. By avoiding formality, small companies also avoid the costs of preparing written systems and procedures, as well as the associated documentation. Instead, the information is in the memories of the experienced personnel. However, this arrangement renders the company vulnerable to the loss of essential information in the event of employee turnover.

The absence of a quality planning function also creates a risk that the small company will remain isolated and static—will fail to keep its planning methods up to date. One proposed solution is to establish quality audits which utilize expertise available in the local community, such as managers from other companies and university professors [for details, see Willborn (1978)].

LESSONS LEARNED

A simple example is seen in the world of sports. Some sports teams arrange for videotaping of their games. Collectively, such tapes present a history which can be analyzed to provide inputs to the quality planning process. Analysis of the history can identify opportunities for improvements such as change of strategy, training to reduce the incidence of predominant errors, revision of the signaling system, and redesign of the equipment.

The lessons-learned concept is applicable to general management as well as to the various functions. An example relative to general management is the post-project appraisals conducted by British Petroleum (BP). BP maintains a full-time postproject appraisal (PPA) organization unit to conduct appraisals of the conduct of large undertakings: acquisitions, joint ventures, and major construction projects. In its first 9 years the unit appraised over 80 such undertakings. The lessons learned from the appraisals include:

How to formulate investment proposals more accurately

How to approve the proposals more objectively

How to execute the undertakings more efficiently

For a detailed explanation, see Gulliver (1987).

Application to Multifunctional Processes. The lessons-learned concept has wide application to multifunctional processes. An important example is the process for developing and launching new products. Such a launching progresses through numerous phases or stages. In some industries it continues for several years. A significant portion of this time is devoted to rework. This rework is caused by chronic deficiencies in the new-product launching system. The outward symptoms of the deficiencies include engineering change orders, process redesigns, and product recalls.

The Log of Problems. For such multifunctional processes, a useful approach to lessons learned is the "historical review." A historian is appointed to review the history of a number of prior cycles of launchings. A part of this review consists of preparing a log of problems encountered in prior launchings. For each such problem, the log specifies the outward symptoms, the causes which were discovered to have been the sources of the symptoms, the remedies to solve the problem, and the estimated amount of damage done (if substantial).

In a sense, the preceding review is a study of the "cost of poor quality" as applied to the product development process. However, some of these costs are quite different from those encountered in manufacture of products. Product development necessarily tries out new ideas, and this inevitably creates problems which are inherent in risk taking. The historical review takes account of this feature of product development problems by studying the consequences of the *time* of discovery of the problems.

The Consequences of Time. This step in the historical review determines, for each problem: at what stage it was first discovered, at what stage it could have been discovered, and what could have been done to discover the problem earlier (or to have avoided the problem altogether).

Kano (1984) makes use of a "T-type matrix" for comparing the actual stage at which problems are found with the stage at which they could have been found. Ingram (1984) describes a history review process comprising five steps—historical setup, grouping and review, creation of a problem log, cause analysis, and remedial action.

The Forms of Improvement.   Most of the improvements consist of new or improved tools for the planners. For example, in the automotive industry a major recurring problem in new-product development has been the inability of the factory processes to meet product tolerance criteria established a year or two earlier during product design. The movement to quantify process capability of manufacturing processes has enabled designers and manufacturing planners to secure early warning of such problems and thus reduce their frequency.

The specific new or improved tools include databases, early warning reviews, procedures, countdowns, and foolproofing measures. Collectively, these tools can significantly improve future launchings. Some problems become extinct—they will not appear at all in future launchings. Other problems will be discovered earlier, so that they will cost less to remedy and will create less delay. Perhaps the most attractive gain is a substantial reduction in the time required to go to market. A company making industrial sewing machines is reported to have cut that time in two, in a space of 5 years.

Organization for Historical Review.   This organization consists of (1) the guidance function and (2) the historian(s).

Guidance is provided by a multifunctional team of managers. Their responsibilities include defining the mission, determining the questions to which answers are needed, providing resources and assistance to the historian, and acting on the findings. The team also takes steps to abolish any atmosphere of blame, in order to assure the objectivity of the historical review.

The historian conducts the detailed review by drawing on various sources: minutes of meetings, correspondence, reports, test results, change notices, and logs. All this is supplemented by interviews with those who actually participated in prior launchings. These interviews are needed to fill in gaps and to clear up biases and vagueness.

A company making process control equipment used the historical review approach to analyze 15 previous projects. The review revealed that certain decisions were being made at too low a level. This, in turn, resulted in improving the performance of certain specific functions, but not in optimizing overall company performance. A second conclusion was that more thorough verification was needed to assure that design changes would, indeed, correct the problems for which the changes were instituted.

Goree and Musson (1984) describe a structured "case study analysis" of a sample of defense products. The analysis used 26 specific elements to review the historical performance in management, contracting, design, test, and evaluation.

For additional discussion and examples, see Section 22 under Diagnosis—General; Diagnosis of Failures in Broad Systems.

Application to Functional Processes.   The lessons-learned concept has been widely applied in all functions. An example in the service function is related by Heskett (1987). The example concerns Hartford Steam Boiler Inspection & Insurance Company (HSB). HSB insures industrial equipment, especially steam boilers. As part of its activity, HSB has compiled a database on the performance of the key types of equipment. This database then serves multiple purposes such as an actuarial base for insurance rates, a source of operating and maintenance data for clients, and a source of information enabling HSB's engineers to provide consulting assistance to clients.

An example in the supplier relations function is a historical review of problems encountered in prior supply contracts (Table 6.2). In this case the frequency of problems in each category of cause helps to identify the vital few areas which should have priority of attention.

TABLE 6.2   Study of Problems in Supply Contracts

Major factors	Totals
Preaward surveys	
Q history (marginal/bad)	13
Contract requirements	
Poorly written	28
Deficient specs and/or drawings	72
Inadequate Q requirements	22
Postaward	
Inadequate conference	5
First article	
Inadequate evaluation	10
First article failure	5
Contract management	
Contractor Q program not viable	76
Contractor financial assets inadequate	29
Contractor physical assets inadequate	13
Contractor CA not sustained	41
Inadequate and/or unqualified contractor personnel	40
Excessive scrap	12
Control of suppliers and subcontractors	6
Miscellaneous factors	
Contractor commitments not met	36
PQAP did not detect problem cause	23
PCO inaction	27
Lack of PCO-Contractor coordination with ACO-QAR	1
Total	459

The concept of historical review has been applied to a great variety of functional problems, such as cancellation of sales contracts, data feedback on field performance, and maintenance of physical facilities. The variety is so great as to suggest that the concept has universal application.

In many cases the benefits of lessons learned can be extended beyond the planners. A common example is the owners' manuals for consumer products. Some of these manuals include tables showing, for various potential problems: the outward symptoms, the likely causes, and the likely remedies. Such tables enable many owners to conduct their own diagnosis and remedy.

The same concept is widely applied to industrial products. See, for example, a table of cause and correction relative to use of industrial grinding wheels ("Grinding Wheel Quality Improvement Hints," 1977).

PLANNING FOR CONTROL

Once planning is complete, the plans are put into operation. The responsibility of the operating personnel is mainly to meet the established goals. They do this through a planned system of quality "control." Control is largely directed at meeting goals and preventing adverse change. This is in contrast to "improvement," which is directed largely at creating beneficial change.

Much human energy is devoted to control. Biologically, this consists of maintaining the body temperature, the blood count, and other physiological functions. Industrially it takes the form of meeting goals: delivery according to schedule, expenses according to budget, and quality according to specification. This control "process" consists of a universal series of steps which, when applied to problems of quality, can be listed as follows:

1. Choosing the control subject, i.e., selecting what is to be regulated
2. Choosing a unit of measure
3. Establishing a goal for the control subject, i.e., specifying the target value for operating performance
4. Creating a sensor—a means of evaluating actual performance in terms of the unit of measure
5. Evaluating actual performance
6. Interpreting the difference between actual performance and goal
7. Taking action on the difference

This series of steps is the regulatory process by which we control anything: in other words, if you know how to control, you can control anything.

The preceding definition of "control" as a process is very different from the meaning given in some European countries to a word of the same pronunciation. The European word, spelled variously as "control," "controle," "Kontrola," "Kontroll," or (Cyrillic) "КОНТРОЛ," is often used in the narrow sense of product inspection. (For an extensive discussion of this universal process, see Juran, *Managerial Breakthrough,* chapters 12 through 20.)

QUALITY CONTROL

The term "quality control" has multiple meanings. In this handbook:

> *Quality control is the regulatory process through which we measure actual quality performance, compare it with quality goals, and act on the difference.*

The other definitions of quality control include:

1. A part of the regulatory process, e.g., product inspection.
2. The name of a department which is devoted full-time to the quality function. In this usage, the term is capitalized, i.e., Quality Control.
3. The tools, skills, or techniques through which some or all of the quality function is carried out.

The term "quality control" has had a short but lively history. Early in the twentieth century, it began to be used as a synonym for "defect prevention" (in contrast to the widely prevailing after-the-fact inspection). However, during the 1940s and 1950s there was a wave of enthusiasm (and overenthusiasm) for the use of statistical methods in quality control. The proponents of this movement coined the phrase "statistical quality control" (SQC) and publicized it so widely that many managers gained the impression that quality control consisted of the use of statistical methods in industry. As a consequence, the SQC movement weakened the use of "quality control" as an accepted term for the regulatory process.

In subsequent decades, various other terms emerged to erode the use of "quality control" as an all-inclusive term for the regulatory process. The term "total quality control" implied that anything else was only partial quality control. Reliability engineers contended that quality control as practiced had been limited to internal quality matters. Advocates of exhortation drives invented new terminology (e.g., "zero defects") to be used as a central slogan. Managers invented terms to represent conduct of the entire quality function (e.g., quality assurance, product assurance). During the mid-1980s there emerged a revival of keen interest in statistical methodology, this time under the name "statistical process control." The end is not in sight.

It would be helpful to agree on a single term for the regulatory process. However, it is difficult to secure such agreement. Most people tend to structure their glossary in a way which affirms their beliefs on organization structure, priority of technique, and other aspects. There have been enough instances in which choice of terminology was decisive in settling jurisdictional disputes to cause people to use terminology as a weapon in such contests. It is not merely a matter of aggression; there are many sincere human beings who feel that broadly standardized terminology is a detriment to their company needs (or personal aspirations) and that, therefore, new, local terminology must be coined to respond to these needs.

On-Line and Off-Line Quality Control.   These terms are used to distinguish (1) the application of the feedback loop to "production line" activities from (2) the progression of events on the quality planning road map. "On-line quality control" is readily visible and even dramatic in appearance. However, "off-line quality control," while less conspicuous, is much more influential in attaining quality. [For elaboration, see Taguchi (1978).]

Self-Control.   This term is applied to situations in which a person is provided with all the means needed to conform to planned goals (for details, see the Concept of Self-Control above).

Quality control is greatly simplified when operating people are in a state of self-control.

THE FEEDBACK LOOP

The universal series of steps (listed under Planning for Control) takes place within a system called the "feedback loop." Figure 6.8 shows in simplified form the flow of events in the feedback loop.

The nucleus of the loop is the control subject—the thing being regulated. A goal or standard is established as the intended value of the control subject. A sensor measures the actual value (performance). A collator compares actual per-

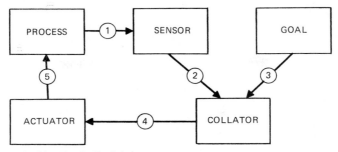

FIG. 6.8   The feedback loop.

formance to goal. When actual performance differs from goal by more than a predetermined tolerance, the loop is closed, actuating the means for restoring the status quo.

The evolution of the modern computer has stimulated the growth of computerized on-line systems of self-control. These computerized systems are used not only in factories but also widely in service industries, as well as in administrative and support operations.

In fully automated processes, the steps of the feedback loop may all be carried out without human intervention. In cases of self-control, the steps may all be carried out by one individual. Lacking self-control, the steps are carried out by multiple individuals. In such cases it is necessary to define with precision who is responsible for carrying out which step.

The Control Subject.   Control subjects exist in very large numbers. At the technological level, there are many quality characteristics of the products being produced: components, units, subsystems, and systems. There are also quality characteristics of the processing conditions (e.g., time cycle, temperature) and the processing facilities. In addition, there are quality characteristics of the input materials and services. Still more control subjects are imposed by external forces: clients, government regulations, and standardization bodies.

Beyond technological quality control subjects are the managerial quality control subjects. These are mainly the performance goals for organization units and the associated managers. Managerial goals extend to nontechnological matters such as customer relations, financial trends (e.g., progress in reducing cost of poor quality), employee relations, and community relations. For elaboration on control subjects at upper management levels, see Section 8, Upper Management and Quality, under Executive Reports on Quality.

The Control Pyramid.   Despite the large numbers of control subjects, relatively few human beings are needed to carry out the necessary controls. They do so by extensive use of the principle of self-control. A great deal of this self-control is built into the technology through use of foolproofing and automated processes which require no human intervention.

Additional self-control is created through job design in ways which meet the criteria of self-control. Such job designs enable the supervisors to delegate most of the burden of human control to the work force. Such delegation enables the supervisors to limit their control activities to the vital few control subjects.

This plan of delegation can be depicted as a control pyramid (Figure 6.9). The bulk of the control is carried out without human intervention. Another large seg-

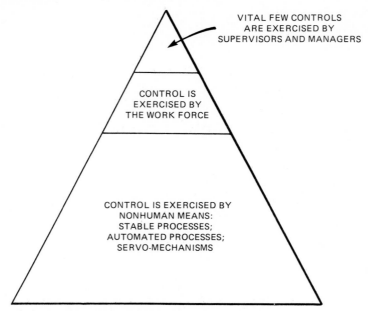

FIG. 6.9   The control pyramid.

ment is carried out by the work force. The remaining vital few controls are carried out by the supervisors and managers.

Control Stations.   In organizing for control it is useful to establish a limited number of centers or control stations. Each such control station then is given the responsibility for carrying out the steps of the feedback loop for a selected list of control subjects. A review of numerous control stations discloses that they are usually located in one of several principal ways:

1. At changes of jurisdiction, to protect the recipients: between stages of major projects (e.g., design review), at movement of products between companies or between major departments, and prior to delivery to finished goods store or to the customer
2. Before embarking on an irreversible path: setup approval before production, product approval before completing a costly operation (e.g., laboratory test before pouring a heat of steel), and product approval before diffusion of a uniform stream
3. After creation of a critical quality
4. At dominant process variables, i.e., the vital few
5. At natural "windows," for economical control

Choice of control stations is aided by preparation of a flow diagram which shows the progression of events through which the product is produced. For examples of flow diagrams, see Figures 16.3, 28.6, 28.9, 28.13, 28.14, 29.7, 30.9, and 30.21 in their respective sections of this handbook. Flow diagrams help planners to visualize the overall process and thereby to do a more logical job of grouping control features into control stations.

Definition of Work.   For each control station, it is necessary to define the work to be done: which quality features are to be measured, the goals and standards to be met, the governing regulations and procedures, the instruments to be used, the data to be recorded, and the decisions to be made. It is also necessary to provide criteria for decision making, such as seriousness classification, sample sizes, and tolerances. Such criteria should be provided by the planners if the control station personnel lack the qualifications to do so.

Assignment of Responsibility.   Often there are a number of people associated with each control station. For example, in a factory department the work of quality control may be shared by setup workers, machine operators, inspectors, supervisors, and process engineers. In such cases it is not possible to determine who is responsible for quality until there has been identification of the actions and decisions needed to attain quality. For details of such identification, see Section 17, under Quality Responsibilities on the Factory Floor.

Unit of Measure.   Communication of quality-related features is best done through numbers. In order to "say it in numbers," it is necessary to create a system of measurement consisting of:

A unit of measure: A defined amount of some quality feature which permits evaluation of that feature in numbers

A sensor: A method or instrument which can carry out the evaluation and state the findings in numbers in terms of the unit of measure.

Units of measure for product and process performance are usually expressed in technological terms; for example, fuel efficiency is measured in terms of distance traveled per volume of fuel; timeliness of service is expressed in minutes (or hours, days, etc.) required to provide service.

Units of measure for product deficiency usually take the form of a fraction:

$$\frac{\text{Number of occurrences}}{\text{Opportunity for occurrences}}$$

The numerator may be in such terms as number of defective units of product, number of field failures, and cost of warranty charges. The denominator may be in such terms as number of units produced, dollar volume of sales, number of units in service, and length of time in service.

Supervisory and managerial controls usually require data in the form of summaries. Preparation of such summaries often requires use of units of measure such as indexes and ratios.

Figure 6.10 shows the interrelation of units of measure at various organization levels.

The Sensor.   Most sensors are designed to provide information in terms of units of measure. At the bottom of the pyramid (Figure 6.10) the sensors are usually technological instruments or human beings employed as instruments (e.g., inspectors, auditors). In the upper layers of the pyramid the sensors are data systems.

There has been a continuing trend to provide sensors with additional functions of the feedback loop: data recording, data processing, comparison of performance with standards, and initiating corrective action in the process. For a discussion of precision, accuracy and maintenance of sensors, see Section 18, under Sensory Qualities.

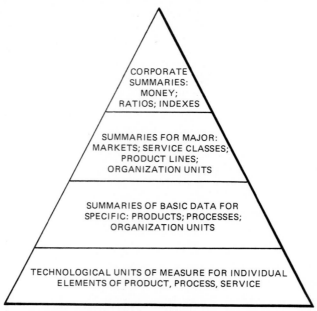

FIG. 6.10 Interrelation of units of measure.

Human Sensing. Much sensing is done by human beings. Human sensing is subject to a variety of errors. Remedies have been evolved for these error types. Table 6.3 summarizes the principal types of human error and the associated remedies. For elaboration, see Juran (1988), *Juran on Planning for Quality,* chapter 6, under Human Errors.

Data Collection and Processing. Additional steps in the feedback loop include data collection by sensors, data entry, and data processing. These steps have all been revolutionized by recent advances in electronic data processing. Sensed data can be entered directly, without the use of paper. The speed of data processing permits real-time display of the processed data. The systems can be programmed to display control charts and summaries in various forms. The systems can also be programmed to carry out analyses, such as identification of the "vital few" problems, and to display these. See generally, Section 27, Computers and Quality.

Analysis for Decision Making. In its most primitive form, this analysis consists of comparing the sensed performance with the quality goals. The observed difference must then be interpreted in terms of its significance. If the difference is "significant," decisions must then be made as to what to do about (1) the deviant process and/or (2) the deviant product.

"Significance" includes statistical significance and economic significance. They are very different in nature.

Statistical Significance; Control Charts. The problem here is to separate false alarms from the real thing. An observed difference between performance and goals can be the result of (1) a real difference or (2) an apparent difference arising from chance variation.

TABLE 6.3 Types and Remedies of Human Error

Type	Remedy
Misinterpretation	Precise definition; glossary
	Checklists
	Examples
Inadvertent errors	Aptitude testing
	Reorganization of work to reduce fatigue and monotony
	Fail-safe designs
	Redundancy
	Foolproofing (errorproofing)
	Automation; robotics
Lack of technique	Discovery of knack of successful workers
	Revision of technology to incorporate the knack
	Retraining
Conscious errors	
Coloration	Design review of data collection plan
Bias	Removal of atmosphere of blame
Futility	Action on reports, or explanation of why not
	Depersonalize orders
	Establish accountability
	Provide balanced emphasis on goals
	Conduct quality audits
	Create competition, incentives
	Reassign the work

A major tool for separating false alarms from the real thing is the Shewhart control chart. This chart is designed to show graphically the limits of variation due to specified chance odds, for instance, 19 to 1. Differences which fall within these limits are then assumed to be due to chance since they could readily have been caused by chance. Differences which fall outside these limits are assumed to be real since the odds against chance causation are so high. For a detailed discussion of the Shewhart control chart, see Section 24.

Starting in about 1980 there emerged in the United States a new wave of interest in the use of statistical tools for quality control. This movement, often called "statistical process control" (SPC), concentrated on use of the Shewhart control chart to distinguish statistically significant variations from those which were not statistically significant. This same movement included extensive training of supervisors and workers in basic statistical tools, with a resulting increase in statistical literacy.

Observed variations which are not statistically significant rarely are acted on because the cause is so often due to chance and hence not "findable." Variations which do have statistical significance become candidates for action (see below, under Economic Significance).

Trend Analysis; Leading Indicators. A useful aid to decision making is trend analysis. The purpose is to create "leading indicators" which help to predict future events. A common example is cumulative forms of data summary. For example, cumulative sum charts have greater sensitivity for identifying trends than do the conventional Shewhart control charts. (See Section 24, under Types of Control Charts, for further discussion.) In like manner, cumulative data on field returns (or field service calls) help to predict the ultimate levels of returns. Similarly, cumulative data on early failures during life testing can facilitate prediction of ultimate failure rates. [For elaboration, see Section 13 under Planning for Time-Oriented Performance (Reliability); Reliability Tests.]

Other Analyses.   There are many varieties of analysis. Data can be organized to separate the vital few problems from the rest. Correlation analysis can be used to discover relationships among variables. Examples of these and other forms of analysis are common in quality improvement projects as well as within the feedback loop. See generally, Section 22, Quality Improvement.

Control Reports.   Most reporting on quality is done by instruments which provide real-time information directly to operating personnel (production workers, office clerks, airline pilots, etc.). Beyond such real-time feedbacks, summarized reports are prepared to enable supervisors and middle managers to become informed and to take action as needed.

Table 6.4 lists some typical subjects for control reports, along with the usual units of measure, sources of data, standards, format, and frequency of reporting.

Upper management levels also require control reports on quality. These are discussed in Section 8, Upper Management and Quality. See especially, Tables 8.1 through 8.4 and associated discussions.

Corrective Action.   The final step in closing the feedback loop is to actuate a change which restores a state of conformance with quality goals.

The term "corrective action" has been loosely applied to two very different conditions:

1. Elimination of *chronic* sources of deficiency. The feedback loop is *not* a suitable means for dealing with such chronic problems. Instead, the need is to employ the quality improvement process as described in Section 22.

2. Elimination of *sporadic* sources of deficiency. The feedback loop is well designed for this purpose.

In such sporadic cases the cardinal issue is what changes caused the sporadic difference to arise. Discovery of those changes, plus action to restore control, can usually be carried out by the unaided local operating supervision (see Section 22, under Troubleshooting).

Economic Significance.   The fact that a nonconformance is statistically significant does not mean that there will be corrective action. In some companies nonconformances are so numerous that the personnel cannot apply corrective action to all of them. In such cases it is customary to establish priorities based on economic significance and related parameters. If the economic significance of some nonconformance is at a very low level, corrective action may not be taken for a long time.

In situations where nonconformances are numerous it is customary to formalize the corrective action process. The cases are documented, and organization machinery is created for decision-making, (e.g., Material Review Boards). See Section 18, under Judgment of Fitness for Use.

Application to Upper-Management Control.   A special and vital application of the feedback loop is for quality control at the upper levels of the company. This application is discussed in Section 8, under Quality Assurance for Upper Managers.

TABLE 6.4 Matrix of Reports on Quality

Control subjects	Typical units of measure	Usual data source	Typical standard	Typical format	Typical frequency*
Product conformance	Parts (defective) per million; average performance	Inspection; test	Engineered; historical	Tabulation; charts	D, W
Outgoing quality based on product audit	Demerits per unit	Product audit	Historical	Charts; narrative	M
Rework	Rework hours per 100 total hours	Accounting; quality	Historical	Tabulation; charts	W, M
Field failures					
Complaints	Number of complaints per 100 units; per $000 of sales	Customer service; accounting	Historical	Tabulation; narrative	M
Returns	Value of returns per $000 of sales	Customer service; accounting	Historical	Tabulation; narrative	M
Warranty charges	Cost per 1000 units under warranty	Customer service; accounting	Historical	Tabulation; charts	M, Q
Service calls	Number per 1000 units under warranty; cost per 1000 units under warranty	Customer service; accounting	Historical	Tabulation; narrative	M, Q
Product reliability	Failure rate; mean time between failures	Quality; customer service	Historical; engineered	Charts; narrative	M, Q
Suppliers' quality performance	Cost of poor quality per $000 of purchases; % of shipments nonconforming	Incoming inspection; accounting	Historical	Tabulation; narrative	Q

*Legend: D = daily; W = weekly; M = monthly; Q = quarterly.

6.39

PLANNING FOR QUALITY IMPROVEMENT

The approach used depends on what kind of quality is to be improved. The two major forms of "quality" consist of:

1. Quality in the sense of "those product features which meet the needs of customers and thereby provide product satisfaction." In general, improvement of this form of quality is done by following the quality planning road map as set out in this section. In effect, the quality improvement results from replanning.

2. Quality in the sense of freedom from deficiencies. In general, improvement of this form of quality is done by the process set out in Section 22, Quality Improvement.

For elaboration of the distinction between the two kinds of quality, see Section 2, under "Quality" Defined.

THE QUALITY MANUAL

A great deal of planning for quality is done with the aid of formal repetitive-use plans often called *systems* or *procedures.* Such procedures are thought out, written out, approved formally, and published to become the authorized, legitimate way of conducting the company's affairs relative to planning for quality. The subject matter of these quality plans ranges over the entire spectrum of the activities through which companies manage for quality. In many companies these plans are published collectively in a document known as a "quality manual" (also "quality assurance manual," "quality management requirements," etc.).

The basic objectives of such manuals are to provide the organization with plans which exhibit certain useful features:

Optimal: The plans are the result of multifunctional discussion and agreement.

Repetitive use: The plans reduce the need for repeated replanning.

Official: The plans are approved at the highest levels of organization.

Readily findable: The plans are assembled into a well-known reference source rather than being scattered among many memoranda, oral agreements, reports, minutes, etc.

Stable: The plans survive despite lapses in memory and employee turnover.

Terminology.   Multiple-use plans are designated by various names. Quality plans for major multifunctional activities are sometimes called quality "systems" or "subsystems." Military and other governmental bodies have favored the term "program." At functional levels the plans may be called "methods," "procedures," or "routines." For major projects requiring tailor-made, single-use plans, the term may be "project plan." For informal plans, the term may be "practice."

Evolution of the Manual.   The predecessors of an organized manual are a wide assortment of memoranda, instructions, marked prints, and other bits of information. These have multiple origins and end up in desk drawers, filing cabinets, people's heads, and wastebaskets. As these things multiply, so does the job of finding authoritative information. Finally a state is reached where the company concludes that a more orderly approach is needed.

The moving force for the first quality manual is usually the quality manager. In consequence, the first manual also tends to be mainly departmental in nature and to emphasize procedures for improving the effectiveness of the Quality Department rather than for optimizing company performance. However, as evolution proceeds, the manual tends to expand into all activities which affect managing for quality.

For some companies, the decisive factor in moving from a narrow-based to a broad-based manual has been a determined customer. One such customer has been the military. For example, the military specification MIL-Q-9585A, *Quality Program Requirements,* includes a provision as follows:

> "3.3 Work Instructions. The quality program shall insure that all work affecting quality . . . shall be prescribed in clear and complete documented instructions. . . . "

This specification is elaborated by setting out various specific requirements and criteria to be met by the quality plans. Other government buying and/or regulatory bodies similarly require that quality plans meet certain specified criteria, some of which are quite demanding.

During the 1980s some major industrial customers undertook to improve their quality in response to increased competition. As a part of their efforts to improve, they demanded improved quality from their suppliers. Those demands went beyond the quality of the products being purchased; the demands extended to the quality *plans* used by the suppliers. A widespread requirement was that the suppliers make use of statistical tools during their process controls (SPC). However, some major buyers established a broad array of requirements to be met by suppliers' quality plans, including use of SPC.

As the company grows and breaks up into divisions which are themselves autonomous businesses, the bulk of the quality plans are contained in divisional manuals. However, there evolves a corporate quality manual which contains corporate quality policies, corporate organization, interdivisional quality procedures, and other matters of a corporate or interdivisional nature.

A second moving force for evolution of a quality manual is a gathering dissatisfaction with quality planning which has been relying on all those scattered memoranda, oral agreements, and so on. Such dissatisfactions in due course culminate in an initiative (often by a quality manager) to create order by organizing an official quality manual.

For some case examples of evolution of a quality manual, see Murray (1976); also Holt (1976).

Contents of the Manual.   The manual is usually organized into modular sections. Such an organization simplifies the job of maintaining the manual as well as providing for selective distribution of the modules.

General Sections.   These deal with broad administration of the manual along with aids to its use. General sections include:

1. A statement by the general manager (or other high official). The statement includes a message relative to the significance of the manual. It sometimes makes some specific assignments of responsibility. It includes the signatures which confer legitimacy.

2. The purpose and the intended use of the manual and how to use it.

3. The table of contents.

4. The pertinent company (or divisional, etc.) quality policies. Often these may be incorporated by reference to the policy document. (See, in this connection, Section 5, under Quality Policies.)

5. The organization charts and tables of responsibility relative to the quality function. (See, in this connection, Section 7, Organization for Quality.)

6. The authorized distribution list for copies of the various modules.

7. Provision for keeping the manual up to date, e.g., periodic audits and scheduled reviews.

8. Supplementary aids for use of the manual. These may include a glossary of terms, a list of acronyms and their meanings, a list of materials referenced, and a bibliography. In some companies the manual includes sample copies of the principal forms cited by the manual, along with instructions for their use.

9. An index.

Managerial Sections. These sections, sometimes called "subsystems," exhibit a good deal of similarity from one company to another. Most manuals include a selection from the following:

Customer relations: Product safety, liability, recall; competitive quality evaluations; preparation of quality-oriented portions of bids for business; order entry process. (See Section 20, Customer Service.)

New-product "cradle to grave" quality planning: Phases or stages; product goals—reliability, mean time between failures, mean time to repair, warranties, etc; design review; model construction and test; software development and test; specifications; qualification testing; configuration and engineering change control. Management for software quality has emerged as a major new area requiring extensive data collection, analysis, and feedback. (See Section 13, Product Development.)

Manufacture: Producibility analysis, equipment specification and procurement, process capability analysis, prove-in of processes, pilot production runs, provisions for traceability. The expanded use of statistical process control (SPC) has expanded the use of quantified process capability as a basis for making decisions relative to manufacturing processes. (See Sections 16, Manufacturing Planning; 17, Production; and 24, Statistical Process Control.)

Supplier relations: Supplier surveys, qualification; quality provisions in purchase agreements; assistance to suppliers, feedback; incoming inspection, test; conversion to "just in time"; supplier rating; certification. (See Section 15, Supplier Relations.)

Inspection and test: Incoming, in-process, and final; visual and other sensory standards; feedback. (See Section 18, Inspection and Test.)

Test equipment: Design, procurement, reproducibility, checkout, calibration, maintenance. (Section 18.)

Nonconforming material: Identification; segregation; Material Review Board; corrective action. (See Section 18.)

Postmanufacture: Identification, packing, storage, transport, installation, checkout. (See Section 20, Customer Service.)

Field service: Service instructions; equipment, tools, manuals; evaluation of use, misuse; visits to dealers, users; analysis of returns, complaints, warranty charges, field failures; administration of warranties; spare-parts provision. (See Section 20.)

Quality assurance: Product audits; competitive ratings; audits of organization, plans (methods, procedures); audit of conformance to plans. (For elaboration, see Section 9, Quality Assurance; also Section 8, Upper Management and Quality.)

Quality-related costs: Classification of costs, collection of cost data (by estimate or from the accounting structure), analysis to find opportunities, reports on trends (see Section 4, Quality Costs).

Quality information system: Information requirements; data sources; data recording, summary, analysis, reporting.

Statistical methodology: Areas of application; statistical tools. (See Sections 23, 24, 25, and 26.)

Corrective action (for sporadic quality problems):   Identification of deviations, diagnosis of causes, restoring the status quo (see Section 22 under Troubleshooting).

Quality improvement (for chronic quality problems):   Project identification, diagnosis of causes, provision of remedies (see Section 22, Quality Improvement).

Human relations: Recruitment, selection; training, qualification, certification. (See Section 10, Managing Human Performance.)

Motivation for quality: Quality awareness, priority; participation in planning, problem identification, problem solving; responsibility for quality planning, control, improvement. (See Section 10.)

Technological Sections.   These deal with the numerous materials, processes, components, products, tests, and other elements which are special to the company. Usually these sections are intradepartmental in nature, and often the publications are not in the company manual but in separate departmental manuals.

"White-Collar" Processes.   Traditionally, quality and quality planning have been regarded as associated with factory-produced goods and factory processes. As a result, the quality manuals of the past have emphasized planning of processes directly associated with design and manufacture of goods.

During the 1980s there emerged a strong trend toward widening the concept of "quality" to include quality of services sold by service companies (see Section 33). This same trend has been extended to include the quality of the administrative and support operations (see Section 21) which contribute to a company's quality image: accuracy of invoices, adequacy of response to customers' inquiries (promptness, courtesy, satisfaction), and so on.

This trend appears to be irreversible. It can, therefore, be expected that quality manuals will increasingly devote attention to quality of administrative and support operations and will assume broader roles in service companies.

Distribution of the Manual.   If the manual is of a modular design, it becomes feasible to make distribution on a selective basis. Tables are prepared showing which organization units are to receive which modules.

Some companies design portions of the quality manual in ways which make them suitable for distribution to outsiders. For example, the module on supplier relations may be designed in a way which is suitable for distribution to suppliers. Other companies design a "showpiece" version of the quality manual to be sent to clients and prospective clients as a sales promotion device.

Provision for Audit.   Any well-designed plan includes provisions for reviewing results to determine whether the execution follows the plan. Sometimes these provisions are written into the plans themselves; for instance, the quality manual may stipulate that there shall be an annual review of execution versus plan. More usually, there is a separate "plan" for audit, sometimes informal, sometimes formal.

The term "audit" has multiple meanings. Applied to quality planning, two of these meanings are vital: (1) audit to determine whether the quality plans are adequate to achieve the quality goals of the company and (2) audit to determine whether the execution follows the plans. (For elaboration, see Section 9, Quality Assurance.)

Limitations of Quality Manuals as Predictors of Good Quality.   Quality manuals are a form of repetitive-use plans. When well prepared, they are the result of participation by those in interest and hence are likely to represent an optimum approach to planning for quality. Companies which prepare such manuals are likely to be armed with better plans, procedures, and so on than are companies which lack such manuals.

These proven values of quality manuals have stimulated many large buyers and regulators to establish criteria to be met by quality plans and procedures. These criteria are mandated in contracts with suppliers. Surveys (or assessments) are conducted to assure that the criteria are met by the conditions in suppliers' facilities and by the provisions in suppliers' quality manuals. Successful compliance is formally recognized—the successful supplier receives a documented status. This status puts the supplier on a favored list.

In some countries there are national standards which establish the criteria to be met by quality plans (e.g., in Great Britain BS 5750). In addition, there are officially designated agencies to conduct the assessments. In such situations a status of having successfully "passed" an assessment can become prerequisite to qualifying as a bidder for certain classes of contracts, such as military contracts. Aggressive promotion by the official assessment agencies can make this status so influential that companies are stimulated to undergo assessment for public relations purposes as well as for the inherent merits.

It does not follow that companies which score well in the assessment will surely deliver high-quality products. A company's top priority may be on some parameter other than quality, such as meeting the delivery schedule. The facilities may be inadequate to produce good quality. Employee training may be inadequate. Human relations, internal and/or external, may be adversarial amid an atmosphere of blame. In still other ways, companies with admirable plans and manuals may fail to deliver good quality. Conversely, there are many companies, with long records of having delivered good quality, whose quality manual, if any, would fail to pass an assessment. See Section 9 under Questions for Quality Surveys; Reference Standards for Surveys.

The assessments do evaluate the state of the procedures and of the written manual. However, there has been no well-researched study to discover the extent to which the results of the assessments correlate with the quality of the subsequent products. [One such research project revealed no correlation; see Brainard (1966).] For this reason, managers should be wary of assuming that the assessments are proven predictors of subsequent quality of product. As in the prediction of creditworthiness, the principal predictor of a supplier's quality is probably that supplier's previous quality performance on similar products.

GENERIC STANDARDS; INFLUENCE ON QUALITY PLANNING

The second half of the twentieth century witnessed an outpouring of generic standards for quality planning. Most of these standards were prepared and published by:

Large industrial buyers (e.g., original equipment manufacturing companies).

Large government buying agencies (e.g., defense departments). One such standard is the well-known MIL-Q-9858A.

Industry associations.

Standardization bodies. Examples of such standards are the U.S. American National Standards Institute standard ANSI Z1.15/1979 and the British standard BS5750.

Government regulatory bodies, usually those oriented to safety, health, and the environment.

Mandated and Advisory Generic Standards. Some generic standards make compliance a prerequisite to the marketing of products. Generally, the generic standards published by large buyers and by government regulators are mandatory.

Advisory generic standards are "guidelines." They do not require compliance. However, in some cases failure to comply makes the product unmarketable, such as use of nonstandard voltages on appliances. In other cases, compliance becomes commercially necessary because compliance has become a tool for marketing.

Purposes of Generic Standards. Generic standards evolve for much the same reasons as quality manuals (see the Quality Manual, above). There are some additional reasons. Generic standards can be designed to serve the broader standardization needs inherent within industries, national economies, and multinational economies. Usually these broad-based generic standards are developed by broad-based committees which are able to enlist the experience and know-how of experts from the various impacted organs of society. The resulting published consensus is more likely to be accepted as a goal and as a reference base for any subsequent surveys (assessments) and the associated certification.

Evolution of Generic Quality Standards. The evolutionary process begins with recognition of the need for a generic standard. A committee (or subcommittee, task force, working group, etc.) is formed to develop a standard in response to the need. In the case of standardization bodies, the committee is broad-based— it includes representatives from producers, users, government, and public-interest groups.

The working group prepares a draft which later is reviewed by the organization hierarchy of committees, agencies, and so on. In the case of government standards, the drafts are usually published, following which public hearings are held. The final draft is formally approved at the highest levels and is published as the official standard.

Adaptation to Diversity. Standards can be designed to be generic, but the areas of application are quite diverse. One way of adapting to this diversity is to design multiple generic standards, each at a different "level" of requirements. For example, the U.S. Department of Defense publishes two such generic standards:

MIL-Q-9858A, *Quality Program Requirements*

MIL-I-45208A, *Inspection Systems Requirements*

The Canadian Standards Association Z299 series, *Quality Program Standards,* is published in four levels:

CAN3-Z299.1-1985 *Quality Assurance Program—Category 1*

CAN3-Z299.2-1985 *Quality Assurance Program—Category 2*

CAN3-Z299.3-1985 *Quality Assurance Program—Category 3*

CAN3-Z299.4-1985 *Quality Assurance Program—Category 4*

(See also Appendix III, "Selected Quality Standards, Sepcifications, and Related Documents.")

In practice, the buyers incorporate into the purchase contracts that level of generic standards judged to be appropriate for the specific application.

An additional way of dealing with diversity is through administrative regulations. For example, contracts involving relatively modest sums of money are often exempted from many of the requirements imposed on large contracts. [For a discussion, see Aboud (1980).]

A further approach is to "tailor" or adapt the requirements to the special nature of the contract. This tailoring is logically arrived at by discussion between buyer and contractor and can involve revision or waiver of provisions in the generic standards. [For elaboration, see Todt (1979) and Bell and Nicholson (1981).]

Adaptation is aided if there is a clear understanding of the markets and "environments" to be served. [For a discussion, see Marquardt (1982).]

Certification; Accreditation. Many purchase contracts and regulations specify suppliers' compliance with generic quality standards. To assure compliance with such standards, use is made of various forms of assurance:

Audit (assessment, survey, review) of the supplier's quality manual to assure that it corresponds adequately to the contract or the regulation

Audit of operations to assure that they conform to the terms of the standards

These audits may be carried out by the buying organization, the regulatory organization, or some third party to whom the audits are subcontracted.

If the audits find that compliance is adequate, some written report or certificate is issued to formalize that finding.

Reliance on such audits requires assurance that the auditing process itself is adequate. To this end, many organizations establish an auditing manual which specifies the auditing procedures to be followed. Such procedures help to assure the completeness and uniformity of the audits. However, much must be left to the resourcefulness and judgment of the auditor.

The latter fact brings up an additional need—how to assure that the human auditors are qualified. Much of this assurance is based on informal criteria such as extent of education, length of experience, and extent of special training. In some cases, formal systems of accreditation are established, requiring successful completion of training courses and examinations. Such accreditation may be extended to suppliers' personnel under controlled conditions of certification.

For further elaboration, including third-party audits, see Section 9 under Quality Surveys.

WHO PLANS FOR QUALITY?

Prior to the rise of the Taylor system (see Juran, 1973), virtually all planning for operations in the United States, including planning for quality, was done by the operating managers, supervisors, and workers. The Taylor system (introduced early in the twentieth century) brought about a revolutionary separation of planning from execution. In due course this revolution spread to the quality function and resulted in the creation of quality specialists, principally in two specialist categories: (1) quality engineers, whose functions were associated with product quality in the factory, and (2) reliability engineers, whose functions were associated with product quality in the field.

These quality specialists did much to evolve concepts and tools which are essential aids to managing for quality. However, the operating managers and line specialists (design engineers, process engineers) were slow to adopt these aids. This lack of adoption was traceable in part to that same separation of planning from execution.

Meanwhile, during the second half of the twentieth century, Japanese industries surprised the Western world by taking over quality leadership in many important product lines. A distinguishing feature of the Japanese quality revolution was their approach to quality planning:

They assigned responsibility for quality planning mainly to the operating managers and line specialists.

They carried out massive training programs to enable the operating managers and line specialists to understand and use the new quality concepts and tools.

The Japanese results caused Western companies to reexamine their assignment of responsibility for quality planning. These companies then began to shift increasing amounts of this responsibility to the operating managers and line specialists, while providing the training needed to support such a change.

Influence of the Scope of the Planning. The options for assigning responsibility for quality planning are influenced by the scope of the planning, mainly according to whether the planning is *inter*departmental or *intra*departmental in scope.

Interdepartmental Processes. These processes link together various intradepartmental processes. Planning of an interdepartmental process requires some sort of interdepartmental organization. The forms most widely used are:

A team of line managers, called a "task force," "committee," etc.

A separate planning (or "staff") function which has responsibility to prepare a plan and then secure approval from the line managers

Intradepartmental Processes. These processes involve multidepartmental tasks or operations. Responsibility for planning of such departmental processes is usually assigned to one or a combination of the following:

The same process planning office which has responsibility for planning of the interdepartmental process

A departmental process planner

The departmental supervision

Tasks and Operations. Tasks and operations make up the base of the hierarchy of processes. At this level of the hierarchy the responsibility for process planning is usually assigned to one or a combination of the following:

A departmental process planner

A local supervisor

The work force

Allocation of Responsibilities. When quality planning is done by staff specialists, it is common for the operating forces to be involved through some form of participation, such as design review. In addition, it is usual for the operating forces to have the final word as to the adequacy of the plan before it becomes effective. The arrangment can be depicted as follows:

	Operating forces	Staff specialists
Prepare the quality plan	X	X
Execute the plan	X	
Audit execution versus plan		X

Future Trends. The trend is to delegate an increasing amount of the quality planning function to the operating people. The trend has been growing and is probably irreversible.

A major premise of the Taylor system was that the supervisors and workers of that day lacked the technological education needed to do planning. That premise was valid in Taylor's time, but it has since become invalid because of the dramatic rise in education levels. That rise has provided the operating forces with the educational base needed to accept increased responsibility for quality planning. However, the transfer of responsibility must be preceded by training in the concepts, skills, and tools of quality planning.

TOOLS FOR QUALITY PLANNERS

Quality planners have developed numerous tools through which the planning becomes economical as well as effective. Some of the major tools have been discussed as major topics in this section (e.g., the quality planning road map, the feedback loop, the quality manual). Subsidiary important tools include the flow digram (e.g., Figure 6.2), the quality planning spreadsheet (e.g., Figures 6.4, 6.5, and 6.6), and the responsibility matrix (e.g., Table 7.3). Additional tools are discussed in other sections of this handbook (e.g., design review, Section 13; process capability analysis, Section 16; project-by-project improvement, Section 22; quality cost analysis, Section 4; supplier surveys, Section 15).

Training in Use of the Tools.   Whoever is to participate in quality planning should be trained in use of the quality planning tools. This training should go beyond education; the training should include solution of actual quality problems with the aid of the tools. For example, training in use of the feedback loop should include planning the work of some control station.

TRAINING FOR QUALITY PLANNERS

Historically, planning for quality was done by people (planners, operating managers, etc.) whose planning responsibility extended to multiple parameters, such as schedule, cost, and safety. Generally these people lacked expertise in how to plan for quality—they had never undergone special training in the subject. In some companies they had access to quality specialists (reliability engineers, quality engineers) who did have special training and expertise in planning for quality.

Since the early 1980s, the trend has been to increase the expertise of the planners and operating personnel by training them in how to plan for quality. This training has been taking place at all levels of the hierarchy.

Division of the subject matter into specific training courses (or modules) has varied among companies. An emerging pattern has been somewhat as described below.

Common Subject Matter.   Certain elements of subject matter have been regarded as applicable to all categories of managers and specialists. These elements include the following: what is quality, effect of quality on sales, effect of quality on costs, external and internal customers, customer needs, the quality planning road map, the feedback loop for control, the universal sequence for quality improvement, measures of quality, quality cost analysis, basic problem-solving tools, quality audits, employee participation, and motivation for quality.

Specialized Subject Matter.   Beyond the commonalities there are topics which are usually special to specific categories of personnel:

Upper management: Companywide quality management (CWQM), quality goals, deployment of quality goals, multifunctional planning to meet goals, allocation of resources, organizing for quality, broad measures of quality, motivation for quality.

Product development: Phase system; customer needs, competitive quality; safety analysis; failure-mode and effect analysis; reliability and maintainability analysis; value analysis; life cycle costing; design of experiment; producibility analysis, process capability, measurement capability; design review; lessons learned.

Process development: Design review; process environment; process capability; measurement capability, adjustment capability; design of experiment; feedback loop; statistical process control; self-control; human error, errorproofing.

Materials management: Supplier survey, selection; supplier relations; process capability; preproduction evaluation; data feedback, quality rating; just-in-time method; quality audit.

Production: Design review; process capability; measurement capability; adjustment capability; controllability (management or worker); feedback loop;

statistical process control; self-control; human error, errorproofing; trouble-shooting.

Marketing: Field intelligence, field performance, competitive performance, complaint analysis, warranty analysis, product liability, life cycle cost, phase system of product development, design review.

Customer service: Field environment; product safety; field operation, economy; field maintenance; customer use, misuse; data feedback.

Quality assurance: All the above; quality manuals, quality audits, quality reports.

Training for Suppliers.   In general, suppliers to large clients must eventually train their personnel to the same level of expertise as is done by those clients for their internal sources of supply. However, there is a time lag. Clients who feel that new levels of training are needed will first train their own people. Subsequently, they urge similar training for suppliers' personnel.

In critical cases this urge is a mandate—the specifications require the use of certified personnel. In less than critical cases the supplier survey may include evaluation of the state of training as an essential parameter.

An approach short of a mandate has been to offer "scholarships" for suppliers' personnel to attend training courses conducted by the client company. This approach emerged during the growth period of "statistical process control."

Training for Clients.   This training has long been done with respect to use of the product. In part, this is carried out by the product literature: owners' manuals and instructions for operation and maintenance. In part, the training is done during product installation and maintenance. Still other forms are training courses and seminars conducted by marketing and customer service personnel with backup by experts in the technology.

An emerging trend is to provide a consulting service to assist clients in efficient use of the product. In many companies such consulting is already being done by technical representatives and/or customer service representatives, but on an informal basis. To expand such consulting (and use it as a marketing tool), it is necessary to summarize the knowledge acquired through prior customer contact and identify the "lessons learned." These lessons learned then become the basis for enlarged consultation, seminars, and other forms of training.

The Quality School.   In very large companies it is customary to maintain an in-house capability—a "school"—for training of all sorts. During the 1980s these schools were faced with responding to a rapidly growing demand for training in managing for quality. Some of the schools responded to the demand by creating a special quality-oriented school to establish the needed curricula and to offer courses to company personnel.

REFERENCES

Aboud, George M., Sr. (1980). "DoD Procurement Quality Requirements (ASPR)." *ASQC Technical Conference Transactions,* Milwaukee, pp. 771–782.

Bell, L. Ferris and Nicholson, Richard H. (1981). "Tailoring Quality Systems for Program Requirements." *ASQC Quality Congress Transactions,* Milwaukee, pp. 263–278.

Bemesderfer, John L. (1979). "Approving a Process for Production." *Journal of Quality Technology,* January, pp. 1–12.

Bhote, Keki R. (1985). "C.W.Q.C.: A New Horizon for American Management." *ASQC Quality Congress Transactions,* Milwaukee, pp. 552–557.

Brainard, Edgar H. (1966). "Just How Good Are Vendor Surveys?" *Quality Assurance,* August, pp. 22–25.

Brunetti, Wayne (1986). "Policy Development—A Corporate Roadmap," *The Juran Report,* No. 8, pp. 20–29.

Caplan, Frank (1980). *The Quality System,* Chilton, Radnor, PA

Caplan, Frank (1984). "Managing for Success through the Quality System." *ASQC Quality Congress Transactions,* Milwaukee, pp. 10–21.

Coonley, Howard and Agnew, P. G. (1941). *The Role of Standards in the System of Free Enterprise.* American National Standards Institute, New York.

Cound, Dana M. (1965). "Quality System Analysis—Key to Recurring Cost Reduction." *ASQC Technical Conference Transactions,* Milwaukee, pp. 109–115.

Follett, Mary Parker (1941). Report in Metcalf, H. C. and Urwick, L. (Eds.), *Dynamic Administration.* Harper & Row, New York.

George, William W. (1977). "Task Teams for Rapid Growth." *Harvard Business Review,* March-April, pp. 71–80.

Goree, Paul F. and Musson, Thomas A. (1984). "DOD/Industry—R&M Case Study Analysis." *Proceedings, Annual Reliability and Maintainability Symposium.* IEEE, New York, pp. 91–98.

"Grinding Wheel Quality Improvement Hints." (1977). *Quality,* April, p. 44.

Gulliver, Frank R. (1987). "Post-Project Appraisals Pay." *Harvard Business Review,* March-April, pp. 128–132.

Hartz, Ove (1982). "Quality Management and Cooperation in Small Firms." *Quality Progress,* April, pp. 18–21.

Heskett, James L. (1987). "Lessons in the Service Sector." *Harvard Business Review,* March-April 1987, pp. 118–126.

Heslop, S. (1981). "Practical Experience in Implementing Quality Assurance in a Small Business." *Quality Assurance,* vol. 7, no. 1, March, pp. 10–14.

Hill, Hubert M. and Sorrell, D. Lynn (1985). "Designing a Quality Assurance System for Information Systems." *ASQC Quality Congress Transactions,* Milwaukee, pp. 416–421.

Holt, J. (1976). "Elaboration and Implementation of a Quality Control System in Nordisk Ventilator Co. A/S." *EOQC Proceedings, Copenhagen.* EOQC, Berne, Switzerland, pp. 65–75.

Ingram, Gary E. (1984). "Historical Processes for Quality Project Management." *Project Management Institute Proceedings,* Philadelphia, pp. 1–3.

Juran, J. M. (1964). *Managerial Breakthrough.* McGraw-Hill, New York.

Juran, J. M. (1988). *Juran on Planning for Quality.* Free Press, New York.

Juran, J. M. (1973). "The Taylor System and Quality Control." A series of articles in *Quality Progress,* May 1973 through December 1973 (listed under "Mangement Interface").

Juran, J. M. (1977). "Quality and Its Assurance—an Overview." *Second NATO Symposium on Quality and Its Assurance.* North Atlantic Treaty Organization, London.

Juran, J. M. (1986). *Planning for Quality.* Juran Institute, Wilton, CT.

Juran Institute (1987). *Juran on Quality Planning* (videocassette series). Juran Institute, Wilton, CT.

Kano, Noriaki (1984). "Problem Solving in New Product Development—Application of T-Typed Matrix." *World Quality Congress Proceedings,* vol. 3. EOQC, Berne, Switzerland, pp. 45–55.

Karabatsos, Nancy (1983). "Quality is Instrumental at Steinway." *Quality,* October, pp. 19–22.

Kofoed, Carl A. (1982). "The Integration Phase." *ASQC Quality Congress Transactions,* Milwaukee, pp. 433–440.

Kohoutek, Henry J. (1983). "Commitment to Quality through a Strategic Plan." *ASQC Quality Congress Transactions,* Milwaukee, pp. 82–86.

Kolacek, O. G. (1978). "So, You Are Going to Have A Quality Assurance Department!" *Proceedings, ICQC '78.* Japanese Union of Scientists and Engineers, Tokyo, pp. C1-45 through C1-50.

Lange, Henry N. (1978). "QA for Small Programs in a Large Industry." *ASQC Technical Conference Transactions,* Milwaukee, pp. 314–320.

Lewis, Wyatt H. (1964). "Design of a Quality System for a Business." *ASQC Convention Transactions,* Milwaukee, pp. 257–259.

Livni, Haim (1985). "Quality Assurance of Technical Specifications." *ASQC Quality Congress Transactions,* Milwaukee, pp. 523–528.

Marquardt, Donald W. (1982). "Comparison of Multi-Level and Generic Standards." *ASQC Quality Congress Transactions,* Milwaukee, pp. 244–248.

Maytag, Fritz (1986). "The Joys of Keeping the Company Small." *Harvard Business Review,* July-August, pp. 6–14 and ES14.

Müller, A. (1971). "Quality Assurance during Manufacturing Engineering Phase." *Quälitat und Zuverlässigkeit,* vol. 16, no. 2, February, pp. 27–32.

Murray, David J. (1976). "The Introduction of a Quality Manual in a Multi-Factory Paint Company." *EOQC Proceedings, Copenhagen.* EOQC, Berne, Switzerland, pp. 207–215.

Norton, Chris E. and Mason, Don L. (1987). "Quality during Transition Construction to Operation." *ASQC Energy Division Newsletter,* Milwaukee, March, pp. 3, 4.

Olsbro, Bertil (1976). "Quality Assurance System for Telephone Equipment." *EOQC Proceedings, Copenhagen.* EOQC, Berne, Switzerland, pp. 169–177.

Roche, J. G. and Sheil, J. (1984). "Quality Practices in Small Manufacturing Firms." *1984 World Quality Congress.* EOQC, Berne, pp. 346–361.

Scanlon, Frank and Hagan, John T. (1982). "Improved Productivity through Quality Management." *ASQC Quality Congress Transactions,* Milwaukee, pp. 491–505.

Taguchi, Genichi (1978). "Off-Line and On-Line Quality Control Systems." *Proceedings, ICQC '78.* Japanese Union of Scientists and Engineers, Tokyo, pp. B4-1 through B4-5.

Todt, Howard C. (1979). "Tailored Requirements for Quality Programs." *ASQC Technical Conference Transactions,* Milwaukee, pp. 608–613.

Veraldi, L. C. (1985). "The Team Taurus Story," MIT Conference paper, Chicago, Aug. 22. Center for Advanced Engineering Study, MIT, Cambridge, MA.

Wilborn, Walter (1978). "Quality Audits in Support of Small Business." *ASQC Technical Conference Transactions,* Milwaukee, pp. 179–185, 979–980.

Wilhelm, W. C. (1980). "Quality Program Modeling for Cost Effective Tailoring." *ASQC Technical Conference Transactions,* Milwaukee, pp. 648–655.

SECTION 7

ORGANIZING FOR QUALITY

J. M. Juran

"Organizing" as used in this section is the process of getting work done by human beings. The organizing process consists of two major activities:

1. Designing the organization *structure*—defining the work to be done and the hierarchical responsibility for doing it. This activity is the subject of this section.
2. Recruiting, training, and motivating the personnel—the inhabitants of the structure. This activity is discussed in Section 10, Managing Human Performance, and Section 11, Training for Quality.

BUILDING THE ORGANIZATION STRUCTURE

The basic building block of the organization is the operation (also called "function," "task," "work element," etc.). An operation is an identifiable type of activity such as edit, assemble, or transport. Many operations are carried out by human beings; others are carried out by nonhuman means. Collectively, the operations carried out by human beings make up the human "work pile."

The organizing process consists of six basic steps:

1. Identify the operations which need to be performed.
2. Assign responsibility for doing these operations, whether to internal or external agencies.
3. Divide the total work pile into logical parcels of work, called "jobs." In general, a job consists of a collection of one or more operations, so chosen that it is feasible to recruit or train people to carry out that collection.
4. Define the responsibilities and authorities associated with each job.
5. Define the relationships of each job to other jobs. These relationships include:
   a. The hierarchical relationship, i.e., the chain of command
   b. The communication and coordination patterns through which interdepartmental activities join to carry out specific purposes
6. Orchestrate the work of the internal and external agencies so that the company's mission is carried out in an optimum manner.

QUALITY MANAGEMENT WORK ELEMENTS AND JOBS

Many of the operations performed in the company directly impact the salability of the company's goods and services. The literature of managing for quality has often referred to these operations as "quality control work elements." In view of the trends in use of the word "control," these operations will be referred to as "quality management work elements."

Some of these work elements have traditionally been carried out by the various functional "line" departments:

Work element	Assigned to
Choose design tolerance	Product Design
Establish process capable of meeting tolerance	Process Engineering
Measure product to determine whether production process is in control	Production
Remedy field failure of products under warranty	Customer Service

This table represents only a small sample. Additional such work elements are discussed in the various functional Sections 12 through 21 of this handbook.

In the United States, other quality management work elements have traditionally been assigned to special departments which are oriented full-time to the quality function. (Such departments are variously called "Quality Management," "Quality Assurance," "Quality Control," etc.) The following list includes those principal work elements which have usually been assigned to such departments.

1. *Broad administration of the quality function.* This involves the following tasks:
   a. Draft quality policies.
   b. Develop major quality objectives.
   c. Develop plans for meeting quality objectives.
   d. Develop the organization structure for carrying out the plans.
   e. Design the system of product quality rating, quality audits, and summarized reports needed to provide quality assurance to upper management.
   f. Conduct quality audits; prepare and issue summarized reports on quality.
2. *Launching new products.* This involves the following tasks:
   a. Study customer needs for quality-oriented parameters.
   b. Review previous performance of similar products to identify chronic problems in manufacture, test, and usage.
   c. Conduct reliability analysis. (This consists of a whole array of work elements: modeling, apportionment, prediction, etc.)
   d. Conduct design review for various quality-oriented purposes: producibility, maintainability, etc.
   e. Establish test programs to evaluate materials, processes, and products.
   f. Conduct inspections and tests of trial production.
   g. Estimate quality costs for bid proposals and for new designs.

3. *Supplier quality relations.* This involves the following tasks:
   a. Prepare the supplier relations quality manual: policies, methods, and procedures.
   b. Prepare the plan for conducting supplier quality surveys.
   c. Conduct surveys of prospective suppliers to judge quality capability.
   d. Maintain quality surveillance of suppliers.
   e. Assist suppliers through seriousness classifications, measurement cross-check, training, etc.
   f. Conduct inspection and test of supplier shipments; provide data feedback.
4. *Manufacture.* This involves the following tasks:
   a. Evaluate quality capability of processes.
   b. Design plans for process control: choice of control stations, definition of control activities, data feedback system, etc.
   c. Conduct process surveillance.
   d. Analyze out-of-control conditions; follow up to secure corrective action.
   e. Design methods for evaluating quality performance of production units.
   f. Prepare and publish quality ratings.
5. *Inspection and test.* This involves the following tasks:
   a. Design the inspection and test plan; choose control stations; define work to be done at each station.
   b. Prepare supplementary standards and criteria as needed, e.g., standards for sensory qualities; standardize test procedures.
   c. Prepare inspection manuals, systems, and procedures.
   d. Prepare inspection job specifications; recruit, select, and train inspectors.
   e. Conduct inspections and tests in accordance with the plan.
   f. Investigate causes of sporadic defects; report findings; follow up for corrective action.
   g. Initiate action to dispose of nonconforming product.
   h. Prepare and report summaries of results of inspection in appropriate ways: by product, by component, by process, by department responsible, by operator, etc.
   i. Provide for measurement of inspector accuracy.
6. *Metrology.* This involves the following tasks:
   a. Design gages, instruments, and test equipment.
   b. Construct or purchase measuring equipment.
   c. Maintain calibration of measuring equipment.
   d. Design and administer systems for ensuring maintenance of precision of measuring equipment.
7. *Customer relations.* This involves the following tasks:
   a. Test finished products. Evaluate adequacy for customer needs.
   b. Evaluate effect of activities which follow final product test: packing, shipping, transport, and storage.
   c. Analyze customer quality complaints, warranty charges, and returns; recommend corrective action.

 d. Evaluate customer experience with product performance; identify the opportunities presented.

 e. Analyze competitors' products relative to customer needs.

 f. Identify customer needs for quality-oriented assistance; develop responsive plans.

8. *Consulting and training services.*   This involves the following tasks:

 a. Analyze costs of poor quality; identify major opportunities for improvement.

 b. Stimulate creation of companywide approaches to quality improvement.

 c. Provide consulting services: analysis of chronic quality problems, reliability analysis, data collection and analysis, and design of experiments.

 d. Design and conduct training courses in various quality-oriented skills and tools.

Published lists of quality management work elements are usually limited to brief statements of each element. However, some lists provide good elaboration of what is meant by the brief statements. The list published by the American Society for Quality Control (1961) is oriented toward a concept of a "profession" of quality engineering, and this orientation has influenced the choice of elements to enter the list.

Assignment of Responsibility.   The quality management work elements may be assigned to various categories of organization units:

1. Functional "line" departments such as Product Development, Manufacture, and Customer Service.

2. Inspection and Test Departments. These departments carry out much of the work of product inspection and test.

3. Quality "staff" departments. The work elements of these departments are mainly planning, analysis, and assurance, and are assigned to quality specialists such as Quality Engineers.

4. Outside agencies. Some work elements are assigned to be performed by suppliers, customers, third-party auditors, and still others.

Choice of which organization unit is to receive which assignment depends on:

1. The extent to which these units have been trained (or are willing to be trained) to perform the work elements.

2. The prior record of initiative or resistance of these units in responding to new ways.

3. The traditions with respect to separating planning from execution and the use of staff versus line. These traditions have a built-in momentum and vary remarkably among companies, industries, and nations.

4. The volume of work. As the company grows in size and complexity, the staff activities tend to proliferate.

Structuring Jobs.   A job is the "bundle of work" assigned to one person. The bundle may consist solely of a single quality-related work element (e.g., inspect, test). In such cases the job title usually is descriptive of the work element being performed (e.g., Inspector, Tester).

In other cases the job consists solely of a mixture of quality-related work elements. Such jobs carry a broader title (e.g., Quality Engineer).

In most cases the job consists of multiple work elements of which only a minority are quality-oriented. In such cases the job title reflects the core responsibilities of the jobholder (e.g., Product Designer, Process Engineer, Customer Service Representative, Order Entry Clerk, Machinist).

While jobs are structured with a view toward stability and toward fitting into a career pattern, the elements which make up the job are not stable. The advance of technology creates new elements and renders old ones obsolete. In addition, elements are frequently transferred from one job to another. For instance, with the development of a simplified instrument, a test which once could be performed only by specialists in a laboratory may be conducted by production workers. The task of computing mean time between failures, previously performed by reliability engineers, may be assigned to designers following a training program.

Because of the mobility and mortality of work elements, there are constant discussions on how to make the assignment. For example, the work element "design test equipment" might logically be assigned to a line manager (Inspection Supervisor), an existing staff specialist (Quality Engineer), or a new staff specialist (Test Equipment Engineer). The choice depends as much on the record of each department in carrying out its assignments to date as on organization theory. Managers tend to give assignments to persons who have demonstrated the ability to achieve results. As a corollary, managers do not assign new duties to persons whose records are mediocre, no matter how "logical" it would appear on the organization chart. If necessary, related duties will be divided, new departments created, and organization charts distorted rather than giving important new duties to persons who have a record of poor performance.

A Major Trend in Assignment of Responsibility.   During the 1980s there emerged in the United States a major trend toward assigning quality management work elements to the functional line departments rather than the Quality Departments. For example:

> Responsibility for reliability analysis began to shift from Reliability Engineers (in the Quality Department) to Design Engineers in Product Development.

> Responsibility for evaluation of process capability began to shift from quality engineers (in the Quality Department) to Process Engineers, Production Supervisors, and production workers in quality control circles.

> Responsibility for design of experiments and analysis of variance began to shift from engineers in the Quality Department to engineers in the functional line departments.

Necessarily, such shifts in responsibility must be preceded by training to qualify the line personnel to be able to perform the newly assigned work. This training has, in fact, also emerged as a major trend.

This trend is a result of the need to increase the expertise used in carrying out the quality-related work elements. Generally the line personnel lacked this expertise because of lack of training. The Quality Department personnel generally had the expertise but lacked the authority to apply it. A joint effort was needed, but some formidable obstacles stood in the way:

> Not being trained or experienced in the use of quality-oriented skills and tools, line personnel lacked awareness of the potential aid to their own traditional responsibilities such skills and tools can provide.

The functional line departments were faced with meeting multiple parameters (schedule, cost, productivity, etc.) in addition to quality. Hence they perceived the quality specialists as special pleaders and advocates for just one of those parameters.

The careers of line personnel were linked to their traditional core discipline (e.g., metallurgy, machine tools) and not to expertise in quality-related skills and tools.

The prevailing merit rating system enforced this same career orientation.

As of the late 1980s, this trend (to assign quality management work elements to the line personnel) has been gaining in momentum and has probably become irreversible.

NONTRADITIONAL QUALITY-ORIENTED WORK ELEMENTS

Few operations directly impact product salability; however, they do impact customers, both external and internal. (*Every* operation produces products of some sort and sends these products on to customers of some sort.)

For example, the process for producing invoices impacts clients as well as internal customers. If invoices are incorrect, the clients endure additional expense and irritation. They publicize the errors not only to the producing company but also to the community, the press, the regulators, and others. The errors may not significantly impact the company's sales, but they damage the company's image as a "quality house." In addition, the errors are costly. It takes work to resolve them, and payment of the invoices is delayed in the process.

In other cases the operations impact clients indirectly. For example, a product design has salable product features but turns out to lack producibility—the available processes are unable to meet the tolerances. In such a case the operation (product design) has produced a product—a design—which does not meet the needs of internal customers. In addition, there are side effects: The resulting delay may cause the loss of some of the potential market, the added costs reduce the profit margin, internal harmony is disrupted, and so on.

In still other cases the operations do not impact external customers at all but do impact internal customers. Examples are the operations which produce employee records or various internal control reports.

Commonalities. All the preceding examples have certain commonalities:

The operations are regular company operations.

The resulting products are not sold to produce the company's income.

Some of the products are deficient.

The deficiencies do not necessarily impact company income.

The deficiencies do cause damage in various forms: higher costs, delays, and irritation.

The deficiencies also damage the company's quality image.

During the 1980s there emerged a new awareness relative to the extent of these deficiencies. It became evident that the damage done by these deficiencies was huge—as large as that associated with factory operations. In response to this finding, much analysis was done to discover the causes of the deficiencies. (See, generally, Section 22, Quality Improvement; also Section 21, Administrative and Support Operations.)

To a large extent the causes were found to be traceable to the original planning of the operations. In turn, the original planning was found to be deficient largely because of the lack of quality planning expertise on the part of the functional department planners. The needed remedies paralleled those for improving quality planning for the "conventional" quality management work elements. (See above, under A Major Trend in Assignment of Responsibility.)

Another Major Trend.   From the findings described above, a dramatic shift in viewpoint and assignment of responsibility for those nontraditional quality work elements has begun to emerge. The shift in viewpoint is to apply the word "quality" to describe the performance of those nontraditional work elements and the resulting products, such as quality of the invoicing process and quality of the invoices. This same shift has widened the perception of the scope of "quality."

The reasons for this shift are rooted in two massive trends: (1) the growing importance of quality to society generally (see Section 34, Impact of Quality on Society) and (2) the intensified competition in quality.

The word "quality" has long had the connotation of something which is good; with the increasing importance of the quality function, the word "quality" has become a useful banner as well. Companies which want to introduce some important change are aided if they can introduce the change under the banner of quality.

Impact on Job Structure.   The main method chosen to upgrade quality for the nonconventional work elements has been to train the functional department personnel in the skills and tools of managing for quality. This approach parallels the trend in progress with respect to the conventional work elements, but with a difference—there is nothing to undo. Previously, the central quality departments were not involved with the nontraditional work elements.

The needed increases in quality expertise have an impact on the job descriptions for the functional line planners. The job requirements expand to include training and experience in quality-oriented skills and tools. The training needs are correspondingly impacted, as are the criteria for qualification. In addition, the merit rating systems are revised to give greater weight to the quality parameter.

In some companies the need to increase quality-related expertise has resulted in creation of new posts within the functional departments (e.g., Director of Quality for the Marketing Department or for the Customer Service Department). These new posts are intended to provide, for those functional departments, the same array of services that quality managers have traditionally provided for the company in general: quality planning, consulting, training, and auditing.

EVOLUTION OF THE QUALITY MANAGEMENT HIERARCHY

Any major industrial function acquires recognition in the form of status on the organization chart and leadership from a member of the management team. During the twentieth century, the quality function attained this status through an evolution which is still in progress.

A Humble Origin. The quality function has emerged from humble origins. From time immemorial, human activity has had the responsibility of meeting multiple needs, including the quality needs of customers. Village crafts people had this responsibility. With the rise of factories, the production departments had this same responsibility.

Under the influence of the Taylor system (Juran, 1973), the emphasis on the productivity parameter increased at the expense of the emphasis on quality. In response, the upper managers created the central Inspection Department which later became the nucleus of a separate quality function.

Organization for Inspection. The early Inspection Department was oriented to quality of goods and of factory processes. It consisted mainly of a hierarchy of inspection supervisors to direct the work of the scattered inspectors. The hierarchy of these supervisors ascended to the new post of Chief Inspector, whose authority also extended to auxiliary activities such as the measurement laboratory and the disposition of nonconforming products.

With the creation of the Inspection Department, it was also necessary to address the issue of whom the Inspection Department should report to. The usual solution was to make it responsible to the factory manager, although there were variations in detail.

In the United States, the concept of the central Inspection Department was widely adopted in the two decades following World War I. By the early 1940s, the majority of industrial companies had adopted it.

For additional discussion, see Section 18, Inspection and Test, under Organization for Inspection and Test.

Organization for Prevention. World War II required industry to make a drastic shift from civilian to military production. Many companies encountered problems in meeting delivery schedules, and a major obstacle was failure to meet quality specifications. It became dramatically evident that what was missing was the means for preventing defects from occurring in the first place.

Quality Control Engineering. After some experimentation, in the 1950s a new department was created to conduct quality planning and analysis, especially for defect prevention. This department came to be known as Quality Control Engineering.

It became necessary to locate the new department somewhere on the organizational tree. To do this, there was created a new post of Quality Manager (or Quality Control Manager) to which the Chief Inspector, the new department (Quality Control Engineering), and the associated services now reported.

The process industries evolved differently. In these industries, inspection for nonfunctional qualities (e.g., appearance) had commonly been done by inspectors responsible to the Production Department. However, the functional testing and the process controls had commonly been done by a laboratory which was responsible to the Technical Department. In consequence, when the new departments of Quality Control Engineering were created in the process industries, they were located in the Technical Department, the precise location being either (1) reporting to the manager of Process Development or (2) reporting to a newly created post of Quality Manager, to whom the traditional laboratory also reported.

Reliability Engineering. During the 1950s a number of companies were faced with new problems of designing and building complex systems to levels of reliability well beyond the usual practice. Traditional approaches to product development and design soon proved inadequate—the field failure rates were unacceptable. One consequence was the rise of a new type of specialist known as a "reliability engineer." These engineers recommended that a separate department be created for them, and the managers usually accepted this recommendation. The activities of this department are discussed below, under Staff Quality Departments.

Organization for Assurance. The term "assurance" is used here in the limited sense of determining with confidence that the company's quality mission is being well carried out.

The managers of small enterprises secured this assurance from personal contact, such as personal examination of the products and processes. As the enterprises grew, this personal contact was delegated to intermediate supervisors and to inspectors, thereby depriving the upper managers of "assurance through personal observation." For many years, the upper managers derived their assurance from their confidence in these supervisors and inspectors, but without creating a substitute for the former "independent" assurance (through personal observation). However, it became progressively evident that some form of independent assurance was essential, so a search began for new forms of such assurance.

One form of such assurance now in wide use requires prior preparation of detailed quality plans plus subsequent reviews and audits to establish that the plans are (1) adequate and (2) being followed. The organization structure through which this is accomplished is as follows:

| | | Staff quality departments | |
| | Line | Quality | Quality |
Activities	departments	planning	assurance
Prepare the quality plans	X	X	
Execute the plans	X		
Audit to determine whether the execution follows the plans			X

Use of this plan of delegation retains for the line departments the full command of their personnel while providing for independent reviews of plans and execution.

For additional discussion, see generally Section 9, Quality Assurance, and Section 8, Upper Management and Quality, under Quality Audits by Upper Managers and under Executive Reports on Quality.

Figure 7.1 shows one of the forms of organizational structure widely adopted during the 1950s.

Proliferation of Quality Function Activities. Once established, the Inspection Department and its successor, the Quality Department, began to acquire an increasing number of functions. The actual assignments have varied remarkably from company to company. Table 7.1 lists a typical sequence of evolution of activities assigned to quality departments.

Some distinct trends are evident from Table 7.1. These trends are summarized in Table 7.2.

TABLE 7.1 Activities Assigned to Quality Departments

Activities	Usual responsibility							See Section
	Analysis	Planning	Consulting	Coordinating	Execution	Audit	Assurance	
Inspection of factory goods: final; in process; supplier		X			X			18
Measurement control		X			X			18
Factory process control		X			X			17
Statistical process control		X			X			24
Inspection planning		X			X			18
Analysis of causes of defects	X		X					22
Field complaint analysis	X		X					20
Supplier surveillance		X			X		X	15
Self-control by workers	X	X						17
Self-inspection by workers		X				X		17
Analysis of cost of poor quality	X			X				4
Defect prevention		X		X				22
New-product reviews	X		X					13

TABLE 7.1 Activities Assigned to Quality Departments (*Continued*)

Activities	Usual responsibility							See Section
	Analysis	Planning	Consulting	Coordinating	Execution	Audit	Assurance	
Motivation for quality	X		X					10
Quality assurance		X			X			9
Product safety; liability	X			X		X		34
Environmental impact	X		X			X		34
Consumerism movement	X		X					34
Government regulation	X		X			X		34
Impact of quality on sales income	X		X					3
Annual quality improvement		X		X			X	22
Companywide quality management		X		X			X	6
Executive reports on quality		X		X			X	8
Training for quality	X	X	X					11

TABLE 7.2   Trends Relative to Quality-Oriented Activities

Early orientation	Trends in orientation
Inspection; detection	Planning; prevention
Factory goods	Goods and services
Conformance to specification	Fitness for customer use
Factory processes	All processes
Empiricism	Statistical methodology
Separation of planning from execution	Participation
Adversary relationship with suppliers	Teamwork relationship
Training of quality specialists	Training for all
Technology	Business: sales, costs
Clients	All customers: external; internal
Factorywide	Companywide

FIG. 7.1   Organization form widely adopted during the 1950s.

THE QUALITY MANAGER

The proliferation of quality-oriented activities has also given rise to a proliferation in job titles and associated responsibilities for persons appointed to head quality-oriented activities. A common generic title is Quality Manager, but there are other titles as well, such as Director of Quality. These Quality Managers are found at various levels in the hierarchy. During the 1980s Quality Managers also began to emerge in such functions as marketing and customer service.

The Plant Quality Manager.   The term "Plant Quality Manager" refers to a Quality Manager who is resident in a plant (a factory) which, in turn, is part of a multiplant division. (In a single-plant division it is usual for the same person to serve as both Plant Quality Manager and Division Quality Manager.)

The Conformance Role.   The basic role of the Plant Quality Manager is to determine product conformance to specification. To this end the manager establishes the laboratories and facilities needed for product inspection and test. The manager also recruits and trains inspectors and technicians to evaluate the product and make the conformance decisions. Borderline and debatable issues come to the manager for resolution. This role of determining conformance applies to all stages of progression of the product within the plant: incoming, in-process, and final.

Under appropriate conditions the work of determining conformance to specification can be delegated to production personnel. See Section 17, Production, under Self-Inspection.

The Role in Cases of Nonconformance.   Each nonconformance requires a new decision: what the disposition of that nonconforming product should be. Decisions to repair or scrap are usually within the jurisdiction of the Plant Quality Manager. However, the optimum disposition may be to use as is: That is, the product may be fit for use despite the nonconformance. [For further discussion, see Sears (1983).]

The Plant Quality Manager participates in the fitness-for-use decision by providing such information as the nature of the nonconformance, the amount of product involved, and the cost of scrap or rework. However, the manager is normally *not* provided with the personnel needed to collaborate with other departments to study such issues as what the client's use of the product will be, what the dangers to society are, and what the urgency is. More usually these matters are studied by divisional personnel, after which they inform the plant of their decisions.

Some buyers mandate the use of material review boards for dealing with nonconforming products. In such cases the Plant Quality Manager is usually a member of the Material Review Board.

In some regulated industries (e.g., nuclear, pharmaceutical) the regulations mandate that nonconformances be recorded and reported to the authorities.

Chronic cases of nonconformance can result in severe pressures on quality managers. The causes of such chronic cases are usually in the system, that is, the product-process planning is inadequate. As a result, Production is unable to produce conforming product. Yet there are schedules to be met and costs to be held down. Such cases call for organization of prevention effort. The Plant Quality Manager can play a constructive role in such effort. (See below.)

The Data Feedback Role.   The Plant Quality Manager also has the role of providing data on product quality to suppliers and to production personnel. Mostly, this data feedback is designed to identify abnormalities, specifically, sporadic outbreaks of quality troubles. The manager also assists in troubleshooting through discovering the precise failure mode, contributing theories as to the causes, and assisting in finding remedies.

Modern electronic data systems have revolutionized the data feedback process. This revolution has made it possible to provide real-time feedback as well as summaries in preanalyzed forms. See Section 27, Computers and Quality.

The Quality Improvement Role.   Companies which set out to improve quality on a systematic basis usually establish quality improvement councils to direct the effort. Some of these councils are at the plant level. The Plant Quality Manager is invariably a member of such a plant council. The manager may also become active in some of the quality improvement projects as a member of the respective project teams.

In addition, the manager is able to assist the quality improvement teams by theorizing as to causes, collecting and providing pertinent data, stimulating remedial action, and evaluating remedial action.

The Training Role. During the 1980s there was increased interest in quality improvement. This, in turn, stimulated a demand for training in quality-oriented skills and tools such as the quality improvement process, team building, and statistical process control. Many Plant Quality Managers accepted responsibility as trainers in these skills and tools.

The Police Image. Some of the roles described above are perceived by production personnel as police roles. Under this interpretation the Plant Quality Manager is viewed as a chief of police, engaged in checking for violations of the law and in reporting offenders to the authorities. This view is deplored and resented by such managers, yet it is really quite a logical analogy from the perspective of the production personnel.

Many quality managers would like to eliminate this police image. The method they commonly employ is logical reasoning. They try to demonstrate by logic that it is important to establish control, test the product, and provide data feedback. This exercise in logical reasoning is normally completely futile—the deeds are more convincing than the words.

The best way to end the police image is to engage in "positive" work. (This positive work is *in addition to,* not instead of, the "negative" work of control.) The most eloquent form of positive work is quality improvement and cost reduction. The improvement process requires creation of teams in which personnel from multiple departments jointly tackle chronic quality problems. The resulting team spirit then carries over into the traditional responsibilities and helps to offset the police image. The Plant Quality Manager who becomes identified with a successful record of "positive" work loses the police image even though the role of "chief of police" remains.

Plant managers have employed additional ways of offsetting the police image:

Being a proponent for resources needed by other departments to improve their quality performance

Periodically "making the rounds" to understand the needs and perceptions of other departments

Helping to establish the conditions which make it possible to delegate greater autonomy to Production, e.g., self-control and self-inspection

Stimulating, within the quality department, an attitude of service to others.

The Qualifications. Qualifications for the job of Plant Quality Manager are mainly of a technological nature. Most job descriptions call for specialized degrees such as in food technology, electronic engineering, and microbiology. Most also require experience in the industry. In recruitment from outside the company there is a universal demand for prior experience as a quality manager. However, within the same company it is not unusual to fill the job of Quality Manager by lateral transfer from other departments. What is seldom demanded in the case of Plant Quality Managers is business training and experience.

The Boss. The Plant Quality Manager normally reports to either the local plant manager or the Division Quality Manager. Life is lived successfully both ways, and there is no clear evidence that the performance of one method exceeds that of the other. Either way, the division quality office participates in establishing the control plan and in audits of plant performance.

An important influence is the criticality of quality with respect to human safety and health and to the environment. In critical cases the upper managers as well as the external regulators tend to mandate that the Plant Quality Manager report to upper management through a separate chain of command.

The Division Quality Manager. The word "division" usually refers to an autonomous organization unit—a profit center—supervised by a general manager. In manufacturing companies, most of such profit centers have been organized in ways which include a Division Quality Manager.

The word "division" has also been used to designate major functional organization units such as Marketing and Customer Service. Previously, Divisional Quality Managers for such organization units were rare. Starting in the 1980s, some major companies established Division Quality Managers in such functional divisions.

An additional new development, also starting in the 1980s, was the movement by companies in the service industries to give higher priority to quality. One feature of this movement was the creation of Quality Managers. Some of these were for profit centers. Others were for functional divisions, or at the corporate level.

Roles of the Division Quality Manager. These roles vary from one company to another but typically consist of a selection from the following list:

1. *Fitness for use:* This involves collecting the information needed for disposition of nonconforming products and then ensuring that the appropriate decision-makers determine the disposition. (The conformance decisions are made at the plant level.)

2. *Quality planning:* Traditionally, this planning focused on the factory process controls and product controls. The trend has been to broaden the areas of quality planning to include essential processes such as the new-product launch cycle, especially the creation of early warning systems to detect potential quality troubles ahead. In some companies the Division Quality Manager's planning role now extends to all phases of activity, including general management of the business, specifically, divisionwide planning for quality.

3. *Quality improvement:* The Division Quality Manager is an essential member of the division quality improvement council. In this capacity the manager shares in the planning and coordination of the quality improvement effort. In addition, the Division Quality Manager is able, through the specialized know-how of the Quality Department, to provide specific assistance to the council and the quality improvement teams in such forms as identifying vital few chronic quality problems, estimating costs of poor quality both overall and in specific areas of concentration, providing the quality improvement teams with data pertinent to their projects, and providing training in quality-oriented skills and tools.

4. *Consulting service:* At the division level the Quality Department usually employs quality specialists who have acquired training and experience in the use of numerous problem-solving tools. This same training and experience can assist in solution of a wide variety of quality problems throughout the division. In consequence, these specialists are able to provide consulting services throughout the division.

5. *Quality assurance:* The Division Quality Manager conducts audits, prepares reports, and in other ways provides an independent source of quality assurance to other divisional managers, including the General Manager. The scope of these forms of quality assurance is described in Section 9, Quality Assurance, and in Section 8, Upper Management and Quality, under Quality Audits by Upper Managers.

The Change to Business Orientation. The growing emphasis on quality has increasingly caused companies to consider managing for quality as an extension of the business plan and to view quality problems as business problems rather than as problems in technology. (See, generally, Section 6, under Companywide Quality Management.)

Many divisions are profit centers, each of which is a near-autonomous business. The General Manager's role is one of business manager, not technologist. (Often the General Manager lacks a technological background.) Of course, some of the subordinate departments (such as Technical, Manufacture, Quality) have a high technological content. Yet the managers of such departments can best help the General Manager by (1) understanding the business mission and (2) directing the resources of their departments toward that mission.

Most Quality Managers have an educational background in technology. Much of their experience has been acquired from the technological departments of the company: the testing laboratories, the factory floor, and the engineering design offices. Their exposure to the business departments (e.g., Marketing, Finance) has been limited. For such Quality Managers, a change to business orientation is a major change. [For elaboration, see Smith (1978).]

To participate in such a change, Division Quality Managers must acquire training and experience in business management—the process of establishing business goals and planning how to meet them. In addition, the division Quality Departments must take steps to transfer many of their technology-oriented activities to other departments. Such transfers must, in turn, be preceded by training those departments in the necessary skills and tools and by establishing means to assure that those departments give continuing priority to the quality goals.

An aid to change in orientation is "making the rounds"—a form of internal marketing research. The Quality Manager visits with each key manager to raise questions such as:

What, in your opinion, are the three company quality problems most in need of solution?

Where lie our best opportunities for improving sales through better quality?

Which are our best opportunities for quality cost reduction?

What major quality threats do we face in the decade ahead?

What are our most urgently needed changes in quality policies, goals, plans, and organization?

Collectively, the responses are revealing (and often full of surprises). They broaden the outlook of the Quality Manager and stimulate the process of change in orientation.

The Boss. During the early stages of evolution the Division Quality Managers were assigned to report to either the Manufacturing Manager or the Technical Manager. The trend has been to make the Division Quality Manager report directly to the Division General Manager. A typical organization chart is shown in Figure 7.2. Since the late 1970s, this organizational form has become the major form in the United States. This same trend in organization form is consistent with the trend toward business orientation of the quality function.

The Department Name. The name has undergone extensive evolution. The first name—Inspection Department—was so descriptive of what the members did that it achieved ready acceptance and standardization.

FIG. 7.2   Typical organization for quality-related activities.

When the function of quality control engineering was added, new names were devised to recognize the broader responsibility. These names competed with each other until some consensus emerged. The name "Quality Control Department" became the most widely adopted replacement for the name "Inspection Department."

In due course the word "control" was "downgraded" from its earlier broad connotation. This led to a search for words with broader implications. One name which met with wide acceptance was "Quality Assurance Department."

This evolution of names continues apace. The shift to business orientation probably calls for a change in the department name. The emerging name will likely include the word "quality"—society at large regards quality as a "good" word. A probable name for the future is Quality Management Department, or simply Quality Department.

(The name Quality Assurance Department has been a source of confusion. In some companies the name is intended to mean broad responsibility over the entire quality function. In other companies the term "quality assurance" is used in a narrower sense—to designate the specialized activities of conducting audits and preparing summarized reports for managers. These activities are discussed in Section 9, Quality Assurance.)

The Corporate Quality Manager.   Some large corporations establish a corporate quality office to provide quality-related services to various internal and external customers. Generally these corporate quality offices are found in multidivisional and/or multinational corporations within which the divisions are linked by some commonality (in markets, products, technology, etc.). The corporate quality office is a service center, not a profit center. It is usually located physically at the corporate headquarters. The corporate Quality Manager is often a vice president and may report directly to the company President or through an intermediate staff Vice President.

The functions of the corporate quality office vary from company to company but usually include the functions listed below. [For a lengthy list, see Robert (1967).]

Assistance to Corporate Management.   This assistance takes such forms as developing corporate quality policies, coordinating the preparation of annual quality goals, preparation of the corporate quality manual, audit of divisional performance, and preparation and publication of reports to management. The trend toward companywide quality management will likely expand the use of corporate quality offices to aid in planning and reporting. Such activities are undertaken only with the clear support of (or mandate from) corporate management. During the 1970s there was much mandating of corporate audits with respect to such matters as product safety and liability.

Assistance to Divisional Management. One form of this assistance is a consulting service. Some corporate quality offices include specialists who can provide consulting assistance. For many problems, an in-house consulting service has advantages over use of outside consultants.

A second form of assistance is training. For certain training courses, it is more efficient to use a corporate capability than to establish self-sufficiency in the divisions.

In some companies, certain quality-oriented services are centralized in order to gain specific efficiencies. An example is a service for conducting supplier surveys and audits. Another example is the laboratory for field failure analysis. When such services are centralized, one option for managing the service is the Corporate Quality Department.

Criteria for Invitation. In general, the central quality office provides services to the divisions only when invited to do so. (The exceptions are in such forms as quality audits mandated by corporate management.) Experience has shown that in issuing such invitations, Division General Managers require that the corporate personnel be

1. Knowledgeable about business matters to an extent which commands the respect of the Division General Manager.
2. Knowledgeable about quality matters to an extent which commands the respect of the Division Quality Manager.
3. Sufficiently personable to minimize the stresses and abrasion which can develop out of such a relationship.

Corporate Quality Managers are well advised to keep these criteria in mind when recruiting their staffs.

Professional Development. The corporate quality office is often the corporate center for collecting and disseminating information on quality methodology. The collection takes place through means such as attending conferences, reading literature, and visiting organizations which are conducting innovative programs. (These organizations may well include divisions within the corporation.)

The resulting information is then disseminated in a number of ways:

Preparation of training programs with associated structured courses and text materials. (Some of the best test materials available in the United States have been prepared by corporate quality offices.)

Publication of success stories through internal news letters or journals.

Organization of internal conferences on quality, with associated committee work, project reports, and discussion of future planning.

Some of those "innovative programs" may be judged to have useful application within the corporation. In such cases the corporate quality office tries to stimulate some division to test them out.

Another form of professional development relates to personnel appraisal.

Many companies require multiple appraisals of their managers. The Corporate Quality Manager is well situated to provide such appraisals with respect to Division Quality Managers and their assistants. (In some companies the Corporate Quality Manager participates in those deliberations which precede filling a vacancy for a post of Division Quality Manager.)

External Relations.   The corporation has numerous relationships on quality matters with outside organizations such as government regulatory agencies, industry associations, standardization bodies, and professional societies. The corporate quality office is often given key roles with respect to such relationships.

Figure 7.3 shows graphically the organization relationship of the corporate quality office to the divisions.

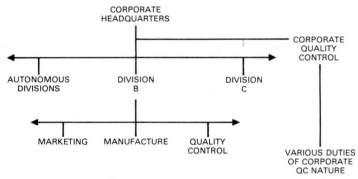

FIG. 7.3   Organization in multidivision companies, featuring corporate quality staff.

The Life Cycle of Corporate Quality Offices.   The preceding list of activities for a quality manager would seem to be a persuasive argument for establishing a corporate quality office. However, there is a cost, without any known measure of return on investment. As a result, the actual establishment usually awaits a favorable financial climate—a time when business is expanding and budgets are liberal. The exceptions have been times of crisis such as the wave of product safety legislation of the 1960s, or the more recent wave of loss of market share to foreign imports, due largely to quality differences.

Once created, it takes a year or two for the corporate quality office to identify the needs of its customers and to arrange to meet those needs. Thereafter the office must survive by earning the support of the Division General Managers.

As viewed by some divisions, the merits of the corporate services are debatable. The costs are quantifiable and real, since in many companies the divisions are "charged" for these costs in the form of mandated overhead burdens. However, the benefits are not quantifiable. As a result, evaluation of the merits of the corporate services are based mainly on the judgment of the Division General Managers.

The real test comes during a time of financial troubles. When business declines and budgets are tight, it is common for the corporate heads to demand a review of each "nonproductive" service to determine whether its continued existence is justified. This review includes securing the judgments of the clients who have been "paying" for the services, specifically, the Division General Managers. At such a time the General Managers do not need to prove that the service has not been worth the overhead charges it imposes on the divisions; their judgments become decisive. The lesson is that *the corporate quality office must earn the support of the divisions before the crisis comes.*

The ups and downs of the business cycle have contributed to a shocking mortality rate of corporate quality offices. In some companies there has actually been a cyclical creation and dismantling of a corporate quality office about once every decade. An added, important variable is the caliber of the corporate quality personnel—to what extent they meet the criteria listed above, under the heading Criteria for Invitation. In too many cases these criteria have not been met, and this has contributed to the mortality rate of the departments.

The emerging trend toward companywide quality management is a new force favoring a role for a corporate quality office. (See generally, Section 6, under Companywide Quality Management.)

Why Quality Managers Fail. Some fail for reasons unrelated to quality, such as lack of leadership skills and poor rapport with peers. (Such reasons can cause any manager to fail.) However, some failures are attributable to quality-related factors such as:

Preoccupation with conformance: This is understandable at the plant or laboratory level. However, at the division level the emphasis should be on meeting the needs of customers.

Emphasis on technology versus business: Here again there is a difference due to level. The plant or laboratory is a technological facility, but the division is a business.

Emphasis on departmental goals: Every Quality Manager has departmental goals and should, of course, meet them. In addition, the Quality Manager is concerned with a broad function which impacts all departments. The quality goals of the division and corporation are much broader than those of the Quality Department. These broader goals impose a broader role on the Quality Manager.

Unfamiliarity with the culture: An obvious example is the case of the Quality Manager who moves from defense-oriented industries to the civilian goods industries. They are two very different worlds with different cultures. The defense world is dominated by an extensive, complex array of mandated specifications and quality plans. It takes much time and effort just to learn what is in those plans and where to apply them. The civilian world also has some mandated specifications and plans, but the dominant force is the competitive marketplace. It places great stress on fitness for use as well as on such parameters as cost and productivity. Quality Managers who move from one such culture to another are in grave danger of failure unless they grasp at the very outset the remarkable change in emphasis.

COORDINATION OF THE QUALITY FUNCTION

"Coordination" as used here is the process of orchestrating all quality-oriented activities so as to attain optimum company results. In the absence of some recognized organization mechanism for assuring coordination, it is easy for departments to emphasize departmental results, to the detriment of company results.

There is a range of alternatives for coordination. While there is a good deal of flexibility in the choice, the most important need is to provide a positive mechanism for coordination rather than leaving it to chance.

The principal forms used for coordination are discussed below.

The Common Boss.   In small companies this is a natural and effective method. Through knowledge of the general needs of the business, the boss can identify the quality needs (objectives) and determine how these needs should be met (plans). Through direct access to all employees, the boss can issue orders to perform those deeds which carry out the plans. Then through this same access, the boss can observe to determine whether the orders have been executed and whether the results have been obtained.

As the company grows, its size and complexity reach a stage such that the common boss can no longer maintain this intimate personal contact with all the people and deeds. Nevertheless, the boss can continue to coordinate personally, provided the company:

Creates special tools analogous to those used for coordinating the finance function (budgets, periodic reports, audits)

Trains the General Manager and subordinate managers in use of these tools

These criteria are central to the concept of companywide quality management discussed in Section 6. If these criteria are not met, the boss lacks the tools for coordination, and coordination must be done by other means.

Self-Coordination.   Where there is no organized provision for coordination, the resulting vacuum may be filled by self-coordination among the various managers. This is certainly what happens when some sporadic trouble flares up. The impacted managers converge on the scene to put out the fire. However, chronic problems tend to go on and on because they lack alarm signals.

An essential ingredient in all forms of coordination is a spirit of teamwork. This is especially necessary if reliance is placed on self-control. Some industry external relationships have long been on an adversary basis: relations with suppliers and relations with unions. Adversary relations can also be present internally; in that event they are a fatal obstacle to self-coordination.

Committees.   Committees (also task forces, teams, etc.) are widely used for coordination. They are at their best when they are closely focused on specific subject matter such as design review, material review boards, and quality improvement projects. For broader matters, the committees can encounter severe jurisdictional complications with line department responsibilities.

In some cases, the committee membership consists of the upper managers themselves. An example is the Quality Improvement Council, the council which directs companywide quality management. In such cases the committee can be effective in a broad undertaking since the members also have line department jurisdiction over the subject matter.

Written Procedure.   This approach is widely used to provide official, repetitive-use plans. (See Section 6, under the Quality Manual.) The result is a form of law and order—a predictable, impersonal means of coordination.

The stabilizing aspect of written procedure can also become an obstacle to progress. Written procedures are intended to provide a predictable, stable plan of action—the precise opposite of improvement. Even worse, in very large organizations (bureaucracies), the procedure can become the end rather than the means.

Precedent. Precedent serves as an informal, unwritten manual of procedure. Despite fallible memories, it is quite useful in small organizations for whom formal, written procedure is too great a burden. Like written procedure, it can also hinder progress.

Staff Departments. This is the main road chosen by companies in the United States. See below, under Staff Quality Departments.

Project Manager. Large, unique projects require extensive planning and coordination, involving multiple major functions. (See Section 6, under Application to Major Programs.) Many such projects are coordinated by a full-time Project Management Department headed by a Project Manager (also called "Program Manager"). Such Project Managers then coordinate for all parameters, including quality.

The "Owner." Many business processes consist of a series of steps, each of which contributes to a final result. Any department head who has command over one of those steps is widely referred to as the "owner" of that part of the process. However, in many cases there is no one in clear command of the entire process, since it progresses through multiple major functions. Some companies have tried to improve the coordination for such processes by assigning each to some manager who then becomes the owner despite not having full command over the process.

Although the owner lacks full command, the designation of "owner" confers certain rights. These rights help the owner to organize informal teams and in other ways establish the means for coordination. The companies are aware of the limitations of informality, so they try to designate, as owners, selected managers whose status and personality are appropriate to give leadership to the coordination effort.

There are variations on the ownership concept. In some companies, each quality improvement project is assigned to a "champion" who is usually a member of the Quality Improvement Council. A project team which encounters a serious organization obstacle can use its access to the project champion to help clear that obstacle.

Matrix Organizations. Matrix organizations exist in various forms. They are used to coordinate for multiple parameters, including quality. What the various forms have in common is the concept of superimposing a team culture on functional departments in order to improve business performance. Team membership is a part-time assignment. The full-time responsibilities of the members are in the business and functional departments.

Experience with matrix organizations suggests that they are at their best in coordination to meet short-range business goals. Such short-range business goals have usually had higher priority than quality goals of a more fundamental nature, such as improving quality on a project-by-project basis and improving the quality planning process.

For an analysis of the matrix organization concept in its various forms, see Cleland (1981a, 1981b).

Crisis-by-Crisis Coordination. This is the coordination of last resort. It takes place when a fire breaks out and all managers rush to do the firefighting. It is also the most expensive form of coordination.

Tools for Coordination. Coordination is aided by use of various tools of quality management: quality policies, objectives and plans to meet them, executive reports, quality surveys, and audits. These tools are the result of coordinated effort, and, once in use, they provide further coordination by the fact of use.

COORDINATION AMONG DIVISIONS

In some multidivisional companies there is much community of interest because the divisions (1) sell their products in the same or overlapping markets, (2) sell under the same company name or brand name, (3) produce components which will enter the same final product, and (4) employ common technology.

In such cases there are obvious needs for coordination with respect to quality. However, any organization for coordination must accommodate the tendency of the divisions to resist invasion of their autonomous status. The more usual forms of coordination include:

1. *An informal council of quality managers:* In this form the various divisional quality managers establish a network of communication by all available means: telephone, correspondence, and meetings. They identify problems of mutual interest and try to establish action programs to deal with these problems. They are, however, handicapped by lack of official recognition (legitimacy) and lack of personnel needed to carry out the numerous associated details.

2. *A formal council of quality managers:* The informal council may succeed in obtaining an official status. This conversion into a formal council provides legitimacy. Now the council has the clear right to call meetings, request data, conduct studies, and recommend action. This same legitimacy also simplifies the problem of securing the personnel and other resources needed to relieve busy quality managers of some of the associated detailed work. For a case example, see Comish (1983).

3. *An international quality office:* This form is widely used in multinational companies. The International Quality Manager typically reports to a corporate staff officer who has broad responsibilities for coordination of foreign subsidiaries, including coordination for quality. Figure 7.4 shows a typical organization form.

The International Quality Manager may be assigned any one or all of the following usual responsibilities:

FIG. 7.4 Organization for coordination through an international quality office.

Provide information and assistance to the subsidiaries in such forms as standards, systems, and procedures.

Receive samples for comparative testing.

Receive data for analysis and comparative reporting.

Assist in interchange of information on projects in progress and on results attained.

Convene international conferences on quality-related matters.

Conduct audits of quality performance, including surveillance visits.

4. *A corporate quality office:* This formal office is not attached to any profit center—it reports to corporate management. It has multiple responsibilities, including coordination, as discussed above, under The Corporate Quality Manager.

In the case of conglomerate companies there is little commonality among divisions (other than financial); hence there is little need for quality coordination among divisions.

In some cases the activities to be coordinated are divided among multiple companies. The need for coordination is especially severe in large, complex systems requiring extensive subcontracting. In such cases the prime contractor engages various subcontractors to design and build the subsystems which are to enter the total system.

For such undertakings, the work of coordination is so extensive that conventional collaboration among the companies does not do the job. Instead, there is need to create a new organization whose main job is coordination. This organization, often called "Program Management," is discussed in Section 31, under the Program Management Function.

Responsibility Matrix.   Organization charts are effective for defining the chain of command. However, the charts are not effective for showing the interrelationships needed for coordination. One way of showing this interrelation is through a responsibility matrix.

Table 7.3 is an example of a responsibility matrix. The horizontal elements consist of specific decisions or actions to be taken. The vertical columns show the various organization units involved. The intersections bear code letters to define the extent of responsibility, whether primary (R) or contributory (C).

STAFF QUALITY ACTIVITIES

In this handbook, the "line" (or "operating") activities are those without which an enterprise cannot exist at all, such as marketing and manufacture. "Staff" activities are those which, while not vital to the existence of the enterprise, are essential to its efficient operation.

Examples of Staff Quality Activities.   Staff quality activities exist in several varieties. The most common are listed in Table 7.4, along with examples in the quality function.

Staff quality activities may be performed at the outset by a staff Quality Department. However, many such activities will in due course be performed by the line departments. This change takes place through a natural, evolutionary life cycle of any staff specialty.

TABLE 7.3 Responsibility Matrix (R—primary responsibilities; C—contributing responsibilities)

Areas of responsibility	General manager	Marketing	Program manager	Engineering	Manufacturing	QC&T*	Finance
Product quality level for business	R	C	C			C	
Initiate program plan, schedules, and budgets		C	R	C	C	C	C
Issue work statement		R	C				
Customer quality requirements		C	R	C		C	
Prepare quality plan						R	
Establish engineering standards				R			
Establish quality standards						R	
Establish product design capability			C	R			
Provide reliability apportionment			C	R			
Prepare design specifications			C	R	C	C	
Perform design review			C	R	C	C	
Accomplish make/buy decision			C	C	R	C	
Provide drawing and change control			C	R	C	C	C

Activity			
Implement production process designs		R	
Implement new design control by reviewing engineering and manufacturing designs against quality standards	C	C	R
Engineering standards	C	R	C
Configuration definition	C	R	
Produce product to design specifications		R	R
Configuration verification			R
Implement incoming material	C	C	R
Design major items of test equipment which require significant design effort		R	C
Design all other test equipment and fixtures and procure all test equipment and fixtures for QC&T, plant and field use; provide QC requirements for engineering designs		C	R

*Quality control and test.

TABLE 7.4 Staff Quality Activities

Types of staff activity	Examples in quality function
Planning—establishing goals and devising ways to reach goals	Preparation of quality manuals; reliability planning; companywide quality planning
Control—ensuring that execution conforms to plan	Product inspection and test; quality audits
Advisory services	Consulting in statistical methodology; design review
Utility services	Data collection and analysis; laboratory test services

Life Cycle of a Staff Quality Activity. A new staff activity has its origin in some new tool (concept, method, technique, etc). Examples in the quality function have included Shewhart control charts, reliability quantification, and quality cost analysis.

The subsequent events are in the nature of a life cycle for the staff activity:

The new tool is tried out in limited areas and it secures good results.

The results are publicized and attract the attention of managers in other areas. These managers want similar results, so they also try out the new tools.

In due course the cumulative results come to the attention of journalists and conference organizers. They propagandize the results and tools through mass media.

The extensive applications build up a body of experience and expertise among the specialists and managers. This expertise is further refined by an evolving literature.

The scholars and philosophers develop models for standardizing the new tools. They also evolve simplified procedures to enable nonprofessionals to apply the tools.

Training is given to the line people so that they can use the simplified tools and procedures to make additional applications on their own.

The staff specialists move to other problems, but they may retain an audit on the line applications as well as providing a consulting service.

STAFF QUALITY DEPARTMENTS

These departments first emerged on a wide scale during the 1940s. Three forces converged to stimulate a rapid growth: a need for improving quality of production of goods required during World War II, a sudden and extensive growth of interest in the use of statistical methodology to aid quality control, and formation of an American Society for Quality Control (ASQC).

Quality Control Engineering. The original emphasis of these staff Quality Departments was on employing the statistical tools. However, it soon became clear that a broader approach was needed. This broader approach required assignment of the bulk of the staff quality activities to engineers (rather than to statisticians). As a result, the emerging dominant title for the personnel became Quality Control Engineer. Correspondingly, the dominant title for the staff Quality Department became Quality Control Engineering.

In due course the Quality Control Engineers became involved with a broad list of quality work elements (see Quality Management Work Elements and Jobs, above). Through this involvement they impacted most of the functions being carried out. For example:

Work elements	*Functions impacted*
Field complaint analysis	Sales; customer service
Quality cost analysis	Accounting
Supplier surveillance	Purchasing
Motivation for quality	Human relations

This same broadening of the scope of quality control engineering also resulted in a broadening of the titles. The title Quality Engineer became more popular than the title Quality Control Engineer.

The one major area not invaded by the Quality Control Engineers was that of launching of new products. When the need arose for modernizing this activity to meet the needs of the computer, defense, and aerospace industries, a new specialty—reliability engineering—was created.

Reliability Engineering. In response to the urging of these new specialists, many companies, notably in the defense and aerospace industries, created new departments for reliability engineering (rather than expanding the scope of the Quality Control Engineering Departments). In some companies a single staff department was retained but was renamed (e.g., Quality Control and Reliability Engineering). The growing competition in reliability of civilian goods then expanded the role of Reliability Engineers into many civilian industries.

The activities associated with the reliability "movement" actually involve two sets of tools: (1) *technological* tools for reliability modeling and quantification throughout the product hierarchy and (2) *managerial* tools to formalize the approach and to assure that it is used. See generally, Section 13, under Planning for Time-Oriented Performance (Reliability).

Interface among Staff Quality Specialties. Establishment of those two categories of quality-oriented engineering also required establishment of jurisdictional boundaries. Generally, the responsibilities of reliability engineering were focused on the launching of new product designs and evaluation of reliability performance throughout all stages of the product life cycle. The responsibilities of quality control engineering related to the remaining quality work elements.

While the areas of responsibility differ, the skills and tools have much in common. Both categories of engineers should have:

An educational background in basic science and in applied science

Understanding of the nature of quality and the processes by which it is attained

Training and experience in using the tools: technological, statistical, and managerial

The respective areas of knowledge do not overlap fully; there are differences as well. Theoretically, it is possible for one person to be qualified to carry out both specialties. (Some individuals hold ASQC certifications both as Quality Engineer and Reliability Engineer.) However, industry practice has largely been to recognize the two categories as separate.

Other Specialties; Staff-Staff Conflicts.   In organizations which employ many quality staff specialists there is a tendency for the work to specialize further and for the titles to proliferate. Examples of such titles have been: Maintainability Engineer, Material Review Engineer, Salvage Engineer, Configuration Control Engineer, Systems Engineer, and still others. In addition, there are "non-quality" specialists whose area of responsibility overlaps that of the quality specialists. Examples are Industrial Engineer, Value Analyst, Operations Research Analyst, Statistician, Standardization Engineer, and Project Engineer.

The presence of multiple specialties with overlapping areas of responsibility sometimes leads to lively conflicts—the respective specialists tend to try to expand their areas of jurisdiction. Running through such staff-staff conflicts is the risk of "rediscovery of scientific management." Once a new, narrow specialty succeeds in obtaining results, it is tempting for those involved to use these results as the basis for securing a broad charter plus associated budget. This is sometimes done by phrasing the specialty in such broad language as to encompass the entire concept of "scientific management." Some of the definitions put forward for operations research, value analysis, systems engineering, and so on have been precisely of this nature.

Managers should be on the alert for this tendency to draft broad staff charters since they are a breeding ground for staff-staff conflicts. Preparing the charter for a new department is similar to launching a new design—in this case, for organizational structure. This design should be subject to close "design review" by all who will be asked to live with it, both line and staff.

ADMINISTRATION OF THE QUALITY STAFF SPECIALTY

This administration is best performed if there is a prior understanding of the perceptions of the major parties in interest.

Perceptions.   The line departments perceive the staff services as a mixture of benefit and detriment. Auxiliary services are often welcomed, but controls are usually resented as imposing delays and interfering with autonomy. The costs are often transferred to the line in the form of overhead burdens. The individual specialists may exhibit abrasive personalities.

The staff Quality Departments view their specialty as vital to the health of the enterprise. However, this view is somewhat self-serving. A staff department is a cost center, not a profit center. The costs are readily quantifiable, but the benefits are not. Such a situation is inherently insecure. To the specialists a possible additional source of security is to convert the specialty into a profession—an essential service to society, with practice limited to licensed professionals. (For further discussion, see Section 11, under Professionalism.)

The managers who preside over both line and staff would like to attain efficient operations at optimum cost and with minimal friction. One attractive solution is to minimize the use of staff quality specialists by transferring staff quality activities to line departments.

Transfer from Staff to Line. A major form of this transfer can come from close attention to the concept of the "product life cycle" of staff quality activities. (See Life Cycle of a Staff Quality Activity above.) According to that concept, a staff department is able to live on and on despite continuing transfer of its activities to line departments. The solution is a continuing development of new products—updating the product line.

For the staff to turn activities over to the line people sounds like economic suicide, and it might well be the case in a static society. However, new problems are continuously arising. These problems require new tools for solution and provide a basis for the staff specialists to modernize their "product line" as they turn the old, matured tools over to the line departments. To continue "doing business at the old stand," in other words, working on solved problems, is the surest way to decay and death of the staff department.

Another method of transfer is to reorganize major functions to provide them with more complete "ownership" of their mission. In a reported case example, a new department—Procurement Engineering—was created within the procurement function. The procurement engineers were trained to provide the procurement function with the technical support previously provided by several staff departments, including the staff Quality Department. For further details, see Brown (1974).

Any method of transfer requires training line specialists to undertake work previously done by quality staff specialists. An example is training product designers in reliability modeling and reliability quantification, as well as in design of experiments.

Budgeting. Budgets for staff Quality Departments are set up to correspond to the types of activity conducted, somewhat as follows:

Activity	*Basis of budget*
Quality improvement	Project-by-project
Planning	Anticipated extent of new products, processes, etc., requiring quality planning
Consulting; control; audits	Previous history, adjusted for expected growth

In their own interest as well as that of their superiors, staff Quality Departments should propose budgets which are dominated by improvement projects. Most of these projects are justifiable on the basis of return on investment. This has strong appeal to upper management as well as to the line departments.

Reports on Staff Quality Activities. Because the bulk of staff work is long range, the frequency of reporting should be infrequent—normally quarterly. Each quarterly report shows the progress made during the last quarter and lists plans for the quarter ahead. The annual report (every fourth quarter) contains the next annual plan as well.

Completed projects are reported on at the time of completion.

In reporting financial results the staff is well advised to enlist the aid of the company's Accounting Department. Upper management gives more credibility to financial figures if they have been "certified" by the Accounting Department.

Much of the content of staff Quality Department reports consists of progress reports on projects of a multidepartmental nature. In such projects the staff Quality Department often plays essential roles in such forms as data collection and analysis or application of quality-oriented expertise. In reporting the results of such projects, the staff people are well advised to lean over backward to give maximum credit to line supervisors. Some staff specialists draft reports on finished projects in the form of joint reports (with the line departments involved).

For a discussion of the contents of managerial reports on quality, see Section 8, Upper Management and Quality, under Executive Reports on Quality.

Introducing Change.   In its creative and project work, the staff department is trying to change the existing order. On the surface, the proposed changes are technological in character. However, any technological change is a potential threat to the "cultural pattern" of those who have a vested interest in the existing order. As a result, a distinct phase in introducing change is dealing with cultural resistance—resistance to the "social" consequences of technological change.

For an extensive discussion as applied to quality improvement projects, see Section 22, Quality Improvement, under Resistance to Change.

Other Staff-Line Relationships.   It is almost universal that responsibility for results of operations rests with the line managers, not the staff managers. For this reason the line managers are given the discretion to either accept or reject the advice of staff specialists. (They do either at their own peril.) This is a good rule. If managers are to be held responsible for results, they should have authority over the means for obtaining those results. To require them to accept staff advice is equivalent to transferring part of that authority to the staff (a form of authority without responsibility).

This very real responsibility of line managers renders the authority of the staff specialist illusory. To be sure, the staff department has status on the organization chart. It has a budget, a table of duties, and other outward symbols of authority. These symbols certainly do confer legitimacy in some important ways—the right to secure information, attend meetings, and present proposals. However, the real authority, that is, the ability to secure action, is not derived from the rank of the staff managers. It is derived from their knowledge, their proved competence in assisting line managers in improving their results, and their individual personalities. The matter of personality is surprisingly important. Although personality by itself solves no problems, it avoids some severe problems by converting the conflicts inherent in the staff-line relationships into innocent rivalries or even good-natured collaboration.

Aside from the conflicts inherent in introducing change, there are others inherent in planning and controlling. Of these, the problem of "two bosses" is probably the most common. The problem arises when staff specialists prepare plans to be executed by line departments. For example, a plant laboratory "reports" to the Plant Manager. However, the Division Quality (staff) Department is a major force in preparing the quality plans to be used and in auditing to ensure that the execution follows the plans. The organization chart itself reflects a dualism. A solid line runs from the laboratory to the Plant Manager. However, a dotted or dashed line runs from the laboratory to the Division Quality Manager.

The solution lies in the fact that the plant laboratory has only one personal boss (the Plant Manager) but numerous impersonal bosses, of which the quality plan is but one. (Others include the personnel manual, the budget, the safety regulations, etc.) As long as there is only one personal boss, the plant laboratory head has a place for appeal to secure the final word.

Careers, Training, and Professionalism for Quality Staff Specialists.   These topics are pertinent to administration of the quality staff specialty. They are discussed in Section 11, under the respective headings.

REFERENCES

American Society for Quality Control (1961). *The Basic Elements of Quality Control Engineering.* ASQC, Milwaukee.

Brown, Arthur W. (1974). "Procurement Engineering." *ASQC Technical Conference Transactions,* Milwaukee, pp. 161–168.

Cleland, David I. (1981*a*). "The Cultural Ambience of the Matrix Organization." *Management Review,* November, pp. 25–28, 37–39.

Cleland, David I. (1981*b*). "Matrix Management (Part II): A Kaleidoscope of Organizational Systems." *Management Review,* December, pp. 48–56.

Comish, John W. (1983). "Managing a Multidivisional Quality Function." *ASQC Quality Congress Transactions,* Milwaukee, pp. 268–271.

Juran, J. M. (1977). "Quality and Its Assurance, An Overview." *Second NATO Symposium on Quality and its Assurance,* London.

Juran, J. M. (1973). "The Taylor System and Quality Control." A series of articles in *Quality Progress,* May 1973 through December 1973 (listed under "Management Interface").

Robert, Paul A. (1967). "Quality Control Management at the Corporate Level." *ASQC Technical Conference Transactions,* Milwaukee, pp. 3–5.

Sears, James A. (1983). "Changing Role of the Quality Inspection Function." *Quality Progress,* July, pp. 12–17.

Smith, Martin R. (1978). "Why QC Need PR." *Industry Week,* October 30, pp. 37–39.

SECTION 8

UPPER MANAGEMENT AND QUALITY

J. M. Juran

"Upper management" as used here refers to the highest leadership posts of an enterprise. Applied to a corporation, upper management includes the president (or chief executive officer) plus the corporate vice presidents. Applied to an autonomous division, upper management includes the general manager and the directly subordinate managers.

Previously, in tiny organizations the chief executive personally directed all activities in the organization, including managing for quality. As organizations grew in size, the volume of activity outgrew the capacity of the chief executive to manage by personal direction. It became necessary to delegate.

A major form of this delegation was through the craft concept. Apprentices were trained in the craft and qualified by examination to become craftsmen. The chief executive—the master—then delegated much of the managing for quality to the craftsmen, subject to inspection and audit by the master.

Growth of organization was sharply accelerated by the Industrial Revolution, which opened the way to mass marketing and mass production. The resulting large enterprises required organization into functional departments. The chief executives delegated to each functional department head the responsibility for managing that function, including the responsibility for quality—for performing the function correctly.

With the growth of technology, products and processes became increasingly complex. To deal with these complexities, many industries adopted the principle of separating planning from execution. Planning of the various functions was delegated to trained planners, leaving to the supervisors and the work force the job of executing the plans. This separation of planning from execution had several major consequences:

A decline in use of the craftsmanship concept

A dramatic rise in productivity

A dispersion of the responsibility of managing for quality among still more organization units

A further distancing of upper management from the job of managing for quality

[For elaboration on the Taylor System of separating planning from execution, and its effect on quality, see Juran (1973).]

The progressive removal of upper management from managing for quality produced negative effects on quality. To offset these effects, various organization devices were adopted. (See generally, Section 7, Organizing for Quality.) Nevertheless, numerous instances arose in which product performance fell short of customer needs. In addition, the companies accumulated huge chronic costs of poor quality.

Despite these quality deficiencies, many companies remained profitable because their competitors had similar problems. This equilibrium was then upset by two major forces: (1) the growing impact of quality on society (see Section 34, Impact of Quality on Society) and (2) the emergence of a new level of competition, notably from Japan.

These new forces severely impacted many companies. The impacted companies then responded in various ways, and with varying results. By the 1980s it had become abundantly clear that those major forces required major responses. It was not enough to make adjustments to the existing approach; it was necessary to go back to fundamentals—to question the premises behind the then-existing approach.

One of those premises was that managing for quality could successfully be delegated to the functional managers (and then on to their subordinates). A second premise was that once managing for quality had been delegated to the subordinate hierarchy, it would no longer be necessary for upper managers to participate personally in managing for quality. These premises had become deeply rooted in Western industrial culture. Many managerial practices, organization designs, areas of responsibility, and even careers had been built around these premises. However, by the 1980s it had become clear that these premises were no longer valid as applied to many of the industries impacted by those major forces. As a corollary, the needed responses from those industries required:

1. A comprehensive, companywide approach to managing for quality
2. Extensive personal participation by upper managers in both the design of the companywide approach and its operation thereafter.

Response through Comprehensive Structure.   One form of response of the impacted industries was to design a more broadly structured approach to managing for quality. In its broadest form, managing for quality is conducted through a structured approach which employs all the processes of the Trilogy: planning, controlling, and improving. This approach is designed to serve the needs of all customers, internal as well as external. It is applied to business processes as well as to technological processes. It parallels closely the way in which companies manage for finance. (For elaboration, see Section 2, the Quality Function, under How to Think about Quality.)

In this handbook, such a comprehensive, structured approach to managing for quality is referred to as companywide quality management (CWQM). It is described in Section 6, under the heading Companywide Quality Management.

Response through Upper-Management Participation.   A second form of response by the impacted companies was through enlisting the personal participation of the upper managers. This participation has ranged across a broad spectrum. At one extreme the upper managers have personally taken full charge of managing for quality. At the other extreme the upper managers have exhorted all personnel to do better, to "do it right the first time," but have limited their own role to such activities as lecturing, blaming, and stimulating others.

PARTICIPATION BY UPPER MANAGEMENT

There is no way known for defining upper-management participation through use of such broad words as "commitment" and "involvement." Instead, it is necessary to define, with precision:

Which specific decisions are to be made by upper managers

Which specific actions are to be taken by upper managers

The more usual decisions and actions which collectively represent upper managers' options for personal participation in CWQM are discussed in the following paragraphs. The actual participation is usually a selection from this list of topics.

For some of these topics, the upper managers' participation is carried out by the upper managers collectively. For other topics the upper managers participate within their respective individual spheres of responsibility.

Establish a Quality Council.   This council (also called "committee," etc.) plays the central role in directing and coordinating the company's efforts to manage for quality. When established at the corporate level, the council plays a role in the quality function analogous to the role played by the Finance Committee with respect to the finance function. If the aim is to establish CWQM, then a corporate quality council is indispensable.

Ideally, CWQM is designed to become a part of the business planning of the company. Such a design is feasible because of the similarity in concept—both business planning and CWQM involve establishing goals, providing the means to meet the goals, reviewing progress against goals, and so on. Where CWQM does, in fact, become an extension of business planning, corporate quality council functions so extensively overlap those of the corporate management committee that the quality council may lose its identity.

In large companies it is common to establish quality subcouncils for major organization segments, such as divisions or functional departments. It is also common to establish councils for major managerial undertakings, such as quality improvement. When subcouncils are established, it is usual to "network" them; that is, members of higher level councils are appointed to be the chairpersons of lower-level councils.

Serve on the Quality Council.   The membership of the council should be in keeping with the scope of the council's mission. Membership on the quality council exposes the members to essential inputs relative to the quality problems requiring solution, the resources needed, and other issues. The council is seldom effective if the members lack decision-making power over the subject matter. In addition, the rank of the council membership sends a message to the rest of the organization regarding the priority of the subject matter.

Establish Quality Policies.   As used in this handbook, policies are guides to managerial action. Once formulated, they are approved at the highest levels of organization. Section 5, under various headings, presents many examples of published quality policy statements at various levels and for various functions.

Upper managers participate in quality policy formation in several ways:

1. *Identifying the need for policies:*   Major evidence of need for policies is found in repeated questions raised at lower levels, asking for directions on broad issues. In many cases the lower levels of management take the initiative in identifying the need for quality policies.

2. *Assigning responsibility for preparing a draft:*   Policy formation usually requires securing inputs from multiple sources—a time-consuming process. In the absence of clear responsibility it is unlikely that a draft will be prepared.

3. *Reviewing, revising, and approving:*   Because policies must be approved at the highest levels, the upper managers must personally review the draft.

Establish Quality Goals.   At upper-management levels the quality goals (also objectives, etc.) are quite broad. See, for examples, Section 5, under the heading Subject Matter of Quality Objectives.

Broad quality goals are properly oriented to the *results* needed by the organization, not to the means used for getting the results. To illustrate, a broad quality goal may be to reduce the cost of poor quality by 50 percent in 5 years. Attainment of such a goal may require raising awareness, training in statistical process control, and other measures. However, at the upper-management level the goal is results-oriented, not technique-oriented or tool-oriented. In general, efforts to improve quality are headed for disappointment if the goals are tool-oriented rather than results-oriented.

Quality goals should be expressed in numbers and should include a time frame—the time during which the goals are to be reached. Lacking such quantification, it is difficult to agree on issues such as what is meant by the goals, what resources are needed, and how to evaluate performance against goals.

Deploy the Goals. Broad goals are merely "wish lists" until they are "deployed." The deployment process consists of allocating the goals to lower levels of organization. These lower levels then propose specific deeds which, if done, will collectively result in meeting the goals. The lower levels also present a list of the resources needed to meet the goals: personnel, facilities, money, and so on. There follows a negotiation process to balance the value of reaching the goals against the resources needed. This negotiation process then arrives at a final list of deeds and resources. During this process the original goals may well have been modified.

Provide the Resources. A major failing of upper managers has been the failure to provide the resources needed to carry out the "list of deeds." Such a failure sends a negative message to the lower levels.

In part the needed resources relate to added burdens placed on subordinates, such as the time required to do the deeds. In part, the resources relate to establishing the supporting infrastructure. For example, major goals for quality improvement may require setting up new organization entities in such forms as a quality improvement council and numerous teams to carry out specific improvement projects. This, in turn, may require setting up a supporting infrastructure which includes a process for choosing projects, a process for making project-by-project improvement, training of facilitators, and training of teams. (See, generally, Section 22, Quality Improvement.)

The resources are a price to be paid for meeting the goals. If the resources are not provided, the perception in the lower levels is that the goals lack priority relative to those goals for which resources are provided.

Provide Problem-Oriented Training. Training is a special form of resource and is a vital element of response to those major forces. It is also a resource which upper managers have generally been willing to provide. However, the upper managers have generally not personally involved themselves with the issue of what training is needed.

The lack of personal involvement by upper managers has led to a good deal of unbalance in training for quality. Until the 1980s, training for quality was largely confined to personnel in the Quality Departments. The emerging quality crisis then stimulated extensive training, principally:

Training for workers in Quality Circles, emphasizing basic problem-solving tools

Training for production supervision and managers, emphasizing statistical tools—"statistical process control"

Training for managerial personnel emphasizing exhortation to do better

Training for managerial personnel emphasizing project-by-project quality improvement

Each of those directions had value, some more than others. In the judgment of the author, the training efforts would have been much better directed and more effective had the upper managers participated in the list of activities set out above. Through such participation the upper managers would have been much better able to identify the quality problems, and thereby to assure that the training activities would be oriented to the solution of those problems. They also would have been better able to judge their personal needs for quality-oriented training.

Serve on Quality Improvement Teams.   There are some persuasive reasons for this form of upper-management participation:

It is a form of leadership by example—the highest form of leadership.

It enables upper managers to understand what they are asking their subordinates to do. In most companies the number of needed improvements runs into hundreds of specific projects, each demanding time of subordinates as well as various resources. There is no better way to understand the nature of these demands than to participate personally in some improvement projects.

Some projects by their very nature require upper managers' membership on the project teams.

Review Progress.   Reviews of progress are an essential part of assuring that goals are being met. The very fact that upper managers do review progress sends a message to the rest of the organization as to the priority given to the quality goals.

Reviews are carried out in two major ways: (1) summarized reports on actual quality performance (see Executive Reports on Quality below) and (2) audits of the processes being used to attain quality (see Executive Quality Audits below).

In conducting reviews it is necessary for upper managers to maintain a constructive approach. The basic purpose of such reviews is, of course, to inform the upper managers of the actual state of affairs. If actual performance falls short of goals, the need is to discover and remove the causes. It is risky, and damaging to morale, to blame subordinates when the cause is not known; often the cause is the system or even the upper managers.

Stimulate Improvement.   One byproduct of review of progress is identification of opportunities for improvement. This is especially true with respect to chronic quality problems. Unlike sporadic problems, chronic quality problems usually originate in the initial planning. The remedy is often to replan, and this is a time-consuming process which is best done as part of a broad undertaking to improve quality. (See, generally, Section 22, Quality Improvement.)

Give Recognition.   The word "recognition" as used here relates to ceremonial actions taken to publicize meritorious performance. These ceremonial actions are typically nonfinancial in nature. They usually focus on activities of an improvement nature rather than on the conduct of operations. In contrast, the reward systems for successful conduct of operations employ such devices as performance appraisal or merit rating and focus on the supervisor–subordinate relationship.

Response to the "major forces" (see Introduction; Background above), requires doing much more than meeting traditional goals; it requires setting and meeting unconventional goals. In turn, to meet these unconventional goals requires extensive revisions in prior practice—virtually a change in culture.

Such a change in culture is accelerated if upper managers give recognition to teams and individuals who make specific contributions to the change. For example, it is common practice for upper managers to preside at ceremonial awards of certificates or plaques to persons who have completed training courses. In some companies, upper managers personally and prominently participate in dinner meetings specifically organized to honor teams who have completed their quality improvement projects. Similar meetings are organized to recognize outstanding contributions made by suppliers. Still other companies establish special awards for teams or individuals whose contributions are judged to be outstanding. These awards are made by upper managers at ceremonial occasions and are publicized through various media such as the company's newsletter, the bulletin boards, and the local press. For case examples, see Gibson (1987) and Onnias (1986).

Revise the Reward System. Many companies employ reward systems in which the rewards include money as well as progress in job grade. In such systems the extent of the rewards depends importantly on the adequacy of performance against operating goals. These goals include quality as well as others (schedule, cost standard, etc.).

For such reward systems, a response to the "major forces" may consist of revising the weight given to the quality component. For example, a large company in the automotive industry revised the merit rating system of its customer service organization by raising to 50 percent (out of 100 percent) the weight given to quality.

Another form of response is to add new parameters to the existing list. Some companies which have undertaken quality improvement on a large scale have added the parameter "performance on quality improvement" to the existing list.

UPPER-MANAGEMENT RESISTANCE TO PARTICIPATION

Many upper managers have exhibited resistance to adding so extensively to their own work loads. In their view they were already quite busy with their traditional responsibilities. In addition, they tended to feel that their contribution could be made by conventional delegation, that is, by establishing the goals and then urging their subordinates to meet those goals. Such conventional delegation was carried out in many companies; it resulted in widespread disappointments. The desired results were not achieved. The lack of results fostered an atmosphere of blame and divisiveness.

The failures to obtain results took the upper managers by surprise. The concept of delegation is vital to all managerial activity. The ability to delegate is an essential attribute of a good manager. However, analysis of a number of the failures shows that there were some serious weaknesses in the delegation strategy:

The new policy of raising quality to a position of top priority was too revolutionary a change to be achieved by a simple act of delegation.

The upper managers were not sufficiently knowledgeable about the subject matter to be able to define the quality goals with adequate precision. Their stated goals (e.g., "Do it right the first time") were too vague to convey to subordinates "What to do differently."

Such vague goals could not compete in priority with the traditional clearly defined goals of meeting specifications, schedules, budgets, etc.

There was no accompanying change in the system of evaluating the performance of subordinates. Hence it was logical for subordinates to conclude that despite the upper-management pronouncements, nothing had really changed. Such a conclusion is especially likely if the company regularly mounts "drives" which come and go with little residual effect.

Despite these serious weaknesses, some companies made significant progress in improving quality. Usually they did so in specific areas where determined middle managers took the initiative, and found ways to supply what the upper managers had failed to supply. Some upper managers feel that such is precisely what the middle managers should do. However, the latter have difficulty in doing so when the former limit their participation to setting broad goals and making broad delegations.

Selective Participation. The upper managers may participate selectively on the basis of perceived specific needs. For example, in some companies upper management has taken the initiative to establish a teamwork relationship with suppliers (to replace the prevailing adversary relationship). Such a change requires support from upper managers in the supplier companies as well, as a result of deeply rooted practices and cultural resistance.

Another example of selective management participation relates to product reliability. The outward evidence is a policy requiring that no new product go to market unless its reliability is at least equal to that of (1) the product it replaces and (2) the product of leading competitors. This policy is then enforced by independent audit.

QUALITY ASSURANCE FOR UPPER MANAGERS

Upper managers have various needs to know what is going on with respect to quality. One of these needs is for *assurance* that all is well with respect to quality. (If not, that need expands into specifics.)

The general nature of quality assurance is described in Section 9, Quality Assurance. The principles and methods discussed there apply widely. However, the application to upper management's needs involves special designs of reports and audits. These special designs are discussed below.

In small companies it is feasible for upper managers to maintain personal contact with all activities in the organization and thereby to secure firsthand assurance as to the state of quality. As the organization grows, the ability to maintain personal contact shrinks. The resulting gap must then be filled by some system of quality assurance. This system consists largely of quality reports and audits.

EXECUTIVE REPORTS ON QUALITY

A major form of quality assurance for upper managers is derived from a battery of executive reports. (The word "executive" as used here is synonymous with the term "upper manager.")

Executive reports on quality have much in common with the feedback loop used at lower levels, such as control subjects, units of measure, data collection systems, and means for summary and analysis. (Table 6.4 shows some examples of the feedback loop as applied to control reports.) The prime difference is the choice of control subject. In turn, choice of control subject affects the other elements of the feedback loop.

Early forms of executive reports on quality tended to be limited to summaries of factory quality information, plus summaries of negative field reports. Table 8.1 lists some typical control subjects and associated units of measure. In large companies such summaries were often prepared by major groupings, such as by factory or by product line.

TABLE 8.1 Early Executive Reports on Quality

Control subjects	Units of measure
Factory quality	
First-time yield	Percent of product accepted on test
Scrap	Percent of material issued
Rework	Percent of direct labor-hours
Field performance	
Rejections by customer	Percent to shipments
Claims	Percent of sales
Complaints	Number
Warranty charges	Cost

With the growth of special quality-oriented departments, various additions and refinements were made to these early forms of reports. A major trend was to enlarge the use of money as the unit of measure for product deficiencies. A second trend was to improve field feedback in order to be able to discover causes of poor quality and identify opportunities for improvement. The availability of electronic data processing greatly simplified data summary and analysis as well as timely reporting. There were also numerous refinements in such forms as: seriousness classification systems, rating systems, and charting to show trends. The Pareto principle was employed to highlight the top few quality problems. Table 8.2 illustrates the nature of executive reports which include these additions and refinements.

TABLE 8.2 Revisions in Executive Reports on Quality

Control subjects	Units of measure
Factory quality deficiencies	Cost of poor quality relative to sales
Finished goods quality	Parts (defective) per million; demerits per unit; demerits per $1000 of sales; demerits per 1000 possible errors
Field quality performance	Percent uptime; maintenance hours per 1000 operating hours
Field quality deficiencies	Cost relative to sales; cost per 1000 units under warranty
Suppliers' quality	Cost of poor quality as a percent of purchases
Top 10 quality problems	Narrative listing
Significant events	Narrative listing

The 1980s accelerated additional trends. Executive reports on quality were increasingly extended to quality performance of business systems. The growing activity in quality improvement required progress reports. The emergence of CWQM necessitated special reporting. An emerging national concern with slow growth in productivity required linking of reports on quality with reports on productivity. The trend toward use of personal computers by upper managers demanded that report systems be "networked" to these personal computers.

Table 8.3 illustrates some of the ways in which executive reports on quality have been influenced by such developments.

TABLE 8.3   Influence of Recent Developments on Executive Reports on Quality

Control subject	Unit of measure
Promptness of service	Days; percent of responses within target goals
Competitiveness in quality	Performance versus top three competitors
Avoidable changes in engineering drawings, purchase orders, etc.	Percent of all changes
Document quality	Percent of pages defective
Software quality	Errors per 1000 lines of code; cost to correct errors
Invoicing errors	Percent in error; cost of correction
Quality improvement	Project data: undertaken, in progress, completed; results of projects collectively; status of major projects individually; percent of managers assigned to projects
Companywide quality management—progress against strategic quality goals	Various

Control Subjects.   The feedback loop is centered on the control subject. Tables 8.1, 8.2, and 8.3 show that the list of control subjects has been undergoing extensive changes. These changes have demanded that upper managers review performance with respect to certain control subjects which previously had been delegated to lower levels. Some of these control subjects are common to many industries: reliability in the field, time required to provide customer service, time required to place new products on the market, parts per million defective, and cost of poor quality. Other control subjects are unique to specific industries: software quality, maintenance hours per 1000 operating hours, and inspection escapes.

Since all control is built around specific control subjects, the choice of these subjects is the most critical element in the entire control system. If a vital control subject is omitted, the managers will lack a vital instrument on their instrument panel. If an unimportant control subject is included, it will receive undue attention while the attention given to more important matters will be diluted.

Because of continuing change in technology, competition, and other factors, it is necessary periodically to update the list of control subjects—to discard those which have outlived their usefulness and add new subjects which have become more important. One way to carry out such updating is through a multifunctional team. Such a team secures from the upper managers their views and nominations for revision. The consensus of these inputs provides the basis for a revised draft of a battery of executive reports. Following review by upper managers, this draft is revised. The "final" design then becomes the executive report battery until the next such updating several years later.

Alternatively, the work of updating is assigned to some individual (usually the quality manager). This individual then makes the rounds, secures inputs, and so on.

Executive Controls and Operational Controls. Because the total number of control subjects is fantastically large, a hierarchy of controls as depicted in Figure 6.9 (the control pyramid) is used. For discussion, see Section 6, under The Feedback Loop.

Table 8.4 shows how the major elements which make up the control systems apply to both operational and upper-management levels. It is evident that although the two control systems rest largely on a common base, they end up as virtually two separate worlds.

Leading and Lagging Indicators. A further distinction in controls is whether they provide information before, during, or after operations. Operational controls are obviously designed to assist in the conduct of day-to-day operations (Table 8.4).

Executive control reports are regarded as lagging indicators because the reports appear weeks or even months after the operations have been performed. Such reports are nevertheless of great value in showing trends, identifying substantial failures to meet goals, measuring performance of managers, and so forth.

The degree of lag varies considerably. The summarized scrap or rework reports

TABLE 8.4 Operational Quality Controls versus Executive Quality Controls

Element	Application to operational quality controls	Application to executive quality controls
Control subjects	Physical, chemical, specification requirements	Summarized performance for product lines, departments, etc.
Units of measure	Natural physical, chemical (ohms, kilograms, etc.)	Various: money; indexes; ratios (see Tables 8.1 through 8.3)
Sensing devices	Physical instruments, human senses	Summaries of data
Who collects the sensed information	Operators, inspectors, clerks, automated instruments	Various statistical departments
When the sensing is done	During current operations	Days, weeks, or months after current operations
Standards used for comparison	Engineered specifications; specified procedures	History; the market; the plan
Who acts on the information	Servomechanisms, nonsupervisors, first-line supervisors	Managers
Action taken	Process regulation, repair, sorting	Replanning; quality improvement; motivation

may lag only one month behind the day-to-day events. However, warranty charges may lag several months behind the date of manufacture and years behind the date of product development.

In contrast, some executive reports are leading indicators. Market research on quality may lead product development by months. Design review is a leading indicator of failure rates. Product audit lags behind date of manufacture but is a leading indicator of quality as received by the user.

The well-balanced system of executive reports makes use of leading indicators ("early warning signals") as well as summaries which lag behind operations.

Onnias (1986) describes how Texas Instruments, Inc. makes use of leading, concurrent, and lagging indicators in its *Quality Blue Book,* which is the central report on progress in quality.

For elaboration on control subjects, see Juran (1964), chapter 13, "Choosing the Control Subject."

Control Subjects which Lack Units of Measure. Ideally, every process should have generally accepted means for evaluating its quality. However, there are many processes for which such means for evaluation are at best in a primitive state. In such cases it is usually easy enough to nominate control subjects but difficult to reach agreement, and even more difficult to work out suitable units of measure.

Table 8.5 lists some examples of functions along with nominations for evaluations which would be useful to managers. When such nominations are made, the lack of ready agreement on units of measure tends to discourage efforts to proceed further.

Actually, control subjects and units of measure follow an evolutionary path. A control subject is proposed. Ideas for units of measure are brainstormed, and a short list is agreed on. For example, a short list for "worker involvement" might emerge as follows:

Percent of workers who have undergone training in statistical process control

Percent of eligible workers who have achieved a self-inspection status

Percent of workers who are active participants on problem-solving teams

Data systems are then designed to collect the information needed to test out the short list. On the basis of the test results, some units of measure are discarded; others are retained and refined. In due course this process of evolution through experience arrives at units of measure which simply could not have been discovered solely by logical reasoning at the outset.

Units of Measure. There are two basic meanings of the word "quality": (1) product features which provide product satisfaction and (2) freedom from defi-

TABLE 8.5 Nominations for Evaluation of Quality Performance

Functions	Nominations for control subjects
Product development	Producibility of designs; avoidable engineering changes
Manufacturing planning	Process capability of processes provided
	Adequacy of technology transfer
Purchasing	Avoidable purchase orders
Production	Worker involvement in quality

ciencies. (For elaborations, see Section 2, under "Quality" Defined.) Each of these two kinds of quality has its own forms of units of measure.

Freedom from Deficiencies.   This aspect of quality is most often evaluated in the form of a fraction. The numerator is a number which expresses the *frequency* of deficiencies minus the number of defects, demerits, field failures, returns, hours of rework, dollars spent in rework, and so on. The denominator is a number expressing the *opportunity* for deficiencies, e.g., the number of units of product manufactured, units of product in service, dollars of sales, and so on. The resulting fractions take such forms as percent defective, demerits per unit, failure rate, percent returned, warranty dollars per 1000 units in service, and so forth.

Note that the above fractions are all in inverse form—the extent of deficiencies rather than freedom from deficiencies. Sometimes the direct form is used, for example, percent yield rather than percent defective, or percent uptime rather than percent downtime.

Product Features.   For this aspect of quality, there is no convenient universal fraction. Instead, there is an extensive array of technological and related control subjects (diameter, speed, etc.) evaluated in technological units of measure (millimeters, revolutions per minute, etc.) by technological instruments (micrometer, tachometer, etc.) Nevertheless, there is a sort of universal rule which applies to units of measure for product features: the units of measure should include the customers' units of measure. To illustrate, suppliers who sell components to an assembler usually include, as a unit of measure, the time required to attach that component to the customer's assembly. Similarly, suppliers of equipment usually include, as units of measure: percent uptime, maintenance hours per 1000 operating hours and other parameters. Yet another application of this universal rule is seen in cases where the internal merit rating system fails to reflect customers' key units of measure. In some companies, merit ratings for the quality parameter are based on demerits per unit found during product audit. Yet the product may be unsalable because of unacceptable field failure rates.

Summaries of Unlike Units of Measure.   The executive report, which is a summary, usually deals with items which are not homogeneous. In consequence, it is necessary to create new units of measure which permit summary of unlike items. There are several ways of doing this:

1. *Arbitrary weighting:*   For example, defects are classified as to seriousness and each class is assigned a weight (demerits). This makes it possible to use demerits per unit of product as new unit of measure.

2. *Conversion into a common natural unit:*   A well-known example is the use of money as a common measure of scrap, rework, service work, etc., despite wide differences in products and processes. Another example is the concept of "opportunities for failure" used as the denominator of indexes of performance. Wilson (1967) developed a measure in terms of demerits per possible error. Brainard (1974) proposed summations in the form of defects per 100 (labor) hours and defects per $1000 (labor). Some companies use failures per million dollars (of sales) as a universal unit of measure across multiple product lines.

3. *Conversion into statistical equivalents:*   In this approach, the historical performance in natural units is equated to 100 percent (for example). A 10 percent departure from this level becomes a score of 90 percent, regardless of what the natural unit is. This method also permits preparation of composite scores for several performances by weighting.

For elaboration on units of measure, see Juran (1964), Chapter 14, "The Unit of Measure."

Data Collection and Summary. Preparation of executive reports on quality requires a good deal of precise coordination among the data sources in order to:

Standardize terminology such as names of defects, parts, and other names which enter the data system.

Standardize the code numbers which are used to translate this terminology into the language of the computer. See, for example, Noyes (1979).

Standardize the calendar dates for defining time intervals (weeks, months) and for meeting report deadlines.

Agree on the form of delivery of information to minimize the problems of preparation of the final executive reports.

Define the respective responsibilities of all departments associated in this cooperative venture.

It is also important to note the distinction between the deeds and the data (which are only the evidence of the deeds). The realities are the deeds, and the surest control is through personal observation of the deeds: "I don't care what the report says—the bins are empty."

The successive layers of summary and the creation of unnatural units of measure all carry the risk that the data will fail to reflect the deeds because of coloration, statistical quirks, and just plain mistakes. Careful checking and auditing are needed to maintain the full connection between deeds and data.

Data processing has been revolutionized by the computer, with dramatic improvements in accuracy and timeliness of reports. See generally, Section 27, Computers and Quality; see also Munro (1982).

Standards of Comparison. The system of executive reports should provide standards against which to compare performance. In the absence of standards, it is easy for managers to overreact to individual complaints or to other alarm signals.

At the technological level the standards are engineered and are embodied into the material, process, and product specifications. Other engineered standards include material usage and labor usage. Next are the historical standards in which current performance is compared with the past. A further standard is the market, that is, what other people do when faced with similar problems. Competitive performance is the most usual market standard for quality. A fourth standard is the plan, such as the budget, quota, and schedule. The plan is established by human judgment after the other inputs—technology, history, and market—are considered.

The recent growth of competition in quality has broadened the use of competitive standards as a basis for judging product performance. This in turn has intensified efforts to discover what is the level of competitive quality. Sources of competitive data include:

1. Customers who purchase from competing sources. Often they are willing to prepare comparative data, although without identifying competitors.
2. Trade associations who become a database, again preserving anonymity.
3. Independent laboratories who publish comparative test results, often naming the competitors.

4. Government regulatory bodies who publish test results, sometimes naming names.

5. Professional society research studies.

To go beyond these sources requires special studies in the form of marketing research. Some of these can be conducted in the laboratory; others require studies in the field. See Section 12 for elaboration.

History as a standard for comparison has long been popular. The data are available, and the standard is known to be attainable. However, use of an historical standard includes a risk of perpetuating poor performances such as high costs of poor quality or carryover of failure-prone designs. This risk can be reduced by judicious design of audits which look for opportunities and threats as well as conformance to standards. For elaboration, see Section 9, Quality Assurance, under Quality Survey. See also Quality Audit by Upper Managers below.

For a broad discussion of standards of comparison, see Juran (1964), chapter 15, "The Standard."

The Executive Report Battery. The growth of upper-management involvement with quality has demanded creation of a battery of reports specially designed to meet the needs of upper management. This battery of reports is variously called the "executive report battery," "the executive instrument panel," etc. Such special design has been an essential element of CWQM.

Texas Instruments, an electronics manufacturer, has used the *Quality Blue Book* since 1981 as the basis of reports to divisional upper managers. The book was deliberately designed to parallel the company's financial reporting system, down to the color of the cover (blue). The report battery is organized into (1) leading indicators (e.g., quality of purchased components), (2) concurrent indicators (e.g., product test results, process conditions, service to customers), (3) lagging indicators (e.g., data feedback from customers, returns), and (4) data on cost of poor quality.

The report is issued monthly and is the basis for annual performance appraisal for managers' contribution to quality. For elaboration, see Onnias (1986).

General Dynamics Corporation, a defense contractor, undertook a form of corporate quality improvement, starting in the early 1980s. One element of the approach is a report battery. The reports deal with numerous parameters, of which 12 are corporate—they are common to all divisions of the corporation. The corporate parameters are as follows:

Avoidable engineering changes

Deviations/waivers

First-time yield

Scrap (labor-hour content)

Scrap (material value content)

Repair and/or rework (labor-hour content)

On-time delivery by Production

Purchased item acceptability

Service report response time

Material review actions

Inspection escapes

Overtime

For elaboration, see Talley (1986).

In 1981, Florida Power & Light (FPL), a public utility, undertook to develop a form of CWQM. Its executive report battery features over 20 parameters, including:

Operating and maintenance cost per customer

Customers per employee

Overtime percent

Extension costs per new service account

Efficiency

Vehicle utilization

Credit memos per 1000 customers

Public Service Commission inquiries

Work-load factor

Service unavailability

Service interruptions

Under its companywide approach, FPL's corporate goals include broad quality improvement goals. These broad goals are then deployed to lower levels for action by project teams. For elaboration, see Brunetti (1987); for additional information concerning the FPL approach, see McDonald (1987), Walden (1987), and Sterett (1987).

For additional discussion concerning the executive report battery and its use for decision-making, see Juran (1964), chapter 17, "Mobilizing for Decision Making." See also Section 20 under Executive Reports on Field Performance.

Opportunities and Threats. Conventional executive reports are designed neither to disclose opportunities available to the organization nor to identify threats which are converging on the organization. These limitations have long been present in financial reporting and have been carried over into reports on quality. Nevertheless, the opportunities and threats are there. What is lacking in many companies is a positive means for identifying them.

One such means is the audit. It is feasible to design the system of audits to provide for identifying opportunities and threats. See Quality Audits by Upper Managers below; see also Section 9, Quality Assurance, under Quality Surveys.

Format. Executive reports should be designed to read at a glance to permit easy concentration on the exceptional matters requiring executive attention.

Tabulations of data are the most primitive format. Some of these consist of forbidding stacks of pages from a computer printout or from a statistical department. These masses of data are an imposition on busy executives, who are, in effect, being asked to do the summarizing which someone else should have done.

Summarized tabulations are a long step in the right direction. They do not give a perspective in time, but they do tabulate the three essential current figures: standard, actual, and variance. In some companies the significant deficiencies or improvements are marked in a distinctive way to simplify the job of reading the tabulation.

Graphic presentation requires added work by the reporting departments but greatly simplifies interpretation by the executive. Blake (1978) dramatizes this principle by producing a single page containing 18 charts, each of which shows the performance trend for some important aspect of operations.

Recent computer development has also enabled managers to display data and graphics on personal computer terminals. The early applications were generally to aid quality managers and engineers (Clements, 1979). However, the trend may well be to provide upper managers with such facilities (Rockart, 1979).

Another approach to visual display is through a "visibility center." Under this concept a special room is fitted with wall charts which are updated monthly. These charts are then viewed and discussed by convening managers. The same room is also used for ceremonial awards. For details, see Frankovich (1978).

Graphic presentation ideally displays a full perspective with respect to time, as shown in Figure 8.1. Typically, a left-hand segment shows some recent history (e.g., several years) on a condensed time scale. The main part of the graph shows current performance against goals (e.g., on a month-by-month basis). The goals are then extended into the near future to show the anticipated results.

Charting technique has been studied exhaustively and is available in the literature. An excellent early reference availably in some engineering libraries is *Time Series Charts—A Manual of Design and Construction,* American Standard Z15.2-1938. (A photocopy of this out-of-print document may be obtained from Engineering Societies Library, 345 E. 47th St., New York, NY 10017.)

When numerous charts are needed, it is feasible to make use of a standardized format to create a coordinated "executive instrument panel." In the absence of such standardization, the managers are faced with a problem of frequent "tuning in and out" because of the variety of format. As a result, their reviews are delayed and the opportunities for error increased.

Publication.   It is useful to assemble the principal executive reports on quality into a comprehensive package which is published regularly and can eventually earn status as the authoritative source of essential information on quality (i.e., an official executive instrument panel). To reach such status requires years of dedicated reporting using unquestioned objectivity, good format, and careful attention to the needs of the executives who are the users.

Interpretation.   The editor of the executive reports can provide useful illumination of the facts through the inclusion of supplemental information which does the following:

Identifies the vital few quality problems. Preferably, this list does not exceed 10 items.

Reports on the status of major quality programs under way; results achieved, work in progress; what the next move is and who is to take it; and need, if any, for action by upper management.

Summarizes the findings of audits and surveys, whether in-house or of suppliers.

Discusses major developments which are taking place with respect to quality as a result of industry programs, government action, competitor action, consumer organizations, and other outside forces.

Previews proposals which will be presented for upper-management consideration.

The editor of the reports must also take pains to avoid the common errors which lead to loss of confidence in the reports. These include:

Failure to distinguish between important and unimportant issues.

Too many false alarms, resulting from failure to check the alarm signals.

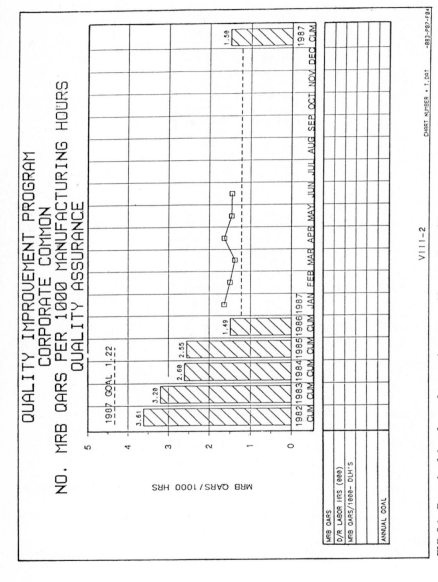

FIG. 8.1 Example of chart format for executive report. *(Courtesy General Dynamics Corp.)*

8.18

An atmosphere of "blame" in the reports, rather than one of constructive search for remedy and improvement.

"Overkill" in its various forms. This is always easier to understand when someone else does it, e.g., government regulators.

A Universal Measure for Quality. In some economies, universal measures have been developed for such social phenomena as gross national product, cost of living, unemployment, and crime. It would obviously be most useful if a corresponding universal measure could be evolved for quality.

As of the 1980s there existed neither such a universal measure for quality nor a generally accepted model which could become the basis for such a universal measure.

For quality in the sense of freedom from deficiencies, a universal measure is theoretically feasible—the model exists. It would require enlarging the accounting systems in order to evaluate how much less the costs would be if there were no deficiencies—in effect, to evaluate the cost of poor quality.

For quality in the sense of product features (which render the product salable), there is no such generally accepted comprehensive model. For certain parameters of this aspect of quality, models do exist (e.g., life cycle costing, product audit based on a system of demerits). However, the parameters are numerous, and many lack models. In addition, efforts to composite the parameters into a single measure requires extensive empirical judgment as to the weights to be assigned to the respective parameters.

Nevertheless, there are forces which press for such comprehensive measures. A growing number of countries have established national awards for quality. The establishment of such awards requires evaluation of the quality performance of companies, as well as their products and the processes they employ. It would be helpful to consumers, many of whom lack technological sophistication, if product quality could be expressed in some simple measure. Many chief executives have urged, "Give me some simple measure for quality, much as I now have for profit or safety."

Qualimetry. Socialist economies have a special need for solving this problem. These economies include a good deal of central planning, and the planners are handicapped in their work if they are unable to quantify so important a factor in the economy as quality. Lacking this quantification, they have greater difficulty in establishing pricing structures for the products, allocating investments for quality, judging what broad programs to undertake, and so on.

Starting in the late 1960s the All-union Research Institute for Standardization of the Soviet Union undertook a project to develop means for evaluating quality. The term "qualimetry" was adopted as a name for the science of evaluating quality (Derbisher, 1971).

Glichev (1985) has summarized the subsequent events under the title "15 Years of Qualimetry: Problems and Prospects." According to Glichev, progress has been made in design of algorithms and models and also in identification of quality parameters. However, practical application has lagged because of various limitations, such as evaluation of sensory qualities, evaluation of long-life parameters, variations in product use and environments, and consumer perceptions.

Future directions appear to involve reliance on market research to secure consumers' evaluations of consumer goods, use of panels of qualified experts to evaluate quality of commercial goods, and computerized data collection and analysis.

Productivity as a Measure. In general terms, productivity is the ratio of output to input, where input consists of labor, material, capital, and services. Methods for evaluation of productivity are in a more advanced state than methods for evaluation of quality. As a result, data on national and industry productivity are widely compiled and published. In turn, the published data are the focus of attention of political leaders, economists, industrial leaders, and others.

To a degree, productivity and quality are interrelated. Projects to reduce cost of poor quality almost invariably improve productivity as well. Attainment of "just-in-time" objectives requires, as a prerequisite, the solution of quality-related problems. However, there are also some important differences. Some of the ingredients of high productivity are not quality-related; some of the ingredients of quality are not productivity-related. The respective planners typically come from different disciplines, for example, industrial engineering as opposed to quality engineering. Improvement of productivity is regarded with suspicion in some quarters as a source of unemployment. In contrast, improvement of quality is universally regarded as a benefit to society.

The overlap between productivity and quality has led to the suggestion that measures of quality be expressed in productivity terms (Midas, 1982). In the judgment of the author, the two measures should be kept separate despite the overlap.

QUALITY AUDITS BY UPPER MANAGERS

Section 9, Quality Assurance, deals extensively with three major forms of quality assurance: quality audits, quality surveys, and product audits. Those forms of quality assurance are typically carried out by full-time quality auditors, sometimes supplemented by middle managers. (The summarized findings are often reviewed at higher levels as well.)

The present topic, quality audits by upper managers, deals with special forms of quality audit in which the upper managers personally participate in conduct of the audits.

Why Quality Audits by Upper Managers? In general, such audits are not undertaken as isolated activities. Instead, they are part of a broader effort to improve performance with respect to quality. The stimulus for such broader effort may come from a threat, such as loss of sales due to lack of quality competitiveness in the marketplace. Alternatively, the stimulus may come from the urge to gain quality leadership and the associated benefits.

The earliest widespread use of such audits was in Japan. Shortly after World War II, many Japanese companies had difficulty selling their goods to the West. A major reason was poor quality. To make matters worse, the long-standing perception of the West had been that Japanese goods were chronically poor. To render the goods salable and to reverse the national quality reputation demanded changes of a revolutionary nature—changes which could be accomplished only through the personal leadership of upper managers. One element of that personal leadership was quality audits conducted by upper managers.

Several decades later, many companies in the West also faced a need for making revolutionary changes in their approach to quality. The needed changes were not merely a matter of improving conformance to policies and goals; what was needed most was revision in policies and goals—revisions in areas which required decisions by upper managers.

The upper managers were then faced with (1) determining what changes were needed, (2) ordering these changes to be made, and (3) assuring that the changes went into effect and remained in effect.

In simplified form, the resulting upper-management participation is as follows:

	Subordinate managers and below	Upper managers
Establish revised policies, goals, plans	X	X
Carry out the plans; meet the goals	X	
Audit		X

The audit is in part a review of results versus goals. However, the personal participation of the upper managers establishes direct contact with various personnel and direct exposure to various realities. These contacts and exposures provide the upper managers with additional vital inputs for decision-making—inputs which are not found in reports of performance versus goals.

Ishikawa (1987) lists the following as benefits of upper-management quality audits when led by the president:

Increased understanding by the president of the state of affairs

Greater objectivity of information coming to the president

Improved human relations with subordinates

Greater stimulus to subordinates through personal participation by the president

Subject Matter of Upper-Management Audits. A useful preview of the emerging content of such audits is provided by the Japanese experience during the decades since World War II. For example, Komatsu Ltd., a manufacturer of construction equipment, conducts audits which serve also as the basis for quality awards to subsidiaries, subcontractors, distributors, and dealers. Figure 8.2 lists the subject matter of these audits along with the weights assigned. For elaboration, see Shimoyamada (1987).

An additional preview is provided by the list of criteria used for awarding the Deming Application Prize in Japan. (The first award was in 1951.) The parameters include:

Policies and objectives

Organization and its operation

Education and its dissemination

Information flow and utilization

Product and process quality

Standardization

Control and management

Quality assurance of functions, systems, and methods

Results

Future plans

For elaboration, see Ishikawa (1987).

Classification / Evaluation item	Domestic Subsidiaries		Subcontractors	Distributors	Dealers
	Production and sales	Mainly sales			
1	Company policy and overall control system	30	30	30	30	30
2	Quality assurance	30	30	30	30	30
3	Product development and technical development	20	20	(30)		
4	Cost control	20		30		
5	Delivery control	10		10		
6	Sales control	20	40		40	30
7	Training, safety, and environment	10	10	10	10	10
8	Priority execution items			30		
	Total	140	130	140 (170)	110	100
	Eagerness and understanding of top management	100		100	100	100

FIG. 8.2 Example of subject matter and weights used in upper management audits. *Note:* Numbers show weights assigned; parentheses around numbers indicate they are for specialized manufacturers only.

The preceding lists are generally applicable to companies in developed countries and, to a degree, to all companies. For companies whose quality revolution is still young, special emphasis is warranted with respect to (1) the functional processes and (2) opportunities and threats.

Functional Processes. These include the processes which determine the quality contributions of such major functions as product development, purchasing, and marketing. They also include numerous business processes of a multifunctional nature, such as launching new products, filling customers' orders, and preparing invoices.

For the major functions, the broad responsibility is clear, but there are inherent weaknesses. For example, in such functions the quality planning has traditionally been done by functional experts who lack expertise in the quality function. It is feasible for the audits to find ways to help overcome such weaknesses. For examples of questions to be raised, see Section 9, Quality Assurance, under Questions for Quality Surveys; Functional Areas.

In the case of multifunctional processes, a major weakness is lack of "ownership." For each step in such processes, there is clear responsibility. However, there is no such clear responsibility for the overall process; the process is supervised by some impersonal procedure or manual which tends to remain static and to acquire inflexibility. Audits by upper managers offer an additional avenue for dealing with weaknesses in such processes.

Opportunities. A major emphasis of the upper-management audit should be on quality improvement. In most companies the pace of creating new quality problems has for years exceeded the pace of solution. The result has been an increasing accumulation of chronic problems which are seriously counterproductive to operations. It takes a determined effort, guided by upper management, to reverse this trend. (See Section 22, Quality Improvement, for details of the improvement process.) A key element is to estimate the cost of poor quality.

Where such accumulation has been continuing for years, it takes years to eliminate it. Nothing short of personal intervention by upper management can supply the necessary leadership. The concept of CWQM includes provision for annual quality improvement. See Section 6, Companywide Quality management; see also Brunetti (1987).

"Opportunities" include the various management movements which are continually emerging over the horizon. Some of these are meritorious; others are cults, or worse. It is sometimes difficult at the outset to tell which is which. One solution is to conduct a tryout at some test site to determine whether the concept has useful application in the company.

Threats.   Threats are a leading indicator of trouble ahead. The upper-management audit should include looking ahead in various directions, such as demographic trends, emerging social forces, trends in legislation, and trends in the marketplace.

Threats can also be internal. A new product under development can, because of lack of early warnings, threaten to create problems for those who will be required to produce the design, or to maintain it. Lack of employee participation may fester into human relations problems. Such internal threats can seldom be sensed from conventional reports. They require personal exposure to the realities.

The Social Responsibility Audit.   "Social responsibility" is a broad term relating to the impact of business on society generally. Widely publicized examples include product safety and damage to the environment, but there are many other impacts as well.

Some of the problems created by such impacts came to a head during the 1960s and spawned new legislation relative to environmental protection, product safety, consumerism, and other issues. In addition, there emerged the concept of a special "social responsibility audit" as an early warning device to assist upper managers in their strategic business planning (see, e.g., Humble, 1973).

A quality audit by upper managers necessarily has some overlap with the concept of a social responsibility audit. The design of the quality audit should consider the degree to which it should extend into the area of social responsibility.

Organization for Quality Audits by Upper Managers.   Normally a quality audit by upper managers is part of a broader effort to improve quality performance. Usually a high-level quality council (committee, etc.) has been created to guide the broad effort. Members of this council typically conduct the audits.

Upper-management audits are preceded by collection and analysis of information pertinent to the subject matter of the audits. This preparatory work is done by subordinate managers in collaboration with staff personnel. The frequency is semiannual or annual. For examples, see Shimoyamada (1987) and Brunetti (1987); see also section 35F, Quality in Japan, under Internal QC Audit by Top Management.

The President's Quality Audit.   In some major Japanese companies the president personally participates in the audit. In such cases it is called "the president's quality audit." For a description of the workings of the president's quality audit, see Section 35F, Quality in Japan, under Internal QC Audit by Top Management; see also Shimoyamada (1987) and Ishikawa (1987).

Third-Party Audits.   Some types of quality audit are subcontracted to third parties for various reasons, such as expertise, economy, and independence. Usually such subcontracting must be authorized by upper managers. In turn, the resulting reports are reviewed by upper managers.

The concept of third-party audits is in wide use. An extensive form is independent test laboratories. Previously these laboratories provided only testing services for goods; some of them now provide auditing services as well. For a discussion of the rationale for this, see Rennie, Morris, and Blackburn (1978).

The growth of the field has attracted other sources of such audits. Standardization bodies in some countries have increasingly organized to provide such services.

An important consideration in employing such services is the independence of the third party. In some cases this independence is the major consideration. (The Deming Application Prize is awarded by an independent committee of experts.)

TRAINING FOR UPPER MANAGERS

A company can undertake a major revision in managing for quality only if its upper managers are trained in the design and supervision of such an undertaking. The needed training is derived from multiple sources, including:

Training "by the book," i.e., through courses and seminars. See, generally, Section 11, Training for Quality, especially under Training for Various Categories of Personnel; Upper Management.

Membership on the quality council. Such membership requires upper managers to address many of the problems faced by the company relative to managing for quality.

Membership on quality audit teams. Such membership brings upper managers into direct contact with many subordinates and the realities faced by them.

REFERENCES

Blake, Geroge B. (1978). "Ideas for Action." *Harvard Business Review,* March-April, pp. 6–8, 12.

Brainard, E. H. (1974). "Quality Measurement and Reporting as Related to Management Cybernetics." *ASQC Technical Conference Transactions,* Milwaukee, pp. 208–217.

Brunetti, Wayne (1987). "Policy Deployment—A Corporate Roadman." *The Juran Report,* No. 8, pp. 20–29.

Clements, John A. (1979). "Interactive Graphics in New Product Quality Assurance Programs." *Quality Progress,* February, pp. 14–16; abstract, Executive Sciences Institute, 1980, pp. 61–62.

Derbisher, A. (1971). "Qualimetry—A New Scientific Discipline." Abstract, Executive Sciences Institute, pp. 939–940.

Frankovich, Jim (1978). "Quality Awareness." *Quality Progress,* vol. 11, no. 2, February, pp. 22–24.

Gibson, Thomas C. (1987). "Looking Back on Three Years of QI." *The Juran Report,* No. 8, pp. 43–49.

Glichev, A. V. (1985). "15 Years of Qualimetry. Problems and Prospects." *Proceedings, EOQC Conference Quality & Development,* vol. 2, pp. 259–269.

Humble, John (1973). *Social Responsibility Audit.* AMACOM, A Division of American Management Associations, New York.

Ishikawa, Kaoru (1987). "The Quality Control Audit." *Quality Progress,* January, pp. 39–41.

Juran, J. M. (1964). *Managerial Breakthrough.* McGraw-Hill, New York.

Juran, J. M. (1973). "The Taylor System and Quality Control." A series of articles in *Quality Progress,* May through December 1973 (listed under "Management Interface").

McDonald, Marshall (1987). "Why FPL Pursued Quality Improvement." *The Juran Report,* No. 8, pp. 17–19.

Midas, Michael, Jr. (1982). "A Measure." *Quality,* August, pp. Q9–Q10.

Munro, Bruce (1982). "The Quality Information System." *ASQC Quality Congress Transactions,* Milwaukee, pp. 327–334.

Noyes, Richard J. (1979). "Quality Measurement System." *ASQC Technical Conference Transactions,* Milwaukee, pp. 434–437.

Onnias, Arturo (1986). *"The Quality Blue Book." The Juran Report,* No. 6, pp. 127–131.

Rennie, D., Morris, W., and Blackburn, K. (1978). "Quality Assurance: The Modern Concept of the Third Party Inspection." *International Conference on Quality Control.* Japanese Union of Scientists and Engineers, Tokyo, pp. C1-27 through C1-32.

Rockart, John F. (1979). "Chief Executives Define Their Own Data Needs." *Harvard Business Review,* March-April, pp. 81–93.

Shimoyamada, Kaoru (1987). "The President's Audit: QC Audits at Komatsu." *Quality Progress,* January, pp. 44–49.

Sterett, W. Kent (1987). "Commitment and Involvement: Vital Components in a Successful Quality Improvement Program." *The Juran Report,* No. 8, pp. 35–37.

Talley, D. J. (1986). "The Quest for Sustaining Quality Improvement." *The Juran Report,* No. 6, pp. 188–192.

Walden, James C. (1987). "Integrating Customer Satisfaction into Daily Work." *The Juran Report,* No. 8, pp. 30–34.

Wilson, Myron F. (1967). "The Quality Your Customer Sees." *ASQC Journal of the Electronics Division,* July, pp. 3–16.

SECTION 9
QUALITY ASSURANCE[1]

Frank M. Gryna

---

[1] In the Third Edition, material on quality assurance was prepared by J. M. Juran.

INTRODUCTION

In this handbook, "quality assurance" is the activity of providing the evidence needed to establish confidence, among all concerned, that the quality function is being effectively performed.

While such is the meaning given in this handbook, the term "quality assurance" has other meanings as well. Confusion regarding this important term can lead to serious misunderstandings. For example, the capitalized term "Quality Assurance" often means the title of a broad-based department which is concerned with many quality-related activities, such as quality planning, quality control, quality improvement, quality audit, and reliability.

This section discusses three forms of companywide quality assurance: quality audits, quality surveys, and product audit. Additional forms of assurance are performed within functional departments. Table 9.1 lists some important departmental assurance activities. Additional examples of assurance can be found in the industry sections of this handbook (see Sections 28 and 29, under The Control Plan; Section 30, under Audit Plan; Section 31, under Critical Tasks; and Section 33, under Quality Audits; see also Section 5, under Quality Policies for Functions; Quality Assurance, and Section 17, under Audit of Production Quality).

Concept of Quality Assurance.   Quality assurance provides protection against quality problems through early warnings of trouble ahead. Such early warnings play an important role in the prevention of both internal and external problems. The assurance is provided from objective evidence, but the type of evidence differs widely according to the persons requiring the assurance and the nature of the product.

For natural products, quality assurance is attained through direct sensory examination of the product—for example, freshness of vegetables in the village marketplace. For manufactured products of a simple, short-lived nature, the sensory evidence must usually be supplemented by laboratory testing. Those who lack test facilities must rely on the word of the manufacturer or on feedback from use testing.

For longer-life products, more elaborate testing (environmental, life) is needed, but most merchants and users lack such test facilities. Hence they must secure their added assurance from such forms as the manufacturer's quality reputation, tests by independent laboratories, or warranties.

For complex products, even data obtained from sophisticated environmental and life tests do not provide full quality assurance, since they fail to guard against inadequate product designs, process designs, and quality planning. They also fail to deal with those aspects of quality performance which show up after final testing (e.g., packing, transport, storage, usage, and maintenance).

To meet these added needs for quality assurance, the manufacturer must not only produce the product but also prepare and make available to the customer the proof that the product is fit for use.

In complex products this proof usually consists of:

1. A formal plan which spells out, for all phases of product progression "from cradle to grave," how fitness for use will be achieved

2. A system of reviews to verify that the plan, if followed, will result in fitness for use

3. A system of audits to verify that the plans are actually being followed

4. A system to provide data on the quality achieved

TABLE 9.1   Examples of Departmental Assurance Activities

Department/assurance activity	Reference pages
Marketing	
Product evaluation by a test market	19.8
Controlled use of product	12.11
Product monitoring	12.11
Captive service activity	12.11
Special surveys	12.12
Competitive evaluations	12.17
Product development	
Design review	13.7
Reliability analysis	13.21
Maintainability analysis	13.43
Safety analysis	13.50
Human factors analysis	13.55
Manufacturing, inspection, and transportation analysis	16.5
Value engineering	13.63
Self-control analysis	13.70
Supplier relations	
Qualification of supplier design	15.12
Qualification of supplier process	15.13
Evaluation of initial samples	15.25
Evaluation of first shipments	15.26
Production	
Design review	16.5
Process capability analysis	16.25
Preproduction trials	16.41
Preproduction runs	16.42
Failure mode, effect, and criticality analysis for processes	16.42
Review of manufacturing planning (checklist)	16.44
Evaluation of proposed process control tools	16.50
Self-control analysis	17.4
Audit of production quality	17.26
Inspection and test	
Interlaboratory tests	18.69
Measuring inspector accuracy	18.94
Customer service	
Audit of packaging, transportation, and storage	20.2
Evaluation of maintenance services	20.10

The foregoing concept has some similarity to the concept of the financial audit, which provides assurance of financial integrity by establishing, through "independent" audit, that the plan of accounting is (1) such that, if followed, it will correctly reflect the financial condition of the company and (2) actually being followed. Today independent financial auditors (certified public accountants) have become an influential force in the field of finance.

The deeds used to provide the evidence for quality assurance masquerade under a variety of names such as "audit," "survey," "surveillance," and "assessment." In the topics which follow, these deeds and their definitions are discussed in detail.

Quality Audit: General.   A quality audit is an independent review conducted to compare some aspect of quality performance with a standard for that performance. The term "independent" is critical and is used in the sense that the reviewer (called the "auditor") is neither the person responsible for the performance under review nor the immediate supervisor of that person. An independent audit provides an unbiased picture of performance.

Quality audits are used mainly by companies to evaluate their own quality performance and the performance of their suppliers, licensees, agents, and others and by regulatory agencies to evaluate the performance of organizations which they are assigned to regulate.

The usual purposes of quality audits are to provide independent assurance that:

Plans for attaining quality are such that, if followed, the intended quality will, in fact, be attained

Products are fit for use and safe for the user

Laws and regulations are being followed

There is conformance to specifications

Procedures are adequate and are being followed

The data system provides accurate and adequate information on quality to all concerned

Deficiencies are identified and corrective action is taken

Opportunities for improvement are identified and the appropriate personnel alerted

Farrow (1987) explains how audits also assist in management decision making, allocation of resources, and improving morale.

The subject matter of quality audits extends across the entire spectrum of the quality function, but the bulk of auditing is performed under several well-established categories:

1. *Audits of policies and objectives:*   This review is conducted at the highest level of company operations and hence is normally done by upper management.

2. *Audit of performance against company objectives:*   Because company objectives are quite broad, this review is also conducted by upper management and is based largely on the data presented by the executive reports on quality.

3. *Audits of plans, systems, and procedures:*   These measures are reviewed to judge their adequacy for enabling the company to meet its quality policies and objectives. This includes audits of computerized systems to detect errors in computer programs. Willborn (1987) discusses the effects of computerization on auditing.

4. *Audit of execution:*   This audit is conducted to determine whether execution follows the plans, systems, and procedures. The term "quality system audit" is often used in contrast to "product audit" described below.

5. *Product audit:*   This audit is conducted to determine whether the product meets specifications and the needs of fitness for use.

Audit categories 1 and 2 are discussed in Section 8, under Quality Audit by Upper Managers. Categories 3, 4, and 5 are discussed below.

Plum (1987) discusses an 11-week implementation plan for an audit program. Ishikawa (1987) identifies four categories of audit by "outsiders" and four categories of audit "from within." Sayle (1981) provides additional detail on many of the steps covered below on conducting audits.

AUDIT OF QUALITY PLANS

The term "audit of quality plans" refers to review of the entire family of elements of quality planning to judge their adequacy for meeting the quality mission of the company. The more complex the product, the greater the need to review the quality plans, systems, procedures, and other measures to judge their adequacy.

Subject Matter. The scope of these audits covers a wide range: all functions affecting quality, a single function (e.g., product development), a broad process (e.g., handling of complaints), or a single activity (e.g., calibration of measuring equipment). Since quality-related activities are numerous, priorities must be determined.

Priorities should emphasize (1) activities impacting on fitness for use and/or contractual requirements and then (2) activities which affect the cost of poor quality. In setting priorities, attention should focus on the opportunity for improvement versus the cost of performing the audit. Thus, as audits identify and help to correct a problem, audit resources should be switched to other areas, or the frequency of audit for the improved areas should be reduced.

Defining clearly just what is the subject matter of specific audits is usually done by:

1. *Identifying the broad areas of quality activity:* Kane (1984) discusses an example which identifies 23 elements (see Table 9.2) for auditing at a manufacturer of refrigeration equipment.

2. *Establishing, for each chosen subject, a detailed checklist of the features to be studied and the questions to be raised:* Checklists benefit both the auditor and auditee (see Sayle, 1981, chapter 8).

TABLE 9.2 Quality Program Requirements

1. Quality policy	13. Purchases and subcontracts
2. Organization	14. Manufacturing activities
3. Quality program documentation	15. Material identification and control
4. Personnel selection and qualification	16. Examination, inspection, and test
5. Document control	17. Nonconformances
6. Measuring and test equipment	18. Special processes
7. Records	19. Handling, storage, and shipping
8. Performance feedback	20. Deliverable software
9. Quality costs	21. Installation and service
10. Corrective action	22. Audits
11. Marketing activities	23. Performance improvement
12. Design assurance	

Source: Kane, 1984, p. 264.

Many checklists have been published and are available in the literature. Hayes and Romig (1977) provide samples of checklists for 10 broad activities. For example, a checklist for "Fabrication" lists 21 elements to be audited, with audit items listed for each element. Element 3, under "Fabrication," is "Adequacy of fabrication work instruction or traveler that denotes and details the job." Recommended items to be audited for this one element are as follows: (1) the function to be performed; (2) sequence of operations; (3) inspection points; (4) setups, equipment, and tools; (5) speeds, feeds, and processes; (6) drawing numbers and revisions; (7) sketches and working drawings; (8) specifications; and (9) raw material, type and size.

Checklists based on the concept of self-control can also be useful (see Section 13, under Concept of Self-Control in Product Development, and Section 17, under Concept of Controllability). Each company, however, should prepare its own checklists.

Reference Standards for Auditing.   Audit of quality plans requires reference standards against which to judge the adequacy of the plans. (Failing this, the audit becomes heavily subjective.) The reference standards normally available include:

The written policies of the company as they apply to quality

The stated objectives in the budgets, programs, contracts, etc.

The customer and company quality specifications

The pertinent government specifications and handbooks

The company, industry, and other pertinent quality standards on product, processes, and computer software

The published guides for conduct of quality audits

The pertinent quality departmental instructions

The general literature on auditing

AUDIT OF EXECUTION VERSUS PLANS

This form of audit is for the purpose of determining whether the conduct of operations is in accordance with the plans, procedures, specifications, and so on. The activities reviewed may be broad (control and improvement of quality costs, response to quality alarm signals) or highly specific (calibration of measuring instruments, documentation of engineering changes).

Audit of execution versus plans reveals a wide variety of activities that are deficient in execution. Some of the more common ones are:

Feedback of inspection data to operating personnel is inadequate.

Quality cost data are not collected.

Chronic quality problems are not identified and pursued.

Obsolete specification documents are used during manufacturing.

Inadequate quality requirements are included in specifications to suppliers.

Test equipments with expired calibration dates are in use.

Detailed process instructions or inspection instructions are inadequate or nonexistent.

Personnel are performing critical operations without being certified in those operations.

In cases where supplier relations are conducted under a plan of assurance rather than incoming inspection, the review of execution versus plan is used widely; this review is often called "surveillance." The customer's representative is extensively engaged in assuring that the supplier is following the agreed-on plan (see Section 15, under Supplier Surveillance).

An important stimulus to audit of execution versus plan has been the growing extent of government regulation of products. As the regulatory agencies gain experience, they turn to the concept of audit as a means of covering maximum ground with the available personnel. When these audits turn up discrepancies which create unwelcome attention and publicity for the companies, the companies respond, in part, by creating or strengthening their own audits (self-audits). A striking illustration of the scope of government audits is the concept of "prudence" audits applied in the utility industry. These audits are retrospective reviews of the decisions, actions, and events involved in the creation of nuclear power plants. From these reviews, state utility commissions have disallowed hundreds of millions of dollars of plant investment from utility rate bases (Charnoff, 1986).

PLANNING AND PERFORMING AUDITS

ANSI/ASQC (1986) identify the main steps in performing audits as initiation, planning, implementation, reporting, and completion. A flowchart describing these steps is shown in Figure 9.1 (adapted from ANSI/ASQC, 1986, pp. 9–13). [Wilborn (1983) abstracts and summarizes existing standards and guidelines for auditing.]

Audit Initiation.   The basic right to conduct audits is derived from the "charter" which has been approved by upper management, following participation by all concerned.

A specific audit is initiated by the manager of the activity to be audited either by request or through approval of a program of audits. It is preferable that an audit be conducted only on request of the manager of the activity.

Audit Planning.   An audit plan should be prepared to inform the manager of the activity being audited and the participating auditors regarding the details of the impending audit. Vital elements of the plan include a definition of the scope and objectives of the audit, identification of the area to be audited, identification of the auditor(s), a schedule including the expected start and completion time for the audit, reference to any relevant standards or procedures, and audit documentation.

Several areas of audit planning warrant highlighting here.

Scheduling.   Most auditing is done on a scheduled basis. This enables all concerned to organize workloads, assign personnel, and conduct other necessary activities in an orderly manner. It also minimizes the irritations that are inevitable when auditors are unannounced. (There are, however, some situations, e.g., bank audits, where the need to avoid "coverup" may require surprise audits.)

Areas to be Audited.   The amount of execution of plans is simply enormous, and priorities must be determined (see above, under Audit of Quality Plans). Conse-

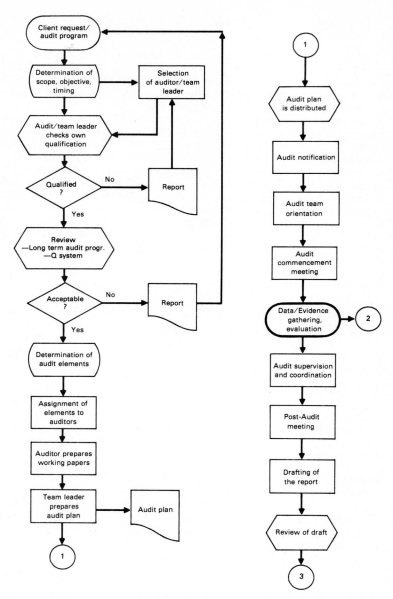

FIG. 9.1 Flow chart for quality audit. *(Adapted from ANSI/ASQC, 1986, pp. 9–13.)*

FIG. 9.1 (*Continued*)

quently, the audit of execution must be based on sampling; even the choice of sampling methods turns out to be an intricate problem. (In contrast, the "sampling" for audit of plans is fairly simple. Plans change slowly, so that periodic audits, even every 2 or 3 years, are adequate.)

In one large electronics company the audit of divisional practice (conducted by corporate staff auditors) employs a plan of sampling based on selected combinations of (1) the product lines made by the company, (2) the functional activities engaged in (e.g., design, production), and (3) the subject matter within these products and activities (e.g., instrument accuracy, recordkeeping).

This sampling approach replaced the former approach of auditing a specific product line within a specific division and reporting the results with recommendations for action (Purcell, 1968).

Another form of audit sampling is by product control centers. In this approach a group of related product control stations is regarded as a center for sampling purposes. Each month or so a sample of about 100 decisions is chosen at random and checked for adequacy. On the basis of the findings, the center is allowed to proceed, the sample is extended, or a product audit is instituted.

Documentation.   The necessary "working papers" for the audit should be identified and/or created. These are all the documents required for an effective audit, including flowcharts, checklists, the auditing approach, forms for reporting observations, and results of previous audits.

Objectivity.   The auditor is expected to be objective. Where objective standards are available, there is less need for the auditor to make a subjective judgment and thereby less opportunity for wide differences of opinion. Provision should be made, however, for challenge of the standard itself.

Discovery of Causes.   In many companies the auditor is expected to investigate major deficiencies in an effort to determine the cause. This investigation then becomes the basis for the auditor's recommendation. In other companies the auditor is expected to leave such investigations to the line people; the auditor's recommendations will include proposals that such investigations be made.

Competence of Auditors.   The basic education and experience of the auditors should be sufficient to enable them to learn in short order the technological aspects of the operations they are to audit. Lacking this background, they will be unable to earn the respect of the operations personnel. In addition, they should receive special training in the human relations aspects of auditing. In 1987 the American Society for Quality Control embarked on a program for the certification of quality auditors. Stenecker (1982) discusses the elements of certification.

Audit Implementation.   The heart of this phase is the collection, analysis, and evaluation of factual information and the drawing of conclusions from these facts. Sayle (1981, chapter 6) proposes that four elements be covered in auditing an activity: (1) person, (2) item, (3) equipment, and (4) documentation.

In making observations, it is important to include a representative sample; for instance, if several shifts are involved, all operating shifts should be at least partially audited.

The information collected in practice consists of a combination of both documented evidence and information obtained through interviews of various personnel.

As a guide, the audit information collected is considered sufficient when it can be seen that the analysis of the evidence by some other qualified person who had not collected the information would reach essentially the same conclusions.

Human Relations.   In theory, the audit is a sort of instrument plugged into the operations to secure an independent source of information. Where it is a physical instrument (e.g., the propeller speed indicator on the bridge of a ship), there is no problem of clash of personalities. Auditors, however, are human beings, and in practice, their relationships with those whose work is audited can become quite prickly. Deficiencies revealed by the audit may be resented because of the implied criticism. Recommendations in the audit may be resented as an invasion of responsibilities. In the reverse direction, auditors may regard slow responses to requests for information as a form of grudging collaboration. These realities warrant extensive discusison and, in addition, indoctrination of both auditors and auditees with respect to the following:

1. *The reasons behind the audits:*   These reasons may have been well discussed with the managers. There is also need to explain to the supervisors and non-supervisors the "why" of the audits. (It is not sufficient to explain that upper management wants audits.) It can be made clear that the managers, customers, regulators, and others concerned likewise require assurance. Ideally, the manager of the activity being audited should be the one who explains the purposes of the audit to the subordinates engaged in the activity.

2. *Avoiding an atmosphere of blame:*   A sure way to cause deterioration of human relations is to look for whom to blame rather than how to achieve improvement. Line managers as well as auditors can fall into this trap. An atmosphere of blame not only breeds resentment; it dries up the sources of information. The audit reports and recommendations should be problem-oriented rather than person-oriented.

There are other advantages to being sensitive to the human relationships involved in auditing. For example, it is useful for the supervisor in an area being audited to accompany the auditor during the audit. This helps to eliminate arguments later as to what was really observed during an audit. For audits running several days or longer, interim reviews of the audit with the auditees are helpful to show the information that has been gathered and what conclusions are being drawn, at least in a preliminary manner. This provides an opportunity to test some of those conclusions.

A self-audit and an independent audit can be combined to provide a "two-tier" audit. Goldstein (1983) describes how the two audits each have an audit plan, execution, and report. The advantages include using the expertise of the person responsible for the function, assuring objectivity with an independent auditor, and minimizing some of the human relationship issues.

The aim of both the self-audit and the independent audit is to build an atmosphere of trust based on the prior reputation of the auditors, the approach used during the audit, and the emphasis on being helpful to the activity audited. Even such small matters as the title of the audit process should be carefully considered. Occasionally people try to avoid the use of the term "audit" when, indeed, what will be done *is* an observation and evaluation. Also, audits may be hidden as part of a company education program. Such subterfuges detract from the trust that must be developed in order for audits to be effective and useful to all concerned.

Burr (1987) provides specific suggestions on overcoming resistance to audits. Sayle (1981, chapter 14) identifies 25 "tactics" to guide auditors in behavioral matters.

Post-Audit Meeting.   An important part of the implementation phase is the post-audit meeting that is held with the manager of the audited activity. At this meeting the audit observations are presented so that the manager can plan for corrective action. In addition, the manager can point out to the auditor any mistakes with respect to the facts that have been collected.

Audit Reporting.   Audit results should be documented in a report and a draft should be reviewed (preferably at the post-audit meeting) with the management of the activity that was audited. The report may be jointly issued by the auditor and auditee. For a report to be viewed as credible, it should be balanced in perspective and be depersonalized.

Balance in Reporting.   An audit which reports only deficiencies may be factual as far as it goes. Yet it will be resented, because nothing is said about the far greater number of elements of performance which are well done. Some companies require the auditors to begin their reports with "commendable observations." Others have evolved overall summaries or ratings which consider not only deficiencies but also the opportunities for deficiencies (see below, under Units of Measure).

One serious and common criticism of audit reports is the tendency for the report to emphasize deficiencies that are minor in nature (at least in the opinions of those who were audited). For audits to be viewed as useful and constructive, the relative importance of the deficiencies reported should be analyzed. Such an analysis must be based on determining what the impact of the deficiency is on other activities (see below, under Seriousness Classification).

Depersonalizing the Report.   In many companies auditors derive much influence from the fact that their reports are reviewed by upper management. Auditing departments should be careful to avoid misusing this influence. The ideal is to depersonalize the reports and recommendations. The real basis of the recommendations should be the facts rather than the opinion of the auditor. (Some auditors follow a practice of noting in the report when a statement is an impression or opinion, without a factual basis.) Where there is room for a difference of opinion, auditors have the right and the duty to offer their opinions as an input to the decision-making process. However, any position of undue advocacy should be avoided, as this tends to reduce the auditor's credibility as an objective observer. (The ultimate responsibility for results rests on the line managers, not on the auditors.) A practice commonly followed to help to depersonalize is to omit the names of any individuals involved, and instead to report the facts on the situation.

The report should include the following items:

Purpose and scope of the audit.

Details of the audit plan, including audit personnel, dates, the activity that was audited (personnel contacted, material reviewed, number of observations made, etc.). Details should be placed in an appendix.

Standards, checklist, or other reference documents that were used during the audit.

Audit observations, including supporting evidence, conclusions, and recommendations.

Recommendations for improvement opportunities.

Recommendations for followup on the corrective action that is to be proposed and implemented by line management, along with subsequent audits if necessary.

Distribution list for the audit report.

Summarizing Audit Data.　In an audit most elements of performance are found to be adequate, while some are found to be discrepant. Reporting of these findings requires two different levels of communication:

1. Reports of each discrepancy to secure corrective action. These reports are made promptly to the responsible operating personnel, with copies to some of the managerial levels.
2. A report of the overall status of the subject matter under review. To meet these requirements, the report should:
   a. Evaluate overall quality peformance in ways which provide answers to the major questions raised by upper managers—for instance: Is the product safe? Are we complying with legal requirements? Is the product fit for use? Is the product marketable? Is the performance of the department under review adequate?
   b. Provide evaluations of the status of the major subdivisions of the overall performance—the quality systems and subsystems, the divisions, the plants, the procedures, etc.
   c. Provide some estimate of the frequency of discrepancies in relation to the number of opportunities for discrepancies (see below, under Units of Measure).
   d. Provide some estimate of the trend of this ratio (of discrepancies found to discrepancies possible) and of the effectiveness of programs to control the frequency of occurrence of discrepancies.

Seriousness Classification.　Some of the audit programs make use of seriousness classification of discrepancies. This is quite common in the case of product audits, where defects found are classified in terms such as critical, major, and minor, each with some "weight" in the form of demerits. These systems of seriousness classification are highly standardized (see Section 18, under Seriousness Classification).

Some audit programs also apply seriousness classification to discrepancies found in planning, in procedures, in decision making, data recording, and so on. The approach parallels that used for product audits. Definitions are established for such terms as "serious," "major," and "minor"; demerit values are assigned; and total demerits are computed (see, e.g., Thresh, 1984, pp. 3–18).

Units of Measure.　For audits of plans, procedures, documentation, and so forth, it is desirable to compare the discrepancies found against some estimate of the opportunities for discrepancies. Some companies provide for this by an actual count of the opportunities, such as the number of criteria or check points called out by the plans and procedures. Another form is to count the discrepancies per audit with a correction factor based on the length of time consumed by the audit. The obvious reason is that more time spent in auditing means more ground covered and more discrepancies found.

Report Publication.　Agreement is reached on report format, responsibility for editing, lists of which managers are to receive what reports, and so on. In some organizations, the report is given only to the manager of the activity that was audited. A followup audit (on progress) can be distributed to upper management. Design of the audit reports is often modular to permit selective distribution. The report should be issued as soon as possible, but no later than 1 month after the post-audit meeting.

Audit Completion. The audit is completed when the report is submitted to the client, except in those circumstances when the verification of corrective action is to be part of the audit assignment and plan.

Responsibility for Corrective Action. Auditors are commonly told to avoid becoming involved in designing remedies and making them effective. Operations managers are required to respond in writing as to what they plan to do with respect to discrepancies found or recommendations made. (Operations managers are not obligated to follow the recommendations. They may conclude not to follow them, in which case they must state why not.) This formality helps to assure that quality audits have a high priority of managerial attention. Auditors are expected to follow up recommendations to assure that some action is taken; thus the recommendation is accepted or is considered and then rejected.

A special situation exists when an auditor documents the symptom of a problem but is unable, during the audit, to identify the cause. Here, the audit report should be directed to the manager of the audited activity even though the underlying cause may rest within that activity or be elsewhere. The report should state steps required to determine the underlying causes.

When deficiencies reported in an audit are serious, the auditor may recommend that a subsequent audit be held to assure that the necessary corrective action has been taken.

Finally, a wrap-up of the audit involves deciding which records from the audit should be retained, for what period of time, and how access should be provided to authorized personnel who need to review such audit documents.

Quality Assurance of Audits. The audit process itself can benefit from the concept of quality assurance. Evaluation of a sample of audits can include examination of the competence and training of auditors, maintenance of auditor independence, documentation of factual information during audits, usefulness of audit reports, handling of human relations problems, and retention of audit records. One approach is to obtain feedback from managers whose activities were audited. Thresh (1984, Appendix) lists 21 questions that examine the fairness, objectivity, audit methods, and usefulness of the audit results—all from the viewpoint of the auditee.

QUALITY SURVEYS

The audits as described above are concerned almost exclusively with conformance of various sorts: conformance of plans to standards of good planning and conformance of execution to plan. Such audits provide answers to some vital questions and must be regarded as an essential element of quality assurance. These audits are, however, not sufficient to provide full assurance to upper management that all is well with respect to quality, since they commonly are not concerned with such matters as:

Relative standing in the marketplace with regard to quality

Analysis of users' situations with respect to cost, convenience, etc. over the life of the product

Opportunities for reducing costs of poor quality

Challenge to product development, design engineering, and other "monopolistic" departments on quality adequacy, perfectionism, cost, etc.

Challenge to top management itself with respect to policies, goals, premises, and axiomatic beliefs

Employee perceptions on quality

To provide such missing elements of quality assurance requires a broader view than the structured audit. The broader review is often called a "quality survey," a "quality assessment," or a "companywide audit." In this section, the word "audit" implies the existence of established criteria against which the plans and execution can be checked. In contrast, the word "survey" implies the inclusion of matters not covered by agreed criteria. (In a sense, the audit discovers discrepancies and alarm signals; the survey goes further and also discovers opportunities and unexpected threats.)

An early form of quality survey was that used by the Bell System in reviewing the adequacy of its approach to quality. These surveys were conducted by personnel engaged full-time in quality matters. The Bell System survey brought together information from six related investigations, as follows:

1. An examination of the product design specifications from the standpoint of product fitness for use, completeness, and freedom from ambiguity

2. An examination of the manufacturing specifications and procedures, for similar reasons

3. A review of customer quality complaints and the action taken in diagnosis and remedy

4. A review of product audit data and shop performance data to appraise the state of product quality and process controls

5. A study of inspection performance, inspector accuracy, test equipment accuracy, and other aspects of inspection integrity

6. An examination into the quality performance and understanding of the shop personnel

The detailed investigations were conducted by full-time staff specialists, and their findings were reviewed by the managers who were members of a survey committee. The resulting reports and followups received the attention of upper management as well as local management.

Another example of a quality survey is that conducted by the Japanese Deming Prize Committee in its examination of companies nominated for this prize. The principal elements examined are as follows: the company's quality policies; organization and management; training in and dissemination of quality control ideas and practices; collection, feedback, and utilization of information; analysis of information data; active utilization of statistical methods; standardization; process control; quality assurance; results attained; and future planning (Mizuno,

1968). The Deming Prize is the most prestigious quality status attainable by a Japanese company.

As an example of a broad survey, a consultant was engaged to evaluate the operations of one division of a large processing company. The objectives of the survey were stated in broad terms:

1. To discover where the company wants to be with respect to quality
2. To discover where the company is now with respect to quality
3. To recommend plans and policies which can economically move the company closer to its objectives

Operations were studied in six different plants, various data were reviewed, and discussions were conducted with plant personnel and with personnel in manufacturing and nonmanufacturing functions at the division level.

The consultant reached five conclusions:

1. The division was generally well equipped to do a good quality job in terms of adequate processes, modern technology, capable personnel, and a favorable organizational climate.
2. Personnel were doing a good job on meeting the quality policies as interpreted by them.
3. Personnel interpretation of policy, however, did not match that of most division executives.
4. A considerable amount of money was being wasted as quality losses, without anyone having a clear idea how much this was or how much of it was readily avoidable.
5. There was a good chance for worthwhile cost reduction, while at the same time improving outgoing quality.

The consultant then presented 14 specific recommendations in areas such as quality policy, losses due to poor quality, machine capability studies, responsibility for deciding whether machines may run, supplier relations plans, measuring outgoing quality, measures of customer complaints and other forms of executive reports on quality, evaluation of the usefulness of process control charts, and evaluation of the effectiveness of lot acceptance plans.

In a different type of survey, a consultant was asked to define specific task responsibilities in the quality program for all major departments of a health care company. The consultant used five questions to interview the department managers:

1. What tasks in your department affect quality?
2. Should any additional quality-related tasks be performed in your department?
3. Should any additional quality-related tasks be performed anywhere else in the company?
4. What quality-related tasks have unclear responsibility?
5. What quality-related tasks currently done in your department require more definitive written procedures?

The consultant summarized the findings as follows: (1) the quality program consisted of 178 tasks performed in 26 functional areas; (2) responsibility was not clearly defined for 19 tasks; and (3) for 27 quality-related tasks, the managers expressed concern about the clarity of the task.

The report included detailed comments on the overall scope of the quality program, key tasks requiring improvement, organization for quality, and the role of upper management.

Some organizations identify the key elements of an overall quality program and evaluate each of these key elements. For example, 23 specific elements of a program are identified in Table 9.2. For each element, a scoring guideline provides a maximum of 100 possible points, allocated equally into four categories: required procedures exist, procedures meet requirements, procedures and practice agree, and results are effective.

The Allis Chalmers Company certifies each of its plants with respect to quality ("We Can, Allis-Chalmers Has," 1981). Ten major elements of "total quality assurance" are evaluated at each plant: management of the quality system, product quality and reliability development, product and process quality planning, supplier quality assurance, product and process quality evaluation and control, special quality studies, quality information feedback, quality measurement equipment, quality training and work force development, and field quality evaluation and control.

Freund and Trulli (1982) explain a method of summarizing the state of an overall quality program through the use of flowcharts, cause-and-effect diagrams, and other inputs. The method evaluates quality parameters that affect the customer. Useful checklists for conducting quality surveys are given by Dobbins (1981), Miller (1982), and White (1983).

QUESTIONS FOR QUALITY SURVEYS

The questions presented in the following subsections, based on a list originally prepared by J. M. Juran, cover companywide issues and issues for functional areas.

Companywide Issues. Questions relating to companywide issues may be categorized as those addressing issues of (1) responsibility to society or (2) quality management.

Responsibility to Society. Questions in this category are:

To what extent is the quality of your product related to human safety and health? To the environment? To regulation by governmental bodies?

Have these responsibilities to society generated any significant problems? What are the three main problems?

How are you organized to prevent these problems from occurring in the first place?

Quality Management. Questions pertaining to this category include:

Are policies, plans, and procedures such that, if followed, quality will be competitive in the marketplace?

To what extent are quality planning, coordination, and so on at the discretion of the Quality Department as opposed to the line managers?

What is the climate for training line managers and supervisors to assume some of these functions now being carried out by specialists in the Quality Department?

Has an estimate been made of the cost of poor quality?

Is the organizational machinery in place to identify and pursue opportunities for increasing sales income and/or reducing costs?

Is the concept of internal customers understood and acted on by all units involved?

Is there an effective system for having early warnings of potential quality problems?

What are your ways for judging the motivation of the personnel (managers, supervisors, workers) with respect to quality in relation to other parameters (productivity, delivery date, cost, etc.)?

On the basis of these ways, what is the adequacy of the present motivation?

How comfortable is the relationship between the management and the work force?

How willing would some of the work force be to receive training in problem-solving and then undertake projects for solution?

Functional Areas.   Questions relating to functional areas may be categorized as (1) questions common to all functional areas and (2) specific questions pertaining to selected areas:

Questions Common to All Functional Areas.   Questions in this category include:

What measures are used to judge the quality of the output? What is the performance, as reflected in these measures?

Have the resources spent in detecting and correcting quality-related problems been estimated?

To what extent are the quality-related responsibilities understood by the personnel?

To what extent have the personnel been trained in the quality disciplines?

To what extent has the capability of key processes been quantified?

Does the data system meet the needs of the personnel?

Questions for Selected Areas

Customer Relations.   Questions pertaining to customer relations are:

Is quality delivered to the customer an asset or a liability to the sales force?

Which qualities are of prime importance to your customers?

How does your quality compare to that of your competitors?

Does field performance meet users' needs?

What are the 10 quality problems most in need of solution from a customer relations viewpoint?

How do you know the answers to the preceding questions: from which sources (complaints, tests, marketing research, etc.)?

What are the leading causes of field failures (product design, purchased components, manufacturing errors, etc.)?

Where do you strike the balance between design for low initial selling price and low life cycle cost?

What part of your profit is derived from sale of spare parts?

Product Development. Questions addressing product development issues are:

What has been the record in launching new designs?

Do specifications originate with the customers? If not, how do you determine what qualities are needed to achieve fitness for use by subsequent processors, merchant chain, ultimate user, and maintenance shops?

How adequate is the system of early warning to detect problems which new products will create elsewhere in the organization or in the field?

To what extent are new and changed designs reviewed by specialists from other departments to evalute producibility, reliability, and maintainability?

What are the top 10 quality problems today? What were the top 10 two years ago? Three years ago? (To what degree are problems carried over from model to model?)

To what extent do product designers become involved in nonconformance questions which affect only internal factory economics?

Supplier Relations. Questions in this category include:

Are factory costs or field failures classified in ways which permit separating out the supplier-related problems?

What is the basic philosophy of supplier relations? Emphasis on contract preparation and enforcement? Less formality but not sharing all information? Teamwork? What is the extent of joint efforts with suppliers on quality planning? On quality improvement?

What is the basis for choosing suppliers in the first place? For allocating purchases among suppliers?

Manufacture. Questions relating to manufacture are:

What is the first-time yield of key manufacturing processes?

Who does the manufacturing planning (technical specialists, production supervisors, workers, etc.)?

Where is the main emphasis placed for manufacturing good products (foolproofing the processes, supervisory attention, motivation of work force, inspection and test following production, etc.)?

Who designs the system of quality controls used on the factory floor (manufacturing engineers, production supervision, workers themselves, quality control engineers, etc.)?

Customer Service.   Questions pertaining to customer service include:

Are field deficiencies acted on?

To what extent is the field service report adequate for providing field intelligence feedback (on quality) to Design, Manufacture, Purchasing, Quality, etc.?

Quality.   Questions in this category include:

What activities are assigned to be conducted by the Quality Department?

To what extent is the Quality Department regarded as a constructive contributor to quality (rather than as a police force)?

Are the line departments making use of the data feedback from the Quality Department?

Do the line departments make use of the specialized know-how of the Quality Department?

Upper Management.   Questions pertaining to upper-management issues are:

What active participation does upper management have on quality-related matters?

To what extent are there policies specifically quality-related?

To what extent does the system of Management by Objectives (formal or informal) include quality-related objectives?

What kind of information regarding quality performance does upper management receive?

Summary of Quality Status.   An overall view of quality status can be obtained by collecting information on three aspects:

1. *The cost of poor quality:*   This represents the internal losses that a company is experiencing due to poor quality. Methodology for estimating such losses is given in Section 4, under Categories of Cost of Poor Quality.

2. *The quality status of the company relative to competition:*   Some methodology for obtaining this information is given in Section 12, under Competitive Evaluations by Field Studies.

3. *Employee perceptions on quality.*   One approach for understanding the culture on quality involves the use of a questionnaire that is distributed to employees. Ryan and Wong (1984) present an example consisting of 14 questions. Wilson Learning Corporation and E. I. Du Pont de Nemours (1986) have prepared a list of 82 questions making up a "Quality Orientation Profile."

These three inputs plus the results from the above questions for quality surveys would provide an overall assessment on quality.

Third-Party Audit or Survey.   Two parties are involved in the purchase of products: the purchaser and the supplier. In the past, the purchaser evaluated the quality from the supplier. Purchasers are now increasingly using the concept of a "third party" to evaluate supplier quality. The third party (a person or an organization) performs the evaluation service for the purchaser but is independent of the purchaser and the supplier. This relieves the purchaser of maintaining a staff with the necessary skills. A third party can either inspect the product, evaluate the quality system, or both.

The concept of third-party inspection is not new. For example, the surveying of ships by the Lloyd's Register of Shipping began over two centuries ago. Rennie, Morris, and Blackburn (1979) describe how the approach has changed from one of primarily witnessing tests and examining components at prescribed stages of manufacture, to one which couples an evaluation of the quality system with periodic inspections of the final product. Underwriters Laboratories performs third-party evaluation by testing products, materials, and systems for public safety (Berman, 1980). The British Standards Institution (BSI) offers a service of assessing the conformance of an organization's quality system to BS 5750, *Quality Systems (The National Standard for Quality Systems in Great Britain)*.

Evaluation by a third party is often associated with formal "certification" and is sometimes coupled with a listing of approved sources, or the issuance of a symbol or mark. For example, an evaluation by the British Standards Institution showing that a firm complies with BS 5750 entitles the firm to use a special symbol in their company literature and to have its name appear in the BSI *Buyers' Guide* for potential buyers of products.

When a really fundamental examination is to be made, the managers guiding the survey should be aware that they are part of the problem. To provide assurance against their own biases, they should have recourse to outsiders who have the independence and competence to identify those problems and causes which have their origin in upper management itself. Most third-party audits, however, are evaluations of product and/or quality systems to some given standard.

A further need is to take note of new forces and phenomena to which traditional programs have not given weight. For example, in previous decades product liability, government regulation, higher levels of customer expectation, competition—both nationally and internationally—on both low price and high quality, increased consumer demands for better servicing of product, the impact of computer software, and still other quality-related problems were not regarded as major factors to be considered in quality policies, objectives, and plans. Subsequently, each of these issues became recognized as a major problem. Those companies who had foreseen some of this through their long-range planning thereby gained important head starts over their competitors. The use of consultants, educators, selected dealers, and other "outsiders" can be useful in assessing the current and expected future status of a company with regard to quality.

Reference Standards for Surveys. In evaluation of an overall quality system, use is often made of reference standards issued by regulatory bodies or by contracting bodies. Examples are MIL-Q-9858A (*Quality Program Requirements*), BS 5750 (*Quality Systems*), and ISO 9000 series (*Quality Systems*).

Such standards provide important benefits. They help to define the activities that are needed to achieve quality objectives, provide criteria for evaluation and thereby increase the objectivity of audits, and are useful during bidding on contracts by providing a common understanding of the activities required of all bidders.

Some cautions, however, must be noted. Most important, it has not been proved that surveys based on such standards are good predictors of subsequent quality performance. (The surveys do, however, provide objective information on the presence or absence of tangible facilities, written procedures, etc.) The best predictor of product quality is the quality performance on similar products in the past. Of course, high quality can be delivered with excessive internal costs. It is important, therefore, to evaluate not only final results but also the activities by which those results were achieved. As another caution, some standards omit such important elements as process capability, training, fitness for use considerations, quality of previous products delivered, etc. Finally, Juran (1977) traces the evolution of quality assurance and discusses the influence of the cultural pattern in different countries on the form of assurance.

If a reference standard is to be used but has not been specified, one must be selected. Pereira (1987) explains how five evaluation factors can help to decide which standard to employ.

PRODUCT AUDITING

Definition and Purposes.   Product auditing is an independent evaluation of product quality to determine its fitness for use and conformance to specification. Product auditing takes place after inspections have been completed. The purposes of product auditing include:

1. Estimating the quality level as delivered to customers
2. Evaluating the effectiveness of the inspection decisions in determining conformance to specifications
3. Providing information useful in improving the outgoing product quality level and improving the effectiveness of inspection
4. Providing additional assurance beyond routine inspection activities

There are often telltale signs indicating the need for product audit. Such signs include:

1. Nonconforming product being received by customers after 100 percent inspection has been performed
2. Damage to product after 100 percent inspection, but before receipt by a customer
3. Product inadequacies that are not evaluated in 100 percent inspection, and so forth

Diggs (1979) discusses some of the indicators of the need for product audit.

Stage of Evaluation.   Ideally, the product audit should compare actual service performance with users' service needs. This ideal is so difficult and costly to administer that most product auditing consists of an approximation (see Table 9.3).

For many simple, stable products, the approximation of test results versus specification is a useful and economic way of conducting the product audit. Even for products not so simple, the majority of quality characteristics identifiable by the user are also completely identifiable while the product is still at the factory. Thus, product characteristics which are essential to use are properly evaluated at some appropriate stage, whether in the factory or in some more advanced stage of progression.

As products become increasingly complex, the product auditing is conducted increasingly at several of the stages shown in Table 9.3. The bulk of the characteristics may be evaluated at the most economical stage, that is, shortly after factory inspection. However, the remaining (and usually more sophisticated) characteristics may be evaluated at other stages.

A useful adjunct to a product audit is a "tear-down" of the product. Cameron (1977) describes how a winding operator on a quality audit team pointed out that

TABLE 9.3 Potential Stages for Product Auditing

Stage at which product auditing is conducted	Pro and cons of using this stage
After acceptance by inspectors	Most economical, but does not reflect effect of packing, shipping, storage, or usage
After packing but before shipment to fields	Requires unpacking and repacking, but evaluates effect of original packing
On receipt by dealers	Difficult to administer at such multiple locations, but reflects effect of shipping and storage
On receipt by users	Even more difficult to administer, but evaluated the added effects of dealer handling and storage plus effects of shipment to user and unpacking
Performance in service	The ideal, but also the most difficult to administer because of the number and variety of usages; can be simplified through sampling

his incoming supplies included two types of diode in the same box. Since the diodes were identical in appearance, the wrong diode could be easily selected and inserted. The action taken: mark each diode with a red or green dot and place them in separate boxes.

In conducting product auditing after shipment to the field, there are further alternatives. If the product consists of small, stable units, it may be feasible to send samples back to a central laboratory for evaluation. If the product consists of large units, it may be more economical to send an audit team out to the field. For example, in the graphic arts industry, a supplier of coated paper may send a team out to the field to observe (1) product in customer warehouses and (2) actual running of the paper on the customer's presses, such as printing of magazines.

Product audit can also be applied at stages during manufacture. "In-line audit" or "work in process audit" are the terms commonly used. Such audits evaluate the effectiveness of previous inspections to detect nonconformances. Thresh (1984) discusses in-line product audits.

A special case of product auditing is that for new products. Love (1982) describes how an audit of new products can facilitate evaluation of the product development program and what went wrong on new product launches and can alert management of the nonconforming product that might be in the distribution system.

Designing the Audit Plan. Because the plan has a wide impact on executive decision making, it is essential that the design be made with the full participation of the departments affected. The usual approach is to designate an interdepartmental committee to guide the preparation of the plan, leaving it to the Quality Assurance Department to do the detailed work in the interim between meetings. (As product auditing becomes accepted, there often evolves a procedures manual to guide the auditors.)

Scope of the Audit. Lacking broad-based participation in designing the plan, the practical burdens of making product audits that depict the quality as the customer receives it often result in less than satisfactory plans.

As one example, the plant manager of an electronics manufacturing firm received a rating of 98 percent on a product audit from the plant. For this rating, the plant received an award for quality. When the mean time between failures of that same product was measured in the field, a value of only 200 hours was experienced. This was a known reason for customer complaints, but such matters were not evaluated by the product audit.

In another case, a vehicle manufacturer had a system of taking a product audit sample weekly from production. A comparison of separate marketing research results with the internal product audit was devastating. Only 18 percent of the characteristics that customers claimed were important to them were being checked in the product audit.

Sampling for Product Audit. When the purpose of the audit remains one of assurance rather than control, the sample size is arbitrary and reflects a balance between the cost of large samples and the unreliability of small samples. The selection of units within a sample should be based on the concepts of random sampling (see Section 25, under Random Sampling).

For products manufactured by mass production, sample sizes for product audit can often be determined using conventional statistical methods. These methods determine the sample size required for stated degrees of risk (see Section 23, under Confidence Internal Estimates). Thresh (1984, section 7) applies these methods to quality audit. Sample sizes for product audit determined by these methods when applied to mass production still represent a small fraction of the product that needs to be sampled. In contrast, for products manufactured as large units or in small quantity, the conventional concepts of statistical sampling are prohibitively costly. In such cases sample sizes are often arbitrary and they seem small from the viewpoint of probability considerations. For example, a vehicle manufacturer uses a product of audit sample consisting of 2 percent of production per shift with a minimum of five vehicles—whichever number is larger. Even though the number of vehicles sampled may be small, the total number of characteristics that are sampled may be quite large. For these vehicles, 380 items are checked on each vehicle and the product audit test includes a 17-mi (27.2-km) road test. In some cases of highly homogeneous production, a sample of one unit taken from batch production can be adequate for product audit. Thresh (1984) recommends a minimum of three units.

Hsiang and Gordon (1982) have proposed a method of determining the sample size that is based on the amount of production, the likelihood that current production is substandard, the cost of correcting problems in the field, the cost of audit sampling, and present quality standards. Unfortunately, the formulas include certain numerical values that must be calculated for particular products.

An allied consideration is the frequency for product audit (daily, weekly, by shift, etc.). Again, practical considerations such as changes in the design, suppliers, production methods, and other factors play an important role.

Reporting the Results of Product Auditing.   Most product auditing is done under a broader concept of preparing a continuing score or "rating" of quality. This running score is then used as one of the inputs for the executive reports on quality.

Seriousness Classification.   The results of product audit appear in the form of presence or absence of defects, failures, and other factors. Because these discrepancies are unequal in importance, a simple summary such as percent defective is not acceptable to the managers involved. In consequence, several levels of seriousness are chosen (e.g., critical, major, minor, incidental). The details of establishing a system of "seriousness classification for defects" are discussed in Section 12, under Seriousness Classification.

Weighting. It is comparatively easy to assign weights to each class to quantify the seriousness. Usually a weight of 100 "demerits" is arbitrarily assigned to the most serious defect class and weights then assigned to the other classes; for instance:

Seriousness classification	Weight or demerit value
A (critical)	100
B (major)	35–75
C (minor)	10–25
D (incidental)	1–10

Summary. In summarizing, defects are converted to demerits to arrive at a composite demerits per unit. For example, the results of product audit on one product line for 1 month were:

Defect class	Weight	Number of defects found	Total demerits
A (critical)	100	2	200
B (major)	50	7	350
C (minor)	10	28	280
D (incidental)	1	26	26
Total			856

Since there were 2500 units of product audited during the month, the demerits per unit totaled 856 ÷ 2500 = 0.34.

For mass production products, the unit of product may be a simple concept (e.g., lamps, gallons, tons). When the product line is miscellaneous in nature, it is necessary to find some common index which expresses the extent of opportunities for defects (e.g., number of electrical connections, weight of airframe, number of quality characteristics, "possible error count"). Use of such a common index facilitates comparison with previous history, with competitors, across product lines, and so on.

The scoreboard in terms of demerits per unit is by no means universally accepted. Managers in some industries want ready access to the figures on critical and major defects, feeling that these are the real problems no matter what the figure of demerits per unit is.

It is often useful to summarize the product audit results in other languages. A manufacturer of consumer products classifies defects at a product audit as visual (V), electrical (E), and performance (P) and then predicts service costs on products in the field. This is done by first establishing classes for each type of defect in terms of the probability of receiving a field complaint, (e.g., a class II visual defect has a 60 percent probability). Service call costs are then combined with the audit data. For example, Table 9.4 shows the results for an audit of 50 units. The expected cost is the product of the probability, the number of defects, and the cost per service call. The expected service cost per unit is then estimated as $269 ÷ 50 = $5.38. Alternatively, as indicated in Table 9.4, the expected number of service calls is the product of the probability and the number of defects. The expected number of service calls per unit is then estimated as 10.8 ÷ 50 = 0.22, or about 22 out of every 100 products delivered to the field is expected to have a service call.

TABLE 9.4   Audit Data

Class of defect	Probability	Number of defects revealed by audit	Cost per service call, $	Expected cost, $	Expected number of service calls
V1	1.00	1	15.00	15.00	1.00
V2	0.60	3	15.00	27.00	1.80
E1	1.00	3	30.00	90.00	3.00
E2	0.60	4	30.00	72.00	2.40
P1	1.00	1	25.00	25.00	1.00
P2	0.60	2	25.00	30.00	1.20
P3	0.20	2	25.00	10.00	0.40
Totals				269.00	10.80

In addition to summarizing the defects found (both number and relative seriousness), the audit results can be tallied by functional responsibility (i.e., design, purchasing, production).

Audit results can also be summarized to show the effectiveness of the previous inspection activities. Typically, a simple ratio is used such as the percentage of total defects which are detected by inspection. For example, if the previous inspection revealed a total of 45 defects in a sample of N pieces and if the product audit inspection revealed 5 additional defects, the inspection effectiveness would be $45 \div 50 \times 100$, or 90 percent.

Standard for Comparison.   To be meaningful, the score on demerits per unit (or the conversion thereof) must be compared with some "standard." The usual standard is previous practice; the managers want to see whether quality is improving or worsening.

To quantify past practice, the auditors conduct the product audit over a sufficient number of months to acquire stable data. This period is known as the *base period.* In calculating the base period, it is usual to exclude known abnormalities such as new-product troubles and the effect of temporary crises. The resulting "refined" base period then becomes a basis for comparison, much as previous years' costs or expenses.

Alternatively, the standard for comparison may be "market quality." In such cases, the product audit plan is applied to competitive products in the same way that it is applied to the company's own products. The methods of securing competitive products follow the practices discussed in Section 12, under Competitive Evaluations.

Action on Discrepancies.   When a product audit reveals defects or discrepancies, the line supervisors are notified for two reasons:

1. To secure their verification of the factual situation so that the subsequent quality rating is based on established facts
2. To alert them to the alarm signals inherent in the presence of defects in the product which has already been approved for shipment to customers

When the product audit sampling reveals critical or major defects, the audit procedures normally provide for documenting these cases fully, just as is done for any other discovery of a serious internal or field failure. A discrepancy form is executed to put corrective action machinery into motion.

Effect of Product Audit on Clarifying Quality Standards.   Introduction of product auditing invariably has a beneficial effect on clarifying quality standards. This effect is the result of:

1. The inevitable discussions between the auditors and the line organizations who contest some of the findings of the auditors.
2. The differences in viewpoint attributable to differences in emphasis. The product audit is specifically set up to reflect the user's viewpoint, whereas the line organizations have a strong tradition of emphasizing conformance to specification.
3. The use of product audit results to provide a running scoreboard of product performance. Such a continuing scoreboard requires that the quality standards be consistent from month to month.

A consequence of the need for clear, uniform standards is that the quality auditors play a role, sometimes the dominant role, in defining quality standards from the viewpoint of the user.

PERSONNEL FOR QUALITY ASSURANCE

Multiple categories of personnel for auditors are generally used, primarily in response to the different types of audits and surveys which must be conducted.

Upper Management.   The role of upper management in conducting company-wide (and other) types of quality audit is discussed in Section 8, under Quality Audit by Upper Managers.

Middle Managers.   A significant number of companies make use of teams of middle managers to conduct quality audits on a part-time basis. These teams include not only quality managers but also managers from other functions as well (e.g., production, personnel, marketing, purchasing). There are advantages as well as limitations to the use of middle managers as auditors.

The Advantages.   Managers have a broader outlook than conventional auditors do and are more likely to consider activities from the viewpoint of the company mission, the needs of users, and the impact on society. The managers do not feel bound by existing plans and are more open to the idea that the plans may need to be revised. They are more likely to identify opportunities (e.g., cost reduction) or threats (e.g., increasing foreign competition) and are more imaginative in recommendations for action. In addition, when a team of managers is seen to be moving from department to department to audit quality, that fact conveys a message to the supervision and the work force.

The Disadvantages.   Managers tend to be undisciplined auditors. They are reluctant to be bound by detailed checklists, so that some aspects of operation are not audited at all. They lack the time to thoroughly analyze their findings; this results in some degree of overreaction, with wear and tear on all concerned. In addition, managers have difficulty in adhering to the schedules for auditing—they are busy people, and their time is subject to being preempted by crises.

A combined approach is to use conventional auditors to conduct the detailed audit. Following this, a team of managers makes a supplemental, broader review and prepares a report for distribution to upper management. Such a combined approach was used by the Bell System for years and was known as the quality "survey" (see above, under Quality Surveys).

Audit Teams. Sometimes, teamwork is useful. Cameron (1977) describes an audit team for electric power systems. The team consists of nine people: unit assembler and assembly supervisor, unit tester, unit inspector and supervisor, winding operator and winding supervisor, methods engineer, manufacturing engineer, project engineer and production liaison engineer, product support engineer, quality engineer, and customer representatives. The audit centers around a teardown inspection (see above, under Stage of Evaluation).

Two work units within the same company may audit each other ("mutual audits"). For example, a manufacturing process and the process following it may exchange teams to audit each other's quality performance (Ishikawa, 1987).

A steel manufacturer has audit teams of middle managers—one from the Corporate Quality Assurance Department, one from the general manager's staff of the plant being audited, and one from another plant in the company.

Some organizations have established an audit group with a strong customer orientation. This audit group can veto the release of a new design or block the release of daily production of a product.

External Auditors. Quality audits are also conducted by persons external to the company. An extensive example is the audits conducted by clients in the form of supplier surveys and surveillance (see Section 15, under Evaluating Supplier Capability). Section 8, under Organization for Quality Audits by Upper Managers; Third-Party Audits, discusses the role of outside consultants.

Full-Time Auditors. The use of full-time auditors greatly improves the competence of the auditing. The auditing job exposes the personnel to a wide variety of company activities so that they undergo intensive training and development, especially during the first 2 years or so of their assignments. As a result, the auditors soon become well-trained professionals. They participate in discussions of quality specifications, standards, procedures, and peripheral "nonquality" matters which nevertheless have a bearing on quality. Their resulting broad exposure also increases their capacity to assume added responsibilities. They are aware of this to such an extent that they become restive after several years. One approach for dealing with this personnel problem is to reassign the person at the end of 3 years or so to a new job which takes advantage of the experience gained on the auditing job.

The common situation of locating a quality audit group within a Quality Assurance Department provides professional supervision, but it can sometimes result in a conflict of interest. This refers to the role of the audit group in identifying weaknesses within a quality system and the typical role of a Quality Assurance Department of attempting to gain acceptance of a variety of techniques for improving quality throughout an organization. An auditor who becomes a strong advocate for certain activities to be performed may unconsciously lose some objectivity and, in turn, damage the credibility of the audit function. Locating the audit function within the Quality Assurance Department can be workable as long as the manager of that department is particularly cautious to stress the objectivity and independence of the audit function.

Product Auditors. Product auditing is usually a full-time job; often the product auditor remains full-time on the same product line year after year.

The general practice is to fill these posts from the ranks of inspectors who have considerable experience and have demonstrated a high level of objectivity and integrity and also have certain special skills required, such as in evaluating the taste of food or drivability of an automobile.

REFERENCES

ANSI/ASQC (1986). *Generic Guidelines for Auditing of Quality Systems.* American Society for Quality Control, Milwaukee.

Berman, Harvey S. (1980). "Quality Assurance in UL's Follow-Up Program." *Quality Progress,* January, pp. 14–17.

Burr, John T. (1987). "Overcoming Resistance to Audits." *Quality Progress,* January, pp. 15–18.

Cameron, R. D. (1977). "Up Your Quality with Show and Tell." *Quality,* May, pp. 24–25.

Charnoff, Gerald (1986). "An Evaluation of the Prudence Consultants Retained by State Commissions and Consumer Counsel." Paper presented at Winter Meeting, American Nuclear Society, Washington, DC (no page numbers).

Diggs, E. J. (1979). "Why Have Outgoing Quality Audits?" *ASQC Technical Conference Transactions,* Milwaukee, pp. 506–512.

Dobbins, Richard K. (1981). "Your Quality Posture—A Profit/Survival Challenge." *ASQC Quality Congress Transactions,* Milwaukee, pp. 485–490.

Farrow, John H. (1987). "Quality Audits: An Invitation to Management." *Quality Progress,* January, pp. 11–13.

Freund, R. A. and Trulli, H. B. (1982). "Quality Assurance Review Technique." *Quality Assurance,* vol. 8, no. 1, March, pp. 17–22.

Goldstein, Raymond (1983). "The Two-Tier Audit System." *ASQC Quality Congress Transactions,* Milwaukee, pp. 14–16.

Hayes, Glenn E. and Romig, Harry G. (1977). *Modern Quality Control.* Bruce (a division of Benzigh Bruce and Glencoe, Inc.), Collier Macmillan, New York, pp. 706–723.

Hsiang, Thomas C. and Gordon, John J. (1982) "New Statistical Methodologies in a QA Audit System." *ASQC Quality Congress Transactions,* Milwaukee, pp. 335–342.

Ishikawa, Kaoru (1987) "The Quality Control Audit." *Quality Progress,* January, pp. 39–41.

Juran, J. M. (1977). "Quality and Its Assurance—an Overview." *Second NATO Symposium on Quality and Its Assurance.* North Atlantic Treaty Organization, London.

Kane, Roger W. (1984). "Fitness Reviews: Key to a Total Quality Program." *ASQC Quality Congress Transactions,* Milwaukee, pp. 263–267.

Love, Kenneth S. (1982). "Quality Auditing of New Products." *ASQC Quality Congress Transactions,* Milwaukee, pp. 534–537.

Marash, Stanley A. (1982) "Conducting an Audit." *Medical Device and Diagnostic Industry,* December, pp. 31–35.

Miller, Ervin F. (1982). "Corporate Quality Audit/Survey." *ASQC Quality Congress Transactions,* Milwaukee, pp. 538–545.

Mizuno, Shigeru (1968). "Quality Systems in Japan." *Reports of Statistical Applications and Research,* Japanese Union of Scientists and Engineers, vol. 15, no. 1, pp. 32–44.

Pereira, Armando Lopes (1987). "Quality Audits and International Standards." *Quality Progress,* January, pp. 27–29.

Plum, Kathryn S. (1987). "A Success Story." *Quality Progress,* January, pp. 32–34.

Purcell, Warren R. (1968). "Sampling Techniques in Quality Systems Audits." *Quality Progress,* October, pp. 13–16.

Rennie, D., Morris W., and Blackburn, K. (1979). "Quality Assurance: Inspection." *Quality Assurance,* September, pp. 71–74.

Riggs, E. J. (1979). "Why Have Outgoing Quality Audits?" *ASQC Technical Conference Transactions,* Milwaukee, pp. 506–512.

Ryan, J. M. and Wong, H. Y. S. (1984). "Breaking Down the Barriers." *Quality,* April, pp. 40–41.

Sayle, A. J. (1981). *Management Audits.* McGraw-Hill Book Company (U.K.), London.

Stenecker, Robert G. (1982). "Proposed ASQC Quality Auditor Certification Program." *ASQC Quality Congress Transactions,* Milwaukee, pp. 830–834.

Thresh, James L. (1984). *How to Conduct, Manage, and Benefit from Effective Quality Audits.* MGI Management Institute, Harrison, NY, pp. 5–7.

Wachniak, R. (1979). "Ten Commandments for Quality Auditors." *Quality,* November, pp. 36–37.

"We Can, Allis-Chalmers Has." (1981). *Quality,* May, pp. 34–40.

White, Bruce (1983). "Measuring the Status of Quality, Part I." *Quality,* August, pp. 63, 64.

Willborn, Walter (1983). *Compendium of Audit Standards.* American Society for Quality Control, Milwaukee.

Willborn, Walter (1987). "Software Quality Auditing." *Quality Progress,* January, pp. 36–37.

Wilson Learning Corporation and E. I. Du Pont de Nemours Company (1986). *Quality Orientation Profile.* John Wiley, New York; Du Pont, Wilmington, DE.

SECTION 10

MANAGING HUMAN PERFORMANCE[1]

Edward M. Baker, Ph.D

[1]In the Third Edition, the section on motivation was prepared by J. M. Juran.

INTRODUCTION

This section of the handbook reviews the factors which influence the amount and type of worker participation and contribution to the planning, control, and improvement of quality. A key dimension of the management process is the establishment and maintenance of a work climate that encourages and makes it possible for workers to behave in ways that contribute to effective individual and organization performance. Only management can create the conditions which enable workers to control the processes over which they preside and to participate with management in projects that seek to achieve breakthrough to new quality levels. In turn, the work must provide meaningful rewards to each worker.

Since the advent of mass production, Western management systems have defined narrow roles for workers. Worker contributions typically have been limited to executing tasks as directed. Worker involvement in work planning, process management, and improvement efforts generally have been limited to providing information when requested. Alternative approaches to human resource management are emerging under a variety of names such as "quality of work life," "work redesign," "sociotechnical systems," "quality circles," "employee involvement," and "participative management." These efforts have goals related to quality and productivity improvement, worker job satisfaction, union-management cooperation, reduction of conflict, and building of trust. These approaches are evolving especially in the United States, from three interrelated influences: (1) behavioral scientists who, with management's support, are attempting to find ways to make work more meaningful for workers and productive for the business, (2) union leaders who are trying to bring to the workplace the same democratic rights and privileges existing in the larger society, and (3) managers who are attempting to apply worker-related management practices which Japanese companies appear to have used to help produce high-quality products and achieve other successful business outcomes.

THE TAYLOR SYSTEM OF MANAGEMENT

Many of the obstacles to meaningful worker contributions to quality performance are rooted in the philosophy, values, and beliefs and their manifestations—the management control systems—developed under the leadership of Frederick W. Taylor. Taylor was a mechanical engineer who joined a factory as a lathe hand, became head of the lathe gang, and then became manager of the machine shop. It was in the late nineteenth century, when factories were beginning their conversion from "many laborers and few machines" to "many machines and few laborers." Taylor concluded that the foremen and workers of those days lacked the educational qualifications to decide how work should be done, what constituted a day's work, or how to select and train workers.

Taylor undertook to remedy all this by changing the shop organization. He created industrial engineers to plan the work methods and to establish standards of a day's work. In other words, he turned the work planning over to the various specialists, leaving to the foremen and workers only the job of executing plans prepared by someone else. Workers had virtually no discretion as to how the work was done. Worker motivation was viewed as an all-or-none situation; workers either were or were not motivated. It was believed that once the proper piecework incentive was established (based on well-defined job tasks), the workers would be motivated to meet the standards of a day's work. Establishment of the proper incentive scheme would eliminate the worker as a source of variation and free the engineers to work on improving the machines, materials, and methods contributing to the operation's efficiency.

Taylor's approach resulted in substantial increases in productivity. These results were publicized by Taylor in his writings (see the compilation of his papers in Taylor, 1947), and they attracted wide attention. This concept of separation of planning from execution became and remains the norm for the practice of management in the United States. In the decades after World War II, when the industrial companies greatly expanded their work of quality planning, they continued to follow the Taylor concept of separating planning from execution. They did so by creating new specialist positions (quality control engineers, reliability engineers, etc.) to do the planning and analysis, leaving it to the line supervisors, operators, and inspectors to execute the plan.

Taylor's approach to efficient mass production in the early 1900s was innovative in many areas including:

Development of concepts and methods for measuring work and analyzing jobs into simple task elements

Recognition of the need to match workers' abilities to jobs through selection and training

The concept that incentives will be most effective if contingent on good performance and provided soon after the work has been completed

Recognition of the need for goals to be specific and clearly understood by all involved in their attainment

However, as workers' economic and education levels increased and job mobility expanded, the dissatisfaction inherent in simple, repetitive tasks that provided only money as a reward with little worker input into planning of daily activities (in contrast with activities outside of work), began to be expressed in various ways: Worker absenteeism and turnover increased; collective bargaining and adversarial union-management relations became the norm.

The unions, when emerging, had two options, according to Cole (1979, pp. 104–105): They could struggle to increase the amount of worker discretion over how the job was to be done; or they could accept the existing power framework and struggle to make quantitative improvements in worker rewards. Faced with management and government power and the lack of worker support, they chose to gain control over job opportunities by working to replace incentive pay schemes (which management preferred) with standard rate structures. The mutual interest of union and management in tight and narrow job definitions reinforced and deepened the division of labor. The union accepted industrial engineering as a way to unambiguously define jobs, thereby institutionalizing seniority as the basis for allocating jobs and pay.

THEORIES OF MOTIVATION AND IMPLICATIONS FOR MANAGEMENT

Since the late 1920s, when behavioral scientists at Western Electric's Hawthorne plant (Roethlisberger and Dickson, 1939) began to investigate the factors affecting worker job satisfaction, there has been a proliferation of theories and research on the subject. A common characteristic of the approaches—and the most significant—is the focus on the work processes, including the social, psychological climate, rather than on economic incentives as a source of satisfaction.

Maslow (1954) postulated that people will work to satisfy needs, but in a hierarchical order of importance, with each lower-level need to be satisfied partially before working to satisfy a higher-level need. Maslow's model has been taught to many managers and has provided the rationale for contemporary approaches to quality motivation. It is restated in Table 10.1 along with some of the usual forms of quality motivation.

Another scheme to understand human performance was proposed by Herzberg (Herzberg, 1971, and Herzberg et al., 1959). Motivating factors exist in the work itself, e.g., challenging work, growth and learning, identification with groups, and responsibility for planning. These provide job satisfaction but will not stimulate superior performance unless the work provides adequate working conditions,

TABLE 10.1 Hierarchy of Human Needs and Usual Forms of Quality Motivation

Maslow's list of human needs	Usual forms of quality motivation
Physiological needs, i.e., food, shelter, basic survival. In an industrial economy this translates into minimum subsistence earnings.	Opportunity to increase earnings by bonus for good work.
Safety needs, i.e., to remain employed at a subsistence level, once it is achieved.	Appeal to job security, e.g.: quality makes sales, sales make jobs.
Social needs, i.e., to belong to a group and be accepted.	Appeal to the employee as a team member not to let the team down.
Ego needs, i.e., self-respect and the respect from others.	Appeal to pride of workmanship, to achieving a good score. Recognition through awards, publicity, etc.
Self-fulfillment needs, i.e., creativity and self-expression.	Opportunity to propose creative ideas and to participate in creative planning.

wages, and other "hygiene" factors. Inadequacy in these hygiene factors is a source of dissatisfaction. Once adequate, they are accepted as normal. They are prerequisites but do not stimulate performance. Instead, "motivators" must be used.

Theories X and Y. McGregor (1960) described the beliefs and assumptions about workers under the titles "Theory X" and "Theory Y."

Theory X. The major beliefs underlying the operation of the Taylor management system are:

Labor is a commodity which can be purchased as needed, like other materials.

Work is inherently distasteful to most people and will be avoided if possible; what people do at work is less important than what they get paid for doing it.

Workers must be influenced to perform in the desired manner with monetary incentives for meeting standards and with penalties for failure.

Few workers want or can handle work which requires creativity, self-direction, or self-control.

Under Theory X, workers are assumed to have no interest in quality. The job of management and supervision is to counter this negative attitude with incentives for meeting standards and penalties for failure, supervise closely, and directly control workers. Tasks must be broken down into specific, simple, repetitive, easily learned operations, which workers are expected to follow. Detailed work routines and procedures have to be established and enforced. Product quality is achieved through use of a separate cadre of inspectors and quality engineers.

Theory Y. McGregor proposed that management adopt an alternative set of assumptions about employees—Theory Y—which could lead to greater organization efficiency and effectiveness. Under this approach:

Workers are viewed as the most important asset of the organization.

The work itself is viewed as a potential source of satisfaction to workers if it provides opportunities for successful accomplishments.

Most workers are viewed as able and willing to exercise self-control and self-direction.

Workers are assumed to have an internal drive for accomplishment and derive satisfaction from producing results of craftlike quality. The organization, however, gives workers meaningless, monotonous jobs which stifle their natural drive.

Workers become frustrated because they cannot attain the satisfaction they want from the job. Management's job is to create the conditions under which workers can contribute meaningfully to the work and exercise self-control.

Table 10.2 compares the quality control approaches of two shops, one operating under Theory X beliefs, the other operating under Theory Y beliefs. Some of the more usual differences in approaches to control of quality are listed. While some aspects of shop operation are alike under both theories (e.g., specifications, processes, inspection, instruments), there are great differences in the design of jobs, i.e., how the work gets done and by whom. To oversimplify, Theory X management does not trust the people and hence relies on the external control system. Theory Y management does trust the people, and exhibits this trust through wider

TABLE 10.2   Shop Operation under Theory X versus Theory Y

Operation under Theory X	Operation under Theory Y
Extensive use of piecework rates and other financial incentives to meet the standard.	Less emphasis on financial incentives; greater use of supervisory leadership.
Emphasis on wage-penalty clauses or disciplinary measures to punish poor quality performance.	Emphasis on the "why" and "how" to improve poor quality performance.
Reliance mainly on inspection personnel for tool control.	Reliance mainly on production personnel for tool control.
Reliance placed mainly on patrol inspectors to see that setups are correct.	Reliance mainly on operators and setup people for correctness of setup.
Reliance on inspection personnel to detect defects.	Reliance on operator self-inspection for process control to prevent defects.
Debates on the factory floor center on authority to shut down machines, and on fixing blame for problems.	Debates on the factory floor center on the interpretation of specifications and measurements, and on fixing problems.
Relationships between operators and inspectors tense, often hostile and acrimonious.	Relationships between operators and inspectors businesslike, often good-natured.
Upper-management response to high scrap in the form of criticism of Inspection and Production.	Upper-management response to high scrap in the form of problem-probing questions to Production and Support Systems.
Operators do not exhibit interest or desire to do a quality job.	Operators do exhibit interest and desire to do a quality job.
Operators largely ignored as a source of ideas for improvement.	Operators frequently consulted for ideas and involved in improvement efforts.

delegation of responsibility and reliance on employee self-control. Berman and Mase (1983) compare management styles for staff jobs.

Theory X or Y? Examples of Theory Y managment are described in Peters and Waterman (1982). There is widespread belief that organizations operating under Theory Y have superior human relations. There is evidence (see Sherwood and Hoylman, 1977) that group participative problem-solving and decision-making processes (e.g., quality circles)—a key aspect of Theory Y operation—can produce higher quality solutions and decisions (as defined by an internal criterion or standard) and a high level of worker commitment to the proper execution of those decisions. However, to date, there has been no exhaustive research study which establishes that one of these theories outperforms the other in terms of the major measures of quality: fitness for customer use, cost of poor quality, etc. Ancedotal cases can be cited to support either theory. The essential management issue is whether employees are able to contribute to quality at each stage of the quality spiral (see Section 2 under The Quality Function). There is nothing inherent in Theory Y which provides for worker involvement in the cross-departmental activities required to carry a product from its inception, through design, development, manufacture, sales, and service. Participative work environments cannot themselves guarantee massive worker contributions to quality breakthrough if workers are not able to work on the system's improvement. Organizations where worker participation in problem solving has led to quality and productivity improvement usually have a means (e.g., a hierarchy of committees, as described by Donnelly, 1977) to pass upward problems requiring management attention.

JAPANESE HUMAN RESOURCE MANAGEMENT PRACTICES

Japanese successes in export product quality and market penetration have focused the attention of Western management on the human (as well as the technical) resource management techniques used by Japanese businesses. The most visible techniques (quality circles, bottom-up consensus decision making, self-inspection, job rotation) are studied by management in order to transplant them to their own companies with the hope of reaping quality improvement. Viewed from a traditional Western business perspective, it is often difficult to determine what to copy, especially to improve quality (see Deming, 1982, and Juran, 1979). What is usually overlooked—or unobservable to the uneducated spectator—are the social, cultural, and economic controls on people's behavior that enable the techniques to work. The techniques work because they are consistent with the values and norms of Japanese society and business life. Many American attempts to utilize the techniques for quality and productivity improvment have not been successful because of a failure to take a total system ("organic") perspective. Rather than assuring that the transplant would be accepted by the organization, typically it is introduced in a programmatic, mechanistic manner akin to installing new equipment. When it is incompatible or in conflict with the rest of the system, it is rejected. Many researchers (e.g., Cole, 1979, Nosow, 1984, Ouchi, 1981, Schein, 1981, and Sethi et al., 1984) have tried to understand the social, cultural, and economic conditions which have made possible worker contributions to quality and productivity improvement in Japan. Their findings have provided a basis for analyzing the successes and failures of these techniques in American companies.

Western Influences on Japan.   Japanese management practices—on the surface—appear consistent with Theory Y precepts and values. In fact, Maslow, McGregor, Herzberg, and other American behavioral scientists have been cited as providing the rationale for instituting contemporary participative management practices (e.g., Kobayashi and Burke, 1976, and Kondo, 1975, 1976, 1977) and job redesign (Takezawa, 1976). Cole (1979, pp. 130–132) notes that the Japanese were interested in the implications of modern Western motivation theories and conducted experiments in the 1960s to redesign jobs, humanize work, and increase worker responsibility. Much of this was done before or at the same time as (but independent of) American efforts.

Takezawa (1976) observed that Japanese managers tend to accept Western behavioral science (Theory Y) models as an idealized goal which is consistent with their own orientation. They are often surprised when they discover that in practice American management fits the scientific management (Theory X) model better than the Theory Y model. Cole explains that the American engineering and managerial professions became locked into the scientific management solution for raising worker productivity. Japanese versions of scientific management allowed for innovation based on modern social science approaches. The history of Japanese industrialization in the twentieth century is one of adapting external methods to fit into the existing culture. Cole (1979, chapter 4) contrasts Japanese and U.S. approaches to scientific management. Taylor's *Principles of Scientific Management* was translated into Japanese soon after its publication in 1911 under the title, *The Secret of Saving Lost Motion.* (It is said to have sold 1.5 million copies.) Much of the effort during this period focused on standardizing work procedures rather than doing time and motion studies. For example, teams of railroad workers conducted a thorough analysis of railcar maintenance operations. Detailed work schedules were developed by the workers, enabling the reduction of repair time. The wage systems in most Japanese industries during this period were not geared toward individual achievement. The Taylor principle of high wages for high efficiency was ignored. Wages were determined by seniority rather than on job determined rates. During the 1920s and 1930s, time and motion studies were applied under a government thrust to overcome worldwide economic depression. These were abandoned in the 1940s as too resource-consuming. In the 1940s, a legal ruling on wage increases prevented the tying of wage rates directly to individual work performance.

Cole notes that the emphasis on paternalism grew in parallel with the rise of scientific management. When first introduced, the principles of scientific management were adapted to complement practices of permanent employment, and pay and promotion according to seniority. Time and motion studies were used primarily to determine "correct" job procedures and played a minor role in wage determination. Management was concerned with motivating workers to look at cost reduction and other management goals as a personal challenge. Thus, even though the Japanese had every chance to incorporate Western-style scientific management, they did it in a way consistent with existing social practices, values, and labor market characteristics.

Cole observed also that the interplay of union and management interests and demands that led to the sharp demarcation of jobs in the United States had exactly the opposite outcome in Japan. Since wages were based historically on seniority rather than specific jobs, there was no model of job control to be adopted by the emerging unions. Management had and still has the prerogative, without union interference, to decide on work assignments, job demarcation, and restructuring to meet changing technology. In order to guarantee employment until retirement, management has the flexibility to meet economic upturns and downturns with transfers and reassignments. Downgrading or undesirable assignments are tolerated because they are viewed as a temporary condition. This is changing (see Sethi et al., 1984, chapter 10).

The major processes through which workers contribute to quality and the underlying social and economic controls are described below.

Quality Circles.   Circles are quality improvement and self-improvement study groups. A circle usually is composed of workers (no more than 10) and their supervisor who functions as leader. The emergence of circles was a natural consequence of a top-down process of statistical and quality management education that began with senior executives and worked its way down the organization pyramid to the engineers, supervisors, and shop-floor foremen. Often cited milestones are Deming's seminar in 1950 (Deming, 1951) and Juran's 1954 lectures. The first circle was registered with JUSE (Japanese Union of Scientists and Engineers) in 1962. See the JUSE publications listed in this section's Supplemental Bibliography for the history, philosophy, and operating methods of circles in Japan. Circles in the United States are discussed later under Quality Circles: Processes, Tools, Administration.

Circles usually are the shop-floor manifestation of a broad range of activities called companywide quality control (CWQC) which gives every employee responsibility for quality. This stems from a philosophy that views each person as having unrealized potential that can be realized through education and study. Improvement of the individual will enable the company to improve. Workers, therefore, are more than a commodity—they are an asset to be developed. The circle process also helps supervisors develop leadership skills.

A primary contribution of quality circles in Japan according to Juran (1967a, 1980) has been in improving workers' knowledge and skills and developing interest in the job by providing opportunities for planning and decision making not present in the daily routine. Circle projects enable workers to interface with management (e.g., through project selection, conduct of studies, presentation of results) which help to prepare some workers for supervisory and managerial responsibilities. As circles gain experience and competence, members may form subcircles (sometimes called "minicircles") and elect a coworker to lead each group. The scope of the group may be expanded to include such topics as cost reduction, safety, absenteeism, delivery, facility planning, jigs and tools, and production control. Circles have spread from the shop floor to the warehouse, from the plant to the office, and from manufacturing to the service sector (see *Quality Control Circles at Work*, in the Supplemental Bibliography). A coalition of two or more circles in an internal supplier-customer relationship may form a joint circle, e.g., production with maintenance or with the warehouse.

Worker participation is supposed to be "voluntary," but that is a relative term given the amount of social control that exists. The supervisor is supposed to have the leadership skills necessary to encourage worker participation. The worker's desire to participate comes from a mix of the supervisor's personal enthusiasm, informing the worker of the need to contribute to the common good of the group and the company (Yamamoto, 1980), and building worker confidence. Confidence is built by proper training, success in tackling projects workers can handle, and recognition of efforts to improve.

Cole (1980, 1981) also has observed that even in Japanese plants recognized as having the best circle efforts, management must continually work at revitalizing circle activities so they do not degenerate into ritualistic behavior, e.g., people attending meetings because participation is expected. Cole (1979, p. 166) reports that one company's morale survey showed 30 percent of workers felt that quality circles were a burden because of competition between groups and pressures to submit suggestions. Circles are not necessarily self-sustaining. Some management techniques to maintain interest are intercompany visits by circle members, conventions within Japan, passing of customer complaints to the circles, and even the goal of helping the company win the Deming prize (Cole, 1979, p. 167). Cole emphasizes that Japanese managers told him they do not have all of the answers to sustaining employee interest and participation. The JUSE has done its part to stimulate quality circle activities by selecting outstanding projects for publication and presentation outside of Japan.

In the opinion of Juran and others (see Cole, 1980, Gryna, 1981, and Sandholm, 1983), quality circles themselves have not been the source of the major upturn in Japanese quality because the members have been limited to working on the "useful many" day-to-day problems within the department. Breakthroughs in quality come mainly from working on the management-controllable systems problems. These require interfaces across departments (see Project Teams below). Cole (1979, pp. 163–167) feels that it is difficult to separate the effect of quality circles from job redesign (discussed later in this section) and technological improvements.

While circles may have contributed directly to only about 10 percent of quality improvement, their efforts have indirectly made possible a great deal of the improvement in management-controllable areas by freeing the engineers and managers to work on the vital few system problems. For example, a number of years ago Toyota discovered that of the quality problems accounting for warranty losses, 50 percent were due to 120 big problems. The other 50 percent of losses came from 4000 small problems. The big 120 were assigned to the engineers while the 4000 were assigned to the circles (see Juran, 1980, "Quality Sagging?" 1972, and Rubinstein, 1973).

Project Teams. These are cross-functional teams created by management to identify, analyze, and solve chronic problems which usually are beyond the scope of the circle. Sometimes the problem is surfaced by a circle. A team often is composed of circle leaders, supervisors, and engineers. In some cases, it may be necessary for the team first to solve the broader problem after which the circle can work on its more narrow project (see Juran, 1966, 1967a, 1967b). Unlike circles which are intended to be permanent, teams usually are formed to work on specific problems or objectives and then disband. (Project team approaches in the United States are discussed later in the section under Team Performance: A Processing System Viewpoint, and in Section 22, Quality Improvement.)

Consensus Decision Making. This is a bottom-up process whereby desired changes to the system (e.g., procedures, methods) can be originated at any level and submitted upward and laterally for approval. This tends to be a time-consuming method, but it brings about understanding from all concerned members of the organization, eliminates surprises, and provides for elimination of disagreements at each organization level. Each higher-level manager can be sure that subordinates endorse fully the recommendations the manager is being asked to approve. (See Sethi et al., 1984, pp. 34–41.)

Self-Control. In the narrow sense, this means the inspection of output by the individual who produces it rather than by an inspector from the quality control department. In the broad sense, it means that the worker participates in the planning (process design, scheduling, etc.) of the work and exercises autonomy and discretion in the way the work is executed. (The conditions necessary for self-control are discussed later in this section.) Self-control pertains to work on individual tasks, as well as involvement in group activities.

There are a number of social, cultural, and economic factors that interact in a complex way to assure that workers will learn and abide by the standards, values, and goals of the company. They create a common viewpoint which guides the behavior of each individual. Ishikawa (1981) has contrasted Japanese and Western cultural values. In his view, one major difference between the two societies is its view of humanity. Whereas the East views people as inherently good and trustworthy, the West views people as inherently evil and not to be trusted. This could be a prime reason why the Taylor system, with all of its external controls, has become institutionalized in Western industry and why the Japanese had little trouble creating systems that institutionalize each individual's responsibility for quality. Schein (1981) has observed that most American students of Japanese management approaches fail to see the subtle way in which self-control is acquired by employees. The system makes it possible for workers to learn the goals of the company, what it is trying to achieve, and its values for how to do things. This provides the worker with a set of criteria regarding what is appropriate behavior in an ambiguous situation. The worker can figure out what to do without asking or waiting for direction from the supervisor. Kondo (1975) notes, for example, that the shop manual is for reference only and not a set of step-by-step procedures workers should follow without question.

Social and Cultural Controls. Employees do what society and the organization expects them to do. In order to do what one's superiors would approve of, one must determine what they are thinking. Not to do so would violate the hierarchical authority structure. The consensus decision-making process reflects a societal and business culture which values overt conformity of viewpoint with one's superiors and the avoidance of conflict. Relationships should be harmonious. The consensus process enables one to learn what others think and feel about an issue so as not to take action that would violate the superiors' expectations and organization norms.

People participate in quality circles (see Cole, 1979, 1980, 1981), contribute suggestions, and do whatever else is expected of them. Failure to do so can lead to social ostracism and the resulting loss of face. The identity and status of workers and their families are gained through the group; there is no identity apart from the identity of the group. Discharge from the company means loss of the social status derived through employment in the company. (See Sethi et al., 1984, chapters 2 and 3.)

Economic Controls. The economic consequences of failing to meet the expectations of the hierarchy are also disastrous. A worker can lose favor to the point of being discharged (lifetime employment exists for about 40 percent of employees in a firm). If some are fortunate enough to obtain jobs with other firms, the seniority-based wage system starts them at the low end of the wage scale.

Lifetime employment, and compensation and promotion by seniority, are intended to promote cooperation, teamwork, and accomplishment of group and company goals. Employees are supposed to recognize that as tenure increases and the company is successful, they will share in the rewards. The lack of external mobility combined with the consequences of having one's internal mobility blocked puts enormous pressures on the individual to conform and participate.

Recruitment, Selection, Education, and Training. Interviews and extensive testing prior to employment assure consistency of the candidate's views with those of the company. Job rotational assignments develop a broad base of technical skills and teach workers how the company philosophy and values guide behavior in the various organizations. They give workers a better understanding of the jobs and needs of other company functions. This facilitates communication and cooperation across departments. At the managerial level, rotational assignments develop managers into generalists with a broad understanding of the business and a network of friendships necessary for developing consensus. Job rotation develops competent workers who are valued for the skills they have rather than the job they are doing at any particular time. This helps develop the individual's concern for the company as a whole rather than any particular unit.

These indoctrination and learning experiences are not intended to teach blind conformity, but rather the exercise of judgment guided by organization goals and values. They are intended to create individual self-control and minimize the need for supervision. The role of the supervisor is less one of issuing direct orders and more one of teacher. Cole's research has led him to conclude (1979, pp. 222–223) that worker-related management practices in Japan reflect a belief that human nature can be perfected, thus the willingness to invest in education and training, career development, and quality circles, and to apply the ideas and findings of behavioral scientists.

Japanese Operations in the United States.   The research of the Japan External Trade Organization, JETRO (1981), has provided the data base for many of the opinions about the form and effectiveness of Japanese management practices applied to their operations located in the United States. JETRO surveyed 230 firms in the United States with varying degrees of Japanese financial interest (most were predominately Japanese-owned) and mix of Japanese and American employees.

Sethi et al. (1984, chapter 8), based in part on their analysis of the JETRO data, found that management strategies ranged from the rigid intact transplanting of the systems and people from Japan to a more flexibile approach with attempts, over time, to acculturate the American workers to the Japanese systems.

Based on his own analysis of the JETRO data, Nosow (1984) concluded the following: (1) The most critical attribute of Japanese companies in the United States is the development of an internal homogeneity that binds all members of the enterprise into a corporate family, (2) development of a corporate family requires commonly understood and shared cultural values, and (3) the specific techniques needed to improve organization performance are not rigidly predetermined, but adaptively selected. Nosow's analysis showed, as an example, that only about 20 percent of the Japanese firms were using quality circles (at the time of the JETRO survey) in the United States, largely because management focused initially on changing relationships and ways of thinking.

AMERICAN HUMAN RESOURCE MANAGEMENT PRACTICES

In recent years, American management practices and systems have been taking two paths, one deriving from predominantly American traditions with some recent adaptations of Japanese techniques and one predominantly a transplant of Japanese techniques.

Predominantly American Approaches.   American approaches are characterized by a growing working relationship between management and human resource development specialists. The historic roots date back to the period 1924–

1932. During that time, studies were conducted at the Western Electric Company, Hawthorne (Chicago) manufacturing plant (Roethlisberger and Dickson, 1939). In a departure from usual industrial practice, management collaborated with behavioral scientists to investigate the effects of various working conditions, e.g., illumination, number of rest periods, length of workday, and time of day on productivity and quality. Experiments were conducted with workers in small groups (there were about five people in a group, compared to the approximately 100 people on the shop floor). Although the experiments were conducted in simulated shop-floor conditions, a number of unusual features were introduced such as asking operators to work at a comfortable pace and discussing changes with them before they were made. It was found that rejects decreased and productivity increased during the early studies as favorable changes were made, e.g., better illumination, more and longer rest periods, and a shorter workday. The improvement continued even after the researchers reversed the changes and brought conditions back to the initial levels. The favorable results were attributed to the improved human relations atmosphere that surrounded the studies, particularly the unusual management attention.

During the following decades, studies continued in various firms. Selection and training systems developed during World War II were implemented as the behavioral scientists turned their attention back to industry. The period beginning with the 1950s has seen a large number of attempts at work improvement, e.g., job enrichment, work redesign, sociotechnical systems, participative management, quality of work life (QWL), and worker involvement. (Quality circles may be one form of group participation in a broader QWL or worker involvement effort.) QWL has been viewed as a process for changing an organization (see Rosow, 1982, for the process steps) from Theory X (with its technological and control systems, and associated beliefs, values, attitudes, behaviors, and relationships) to one consistent with Theory Y. QWL also has been viewed as an outcome of the change process, its success being measured in terms of employee attitudes and work satisfaction. These efforts have been led by behavioral scientists, but with influences from some American union leaders who were trying to bring about "social democracy" in the workplace, as well as influences from European industrial democracy efforts. For more on these efforts see, for example, Burck (1981), "The New Industrial Relations" (1981), Davis (1983–1984), Guest (1979), and Walton (1979). The union's role and issues surrounding union-management collaboration are discussed later in this section under Role of the Labor Union and in Batt and Weinberg (1978), Bluestone (1977), Burck (1981), Lawler and Ozley (1979), and Rubinstein (1982).

An assumption implicit in some QWL approaches is that job satisfaction is a prerequisite for high-quality, productive work. An alternate view is that job satisfaction is a result of–not a condition for–quality performance. Satisfaction comes when management removes the obstacles and provides the processes that enable workers to perform well. Good performance brings satisfaction and pride.

A trend now emerging appears to be one of integrating fully the human resources management expertise (the managers and specialists) into the business management team. The human resource development function is being elevated to the status of a key business system requiring strategic planning and a long-range outlook encompassing culture change rather than a simple technique or programmatic orientation (Golden and Ramanujam, 1985, and Tichy, 1983). Human resource specialists are taking a broader systems perspective, learning more about the business and the ways in which their approaches can contribute to business success (especially quality). The specialists previously had focused on the quality of work life or worker involvement process as an end in itself, with quality and productivity a desirable by-product. There is now growing awareness that quality is also a desirable focus since it (1) is necessary for business health and (2) will require greater worker involvement and self-control. Conversely, line managers are acquiring more of the human resource development knowledge, skills, and roles formerly delegated to the personnel function. This is a development parallel to the shifting of *other* key quality functions from the quality control department to line management.

Certainly there have been false starts and setbacks due to attempts to play "catch-up" to the Japanese and compress the time needed to build a collaborative relationship with the union and bring about the necessary changes. There have also been some dramatic demonstrations of worker contributions to improved product and process design when management shared its prerogatives with the workers, and the union relaxed work rules (see Main, 1983). Longer-term views are beginning to prevail as well as recognition of the need to better integrate human resource management systems and technological innovations (automation, scheduling, inventory controls, etc.) into a coherent work system.

Sethi et al. (1984) list a number of companies—some of which are on Peters and Waterman's (1982) list of "excellent" companies—which have a history of human resource management practices similar to those associated with Japanese companies. These companies devote a great deal of energy to creating a work environment in which workers can closely identify their interests with those of their employers. There is heavy emphasis on product quality, innovation, and customer satisfaction. Features of these organizations include sharing of financial rewards at all levels in the organization, no layoffs, a largely salaried rather than hourly based wage system, above-average compensation, worker training, promotion from within, and a genuine interest in all aspects of employee welfare.

Ouchi (1981) has observed the similarity of these practices—which he calls Type Z—to those of companies in Japan. He has cited Type Z companies to support his view that Japanese management practices can be applied successfully in the United States. Sethi et al. (1984, pp. 221–223, 265–271) and Nosow (1984) argue that the practices of these Type Z companies derive from a uniquely American social, cultural, and political environment. Sethi and his colleagues, based on their own research and that of others (e.g., Bruce-Briggs, 1982, and Sullivan, 1983), believe that traditional Western business organizations will have difficulty developing quickly into a Type Z organization. They also note (with criticism of the authors' methodology) the performance decline of some of the Peters and Waterman "excellent" companies since publication of their book in 1982. Much of the success of these companies was attributed to progressive human resource management practices and entrepreneurial type leadership (see also "Who's Excellent Now?" 1984).

American approaches will be discussed in more detail in subsections to follow such as Processing System Design.

Transplanted Japanese Techniques.   U.S. management interest in quality circles was stimulated primarily by Juran's (e.g., 1967*a*, 1967*b*) observations of circle operations in Japan as well as by Rubinstein's (1971) efforts during the 1960s to involve operators—in small groups—in quality improvement. Circles were introduced to American business in the early to middle 1970s through use of adapted JUSE training materials and guidelines (for more history see the ASQC 1976 and 1983 references in the Supplemental Bibliography). During the following 10 years, there was a proliferation of research, consultants, training materials, convention presentations, papers, and books. (Circles also spread to Western Europe and South America.) The New York Stock Exchange study, *People and*

Productivity (Epstein and Freund, 1984), showed 44 percent of all U.S. companies with more than 500 employees had quality circle programs. Nearly three out of four started after 1980. Lawler and Mohrman (1985) estimate that over 90 percent of the Fortune 500 companies have quality circle programs. Circles have been applied on the shop floor and in the offices, in manufacturing, and in service industries (see, for example, Ingle and Ingle, 1983).

Sethi and his associates (1984) characterized the use of quality circles by some U.S. companies as "cosmetic." These companies are usually midsized and have market share niches that partially protect them from intensive competition. Their approach usually has the following features:

Introduction is accompanied by a tremendous fanfare in the in-house magazines and the local media. The emphasis is on conveying an image to employees and community that the company is forward-looking in its industrial relations and willing to experiment with new modes to improve productivity and worker relations. But the principal organization concept of top-down management remains unchanged.

Programs are directed by the personnel or public relations departments, and there is little real top management involvement or commitment.

There is inadequate resource allocation, and once the program is initiated, there is insufficient follow-through.

The new practices are too often introduced without enough prior training for the involved workers and plant supervisors as to what is expected of them and how the circles are supposed to function. There is greater attention to form than to substance.

The program often is consultant-driven. A convincing sales presentation leads management to expect great results. In the experience of this author, many (although not all) of the consultants have little expertise beyond delivering training. They do not work with top management to remove inhibitors to meaningful worker participation.

Circles implemented under these conditions usually have a life of 9 months to 2 years. Their growth and decline follow a characteristic pattern (see Cole and Tachiki, 1984, and Lawler and Mohrman, 1985). The program runs into trouble when management is required to go beyond words and become involved personally, for example in face-to-face meetings with workers to listen to a project proposal and a request for management support. While some local problems may be solved, management itself does not form its own circles to address systems issues surfaced by workers. Nor do the circles lead to other forms of participation (e.g., cross-functional project teams) where workers can work with management on systems improvement. (See discussion of improvement project teams in Section 22 as well as: Deming, 1982, pp. 84–86, 107–110, and Gryna, 1981.) Worker enthusiasm is replaced with frustration, and participation fades. When management expectations for results are not met, a scapegoat (e.g., the union, the method) is found for the failure. Morale and trust are worse than before the circle program.

Sethi et al. (1984) have identified a category of companies which follow an approach they call "exploitation." Quality and productivity improvements are sought *through* rather than *in collaboration* with workers. Most of the firms taking this approach have no union. Characteristics are:

The management strategy toward worker relations is essentially authoritarian in character, combined with a large measure of paternalism.

The machine aspects of production rather than the human aspects of management are emphasized.

A great deal of emphasis is placed on the measurement of individual worker productivity, and the reward system emphasizes individual production versus group output.

The primary mode of worker motivation for participating in group activity—whether it involves quality control or increased production—is fear. The highly paternalistic management orientation ensures that this fear is never brutally exercised or overtly manifested, but cooperation and acquiescence on the part of workers is expected and taken for granted.

Management makes every effort to keep as large a share of the gains from productivity as possible. The workers' share is often minimal, grudgingly given, and carries a large measure of acclaimed management generosity.

Management keeps itself insulated from the work force. Top-down communication consists of requests for information, not suggestions or opinions. Bottom-up communication is one of providing the facts. Management does what is minimally required to get workers involved without delegating any of its authority and prerogatives. The primary focus is on things that can be accomplished on the shop floor, and involves streamlining production processes and reducing the number of workers rather than increasing the intellectual contributions of workers.

Companies using this approach still have in place the bureaucratic, autocratic, Theory X management systems. Management does not want worker participation because it fears loss of its own authority. Workers do not trust management. Thus, the system does not encourage meaningful worker participation nor provide mechanisms for it. Quality circles, when used, are viewed strictly from an engineering rather than a human relations perspective. Results are periodically evaluated to see if the costs are justified.

MANAGEMENT'S ROLE

Lessons from and for Japan. The Japanese successes in application of the various techniques—as has been shown—were made possible because they were consistent and supported by the social, cultural, and economic environment. Western failures to reap fully the benefits of these practices occur when the prerequisites for success do not exist or the organization does not create the personnel systems and work climate to encourage, enable, and reward workers for contributing their energies and ideas. The importance of these environmental controls in sustaining worker-related management practices was made evident by the Japanese over the history of their industrialization, and particularly since 1950. The importance of these factors is being demonstrated today in Japan, but in a different way. In a number of companies—particularly high technology—the slowdown of economic growth has reduced management's ability to reciprocate worker loyalty and dedication to the company with guarantees of jobs for life and built-in promotions and salary increases. Sethi et al (1984, chapter 10) describe a weakening of the foundation upon which past Japanese successes were built resulting from cost competition from other Asian producers (e.g., Korea and Taiwan), requirements to compete in high-technology markets requiring innovation and fast response, and internal cultural changes (e.g., role of women).

Thus, under cost and technological competitive pressures, worker-related management practices of a number of Japanese companies are becoming more like those of some American companies, with similar disastrous results on worker attitudes and loyalties. Younger workers with high technology skills have greater mobility than before and are less willing to accept a system that requires conformity or does not compensate them adequately.

Defining and Creating a Responsive Corporate Culture. Worker-related management systems and practices should enable the business to be responsive and flexibile in anticipating and meeting customer needs and requirements under changing market, economic, political, social, and government-regulatory conditions. The recent experiences of American and Japanese companies suggest that workers cannot and will not contribute fully if the company operates in a manner that is inconsistent with workers' abilities, needs, values, and expectations which have been conditioned by the larger society. (In a sense, workers as internal customers of the company's management systems have user input requirements.)

The nature of work and the work force is changing in a way that requires management to evaluate explicitly how its systems and practices affect the loyalty, dedication, and commitment of employees (all levels) to the company and whether they promote or inhibit the full contribution of employee skills, knowledge, and creativity. The research of Yankelovich and Immerwahr (1983) has documented a widening "commitment gap" between employees' perception of their ability to perform and their actual performance. For example: 75 percent of those surveyed felt they could be much more effective; 63 percent felt they had a great deal of discretion over the quality of their work, but 44 percent reported giving only the minimum amount of effort required. As technology continues to change jobs, even on the shop floor, to predominantly high-discretion, information-processing, knowledge work, then employee discretion and capability to contribute to the control and improvement of quality will increase (see Davis, 1983–1984, Howard, 1984, Miller, 1984, and Sethi et al., 1984, especially chapter 11). Management should look closely to see whether traditional organization characteristics ranging from rewards, punishments, and compensation practices, to forms of involvement in planning and decision making are consistent with the ability of the company to be competitive in quality and productivity.

Workers are better educated than their predecessors, both technically and in financial aspects of the business. They want the democratic freedoms, rights, and responsibilities they exercise in private life extended to the workplace. Sethi et al. (1984), Miller (1984), and others contend that Western business organizations cannot meet future demands by copying the techniques of currently successful companies, American or Japanese. Harmonious relations, a spirit of cooperation, and worker loyalty cannot be created by imposing groupism. Rather, American management practices are best based on American traditions and culture which place great value on the individual's freedom of choice, particularly in the participation in various activities and selection of one's associates. In a high-discretion environment, imposition of tight controls would not produce more than the minimum contribution. Workers need to feel that management is reasonable, is competent to make the request, and that the worker will benefit. Juran (1964, chapter 21) has observed that freedom is a relative term. People do consent to the imposition of organization controls in return for various rewards. There is always a tradeoff. Extreme individualists are out of place if they join bureaucratic organizations, or if they do, they are best placed in jobs of high autonomy, e.g., researcher.

Schein (1981) suggests that a key role of management is to know when individual contributions are needed and when team contributions are needed in order to create the norms and reward systems that will produce appropriate forms of behavior as required. This is much like the job of a sports team coach who has to create a team effort while maximizing the contribution of individual player talents. In addition, this must be done in a way that maintains individual responsibility and accountability. Accountability requires self-control.

Companies will compete successfully if they have created a system of values, beliefs, and behaviors (individual and team)—a culture—necessary for that success. Miller (1984) observes that typically top management develops financial, market, and product strategies without asking if the work environment will enable and encourage people to accomplish these company plans. In the future, management will need to define and create the culture necessary to optimize business performance. The achievement of the desired culture requires planning. Miller has identified eight primary (general) values which promote worker loyalty, productivity, and innovation in American companies—purpose, consensus, excellence, unity, performance, empiricism, intimacy, and integrity. His ideas are representative of the thinking of a growing number of behavioral scientists and managers regarding the new roles facing management. (See, for example, Berman and Mase, 1983; Kanter, 1983; Myers, 1981, chapter 7; Peters and Waterman, 1982; Sethi et al., 1984, chapter 11; and Yankelovich and Immerwahr, 1983.) Many of these ideas are not new. Decades ago Juran (1956) proposed that the anthropologists' concepts of culture could be applied to business organizations by managers desiring to create beneficial change. Miller's eight values, summarized below, provide a framework to define the existing culture, the desired culture, and develop a plan for change.

Purpose. The goals of the company are stated, not in accounting terms (e.g., return on investment, or ROI), but in terms of product or service and benefit to the customer. Miller talks about "power of purpose," the energizing effects of working toward a worthy cause, a noble goal, a vision. It gives meaning to people's efforts.

Consensus. Organizations, according to Miller, should broaden the available forms of decision making beyond the traditional top-down command styles. How and by whom problems are solved, decisions are made and carried out should be determined by what will produce the highest quality results. Miller describes three forms of managerial decision-making styles that can be matched to the particular situations:

1. *Command:* The individual manager makes the decision without discussion with subordinates or peers. This is used for short-term operating decisions where it would be inappropriate to disrupt or take the time of others. It also may be appropriate in crisis situations where there is no time to get the ideas of others.

2. *Consultative:* The individual manager makes the decision after discussion, either one-on-one or in a small group, with others who have knowledge or interests related to the decision.

3. *Consensus:* A group of the manager's subordinates or peers who have the necessary knowledge and information and who will be affected by the decision participate in the discussion until a decision is reached which they all agree to support.

A more detailed discussion of the range of decision-making styles, levels of employee involvement, and the criteria for their selection is given by Baker (1982), Sherwood and Hoylman (1977), and Tannenbaum and Schmidt (1973). (Individual self-control where, in a sense, the individual manages a process, will be discussed later.)

Excellence.   Management's job is not to promote satisfaction with the way things are but to create dissatisfaction with the way things are and could be. Closing this gap would be energizing. Management can create an environment of intellectual inquiry in which the pursuit of knowledge becomes the norm by (1) demanding and rewarding individual initiative and improvement, (2) publicly recognizing those who excel, and (3) designing the systems and organization structures that cause individuals to feel they can control their own destinies in a way that promotes acceptance of responsibility. (Juran's "breakthrough" sequence and Deming's continuous improvement cycle, discussed later, are processes to help accomplish these ends.)

Unity.   In a theme consistent with the views of Juran (1964), Deming (1982), Myers (1981), Sethi et al. (1984), some union leaders (e.g., Bluestone, 1977), and others, Miller feels that companies must try to return to earlier American craft traditions for their workers. Ownership and identity with the work and the product were a source of pride. Personal ownership, replaced by the alienation of impersonal mass production systems, can again be made possible by information technologies that change the nature of work from doing to thinking. Workers are prepared to accept new relationships and responsibilities. The bureaucratic divisions that separate manager as thinker from worker as doer are barriers to competitive quality and productivity and can be overcome by management practices which are directed at creating harmony of purpose and creation of common interests. Miller (1984, chapter 5) describes a number of plants where management increased its power to perform effectively by delegating to employees more self-control for day-to-day decisions. To accomplish this, he concludes that management should:

Design an organization structure to eliminate unnecessary layers and give greatest possible responsibility to lowest possible levels.

Redesign compensation systems to create a common concern rather than accentuating distinctions between management and labor (e.g., hourly versus salaried employees).

Seek the greatest possible degree of involvement from people at all levels.

Exhibit through personal style and example, the trust and unity they feel with employees.

The unification of people, processes, and organization unit is discussed in detail later under the subsections The Processing System, Worker Participation in Process Management, and Team Performance: A Processing System Viewpoint.

Performance.   Performance will matter to the individual if rewards are dependent on performance. Financial rewards are part of a total array of positive consequences for performance. Performance measurement can serve to let individuals know how they are doing. Evaluation can be made against the individual's or group's prior performance rather than against arbitrary and artificial standards. (See the topic Managing the Consequences of Performance later in this section.)

Empiricism. Effective organization performance is promoted by the use of scientific logic, the encouragement of intellectual curiosity and questioning of why something is known and the reliance on statistical thinking that provides a common basis for the interpretation of data. Employees at all levels will perform measurably better if they know how they are performing. This was clearly demonstrated to this writer in a discussion with an operator in an automotive plant. In describing the resolution of some problems, the operator pointed to the statistical process control chart and said: "This chart is great. I can't remember what I had for dinner last night, but I can see what this process was doing 3 months ago." He went on to describe how the chart was like a scoreboard which helped him see his contributions (physical and mental) to the control and improvement of the process.

Intimacy. This relates to the ability of individuals to share ideas, feelings, and needs in an open, trusting manner, without fear of punishment. The business relies less on procedures, forms, and technology and more upon the cohesiveness of its people.

Integrity. Action is based on what is ethical, not just legal. Deeds are consistent with words. Managers are role models of integrity that inspire their subordinates to believe the purpose of the organization is right, just, and worth sacrificing for. Management's role is to create and manage a culture consistent with the organization behaviors needed to execute the business plan.

Management's Task: Applying the Knowledge. The application of behavioral science knowledge often is a difficult task. Even if one believes that a Theory Y approach is a more effective (and ethical) way to manage human resources, it is not easy to translate the behavioral scientist's concepts, principles, and research findings into action. A major source of difficulty is the abstract language used to explain why people behave as they do in complex industrial organizations. Discussions typically focus on internal events within the individual. Rather than dealing with factors the manager can observe, measure, and influence, the subject matter is one of internal "psychological" events, e.g., motives, attitudes, needs. These abstractions need to be transformed into concrete actions a manager can use.

Organization effectiveness does not depend solely on good people management systems or good technology management systems, but rather on the interaction of all business systems. It may be useful to view business performance as dependent on three related categories of systems:

Technical processing systems: Employee technical skills and knowledge, equipment, technologies, methods, etc.

Social/cultural systems: Beliefs, values, and preferred modes of behaving; reward systems; willingness of people to contribute and cooperate.

Process management systems: Concepts, methods, tools to integrate the social/cultural and technical systems in order to control and improve processes and properly link them across the areas of the business.

Deficiencies in any of these areas can degrade quality and jeopardize competitive viability. The approach to applying human performance management techniques will be described later within a process management framework.

ROLE OF THE LABOR UNION

Irving Bluestone, a former United Auto Workers vice-president, has discussed (reported in Yankelovich and Immerwahr, 1983) the need for management and the union to overcome traditional relationships that are preventing cooperation on issues of mutual concern. There are factors on both sides that label efforts to cooperate as "collusion," "being in bed with the enemy," etc. Cooperation is viewed by union militants as selling out to the company. It is viewed by certain managers as giving away the company to the union. The economic challenge has made the health of the business a common concern. A process is needed to enable appropriate adversarial roles to be exercised while finding ways to work together for mutual benefit.

Trade unions, in the tradition of their craft guild predecessors, have prepared their members to exercise the self-control implicit in their jobs. Long apprenticeships teach the knowledge and skills to bring equipment and facilities to a state of fitness for use (or to specification). Industrial unions, on the other hand, have not traditionally focused on self-control, but have defined their primary roles as one of establishing equitable pay systems. To the extent that mutual trust could be established with management, and the union and its members could benefit, the union has collaborated on quality-of-worklife projects. Some of these efforts have given workers wide latitude in how work is accomplished. However, there have been setbacks when the union felt that management had not generalized its open, cooperative approach beyond the specific quality-of-work-life projects and consulted with the union.

The Yankelovich and Immerwahr study found that blue-collar workers, particularly union members, have the least discretion of all of those surveyed. The union faces new challenges in helping its members close this "commitment gap." Unions and management must find a process to undo many of the features of the Taylor system and turn over some of the specialist functions to the operator.

Joint labor-management committees have provided a way for both parties to cooperate outside of the labor contract. They have been especially successful in business and industries facing an economic threat. Some of the gain-sharing plans offer a model for providing an institutionalized basis for cooperation in matters of quality and productivity (e.g., see Rubinstein, 1982). According to Batt and Weinberg (1978), Scanlon gain-sharing plans (although not widespread) have proven successful as a cooperative effort because:

The plan does not depend on the support of any individual union official or manager who is subject to change. Everyone has a visible, measurable stake in its continuation—the monthly bonus check.

This plan is agreed to voluntarily by union and management, outside the contract, with the acceptance of a majority of employees. Final adoption is decided after a 1-year trial period.

The benefits reach everyone immediately.

There is a continuing incentive for communications to improve in all directions. The monthly bonus provides immediate feedback on company performance. Everyone comes to realize that the success of each person and group depends on the success of the enterprise.

Based on his research, Schuster (1984) attributes a good deal of the plan's success to the management philosophy necessary to establish employee participation, information sharing, and mutual trust.

Although union-management collaboration in work environment improvements does not replace the fundamental adversarial relationship of both parties, there is a mutual willingness to explore new forms of cooperation. For example:

A provision of the 1982 Ford and General Motors collective bargaining agreement authorized mutual growth forums (Katz, 1982).

AT&T and the Communications Workers of America have created "common interest forums" to discuss long-range employment efforts of new telecommunications technologies (Hanlon, 1985).

The 1983 agreement between the Steelworkers of America and the major steel companies established labor-management participation teams. Teams work on any area of mutual interest not specifically excluded by or in violation of the contract (Rubinstein, 1984).

General Motors and the United Auto Workers in 1983 set up a joint committee to study the social, technical, and management system requirements for a new automobile manufacturing organization. This resulted in the formation of the Saturn Corporation, a General Motors subsidiary (Ephlin, 1985).

This type of union-management cooperation is associated with quality and productivity improvement, although the specific linkages are not well understood (Hanlon, 1985). These efforts tend to improve communication and trust to a level where the union is flexible in its acceptance of innovative human resource management practices, (e.g., self-managing work teams) and new technologies. In turn, management accepts the union's job security provisions. Such companies are characterized by effective group problem solving, innovative employee suggestions, and low rates of grievances, disciplinary actions, absenteeism, and turnover.

Reisman and Compa (1985) take the opposite view. They believe that the adversarial character of American labor-management relations is organic to an economic system propelled by hard-driving managers seeking to maximize profits. Both the historical roots of American unionism and the underlying pressures that drive management suggest that those who recommend a new spirit of labor-management cooperation are asking for a cultural revolution that has no basis in industrial reality. The "new era" in labor-management cooperation is a repeat of the cycle of "new eras" that has existed for as long as unions have existed. They maintain that the traditional adversarial relationship is better for both sides than one based on cooperation. Adversarialism is a positive concept. It includes room for give and take in solving shop (or office) problems, in improving quality and productivity, and in meeting workers' needs. From the union's viewpoint, economic progress and shop-floor autonomy are best achieved by having labor and management negotiate from opposite sides of the table where both sides are conscious of inherent differences and respectful of each other's interests, and where the strength of each side serves to check the reach of the other.

The history of some cooperative efforts can reinforce this skepticism. Schuster (1984), Rubinstein (1984), and Cohen-Rosenthal and Burton (1986) acknowledge that the failures have occurred, but the causes were more in process implementation than in philosophical differences or profit motives. Difficulties were found to stem from high management mobility, competitive and adversarial relationships between management functions as well as between operating management and technical staffs, weak union leadership, and absence of expert consultants and practitioners skilled in implementing change in union settings. These writers describe methods for successfully overcoming these obstacles.

THE PROCESSING SYSTEM

Any business organization can be viewed as a network of interdependent functions working to accomplish the organization's purpose. This is done through a diffusion of goals and objectives horizontally and vertically throughout the organization. Most of the individuals, however, may not understand how what they do relates to that higher purpose, and how they affect the ability of other organization members to contribute to that purpose. The processing system concept described below represents a synthesis of various systems approaches to analyzing human performance in organizations (e.g., see Brethower, 1982, Connellan, 1978, Kast and Rosenzweig, 1979, Lawler, 1976, Myers, 1981, and Rummler, 1981). A systems perspective can provide a useful framework for understanding and managing the factors that affect people's performance in any line, service, or administrative and staff work—at any level in the hierarchy. It applies to the production of hardware and to "software" (information, ideas, etc.). If the primary purpose of the enterprise is defined as the production of goods and services that satisfy customers' needs and expectations, the concept of fitness for use may be extended throughout the entire enterprise. It may be useful for each suborganization to view its own purpose as one of satisfying internal customer requirements. These ideas have their origins in the same kinds of systems thinking that gave rise to Japanese companywide quality control practices (see, for example, Ishikawa, 1985, Juran, 1964, Kogure, 1970, and Suzuki, 1978). See also Section 6 under The Triple Role Concept.

Internal Supplier–Customer Network. Figure 10.1 shows three stages of a larger processing system that produces goods (e.g., parts manufacturing or assembly) or services (e.g., accounts payable, scheduling). Activities at each stage transform inputs to outputs of greater value. Each stage is a supplier to subsequent stages and customer of previous stages. Each individual employee, as "process manager," plays these two roles of customer and supplier.

System Components. The system components necessary for quality performance are illustrated in Figure 10.2 for a single supplier-customer interface and are described below.

FIG. 10.1   Dual roles of the process manager in the network of supplier-customer interfaces.

FIG. 10.2 Processing system components necessary for quality performance. *Note*: User's input requirements derived from own output requirements established to satisfy subsequent customers.

Supplier (Producer) Processing System. The "supplier (producer) processing system" can represent the job of the individual worker who, although not a manager in the traditional sense of managing subordinates, can be viewed as presiding over a process, managing the resources at his or her disposal. "Presiding" is a relative term. It can mean that individual simply follows procedures and executes tasks as told; or it can have a broader definition where the worker exercises discretion and self-control over how the work is done and participates in all of the management control functions for that job. The individual uses personal efforts, skills, knowledge, and intellect to blend the other input resources (process sheets and other "how-to" documents, equipment and tools, materials, etc.) to create outputs of value to the organization.

The person illustrated above each processing system box can represent a production operator or tradesperson on the shop floor, an engineer, production control specialist, finance analyst, secretary—any nonsupervisory professional, technical, or clerical employee. Inside each box are the tasks and related process activities which could be detailed by a process flow diagram. This framework also may be used to depict the processing system of any higher-level employee—supervisor, manager, etc. A manager's system contains the processing systems that contribute to the products and services provided by his or her organization. This could include staff, service, support, and administrative functions which do not report to the manager. This concept is explained further in a subsequent subsection, Team Performance: A Processing System Viewpoint.

Outputs. These are the products and services. The output of plant engineering, for example, could be "serviced machines"; of material control, "delivered parts"; of accounts payable, "paid invoices." It is the vital few important characteristics of the output—the *critical outcomes*—which are measured. As one moves up the organization hierarchy from microlevel processing systems to macrosystems presided over by middle- and higher-level managers, the process output measurements change in the frequency with which they are generated and in their complexity. Measurements are taken less often and tend to be indexes and composites.

Inputs. These are resources that, for convenience, can be summarized into five categories: people—their knowledge, skills, intellect, creativity, and energy; equipment—machines and tools; methods—e.g., process sheets, shop manuals, instructions; materials and information; environment—the psychological and social as well as the physical. Inputs function in two ways. There are those which *do* the transforming and may be consumed (oil burns off, tools wear, people get tired). The inputs *to be* transformed are *throughputs* to the system. Rather than being consumed, they emerge as outputs with greater value than when they entered (e.g., raw materials to become functioning parts, equipment to be rehabilitated, people to be trained or advised, invoices to be paid, management reports to be acted upon).

Output Requirements. The measured value or values (target, aim, standard, objective, specification, etc.) for the outputs that the processing system—as supplier—intends to achieve.

Customer (User) Processing System. Any system is in a customer role when it uses a supplier's outputs as inputs to its own processes. Each customer becomes the producer for subsequent users.

Customer Input Requirements. These are the types and characteristics of inputs the processing system—as customer—needs from the supplier to perform effectively (i.e., to meet the customer's own output requirements). Value added by the supplier can be evaluated in terms of how well the customer's requirements have been met.

Supplier's External Feedback Loop: Customer Satisfaction. This is information about how well the supplier's outputs are meeting customer requirements. The information may be used for decisions affecting output (e.g., what characteristics to measure and control) or process (e.g., what can be changed to reduce processing time or output variability).

Supplier's Internal Feedback Loop: Process Control. This is information about process stability (repeatability) and output uniformity needed for process regulation. (See Juran, 1964, for a detailed discussion of the manager's feedback loop for control; see also Section 6 under The Feedback Loop.)

WORKER PARTICIPATION IN PROCESS MANAGEMENT

There are two distinct, but intertwined, sets of process management activities necessary to produce quality products and services continuously:

Process control: the prevention of adverse, undesired change; maintenance of the status quo, of a stable state

Process improvement: planning and creating beneficial, desired change

Process Control and Improvement Cycles. A four-stage cycle for each set of activities is shown in Figure 10.3. An early version of the cycle was introduced to Japan by Deming (1951) in his statistical quality control lectures in 1950. Deming (personal communication) derived the cycle from Shewhart's three-stage cycle of activities necessary to manage a production process: specify, produce, inspect. Shewhart (1939, pp. 44–49) observed that these activities were analogous to the

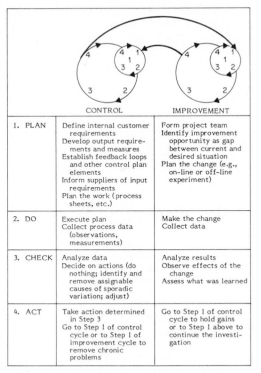

	CONTROL	IMPROVEMENT
1. PLAN	Define internal customer requirements Develop output requirements and measures Establish feedback loops and other control plan elements Inform suppliers of input requirements Plan the work (process sheets, etc.)	Form project team Identify improvement opportunity as gap between current and desired situation Plan the change (e.g., on-line or off-line experiment)
2. DO	Execute plan Collect process data (observations, measurements)	Make the change Collect data
3. CHECK	Analyze data Decide on actions (do nothing; identify and remove assignable causes of sporadic variation; adjust)	Analyze results Observe effects of the change Assess what was learned
4. ACT	Take action determined in Step 3 Go to Step 1 of control cycle or to Step 1 of improvement cycle to remove chronic problems	Go to Step 1 of control cycle to hold gains or to Step 1 above to continue the investigation

FIG. 10.3 Plan-do-check-act (PDCA) processing system management cycle.

steps of the scientific method for acquiring knowledge: hypothesize, experiment, test the hypothesis. The cycle, hence, is a process for learning and improving. The stages have been labeled "plan-do-check-action" by the Japanese (see Ishikawa, 1985, and Kondo, 1977) and for convenience will be referred to as the PDCA cycle. The cycles are similar to the universal control and breakthrough sequences developed by Juran (1964).

According to Shewhart and Deming, a process must be stable before it can be improved. Without statistical control there is no consistently reproducing process. Stable performance requires a process control feedback loop. A PDCA cycle is shown within the planning stage, indicating that the planning for control and improvement also requires a series of activities such as identifying intended suppliers and customers who can form teams to work on process control and improvement. This will be discussed in subsequent subsections.

When Western industry organized for mass production with its dependence on large quantities of unskilled labor, it separated the "doing" from the rest of the cycle. Prior to mass production, most—if not all—functions were integrated within the same individual. The worker was both producer and entrepreneur, carrying out all of the activities of the management cycle from the planning and design of product and process, to the manufacture and sale of the goods. The controls on the worker's behavior came directly from feedback from the customer in the marketplace. Income and reputation required making goods fit for use. In order to stay in business, resources had to be managed efficiently with little waste. The individual had the control and flexibility needed to make the necessary decisions and tradeoffs between internal costs and market forces in order to produce a decent return (see Juran and Gryna, 1980, p. 138).

In most Western industrial organizations (which are based on the Taylor model of functional specialization), the steps of the control cycle are carried out by different people. Managers and engineers plan the work and design the process and tell workers the "right way" to do the work. Workers follow the prescribed methods and inspectors check their work. It is assumed that when things are going well it is because of the system. Since management, not workers, designed the process and set the goals, management, not workers, deserves the credit. Workers are being paid, and that, it is thought, is sufficient. When problems occur, e.g., scrap or rework, workers receive feedback (negative) from supervisors, inspectors, and others. Feedback is used in an attempt to restore control, not maintain control. It takes the form of warnings of what will happen if the worker does not follow procedures. Unfortunately, this approach usually induces overcontrol producing process instability, greater product variability, and high defect rates along with conflict, finger pointing, defensiveness, and other dysfunctional human behavior.

The management systems put in place for mass production may have done three things for workers:

1. Reduced their effectiveness by not giving them the information they need (feedback) to regulate and maintain control of the process
2. Made the work itself essentially meaningless by also removing the planning and other activities needed to give the work continuity, a clear purpose, and provide a sense of accomplishment
3. Precluded participation in planned improvement projects to breakthrough to new quality levels

In this writer's opinion, many white-collar jobs have the same characteristics. Whether in engineering, accounting, or other areas, white-collar work often is characterized by limited positive feedback to employees when results are good, abundant negative feedback when results are poor, and a limited employee role in planning, goal setting, and decision making.

Process Management and Worker Self-Control

Self-Control in Sports and Recreation. A number of writers (Connellan, 1980, Kondo, 1976, Myers, 1981, and Miller, 1978), trying to better understand the factors affecting human behavior, have been intrigued by the willingness of people to participate and try to do well in sports, games, and other leisure and recreational activities, under conditions that they would not tolerate at work. The authors ask, for example:

Why do people who are fatigued at work find energy the same evening to play three sets of tennis or two games of racquetball?

Why do people get up at 5:30 in the morning to play golf in the rain?

Would golf be as much fun if it were part of work and the boss directed the employee to shoot an 80?

Why do people voluntarily play cards or bingo when it is usually done in smoky, noisy, poorly lighted rooms at night after working all day?

Would bowling be as much fun if the bowler could not see what happens to the pins after the ball was launched; or if one had to wait until the end of the evening (or end of the season) to find out the score?

It is obvious why people play a Las Vegas "one-armed bandit"; but why will they pay to play an electronic "pinball machine," and do this hour after hour even when there is no monetary payoff?

The answers to these types of questions can shed light on why work is "work" and play is "fun," and provide an understanding of the essential elements of jobs that encourage ("motivate") people to expend effort, try to improve, and make it possible for them to improve the results of their efforts.

Analysis of these activities indicates that people engaged in sports or recreation have the means for self-control:

1. They know what they are supposed to do. Goals and targets are visible. The relationship (contingency) between performance and reward is known.

2. They know what they are doing. Output is measurable (the score) and there is immediate feedback on performance (the scoreboard). The cheers and encouragement of the other participants provide additional feedback and social recognition that is positively reinforcing and causes effort to be maintained or increased; scores do not have to be related to money or other material rewards to reinforce behavior.

The knowledge that one has achieved the goal also is a source of positive reinforcement.

3. They have the ability to regulate. The method of doing the task is not tightly specified; people can do it in a way that is comfortable for them.

Feedback of results and knowledge of goals makes it possible to change one's own behavior if desired results are not being achieved.

Participation in the sport (which includes selecting ones associates and leaders) and the setting of one's own goals is voluntary; achievement of goals which people have set for themselves is usually more rewarding than achieving someone else's goals.

The freedom afforded individuals causes their creativity, intelligence, and skill to be challenged.

Self-Control in Processing Systems.   When employees, whether on the shop floor or in the offices, are not provided with the means for self-control, they cannot be held accountable for failure to achieve the desired results. Deficiencies may exist in the process itself, e.g., equipment design, work organization and layout, tools, and job aids; or they may exist in the feedback loops (e.g., cannot communicate with supplier or customer) or in the consequences of performance. These affect the worker's knowledge of "supposed to do," "is doing," and ability to regulate (take action), summarized below.

See the following related discussions: Section 17 under Concept of Controllability explains the concept of self-control and includes checklists applicable to the production function. Section 13 under Improving the Effectiveness of Product Development discusses the application to product development (see particularly Table 13.17); see also Juran and Gryna, 1980, chapters 5, 13, 14; May, 1978; and Myers, 1981, chapter 3. The effect of broader responsibility for planning and organizing on the meaningfulness of work is discussed later in this section under Work Redesign.

In a state of self-control, workers follow the PDCA cycle to manage their own processes.

Knowledge of "Supposed to Do." Workers know (and may have been involved in establishing) the intended outcomes of the process from engineering specifications, budgets, sales quotas, delivery schedules, or other statements of process aim, target or objective, etc. There also is knowledge of how to do the work. This can come from training, instructions, job aids, shop manuals, etc. According to Kondo (1977), the "how to" is described in a way that does not restrict the worker's freedom to exercise judgment in the accomplishment of the process aim. Specification of method is detailed and restrictive only where fitness for customer use is at stake, as for example, in areas of worker and customer safety. The reasons for the restrictions are explained to workers. Within these limitations, workers are encouraged to do the work in ways best suited for each of them. Manuals and other "how to" instructions are for reference only. Workers, for example, are able to:

Refer to product specifications, product sample, or other definition of the end result to be obtained

State the critical (vital few) quality characteristics and why they are important to customers, i.e., describe how the outputs of the process are used

Describe what to do with defective raw material or defective output

Knowledge of "Is Doing." Workers are able to determine the relationship between their own behavior and the outcomes the process is producing. This requires feedback. (Guidelines for developing performance feedback systems are provided by Fairbank and Prue, 1982.) Feedback is provided in the three ways described below (see Figure 10.2).

During the Process Operation. Information is continuously provided to the workers through their senses directly or through the mediation of measuring instruments. This helps workers regulate their behavior on a continuous basis to "home in" on the target while creating the output (see Pettigrew, 1983). Obviously the accuracy, repeatability, and ease of use of the instruments are critical.

Direct Feedback after Output Production. On the shop floor, control charts can provide information on process stability (statistical methods for process control are reviewed in Section 24 of the handbook). They tell the worker when to leave the process alone, when to adjust, and when to seek assistance from management. It is preferable that this information be provided directly to the worker without intervention from the supervisor or other "experts" who may exercise pressure to "do something" when the chart provides no evidence that quality can be improved by employee regulatory actions.

The responsibility of management and supervision for understanding control charts has been discussed by Deming (1982). Inability to "read" a chart and failure to abide by the statistical decision rules will produce overadjustment, increase the variability of outputs, and increase the proportion of defectives. Charts provide a guide to appropriate action for workers and for management. A process in statistical control and capable of meeting specifications can not do better unless a change is made in the system. Only management actions, not operator adjustments, can improve the capability. Management can provide the worker with a significant role in improvement, for example, by participating in breakthrough projects. This is discussed later in this section under the topic Quality Campaigns and in Section 22, Quality Improvement.

Feedback from Customers.   Feedback from customers directly or through others (e.g., supervisor) can show workers the importance of their work to overall product quality. Feedback from internal customers such as may be obtained in worker group problem-solving sessions can lead to recommendations to management for changes to improve process capability or modify internal customer requirements. Periodic feedback discussions with supervisors, particularly regarding process performance shown on the control charts, can provide opportunities for the supervisor to positively reinforce workers for their work in maintaining process control. This is discussed in more detail under Managing the Consequences of Performance.

Ability to Regulate.   Workers have both the authority and means to take action when there is evidence (e.g., on the control chart) that an unplanned change has occurred. Some companies provide criteria to guide worker actions in such cases. A change can be sporadic or sustained. The worker has the diagnostic skills to identify the causes and respond with adjustments or other actions to correct the situation. It may be necessary on occasion to summon additional help, e.g., supervision or engineering. If a sporadic change was in the direction of improvement, e.g., a reduction in defects by the occurrence of a special (assignable) cause, management should be informed so that this condition can be made to happen all of the time, i.e., become a common cause. Workers may not be able to regulate the process because of the design of the equipment, tools, job aids, workspace, or organization of the work. These types of factors are discussed extensively in a number of human factor engineering books (see, for example, Harris and Chaney, 1969, and McCormick and Sanders, 1982).

Feedback and Self-Control at Hawthorne.   The classic "Hawthorne effect" can be better understood in terms of the availability of performance feedback and consequences. This milestone research was reviewed four decades after the original studies, by H. M. Parsons (1980), who also interviewed one of the workers who participated in the studies. He and other behavioral scientists (Connellan, 1978, pp. 160–163; Miller, 1978, pp. 368–369) emphasized the importance of feedback on the workers' ability to control their own behavior. Unlike conditions on the shop floor, the experiment procedure provided frequent feedback on group productivity. Incentive pay was based on the amount by which the group exceeded production standards. Since each group consisted of five employees (rather than 100), each individual could better relate payment to individual efforts. This provided workers the opportunity to set production targets for themselves. Feedback on group performance was available throughout the day. It informed workers how well they were doing with respect to the targets and the payment which followed.

Division of Responsibility.   When a process has changed, e.g., entry of a new supplier of materials or installation of new equipment, it is management's responsibility to bring the process into statistical control. Self-control enables the worker to maintain the quality only at the level which the process is capable of achieving. It does not guarantee defect-free performance. It is up to management to create the policies and procedures in all of the business systems, e.g., purchasing, maintenance, training, etc., so that variation due to materials, equipment, people, etc., will be small relative to the targets, specifications, etc.

Workers also have a responsibility to bring to their management's attention situations in which they do not have the means for self-control. It sometimes happens, when workers attempt to inform management of deficiencies in these areas, they are ignored, told they are making excuses, etc. That discourages them from further attempts to communicate with management.

Self-control gives each employee, management and non-management, a reasonable (vital few) number of things to regulate. It makes possible broad spans of management control.

DIAGNOSING WORKER PERFORMANCE

People are an integral part of processing systems in which they work. What they do, or fail to do to produce quality goods and services depends on:

1. The capability of the system in which they operate and the extent to which they are given self-control, as described previously.

2. What actually happens to them as a result of their performance, i.e., the consequences from output quality (or quantity, cost, schedule, etc.), or from how and what they did to produce those outputs—their behavior. These consequences greatly influence future performance. Deficiencies in worker contributions to processing system performance are classified below.

Execution Deficiencies. Even when workers want to perform well, they cannot. They do not have the skills, knowledge, abilities, information, communication links, or other process resources (performance antecedents) needed to achieve performance goals. The process is not capable. These deficiencies are correctable by management through better systems of selection, training, information (feedforward, e.g., process sheets, and feedback), equipment, design, etc. Tools and machines, for example, can be designed to be compatible with abilities and limitations of the operators and maintenance personnel—the users of the equipment (see McCormick and Sanders, 1982).

Motivation (Consequence) Deficiencies. Even though the process is technically capable of achieving objectives, i.e., the people and equipment are able to do things correctly, the performance is degraded because people have little or no reason to do the right things, or in fact may have reason to avoid doing the right things.

Most of these kinds of behaviors are rational worker responses to the organization's reward system. People tend to behave in ways that help them achieve positive consequences and avoid negative ones. Whereas execution deficiencies place limits on how well an individual *can* perform, consequence deficiencies place limits on how well an individual *will* perform. The vast majority of these motivational deficiencies are correctable by the proper management of consequences to workers (discussed below), and through leadership that inspires people to work toward a goal whose achievement is reward in itself. There will be instances, however, where the nature of the work does not provide the worker with sufficient challenges or other rewards to elicit the desired performance. This can be remedied through better design of selection systems.

An operator, for example, may find that taking the time to monitor and regulate the process (make proper adjustments, call for maintenance to help remove an assignable cause of variation, etc.) does not bring supervisor praise for these quality-oriented actions. The supervisor may, in fact, say nothing about the defective items that could result from improper regulation, and criticize the operator for jeopardizing production counts. The operator quickly *learns* that life will be a lot more pleasant if the production goals are met. The supervisor in turn, who is responding to his or her own reward system, suffers no negative consequences for failing to service the equipment. The equipment is serviced between shifts or by the next shift supervisor who has to keep the equipment running to meet production goals. The supervisor in turn is responding to his or her reward system which has established accountability for production volume only with no negative consequences for defect rates or running equipment into the ground. The consequences reinforce undercontrol of the process.

Combination of Execution and Motivation Deficiencies. Many worker performance problems are difficult to diagnose because they result from a combination of execution and motivation deficiencies. When workers, for example, do not have the necessary information, proper equipment, and discretion to act, they can become frustrated and discouraged to the point that they no longer want to contribute beyond the minimum required, if that. Even highly motivated individuals eventually will be demotivated by the failures which an incapable process forces them to experience. For example: Equipment may be poorly designed; grease, oil, or metal filings piled on the floor may make it a difficult and unpleasant task to get to the controls; it may be inconvenient to contact the supervisor or engineers to discuss the problem. It may just not be worth the effort to deal with the problem in comparison to the potentially few negative consequences for failing to act.

The use of process overcontrol can also be used to illustrate the interactive nature of execution and motivation deficiencies. There may be the best intentions to reduce product variation and prevent output from exceeding specifications. Lack of knowledge (execution deficiency) of the phenomenon of natural process variation (see Section 24, Statistical Process Control) can lead to overreaction to output fluctuation. In order to avoid negative consequences for producing defective parts or for standing by and doing nothing, the operator will feel pressured to "do something." Statistical theory and practice tells us that reacting to random piece-to-piece variation as if it had an assignable cause will, in fact, increase variation and increase the number of defectives. A vicious cycle develops of frustration and anger whereby more action is taken and more people become involved (perhaps the parts supplier, tool engineer, middle management) with behaviors focused on avoiding blame.

The capability of the processing system to repeatedly accomplish its goals and objectives, meet the product specifications, etc., is management controllable. It is common experience to hear of a quality problem diagnosed as worker "laziness," "carelessness," or "lack of concern." Resolution is sought through pleas for better performance, e.g., through use of motivational posters, or by fixing blame and warning of dire consequences if things do not improve. It automatically puts the burden of responsibility for improvement on subordinates without diagnosing the higher management-controllable causes. It forces people into a no-win situation because they do not have the means to change the system. This can be said of all employees, at every level in the hierarchy. Managers are part of the system like everyone else and there are factors affecting their performance which are beyond their own direct control and require upward and lateral communication.

People's performance can be improved by following the improvement cycle shown in Figure 10.3. Techniques for diagnosing problem sources (deficiencies of execution, motivation, or both), as well as identifying solutions, are described by Connellan (1978, 1980), Gilbert (1982), Miller (1978, chapter 11), and Zemke and

Kramlinger (1982). See also Section 22 under Test of Theories of Worker-Controllable Errors.

MANAGING THE CONSEQUENCES OF PERFORMANCE

People tend to behave in ways that enable them to achieve positive consequences and avoid negative ones. Consequences can be positive, negative, or neutral depending on the individual employee, and the circumstances. Whether a consequence is positive or negative for an individual cannot be assumed in advance. For example, a worker may not want the additional responsibility of self-inspection, particularly if it is hard to do with the present process design. Thus, what is positive and what is negative for workers can best be determined by asking workers or by observing the effects on their performance.

Reinforcement and Punishment: Definitions.   A *positive reinforcer* is a desirable consequence that causes people to maintain or increase their level of contribution (of physical and mental energy). The individual performs because the outcome will produce a desirable consequence, e.g., peer or supervisor recognition for solving a problem or keeping a process in control. A *negative reinforcer* is an undesirable consequence. It also maintains or increases employee behavior, but the type of behavior that enables the individual to avoid the consequence. Examples are: an employee returns to the desk or machine after lunch to avoid losing pay or being reprimanded; an employee consistently turns in reports late rather than on time, since on-time reports are returned for correction and additional explanation, while late reports are rarely returned for rework; a manager does not report savings that brings the department in under budget in order to avoid losing that amount in the next budget; work is done a certain way to avoid unpleasant or potentially harmful consequences (shock, bruises, fatigue, etc.) from the equipment or environment.

   Punishment results when the employee fails to avoid a negative consequence. Its effect is to reduce the tendency of the employee to behave in the way that brought the punishment, e.g., after a reprimand for coming to work late, the employee comes in on time; after the department has been charged with the cost of errors, the supervisor warns workers that their performance reviews will be downgraded if errors continue. Punishment, however, only temporarily reduces or eliminates the occurrence of the undesired behavior (not following guidelines, omitting information, coming in late, etc.) which reappears when the punisher leaves, or punishment is not administered, or can be avoided in other ways. (Once the employee behaves in ways to avoid the punishment, that negative consequence becomes a reinforcer of avoidance behavior.) Although punishment is usually a quick short-term solution, it is not a viable way of bringing about long-term behavior change for two major reasons: (1) it typically depends on external control of someone else, usually the boss, who must spend an exorbitant amount of time being a police officer. (2) The persons delivering the punishment stand a good chance of being punished in return by the worker (e.g., equipment sabotaged, critical information omitted from reports, no meaningful participation in problem-solving meetings when led by the same supervisor who delivers the punishment).

   The most effective way to manage consequences (particularly to instill self-control) is through the identification and administration of positive reinforcers. Positive reinforcement makes people feel good about themselves and feel like winners. Reliance on aversive consequences by punishment or negative reinforcement as a control mechanism is an "I gotcha" mentality. It betrays lack of trust of the person to do the job without being watched, and makes people feel like losers. It creates fear, inhibits risk-taking, creativity, and innovation. People behave in a way that enables them to avoid negative consequences, and no more. Chambers (in Deming, 1982, pp. 208–210) describes a case where the defect rates reported on the control chart fluctuated below the manager's quality objective. The chart itself displayed an unnatural tight pattern of variation "hugging" the central line. Interviews of the inspector who maintained the charts revealed that the unusual pattern of variation shown on the chart was "fudged" because of worker fear of punishment for failure to meet management's quality goals and did not reflect actual process performance.

Planning and Administering Performance Consequences. The way consequences are used to control worker behavior communicates to workers how much trust and confidence management has in their abilities to take on greater responsibility. Control by negative consequences will induce fear in workers. It will make it difficult, if not impossible, to establish self-control and will discourage worker involvement in improvement efforts. Most organizations seem to rely on negative consequences. For example, people may come to work on time not because of the positive consequences for that effort, but to avoid negative consequences such as reprimand or loss of pay. The use of negative reinforcement puts a limit on improvement. People generally will do no more than is minimally necessary to avoid the negative consequences. There is no incentive to do better. Positive consequences, on the other hand, seem to be a consistent and efficient (in terms of the manager's time) means for establishing and maintaining process stability through self-control and for eliciting contributions to quality improvement.

Balance of Consequences. A person desiring to change the behavior of others (superiors, subordinates, coworkers) can look at the effects of consequences as a net ledger balance after subtracting debits (negative consequences) from credits (positive consequences) or as a balance scale with weights accumulating on the positive and negative sides. The tendency of people to act in certain ways is affected by that balance.

Determining Which Consequences Are Positive. It has been stated previously that positive consequences can best be defined for each employee through investigation. In a sense, workers are the customers of the person for whom they work. Thus, some "market research" by supervisors most likely will be necessary to determine the kinds of things the workers value and will work to achieve. This can be done in a number of ways:

Ask them directly what they like about the job or what they like to do off the job.

Questionnaire survey.

Listen to what people discuss among themselves.

Trial and error.

Potential Positive Consequences. One of the most powerful consequences for workers is positive feedback regarding how they are doing with respect to goals which they participated in establishing. Knowledge that one has accomplished the goal, or at least is moving in that direction, is a positive consequence that can accompany the feedback provided by the control chart, or feedback from fellow workers (i.e., from the next customer and from discussions with the supervisor regarding performance).

Examples of consequences which workers may find positive are:

Self-control and increased job responsibility, e.g., opportunity to schedule own work, flexible working hours.

Recognition for job well done, e.g., sincere and thorough praise, being listened to, having ideas used, public acknowledgement of contributions, more interesting work, training for a better job, time off when work is complete. Daniels and Rosen (1983, p. 91) present research findings indicating that managers and supervisors may overestimate how often they provide workers with recognition for good work.

Personal growth, e.g., being sent to a trade show, professional association meeting, or seminar; participation in goal-setting or in problem-solving groups.

Economic gains, e.g., bonus, stock options, stock ownership—a stake in the company, merit pay, fringe benefits (especially "cafeteria" style where workers are able to choose benefits appropriate to their needs combined with a sharing in savings resulting from use of the plan). The effect of pay on performance has been widely studied (e.g., Lawler, 1976). Pay may be an incentive only when it is dependent on performance. (See Reinforcement Contingencies below.) Generally when people do what is necessary to avoid losing pay, rather than working to achieve it, pay is a negative reinforcer. Thus, even though one may believe that people are "paid to work," that is not the case unless pay is tied to performance. Compensation and profit sharing must depend on worker performance to have an incentive effect.

Group incentive programs which reward the performance of organization units (a profit-sharing plan rewards on basis of entire company's profits). The Scanlon, Rucker, and Improshare plans are the best known of the hundreds of methods and formulas to define and distribute incentives. Many plans emphasize quality, e.g., returns will be charged as costs against the plan. See the following references: Bullock and Lawler (1984), Ross and Hauck (1984); see Majerus (1984) for a union leader's viewpoint.

Positive Reinforcement Contingencies. A positive consequence is not necessarily a reinforcer of behavior. The consequence, whether provided for the behavior (how the work is done) or the outcome (what is produced), will maintain performance only if it depends on the occurrence of the performance. There must be an "if–then" time relationship between the performance and the consequence:

If the performance occurs, then the consequence follows.

If the performance does not occur, the consequence does not follow.

Connellan (1978, p. 31) notes that managers often reverse this sequence, e.g., "You can have this afternoon off if you will do it correctly tomorrow."

A contingency (based on positive consequences) can be established when workers have the means for self-control: They know the targets, goals, standards (the "supposed to do") that constitute the "if," part of the "if–then" relationship; they know the "then"—the consequences—and these must occur according to the expectations created.

Intermittent Reinforcement. In general, positive consequences are most effective when given on an intermittent basis, i.e., occasionally rather than continuously. Usually, it is not feasible to provide a positive consequence every time the desired performance occurs. The supervisor would have to spend all the time observing the workers to "catch" them doing the right thing. Constant supervision contradicts the self-control concept and undoubtedly will be negative for most workers. Intermittent reinforcement is feasible and lets the workers know that rewards will be forthcoming for good performance, even though they may not occur at the time of performance. The length of time between reinforcement can be relatively short, e.g., every few hours, every morning at the start-of-shift meeting, or longer, as with formal performance appraisals.

Additional discussion on the subject of consequences management with examples and supporting evidence is provided in the following references: Connellan (1978, 1980), Daniels and Rosen (1982), Frederiksen (1982), O'Brien et al. (1982), and Miller (1978).

Performance Appraisal. Unlike coaching, counseling, and other forms of frequent feedback which focus on a specific task performance, the performance appraisal is a general review of results achieved and the activities (process) which produced those results.

The appraisal can provide an opportunity for supervisor and subordinate to work together to improve the worker's—and hence the supervisor's—performance as an individual contributor and as a member of the organization team. It typically is underutilized for this purpose. Following the cycle shown in Figure 10.3, the improvement process could include the following activities:

Planning. Identifying a gap between current and desired performance; planning of a method to identify and remedy execution and motivation deficiencies producing that gap.

It is extremely helpful to avoid characterizing performance with abstractions and generalities, e.g., "lazy," "not aggressive," "terrible" which imply that the worker is at fault and could do the job if only there was the desire. This approach deflects the responsibility for improvement away from management. Focusing on the specific behaviors and outcomes (upon which the abstraction was based) will help point the way to improvement.

Doing. Collecting existing data and records as well as interviewing the worker's suppliers and customers.

Checking. Analyzing the sources of improvement.

Acting. Better supervisor use of positive reinforcement; more worker training; better cooperation from others (suppliers and customers) in the organization.

In the latter case, for example, a plan (step 1) to gain that cooperation would need to be developed and the improvement cycle repeated. The "interlocking objectives process," described in a subsequent subsection, is one way of helping the individual's performance by strengthening teamwork.

Performance evaluation is a process that—as with any process—needs to be controlled. The rater must have proper training, instructions, rating formats and information. Without this, worker ratings can be as much a function of poor evaluation as actual performance. Baker and Schuck (1975) offer theory and evidence to show that a rater can be affected by factors unrelated to the worker's performance.

Additional discussion of performance appraisals is provided by Deming (1982, chapter 10), Juran (1964, pp. 247–249), Latham and Wexley (1981), Myers (1981, pp. 234–244), and Scherkenbach (1985).

PROCESSING SYSTEM DESIGN

Under the precepts of Taylor, manufacturing production operations have been organized into a series of tasks with some being performed at each sequential processing station. This concept has been carried over to administrative and service areas, particularly where a large volume of transactions occur. Engineering and other support functions often show signs of the Taylor influence where workers are responsible for only a small part of the total product or service and do not understand how they contribute to the larger organization mission. Often they do not know their internal suppliers, the customers who receive the output of their efforts, and how it is used. There are, however, many forms of job (process) design which can provide workers with greater self-control and sense of purpose, and contribute to individual and organizational effectiveness.

Job Characteristics.   Hackman and Oldham (1980) describe five characteristics of jobs which they have found contribute to the meaning and satisfaction workers derive from the work. Jobs that are high in these characteristics are sometimes referred to as "enriched." Table 10.3 summarizes these job characteristics and the management actions that can be taken to enrich jobs in these characteristics. A number of approaches which have been used to redesign jobs are described in more detail below.

Horizontal Job Enlargement.   Workers are given a greater number of production tasks, but requiring the same skill level. For example, an assembly line of 40 workers can be redesigned to consist of five lines of eight workers each. While this

TABLE 10.3   Job Enrichment Characteristics and Management Actions (Based on Work of Hackman and Oldham, 1980)

Characteristic	Definition	Action
1. Skill variety	Degree to which the job has a sufficient variety of activities to require a diversity of employee skills and talents	Combine sequential tasks to produce larger work modules (horizontal enlargement)
2. Task identity	Extent to which work requires doing a job from beginning to end and results in a completed visible unit of output	Arrange work into meaningful groups, e.g., by customer, by product
3. Task significance	Extent to which the job impacts internal and external customers	Provide means for direct communication and personal contact with customer
4. Autonomy	Amount of employee self-control in planning and doing the work	Provide employee greater self-control for decision making (vertical enlargement)
5. Feedback	Degree to which direct knowledge of results is provided to employee	Create feedback systems to provide employees information directly from doing the job

gives each worker greater variety, it may not make work more satisfying and meaningful if all the tasks are inherently boring. Some of the other job enrichment characteristics will also have to be incorporated such as enabling workers to see how their efforts contribute to an identifiable product. In the extreme examples of horizontal enlargement, the assembly line is eliminated and each worker assembles the complete product unit. Examples of quality improvements resulting from horizontal job enlargement are given by Huse and Beer (1971) and Tuggle (1969). An alternate approach to horizontal job enlargement is to train each member of a unit to do all the jobs with tasks assigned on a rotating basis (this may require a higher pay rate).

Vertical Job Enlargement.   The job can be vertically enlarged by giving the work unit responsibilities previously restricted to the supervisor, e.g., assigning the work, scheduling breaks, establishing work rules, and interviewing and hiring job applicants. Production operators may be given the added duties of product inspection, tool control, inventory control, recordkeeping, etc. The individual becomes a "minimanager" for that work station.

In one case (Maher et al., 1969), the job of process inspectors was enlarged by adding unconventional duties such as trouble-shooting, disposition of nonconforming product, conducting process capability studies, planning production station quality control criteria, establishing prevention programs, and assisting in design reviews.

Myers (1981, p. 97) provides additional examples of vertical enlargement:

1. Assemblers on a radar assembly line are given information on customer contract commitments in terms of price, quality specifications, delivery schedules, and company data on material and personnel costs, break-even performance, and potential profit margins. Assemblers and engineers work together in methods and design improvements. Assemblers inspect, adjust, and repair their own work, help test completed units, and receive copies of customer inspection reports.

2. Electronic assemblers involved in intricate assembling, bonding, soldering, and welding operations are given training in methods improvement and encouraged to make suggestions for improving manufacturing processes. Natural work groups of 5 to 20 assemblers each elect a "team captain" for a term of 6 months. In addition to normal duties, the captain collects work-improvement ideas from team members, describes them on a standard form, credits the suggestors, presents the recommendations to their supervisor and superintendent at the end of the week, and gives the team feedback on idea utilization. Though most job operations remain the same, vertical job enlargement is achieved by providing workers increased opportunity for planning, reorganizing, and controlling their work.

Job Enlargement, both Vertical and Horizontal.   Myers (1981, p. 97) describes two examples of jobs incorporating both horizontal and vertical characteristics:

1. Jobs are enlarged horizontally in a clad metal rolling mill by qualifying operators to work interchangeably on breakdown rolling, finishing rolling, slitter, pickler, and abrader operations. After giving the operators training in methods improvement and basic metallurgy, jobs are enlarged vertically by involving them with engineering and supervisory personnel in problem-solving sessions for increasing production yields.

2. Jobs in a large employee insurance section are enlarged horizontally by qualifying insurance clerks to work interchangeably in filing claims, mailing checks, enrolling and orienting new employees, checking premium and enrollment reports, adjusting payroll deductions, and interpreting policies to employees. Vertical enlargement involves clerks in insurance program planning meetings with personnel directors and carrier representatives, authorizes them to sign disbursement requests, attend a paperwork systems conference, recommend equipment replacements, and to rearrange their work layout.

Hackman and Oldham (1980) describe the redesign of keypunch operator jobs in a large insurance company. Before the change, operators were strictly limited to keypunch tasks. They were isolated from their customers by assignment clerks who distributed the work in batches that could be completed in 1 hour. The operators did not know who was their customer or the impact of their work on the customer. Since the supervisors reviewed their work for errors and assigned corrections to someone other than the original operator, there was no opportunity for feedback. The performance situation was characterized by high error rates, missed schedules, high costs, and absenteeism. This situation was dramatically improved after introduction of the following changes:

1. Each operator was given the responsibility for all of the work for a number of accounts. In addition to keypunching, the operators planned and scheduled their work.
2. Operators interfaced directly with their customers. They personally inspected incoming work for corrections and legibility. Any customer concerns were discussed with the operator who had the freedom to correct errors without checking with the supervisor.
3. Operators kept their own records which were used for regular performance reviews.

Juran and Gryna (1980, p. 161) cite a case where the telephone company revised the job of preparing telephone directories for publication. Each step of the 21 steps of the process previously was done by one or more different workers. The revised approach allowed each worker to assemble an entire directory, i.e., to perform all 21 operations. There was a dramatic reduction in turnover, absenteeism, and errors.

Autonomous Work Groups. A work team may become self-managing by taking over some of the PDCA control functions usually performed by a supervisor. Teams are also referred to as semiautonomous since they are constrained by the organization's control systems. Creation of autonomous work teams will not guarantee improved performance if the team structure is imposed on workers and they have to operate in a tight top-down environment without the opportunity for significant decisionmaking (see Bluestone, 1977). Juran and Gryna (1980, pp. 160–161) describe the case of a Swedish company which redesigned its process to enable a team of approximately 10 employees to assemble the entire engine. The team decides which members perform the various operations. The team also performs some of the administrative and service functions related to materials supply, tool maintenance, inspection, and recordkeeping. Self-managing groups may be a local effort or part of a broad organization work restructuring effort. See the following for additional studies and bibliographies: Gyllenhammar (1978), Ketchum (1984), Tichy (1976), and Woodman and Sherwood (1977).

Self-Inspection. Responsibility for in-process inspection of their own work can be given to the production operators. Kondo et al. (1982) report an increase in operator motivation, a decrease in time for corrective action, and 40 percent decrease in defects. This can also help the operator close the feedback loop to "upstream" operations. (See Production, Section 17 of this handbook.)

Job Design: The Investigation. Hackman and Oldham (1980) recommend a cautious approach be taken to job redesign. There are definite differences between employees as to how much freedom and complexity they want, or have the ability to take on. Most, but not all, people want a more demanding, challenging job. Putting employees in jobs for which they are not trained or otherwise suited can cause them to fail. Investigation should be conducted to assess the appropriate types of job design. All persons directly affected or whose support will be needed to conduct the investigation and help in the change should be involved. This includes management and supervisors, union leaders, and workers. Without their participation and education, changes could be perceived as threatening, and result in overt or covert resistance (see also Myers, 1981, pp. 108–114).

Hackman and Oldham (1980) recommend six criteria that can be used in deciding if and how to redesign jobs. In summary, job design is appropriate where:

1. Job design solves an existing problem or takes advantage of an opportunity.
2. The problem or opportunity involves work effectiveness (quality and quantity of output), motivation, or satisfaction.
3. Job design appears to be a solution, rather than supervisor training, or change in the reward system.
4. The five job enrichment characteristics which redesign is to address have been identified.
5. Workers are enthusiastic about the change.
6. The organization is receptive to the needed changes.

High Technology and Work Redesign. The implications of high technology for effective worker performance have been discussed by Davis (1983–1984). Manufacturing systems are becoming more automated through the use of robots and the linking of individual machines into complex, computer-controlled, integrated systems where failures in any part of the system can have serious consequences for the entire system. In this arrangement, the worker no longer has simple repetitive tasks. The job is one of monitoring, diagnosing, and correcting the causes of instability. The diagnostic and correction process is complex, due to the multiplicity of potential failure modes. It is not sufficient to train workers in advance to deal with a limited number of potential assignable causes of instability. Workers need a broad repertoire of skills and knowledge to deal with failure modes that are hard to anticipate. In addition, they need to have the flexibility and self-control to respond rapidly and decide where, whether, and when to intervene without having to take the time to get permission from supervision or engineering.

Davis (1983–1984) cites the Three Mile Island nuclear plant near-disaster of 1979 to illustrate the results of failure of organizations to recognize the demands technology places on an organization and its personnel. The series of events leading to the disaster involved a combination of conditions which made it impossible to correct the malfunction promptly, e.g.:

Control room deficiencies.

Lack of clarity in operating procedures.

Operator training deficiencies: no worker or engineer knew how to operate more than a small segment of the total system.

Negotiated work rules precluded a quick response. Engineers were not allowed to do the operator's work of turning knobs or moving levers; workers were prohibited from doing any "engineering calculations."

In Davis's view, the use of the single approaches such as job enrichment, incentives, and profit sharing do not promote the degree of organizational adaptability and flexibility of response as does an integrated approach that matches the technical and social system requirements. Sociotechnical systems have been implemented in a number of new plants beginning in the 1970s. Common characteristics are (Davis, 1983–1984, p. 13):

Little or no plant middle management

Self-regulation of process by work teams

Workers with wide repertoires of skills and no specific jobs or job descriptions

Localized planning and decision making

Open flow of information across and between all levels of the organization

Weekly team meetings to review progress and difficulties, and plan and solve problems

Fairly open job progression

Wage schemes based on payment for knowledge and skills

Work team representatives who sit on plantwide committees and participate in the selection of new employees

The performance of these new plants was superior to other plants in the same company operating under more traditional systems. They had higher product quality, lower costs, fewer grievances, lower worker turnover, and less reported dissatisfaction.

TEAM PERFORMANCE: A PROCESSING SYSTEM VIEWPOINT

A spirit of teamwork (as well as substantive individual contributions) can be built when people recognize that it is in the best interests of themselves and their organization to cooperate with others. Obviously, cooperation is easier when one knows with whom to cooperate, as in groups with a special identity and common purpose (e.g., autonomous work groups, quality circles, quality breakthrough project teams, ad hoc task forces). When the common purpose and mutual dependencies of the members are not obvious to each member, there is no team.

Organization Barriers to Teamwork. The entire enterprise can be viewed as a network of people in interdependent supplier (producer)–customer (user) relationships as illustrated in Figures 10.1 and 10.2. These relationships typically are not well understood, either by employees at the lower organization levels or by middle and higher level managers. This is especially true of hierarchical, bureaucratic organizations whose structures and management systems make it difficult for people to see how they contribute to the common good. Juran (1964, pp. 131–133) pointed out years ago the impediment of "provincialism" to quality improvement. Deming (1982) calls it "departmental barriers." Ishikawa (1985, pp. 107–109, 125) describes his attempts years ago in Japan to resolve hostility between production areas by having each worker view the next process as a customer. Similar attempts were made to reduce "sectionalism" between staff and line employees.

This separateness produces the phenomenon of organization suboptimization. Department or functional objectives are not linked in a coherent way that is in the best interests of the overall business purpose and goals. Hence, even though people meet their individual objectives, the enterprise as a whole fails to fully accomplish its larger mission. Organization effectiveness is diminished by the costs associated with waste, inefficiencies, rework, in-fighting, and other dysfunctional behaviors. Engineering, for example, may release drawings to meet manufacturing schedules, even though all engineering and test work has not been completed. Subsequent inevitable engineering changes have cost and quality ramifications throughout the organization. Sales, for example, may promise customers option combinations and quantities that exceed the plant's production capability. Then the orders are submitted to the plant with insufficient information or errors that require the order to be returned to Sales. Conversely, the plant may give Sales unrealistic production schedules or fail to inform them of planned shutdowns.

Barriers between organizations can be made even more impenetrable by the special languages of each function and the failure to work at establishing common understandings [see Juran (1964, pp. 212–213) and Deming (1982, chapter 15 on Operational Definitions)]. In addition, communication across organizations may occur at managerial levels well above the employees who need or provide the information.

Teamwork: Linking Customer and Supplier Requirements. The establishment of process output requirements—specifications, objectives, schedules, quotas, budgets, etc.—can be viewed as a two-way street that considers both the customer's needs and the supplier's capability. Admonishing people to cooperate and help each other will not bring about the intended results. Teamwork requires: (1) a process that will overcome bureaucratic complexities and barriers, and (2) a system of rewards that reinforces use of the process.

This is being accomplished in Japanese business through companywide quality control. Using a variety of techniques and activities known as "quality function deployment," the critical interdependencies between the organization's processing systems are identified (e.g., see Kogure, 1984, Kogure and Akao, 1983, and Sullivan, 1986). The mutual requirements—supplier to customer and customer to supplier—are established in a way that coherently links the processes to each other and to the requirements of the final customer.

Various approaches to overcoming the barriers imposed by traditional hierarchical, functionally separated organization structures are emerging outside of Japan. These are not attempts to copy Japanese companywide quality control.

They derive, however, from the same kind of systems thinking that recognizes the need to meaningfully integrate people, units, and processes within the enterprise in order to generate the responsiveness and innovativeness to anticipate rapidly changing customer demands. Hermann and Baker (1985) describe an "interlocking objectives" process to link individual and unit objectives across the plant and to the objectives and goals of the plant manager. Pettigrew (1983) used a "process intent" approach to link operators in an automotive assembly plant. Brethower (1982) describes application of this concept to help a plant manager and sales manager—each of whom are suppliers to and customers of the other—establish mutually supporting objectives. Efforts to build teamwork by linking internal customers and suppliers in administrative and service processes such as accounts receivable, document distribution, and marketing are described by Baker and Artinian (1985), Kane (1986), Melan (1985), and Nickell (1985). Kotter (1985) describes the manager's role and approaches to managing cross-functional relationships and interfaces within the political realities of organization life.

Effective Team Functioning: The Behavior of Groups.   A team is a group of individuals each with specific skills and knowledge and interests that enable the members to contribute to the accomplishment of a common purpose. (See, for example, the team approach to quality improvement taken by the Florida Power and Light Company, 1982.) The team's purpose may be accomplished in a relatively short time after which the team is disbanded; or, it may have a longer-term purpose requiring ongoing activity. Whether participation is voluntary or mandatory depends on the purpose, who is needed, and the time available. Team leaders typically are from supervision and management, although a nonsupervisory employee may be elected by the group when appropriate. The team may be composed of people from the same local organization unit (e.g., a quality circle of operators reporting to the same supervisor; an autonomous work group) or formed within a given function (e.g., electricians, accountants). Cross-functional teams are formed where expertise and a vested interest in the outcome rests in a number of different organization units, departments, or functions. (Numerous team approaches to quality improvement are described in the *Juran Report*—see Supplemental Bibliography.) A team may have members from the same organization level (e.g., all operators, supervisors, or managers), from a vertical slice within the organization or function, or a diagonal slice of organization levels and functions. In some cases, e.g., joint union-management quality of work life committees, a special structure may have to be created to accommodate the new roles and relationships (see Carlson, 1978, Rubinstein, 1982, and Stein and Kanter, 1980). Finally, the team may be characterized by the scope of its purpose and amount of its discretion to gather information, make decisions, and take action.

Teams may be formed, as needed (perhaps on an ad hoc basis) to fight fires and solve local problems (remove assignable causes) to maintain process control. On the other hand, with the support of higher management, a team may work on improving the system (e.g., a quality "breakthrough" project) by working on management-controllable issues, but where discretion has been delegated to the group and the means have been provided to develop and recommend a change, and perhaps implement the change (e.g., Davidson, 1982, and Kondo, 1981). A team formed of internal customers and suppliers, working through the control and improvement cycles (Figure 10.3), can constitute a powerful force for positive change. Moehlenbrock (1985) contrasts control teams with breakthrough teams. Each manager can set the stage for effective teamwork by guiding subordinates through the planning activities needed to identify critical supplier-customer interfaces. An early step, usually done at the department level, is the development of processing system flow diagrams. This is done first at a macrolevel of analysis to identify supplying and using organization units or functions. Then each individual can develop a microflow which details specific tasks and pinpoints specific individuals who are suppliers and customers. It is an iterative process (a PDCA at the planning stage, as illustrated in Figure 10.3) because additional information usually needs to be gathered. In addition, there often are differences of opinion within the department regarding the process flow that have to be reconciled. Then arrangements can be made for people to meet with their customers and suppliers. Table 10.4 provides an idea of the kinds of questions that need to be answered and can serve as a guide for supplier-customer discussions (they may interview each other). This can help the team identify improvement areas, particularly in components of the system, e.g., poor or nonexistent feedback loops.

A team is a processing system producing outputs (problem solutions, decisions, recommendations, strategic plans, policy statements, engineering drawings, repaired equipment, etc.) for a user, e.g., a manager, another team, its own members. High-quality outputs (innovative solutions) are likely because the idea generating and evaluation processes used by groups (e.g., Sink, 1983) can produce results usually not possible by simply combining the ideas and efforts of people working alone. This synergy of ideas is supported by the energy created by the positive reinforcement inherent in working for a worthy goal and the ability of individuals to see that the group's success depends on each person's contribution and cooperation.

The behavior of people in groups can be more difficult to manage than their behavior as individuals. The strength of the group comes from the diversity of viewpoints, backgrounds, and special knowledge of the individual members. These differences can be a source of disfunction unless there are controls to guide

TABLE 10.4   Guide to Help Identify Processing System Components Necessary for Teamwork

---

1. Processing system as supplier (producer).
   a. What products and services are produced?
   b. For whom? (List your customers—individuals, units, functions; be as specific as possible.)
   c. What is the value to customers of these output products and services?
      • What is their purpose? Why are they needed?
      • How are they used? Under what conditions?
      • What are the customers' usage (input) requirements?
   d. How do you know if you are meeting these requirements? (Are you capable?)
      • Do you find out? When? How Often?
      • Do your own output requirements (standards, goals, targets) relate to your customers' input requirements?
      • What do you measure, and why? Are you your own customer?
   e. How do you evaluate output fluctuation and deviations from targets? Do you have a statistical definition of process stability?
2. Processing system as customer (user).
   a. What inputs (material, information, tools, other resources) do you receive?
   b. From whom? (List your suppliers.)
   c. Do they know your input requirements?
   d. Do you communicate with your suppliers? When (e.g., only when there is a problem)? How (e.g., face-to-face, mediation by someone else)?

---

people's behavior in the same direction. The following conditions will contribute to effective group functioning:

The group's purpose is clearly understood and supported by all members.

There is a process for establishing and prioritizing goals and objectives to the vital few that can be accomplished. The roles and responsibilities of each member for specific tasks or functions are clear and agreed upon by all members. This is especially true of the leader's role.

Individual accountability is established for the accomplishment of specific, measurable outcomes.

Feedback to individuals, e.g., from the leader or other team members, is specific and nonpersonal so individuals can evaluate the effect of their behavior on the group performance.

A process (e.g., procedures, guidelines, rules, etc.) exists for getting the work done. This includes a method for assigning work to individuals, coordination of efforts, exchange of information, discussion, and problem-solving and decision-making processes.

Rubin et al. (1978) have found that most of the conflict, mistrust, and counterproductive behaviors of people in groups are symptoms of failure to clarify and agree upon goals, roles, and procedures—in that order. A great deal of literature is available describing the principles, processes, and techniques of effective group and team functioning. Examples are Fisher (1980), Rubin et al. (1978), Zander (1983), and the *Handbook for Group Facilitators* (updated each year, it provides a compendium of concepts and tools—see the Supplemental Bibliography). Prince (1970, 1972) describes a process for stimulating creative and innovative ideas.

Juran (1956) observed that blind opposition often faces the proponent of change who fails to properly understand and deal with the concerns of others who will be affected by the change. Opposition may be expressed in many ways, e.g., "We tried that before and it didn't work." Connellan (1980, pp. 104–105) lists dozens of "killer phrases" which can arise in team discussions which will prevent ideas from budding. He recommends the learning of a new vocabulary of "booster phrases" which can help team members positively reinforce each other's generation of creative ideas.

Quality Circles: Processes, Tools, Administration.   The likelihood of success will be increased greatly if management thinks through what it hopes to accomplish with this form of worker involvement and develops a common understanding regarding a number of related issues:

Will circles constitute a stand-alone program—a separate appendage to the organization—guided and promoted only by the manufacturing or quality control departments? Or will they be a logical consequence of a business strategy that integrates human resources management planning into the overall business process in a context analogous to companywide quality control?

Is the purpose of the circles to solve local quality problems (typically sporadic) or to work with management and other circles on chronic, systems problems?

Is the purpose equally to improve work relationships between workers, management, and the union?

What is the state of union-management relations? Can circles be undertaken as a cooperative effort? Can structures, e.g., union-management committees, be created to jointly manage the effort? Is preparatory work needed to build union-management relations? What is the risk in proceeding without an active union role?

What will be the role of middle and top management?

Is this intended to be a short-term or ongoing effort? Is the purpose consistent with the planned or likely duration of circles in the organization?

See Barra (1983), Gryna (1981), Ingle (1982), Ishikawa (1985), Shea (1986), and the Supplemental Bibliography for more on these and other quality circle issues discussed in this subsection. The role of management and the functions of a steering committee are discussed in the next subsection, Quality Campaigns. The participation of the union is discussed in a previous subsection, Role of the Labor Union.

Circles are composed of workers reporting to the same supervisor. As discussed in early subsections, this limits their ability to directly tackle and influence chronic systems problems which typically requires cross-functional collaboration, as with project teams.

The circle leader usually is the supervisor. If a circle is subdivided into mini-circles (of three to five workers), one of the members is elected to be leader. Worker presence may be mandated (depending on labor contract provisions if workers are represented), but worker involvement cannot be ordered or achieved through coercion. Worker commitment to the process has been found to be best achieved through voluntary participation based on an understanding of the circle's purpose and benefits. Circles usually meet about 1 hour per week on regular time. If there is a need to meet more frequently, this may occur on regular time or overtime. Practice varies. Additional time is often needed to work on the project, attend training, study, etc.

Coordination and facilitation functions may be assumed by the same individuals. Large plants and multidivision plants may have two or more facilitators. In many cases, facilitators report to a line manager—even the plant manager—with a dotted-line relationship with a division coordinator. Practice varies. In the discussion below, both functions will be treated as the responsibility of a single individual or individuals with the title of facilitator. In joint union-management efforts, these roles are often shared by a union member and nonunion employee.

The facilitator's primary roles are those of change agent, counselor, promotor, and trainer with additional administrative tasks, e.g., recordkeeping and scheduling. The following attributes are necessary for facilitator effectiveness:

1. Good interpersonal and communications skills to interact with people at all levels of the organization, resolve conflict, and break down resistance to change
2. Trust and respect of union, management, and workers
3. Sufficient knowledge of the organization's processes and products to speak the language, follow up, etc.
4. Technical knowledge of circle processes, e.g., PDCA cycle, tools, management presentation techniques
5. Administrative skills for self-management and circle management (e.g., develop and follow up plans and monitor progress, provide timely feedback)

The facilitator is a critical vertical and lateral link, particularly during the period of introduction of circles to the organization and during the first 6 to 9 months of any circle. It is common for the facilitator to participate as an active member of the organization steering committee.

Quality circles use statistical tools and related graphical techniques to provide input to various stages of the PDCA cycle (Figure 10.3). For example:

Checksheets are used to record observations and measurements made during the *do* stage. These data are inputs to the *check* stage where they are summarized and transformed into Pareto diagrams, control charts, or graphs.

Control charts developed in the *check* stage provide information to the *act* stage where actions are taken depending on the sporadic or chronic nature of the process variation and whether improvements are locally controllable.

Pareto diagrams provide input to the *plan* stage to help prioritize the efforts and allocation of resources according to improvement potential.

Flow diagrams provide input to the *plan* stage by describing how process resources—people, parts materials, information, paperwork, etc.—move through the system, who acts on them, and interacts with them. This tool helps identify improvement opportunities by showing where waste, cost, redundancy, rework, and scrap can be reduced or eliminated.

Cause-effect diagrams, and their variants, e.g., "why-why," "how-how," "interrelationship" diagrams (see also Fukuda's, 1983, modification, "CEDAC" or cause-effect diagrams with the addition of cards), are used to surface potential problem causes or process improvement sources which can be used to *plan* a study, test, or experiment.

These and other basic tools and recommendations for training in their use are discussed in Barra (1983), Ingle (1982), Ishikawa (1983), and the JUSE and other quality circle references in the Supplemental Bibliography; see also this handbook, Sections 22, Quality Improvement; 23, Basic Statistical Methods; and 24, Statistical Process Control. More sophisticated methods, e.g., design of experiments, are used less frequently (see papers of I. Kusaba and T. Sugimoto in *Reports of Statistical Applications Research,* Japanese Union of Scientists and Engineers, vol. 25, no. 2).

Management can support and sustain circle activities in a number of ways, including:

1. Recognizing and rewarding (not necessarily monetarily) workers' efforts, even if recommendations are not adopted. Giving workers increased discretion and self-control to act on their own recommendations is an excellent reward.

2. Offering monetary rewards through the suggestion program (which may have to be modified to accommodate joint submission by circle members).

3. Providing sufficient training to expand worker skills to take on more complex projects.

4. Establishing a system for circles to expand into cross-functional teams when it appears to be a logical step. Circles may become "fatigued" when they feel they have accomplished about all they can by themselves and see the need to work with their internal suppliers and customers.

5. Training of middle managers in circle tools and techniques so they can ask their subordinates the "right questions" and not be "outsiders." These tools are also useful for the managers' own processes.

6. Addressing middle management resistance when diagnosed. Typically, management is concerned about a loss of authority and control.

7. Measuring effectiveness by focusing on the quality of the process—e.g., the training, the group discussion process, the interpersonal relationships, supervisory leadership style—rather than outcomes (e.g., reduction of scrap and

costs). If the process is right, the outcomes will be also and that will reinforce employee involvement, as well as management commitment.

QUALITY CAMPAIGNS

Intensive drives and campaigns sometimes are used in an effort to bring about quick improvements in quality. The kind of management thinking that seeks remedy in short-term programs is usually the kind of thinking that brought about the poor quality performance in the first place. When a campaign is sought, what is actually needed is a change in management systems that will enable people to consistently produce high levels of quality. This requires a "breakthrough" approach, of the type described by Juran (1964; see also Section 22 of this handbook), in which the organization transition to improved processes and systems is guided by the results of planned experimentation and investigation.

The pressures for immediate quality improvements do occur, however. They may result from poor performance in a number of areas, e.g., competitive quality position, field failures, warranty costs, waste, and other internal costs, with urging of the customer to "do something" to turn around. The "zero defects" campaigns of the 1960s in the defense and aerospace industries resulted primarily from the insistence by government officials that suppliers undertake such campaigns.

Campaigns typically are initiated by top executives who are responding to a high-visibility problem. The campaign, therefore, should be viewed as an opportunity to begin to put in place needed changes which can be instituted on a long-term basis when the campaign ends. In the campaign, the needed resources usually are made available, the usual red tape and other obstacles disappear, and there is a chance to try out new approaches.

Some grievous errors have been made in quality campaigns which have left the organization in worse shape, with less performance capability than before the campaign, even when the stated objectives of the campaign were met and short-term results obtained. The major assumption underlying most short-term programs is that deficient quality performance (errors, defects, etc.) results from an unwillingness of workers to pay attention to the details necessary for quality. Hence, the thrust of the campaign is to convince workers to take greater care and pride in their work without providing a method to improve. This was characteristic of many of the "zero defects" programs of the 1960s—lots of hype, but little substance.

These assumptions of worker inattention were made without adequate diagnosis. They also are unsound from the viewpoint of behavioral psychology, and unsupported by the facts. The majority of defects are inherent in the system and, therefore, only management can create the conditions for improvement. This is true even where defects are attributed to causes within the worker such as "lack of concern," "unwillingness" to put forth the best effort, and even behaviors that seem to be worker-controllable. In most cases, the root cause of worker behavior of this type can be traced to heavy management reliance on punishment or to setting of poor examples with regard to quality. Thus, even most "conscious" errors are management-controllable (see Section 22 under Test of Theories of Worker-Controllable Errors for more on types of human errors).

Improvements that came out of zero-defects type campaigns can be explained better, not by "increased motivation and attitude," but by changes actually made in the way work was done, e.g., use of checklists that were not used before. Often product inspection was increased. This may have improved short-term outgoing quality but also added cost and did little to improve the production process.

In addition to the propaganda, campaigns need a roadmap for improvement. If not, after the excitement of the campaign—with its banners, posters, pins, and management speeches—has passed, there most likely will be a great letdown and loss in worker morale. Workers may recognize that the blame for poor quality and the responsibility for its improvement was placed with them, but without adequate means to produce the improvement and without meaningful management involvement. Management, on the other hand, may become frustrated and angry at the work force when their high expectations for success have not been realized. A possible result is a management decision to impose tighter external controls and establish other conditions which provide no basic improvements.

The opportunity to build a base for longer-term positive change can be enhanced by treating the program as a "breakthrough" effort with three phases:

1. Prelaunch planning and preparation of communications to inform people about the "why" and promote the effort (the motivation component), and of the "how"—the necessary training, communications, and project methodologies to bring about improvement (the execution/prevention component)
2. Launch
3. Implementation

Prerequisites. The conditions which favor a successful campaign are mainly as follows:

1. The company has already done a respectable job of reducing management-controllable defects and hence is coming to the worker body with clean hands.
2. The worker-controllable defects are substantial enough, for economic or usage reasons, to warrant a serious effort of this type.
3. The extent of mutual confidence between management and workers and union leadership is such that worker participation in a campaign is likely to be genuine.
4. The top managers are willing to show personal interest, especially to set an example by changing their priority of emphasis on quality in relation to other company goals.
5. The intermediate supervision is sufficiently openminded to be willing to listen seriously to the ideas and suggestions of the workers.
6. Management is willing to provide the staff people needed to conduct the numerous detailed studies (discovering the knack of superior operators, investigating worker proposals, etc.; see Juran, 1966).

Phase 1: Prelaunch Planning and Preparation. The following steps are recommended before getting workers and managers actively involved in quality campaigns:

Form a Steering Committee. This is a corporate-level committee which provides overall guidance, direction, and review. The committee demonstrates management's involvement and support of the effort by participation in review meetings, plant visits, awards dinners, and other activities that provide opportunities for direct communication to workers and recognition of their accomplishments. The committee is chaired by a senior executive, preferably the chief executive officer, and includes key executives from the major line and staff organizations. The top union official may be invited to participate as a member. The union may have a consultative role. If the program was initiated as a joint union-management effort, the senior labor relations executive and top union officer may co-chair the committee. A full-time administrator also is needed.

Form Subcommittees. In large companies, it is necessary to create division and plant subcommittees, similarly constituted, with people from these organizations who are responsible for local planning and implementation. Part-time coordinators may have to be appointed from the divisions and plants. The line departments (production, marketing, design, etc.) need representation, since their people will take the bulk of the action. In addition, staff department representation is needed. The campaign will give each participant an opportunity to improve their own performance, as well as enabling them to contribute needed skills and talents to the overall effort. For example:

Advertising can help in designing the publicity, exhibits, etc., to have high positive impact on workers.

Personnel and public relations can provide communications through the existing company media (bulletin boards, newspapers, etc.) and design new means of communication internally and outside the company.

Quality engineering can provide guidance to the corporate steering committee and line organizations regarding the tools and methods of investigation used for the diagnosis of quality problems.

The corporate steering committee and subcommittees can provide a model of cooperation and clarity of goals by defining overall program goals, their own committee goals, roles, tasks of their members, and working relationships.

Budget.   There are three categories of costs to be considered.

1. Promotion and training materials.
2. Salary of the full-time administrator.
3. Time spent by all employees including managers and supervisors in coordinating, recordkeeping, and diagnostic activities

Budget planning is done in advance of the implementation phase to assure that the necessary resources will be allocated to the program and not be in conflict with other objectives and commitments. The same budget planning subsequently becomes an aid to evaluation of the program. Cost-benefit analysis may be difficult, since improvements in working relationships may take a while to be reflected in performance measures.

Communication Plan, Worker Recognition Methods, Training Manuals, and Information Materials.   These are given attention by subcommittees and the steering committee to assure consistency with program objectives, corporate culture, and external image. Information review by various disciplines, e.g., product and quality engineering, industrial relations, will help ensure that a sound quality message is conveyed to the public. For example, some published advertisements stress the extensive use of quality control inspectors to assure quality. The risk is that the public will question whether the company is using good production methods if its product needs all that inspection, and wonder who is really paying for that inspection.

Education and Training

Awareness. The same pressures that initiated the campaign often produce a desire to launch the program promptly without taking the time to have a top-down educational process. However, it is unrealistic to think that workers will accept the program if supervisors and managers do not understand and believe in the program's merits. Managers and supervisors, as well as union representatives, need the opportunity to learn the details of the program, their respective roles, and to discuss the benefits and their concerns. Many early quality circle efforts failed in the United States because the educational process bypassed middle management (Gryna, 1981).

Manager and Supervisor Skill Development. Success will be promoted by training in the following participative management skills: managing team goal-setting; group dynamics; group leadership; positive reinforcement, for individuals and its use in groups; delivering feedback; PDCA cycle tools (e.g., graphs, control charts, Pareto charts) for planning, monitoring, and evaluating process changes.

Schedules. Accomplishment of tasks will be facilitated with benchmark dates established for the prelaunch, launch, and implementation phases.

Goals and Accountability. It has been universal for campaigns to set improvement goals. Goals at the local department and unit level can be set jointly by workers and supervision, based on analysis of what is achievable at their level. During the period immediately after launch, accountability for proper implementation process will assure that the right things are done; for example: interpersonal, planning and problem-solving skills are learned; positive reinforcement and recognition are used; support groups provide assistance as needed; meetings are held on schedule; workers are provided adequate and timely responses to their suggestions.

Prior Publicity. Proper interpretation internally and by the public of the need for the program can be addressed when considering publicity approaches. Sources of publicity are local newspapers, TV and radio, house organs, payroll envelope inserts, information booklets, and teasers that something is going to happen.

Measurement of Performance. The usual quality measures can be used to evaluate shop floor performance, e.g., reduction in percent defective (or increase in percent conforming), reduction in error rate, or reduction in variation around a target value. However, since the programs are companywide, the need to measure goes beyond the "hardware" departments involved in production; it extends to the "software" departments performing support activities—engineering, accounting, data processing, finance, marketing, material control, etc. While all these departments have quality problems, not all of them have a quantified measure of quality. It may be necessary to develop new units of measure for this purpose. In some cases it may be necessary to resort to a universal measure such as errors per 100 worker-hours. When measurement of outputs is not feasible, audits of the process, e.g., of materials handling, can be conducted and points awarded for positive accomplishment. It is always better, however, from the point of view of objective measurement and employee participation, if each work team, nonproduction as well as production, defines what it wants to measure and how it will be done. Improvement can be evaluated by the graphs, control charts, Pareto charts, or other statistical methods. Guidelines can be developed which describe proper ways to measure performance and how to provide positive reinforcement for doing the right things (good process) even if objectives are not accomplished fully.

Posting of work team or department performance charts can help maintain a positive spirit. Clear depiction of current performance can provide positive reinforcement for movement toward the goals and encourage discussion about how the individual members are doing (see Leek and Riley, 1978). Since the products, processes, etc., differ between groups, the basis of competition can be in terms of universal measures such as percent improvement for the month. A statistical basis for evaluation will help assure that meaningful improvement is recognized. If the "best" performing group is there by chance, then recognition awards are nothing more than a lottery (see Deming, 1982, pp. 219–220). Obviously, each week or month someone will be on top and someone at the bottom. It is incumbent on management to make sure the performance being recognized is really at a new level. If not, recognition can be provided for the positive things the group has done, e.g., cooperation. If "chance" performance is rewarded, there is risk of a letdown during the next period if the low side of the chance distribution occurs and performance "appears" to have worsened.

Awards to groups are plaques or trophies which stay in the possession of the winning group for a month and then travel to the next winning group. Certificates may be awarded to individual members to be retained permanently.

Individual Performance.   Programs may also recognize individual workers. The cautions discussed for group performance also apply here. Companies generally avoid publication of the performance of individuals other than in the exceptional cases when an award is to be given. Praise of individuals may be in public, but criticism is best given in private.

Awards to individuals are made by an awards committee on recommendation of the supervisor. In some companies, individual recognition may be granted by financial rewards such as cash prizes, paid holiday, trips, and merchandise prizes. Other companies provide nonfinancial recognition: designation of crafts worker of the day, badges or plaques, special parking privileges. Care must be taken not to use an award that "cheapens" the accomplishments. Whether financial or nonfinancial, the awards are made at a ceremonial presentation. Pictures and narratives appear in the house organ, in the public press, on the local television, or on the "wall of fame." Commendation letters, sometimes sent to the worker's home, are used.

Extension to Include Suppliers.   Some companies believe that suppliers should be included in the program in view of the impact of supplier quality on the final product. The question of whether it is "right" for a company to "shove the program down the supplier's throat" is resolved by applying the same rule as is applied to workers—it should be voluntary on the part of the supplier. The conventional approach to suppliers parallels that used for workers, but scaled up to size. The activities usually include:

Informing the suppliers of the company's action in launching a quality improvement campaign

Sending each supplier copies of the materials used to indoctrinate the company's supervisors

Structuring means for measuring supplier performance

Organizing seminars for suppliers to discuss supplier relations problems and solutions

Creating a principal award, e.g., quality supplier of the month (do not make this a lottery)

Creating subsidiary awards, e.g., outstanding supplier

Making ceremonial awards and publicizing these to all suppliers

Preparing and distributing periodic summaries on the company's progress in supplier relations

Choice of a Name for the Program.   The name can be chosen in a way which merely describes the program contents. However, because these programs require selling to many people and have customer relations implications, it is usual for companies to derive added benefits by choosing a name which:

Takes advantage of currently favorable publicity

Responds to the wishes of important customers

Provides a catchy slogan to improve the salability to workers

In the absence of some currently favorable publicity, it is usual for companies to build a name around their usual sales slogans or public relations image. Alternatively, a theme is invented specially for the program, and the name relates to this theme.

Phase 2: The Launch.   The dramatic launch has for centuries been used by leaders to convey to followers the nature and importance of a new campaign. In several ways, the dramatic launching can be of aid to the program.

It constitutes a spectacle—a memorable occasion—and thereby gives the program significance and importance.

It convenes a host of people, proposes a meritorious cause, and provides opportunity for membership in this meritorious cause.

It assembles the recognized leadership and shows them to be actively behind the program.

It introduces and legitimizes the individuals designated to guide the program, i.e., the committees and the administrator.

It pledges the managers to a new level of conduct on some matters which have in the past been obstacles to motivation, e.g., action on ideas for improvement.

Collectively these are forceful reasons for conducting the dramatic launching—so forceful that any excess of advertising can detract from the value of the meeting.

The meeting may be convened in any large hall, or outdoors, or even via closed-circuit television if several locations are involved. The dignitaries include the senior executive of the company, national and local political leaders, the union head, an important customer, a guest of honor who is a well-publicized figure. Speeches are made explaining and supporting the program. The committee and the administrator are introduced. Films are shown. Pledge cards are usually used and the first ones are signed (by the senior executive and the union head). The messages can establish clearly that:

Top management regards quality as one of its highest priorities and will play an active role.

Worker involvement is a key element of the program—it cannot succeed without the voluntary participation of workers (the program is not optional for supervision and management).

Quality is a key factor in sales—and hence in jobs; management also will play an active part.

Program identity typically is established through use of slogans, banners, posters, pins, etc. Care must be taken not to cheapen the effort, insult workers, or put the responsibility for improvement solely on workers (pledge cards often do the latter). To the extent that publicity information provides guidance on ways to do things better rather than simply stating goals, management will have demonstrated its intention to provide the means to improve.

Phase 3: Implementation.   Management operating through the corporate and local steering committees provides workers with the means and desire to contribute to quality improvement through individual and team effort. Activities are directed at reducing worker-controllable defects and management-controllable defects. After the launch, communications activities become an integral part of the implementation phase, both to increase worker awareness of the company products and inform them about their own role in the quality of those products, as described below.

Product Exhibits and Demonstrations.   The purpose is to help workers understand how the product is used, what will happen if the product fails, and how their work relates to all this. In some cases, simple exhibits can be set up to demonstrate product use. In other cases, special effort is needed. For example, in an automotive parts plant, the managers were faced with showing the metal finishers in the "white" stage the unfinished component (an automobile hood) adjacent to the corresponding finished component. The left side of each hood had various defects; the right side had none. The display made it very easy to see the real damage done by the process defects. The same approach can be taken by placing competitive products side by side so that similarities and differences can be contrasted. Where exhibits are not feasible, they may be approximated through visual presentations: posters, pictures, videotapes, etc.

Worker Participation in Company Advertising.   Advertisements in which workers describe their contributions to quality can be combined into a package (television or printed media) and shown to fellow workers.

Usage Information.   The impact of quality on customers and users can be shown in various ways: arranging visits to customer locations; inviting customers to come to the plant; display of customer letters resulting from good work (repeat orders) or from bad work (complaints). Well-known users, e.g., athletic stars and TV celebrities, may be invited for memorable occasions. Visits can be made to supplier and customer plants to "close the feedback loop."

Communications also serve to inform workers about program status, provide feedback about the effectiveness of their efforts toward improved quality levels ("scoreboard"), maintain a spirit of positive competition, and provide recognition for individual and group accomplishments (reduction of worker and management-controllable defects resulting from worker suggestions).

Communications vehicles may include newsletters, bulletin boards, quality visibility centers (Leek and Riley, 1978), awards dinners, periodic meetings (weekly, monthly, etc.), and letters of recognition.

Improvement Projects. Quality campaigns, by themselves, do not result in lasting improvements in quality. Potential benefits in quality and work climate are realized through improvement projects. The process of identifying organizing, and executing these projects is disucssed in Section 22, Quality Improvement.

ACKNOWLEDGMENT

The author thanks one of his major suppliers, Carol Gestwicki, for her expert transformation of the manuscript to meet the publisher's requirements.

REFERENCES

Baker, E. M. (1982). "Managing for Quality through Employee Involvement." *ASQC Quality Congress Transactions,* Milwaukee, pp. 282–284.

Baker, E. M. and Artinian, H. L. M. (1985). "The Deming Philosophy of Continuing Improvement in a Service Organization: The Case of Windsor Export Supply." *Quality Progress,* vol. 18, no. 6, pp. 61–69.

Baker, E. M. and Schuck, J. R. (1975). "Theoretical Note: Use of Signal Detection Theory to Clarify Problems of Evaluating Performance in Industry." *Organization Behavior and Human Performance,* vol. 13, pp. 307–317.

Barra, R. (1983). *Putting Quality Circles to Work.* McGraw-Hill, New York.

Batt, W. L., Jr., and Weinberg, E. (1978). "Labor-Management Cooperation Today." *Harvard Business Review,* vol. 56, no. 1, pp. 96–104.

Berman, D. L. and Mase, H. (1983). "The Key to the Productivity Dilemma: 'The Performance Manager.'" *Human Resource Management,* vol. 22, no. 3, pp. 275–286.

Bluestone, I. (1977). "Creating a New World of Work." *International Labour Review,* vol. 115, no. 1, pp. 1–10.

Brethower, D. M. (1982). "The Total Performance System." In O'Brien, Richard M. et al. (eds.). *Industrial Behavior Modification: A Management Handbook.* Pergamon, New York, pp. 340–369.

Bruce-Briggs, B. (1982). "The Dangerous Folly Called Theory Z." *Fortune,* May 17, p. 44.

Bulock, R. J. and Lawler, E. E. (1984). "Gainsharing: A Few Questions, and Fewer Answers." *Human Resource Management,* vol. 23, no. 1, pp. 23–40.

Burck, C. G. (1981). "What's in It for the Unions." *Fortune,* August 24, pp. 88–92.

Carlson, H. C. (1978). "The Parallel Organization Structure at General Motors." *Personnel,* July–August, pp. 64–69.

Cohen-Rosenthal, E. and Burton, C. (1986). *Mutual Gains: A Practical Guide to Union-Management Cooperation.* Praeger, New York.

Cole, R. E. (1979). *Work Mobility and Participation: A Comparative Study of American and Japanese Industry.* University of California Press, Berkeley, CA.

Cole, R. E. (1980). "Will QC Circles Work in the US?" *Quality Progress,* vol. 13, no. 6, pp. 30–33.

Cole, R. E. (1981). "Common Misconceptions of Japanese QC Circles." *ASQC Quality Congress Transactions,* Milwaukee, pp. 188–189.

Cole, R. E. and Tachiki, D. S. (1984). "Forging Institutional Links: Making Quality Circles Work in the U.S." *National Productivity Review,* vol. 3, no. 4, pp. 417–429.

Connellan, T. K. (1978). *How to Improve Human Performance: Behaviorism in Business and Industry.* Harper and Row, New York.

Connellan, T. K. (1980). *How to Grow People into Self-Starters.* The Achievement Institute, Ann Arbor, MI.

Daniels, A. C. and Rosen, T. A. (1983). *Performance Management: Improving Quality and Productivity through Positive Reinforcement.* Performance Publications, Atlanta, GA.

Davidson, W. H. (1982). "Small Group Activity at Musashi Semiconductor Works. *Sloan Management Review,* vol. 23, no. 3, pp. 3–14.

Davis, L. E. (1983–1984). "Workers and Technology: the Necessary Joint Basis for Organizational Effectiveness." *National Productivity Review,* vol. 3, no. 1, pp. 7–14.

Deming, W. E. (1951). *Elementary Principles of the Statistical Control of Quality.* Nippon Kagaku Gijutsu Remmei, Tokyo, Japan.

Deming, W. E. (1982). *Quality Productivity and Competitive Position.* MIT Center for Advanced Engineering Study, Cambridge, MA.

Donnelly, J. F. (1977). "Participative Management at Work." *Harvard Business Review,* vol. 55, no. 1, pp. 117–127.

Ephlin, D. F. (1985). "Launching Saturn: The UAW Perspective on Quality." *Quality Progress,* vol. 18, no. 4, pp. 55–57.

Epstein, E. and Freund, W. C. (1984). *People and Productivity: The New York Stock Exchange Guide to Financial Incentives and the Quality of Work Life.* Dow Jones–Irwin, Homewood, IL.

Fairbank, J. A. and Prue, D. M. (1982). "Developing Performance Feedback Systems." In Frederiksen, L. W. (ed.). *Handbook of Organizaitonal Behavior Management.* John Wiley & Sons, New York, pp. 281–299.

Florida Power and Light Company (1982). *FPL Quality Improvement Program.* Miami, FL.

Fisher, B. A. (1980). *Small Group Decision Making: Communication and the Group Process.* McGraw-Hill, New York.

Frederiksen, L. W. (ed.) (1982). *Handbook of Organization Behavior Management.* John Wiley & Sons, New York.

Fukuda, R. (1983). *Managerial Engineering.* Productivity, Inc., Stamford, CT.

Gilbert, T. F. (1982). "Analyzing Productive Performance." In Frederiksen, L. W. (ed.). *Handbook of Organizational Behavior Management.* John Wiley & Sons, New York, pp. 117–144.

Golden, K. A. and Ramanujam, V. (1985). "Between a Dream and a Nightmare: On the Integration of the Human Resource Management and Strategic Business Planning Processes." *Human Resource Management,* vol. 24, no. 4, pp. 429–452.

Gryna, F. M., Jr. (1981). *Quality Circles, a Team Approach to Problem Solving.* AMACOM, American Management Association, New York.

Guest, R. H. (1979). "Quality of Work Life—Learning from Tarrytown." *Harvard Business Review,* 57, July–August, pp. 76–87.

Gyllenhammar, P. G. (1978). *People at Work.* Addison-Wesley, Reading, MA.

Hackman, J. R. and Oldham, G. R. (1980). *Work Redesign.* Addison-Wesley, Reading, MA.

Hanlon, M. D. (1985). "Unions, Productivity, and the New Industrial Relations: Strategic Considerations." *Interfaces,* vol. 15, no. 3, pp. 41–53.

Harris, D. and Chaney, F. B. (1969). *Human Factors in Quality Assurance.* John Wiley & Sons, New York.

Hermann, J. A. and Baker, E. M. (1985). "Teamwork Is Meeting Internal Customer Needs." *Quality Progress,* vol. 18, no. 7, pp. 12–16.

Herzberg, F. (1971). "An Interview with Frederick Herzberg." *The Management Review,* July, pp. 2–15.

Herzberg, F., Mausman, B., and Snyderman, B. (1959). *The Motivation to Work,* 2nd ed. John Wiley & Sons, New York.

Howard, R. (1984). "High Technology and the Reenchantment of the Work Place." *National Productivity Review,* vol. 3, no. 3, pp. 255–264.

Huse, E. F. and Beer, M. (1971). "Eclectic Approach to Organizational Development." *Harvard Business Review,* September–October, pp. 103–112.

Ingle, S. (1982). *Quality Circles Master Guide.* Prentice-Hall (Spectrum), Englewood Cliffs, NJ.

Ingle, S. and Ingle, N. (1983). *Quality Circles in Service Industries.* Prentice-Hall (Spectrum), Englewood Cliffs, NJ.

Ishikawa, K. (1981). "Company-Wide Quality Control—Revolution—Management." *ASQC Quality Congress Transactions,* Milwaukee, pp. 124–131.

Ishikawa, K. (1983). *Guide to Quality Control.* Asian Productivity Organization, Tokyo, Japan. Distributed by UNIPUB, New York.

Ishikawa, K. (1985). *What is Total Quality Control? The Japanese Way.* Prentice-Hall, Englewood Cliffs, NJ.

Japan External Trade Organization, JETRO (1981). *Japanese Manufacturing Operations in the United States,* September, Toyko, Japan.

Juran, J. M. (1956). "Improving the Relationship between Line and Staff." *Personnel,* May.

Juran, J. M. (1964). *Managerial Breakthrough.* McGraw-Hill, New York.

Juran, J. M. (1966). "Quality Problems, Remedies and Nostrums." *Industrial Quality Control,* vol. 22, no. 12, pp. 647–653.

Juran, J. M. (1967a). "The QC Circle Phenomenon." *Industrial Quality Control,* vol. 23, no. 7, pp. 329–336.

Juran, J. M. (1967b). "The Japanese QC Circle: Questions and Answers." *Quality,* summer, no. 2, pp. 37–38.

Juran, J. M. (1979). "Japanese and Western Quality—A Contrast." *Quality,* Part I: vol. 18, no. 1, pp. 8–12; Part II: vol. 18, no. 2, pp. 12–14.

Juran, J. M. (1980). "International Significance of the QC Circle." *Quality Progress,* vol. 13, no. 11, pp. 18–22.

Juran, J. M. and Gryna, F. M., Jr. (1980). *Quality Planning and Analysis,* 2nd ed. McGraw-Hill, New York.

Kane, E. J. (1986). "IBM's Quality Focus on the Business Process." *Quality Progress,* vol. 19, no. 4, pp. 24–33.

Kanter, R. M. (1983). *The Change Masters.* Simon and Schuster, New York.

Kast, F. E. and Rosenzweig, J. E. (1979). *Organization and Management: A Systems and Contingency Approach.* McGraw-Hill, New York.

Katz, H. C. (1982). "Assessing the New Auto Labor Agreements." *Sloan Management Review,* vol. 23, no. 4, pp. 57–63.

Ketchum, L. D. (1984). "How Redesigned Plants Really Work." *National Productivity Review,* vol. 3, no. 3, pp. 246–254.

Kobayashi, M. K. and Burke, W. W. (1976). "Organization Development in Japan." *Columbia Journal of World Business,* summer, pp. 113–123.

Kogure, M. (1970). "On the Systems Approach in Japan's Quality Control." *ASQC Technical Conference Transactions,* Milwaukee, pp. 429–439.

Kogure, M. (1984). "Quality Control in the Japanese Service Industry." *Reports of Statistical Applications and Research,* Japanese Union of Scientists and Engineers, vol. 31, no. 4, pp. 15–27.

Kogure, M. and Akao, Y. (1983). "Quality Function Deployment and CWQC in Japan." *Quality Progress,* vol. 16, no. 10, pp. 25–29.

Kondo, I., Wakimoto, K., and Hanawa, N. (1982). "Operator Inspection at a Japanese Steelmaker." *Quality Progress,* vol. 15, no. 12, pp. 14–16.

Kondo, Y. (1975). "Human Motivation and Quality Control." *Joint Conference Proceedings, European Organization for Quality Control—International Association for Quality,* Venice, vol. 1, pp. 139–150.

Kondo, Y. (1976). "The Roles of Manager in QC Circle Movement." *Reports of Statistical Applications Research,* Japanese Union of Scientists and Engineers, vol. 23, pp. 71–81.

Kondo, Y. (1977). "Creativity in Daily Work." *ASQC Technical Conference Transactions,* Milwaukee, pp. 430–439.

Kondo, Y. (1981). "Participation and Leadership." *ASQC Technical Conference Transactions,* Milwaukee, pp. 110–117.

Kotter, J. P. (1985). *Power and Influence.* Free Press, Macmillian, New York.

Latham, G. P. and Wexley, K. N. (1981). *Increasing Productivity through Performance Appraisal.* Addison-Wesley, Reading, MA.

Lawler, E. E., III (1976). "Control Systems in Organizations." In Dunnette, M. D. (ed.). *Handbook of Industrial and Organizational Psychology.* Rand McNally College Publishing Company, Chicago, pp. 1247–1291.

Lawler, E. E., III, and Mohrman, S. A. (1985). "Quality Circles after the Fad." *Harvard Business Review,* vol. 63, no. 1, pp. 65–71.

Lawler, E. E., III, and Ozley, L. (1979). "Winning Union-Management Cooperation on Quality of Worklife Projects." *The Management Review,* March, pp. 19–24.

Leek, J. W. and Riley, F. H. (1978). "Product Quality Improvement through Visibility." *ASQC Technical Conference Transactions,* Milwaukee, pp. 229–236.

Maher, J., Overbach, W., Palmer, G., and Persol, D. (1969). "Enriched Jobs Mean Better Inspection Performance." *Quality Assurance,* November, pp. 23–26.

Main, J. (1983). "Ford's Drive for Quality." *Fortune,* April 18, pp. 62–70.

Majerus, R. E. (1984). "Workers Have a Right to Share Profits." *Harvard Business Review,* vol. 62, no. 5, pp. 42–50.

Maslow, A. H. (1954). *Motivation and Personality.* Harper and Bros., New York.

May, E. (1978). "Operator Participation in Quality Control, Also Called Self-Control." *Proceedings of the International Conference on Quality Control, Tokyo.* Section A4, pp. 17–22.

McCormick, E. J. and Sanders, M. S. (1982). *Human Factors in Engineering and Design,* 5th ed. McGraw-Hill, New York.

McGregor, D. N. (1960). *The Human Side of Enterprise.* McGraw-Hill, New York.

Melan, E. H. (1985). "Process Management in Service and Administrative Operations." *Quality Progress,* vol. 18, no. 6, pp. 52–60.

Miller, L. M. (1978). *Behavior Management.* John Wiley & Sons, New York.

Miller, L. M. (1984). *American Spirit: Visions of a New Corporate Culture.* William Morrow, New York.

Moehlenbrock, M. (1985). "Control Teams Contrasted with Breakthrough Teams." *The Juran Report: Proceedings of Annual Conference (IMPRO 84) on Quality Improvement,* winter, no. 4, pp. 175–179.

Myers, M. S. (1981). *Every Employee a Manager,* 2nd ed. McGraw-Hill, New York.

"The New Industrial Relations." (1985). *Business Week,* May 11, pp. 85–93.

Nickell, W. L. (1985). "Quality Improvement in a Marketing Organization." *Quality Progress,* vol. 18, no. 6, pp. 46–51.

Nosow, S. (1984). "A Lesson for American Managers: Learning from Japanese Experiences in the U.S." *National Productivity Review,* vol. 3, no. 4, pp. 407–416.

O'Brien, R. M., Dickinson, A. M., and Rosow, M. P. (1982). *Industrial Behavior Modification: A Management Handbook.* Pergamon, New York.

Ouchi, W. G. (1981). *Theory Z: How American Business Can Meet the Japanese Challenge.* Addison-Wesley, Reading, MA.

Parsons, H. M. (1974). "What Happened at Hawthorne." *Science,* vol. 183, pp. 922–930.

Peters, T. J. and Waterman, R. A., Jr. (1982). *In Search of Excellence.* Harper and Row, New York.

Pettigrew, T. J. (1983). *Process Quality Control: The New Approach to the Management of Quality in Ford.* SAE Australasia Seminar on Development Trends in Automotive Quality Control, April.

Prince, G. M. (1970). *The Practice of Creativity.* Harper and Row, New York.

Prince, G. M. (1972). "Creative Meetings through Power Sharing." *Harvard Business Review,* vol. 50, no. 4, pp. 47–54.

"Quality Sagging? Workers Depressed? Try these Ideas." (1972). *Iron Age,* vol. 210, no. 23, p. 29.

Reisman, B. and Compa, L. (1985). "The Case for Adversarial Unions." *Harvard Business Review,* vol. 63, no. 3, pp. 22–36.

Roethlisberger, F. J. and Dickson, W. J. (1939). *Management and the Worker.* Harvard University Press, Cambridge, MA.

Rosow, M. P. (1982). "Quality of Working Life: A Behavioral Process for Organizational Change." In O'Brien, Richard M. et al. (eds.). *Industrial Behavior Modification: A Management Handbook.* Pergamon, New York, pp. 335–349.

Ross, T. L. and Hauck, W. C. (1984). "Gainsharing in the United States." *Industrial Management,* vol. 26, March–April, pp. 9–14.

Rubin, I. M., Plovnick, M. S., and Fry, R. E. (1978). *Task Oriented Team Development.* McGraw-Hill, New York.

Rubinstein, S. P. (1971). "Participative Quality Control." *Quality Progress,* vol. 4, no. 1, pp. 24–27.

Rubinstein, S. P. (1973). "Engineering Management Attitudes and U.S. Productivity Challenges." *Professional Engineer,* vol. 43, no. 7, pp. 37–39.

Rubinstein, S. P. (1982). "Labor Management Quality Systems." *ASQC Quality Congress Transactions,* Milwaukee, pp. 674–682.

Rubinstein, S. P. (1984). "Quality Control Requires a Social and Technical System." *Quality Progress,* vol. 17, no. 8, pp. 22–27.

Rummler, G. A. (1981). *A View of the Management Process.* The Rummler Group, Summit, NJ.

Sandholm, L. (1983). "Japanese Quality Circles—A Remedy for the West's Quality Problems?" *Quality Progress,* vol. 16, no. 2, pp. 20–23.

Schein, E. H. (1981). "Does Japanese Management Style Have a Message for American Managers?" *Sloan Management Review,* vol. 23, no. 1, pp. 55–68.

Scherkenbach, W. W. (1985). "Performance Appraisal and Quality: Ford's New Philosophy." *Quality Progress,* vol. 18, no. 4, pp. 40–46.

Schuster, M. (1984). "Cooperation and Change in Union Settings: Problems and Opportunities." *Human Resource Management,* vol. 23, no. 2, pp. 145–160.

Sethi, S. P., Namiki, N., and Swanson, C. L. (1984). *The False Promise of the Japanese Miracle.* Pitman, Marshfield, MA.

Shea, G. P. (1986). "Quality Circles: The Danger of Bottled Change." *Sloan Management Review,* vol. 27, no. 3, pp. 33–46.

Sherwood, J. J. and Hoylman, F. M. (1977). *Utilizing Human Resources: Individual versus Group Approaches to Problem-Solving and Decision-Making.* Paper No. 621, Institute for Research in the Behavioral, Economic, and Management Sciences, Krannert Graduate School of Management, Purdue University, West Lafayette, IN.

Shewhart, W. A. (1939). *Statistical Method from the Viewpoint of Quality Control.* Lancaster Press, Lancaster, PA.

Sink, D. S. (1983). "Using the Nominal Group Technique Effectively." *National Productivity Review,* spring, pp. 173–184.

Stein, B. A. and Kanter, R. M. (1980). "Building the Parallel Organization: Creating Mechanisms for Permanent Quality of Work Life." *Journal of Applied Behavioral Science,* pp. 371–386.

Sullivan, J. J. (1983). "A Critique of Theory Z." *Academy of Management Review,* vol. 8, no. 1, p. 133.

Sullivan, L. P. (1986). "Quality Function Deployment." *Quality Progress,* vol. 19, no. 6, pp. 39–50.

Suzuki, T. (1978). "Quality Function and Industrial Cybernetics." *Proceedings of the International Conference on Quality Control, Tokyo,* Section B4, pp. 39–43.

Takezawa, S. (1976). "The Quality of Working Life: Trends in Japan." *Labour and Society,* vol. 1, pp. 29–48.

Tannenbaum, R. and Schmidt, W. H. (1973). "How to Choose a Leadership Pattern." *Harvard Business Review,* vol. 51, no. 3, pp. 162–173.

Taylor, F. W. (1947). *Scientific Management.* Harper and Bros., New York.

Tichy, N. M. (1976). "When Does Work Restructuring Work? Organizational Innovation at Volvo and GM." *Organizational Dynamics,* vol. 5, no. 1.

Tichy, N. M. (1983). *Managing Strategic Change: Technical, Political, and Cultural Dynamics.* John Wiley & Sons, New York.

Tuggle, G. (1969). "Job Enlargement." *Industrial Engineering,* February, pp. 26–31.

Walton, R. E. (1979). "Work Innovations in the United States." *Harvard Business Review,* vol. 57, pp. 88–98.

"Who's Excellent Now?" (1984). *Business Week,* Nov. 5, pp. 76–86.

Woodman, R. W. and Sherwood, J. J. (1977). "A Comprehensive Look at Job Design." *Personnel Journal,* August, pp. 384–418.

Yamamoto, M. (1980). "The Japanese—Homogeneity Promotes 'Ikigai.'" *Quality Progress,* vol. 13, no. 9, pp. 18–21.

Yankelovich, D. and Immerwahr, J. (1983). *Putting the Work Ethic to Work.* The Public Agenda Foundation, New York.

Zander, A. (1983). *Making Groups Effective.* Jossey-Bass, San Francisco, CA.

Zemke, R. and Kramlinger, T. (1982). *Figuring Things Out.* Addison-Wesley, Reading, MA.

SUPPLEMENTAL BIBLIOGRAPHY AND RESOURCES

American Periodical Publications

Harvard Buisness Review. Published bimonthly by the Graduate School of Business, Harvard University, Boston, MA 02163.

Handbook for Group Facilitators. Published annually by University Associates, 8517 Production Avenue, San Diego, CA. It is a source of ideas and techniques for managing group meetings and team performance.

Human Resource Management. Published quarterly (for the University of Michigan Graduate School) by John Wiley & Sons, 605 Third Avenue, New York, NY 10158.

Juran Report. Published by the Juran Institute, 88 Danbury Rd., Wilton, CT 06897. Contains proceedings of Annual Quality Conferences—IMPRO—which describe project team approaches to quality improvement.

Management Review. Published monthly by the American Management Association, 135 West 50th Street, New York, NY 10020.

National Productivity Review. Published quarterly by Executive Enterprises Publications Co., 33 West 60th Street, New York, NY 10023.

Organization Dynamics. Published quarterly by AMACOM Division of the American Management Associations, 135 West 50th Street, New York, NY 10020.

Performance Management Magazine. Published quarterly by Performance Management Publications, 3531 Habersham at Northlake, Tucker, GA 30084.

Productivity Newsletter. Published by Productivity, Inc., P.O. Box 16722, Stamford, CT 06905.

Quality Progress. Published monthly by the American Society for Quality Control, 230 West Wells Street, Milwaukee, WI 53203.

Sloan Management Review. Published quarterly by the Sloan Management Review Association, Alfred P. Sloan School of Management, Massachusetts Institute of Technology, 50 Memorial Drive, Cambridge, MA 02139.

Training and Development Journal. Published monthly by the American Society for Training and Development, Suite 305, 600 Maryland Avenue S.W., Washington, DC 20024.

Publications (in English) of the Japanese Union of Scientists and Engineers (JUSE).

Available from JUSE, 5-10-11 Sendagaya, Shibuya-ku, Tokyo 151, Japan (additional materials are cited in the References):

Reports of QC Circle Activities. Published annually since 1968. Each booklet contains numerous reports of Japanese quality circle projects presented in the West. JUSE also publishes *Reports of QC Circle Activities in Japan.* These contain quality circle team presentations given within Southeast Asia.

International QC Circle Convention Proceedings. Contains reports of Japanese and foregin quality circle activities presented in Japan.

Reports of Statistical Applications Research. This quarterly journal sometimes includes descriptions of quality circle projects. Volume 21, no. 4 (December 1974) was reprinted as the booklet, *Training for Foremen and QC Circle Leaders.* Volume 25, no. 2 (June 1978) contains a listing of statistical courses for quality circle members, supervision, and management, within the context of companywide quality control.

Ishikawa, Kaoru (ed.) (1983). *QC Circle Activities.* A comprehensive history and description of the quality circle movement.

QC Circle Koryo: General Principles of the QC Circle (1980). A translation of the original Japanese book.

Other Japanese English-Language Publications

Ishikawa, Kaoru (1983). *Guide to Quality Control.* Asian Productivity Organization, Tokyo, Japan. Distributed by UNIPUB, New York.

Jishu Kanri Activities in the Japanese Steel Industry (1971). Japan Iron and Steel Federation, Tokyo.

Quality Control Circles at Work: Cases from Japan's Manufacturing and Service Sectors (1984). Asian Productivity Organization, Tokyo. Distributed by UNIPUB, New York.

American Experiences with Quality Circles

American Society for Quality Control (1976). *QC Circles Applications, Tools, and Theory* [Amsden, R. T. and Amsden, D. M. (eds.)]. Available from ASQC, 310 West Wisconsin Avenue, Milwaukee, WI 53203.

American Society for Quality Control (1982). *Quality Circles and Quality of Work Life—Directory of Resources.* Available from ASQC (includes extensive bibliography).

American Society for Quality Control (1983). *Quality Circle Papers: A Compilation.* Available from ASQC.

The Quality Circles Journal. Published quarterly by the International Association of Quality Circles, 801-B West Eighth Street, Suite 301, Cincinnati, OH 45203.

SECTION 11
TRAINING FOR QUALITY[1]

Frank M. Gryna

---

[1] In the Third Edition, the material on training was prepared by J. M. Juran.

INTRODUCTION

All companies organize their activities along functional lines. Each of the resulting functional departments trains its members in the concepts and tools needed to carry out the departmental function. One such functional department is called the Quality Department (or similar name). Its members are exclusively engaged in quality-related activities. In consequence these members are extensively trained in quality-related concepts and tools. Other departments engage in quality-related activities to only a limited degree, and hence their members have had only limited training in quality-related concepts and tools. For many years, the practice of functional training was sufficient to enable companies to make products of a quality which could compete successfully in the marketplace. For some products this is still the case, but it is no longer the case for sophisticated modern products.

The need is to extend training in quality-related matters to personnel in all functions. To help explain this need it is useful to resort to an analogy with finance. There is a considerable body of finance-related concepts and tools: budgets, cost controls, balance sheets, etc. In some companies only members of the finance department have been trained in these concepts and tools. In other companies such training has been provided to the entire management team. This difference in training strongly influences the respective financial performances.

In like manner, companies differ in their extent of training in quality-related concepts and tools. Companies in the west have traditionally concentrated such training in the Quality Department. In contrast, many Japanese companies have extended this training to all departments. This difference in extent of training has strongly influenced the respective performances with respect to quality. The same difference in training has also contributed to a quality crisis in Western countries, and the crisis has led to a revision in Western training policy. The underlying premises for this revision are set out below.

PREMISES AND GUIDELINES

The need for the West to revise its approach to training for quality is based on the following premises:

1. There is a body of quality-related knowledge which is an essential element of modern competition in quality. This body of knowledge will be called the "quality disciplines." These disciplines consist of quality-related concepts, tools, techniques, etc. A listing of most of these disciplines is given in Table 11-1.

TABLE 11.1   The Quality Disciplines

Major managerial concepts
  Fitness for use
  The quality function
  Parameters of quality
  Quality specifications and standardization
  Quality planning
  Quality control
  Quality assurance
  Quality improvement
  Reliance on the laws of nature
  The factual approach
  Quantification
Tools for functional areas
  Sales
    Marketing research for quality
  Product development
    Design review
    Errorproofing
    Failure mode and effects analysis
    Fault tree analysis
    Quantification of reliability,
      maintainability, availability, and safety
    Weibull analysis of data
    Design of experiments
    Setting tolerances
  Supplier relations
    Supplier surveys
    Quality requirements
    Quality planning
    Supplier surveillance
    Incoming inspection
    Audit of decisions
    Data banks
    Supplier rating
  Manufacture
    Manufacture planning
    Process capability
    Tolerances for interacting dimensions
    Statistical control charts

    Errorproofing
    Design of experiments
    Computer controls
    Self-control
    Self-inspection
    Troubleshooting
  Inspection and test
    Inspection planning
    Inspector accuracy
    Classification of characteristics
    Classification of defects
    Reproducibility of measurements
    Sensory tests
    Calibration systems
  Field performance
    Complaint procedures
    Analysis of field data
    Preventive maintenance
  Quality improvement
    Sporadic versus chronic problems
    Pareto concept
    Project concept
    Diagnosis
    Management-controllable defects
    Worker-controllable defects
    Quality circles
Broad management of the quality function
  Policies
  Objectives
  Quality cost
  Company-wide planning
  Organizing
  Coordination
  Motivation
  Recruiting and training personnel
  Quality and society
Data collection and analysis
  Planning for data collection
  Statistical tools

2. These quality disciplines apply to all activities and at all levels of the company. (This is identical to the finance-oriented disciplines.)

3. In companies in the West, training in the quality disciplines has largely been concentrated in one specialized department—the "Quality Department" (or similar name).

4. In companies in Japan, training in the quality disciplines has largely been companywide rather than concentrated in one specialized department.

5. The evidence is overwhelming that the Western approach of concentrating this training only in the Quality Department is unable to compete with the approach of companywide training in the quality disciplines. Line personnel in the West, and especially in the United States, have access to assistance from well-trained quality specialists. However, experience has shown that the line people make only limited use of this assistance. *Unless the tools are put into the hands of the line people, the amount of this use will remain limited.* As a result, many quality-related activities are poorly performed and some are not performed at all.

6. Hence, the West is now faced with undertaking a massive program of company training in the quality disciplines, much as was undertaken by the Japanese starting in the early 1950s. (To fully understand the impact of the training effort in Japan, it is useful to visit Japan and witness at first hand the knowledge that has been acquired by all personnel.)

Effect of Massive Training for Line Departments. Such "massive training" for line people has a profound effect on organization for quality. A preview of this effect is seen in the conduct of quality-related activities in Japan. There the line specialists (e.g., product designers and manufacturing planners) perform most of the work of quality planning and analysis which in the United States is done by reliability engineers and quality engineers. The line supervisors do most of the planning of quality systems, and make them work. The line supervisors are also active in initiating and carrying out projects for improving quality and reducing quality-related costs. In addition, millions of workers in the quality circles are active in devising control plans and in finding ways to improve quality and reduce costs. This training in the quality disciplines and the associated experience has made the line people more self-sufficient in quality matters and hence better able to meet future competition.

There is much cultural resistance to accepting such training, and especially to the consequences of using it. The former resistance comes from line people who have long conducted their affairs without training in the quality disciplines. The latter resistance comes from Quality Departments and quality specialists who see a threat to their vested interests. Collectively all this resistance can delay and even defeat the training program. It follows that companies should understand the nature and extent of this cultural resistance before embarking on any program which is to extend throughout the hierarchy. The conclusion may be that such a broad program is premature and that what is needed at the outset is selective training which responds to the more obvious and urgent company needs.

Major Issues to be Considered. Training must be specially tailored to each company's needs. Each company has a uniqueness due to:

1. The quality problems and challenges faced by the company.

2. The knowledge and skills needed to solve these problems and meet these challenges. The purposes of training can be designed to provide an awareness of the significance of the quality issue, to provide problem-solving tools to correct

current problems, and to show individuals how quality can be integrated into their own positions. The skills may be technological, managerial, or statistical. These skills must be identified on a job-by-job basis; i.e., for each job, it is necessary to determine what skills are required to perform the quality-oriented tasks contained within that job.

3. The knowledge and skills actually possessed by the jobholders. To understand this requires that an inventory be taken to discover the prevailing levels of knowledge and state of skill.

4. The training facilities and processes already in existence. These may include apprentice schools, on-the-job training by supervisors, self-training through manuals, company Training Department courses, collaboration with local university extention services, etc. These existing forms are supported by vested interests, and the organizer of any new program is well advised to secure the use of their services.

5. The prevailing climate for training, based on the record of past programs.

6. "What is different?" Most personnel believe that they are already doing what is needed to achieve the desired quality. The critical question in the minds of the people being trained is: "What do you want me to do different in my job that I am currently doing today?" The training program should provide specific responses to that question.

PLANNING THE TRAINING PROGRAM

Example of a Companywide Program.   Table 11.2 is an extract from the training program for a Japanese company.

It is evident that this program goes from top to bottom in the organization and covers managerial, technological, and statistical subjects. It also provides training that is at the awareness level in addition to training that will enable people to perform specific quality-related activities.

For Western companies, a program of companywide training in the quality disciplines is a radical departure from the past. Clearly, such a program is more likely to become successful if there is careful planning beforehand. Planning is needed to answer these questions:

Who is to be trained?

Training in what?

Where will we get the training materials?

How will we secure leaders to do the training?

Should we train in-house or elsewhere?

How much will it cost?

How long will it take?

What should be the schedules and priorities?

Many of these questions are discussed in this section of the handbook.

Who Plans?   A widely used approach is to create a broad-based task force to do the planning. Such a task force includes:

Several managers from major line departments, e.g., Product Development, Manufacture, Marketing

TABLE 11.2   Training Program in Matsushita Electric Industries Co.

Title of course	Held for	No. of persons	Hours	Contents
Management Course	President and directors	8	21	Introduction to QC, statistical way of thinking, quality assurance, development of new products, organization and administration of QC
Course for Chiefs of Departments	1. Factory manager, Chiefs of departments at head office	22	18	Same as above top management course
	2. Sales managers	15	6	Introduction to QC, market survey
Middle Management Course	Chiefs of departments at factories, chiefs of sections (out of 200 persons, 60 persons attended QC:MC course held by JUSE)	200	6	How to introduce and promote QC
Engineer's Course	QC engineers OR workers			Attended the courses held outside the company
Intermediate	People in charge of design and research	60	144	QC application method, statistical method, control chart method, sampling inspection method, sampling, etc.
Introductory Course	Engineers in general (out of 260 persons, 20 persons attended the courses held outside the company) (this course has been held five times)	260	36	Received the training under the course corresponding to introductory course held by JUSE
Foreman Course (Primary)	Foremen	200	12	Foremen's QC text (A) used
Foreman Course (Secondary)	Foremen picked up from those getting primary course	80	30	Foremen's QC text (B) used

Source: Ishikawa, K. (1969). "Education of Quality Control in Japanese Industry." *Reports of Statistical Applications and Research,* Japanese Union of Scientists and Engineers, vol. 16, no. 3, p. 21.

Several managers from major service departments, e.g., Finance, Industrial, Engineering

A manager from Management Development or Training

A manager from Quality

A major appliance manufacturer established a high-level management team to do the broad planning for the training program. This team first took a 30-h training course covering managerial, statistical, and technological topics. At the start of the course, presented by this author, the president announced that the purpose was (1) to provide knowledge for upper management and (2) to help upper management decide what elements of the training should be provided to the various departments. Then, at the end of the course, the president asked each of the managers for recommendations on training for quality.

The broad-based task force can lay out the training program in general terms. However, there is also a need for much detailed planning. The detailed planning can be done either by the central training department or it can be decentralized to various organization units: division, functions, offices, plants.

Corporate Plan or Not?   The practice varies. Some large companies have left it to each division to work up its own plan of approach, with only limited coordination by corporate headquarters. Smaller companies tend to do the planning on a corporate basis, with participation by the divisions (or plants).

Where broad corporate planning is used, it tends to concentrate on broad matters:

Coordination with other active programs (e.g., productivity improvement, participative management).

Training for upper managers

The budget for major expenditures

Development of training materials which are applicable to multiple divisions

Development of leaders for the seed courses

Example of Planning a Quality Training Program.   Hill and McClaskey (1980) described the approach used at the Tennessee Eastman Company. The approach consisted of the following steps:

1. *Define the purpose:*   Their discussions resulted in a list of nine alternative purposes. The one selected was "To make each level of management aware of its quality responsibilities." The Development and Control departments for several areas were selected as a target group for the training program. Management was defined to include all members of the Development and Control departments, from workers to department superintendents.

2. *Identify alternatives that will achieve the purposes:*   Brainstorming was used, and several dozen alternatives were generated. These were narrowed to a list of seven:

   a. Set up a company system to develop, evaluate, and certify quality control programs
   b. Prepare written quality plans for every product
   c. Require position guides that include quality responsibilities
   d. Teach about quality responsibilities

   e. Have standard administrative procedures that assign quality respon-
      sibilities

   f. Establish improved communication among various groups

   g. Have a central quality organization responsible for the coordination of
      quality program development and knowledge dissemination

   3. *Analyze the alternatives:*   The seven alternatives were compared using five
criteria with weights assigned, as follows:

Criteria	*Weight*
Chance of implementation	9
Completeness	8
Flexibility of format	4
Levels of management reached	3
Probability of reducing cost of internal and external failures	2

   Each alternative was given a raw score which was multiplied by the weight for
each criterion. These weighted scores were then added and the sum used as a score
for each alternative. The alternative with the highest score was "teach about quality responsibilities."

   4. *Design the actual program:*   The following design criteria were developed
for planning the individual courses. The criteria stated that courses should:

   a. Create awareness of quality responsibility

   b. Cover total learning needs in quality awareness

   c. Be modifiable to meet specific needs

   d. Be designed for intended audience

   e. Be used only by people requiring the knowledge

   f. Be limited in content to fill a specific need

   g. Be developed so that specific curricula can be selected for individual
      needs

   h. Be usable by individuals or small groups at random times

   i. Have a maximum length of 2 hours

   j. Be portable and usable near work area

   k. Be used just before knowledge is needed

   l. Have pre and post tests

   m. Have the development costs monitored

   n. Be reviewed for quality, consistency of terminology, and accomplish-
      ment of objectives

   The personnel were surveyed to identify course needs. The survey form listed
40 potential courses and 13 different job categories. The courses covered management, quality engineering, quality assurance, operations, and statistical methodology. An analysis of the survey results revealed the need for 16 new courses.

   5. *Implement the solution:*   The task force decided that the 16 courses should
be developed in house. A company "expert" was selected to develop each course,
and a steering committee reviewed the outline, drafts of the course material, and
the final script and slides. To track the cost of developing each course, a set of
charge codes was established and expenses were accumulated.

6. *Evaluate the results:*   For each course the transfer of knowledge was evaluated by the use of pre and post tests.

ANALYSIS OF TRAINING NEEDS

The analysis to determine training needs should not be left in the hands of a quality specialist, but instead should be under the direction of a broad based task force planning the training program. One approach to obtaining input is to "make the rounds" of all the managers who will be sending people to the training program. Each manager should be asked to describe those quality-related problems which require response in the training program. With that information as a base, discussions should then be held with specialists to decide which tools and techniques to incorporate into the training program.

Some companies find it useful to create a matrix relating subject matter of training to the types of personnel to be trained. To construct such a matrix, potential training topics (e.g., the items in Table 11.1) are listed vertically. Then columns are identified with headings for various personnel (e.g., the categories listed later in this section under Training for Various Personnel). The matrix is completed by checking the topics needed for each category of personnel.

One large company (IBM) has identified five major elements of education for quality, as follows:

1. Quality awareness
2. Quality truths
3. Attitude change through case studies
4. Quality science, i.e., tools and methodology
5. Implementation

WHY QUALITY TRAINING PROGRAMS FAIL

Training programs are often conducted to change the attitude or to change the behavior of personnel. If these changes do not take place, the training program has failed. Experience has uncovered several reasons:

1. *Cultural resistance by line managers:*   Often, line managers believe that they and their people have all the information necessary to do "a quality job." They see no need for additional training, and many regard it as a waste of time that could better be spent on other activities. Some remedies are (*a*) present factual information describing the need for such training, (*b*) secure the full support of upper management, and (*c*) start the training at upper management levels.

2. *Doubt as to the usefulness of the training:*   An approach to overcome this doubt is to develop some case examples within the company. These examples can then be included in the training course. One "inside" example can work wonders.

3. *Lack of participation by line managers:*   Line managers clearly have an interest in these training programs. The hours their subordinates spend on training are hours deducted from productive time. The line managers face the realities of quality-related problems and hence are an essential source of inputs to planning the training. As a minimum, the views of these managers should be solicited. Better yet, some of the line managers should be members of the task force which designs the training program.

4. *Technique versus problem orientation:* Many courses on quality have been designed around specific techniques rather than around the quality problems which require solution. Making the rounds of line managers to collect the list of quality-related problems can help ensure that the course will be problem-oriented.

5. *Inadequacies of leaders:* When a large amount of training is undertaken, one of the key decisions is the selection and preparation of leaders. These leaders should not only be competent teachers; they should also have high credibility as professionals in the area of knowledge of the course.

6. *Mixing of levels of participants:* In some companies, if the same "class" includes "students" from several ranks in the hierarchy, the effect can be to inhibit discussion. Ideally, the students in a class should be in the same or similar levels of rank.

7. *Lack of application during the course:* The ideal approach is to design the course so that the participants must apply the training during the course. One of the best learning experiences is the application of the material being taught. This was successfully done during World War II in the area of work-simplification programs. More recently, value engineering seminars often have a project included as part of the seminar. Quality circles also use the concept. In the first half of a circle meeting, the leader instructs the members in a new problem-solving technique. During the remainder of the meeting, the technique is applied to the problem currently pursued by the circle.

8. *Language too complex:* Some courses fail because the language used is too complicated for the audiences. This has been particularly so in the area of statistical techniques. What the statistician considers as a "simple" technique may be too complex for some people. The remedy is not only careful preparation and aids to presentation, but preferably a test run of the material before a small pilot group.

9. *Lack of participation by the training function:* Large companies often have a training department with people who are knowledgeable about the design and execution of training programs. These people are not necessarily knowledgeable about specific quality-related techniques, but they can provide excellent inputs into the overall design, execution, and evaluation of training programs. Their expertise should be utilized.

10. *Operational and logistical deficiencies:* Some courses fail because of poor physical environment and facilities. These matters involve control of environment (e.g., noise), space available for each student, audio-visual facilities, luncheon arrangement, and a myriad of other details. Again, a corporate training department can be helpful based on their experience in conducting many courses.

To avoid some of these pitfalls, allow sufficient time for thorough planning and for a pilot run of the course.

MEANS OF PROVIDING TRAINING

The classroom is not the only method of providing training. The other methods include:

Job Experience. One of the most effective ways of acquiring knowledge is from experience in work situations. This can be a useful form of training at all levels. For example, as upper managers become more involved in quality matters, they need to acquire knowledge of quality issues and methodologies. One way to acquire such knowledge is through conduct of quality audits. (See Section 9 under Quality Audits.) At each of these audits, managers in some area of the company are asked to respond to a structured list of questions concerning quality issues and activities in their area. These audits are conducted by members of upper management and hence become a part of their training. At a different level, a quality specialist is assigned a specific problem to solve, such as locating the cause of rejects on a particular operation or preparing an inspection plan for a new product. The experience acquired in executing these projects is an important method of training the quality engineer (Reynolds, 1979).

For production workers, training is often a major responsibility of the supervisor. To an important degree, the supervisor personally is the trainer in:

1. Job induction, when the employee first starts on a new task
2. Job rotation, when the employee is assigned to a variety of tasks
3. Self-teaching, when the employee must study the procedures and other documentation as part of the preparation for doing the job

A special form of on-the-job training is "vestibule training." Here, employees are taught their particular operations by building product in a special classroom before they are sent out to the production line. For example, a manufacturer of disk drives for computer systems requires that all new production employees receive vestibule training before they ever see the real assembly line. The training ranges from several days to several weeks depending on the nature of the job. Before an employee joins the assembly line, dozens of disk drives will have been built under the supervision of an instructor. By the end of the first week, the trainee is able to build a complete disk drive. This company reports that in the final test in assembly areas, yield by untrained employees was about 75 to 80 percent. After trained employees joined the line, the yield rose to over 90 percent ("Vestibule Training," 1981).

Rotational Job Experience. The concept here is that employees will perform better if they are aware of the effects of their activity on other activities in the company, or on the performance of the product. An example of this is the practice followed by the Matsushita Company in their training program for design engineers. The young graduate undergoes a 1-year indoctrination program before being assigned to a specific design activity. For the first 3 months, the engineer works full time at a dealer's facility. Here, knowledge is gained on how the sets are sold, the needs of customers, and typical field service problems. The engineer then spends an additional 9 months full time in the production shops working at production stations, learning the manufacturing processes, and helping to introduce new designs into manufacturing processes. Later steps in the overall training program require formal classroom work and a second round of field experience for those being considered for promotion. In the United States, designers at the Maytag Company spend 6 months in the factory before going on to their engineering assignments. Similarly, one division of the Westinghouse Company assigns new designers for 6 to 12 months on the factory floor as training prior to design. Many Quality Departments provide rotational experience to broaden the knowledge of various quality specialists, e.g., staff people are assigned full time to line operations in order to "live" the problems of the line. Such experiences can be sobering and invaluable in the development of the staff specialist.

There are many opportunities for applying the rotational experience concept, but it does require a plan and the determination to follow the plan.

Classroom Training. This widely used training form has broad application to training programs in quality. Effective use of the classroom requires care in dealing with several elements of the learning process:

A training content which links the quality mission of the company, the unsolved quality problems, and the role of the trainee in solving those problems

A clear course outline plus prepared text material, so that the trainee can see what will be coming up and can do some advance preparation

Competent instructors, both as to the subject matter and as to ability to communicate

Well-designed teaching aids

In addition, it is well to do some judicious screening so that trainees do not get into courses for which they are seriously overqualified or underqualified.

The classroom training may consist of courses designed and conducted by company personnel, public courses, or courses provided on-site by outside consultants. Several organizations have extensive activities in presenting public and on-site seminars. These organizations include the Education and Training Institute of the American Society for Quality Control, the American Management Association, Juran Institute, and Philip Crosby Associates.

Self-Instruction. This can be accomplished through:

1. *Video cassettes:* Here, the knowledge is presented through a series of video cassettes that are usually supplemented with a workbook. Typically, the cassettes are viewed by a group of people who discuss each cassette and the potential applications within their own company.

2. *Training films:* There are increasingly available a wide variety of films ranging from quality awareness topics to metrology, statistical methods, reliability and maintainability, and other topics.

3. *Programmed instruction:* In this form, written materials are prepared and designed to present successive "frames" or small segments of information for self-study. The design further permits immediate feedback to the student to judge the absorption of the knowledge.

Further details on each of these three methods are presented under Instructional Technology, below.

Supplements to Formal Training Approaches. These include:

1. *The quality control manual:* These manuals are used for reference when procedural questions arise and for the induction of new people into jobs. Well-prepared manuals can help an employee learn a good deal about the new job. In special situations, the manual can be used as a text for training seminars.

2. *Visits to other companies:* Such visits can be to customers, suppliers, or other companies. Not only can specific knowledge be acquired, but viewing quality activities in other companies can help to change attitudes and broaden horizons.

3. *Membership in professional societies:* Attendance at monthly society meetings can be a source of new knowledge from outside speakers and also from the contacts made with local people at the meetings. Some professional societies reserve one of their evening meetings for programs specially designed for

managers. This can be part of the program for training managers in quality. Some sections of the American Society for Quality Control present a variety of courses each year to meet the needs of the local member (for an example, see Rado, 1976).

4. *Publications:* Books and journal articles make wide use of case histories showing how some companies have solved quality problems. Making this information available within a company can be part of the overall training program. With the enormous amount of literature available, it can be helpful to subscribe to an abstracting service. Such services exist for quality. One service is *Quality Control and Applied Statistics,* an international literature digest published by Executive Sciences Institute, Whippany, NJ 07981.

The service provides abstracts of articles taken from journals all over the world.

TRAINING FOR VARIOUS CATEGORIES OF PERSONNEL

Upper Management. Ideally, the quality training program in a company should include the entire managerial and supervisory hierarchy, *starting at the top.* Such a proposal was, until the 1980s, seldom welcomed by upper managers. Their instinctive belief was that upper managers already know what needs to be done and that training is for others—the work force, the middle managers, the engineers. The present atmosphere of crisis in some countries is forcing a reexamination of this belief.

The training for upper management should include a broad coverage of all of the quality activities in the company, but more importantly should show exactly what role upper management should take in the overall program.

Course Leadership. Experience in conducting training courses for upper managers has generated some feedback:

Upper managers regard themselves as business managers. Hence, the training should establish a clear linkage to business goals.

Upper managers are results-oriented—they are measured by business results. Hence the training should be oriented to results, not techniques.

Upper managers are usually aware that they themselves may be a part of the problem. Hence they look for answers to the question: What should I be doing different that I am doing now?

Upper managers strongly prefer to be in training meetings with other upper managers. They feel that no one else understands the problem faced by upper managers.

As a consequence of the foregoing, upper managers are reluctant to accept insiders or subordinates as instructors. Instead, their preference is to listen to outsiders. These outsiders may be upper managers from other companies. Alternatively, the outsiders may be consultants who appear to be:

Knowledgeable in quality-oriented matters.

Able to convey this knowledge in ways which relate squarely to the business realities faced by upper managers.

Able to provide answers to the question: What should I do different than I am doing now?

Outlines of Some Courses.   The Japanese Union of Scientists and Engineers has provided a course for upper management since 1957. The outline for the 1980 version of the course is shown in Table 11.3.

A 1-day seminar presented by Juran Institute consists of the topics shown in Table 11.4.

The outline for a top management course at IBM is shown in Table 11.5.

TABLE 11.3   Course for Upper Management (Japanese Union of Scientists and Engineers)

Topic	Hours
Role of top management in implementing QC	1.5
QC in new product development	2.0
Statistical methods	3.5
Management of QC	3.5
QC in manufacture	3.5
QC in purchasing and sales	3.5
Quality assurance	3.5
QC in Japan and in the world	3.5
Group discussions on promoting QC in the companies	3.0
Reports of group discussions	3.0
Total	30.5

TABLE 11.4   Topics of 1-Day Seminar for Upper Management*

The job of upper management	Training for quality
Annual quality improvement	Motivation for quality
Audit of departmental activities	The Japanese quality revolution
Audit of coordination for quality	Epilogue

*Presented by the Juran Institute.

TABLE 11.5   Top Management Course Outline*

1. Quality awareness
   - Fundamentals of quality
   - Worldwide quality challenge
   - Quality's impact on productivity
   - White collar and blue collar quality
2. Assessment of IBM's quality status
   - IBM's goals for the 1980s
   - Worldwide computer performance
   - Corporate quality direction
   - Corporate quality staff strategy
3. Life cycle quality costs
4. IBM managers' role in quality
   - Behavior change
   - Requirements setting

   - Measure of quality performance
   - Setting and improving quality goals
5. Overview of quality programs across IBM
   - Software
   - Manufacturing
   - Marketing
   - Service
   - Finance
   - Administration
6. Quality tools
   - Statistics
   - Managing breakthrough
   - Problem analysis methods
   - Special tools

*Presented at IBM.

Quality Managers. Many quality managers have risen to their positions through experience in inspection, quality engineering, product development, manufacturing, or field service. For these managers, there is often a need for formal training in the management of the broad quality function, i.e., the business orientation.

Course Leadership. For large corporations, it may be economic to establish in-house courses for quality managers. The courses can be conducted by corporate personnel or by outside consultants. What is critical is that the leaders have high credibility for their knowledge of the managerial and business aspects of the overall quality function.

Outline of a Course. The outline for a 4-day course on Management of Quality presented by Juran Institute is shown in Table 11.6.

TABLE 11.6 Management of Quality*

The quality mission	Worker errors
Quality and sales	Motivation for quality
Product development	Quality cost analysis
Supplier relations	Policies, objectives, planning
Manufacture	Organizing: role of upper management
Inspection and test	The quality manager
Field performance	Quality assurance
Improvement: projects	Quality and society
Improvement: organizing	The quality disciplines
Improvement: diagnosis	Training and quality
Improvement: remedy	The decade ahead

*Four-day course presented by Juran Institute.

Other Middle Managers. The role of "middle manager" covers a wide spectrum of responsibility. In large companies, the training program for middle managers who are at the high end of this spectrum will have much in common with the program set out above for upper management. At the lower end of the spectrum the training program will tend to overlap that used for first line supervisors. Since companies vary widely in size and systems of delegation, the planning task force may be well advised to look beyond simplistic labels such as "middle management" and examine the responsibility pattern as well.

A major question for the planning task force is whether to offer a single standardized training program for middle managers broadly, or to design special programs for the various categories of middle managers. There are persuasive reasons for specializing the courses. Middle managers operate at various levels of responsibility, in different functional activities, in different types of business, markets, product lines. However, it takes a lot of work to agree on the special needs, prepare the specialized training materials, train the leaders, etc.

Course Leadership. All managers are results-oriented. However, middle managers also have departmental responsibilities. In large companies these departmental responsibilities can dominate the attention of middle managers; i.e., they are judged based on measures of departmental performance. This same domination will have its effect on such wide-spectrum training programs as annual improvement. In such programs these middle managers will strongly prefer that case examples and illustrative improvement projects come from their specialty.

All of this has its effect on the content of the training materials and on the choice and development of leaders. There may well be need for multiple leaders, i.e., some to deal with the broader companywide matters and others to deal with specialties.

Outline of Some Courses. If it is decided to offer a single standardized training program for middle managers, then an adaptation of an outline such as the one given in Table 11.6 is appropriate. If it is decided to offer special courses then separate outlines may be required for courses for managers of product development, purchasing, manufacturing, field service, and other functional areas.

Training for Quality Improvement. An important part of the training program is that directed at quality improvement. Section 22, Quality Improvement, explains the project-by-project approach to improvement. This approach makes use of cross-functional teams working on selected problems. Implementation of the project approach requires that upper management, middle management, first-line supervisors, professional specialists, and selected line personnel be trained in the improvement process.

Various levels of middle management and line and staff specialists comprise the membership of most of the project teams. As membership on a team is drawn from several functions, the importance of having members work effectively together must be recognized in the training. In addition, the tools of problem solving (see Section 22 under Diagnosis) must be provided in the training. The training, therefore, includes the project approach, conducting team meetings, group dynamics, and problem solving. Table 11.7 shows the relative emphasis of these four areas for team leaders, team members, and facilitators. An outline of a video cassette course providing the methodology for the project approach is presented in Table 11.8.

Specialists. In the United States, many quality specialists have received an extensive amount of training. This training has been concentrated in areas such as statistical methodology, quality costs, quality audit, reliability engineering, and other subjects.

There is also a need to train the line specialists such as design engineers and manufacturing engineers.

As of the early 1980s such training was largely on a voluntary basis. The subject matter was dominated by statistical methods, but there was much variation by industry and function. Specialists in the chemical industries exhibited much interest in advanced statistical tools such as evolutionary operation and response

TABLE 11.7   Training for Project Teams

	Project approach	Conduct meetings	Group dynamics	Problem solving
Leaders	P	P	P	P
Members	S	...	P	P
Facilitators	P	P	P	S

Note: P = primary; S = secondary.

TABLE 11.8   Video Cassette Course on Quality Improvement*

Proof of the need
Project identification
Projects to improve product salability
Organizing for improvement
Organizing for diagnosis: the diagnostic journey
Operator-controllable errors
The diagnostic tools
The remedial journey
Motivation for quality
Holding the gains

*Courtesy, Juran Institute.

surface methodology, whereas product designers were more interested in reliability-oriented training.

Despite the availability of these courses the volunteers were few. As a result, use of the quality-oriented tools required collaboration between:

1. The line managers and specialists whose work would benefit by use of the tools

2. The quality specialists who were trained in use of the tools

In most companies this collaboration was limited—so limited as to warrant the conclusion that *the tools will be used only if the line people are trained in their use.*

Starting in the early 1980s there evolved a trend to make such training courses mandatory for line specialists.

It is feasible to take soundings on the extent to which some of the quality-oriented tools are used by or even known to the line specialist. An example of a census form is shown in Table 11.9.

Course Leadership.   In some large companies, qualified trainers are available in the form of internal consultants from corporate service departments such as Corporate Quality Assurance. Such departments have been an important source of training materials and training expertise for in-house use.

In those companies where in-house sources are not available it is necessary to use outside sources at the outset. Potential trainers can be chosen and sent to outside courses. Alternatively, outside trainers are brought in to conduct the seed courses. (Some training materials are specially designed to simplify use by in-house trainers.)

In small companies it is seldom economic to develop in-house training at this level. Hence outside sources are used, e.g., training at outside courses, use of consultants, etc.

Professional organizations are a source of courses useful for members and others interested. For example, the American Society for Quality Control presents courses and seminars on a variety of quality-related topics. (See Table 11.19 for a list of offerings of ASQC.)

Outline for Some Courses.   An outline of topics for a statistical quality control course developed by the General Electric Company and aimed at manufacturing engineering, shop operations, and quality department personnel is shown in Table

TABLE 11.9 Census on Diagnostic Tools

In my organization the status of these tools is about as follows:

Diagnostic tools	Degree of our understanding			Extent of our use		
	Well understood	Not well understood	Unknown	Often	Seldom	None
Data sheets						
Frequency distribution						
Average and standard deviation						
Frequency histogram						
Process capability analysis						
Pareto analysis						
Orderly arrangement of theories						
Process dissection						
Time-to-time analysis						
Cumulative failure analysis						
Weibull analysis						
Concentration diagrams						
Correlation analysis						
Experimental designs						

TABLE 11.10 Applied Statistics in Manufacturing

Course topics	
Achieving parts per million defect levels	Process control charting
Process variability concept	np $\quad X, R$
Measuring variability	p $\quad \tilde{X}, R$
Sample size requirements	c $\quad \overline{X}, R$
Process capability analysis	u
	Control chart implementation
	Getting the process into control

Note: $\tilde{X}$ is the median value of X.

11.10. In this video-based course, participants apply techniques by interacting with a computer simulation of a manufacturing process.

Applying training to specific industries, products, processes, etc., often requires specialized training materials and leadership. For example, a discussion of training needs for microcontamination control is given in Trimble (1983). Another example in the area of handling of hazardous waste is Coop (1982).

First-Line Supervisors. This category has long been exposed to training courses. Traditionally the course content has emphasized elements of supervision, work planning, job technology, cost control, etc. Until recently the quality-oriented content has been minimal. Then, in the early 1980s there came a shift in emphasis due to the growth in competition in quality plus the explosive interest in quality circles. This shift in emphasis has in turn resulted in a growth in quality-oriented training courses for first-line supervisors, notably production supervisors.

Course Leadership. In large companies the number of first-line supervisors is also large. Such members require the development of in-house facilities and leaders. The seed courses may be provided from the outside, along with training of those who are to be the in-house leaders. Thereafter the in-house leaders take over.

At this level, some of training will relate to the company's broad approach to quality: quality policies, goals, planning, organization, systems, procedures. In many companies the Training (or Management Development) Department includes specialists who are qualified to conduct in-house training in such matters. Similarly, when training requires interplay among trainees (as in project teams for quality improvement), there is need for leadership with skills in group dynamics. Such leadership is commonly available on an in-house basis in the form of trainers or "facilitators" from the Training Department.

Another substantial area of training is at the technique level. Leaders for training in techniques can be developed on an in-house basis, either from the Quality Department or from the Training Department.

Outlines for Some Courses. In Japan the training courses for first-line supervisors have become well standardized, and deal with the subjects listed in Table 11.11. A basic textbook in the foregoing topics is Ishikawa (1972).

The Japanese training materials have been translated into many languages. In most countries these translations, with local modifications, have become the dominant training materials used in courses for first-line supervisors.

The topics for a typical course for inspection and test supervision are shown in Table 11.12.

TABLE 11.11 Course for First-Line Supervisors

What is quality control?	Binomial probability paper
Role of the supervisor	Process improvement and control
Pareto diagram	Sampling concepts
Ishikawa cause-and-effect diagram	Application
The statistical viewpoint	Quality circle activities
Control charts	Quality assurance

Nonsupervisors. Quality-oriented courses for nonsupervisors had their origin in Japan in 1962. Since then millions of Japanese workers have undergone such training as part of the QC circle movement. (A basic text, translated from the Japanese, is *QC Circle Koryo,* 1980.) Part of the course is "by the book," and this book portion consists largely of the technique portion of the production supervisors course. After the training in techniques, the circles study improvement projects which have been successfully carried out by other Circles. (See, for example, *Quality Control Circles at Work,* 1984.) Such projects show how the techniques were applied in actual work situations. Finally, the circle undertakes improvement projects to be worked out by its own members.

During the late 1970s the quality circle movement became popular in the United States. The training courses were based on translations of Japanese materials.

Course Leadership. In the United States, wide use is made of consultants who specialize in quality circle training. These consultants conduct the seed courses for leaders, facilitators and even for the pioneering quality circle members. With the growth of a demand of quality circle training (during the early 1980s) there have emerged courses which offer to train leaders directly from the training materials.

Outlines for Some Courses. A typical training program for quality circles consists of 10 modules. An example, from the Harley-Davidson Company, is shown in Table 11.13. Many circles teach a technique in the first half of the circle meeting and then apply the technique to the circle project in the last half of the meeting. Some companies also give an advanced course primarily of statistical tools, such as sampling, control charts, and scatter diagrams.

Specialized courses have been developed for nonsupervisors. See Overturf (1977). This example makes use of audio and video cassettes, modules, workbooks, pocket guides, and sample bottles with a suitable measuring gage. For training of technicians, see Hromi (1980).

TABLE 11.12 Course for Inspection and Test Supervisors

Supervision	Conformance
Job technology	Troubleshooting
Measurement	Inspection and test
Statistical methodology	data

TABLE 11.13 Typical Modules for Quality Circle Training

Introduction to quality circles	Histograms
	Check sheets
Brainstorming	Case study
Cause-and-effect diagrams	Graphs
Pareto diagrams	Presentations

Support Areas. Increasingly, attention has been given to the effect on quality of activities in support areas such as materials handling, production control, order filling, and accounting. In some companies, efforts have been made to train supervisors of support areas by including them in training courses being held for the manufacturing and product design functions. The approach has not been successful. The applications discussed here are oriented to design and manufacturing activities, and many personnel in support areas find it difficult to make the transition.

It is likely that separate courses will have to be developed for the support areas. These courses will need to stress two issues:

1. What is the effect of the activities in the support area on the quality of the outgoing product or service?
2. How can the quality of activities in the support area be improved?

When mistakes are made in a support area, the work is repeated and the "rework" absorbed as part of the regular workday. However, the rework is a part of the cost of poor quality and represents an opportunity for cost reduction and quality improvement. Training courses should address that potential.

The emergence of quality circles of hourly workers and also quality improvement teams of personnel at higher levels has included projects in support areas. Experiences with these projects can provide case examples for training programs.

Service Industries. Managers in the service industries have traditionally felt that their business is "different." In consequence they have rejected training in courses based on materials oriented to manufacturing industries.

Starting in the early 1980s, training courses specially oriented to service industries began to come on the market. (A pioneering example is Quality Improvement for Services, Juran Institute, 88 Danbury Road, Wilton, CT 06897.)

This trend will likely continue until courses are developed to be applicable to any and all industries.

Outsiders. Training in quality-related matters must also extend to people outside of the company. This includes suppliers, clients, and others.

Suppliers. Some companies make extensive use of outside suppliers, contractors, and subcontractors. Quality-oriented training for these outsiders is clearly as necessary as for inside sources of supply.

In a major construction company, one of the vice-presidents has been largely occupied with preparing and conducting training courses for subcontractors on the subject of attaining and improving quality. As a byproduct of this training it became possible to organize multitrade teams of supervisors and tradesmen to tackle projects for solving some long-standing quality problems. The teams were so effective that their results came to the attention of the respective presidents of the subcontracting companies. These presidents, in turn, organized multicompany teams to tackle still other projects which were beyond the scope of the lower-level teams.

An outline for a 1-day training seminar for suppliers for an appliance manufacturer is given in Table 11.14.

TABLE 11.14   Supplier Seminar

Introduction
Concept of variability
Improvement of quality of current products
Prevention of quality problems—product engineering
Prevention of quality problems—manufacturing engineering
Role of upper management

Clients.   In some cases it is the supplier who is large and whose clients include numerous small companies with limited training in the quality disciplines. In such cases, training of clients may be a means of increasing share of market for the supplier. Such training becomes an extension of conventional technical service.

Others.   The Japanese have introduced the concepts of quality circles into the consumer area. (See Takahashi, 1981.)

Others can also include government regulators, independent auditors, union officials, and the media. They may be invited to attend regular courses. They may also be invited to attend special briefings organized to provide them with a depth of understanding of quality-related matters which they could never acquire solely through official contacts.

Training for Course Leaders.   In the foregoing the approach to training of leaders has included:

1. Use of consultants.
2. Use of outside training courses.
3. Self-training from specially designed training materials.
4. "Leader train leader." During each course the leader identified those trainees who might be good candidates to become leaders for future courses.
5. Learn from new trainees. Any idea that the learning is all in one direction is naive. The trainees have extensive experience in the realities of the subject matter. They bring up cases for discussion. They raise pertinent questions. They challenge the course materials and the assertions of the leader. All these constitute inputs for improving the content of the training materials and the knowhow of the leader. In this way, a training course may be launched with the awareness that it will be "debugged" during the first several classes!

Many organizations have reported that there is need for improving the training of leaders of quality circles. Such training should include the following:

Group dynamics: The leader is trained to conduct circle meetings so that the decisions are made more by consensus than by a majority vote.

Motivation: The concept of motivation coming from within individuals is emphasized, and this is illustrated by showing how quality circles can contribute to self-motivation, leadership, and communication. The importance of communication as an expression of leadership style is emphasized. Several barriers to communication are described and applied to conducting problem-solving discussions in circle meetings.

Problem-solving tools: These were discussed above, under the heading "Nonsupervisors."

The aim of training circle leaders is to show them how to function as coach, coordinator, and trainer in the quality circle. The agenda for a leader-training program at 3M is given in Table 11.15 (Gryna, 1981).

TABLE 11.15   Agenda for Quality Circle Leader Training at 3M

January 15	
8:00 a.m.	Introduction—Meet each other
	History
	Training materials
	(Audiovisual) Introduction to quality circles
	Why quality circles?
	Brainstorming—Quality circle objectives
9:30	Break
9:45	Group dynamics (wilderness exercise)
10:45	Cause and effect I
11:30	Morning summary
11:45	Lunch
12:30 p.m.	Motivation
1:15	Pareto
2:00	Break
2:15	Starting, training, and operating your circle
3:15	Group discussion
4:15	Training assignments and summary
January 16	
12:30 p.m.	Review
1:00	Brainstorming (leader teach)
1:45	"What circles are doing"
2:15	Break
2:30	Cause and effect II (leader teach)
3:15	Histograms (leader teach)
4:00	Summary
January 17	
8:00 a.m.	Review
8:15	Communications and leadership
9:00	Graphs (leader teach)
9:30	Break
9:45	Check Sheets (leader teach)
10:30	Case Study (leader teach)
11:00	Management presentation (leader teach)
11:45	Lunch
12:00 p.m.	Management presentation (continued)
1:15	Group discussion
1:30	Simulation
4:00	Summary

CLASSROOM TRAINING METHODS

For training in the industrial setting, the straight lecture approach is not enough. Among the means of supplementing the lectures are the following.

Application to Company Problems. For a course given within a single company, the instructor asks the attendees to apply specific training topics to specific company problems. For example, small groups can be assigned to problems such as drafting specific quality policies, identification of quality improvement projects, or development of a design review checklist. On an individual basis, participants can be asked to rate the company with respect to specific activities covered in the lecture. A rating form for evaluating the elements of a quality improvement program is given in Table 11.16. This census form can be filled out by each person. The class results are then summarized on a transparency, followed by a discussion of the strengths and weaknesses of the company. Similar census forms can be developed for other aspects of the quality program.

Case Examples. It is essential that an abundant supply of case examples be included in classroom training. Where possible, the examples should come from the company and preferably be presented by the individuals who did the work. In the industrial setting it is best to present a series of cases first and then generalize later. Case examples can be presented by the instructor or they can be

TABLE 11.16 Census of Company Practices in Quality Improvement
(Do not sign your name)
In my company the effectiveness in quality improvement is about as follows:

Elements of quality improvement	Strong	Adequate	Weak	No opinion
Atmosphere for breakthrough activity				
Proof of the need				
Use of the language of management				
Use of Pareto analysis				
Establishment of clear priorities for projects				
Clear responsibility for guiding projects				
Clear responsibility for diagnosis				
Use of controllability concept				
Diagnostic competence				
Overcoming resistance to change				
Action on the findings				
Control at the new level				

assigned as exercises for the students. Some textbooks have case examples for the students. For example, one source of case examples for students, along with suggested solutions, can be found in the instructor's manual for *Quality Planning and Analysis* (Juran and Gryna, 1980). Another source is Heldt (1975).

Role Playing. Role playing can be an effective way to demonstrate concepts. (For a description of four scenarios, see Heldt and Pinschmidt, 1977.) At several ASQC conferences, role-playing has been staged for supplier relations problems. The concept has also been applied to product liability (see Mundel, 1982).

Simulation. Simulation, particularly using a computer, can be an effective way to liven up the classroom. The United States Air Force Institute of Technology has made extensive application of the simulation technique in the areas of quality and reliability training. Two specific areas are:

Reliability management simulation: The student is required to make decisions comparable to those which arise in the development, production, testing, and field usage of a system. (See Rehg, 1969.)

Product life cycle: Random number generators are explained and then used to produce simulated data on equipment failure times, repair times, results after repair, lead times for inventory replacement, personnel availability, and other related processes. All of this is put together in a life cycle cost model (see Rehg, 1973).

INSTRUCTIONAL TECHNOLOGY

The technology available has expanded beyond written material and now includes audio-visual material, films, and teaching aids.

Textbooks: Broad Orientation

Feigenbaum, A. V. (1983). *Total Quality Control,* 3rd ed. McGraw-Hill, New York.

Hayes, Glenn E. and Romig, Harry G. (1982). *Modern Quality Control.* Bruce, Benziger & Glencoe, 17337 Ventura Boulevard, Encino, CA 91316.

Juran, J. M. (1981). *Management of Quality,* 4th ed. Juran Institute, 88 Danbury Road, Wilton, CT 06897.

Juran, J. M. (1982). *Upper Management and Quality,* 4th ed. Juran Institute, 88 Danbury Road, Wilton, CT 06897.

Juran, J. M. and Gryna, Frank M., Jr. (1980). *Quality Planning and Analysis,* 2nd ed. McGraw-Hill, New York.

Textbooks: Statistical Orientation. The more basic books include the following:

Charbonneau, Harvey and Webster, Gordon L. (1978). *Industrial Quality Control.* Prentice-Hall, Englewood Cliffs, NJ.

Grant, E. L. and Leavenworth, R. S. (1979). *Statistical Quality Control,* 5th ed. McGraw-Hill, New York.

Moroney, M. J. (1969). *Facts From Figures,* 3rd ed. Penguin Books, Baltimore.

Ott, E. R. (1975). *Process Quality Control.* McGraw-Hill, New York.

Small, Bonnie B. et al. (1956). *Statistical Quality Control Handbook.* Western Electric Company, New York.

Books on advanced statistical methodology include:

Box, G. E. P. et al (1978). *Statistics for Experimenters.* John Wiley & Sons, New York.

Daniel, C. (1976). *Applications of Statistics to Industrial Experimentation.* John Wiley & Sons, New York.

Duncan, A. J. (1974). *Quality Control and Industrial Statistics.* Richard D. Irwin, Homewood, IL.

Johnson, N. L. and Leone, F. C. (1977). *Statistics and Experimental Design in Engineering and the Physical Sciences,* 2nd ed. Wiley-Interscience, New York.

Miller, I. and Freund, J. E. (1977). *Probability and Statistics for Engineers,* 2nd ed. Prentice-Hall, Englewood Cliffs, NJ.

Schilling, Edward G. (1982). *Acceptance Sampling in Quality Control.* Marcel Dekker, New York.

Books: General

Carruba, Eugene R. et al. (1975). *Assuring Product Integrity.* Lexington Books, Lexington, MA.

Crosby, Philip B. (1979). *Quality is Free.* McGraw-Hill, New York.

Juran, J. M. (1988). *Quality Control Handbook,* 4th ed. McGraw-Hill, New York.

Simmons, David A. (1970). *Practical Quality Control.* Addison-Wesley, Reading, MA.

Smith, Martin (1980). *Quality Sense.* American Management Association, 135 West 50th Street, New York, NY 10020.

Journals

Quality Progress, a journal of the American Society for Quality Control (ASQC), 310 West Wisconsin Avenue, Milwaukee, WI 53203.

Journal of Quality Technology, a journal of ASQC.

Technometrics, a journal sponsored by ASQC and the American Statistical Association.

Annual Conference Transactions, the papers presented at the National Conference of ASQC.

IEEE Proceedings, Annual Reliability and Maintainability Symposium, published by the Institute of Electrical and Electronic Engineers, 345 East 47th Street, New York, NY 10017. (Also serves as the Journal of the Electronics Division of ASQC.)

Quality, published by Hitchcock Publishing Company, Box 3002, Wheaton, IL 60187.

Quality Assurance, journal of the Institute of Quality Assurance, 8110 Grosvenor Gardens, London SW1, England.

EOQC Quality, journal of the European Organization for Quality Control, P.O. Box 2516, CH-3001 Berne, Switzerland.

In the area of quality circles, written and audio-visual material is available from consultants.

Audio-Visual Systems.   Video cassettes appear to be emerging as the dominant form for instructional systems. One example is *Juran on Quality Improvement:* This is a series of 16 color video cassettes on the subject of quality improvement and reduction of quality-related costs published by Juran Institute, 88 Danbury Road, Wilton, CT 06897. These cassettes are available in nine languages.

Other video cassettes are oriented to statistical methodology and reliability.

Dr. J. Stuart Hunter's course on Design of Experiments: A comprehensive series of 32 cassettes on experimental design by a leading authority, with Dr. George E. P. Box as technical consultant. Available from: Office of Continuing Education and Training, 779 Anderson Hall, University of Kentucky, Lexington, KY 40506. Also available on film.

Statistics in Quality, Productivity, and Problem Solving: This is a series of 11 color video cassettes prepared by Dr. Lloyd S. Nelson. Available from MIT Video Courses, Massachusetts Institute of Technology, 77 Massachusetts Avenue, Room 9-234, Cambridge, MA 02139; telephone (617) 253-7444.

Dr. Sanford Thayer's courses: There are several of these, each involving 10 cassettes. Available from ERG Director, Colorado State University, Fort Collins, CO 80523; also from Massachusetts Institute of Technology, Center for Advanced Engineering Study, Cambridge, MA 02139.

Computer Interactive Instruction.   The increased capabilities of computer hardware and software combined with a decrease in computation costs has broadened the interest in computer interactive instruction. Commercials extol the use of computers in classrooms. For example, children are portrayed at computer terminals at which they learn elementary spelling and arithmetic. The reported benefits stemming from such instruction, e.g., self-paced instruction, increased enthusiasm, or the ability to summarize individual students' problem areas, have provided the impetus for expanding application areas to industry.

One corporation has used computer interactive instruction to train engineers in problem-solving skills. Instruction is conducted via personal computer, video disk player, and a monitor. After a particular topic is played on the video monitor, the computer guides the engineer. If the engineer answers correctly, the presentation continues. If the answer is not correct, the computer cues back the relevant video instruction segment, and then the engineer is asked to choose another answer.

Training Films.   Motion picture films, strips, and transparencies are among the media available for in-house training or for training through local university and professional society sections. There are numerous distribution houses which offer such films for sale or rental. Some of these films are general or motivational in nature. Others deal with specifics, e.g., metrology, statistical methods.

In 1974 ASQC turned its films over to one such distribution house (ROA Films, 1969 North Astor Street, Milwaukee, WI 53202).

Another approach makes use of the "talk-back television" concept. In one example, 1-day workshops were conducted (in various locations) in discussions by means of two-way communication. Attendees received workbooks, and graduate students were available at each location to aid participants in understanding the material. (See "Oklahomians," 1977.)

Home Study Instruction.   The American Society for Quality Control has prepared quality assurance training material for use by individuals or groups on a home study basis. Examples of courses are statistical methods and nondestructive testing. The courses are designed to permit students to evaluate their progress on specific topics before proceeding on with the next material. Leader guides are available. (See Leaman, 1975 and 1979.)

Teaching Aids.   Presentations can be enlivened by some ingenious teaching aids. They include:

1. *Attribute sampling demonstrators:*   These consist of a supply of wooden beads, some of which are colored to represent defects. Pitted paddles are thrust into the bead pile to collect a sample in the pits (Fig. 11.1). This sampling can be done by each member of the class, and the results can then be tabulated and analyzed.

A typical proportion of colors is as follows:

Color A	1 percent		Color D	8 percent
Color B	2 percent		Color E	16 percent
Color C	4 percent		Natural	69 percent

By adding various combinations, a percent defective anywhere from 1 to 31 percent can be simulated.

FIG. 11.1   Attribute sampling demonstrator.

2. *Galton's quincunx:*   This creates frequency distributions by letting beads tumble over multiple rows of pins. At each row the bead can fall to the right or the left of the pin. After a random journey over numerous rows of pins, the bead drops into a vertical slot. When many beads are dropped, the result is a frequency distribution (Fig. 11.2).

The device makes it easy to simulate a manufacturing process in the classroom. Each bead becomes a unit of product which can be "manufactured" and measured before the eyes of the audience. As a series of units is measured, the frequency distribution takes shape. The central tendency and dispersion can then be calculated, the latter representing process capability.

In addition, the device can be used to demonstrate the nature of the control chart for averages and ranges. Limit lines for the "process" are calculated and drawn on the blackboard. Samples generated by the device represent process subgroups. The averages and ranges for these subgroups can be plotted to test for out-of-control, both when the process is undisturbed and when it is deliberately changed. (Some devices are designed to permit ready change of average; the others can only be tilted.)

3. *Statistical tolerancing simulator:*   This device consists of several sets of blocks, each simulating a set of components waiting to be assembled. The purpose is to demonstrate that as random assembly takes place, the extremes will seldom

FIG. 11.2   Galton's quincunx.

TABLE 11.17   Simulator for Statistical Tolerancing*

Size, in	Silver	Black	Red	Blue	Orange	Total
0.500						
0.600					1	1
0.700		1	1	1	1	4
0.800	1	3	2	1	2	9
0.900	5	6	4	3	4	22
1.000	8	6	6	5	4	29
1.100	5	3	4	5	4	21
1.200	1	1	2	3	2	9
1.300			1	1	1	3
1.400				1	1	2
1.500						
Totals	20	20	20	20	20	100
$s =$	0.095	0.116	0.145	0.163	0.192	

*The maximum assembly is 6.5 in and the minimum is 3.5 in. However, since s of the composite of all five distributions figures out to be 0.327, further calculation shows that only about 2 of 100 assemblies will actually be outside of ± 0.750 around the average of 5.0.

come together. A typical set of blocks is described in Table 11.17. The class participates in assembling the "parts" at random and demonstrates the difficulty of reaching the worst-case dimensions.

Lacking the more sophisticated teaching aids, the instructor can resort to use of ordinary six-faced dice, coin tossing, and still other simple devices.

Sometimes the classroom must be brought to the field. An automobile manufacturer constructed a mobile facility completely equipped as a classroom for training dealer personnel. The facility was moved to different locations for presenting a 1-day course. Technicians from several nearby dealers were brought to one location thus saving expenses and providing an opportunity to exchange experiences. The local dealer furnished a car to provide for hand-on work (see "Datsun's Mobile Training Vehicle," 1977).

Facilities and Operational Matters for Courses.   These are matters that must be planned by experienced people—not well-intentioned amateurs. They include:

1. Size and physical layout of the room.   Particularly, if the course is to be longer than one day, people must have sufficient space to sit comfortably. Tables are preferable (to spread out course materials) and each person needs about 3 ft of table space.
2. Control of room temperature.
3. Proper audio-visual aids and lighting.
4. Provisions for taking phone messages.
5. Location off-site or on the company site.
6. Provisions for meals and coffee breaks.

Although such matters are details, they can make the difference between a successful and unsuccessful course. The corporate training department is an excellent source of advice.

EVALUATION OF TRAINING PROGRAMS

The ultimate measure of the value of training is the degree of success in applying the concepts. Although there is no known way to evaluate the return on investment, it is feasible to evaluate some of the aspects of the training.

Implementation of Concepts. A potential source of evaluation is a newsletter to collect and disseminate results which are traceable in part to the training programs. The newsletter may be a new medium specially established to serve the needs of quality-oriented programs. Alternatively, some existing media (e.g., a company newspaper or bulletin board) may establish a special supplement for quality-related information.

Contents of such a newsletter typically include:

Case examples of how the training helped to secure improvements in quality, costs, etc. Such case examples become a supplemental source of training materials, including postgraduate training for those who have completed the course work.

New uses for the training course, e.g., to help improve supplier performance, to inform clients of efforts toward continued improvement.

Pictures and conventional news stories (e.g., interviews) relative to trainees, leaders, etc.

Messages from senior managers, major clients, other important people.

These and other contents not only help to maintain a lively interest; they constitute a deeply appreciated form of recognition for those who are active in securing results.

Feedback. All instructors need feedback. Provisions must be made to obtain the feedback in specific terms (e.g., most and least useful subjects, duration of the training, instructors, physical facilities). Again, a corporate training department is an important source of experience.

The United States Army, through a "quality control division" at one of the training centers, has a program for evaluating the basic combat training provided to recruits. Through a series of four formal test programs, the knowledge acquired by the soldiers is evaluated, problem areas identified, and formal feedback given to the instructors in the program. (See Binstock, 1977.) For a description of a program involving seminars and factory visits along with results of the evaluation, see Stephens (1982).

Examinations. To date, companies have avoided the use of examinations and certificates with respect to courses for managers. It is in fact difficult to write examination questions on managerial subject matter, i.e., to secure objectivity in questions or answers. In addition, managers have exhibited considerable cultural resistance to being examined. They prefer to be judged by results on the job.

At nonmanagerial levels (specialists, first-line supervisors, the work force), much of the course content consists of techniques and tools. These do permit objectivity in questions and answers. In addition, there is less cultural resistance. Hence some companies do conduct examinations with purposes in mind such as:

To evaluate the trainees' grasp of the subject matter

To provide a form of recognition to those who are successful in the examination

CAREERS IN THE QUALITY FUNCTION

The growing importance of the quality function has required that industrial companies establish major quality-related departments. Whether such departments can provide a lifetime career depends largely on the activities assigned to them.

In the United States, many companies have established large central Quality departments which include numerous full-time inspectors and staff specialists. In such departments a lifetime career in quality is entirely feasible. Inspectors can progress horizontally into higher inspection and test grades. Through added education and experience, they can progress into engineering grade work. Alternatively, they can progress vertically into supervisory and managerial posts. In like manner, quality engineers and reliability engineers can progress horizontally into such posts as product designer or field engineer. Alternatively, they can progress vertically into the supervisory and managerial hierarchy, whether in Quality or some other department, e.g., Production.

Any job is a mixture of management and technology, the proportions changing over the years. Figure 11.3 is a reminder that as the job shifts the incumbent must shed the technological and grasp the managerial.

In many U.S. companies the quality manager reports directly to the division general manager. Such an organizational link makes the quality manager one of the competitors for the post of general manager. Any such promotion obviously has considerable significance to persons who contemplate a career in the quality function. (The fact of such promotion is propagandized to aid in recruitment and retention of employees.)

In companies which use different organization forms the career pattern can differ. An electronics engineer may be assigned full time to activities of a reliability engineering nature. In the United States the title would usually be "reliability

FIG. 11.3 Job progression management and technology.

engineer." In many European companies the engineer continues to use the title of "electronics engineer." The reason is that he or she regards electronics engineering as a better recognized and more secure career than reliability engineering.

Although large, central Quality Assurance departments have been widely established in the United States, the mid-1980s saw the beginnings of a trend toward the Japanese concept of organization for quality. Under that concept, line engineers receive extensive training in the quality disciplines, thereby reducing the need for quality engineers and reliability engineers. In addition, the Japanese companies have less need for inspectors as a result of their revolutionary rate of quality improvement. Moreover, the full-time inspectors are not part of the Quality Department; they are part of the Manufacturing Department. (Audit inspectors reside in the Quality Department.)

If the trend toward the Japanese concept of organization were to grow to large proportions, it would obviously have a major impact on the extent to which the quality function can provide a lifetime career.

Professionalism. In the United States the growing numbers of quality specialists and managers have stimulated interest in attaining the status of a recognized "profession" for the quality function. (The outstanding example of a recognized profession is medicine. For a discussion of the "components" of several professions, see Hoppmann et al., 1980.) Numerous collective actions have been taken in the direction of establishing a professional status.

The American Society for Quality Control (ASQC) was formed in 1946. By June 1987 it had over 54,000 members.

Much has been done to evolve an organized, special body of knowledge (books, papers, standards, etc.) to serve as the basis for training in the quality profession.

Training courses have been established to enable persons who enter the field to acquire this special body of knowledge.

Many states require continuing education for various professions. As of 1979, Iowa was the only state with such a requirement for engineers. (See Courter, 1980.)

Examinations have been evolved to provide a basis for certificated recognition of the acquisition of this special knowledge. By April 1986 there were about 2000 certified reliability engineers, and 12,000 certified quality engineers.

As of 1980 none of the states in the United States had authorized a license and a monopoly for the practice of quality engineering. No such action is likely during the 1980s. One state (California) has established an examination and certificate for the *title* of Quality Engineer. However, this confers a monopoly only as to the use of the title. Anyone may do the work.

The outward evidences of steps toward professionalism have been most obvious in the United States. (See Juran, 1976.)

However, some of the European societies have been considering the matter of certification. (Virtually all European countries have created a national society for quality and have evolved literature and training courses relative to the quality function.)

UNIVERSITY-LEVEL TRAINING IN QUALITY

At the university level, training is provided either in individual courses, 2-year programs, 4-year degree programs, or graduate programs.

Individual Courses.   Courses are usually located in departments of Industrial Engineering, Business Management, Industrial Technology, or Statistics. The majority of these courses emphasize statistical quality control as applied to manufacturing. Some schools have courses in reliability engineering, maintainability engineering, engineering statistics, and the management of quality control. Quality-related topics are often included as a part of other courses, e.g., a course in production management in a college of business. (See LaForge, 1981.) Some courses and seminars are given on a credit basis; others are on a noncredit basis.

Two-Year Degree Programs.   These programs aim primarily at training quality technicians, although they have been useful for others in the quality function. The programs, which lead to an associate degree, consist of about 35 percent general education, 30 percent quality and related disciplines, 25 percent science and mathematics, and 10 percent business. As of 1985, 67 colleges reported having a 2-year degree program in quality. The state of California is one of the leaders in the development of 2-year programs. In addition to these degree programs, 44 institutions reported having a 1-year certification program.

Four-Year Degree Programs.   As of 1985 there were eight colleges that provided a 4-year degree program in quality. The programs follow a curriculum similar to that described for the 2-year programs but with additional courses in each area. Universities have been reluctant to make the investments for new 4-year programs which they regard as overly specialized—such as a program in quality. Overcoming this reluctance has usually required the strong moral and tangible support of local industry.

Many industrial engineering programs provide an excellent background for quality engineers because of the emphasis on the cost, schedule, and quality parameters. The typical program includes general education, mathematics, pure science, engineering science, computer science, communication skills, and problem-solving courses. Courses in statistical methods are required, and some schools require courses in quality control. Some offer elective courses in reliability, advanced statistics, design of experiments, and other areas useful to the quality engineer.

Graduate Programs.   These degrees lead to a master's degree in applied statistics, business administration, or engineering. The programs in business administration and engineering follow a basic graduate program with elective courses taken in quality disciplines. There are also nontraditional degree programs that grant credit for job experience and combine it with formal classes. (See Land and Heldt, 1981.)

The American Society for Quality Control has cooperated with universities to develop educational programs. (See Constable, 1983; also Leaman, 1981.)

NATIONAL APPROACHES TO TRAINING

The Japanese have made the greaest strides in training, but other countries have also been active.

Japan.   After World War II, the Japanese industrial leaders decided that until their quality of products was raised to levels which could compete in the international market, Japan would remain a developing nation. In consequence, the leaders took bold steps to create a revolution in quality. One of the major steps taken was a massive training program in quality.

The Japanese training in management of quality *started at the top* with seminars for company presidents.

That was only the beginning. Two Japanese professional societies—the Japanese Union of Scientists and Engineers (JUSE) and Japan Standards Association (JSA) designed followup on courses. Over the years courses in quality management and/or methodology were widely given to presidents, directors, managers, superintendents, supervisors, engineers, etc. (see Table 11.18). In a sense, all managers in the hierarchy concluded that they could put their training to better use if their subordinates were similarly trained. The result was that all levels of the hierarchy in all company functions received training in quality management and/or methodology appropriate to their roles. Much of the training was done in courses sponsored by JUSE and JSA. In addition, large companies established in-house training, usually for the lower levels of the hierarchy. In the case of supervisors, training courses were also offered on the national radio. Beyond the supervisors, training was provided to hourly workers through the concept of Quality

TABLE 11.18   JUSE Education and Training Courses (1985)

Quality Control	Design of Experiment
Basic Course	Basic Course
Middle Management Course	Osaka Course
Top Management Course	Introductory Course
Introductory Course	Multivariate Analysis
Executive Course	Advanced Course
Basic Course for Foremen	Seminar (Osaka)
Course for Sales Department	Basic Course
Course for Purchasing Department	Operations Research
Correspondence Course	Basic Course
Circle Instructor Course	Corporate Strategy, Manager Course
Circle Top Management Course	Corporate Strategy, Executive Course
Basic Course for Group Leaders	Industrial Engineering
Introductory Course for Sales Department	Basic Course
(Osaka)	Basic Course for Foremen
Instructor Course	Marketing
Course for GMP (Pharmaceutical)	Seminar
Circle Leader Course	Sensory Test
Circle Course for Clerical Work	Sensory Inspection Seminar
Introductory Course for Executives	Product Liability
and Managers	Prevention Introductory Course
Introductory Course for Purchasing Dept.	Other Management Techniques
Introductory Course for Sales Department	Statistical Application Seminar for Clinical
(Tokyo)	Test
Introductory Course for Service Ind.	Finite Element Method Seminar for Fluid
Introductory Course for New 7 Tools for TQC	Mechanics
Reliability	Software Production Control Seminar
Basic Course	Cost Reduction Seminar
Introductory Course	Numerical Analysis in Geotechnical
Management Course	Engineering
Course on FMEA-FTA	VE Basic Course for Foremen
Course on Design Review	
Six-Day Course (Osaka)	
Course on Probability Paper	
Course on Test	
Course on Failure Analysis	

Circles. The Japanese have also extended their training programs to developing countries. (See Mizuno and Kume, 1978.)

The United States. Most training in the United States is done by industrial companies, consultants, professional societies, and universities. Some organizations (e.g., AT&T, IBM, TRW, and Westinghouse) have extensive programs in training for quality. The American Society for Quality Control through its Education and Training Institute presents a variety of courses throughout the country (Table 11.19). Until recently, the emphasis in the United States has been on training quality specialists. This is in contrast to Japan where the training is companywide.

Other Countries. The affiliate organizations of the European Organization for Quality Control (EOQC) also sponsor quality courses.

Since 1973 the United Nations Industrial Development Organization (UNIDO) has provided training for engineers in about two dozen countries. (See Sandholm, 1976.) The program, consisting of 10 weeks in Sweden and 2 weeks in the developing countries, has the following structure:

A theoretical portion lasting 4 weeks covering statistics, metrology, inspection, and reliability

A practical study session in industry of 1 week

A second theoretical portion lasting 2 weeks and covering management topics

A second practical stage of 1 week in which the participants study quality control in a company similar to their own

A final 2-week seminar dealing with a variety of management topics

The Japanese, under the auspices of the Association for Overseas Technical Scholarships, also provide a course for developing countries. The course is held in Japan and consists of a curriculum of 6 weeks:

First week: Orientation and introductory lectures on Japanese management systems, history, characteristics of quality control in Japan, and concept of quality control

TABLE 11.19   List of ASQC Courses (1986)

Fundamentals of Quality Control
Basic Statistical Quality Control
Statistical Process Quality Control
Quality Audit-Development and Administration
Design of Industrial Experiments
Reliability Engineering
Quality Engineering by Design—The Taguchi Approach
Quality Engineering
Software Quality Assurance
Managing for Quality
Quality Management for Supervisors
Managing Quality for Profits
Managing the Inspection Function
Introduction to Quality Costs
Quality in the Service Industries

Second, third, and fourth weeks: Fundamental quality control techniques through lectures, classroom, and in-plant participation

Fifth and sixth weeks: Lectures, factory visits, and discussions on topics such as vendor-vendee relations, QC promotion system, quality circles, and the human aspects of quality control.

West (1981) reports experiences of an American organization that provided training in quality for a developing country.

Training on quality prevails throughout other countries. For an example from Turkey, see Stephens (1982). For an example from India, see Gopal et al. (1981).

BUDGETS FOR TRAINING IN QUALITY

There is no consensus on what constitutes a "right" budget for quality-oriented training. A few quality managers have proposed use of a budget equal to 10 percent of the cost of poor quality. That proposal has a degree of logic behind it but there is no experience to back it up. Until some experience is acquired, the approach must be to plan the training, translate the plans to money, and judge whether the total is reasonable in relation to other priorities.

Such a budgeting process is quite straightforward. The planning team can:

Design training courses which are appropriate for the various categories of persons to be trained

Estimate the class hours consumed by in-house courses and thereby the hours of time required from leaders, attendees, and facilities

Estimate the cost of preparing or buying the training materials

Estimate the cost of outside course fees along with the travel and living expenses

The budgeting is also influenced by the scheduling. The programs will likely extend over a span of several years (see below) so that the annual budget will be only a fraction of the total.

SCHEDULES FOR TRAINING

A program to train the entire company hierarchy in the quality disciplines cannot be carried out in a single year. Such a pace is beyond the digestive capacity of company training facilities and leaders. For large companies such a program will likely need to be spread over a range of 5 to 10 years. Accordingly, the planning team is faced with establishing schedules and priorities. The variables to be considered in setting priorities are:

Multiple businesses, i.e., divisions, profit centers, major contracts

Multiple levels of managers

Multiple types of technical specialty

Multiple locations (plants, laboratories, offices)

Multiple functional departments

Some groups wish to be among the first to be trained; others wish to be among the last.

For the longer range the planning team should bear in mind that after a few years there will arise a "maintenance" level of training. With cumulative turn-over, promotions, transfers, etc., there will be need for a program to maintain the training at the new level.

REFERENCES

Binstock, S. L. (1977). "Quality Control in Combat Training." *Quality Progress,* May, pp. 10–12.

Constable, Gordon K. (1983). "The Role of ASQC in Academic Programs." *ASQC Quality Technology Program Accreditation Update,* pp. 49–53.

Coop, Philip G. (1982). "Training as a Key to Hazardous Waste Compliance." *ASQC Quality Congress Transactions,* Milwaukee, pp. 653–658.

Courter, Sandra Shaw (1980). "Continuing Education: A Growth Industry." *Quality Progress,* April, pp. 16–21.

"Datsun's Mobile Training Vehicle" (1977). *Quality,* September, p. 47.

Gopal, Krishan, Rai, Suresh, Aggarwarl, K. K., Gupta, J. S. (1981). "Reliability Education in India, Present and Future." *Institute of Electrical and Electronic Engineers Transactions on Reliability,* vol. I-30, no. 1, April, pp. 4–7.

Grant, E. L. and Leavenworth, R. S. (1979). *Statistical Quality Control,* 5th ed. McGraw-Hill, New York.

Gryna, Frank M., (1981). "Quality Circles—A Team Approach to Problem Solving." *AMA-COM Journal,* pp. 57–58.

Heldt, John (1975). *Quality and Reliability Cases, Projects and Exercises.* Published by the DeAnza College Book Store, Los Altos Hills, CA.

Heldt, John J. and Pinschmidt, Robert J. (1977). "Learning by Doing." *Quality Progress,* August, pp. 30–32.

Hill, Hubert M. and McClaskey, David J. (1980). "Developing Awareness of Quality Responsibilities." *ASQC Technical Conference Transactions,* Milwaukee, pp. 160–167.

Hoppmann, W. H., II, Liu, James C. C., and Rivello, J. Roberto (1980). "Models of Professions: Law, Medicine, and Engineering." *Mechanical Engineering,* May, pp. 44–49.

Hromi, John D. (1980). Training Quality Control Technicians." *Quality Progress,* October, pp. 35–37.

Ishikawa, K. (1972). *Guide To Quality Control.* English language translation available from UNIPUB, 345 Park Avenue South, New York, NY 10010.

Juran, J. M. (1976). "Emerging Professionalism in Quality Assurance." *Quality Assurance,* vol. 2, no. 3, September, pp. 71–77.

Juran, J. M. and Gryna, Frank M., Jr. (1980). *Quality Planning and Analysis,* 2nd ed. McGraw-Hill, New York.

LaForge, R. Lawrence (1981). "Education." *Quality Progress,* June, pp. 13–15.

Land, William E. and Heldt, John J. (1981). "New Dimensions in Quality Education." *Quality Progress,* July, pp. 20–22.

Leaman, David C. (1975 and 1979). "Education and Training" column of *Quality Progress,* November 1975, p. 34, and December 1979, p. 5.

Leaman, David C. (1981). "Quality Technology Program Accreditation Update." *Quality Progress,* May, pp. 4, 5, and June, pp. 4, 5.

Mizuno, Shigeru, and Kume, Hitoshi (1978). "Development of Education and Training in Quality Control." *Reports of Statistical Applications and Research,* Japanese Union of Scientists and Engineers, vol. 25, no. 2, June, pp. 36–59.

Mundel, August B. (1982). "Product Liability Trial." *ASQC Quality Congress Transactions,* Milwaukee, pp. 791–793.

"Oklahomians Learn about Quality Assurance via Talk Back Television." (1977). *Quality Progress,* February, p. 9.

Overturf, George (1977). "Roll On Bottle Closures." *Quality Progress,* November, pp. 12–16.

QC Circle Koryo, 3rd ed. (1980). Japanese Union of Scientists and Engineers. Available from the American Society for Quality Control.

Quality Control Circles at Work (1984). Asian Productivity Organization, Tokyo (in English).

Rado, Leonard G. (1976). "Status Report: Quality Training." *Quality Progress,* March, p. 25.

Rehg, Virgil (1973). "A Computer Simulation of the Life Cycle." *Institute of Electronic and Electrical Engineers Transactions on Reliability and Quality Control.* IEEE, New York, pp. 564–675.

Rehg, Virgil (1969). "Reliability Management Simulation Exercise." *Institute of Electronic and Electrical Engineers Transactions on Reliability and Quality Control.* IEEE, New York, pp. 68–71.

Reynolds, Edward A. (1979). "The Value of 'Hands On' Training for the Quality Engineer." *Quality Progress,* May, pp. 34, 35.

Sandholm, Lennart (1976). "United Nations Training Programmes in Quality Control." *Quality,* vol. 20, no. 2, pp. 8–11.

Stephens, Kenneth S. (1982). "Quality Control in Turkey," *Quality Progress,* January, pp. 16–21.

Takahashi, Hiroyuki (1981). "QC Education for Consumer's Opinion Leader." *ASQC Quality Congress Transactions,* Milwaukee, pp. 703–708.

Trimble, John M. (1983). "It's Time to Assess Your Training Needs." *Microcontamination,* June-July, pp. 52–55.

"Vestibule Training." (1981). *Quality,* January, p. 57.

West, Andrew H. (1981). "Transferring Q.C. Technology to Developing Nations." *ASQC Quality Congress Transactions,* Milwaukee, pp. 359–364.

SECTION 12
FIELD INTELLIGENCE[1]

Frank M. Gryna

---

[1]In the Third Edition, material on Field Intelligence was prepared by J. M. Juran.

12.1

CONCEPT OF FIELD INTELLIGENCE

This section of the handbook is mainly devoted to the first step on the Spiral of Quality (Figure 2.1). That step is called marketing research.

Marketing research for the quality parameter is needed for (1) developing new products and (2) monitoring the performance of current products.

All companies collect a variety of information for new and current products, but the information related to product quality often has serious weaknesses. It concentrates on "product dissatisfaction" information, i.e., complaint data. Also, the planning for collection of the information is often minimal and leads to results that have low credibility. To be competitive on fitness for use, organizations must have a clear understanding of user needs. Often, the information needed is not available in the form or depth required and additional information must be captured through marketing research.

The term "field intelligence" will be used as the label for all information on product use whether relating to in-house use (other departments, sister divisions) or external use (merchants, processors, ultimate users). It includes information about product performance and the impact of that performance on all concerned—the merchant chain, users, service shops, society, government, the press, and the advocates.

This section of the handbook concentrates on that field intelligence needed for use in the next step on the Spiral—product development. Other sections of the handbook cover additional subjects that are allied to field intelligence. The section on Quality and Sales Income discusses the broad issue of the effect of product quality on sales income; Section 19 on Marketing covers quality issues during the process of marketing the product; Section 20 on Customer Service discusses the significance and processing of customer complaints; see also Section 8 under Quality Audits by Upper Managers.

Needs and Sources of Field Intelligence Information.   To develop and market its products, an organization requires information about quality in the marketplace. Some of this information is readily available in the form of feedback from customers. This feedback may include complaints from individual customers or changes in market share due to product quality or other parameters. Such information is not only used to monitor the performance of current products but also serves as input to the development of future products. Table 12.1 summarizes the principal needs for field intelligence and the sources for obtaining the knowledge.

Feedback on Performance of Current Products.   The feedback on current products provides an important source of information both for designing future products and for monitoring the performance of current products. This feedback often provides alarm signals that must be acted on to maintain good customer relations. The main effect of an individual alarm signal (a complaint from one customer) is to stimulate action that provides satisfaction to the customer. Collectively, these signals supply one measure of overall customer dissatisfaction. However, they are a poor measure of product quality, since many quality failures do not result in alarm signals. (See, in this connection, Section 20 under Quality Complaints.)

Loss of customers due to quality failures is another form of alarm signal, and sometimes the signal can be quite dramatic (see Table 12.2). This case involves a consumer product in which four models are sold to one major distributor. The letters in the table indicate the source of supply for each model by year. In 1979

TABLE 12.1 Needs and Sources of Field Intelligence on Quality

Needs for market quality information	Forcibly brought to company attention by "alarm signals"	Readily available but requires analysis	Not readily available; must be created by special studies
Individual dissatisfactions of customers	Complaints, returns, failure reports, claims Loss of customers Reports of Sales and Service personnel Safety and liability cases Supplier ratings		Study of failures beyond guarantee period Study of users' quality costs Interviews with users
Widespread customer dissatisfactions	Loss of customers Guarantee account charges	Pareto analysis of complaints, returns Pareto analysis of sales reports Analysis of decline in share of market Analysis of sale of spare parts	
Relative priorities of customers			Study of quality versus other parameters; study of quality-related attributes
Competitive quality status		Ratings from customers Ratings from consumer journals Government reports Share of market reports Salesforce reports	Laboratory test of competing products Usage test of competing products by customers and consumers
Opportunities for improving income through quality	Pareto analyses to identify major causes of dissatisfaction Projects to eliminate these causes	Summary of above analyses; projects for improvement based on these summaries	Special studies to study use of product Purchase of performance data Use of product by company personnel Projects based on above

TABLE 12.2 Change in Suppliers of Product*

Model	1979	1980	1981	1982
High price	A	C	C	C
Middle price	B	B	C	C
Low price	C	C	C	C
Special model	B	B	B	C

*A, B, C indicates suppliers.

Company B was the supplier for two of the four models, but by 1982 they had lost all of the business to Company C. Analysis revealed that Company B was competitive on price, delivery, and product features, but lost the business because of poor quality.

The situation does not have to become such a disaster before the alarm signals sound a warning. See below under Competitive Evaluations and also Section 20 under Data Analysis Techniques.

Limitations Inherent in Feedback of Information on Current Products. Routine feedback from current customers can provide valuable input, but it can also be completely silent on other areas that are critical. There are several such areas.

1. Dissatisfied Customers who Silently Switch to a Competitor's Product. Current customers are certainly a main source of business for the future, but those customers will switch to a competing product if they believe that the other product is superior. Often, the customer has no complaint about the product currently in use, but discovers a competing product that has superior performance or value. Thus the customer will quietly buy the other brand, and the original company will miss the problem until enough customers switch to cause a broad decrease in sales. The product probably conforms to specifications but it simply is not competitive with respect to fitness for use. Here are some examples:

A semiconductor manufacturer supplied parts to another manufacturer and the parts met specifications. However, the customer reported that the parts simply did not work as well in the printed circuit board as did parts from another manufacturer. The customer changed suppliers.

A manufacturer of surgical needles noticed a significant decline in market share from some major customers. Again the product met all specifications. Discussions with the customers revealed that a competitor had created a sharper needle that did not become dull as fast and performed more effectively during surgery. The original manufacturer changed the design of the needle, but several years later was still trying to regain the market loss.

A manufacturer of abrasive cloth, competitive on price and conformance to specification, gradually lost a significant market share to a competitor. Investigation revealed that the competitor had developed an abrasive cloth which cut the user's costs significantly. (The user measured fitness for use based on "cost per 100 pieces polished" and had compiled data for each supplier of cloth.)

In all three examples the product met specifications and there was no product dissatisfaction. Customers simply changed to another brand because of greater product satisfaction—a superiority in fitness for use. The lack of alarm signals underscores the need for field intelligence on fitness for use.

Absence of product dissatisfaction is sometimes confused with fitness for use. Some managers reason that if no one is dissatisfied then everyone must be satisfied. The fallacy is a subtle one: *Product dissatisfaction and product satisfaction are not opposites.*

2. Noncustomers. A major gap is information on the needs and attitudes of people who are not customers. Intelligence is needed to learn why they are not customers, and what it would take to cause them to purchase the product.

3. Product Dissatisfaction beyond the Warranty Period. All companies have extensive systems for keeping track of product performance during the warranty period. However, the warranty period is usually between 10 and 20 percent of the actual product life expected by the customer. Once the warranty period is passed, the feedback of information from the customer to the company becomes sporadic at best, and thus the company lacks information about the complete history of the product. As fitness for use applies for the life of the product, field intelligence information is needed over the lifetime.

ANALYSIS OF AVAILABLE FIELD INTELLIGENCE

The raw data for some types of field intelligence are readily available (see Table 12.1), but full use is not made of the data for two reasons: (1) the data are not recognized as valuable in planning for future products; and (2) the data are not in a form useful to product development and other functions.

Decline in Sales. All companies have data systems to compute the volume and trend of sales. Seldom are these sales analyses structured to permit evaluation of the effect of quality on sales. The concepts for arriving at such an evaluation are clear enough. At periodic intervals, the sales summaries are published. These summaries show which accounts and/or product types have gone up in volume and which have declined. It is then feasible to analyze individually those which have undergone a significant change. These analyses require going into the individual accounts and product types to see whether volume changes were due to quality or other reasons. However, in practice it is not a simple matter to draw conclusions. The analyses require a joint effort among marketing, quality, and other departments to draw the proper conclusions. A discussion of the effect of quality on sales income is provided in Section 3, Quality and Sales Income.

A further indicator of the effect of quality on sales is a change in the price premium connected with a product. A change in price premium can be due to a number of factors including product quality. For example, a chemical manufacturer noted that the amount of a price premium had declined on a product, but the reason was not obvious. A marketing research study showed that product quality was one of the key reasons for the decline. (See below under Competitive Evaluations by Field Studies.)

Another source of information is the company's performance during its bidding for contracts. Table 12.3 shows an analysis involving 20 unsuccessful bids. Quality of design was a major contributor in the pattern. From knowledge of the users' specific objections to the designs and other users' preferences in successful

TABLE 12.3　Analysis of Unsuccessful Bids

Contract proposal	Quality of design	Product price	Installation price*	Reciprocal buying	Other
			Bid not accepted because of		
A 1	· · ·	X†	X	· · ·	X
A 2	· · ·	· · ·	XX	· · ·	· · ·
A 3	XX†	X	· · ·	· · ·	· · ·
A 4	XX	· · ·	X	· · ·	· · ·
A 5	XX	· · ·	· · ·	· · ·	· · ·
A 6	XX	· · ·	· · ·	· · ·	· · ·
A 7	· · ·	XX	· · ·	· · ·	· · ·
A 8	· · ·	XX	· · ·	· · ·	· · ·
A 9	· · ·	· · ·	XX	· · ·	· · ·
A 10	· · ·	· · ·	XX	· · ·	· · ·
B 1	X	· · ·	X	· · ·	· · ·
B 2	· · ·	· · ·	· · ·	XX	· · ·
B 3	· · ·	· · ·	· · ·	XX	· · ·
B 4	· · ·	· · ·	· · ·	XX	· · ·
B 5	· · ·	X	X	· · ·	· · ·
B 6	· · ·	X	XX	· · ·	· · ·
B 7	XX	· · ·	· · ·	· · ·	· · ·
B 8	· · ·	X	X	· · ·	· · ·
B 9	· · ·	· · ·	· · ·	X	· · ·
B 10	X	X	X	· · ·	· · ·
Totals	7	8	10 (of 14)	4	1

*Only 14 bids were made for installation.
†X = contributing reason; XX = main reason.

bids, the needed remedies emerged much more clearly than was evident merely from the memory of the managers involved.

Field Complaints.　Most organizations have systems of collecting and analyzing information on customer complaints. (For a discussion of these systems see Section 20 under Processing of Complaints.) A Pareto analysis of field failures, complaints, product returns, etc., serves to identify the vital few quality problems to be addressed in both current and future products. This type of analysis is in wide use. Table 12.4 shows a Pareto analysis of field complaints on fuel nozzles using several different indices. A conventional Pareto analysis would rank the various types of complaints according to the frequency of occurrence; but when those complaints are evaluated on an economic basis, the ranking changes. Note also that there are several possible economic indices such as warranty costs or effect on the user. The priorities for future product development can be quite different depending on the measure used in the Pareto analysis.

Salespersons' Reports.　Salespeople, distributors, and other people in the marketing process are a natural, though imperfect, field intelligence system. Their reports on quality usually deal with troubles which jeopardize current customer relations. In addition, the salespeople report on competitive products which are

TABLE 12.4   Pareto Analysis of Complaints on Fuel Nozzles

Failure mode	Ranking based on various measures		
	Frequency	Warranty charges	Effect on user
G	1	4	3
A	2	1	6
D	3	2	1
F	4	5	4
N	5	7	8
L	6	3	2
P	7	6	5
R	8	8	7

creating difficulties for them. Although such input is clearly part of the field intelligence system, the emphasis is understandably on those aspects which will aid in meeting marketing departmental goals such as sales volume and sales expense. As a result, the amount of factual information on quality matters is often limited. There are too many cases in which input from the marketing department on quality matters has such low credibility with technical people that it is ignored. In the worst case, complaints from marketing personnel about poor quality are viewed as an excuse for failure to meet sales quotas. Such episodes illustrate the need for marketing, product development, and quality personnel to work jointly together to agree on what facts need to be collected.

Sale of Spare Parts.   These sales are often regarded as a benefit to the company because of the contribution to sales income. In many cases, customers have become accustomed to the routine replacement of certain parts, and it occurs without any complaints. From the customer's point of view, the need for spare parts not only means the additional cost of the parts but also the time and expense to install those parts. (In some cases an additional element is an expensive cost of equipment downtime.) Despite the fact that many users put up with these replacements as a necessary evil, the manufacturers should analyze the sales of spare parts to identify major field problems from the viewpoint of the customer. The high usage of a certain part for replacement as spares may indicate a need for new product development to search for alternatives that would reduce the requirement for spare parts. This would of course reduce the sales income from the sale of spare parts. However, it would guard against losing the entire business to competitors who come up with products of higher reliability.

Data from Customers.   Information from customers not only consists of complaints but can include other information on quality.

A simple form of this information consists of warranty cards returned by customers upon receipt of the product. These cards can provide some information about the customer's perception of product quality upon delivery. They can also record the approximate date that the product was placed in operation (a useful input for later reliability analyses).

A broader type of information is provided in the form of supplier rating data (see Section 15 under Supplier Quality Rating). The customer keeps track of quality and other data from suppliers and summarizes the information in the form of comparative ratings. These ratings are often sent to the suppliers to stimulate action, and the effect can be dramatic. Generally supplier names are coded, but an individual company will be told its ranking relative to competitors.

Purchasers of expensive equipment usually have detailed data systems for recording maintenance and repair work. Examples include construction, transportation, and manufacturing processing equipment. These data systems become a gold mine of information for the manufacturers of the equipment. The challenge is to work out arrangements with the customers to obtain the performance data in a form that will be useful for future product development. Contracts to buy such data are not unusual.

Government Reports.   Governments are increasingly involved in product evaluation, mainly in their capacity as regulators but also in their capacity as purchasers. Sometimes the data on performance of companies are published in aggregate form, but in other cases data are given on the performance of products from individual companies. Whatever the form of the information, it is a valuable input for product development. An example of such information is the reporting on tests conducted to evaluate the safety of automotive vehicles.

Independent Laboratories.   These include consumer journals, standardization organizations, and still others. Some of these laboratories make comparative tests for competing lines of products. They then publish the results for the benefit of their subscribers as an aid to making purchasing decisions.

There is some confusion about interpreting the comparative analyses published in consumer journals. Generally, these journals publish analyses based on tests of only one or a few items from each supplier of a product. These analyses provide factual information about the *design* of the product and often draw some conclusions about the adequacy of the design for fulfilling typical consumer needs. The journals point out that because of the limited sample size, they are unable to draw conclusions about the ability of the manufacturer to produce, in volume, products that meet the design specifications. This distinction between quality of design and quality of conformance is often not understood by the consumer. Thus, a consumer may buy a product that was rated high in a consumer journal and then be dissatisfied with the product because of conformance defects.

Manufacturers do not always agree with the ratings given in consumer journals, but the evaluations are publicly available and do influence consumer perceptions. Hence they are properly one more input for new product development.

ORGANIZATION FOR FIELD INTELLIGENCE

Team Approach.   Normally there exists no separate department whose basic activity is one of collecting and analyzing field intelligence. Instead, this activity is dispersed among several departments: sales, customer service, quality assurance, complaint investigation, technical service. Under this typical form of organization, the field intelligence activity suffers through lack of effective leadership and coordination. One solution to the problem is to create a team of members from the pertinent departments—those who need field intelligence and those who can provide it. Such a team can take on the job of identifying what are the needs for field intelligence and what means should be used for satisfying the needs.

Specific Assignment for Coordination.   A second approach is to assign coordination of field intelligence to some specific, designated department. Such an assignment increases accountability for getting action. In addition, it gives the field intelligence function a sponsor who has a legitimate place in the hierarchy.

In clarifying who is responsible for doing what, it is useful to create a matrix of responsibilities. A chemical company prepared such a matrix for one area of field intelligence, i.e., the determination of fitness-for-use needs for new products (see Table 12.5).

TABLE 12.5   Responsibility Matrix for Analyzing Fitness-for-Use Needs

Actions	Marketing	Technical service	Production	Development and control	Research
Contact customer to learn needs	R	C			
Identify critical properties		C		C	R
Learn process capability			R	C	
Identify critical measurements			C	R	
Determine if measurements reflect fitness for use	C	R			
Collect cost information		C	R	C	
Integrate all information and finalize specifications		C	C	R	

Note: R: primary responsibility; C: contributing responsibility.

Special Field Intelligence Department.   A third form of organization is to create a separate department whose prime responsibility relates to field intelligence. This form is quite useful if the company needs an aggressive revision of its approach. Such a department, when first created, is not content with the available sources and methods for securing field intelligence. Instead, it comes up with proposals for developing new sources such as creation of dealer councils or in-depth interviews with a sample of users.

Planning for Field Intelligence.   As noted in Table 12.1, the main needs are to:

1. Discover customer dissatisfactions not evident from complaints or other alarm signals.
2. Discover the relative priority of quality versus other product parameters.
3. Discover the status of quality in relation to competitors.
4. Determine the specific fitness-for-use needs of customers.
5. Identify opportunities for improving income by improving fitness for use.

Such broad needs make it necessary to carefully plan the approach to data collection.

The Data Plan.   Field intelligence can be useful to the manufacturer in various ways—to improve product designs, processes, tests, field service, marketing strategy. The wide range of purposes served makes clear that no single department can identify the company's needs for field intelligence. An interdepartmental team is able to come up with a list of needs such as:

The vital few quality characteristics on which information is needed

Product performance with respect to those vital few characteristics, expressed in agreed units of measure

Information on users' costs and satisfaction as well as dissatisfaction

Failure information, including exact failure modes

Environments of use, both for successful use and for failures

The team can, in addition, usefully face up to the problem of data communications—preparation of a glossary of terms and a system of code numbers to facilitate data entry to computers, and other matters to improve field feedback.

Data Sources.   In addition to using the available sources of field intelligence previously discussed, other approaches to data collection may be necessary.

1.   Natural Field Contacts.   Every company has some employees who are in direct contact with the field: the sales force, complaint investigators, technical service specialists, service shop personnel. It is feasible to secure some field intelligence through these contacts, but only if certain special steps are first taken:

Prepare a detailed plan setting out just what information is wanted.

Provide the time and assistance needed for acquiring the information.

Motivate the employees to accept responsibility for acquiring the planned field intelligence as part of their job.

The last step is usually the most difficult. When the "regular" job is something else (e.g., service calls), then field intelligence is incidental and is not readily accepted as part of the job.

2.   Controlled Use.   In some cases a company makes enough use of its own products to serve as a significant data base on product performance. In such cases it is feasible to design a data plan and to acquire useful field intelligence. In other cases the need may be to create an outside data base, as by placing household appliances in employee homes or by sending packages of food to a consumer panel. The users get free use of the product but they pay in data through keeping a complete log on quality-related performance.

3.   Purchase of Data.   Contracts may be made to buy data from users of the product. The arrangements specify the data plan to be followed. They also provide for such associated features as training of personnel, audit of validity of data, and return of failed samples. For example, one automobile manufacturer agreed to pay all of the repair expenses for its cars at a car rental agency in return for getting complete detailed data on the repairs. In another case, a manufacturer designed a repair information system for its customers and provided the service of analyzing the data and presenting summaries to the customers. This analysis was done not only for the manufacturer's product but also for competitors. In such cases, the manufacturers participate in the design of the data plan so that the joint needs for data are given.

4. Product Monitoring.   There is a growing technology which enables the "health" of products to be monitored during operation. An example is the in-flight instrumentation used to monitor aircraft engine performance. Periodic spectroscopic analysis of the engine oil is a related example. In another case, an independent entrepreneur developed instruments to monitor the performance of computers. Users were asked to install the instruments as a means of collecting data on error rates. The data were then *(a)* used by clients to compare competing systems and *(b)* sold to manufacturers of the computers.

5. Captive Service Center.   Some consumer product companies maintain serv-ice centers throughout the country at which repair work on their products is per-formed. Thus, information on product performance, failure modes, and the cost of repairs is accumulated as part of the process of providing the repair service. The acquisition of field intelligence from such operations does not occur auto-matically. Repair organizations view their objective as providing the repair serv-ice to customers, and not as collecting data and writing reports. There must be explicit cooperation between that repair service and product development in order to obtain the field intelligence needed. In one company there was great dif-ficulty in achieving this cooperation, and an unusual approach was developed. A sample of customers were told to send any products requiring repair to the Qual-ity Control Department. The department performed the repair work and returned the products to the customers. However, as part of their repair work they collected the kind of information needed for future product planning.

6. Maintaining the Product for the Customer.   A variation of the captive service center is the mobile service center. In this form, a field force of repair people visits the customer's site and performs all preventive and corrective maintenance work on the product. Examples include computers and office equipment.

7. Following Progression of the Product on Site.   In this approach a company "staples itself" to its product and observes how the customer uses the product. The idea is to identify opportunities for improving fitness for use. For a further discussion of this, see Discovering Market Opportunities, below.

8. Special Surveys and Studies.   These are special marketing research studies conducted on an infrequent basis to obtain evaluations of quality versus compe-tition, answer specific questions about a product, or learn about customer percep-tions of the relative priority of quality versus other product parameters. Examples of such studies are discussed below under Competitive Evaluations by Field Studies.

9. Continuing Measurements to Obtain Customer Perception on Qual-ity.   Increasingly, companies are trying to identify measures that can be contin-uously used to evaluate how customers feel about quality. For example, a division of one of the large electronics companies developed a six-point program for qual-ity improvement. One of the six points was to create quality and reliability "expe-rience measures" that measured performance throughout the complete product life cycle. In an organization making copier and duplicator products, a series of competitive benchmarks were developed that became the basis for establishing quality, cost, and delivery targets. These benchmarks were incorporated in both the annual operating plan and the 5-year business plan. Their experience showed that many of the prior measurements used did not reflect the realities of the marketplace (Pipp, 1983).

The Sampling Concept. A common and fatal error in the pursuit of field intelligence is to go after 100 percent of the data. Normally a well-chosen sample will provide adequate field intelligence, and at a cost which is reasonable rather than prohibitive.

For example, a vehicle maker tried to secure complete field data from its 5000 dealers. The data quality was poor and the cost was high. The company then changed its approach. It concentrated on data from a sample of 35 dealers who were well distributed geographically and who accounted for 5 percent of the sales. The result was a more prompt feedback of a better basis for decision making, and at a much lower cost.

Section 23 under Statistical Estimation discusses methodology for determining the sample size required.

SOME SIMPLE TOOLS FOR COLLECTING FIELD INTELLIGENCE

Like certain statistical tools, the simpler marketing research tools seem almost trite, but can be surprisingly effective.

Warranty Cards. Upon the purchase of the product, the customer is asked to return a card showing the customer's name, address, date, and source of purchase, and the condition of the product when it was received by the customer. The information is limited, but it is one snapshot of the product, taken by the customer.

Telephone Calls to the Customers. Here, customers are called and asked for impressions on the quality of the item they purchased. The information gained can provide a general impression of quality, but it can also lead to important contacts for obtaining more information. Two examples will illustrate this tool.

The Sales Department in a high-technology company complained that "about 20 percent of the customers say quality is poor, and this is making it difficult for us to get repeat orders—no wonder we're having trouble meeting our sales goals." The design and manufacturing departments were amazed because they had recently taken steps that they believed had resulted in superior quality. The Quality Control Department contacted some customers, and they heard a different story. Problems had occurred with early units of a new model, but the problems had been corrected and, said the customers, "Your overall quality record is really fine." Thus, the salespeople heard about problems but not about good performance and had therefore concluded that quality was poor.

Contacting the customers resulted in clarification of customer perception, but it also led to positive action. First, the salespeople were given information on product quality to make them believers of the superior quality level, and they highlighted this information in their selling efforts. Second, the positive reaction of customers resulted in Sales giving additional customer names to the Quality Department and encouraging them to contact customers on a planned basis.

Customers appreciate being asked their views about product performance. One customer offered to give the manufacturer the log of all events that occurred during the initial usage of the product. The offer was accepted with enthusiasm; imagine the usefulness of that information to the product development and manufacturing functions.

In another example, phone calls were made to 192 housewives who were asked about the performance of their washing machines. The owners of brand B were delighted, but brand A was another story. Many owners of brand A complained that the clothes got tangled during washing. The manufacturer stated that the tangling problem had been corrected in a new model. Unfortunately, records showed that the source of complaints on the tangling problem included owners of the "improved" model. A change had been made but it just did not solve the tangling problem. The change reduced the amount of tangling and the manufacturer rationalized that the problem was corrected, but the housewives said the clothes still got tangled. (Their friends used other brands that didn't tangle the clothes.) Of brand A's present customers, 10.5 percent said they would not buy brand A again (because of the tangling and other quality problems), while only 1.1 percent of brand B owners planned to switch brands. Some simple marketing research on the improved model would have given a warning that the redesign was not adequate. Thus, the inadequacy would have been discovered before the "improved" model was released for full production (Gryna, 1970).

Visits to Individual Customers. Another form of research is the periodic visit to major customers by a marketing or engineering representative of the company. These visits are not made in response to complaints but are designed to learn about customer experiences with the product. These visits should be structured to provide answers to specific questions. (In practice, the visits are often not structured and are only partially successful in collecting useful information.)

In one example, a manufacturer of disposable medical items for hospitals was investigating a decline in market share. For the product involved it was usual for a hospital to use the product for about a year and then make a decision on a long-term purchase contract.

Historically, about 65 to 70 percent of customers became regular customers after the trial period, but for product X only about 40 to 50 percent were signing up with the company. To learn why, visits were made to some of the hospitals that rejected a long-term arrangement. Prior to the research there had been pressure on the manufacturing function to improve quality in four key areas. As a result of the visits to customers, two of the four areas were confirmed as needing improvement, the other two were shown not to need improvement, and there were three new reasons for dissatisfaction that had not been previously revealed. These additional reasons centered around the product design.

In another case, a manufacturer of car wax held discussions with customers to learn how customers evaluated quality of wax. Within the company, high priority was attached to the "gloss" properties of the wax. The research revealed that the customers did not associate this property with car wax (although it was associated with house paint). Even when the term "gloss" was brought up for discussion it generated little reaction by the customer. What the customers did talk about was the "beading" property of the wax. Customers described beading as "when the water rolls off the surface." About 82 percent of the respondents indicated that they used "water beading" as a measure of continued wax performance. This study led to a change in priorities for the manufacturer and even influenced the selection of a name for the wax.

Mail Surveys. Still another means of collecting field intelligence is the questionnaire. For example, a manufacturer of programmable controllers makes an annual customer survey by sending a questionnaire consisting of the following questions:

Model number used

Approximate date of installation

Other programmable calculators used

How would you rate:

    The quality/reliability of our controller?

    The quality/reliability of our controller versus other manufacturers?

    The quality of the documentation you have received from us?

    The quality of hardware service you have received at your site?

    The response time on service?

    The quality of application programs support you have received?

    The training provided (separately on hardware and program logic training)?

    The quality of the sales support you have received?

    The repair turnaround?

    The quality of the repaired units?

Are there any other comments or suggestions you would like to make?

To most of the questions the customer is asked to respond by checking off excellent, very good, good, fair, or poor. These responses are converted to a numerical scale and the results are summarized in quantitative form.

Kukla (1981) explains how a questionnaire was used for transmission and axle customers of an equipment company. This questionnaire asks for responses on an absolute basis, a comparison to competition, and also the relative importance of the attribute being evaluated.

Special Arrangements with Individual Customers. A simple but effective approach for gaining field intelligence is to establish a special arrangement with a few customers to obtain information in depth. An electronics manufacturer does this with two or three key customers in each of several industries. The manufacturer offers, with the help of the customer (the "quality partner"), to maintain detailed records on the performance of the equipment in the customer's plant. The records benefit the manufacturer by relating performance to specific applications and environments rather than to assumed conditions. The customer benefits by having a direct link to the manufacturing and engineering operations of the manufacturer.

Focus Groups. In order to better understand customer perceptions of their company's products, a food company sponsors meetings of small groups of customers to discuss product requirements. (The company holds an average of one such meeting per day.) The technique is called a focus group. A focus group consists of about eight to ten current or potential customers who meet for a few hours to discuss a product. Here are some key features:

1. The discussion can focus on current products, proposed products, or future products.

2. A moderator who is skilled in group dynamics guides the discussion.

3. The moderator has a clear goal as to the information needed and a plan for guiding the discussion.

4. Often company personnel observe and listen in an adjacent room shielded by a one-way mirror.

Focus groups can discuss many facets of a product or can discuss quality only. A discussion on quality can be broad (e.g., obtaining views on what are the factors comprising fitness for use) or can have a narrower scope (e.g., determining customer sensitivity to various degrees of surface imperfections on silverware).

Depending on the goals, the participants in a focus group may be average customers, noncustomers, or special customers. Sometimes the participants are a special segment of society: For example, a toy manufacturer assembles a focus group of youngsters and provides them with a variety of toys for use in the group session. The children are observed to see which toys command the most attention and what kind of abuse the toys must take. The parents get their chance to talk in a separate focus group. A manufacturer of hospital supplies uses focus groups of nurses who apply products under simulated hospital conditions and offer comments while the product designers are observing and listening behind a one-way mirror. The designers translate the comments of nurses as wisdom based on experience, while the feedback of company marketing personnel is viewed as gossip.

Focus groups provide information quickly and at low cost. Calder (1977) provides some incisive views on focus groups. Some marketing research specialists are concerned that the technique may be viewed as a cure-all. Focus groups can pinpoint problems, obtain specific information on quality matters, and identify issues that need to be explored with quantitative or other techniques.

The following example illustrates the use of questionnaires and focus groups. An annual mail survey of automobile customers revealed a significant number of complaints on "fit of doors." Within the company this term meant problems of "margin" and "flushness." Margin is the space between the front door and fender, or between the front and rear doors. Sometimes the margin was not uniform, e.g., a different amount of space at the top as compared to space at the bottom of the door. Flushness refers to the smoothness of fit of the door with the body of the car after the door is shut. The manufacturer took action, but it was doomed to failure. Steps were taken during processing and assembly to correct the margin and flushness problems, but the action didn't correct the problem—a later survey again reported a problem on fit of doors.

Fortunately, there was other marketing research input. The company also held periodic focus group meetings in which a group of people were paid to attend a meeting where they answered a questionnaire and also discussed issues in detail. The questionnaire listed fit of doors as one category of problems, and some customers in the clinic checked it. On the spot they were asked, "What do you mean by fit of doors?" Their answer was not margin or flushness but two other matters. First, fit meant the amount of effort required to close the door. They complained that they had to "slam the door hard in order to get it to close completely the first time." Second, fit meant sound. As the door was shut they wanted to hear a solid "businesslike" sound instead of the metallic, loose sound they heard (telling them the door was not closed) as they walked away from the car. The marketing research gave a better understanding of the symptom, and then the company pursued the right problem, which required changes in the product design and the manufacturing process. The company had long realized that fit of doors was important, but the first time the company acted, it solved the wrong problem.

A method similar to a focus group is a council of consumer advisors. Such a council is a relatively permanent group and meets periodically to discuss issues of concern to the manufacturer.

COMPETITIVE EVALUATIONS

An important part of field intelligence is to learn where a company stands on quality with respect to competition. In some cases, the necessary knowledge can be learned from laboratory testing. In other cases it is necessary to conduct field studies.

Laboratory Evaluations. These provide useful technical data at modest expense. In some companies, competitive studies are part of the annual product planning program. A manufacturer of floor tiles made an annual comparison with competition (see Table 12.6). From such a comparison, the planners can consider whether characteristics T and U, now below market, should be improved. In the case of characteristic R and S, where the company now excels, they can consider whether this excellence can be sold or whether it should become the basis of a cost reduction. This program worked out so successfully that it is now performed on a semiannual basis and is one of the key inputs for a semiannual visit by corporate management to each plant.

TABLE 12.6 Comparison of Competitive Products

Characteristics of the product	Ranking of the companies				
	Home Co.	Competitors			
		A Co.	B Co.	C Co.	D Co.
P	3	2	1	4	5
Q	2	4	3	1	5
R	1	3	2	5	4
S	1	5	3	4	2
T	5	2	3	1	4
U	4	1	2	5	3

Many companies purchase competing products and not only test them but disassemble them to evaluate the design concepts. For products not involving destructive tests it may be feasible to inspect and test such products at some friendly dealer. Carpets and watches are examples of products for which competitive evaluations have been made without purchase. (In the carpet example, a traveling laboratory was set up so that the examinations were performed in the storage warehouse.)

COMPETITIVE EVALUATIONS BY FIELD STUDIES

The ultimate evaluation of quality is made by the user under the conditions of the marketplace. The field intelligence gathered on these evaluations must be based on factual inputs and not on hearsay. These evaluations aim to discover the users' viewpoint on fitness for use, and also to provide a comparison to competitors. The distinguishing feature of the field studies is that the user is the prime source of data.

Such studies should not be planned by any one department but by a team involving members from marketing, product development, quality, manufacturing, and other areas as needed. This team must agree beforehand on what questions need to be answered by the field study. The types of questions which should be considered are:

1. What is the relative importance of various product qualities as seen by the user?
2. For each of the key qualities, how does our product compare with competitors' products, as seen by the users?
3. What is the effect of the quality differences on user costs, well-being, and other aspects of fitness for use?
4. What are users' problems about which they do not complain but which our product might nevertheless be able to remedy?
5. What ideas do users have that might be useful in new-product development?

Examples of Field Studies. In a case involving an industrial product, a field study was made as part of a strategic planning analysis. Although both failure costs and customer complaints were low, the product had been losing market share for several years. Quality was one of five areas of strategic planning that was studied in order to improve market share. (See Utzig, 1980 and 1981.)

Table 12.7 shows a summary of the results. The six attributes studied were collectively a measure of fitness for use. On a scale of 1 to 10, customers were asked for two responses—the relative importance of each attribute and a perceived performance rating versus two key competitors. The average score for General Electric was lowest—not just for one attribute but for all of them. These unpleasant findings were not believed. (After all, the failure costs were at an acceptable level and complaints were few.) The study was repeated. It was repeated again. Three geographical areas, covering all types of customers, were studied before the results were believed. The details revealed that customers not only wanted fewer failures; they also wanted to improve their own productivity, and this meant purchasing products with higher efficiency, durability, and better maintainability and serviceability. The desire for improved service was a surprise.

TABLE 12.7 Customer-Based Measurements

Product attribute	Mean importance rating	Competitor performance ratings		
		GE	A	B
Reliable operation	9.7	8.1	9.3	9.1
Efficient performance	9.5	8.3	9.4	9.0
Durability/life	9.3	8.4	9.5	8.9
Easy to inspect and maintain	8.7	8.1	9.0	8.6
Easy to wire and install	8.8	8.3	9.2	8.8
Product service	8.8	8.9	9.4	9.2

Source: Utzig, 1980, p. 150. Copyright 1980, American Society for Quality Control. Reprinted by permission.

The company thought they were the leader on service (because theirs was a comprehensive service organization). However, the customers reported that the speed and quality of service were not equal to that of the competition. All of this led to the development of a plan including actions in product design, the manufacturing processes, product service, and the quality assurance system.

In another example, a manufacturer of equipment was also going through an era of declining market share. Complaints about "quality" led to a proposal to "beef up the inspection." Discussions within the company revealed uncertainty about the nature of the complaints, so it was decided to conduct a field study to learn more about customer view. A team was formed to plan and conduct the study. Visits were made to about 50 customers.

In one part of the study, five attributes were identified and customers were asked to rate the company as superior, competitive, or inferior to competition on each of the attributes (see Table 12.8). The results were stunning. The hardware problems were confirmed, but the study revealed the presence of both design and manufacturing causes. Also, documentation and field repair service were identified as weak areas (these were surprises to the company involved). The action taken was dramatic. A broad approach to quality was created, starting in initial design and continuing throughout the Spiral of all activities affecting fitness for use. This was in stark contrast to the original proposal of adding inspectors. The study required about seven worker-months of effort, including the planning, customer visits, analysis of results, and preparation of a report—a small price to pay to develop a proper strategy.

An example from a chemical company involves a specialty product that is used exclusively in one industry (Gross, 1978). The product had been granted a premium price by the market but the amount of the premium was declining. The study investigated the relationship of price and product attributes. For each of six attributes, customers were questioned. An analysis of the responses provided information on:

The relative importance of each attribute (the study referred to this as "value")

The relative rating of the product versus competition on each attribute ("perception")

The contribution to the price premium for each attribute

TABLE 12.8   Heavy Equipment Case

Parameter	Comparison to competition, %		
	Superior	Competitive	Inferior
Analysis of customer needs			
Preparation of quality requirements and purchase order			
Preparation of specifications and technical documentation			
Quality of equipment			
Quality and availability of spare parts			
Quality of field repair service			

Source: Private communication.

Some of the results are shown in Table 12.9. The relative importance ("value") numbers were determined by means of a trade-off analysis. Two realistic levels of performance for each attribute were defined. For the quality attribute, a high level was defined as impurities of less than 1 part per million (ppm.); a low level was defined as impurities of less than 10 ppm.

> The respondent was told, first, to consider an offering with all of the attributes at the high level; and, next, to suppose that the company making the offering was faced with increasing costs and, rather than raise the price, was considering sacrificing performance on one of the attributes by reducing it to the lower level. The respondent was then given a pair of attributes (such as product quality and speed of delivery) and asked which he would rather see kept at the higher level, and the degree of his preference. (A number of additional pairs of attribute sacrifices were given for similar ranking.) Finally he assigned dollar values to the price difference he would tolerate to retain the higher level of performance on each attribute. As a result of this questioning, and the use of statistical analysis, we were able to construct a scale of the relative dollar value of each attribute for each respondent. (Gross, 1978, pp. 35, 37)

The average results are shown in the "Value" column of Table 12.9. To no one's surprise, the quality attribute was regarded as the most valuable. Somewhat surprisingly, product innovation was second on the value list. The other four attributes trailed far behind the first two. Note that although quality was the most valued attribute, it was not the largest contributor to the price premium. The detailed responses revealed that the customers perceived quality to be about equal to that of its principal competitor—equal but not superior. The results of this study provided the company with an opportunity for making certain changes to protect the price premium.

TABLE 12.9   Research on a Speciality Product

Attribute	Value, $	Perceived performance				Contribution to price premium, $
		DuPont	A	B	C	
Quality	108					1.70
Innovation	105					2.00
System	103					0.80
Service	102					0.25
Delivery	101					0.15
Retraining	101					0.40
						5.30

Source: Gross, 1978, p. 39.

Studies of this type often reveal differences between the customers' perceived performance of some product attribute and the actual performance of that attribute. In some cases, customers may perceive the level of an attribute as poor when in reality the performance of that attribute is good. In such cases, the need is to take action to change the perception of the customers. In other cases the level may be correctly perceived as poor. This then requires an improvement in the level of performance rather than a change in the perception of the customer.(For further discussion of perceived quality, see Goble et al., 1981.)

A final example of a field study on competitive quality comes from a manufacturer of health products. This was also a "multiattribute study" in which customers were asked to consider several product attributes and indicate both the relative importance and a competitive rating. The results for one product are shown in Table 12.10. Note that an overall score is obtained for each manufacturer by multiplying the relative importance by the score for that attribute and then adding up these products. (For an extension to include costs, see Gryna, 1983.)

In generalizing about these examples, it should first be observed that all were based on a study of customers who were experienced in using the product involved. The studies determined both the relative importance of a number of attributes and a competitive rating for each of those attributes. Also note that the attributes involved can encompass quality as well as other business factors or be restricted to quality-related issues. For example, the chemical example was general in the sense that quality was just one of a number of business attributes, whereas the example of an industrial product was more specific with respect to quality as each of the attributes listed was a facet of fitness for use. It is useful to make multiattribute studies from both a general point of view and a more specific point of view. Most studies are general, but additional studies at a more detailed level will provide valuable information to product development, manufacturing, customer service, and other functions. (See also Utzig, 1981.)

DISCOVERING MARKETING OPPORTUNITIES

The search for ideas to achieve a unique position in the marketplace is perpetual. (Market quality is a moving target.) One important avenue is to seek ideas for the improvement of fitness for use. The broad steps are: analyze the present use of the product, analyze the total system of use, and strategically plan for quality.

Analyze the Present Use of the Product by the Customer.   This includes:

Collect and Analyze All Available Information on Current Product Usage.   (See, generally, Section 20, Customer Service.)

Visit the Scene of Action.   That is, go to the places where the product is used. There is no substitute for "stapling ourselves to the product." The observation on site provides information about:

1.   Conditions of Use.   Actual conditions of use can differ markedly from those assumed by the product designer, but field conditions are the realities.

2.   Problems Reported by the User.   These problems can be of several types. One type of problem involves inconvenience during use. One instrument manufacturer learned from customers that it was difficult to read the scale on an instrument through the normal 3-in.-high window ("Beckman Gets Customers to Design," 1974). The design was changed to provide a 6-in window. A second type of problem relates to the effects of a product failure. The effects of downtime due to failures can be significant, but there may be other consequences as well. A manufacturer of process control devices learned from a study that the devices were so unreliable that they represented the single biggest maintenance problem of the customer. A third type of problem is a disagreeable chore imposed on the user. An example is the disposal of garbage created by the product. The early instant cameras made use of a peel-back film that required the user to peel off a surface from the photo and then dispose of it. In a later model of the camera, the peel-back feature was eliminated.

TABLE 12.10   Multiattribute Study

Attribute	Relative importance, %	Company X		Competitor A		Competitor B	
		Rating	Weighted rating	Rating	Weighted rating	Rating	Weighted rating
Safety	28	6	168	5	140	4.5	126
Performance	20	6	120	7	140	6.5	130
Quality	20	6	120	7	140	4	80
Field service	12	4	48	8	96	5	60
Ease of use	8	4	32	6	48	5	40
Company image	8	8	64	4	32	4	32
Plant service	4	7.5	30	7.5	30	5	20
Total			582		626		488

Source: Private communication.

12.21

3. Problems Not Reported by the User. Sometimes the user reports being perfectly happy with a product when in reality a problem exists. As part of a field intelligence network for a television manufacturer, company executives visited the homes of consumers. Although the consumers were satisfied with the picture, the executives realized that the picture was not as good as what had been engineered in the laboratory. The problem was a lack of fine adjustment by the owners. The company had been working on an improved tuning system, but the intelligence led to establishing a high priority for developing single-button tuning. It was on the market within a few months. (See Reavey, 1973.)

4. Remedial Steps Already Taken by the User (or Contemplated by the User) to Improve the Product. This source of ideas for product changes even includes some built-in field testing.

5. Needs for Which the User Sees No Present Solution. These needs represent an opportunity for the product development function to create a new design that would be unique in the marketplace.

Visits to the customer sites need not require a large amount of resources; a sample of customers is sufficient. However, before the visits are made, a plan must spell out the questions to be answered and the procedures to be followed to collect the information. One company has a built-in mechanism for continuously obtaining knowledge on conditions of use, problems of the user, and any special steps taken by the user. This company manufactures tools for automobile mechanics and has its marketing function literally in a truck. As sales are made at the customer site, the salesperson observes the conditions of use and learns about any customer dissatisfaction.

Quantify the User's View of the Product. This includes:

1. Information on the costs to the user of operating and maintaining the product throughout its life. Data of this nature become targets for the product development function to beat through future product designs.
2. Information on the amount of employee training required to operate the product. To the extent that future designs can reduce the training, the design will be superior.
3. Information on the amount of technical service required to support the product. An example includes the amount of diagnosis and maintenance work required to repair product failures.

An electronics company now has a product that can be linked by telephone from the user's site to diagnostic equipment at the factory. For certain types of products, such self-diagnosis can solve 90 percent of the service problems. Another example involves the setup of equipment. Traditionally, some computers and terminals have been considered too complex to be set up by the user. However, the advent of self-testing diagnostic capabilities now provides an opportunity to design new products that can be set up and installed by the user (see Richardson, 1981).

The study of the user's operation can be aided by dissecting the process of use. This is done by documenting all of the steps, analyzing them, and identifying opportunities for new-product development. Such information is valuable input to the product development function as that group embarks on a new design project. Section 13 under Planning for Basic Functional Requirements shows an example using a functional flow diagram and a requirements allocation sheet. In another application, a certain clamp controlled the amount of flow of fluid from an external source to a patient during a dialysis process. An analysis showed that the proposed clamp was excellent in controlling the flow of fluid, but it was inconvenient in a later step that required the patient to wear the product under clothing. The original focus was on performance of the product, but the block diagram pinpointed a later problem of inconvenience to the patient.

The opportunities for improvement span the full range of customer use from initial receipt through operation. The primary stages and examples of ideas for improving fitness for use are given in Table 12.11.

TABLE 12.11   Opportunities for Improving Fitness for Use of an Industrial Product

Stage	Opportunities
Receiving inspection	Provide data so incoming inspection can be eliminated
Material storage	Design product and packaging for ease of identification and handling
Processing	Do preprocessing of material (e.g., ready mixed concrete); design product to maximize productivity when it is used in customer's manufacturing operation
Finished goods storage warehouse and field	Design product and packaging for ease of identification and handling
Installation, alignment, and checkout	Use modular concepts and other means to facilitate setups by customer rather than manufacturer
Maintenance, preventive	Incorporate preventive maintenance in product (e.g., self-lubricated bearings)
Maintenance, corrective	Design product to permit self-diagnosis by user

Analyze the Total System of Use of the Product.   To a degree, fitness for use can be improved by refining the steps in the current use of the product. However, the most spectacular historical benefits have come not from such refinements but rather from discarding the existing progression entirely in favor of some new concept of serving the user. The term "systems approach" is here used to designate any approach which tries to improve fitness for use by restudying the entire progression rather than by accepting the present progression and refining the elements within it.

There have been a number of examples of the systems approach that enable us to identify some distinct categories:

Transfer of decentralized processing to a central process facility (e.g., frozen food, instant photography)

Modular concepts (e.g., prefabricated housing modules)

Elimination of user maintenance (e.g., self-lubricated bearings, aluminum exteriors)

New centralized service (e.g., centrally generated gas for heating, a central computer center into which various terminals feed)

Extending the shelf life of a product—e.g., by making a basic change in the manufacturing process, the shelf life of a brand of potato chips was increased from 2 months to 1 year (Vanderwicken, 1974)

Making a product compatible with other products (e.g., linking of products to a computer)

A listing of the main steps in the progression of an industrial product and examples of potential areas of improvement are shown in Table 12.11. The benefits to the user may take the form of:

Eliminating some of the users' work entirely

Transferring work from the user to some other stage in the progression of events at which it can be done more easily

Improving the effectiveness of such work as still remains

Strategic Planning for Quality. Companywide strategic planning focuses on the opportunities and threats that lie in the future and the subsequent decision making that defines organizational aims, policies, and plans. An important element of strategic planning is to differentiate the product in a way that will result in a competitive advantage. One strategy is to differentiate on the basis of cost; another strategy is to differentiate on the basis of quality. A discussion of the many issues involved is provided in the section on Quality and Sales Income. For a discussion of the key questions involved in strategic planning, see South, 1981. An example of strategic planning using quality as part of the strategy is given in Utzig, 1980.

REFERENCES

"Beckman Gets Customers to Design its Product." (1974). *Business Week,* Aug. 17, p. 54.

Calder, Bobby J. (1977). "Focus Groups and the Nature of Qualitative Marketing Research." *Journal of Marketing Research,* August, pp. 353–364.

Goble, J., Gruska, G. S., and Bajaria, H. (1981). "Perceived Quality." *ASQC Quality Congress Transactions,* Milwaukee, pp. 639–645.

Gross, Irwin (1978). "Insights for Pricing Research." In Bailey, E. L. (ed.), *Pricing Practices and Strategies.* The Conference Board, New York, pp. 34–39.

Gryna, Frank M., Jr. (1983). "Marketing Research and Product Quality." *ASQC Quality Transactions,* Milwaukee, 385–392.

Gryna, Frank M., Jr. (1970). *User Costs of Poor Product Quality.* Doctoral dissertation, University of Iowa, Iowa City.

Kukla, Robin (1981). "How Do We Rate in the Market Place?" *Quality Progress,* May, pp. 18–20.

Pipp, Frank J. (1983). "Management Commitment to Quality: Xerox Corp." *Quality Progress,* August, pp. 12–17.

Reavey, Edward P., Jr. (1973). "Motorola Executives Call on Consumers in Their Homes." *Harvard Business Review,* November–December, pp. 6–7.

Richardson, Hugh (1981). "Designing for Customer Set-up." *Quality,* October, pp. 62–65.

South, Stephen E. (1981). "Competitive Advantage: The Cornerstone of Strategic Thinking." *The Journal of Business Strategy,* Spring, pp. 15–25.

Utzig, Lawrence (1981). "Customer Based Measurements Close the Loop." *ASQC Technical Conference Transactions,* Milwaukee, pp. 673–683.

Utzig, Lawrence (1980). "Quality Reputation—A Precious Asset." *ASQC Technical Conference Transactions,* Milwaukee, pp. 145–154.

Vanderwicken, Peter (1974). "P & G's Secret Ingredient." *Fortune,* pp. 76–77.

SECTION 13

PRODUCT DEVELOPMENT [1]

Frank M. Gryna

---

[1] In the Third Edition, this section was prepared by H. D. Voegtlen.

INTRODUCTION

This step on the Spiral of quality activities concerns the process of translating the needs of the user, learned from field intelligence, into a set of product design requirements for manufacturing. The activity is often called product development, research and development, engineering, or design.

In this handbook, the business aspects of launching new products are discussed in Section 3, Quality and Income, and Section 19, Marketing. The broad planning approach for quality is discussed in Section 6, Companywide Planning for Quality. Section 12, Field Intelligence, discusses the collection of information needed as inputs to initiate the product development process. The present section concentrates on the managerial and technological steps needed during product development to assure that the user needs are reflected in the product design.

Importance of Product Development.   There is increasing evidence that many fitness-for-use problems can be traced to the design of the product.

In a classic study of 850 field failures of relatively simple electronic equipment, 43 percent of the failures were due to engineering design (Juran and Gryna, 1980).

In a study of seven space programs, 35.2 percent of component failures were due to design or specification error (Juran and Gryna, 1970).

During a typical period of 11 months at a chemical plant, 42 percent of the rework dollars were traced to research and development (consulting experience of the author).

In a study of "quality calamities" by the British Institute of Management, 36 percent were due to lack of proving new designs, materials, or processes and 16 percent were due to lack of or wrong specifications (Belbin, 1970).

In one chemical company, a startling 50 percent of the product shipped was out of specification. Fortunately the product was fit for use. A review concluded that many of the specifications were obsolete and had to be changed (consulting experience of the author).

For mechanical and electronics products of at least moderate complexity, it is the author's opinion that errors during product development cause about 40 percent of the fitness-for-use problems. Where Product Development is responsible for both creating the formulation (design) of the product and also responsible for developing the manufacturing process, as in chemicals, about 50 percent of the problems are due to development.

The amount of activity within product development to correct deficiencies in products can be surprisingly high. In one typical year, an electronics organization determined that the cost of design changes was about 67 percent of the operating profit. Some of these changes were initiated by the customer but over 80 percent of the changes were related to design deficiencies.

Traditional and Modern Products.   Times have changed, products have changed. A comparison of traditional and modern products is shown in Table 13.1. The traditional product is shoes, a garden tool, bread, or an aspirin. The modern product is a printed circuit board, an electronic computer, or a nuclear reactor. In practice, products are on a continuous spectrum from traditional to modern. Some products move on that spectrum. For example, the earliest automobiles and telephones were traditional in simplicity but now are modern in complexity; the advent of microwave cooking has changed the stove industry from traditional to modern; requirements on lead-free chemicals have changed some chemical companies from traditional to modern. The change from traditional to modern products is often gradual and can mask the need for new approaches in product development.

Two processes are needed for launching new products: (1) the traditional process for traditional products and (2) a revolutionary process for modern products. Traditional methods are not adequate to launch modern products. They were tried and they failed. As a corollary, the fact that revolutionary ways are available does not mean that they should be used for traditional products as well. For many traditional products the traditional ways are adequate and the use of modern ways is uneconomic.

All products, traditional and modern, have two types of requirements: "functional performance" requirements and other, fitness-for-use requirements such as

TABLE 13.1 Traditional versus Modern Products

Aspects of products	Traditional	Modern
Simplicity	Simple, static	Complex, dynamic
Precision	Low	High
Need for interchangeability	Limited	Extensive
Consumables or durables	Mainly consumables	Mainly durables
Environment in which used	Natural	Unnatural
User understanding of product	High	Low
Importance to human health, safety and continuity of life	Seldom important	Often important
Life cycle cost to user	Similar to purchase price	Much greater than purchase price
Life of a new design	Long; decades and even centuries	Short; less than a decade
Scientific basis of design	Largely empirical	Largely scientific
Basis of reliability, maintainability, etc.	Vague: "best effort"	Quantified
Volume of production	Usually low	Often high
Usual cause of field failures	Manufacturing errors	Design weaknesses

reliability, maintainability, and safety. For traditional products, the design work done to achieve the performance requirements is usually sufficient to meet the other parameters. Modern products have more exacting needs that require additional managerial methods and technological tools.

BASIC CONCEPTS

Cost-Effectiveness Concept. For modern products, attainment of fitness for use involves a balance among competing parameters and costs. The aggregation of these parameters and costs, from the inception of the design to the end of the operational life is called the cost-effectiveness concept (Figure 13.1). Zaludova (1981) discusses a similar model and gives examples of individual characteristics of the effectiveness features. Many of the technical and economical parameters in the model are discussed in this section of the handbook.

The Phase Concept of Product Development. The broad concept of cradle-to-grave quality planning is discussed in Section 6, Companywide Planning for Quality. The reader is urged to study this broad planning in conjunction with the present topic.

A major segment of the cradle-to-grave quality planning is "product development." This segment logically breaks down into a number of recognized phases.

1. *Concept and feasibility phase:* In this phase the known or anticipated need for a product is studied in enough detail to determine if it is feasible to design and

FIG. 13.1 Cost-effectiveness.

manufacture a product responsive to the need. An important element of this feasibility is the expected cost to the company and to the customer. This phase culminates in a conclusion that it is feasible (or not feasible) to continue with the project. This conclusion recommends one or more design concepts that appear to be promising to explore in the future.

2. *Detailed design phase:* In this phase, the alternative design concepts are evaluated, the most promising one is selected, and the product is designed in sufficient detail to prepare purchasing specifications for parts and materials and to plan the manufacture of products for prototype testing. For complex products, the detailed design phase may consist of two major subphases: (1) a more detailed exploration of several design concepts uncovered in the feasibility stage (these explorations may be conducted simultaneously or sequentially), and (2) selection of a final design concept followed by a full, detailed design.

There is always the possibility that during or after the detailed design phase, the design concept selected may prove to be poor and may have to be discarded. The cycle then starts all over. (The detailed design phase may also include major work in new-component development and may go beyond and include fabrication of hardware to evaluate the design proposed on paper.)

3. *Prototype phase:* In this phase, the first essentially complete units of the product are built and tested. The tests may evaluate such factors as basic design capability, effects of extreme environments, and reliability for extended periods of operation. The units built may not be complete, but are complete enough to test the adequacy of the basic design approach. The prototype tests should indicate that the initial design approach can be adopted and completed in detail. If not, "back to the drawing board."

Ideally, prototype units are built using the manufacturing procedures and equipment planned for full-scale production, but this is sometimes not possible. In such cases, the test results may not be completely representative of what the production units will do. However, the prototype phase is a valuable means for the designer to evaluate the adequacy of his or her design approach ("technical feasibility") and to revise the design prior to setting up manufacturing procedures.

In this phase, some companies sell the product on a limited basis (a "test market") to measure potential sales performance and identify weaknesses in the product or in the marketing plan. (See Section 19 under Role of the Marketing Department During the Launching of New Products.)

4. *Preproduction demonstration:* In this phase a "production design" is prepared and is evaluated for producibility and performance.

The production design differs from the prototype design, due to design changes made for a variety of reasons: to simplify manufacturing processes, cut the cost of materials, standardize for greater interchangeability with existing products, utilize present production facilities, etc.

Next, a preproduction lot of product is made according to the production design, using the production equipment. (See Section 16 under Preproduction Trials and Preproduction Runs.) This "pilot run" is then tested, sometimes under simulated-use environments (proving grounds) and sometimes by selected customers under conditions of actual use.

Based on the results of the tests and the experience of manufacture, the design is either released for full-scale production or sent back to be reworked.

5. *Full-scale production:* This is the regular production for sale and delivery to customers.

6. *Design changes:* Based on experience gained in production, marketing, and use of the product, design changes are made to improve product performance and to eliminate field failures which showed up under the conditions of use. These design changes go through one or more of the previous phases of the life cycle.

7. *Customer use:* This is the entire period of product useful life, including the warranty interval (if provided) and all service and repair until the product is discarded, traded in, or replaced.

There are other methods of dividing the cradle-to-grave progression into logical phases. For example, some practitioners divide the prototype phase into three subphases, i.e., prototype design, prototype construction, and prototype testing. There is no single method which fits all companies or even all projects within a single company. Renna and Howard (1979) discuss the phases of a development cycle for a television camera and identify some of the quality-related tasks that are needed.

The need for careful evolution of a new product is not restricted to products having complex hardware. The evolution of a new antiperspirant is an example (*Wall Street Journal,* 1978). It started with a formal market research study that established the need for a new product, one that "did not go on wet and make you wait to get dressed." First, a volatile silicone was used as a substitute for water, but the silicone dissolved part of the applicator. The next model corrected the problem but was "too oily." The next model looked promising until it became a rock-hard gel that could not be removed from the package. The next model had several problems: (1) The product leaked out of most containers, (2) the new dispenser was too confusing, and (3) users felt the product was too dry on application and, therefore, they were not sure that the product was working properly. After other futile attempts to develop a new applicator (including one with a clicking noise to assure users that it was working), a conventional applicator was chosen and the new product was released for production. The cost of this development was $18 million over a 2-year period—and the product was a simple one with just a few moving parts. Hammel (1974) describes the development effort for a new line of dolls. This involved 5 years of research, much trial and error, and world-wide searches for sources of materials, manufacture, and skilled labor.

Early Warning Concept and Design Assurance. The frequency and severity of problems caused by design has stimulated companies to develop more and better forms of early warning on impending troubles. These early warnings are available in a variety of forms (Table 13.2). All companies make use of some combination of these alternatives, the specific choice being tailored to the unique conditions present in the company. In addition, much has been done to evolve special quality-oriented tools to help evaluate the designs and to improve the design process itself. Collectively these early warnings and quality-oriented tools provide added assurance that the new designs will not create undo trouble as they progress around the Spiral. Many of these forms of early warning are administered by reliability, maintainability, and other specialists. The timing of their inputs is critical. Early timing can provide constructive help; late timing causes resistance to the early warnings and often creates an atmosphere of blame.

The forms of early warning can be enhanced by other steps taken to improve the overall effectiveness of the product development function (see later in this section under Improving the Effectiveness of Product Development).

Design Review. During the development cycle, the product undergoes several reviews. One form is a business review in which the results to date of the development effort are summarized and a decision is made whether or not to proceed further. Another type of review is technical in nature and is usually called design review.

Design review is a technique for evaluating a proposed design to assure that the design (1) will perform successfully during use, (2) can be manufactured at low cost, and (3) is suitable for prompt, low-cost field maintenance. Design review is not new. For traditional products the design review is carried out by the head of the enterprise, by the head of the technical department, by a new-products com-

TABLE 13.2 Forms of Early Warning of New-Product Problems

Phases of new-product progression	Forms of early warning of new-product troubles
Concept and feasibility study	Concept review
Prototype design	Design review, reliability and maintainability prediction, failure mode, effect, and criticality analysis, safety analyses, value engineering
Prototype construction	Prototype test, environmental test, overstressing
Preproduction	Pilot production lots, evaluation of tolerances
Early full-scale production	In-house testing (e.g., kitchen, road), consumer use panels, limited marketing area
Full-scale production, marketing, and use	Employees as test panels, special provisions for prompt feedback
All phases	Failure analysis, data collection and analysis

mittee, or by manufacturing planning specialists. For these products, an informal review is sufficient.

Modern products require a more structured program. The characteristics of a program include:

1. Design reviews are made mandatory, either through customer demand or through upper-management policy declaration.

2. The design reviews are conducted by a team of specialists who are not directly associated with the development of the design. These specialists must be highly experienced and bring with them the reputation of objectivity. Table 13.3 (derived from Jacobs, 1967) shows the possible membership and responsibilities of a design review team for three phases of design review. Special members could include an industrial designer, a representative from a university, or the technical press.

3. The ultimate decision on inputs from the design review rests with the designer. The designer must listen to the inputs, but on matters of structural integrity and other creative aspects of the design, the designer retains the monopoly on decisions. The control and publication of the specification remains with the designer.

4. Design reviews are formal. They are planned and scheduled like any other legitimized activity. The meetings are built around prepared agendas and documentation sent out in advance. Minutes of meetings are prepared and circulated. Follow-ups for action are likewise formalized.

5. The parameters can include reliability, performance, maintainability, producibility, testability, interchangeability, installation, safety, ergonomics, appearance, and cost and value. Other special parameters can also be included when needed for a particular product. Alternatively, design review can be restricted to just several of the parameters cited.

6. As much as possible, design reviews are made to defined criteria. Such criteria may include customer requirements, industry standards, government regulations, and checklists based on experience with previous products. The computer can help in the capture, recording, and retrieval of previous experience. (For an example, see Section 27 under New Product Quality Design Review.)

7. Design reviews are conducted at several phases of the progression of the design, such as design concept, prototype design and test, and final design. Reviews are made at several levels of the product hierarchy, such as system and subsystem.

The adoption of the design review concept takes place in several ways. These include: by mandate from upper management in response to an undue extent of field troubles traceable to inadequacies in designs; through pressure from outsiders (e.g., clients, regulators, or insurance companies, who want assurances with respect to public safety or health); and through internal evolution (designers gradually become aware that useful inputs can be obtained from specialists such as reliability and maintainability engineers). Acceptance of the concept is best gained by having a successful case example of design review within the company. A design review that identifies potential problems and results in design changes carries more weight than a discussion of the logic of design review. Another approach is to try out a retrospective design review, on several previous designs. For each design, a list of problems that required design changes is prepared. This list is evaluated and the question asked: "Suppose we had a design review, would the review have detected this problem?" If many of the problems are detected,

TABLE 13.3   Design Review Team Membership and Responsibility

Group member	Responsibilities	Type of design review* PDR	IDR	FDR
Chairperson	Calls, conducts meetings of Group, and issues interim and final reports	X	X	X
Design Engineer(s) (of product)	Prepares and presents design and substantiates decisions with data from tests or calculations	X	X	X
Reliability Manager or Engineer	Evaluates design for optimum reliability consistent with goals	X	X	X
Quality Manager or Engineer	Ensures that the functions of inspection, control, and test can be efficiently carried out		X	X
Manufacturing Engineer	Ensures that the design is producible at minimum cost and schedule		X	X
Field Engineer	Ensures that installation, maintenance, and user considerations were included in the design		X	X
Procurement Representative	Assures that acceptable parts and materials are available to meet cost and delivery schedules		X	
Materials Engineer	Ensures that materials selected will perform as required		X	
Tooling Engineer	Evaluates design in terms of the tooling costs required to satisfy tolerance and functional requirements		X	
Packaging and Shipping Engineer	Assures that the product is capable of being handled without damage, etc.		X	X
Marketing Representative	Assures that requirements of customers are realistic and fully understood by all parties	X		
Design Engineers (not associated with unit under review)	Constructively reviews adequacy of design to meet all requirements of customer	X	X	X
Consultants, Specialists on components, value, human factors, etc., (as required)	Evaluates design for compliance with goals of performance, cost, and schedule	X	X	X
Customer Representative (optional)	Generally voices opinion as to acceptability of design and may request further investigation on specific items			X

*P = Preliminary; I = Intermediate; F = Final.
Source: Jacobs, 1967.

this suggests that design review should be tried on future designs. This approach can enlist the support of personnel from manufacturing, field service, marketing, and other areas.

The track record on formal design review is mixed. Many companies have tried design review, but only a minority report success. Sometimes the remark is heard that "a designer who is a good salesperson can often sell a poor design during the design review process." The ingredients for a successful design review include:

1. *An emphasis on constructive input to designers, rather than criticism:* A universal obstacle to design review has been the cultural resistance of the design department. It has been common practice for this department to hold a virtual monopoly on design decisions; i.e., these decisions have historically been immune from challenge unless actual product trouble was being encountered. With such a background, it was not surprising that the designers have resisted the use of design reviews to challenge their designs. Some people believe that the designer's resistance to design review borders on arrogance. However, a review is interpreted by the designer as a criticism of the design work. Designers, like other human beings, are sensitive to criticism—particularly if it is presented to management. One approach that has been tried is the concept of a "peer walk-through." These are a series of meetings in which technical specialists provide input to the designers without any management people being present. This identifies potential problems and allows time for design changes before the formal design review is held.

2. *Avoiding any competition at the technological level that results in the designer feeling that there are others competing for the role of designing the product:* The resistance to design review is aggravated when reliability engineers propose competing designs. The designers resist the idea of competitors even more than they resist the idea of design review.

3. *Realistic schedules:* If the review is held close to the time of design release, there will not be sufficient time to investigate a potential weakness and change the design. The reaction then is: "Why didn't you tell us this sooner?" This can be minimized by scheduling several stages of design review (e.g., preliminary, intermediate, and final design reviews).

4. *Sufficient resources:* The team membership must provide the knowledge needed to cover the many parameters of fitness for use. (Of course, to facilitate discussions the number of members should be kept to a minimum.) Members must have enough time to prepare for and follow up on meetings. In addition, they must have a high level of competence and credibility. Such people are in great demand and it is easier to assign others who do not have sufficient knowledge and experience. The result may be marginal inputs to the design review— and rejection by the designers.

5. *Adequate planning for design review meetings:* The responsibilities of team members should be made clear (Table 13.3). Also, prior to meetings, documentation should be collected and sent out to the design review members for study. Such material includes specifications and design review checklists. Lawlor (1978) provides examples of checklists for several product development stages. Either before or during the design review meetings, other analyses can be presented including failure mode effect, and criticality analysis, reliability predictions, and results of reliability tests.

6. *Focusing on the unproven and untried features of a design.*

7. *Sufficient structure in the design review process:* This assures that design weaknesses are identified, documented, and provision for follow-up and resolution is made. Generally the chairperson of the design review team is someone from the line design function that was responsible for creating the design, e.g., the project engineer. This helps to promote implementation of inputs from the design reviews. (In other organizations, the project manager chairs the reviews.) Much of the success, however, of design review depends on the planning for review meetings and on the follow-up after the meetings—a role for the quality and reliability specialist. Some companies have found it useful to conduct a training course in design review.

8. *A realization that the design review may uncover some interdepartmental conflicts:* Means should be available to resolve these conflicts.

9. *Management directive:* Management must formalize the design-review process to make it clear to all concerned that resources, time, and priorities must reflect the importance of the activity.

Burgess (1985) identifies some common problems encountered in design review and explains how these can be overcome.

POLICY ISSUES

There are basic issues in product development that deserve deliberation and decision making by management. Where such issues are not explicitly faced, policies are developed by default at lower levels of the organization. These policy issues go beyond technology; they can involve legal, financial, and marketing matters as well. Such matters are normally beyond the designer's training and experience.

Level of Quality of Design. Several alternative quality strategies exist for new-product development—quality superior to competition, quality equal to the average of competition, and quality at a minimal acceptable level so that cost and other parameters can receive higher priority. Many organizations have evolved an unwritten policy from past experience. In other organizations, however, product development personnel receive little guidance from either past experience or a policy from management.

Carryover of Failure-Prone Designs. New models of a product often use design features of previous models. If such design features are failure-prone, these weaknesses are carried over into the new model. Such a condition can be revealed by summarizing past history in a matrix. The columns of the matrix are product models listed in chronological order; the rows of the matrix are the failure-prone features. Of course, the solution to the design weakness may be unknown, or known but not economically feasible. The problem of carryover is intensified by pressures for new models, along with a preference by designers to work on new models rather than to correct deficiencies on old models. The policy issue is the relative priority of correcting carryover weaknesses versus developing new features. Concentrating on new features runs the risk that competition will develop a product free of the carryover weaknesses and thereby have a competitive advantage.

Design for Intended Use versus Design for Actual Use. Actual use of a product can differ from what the designer regards as the intended use. The difference can be due to variations in environment and other conditions of use. In addition, some users will misapply or misuse the product (in liability cases, juries and judges have been notoriously unsympathetic to defense contentions that the products have been misused). The policy question is: Should the design be based on how the product is intended to be used, or based on how the product will actually be used (and misused)? In most companies this question has never been placed before upper management for decision. Hence, by default, designers make the decision.

Design for High Reliability and Design for Maintainability. For complex products, reliability and maintainability are important parameters of fitness for use. The policy issue is: What should be the relative priorities of reliability and maintainability? Evaluation of this issue requires consideration of the effect on costs (both to the manufacturer and the user), trade-off analyses for uptime, and the relative importance of reliability and maintainability as perceived by customers. Helland (1978) reports two examples involving office reproduction equipment.

Quantification of Reliability and Other Parameters. Traditionally, performance parameters (power generated, pH temperature rise, parts per million of impurities) have been quantified during design; other fitness-for-use parameters (reliability and maintainability) have not been quantified in many companies. Designers understand that reliability and maintainability are important, but without quantification, these parameters do not receive the same degree of formal evaluation as performance parameters. The policy issue is whether reliability, maintainability, and similar parameters should be quantified. Quantification means establishing numerical requirements, evaluating the design before release to see if those requirements have been met, and measuring field performance. Staff specialists can recommend quantification, but it will not be effective without management affirmation. In one organization with such specialists, management made the decision to quantify—but only after a serious failure of a new model due to poor reliability.

The Learning Curve as Inevitable. The process of developing a new product design often consists of many trials before the "learning curve" results in an acceptable design. In manufacturing operations, a large amount of rework on product is viewed as a deficiency, and attempts are made to identify the causes and take action. In product development, however, there often is not that same sense of urgency because the learning curve is accepted as inevitable. The policy issue is whether to let learning take place fortuitously, or to take the initiative— to formally study product development as a process and learn from the past in order to improve the process for the future. See Section 6 under Lessons Learned and Section 22 under Diagnosis—General.

Jurisdiction in Product Specifications. Usually, product specifications are issued and any changes are made by the product development function. Many specification characteristics affect fitness for use, but there are other characteristics that do not—they only provide internal manufacturing information. The policy question is whether the production function should be allowed to set and change specifications on those characteristics that do not affect fitness for use. More realistic specifications could be the result.

Requirement of a Formal Product Development Process. The simplicity of traditional products permits product development to be done with a modest amount of effort. The complexity of modern products and the consequences of releasing deficient designs can mean that product development must be structured with phases (see above under The Phase Concept of Product Development) to assure that the designs released are adequate. The establishment of a formal product development process is a policy decision for management.

Release of Design Prior to Production Capability Verification. History is replete with designs that were released and then caused many problems during manufacturing. For example, the specifications on a chemical product are based on a few laboratory results, minimal input on customer needs, and no information on process variability. Such a situation breeds future problems and costly changes. The policy issue is whether the capability to manufacture should be formally verified before the design is released.

Breaking the Monopoly of Designers. The ultimate responsibility for the design of a product rests with the product development function. With modern products, it is virtually impossible for individual designers to possess all the knowledge needed on all of the attributes of fitness for use. Thus it becomes necessary that the designer's knowledge be supplemented with the knowledge of specialists in other areas such as reliability, maintainability, and producibility. What is needed is a policy decision on whether an independent evaluation of the design will be performed before the design is relased for full production.

Examination of these and other policy issues can be a part of an audit of product development by upper managers. See Section 8 under Quality Audit by Upper Managers.

PLANNING FOR BASIC FUNCTIONAL REQUIREMENTS

Examples of basic functional requirements are weight, power consumption, and speed. The achievement of these requirements, the heart of the product development task, rests on a foundation of technological disciplines such as chemistry, electrical engineering, and mechanical engineering. Product development efforts to achieve the functional requirements are related to fitness for use:

1. Fitness for use includes the functional requirements. Unless these are provided at some adequate level, there is no product to market.
2. Designing for functional capability can result in high complexity. High complexity, in turn, is a breeding ground for problems in reliability and maintainability—important parameters of fitness for use. Trade-offs may need to be evaluated between additional functional capability and the effects on other fitness-for-use parameters.

Product development translates customer expectations on functional requirements into specific engineering and quality characteristics. For traditional products, this process is not complicated and can be achieved by experienced design engineers without using any special techniques. For modern products, it is useful to document and analyze the design logic. This means starting with the desired product attributes and then identifying the necessary characteristics for raw materials, parts, assemblies, and process steps. Such an approach goes under a variety of names such as systems engineering, functional analysis systems, technique, structured product/process analysis, and product quality deployment.

One example of this approach is shown in Figure 13.2 [Kogure and Akao (1983)]. This figure shows a matrix of customer requirements ("required quality")

REQUIRED QUALITY									
STAGE	No.	Primary	No.	Secondary	No.	Tertiary	Importance	Thickness	Weight
STAGE OF SEWING	1	Easy to sew	11	Easy to stitch and cut	111	Light	C		O
					112	Does not stick	B		
			12		121	Easy to work on sewing machine	B		
					122	Surface coating does not fall off	B		
			13	Can use adhesives	131	Withstands organic solvent	C		
STAGE OF USAGE	2	Protect passengers	21	Does not let rain seep	211	No hole, no tear	A		
			22	No change in atmospheric pressure in tunnel	221	Airtight (no pinhole)	A		
			23	Does not tear under pressure	231	No tear under air pressure	A		
					232	No tear from poking from inside	A		
					233	No tear from shocks of starting or stopping	A		

FIG. 13.2 Matrix of required quality and counterpart characteristics.

COUNTERPART CHARACTERISTICS				
Tensile strength	Tear strength	Extension ratio	Anticrumple strength	Water pressure resistance
				•
•	•		•	
•	•	•		
•	•	•		

and product quality characteristics ("counterpart characteristics") developed for the hood that connects railroad cars of a train. The left-hand side of the matrix shows customer requirements in terms of primary, secondary, and tertiary needs, along with importance ratings of A, B, or C; the right-hand side of the matrix shows the technological characteristics that are needed to achieve the requirements. Thus the design value of tensile strength can be determined by considering requirements 231, 232, and 233. Traditionally the strength would have been determined by a design engineer based on prior experience. This matrix approach provides a more methodical way of converting customer needs into product characteristics. When this is done for all customer needs, specific responsibilities can then be assigned for the various characteristics ("deployment of the quality function").

Vinson and Heany (1977) describe the development process for a new fluorescent lamp starting with customer expectations and proceeding through design logic and the creation of product and process characteristics.

Baxter Healthcare Corporation, a manufacturer in the health care field, uses the following approach:

1. Prepare a functional flow block diagram to show the normal flow of manufacturing and use for the product. Figure 13.3 contains a partial reproduction of a functional flow diagram.

2. Assign requirements to each block of the diagram (an example of this for one subfunction is shown in Figure 13.3). Each design requirement is allocated to one or more components.

3. Sort the requirements by component and prepare a separate requirements document for each component.

4. Add nonfunctional requirements such as quality verification methods to each component specification.

5. Generate the basic product system specification capturing system requirements and references to the component specifications.

The company cites the following benefits:

1. It provides a disciplined approach to defining requirements—particularly helpful to less experienced design project leaders.

2. Analyses made can be used during the development of new products using the same or similar components. This saves much labor and paperwork. In addition, the approach provides a methodical way to establish test methods to assure verification of requirements.

3. The approach starts with customer expectations and emphasizes customer use of the product.

4. The potential for interface problems between design groups is reduced by the analysis and documentation.

5. A means is provided to communicate and manage mandatory versus desirable marketing issues.

6. The approach provides a trail to allow a designer to determine what other components may be affected by a design change.

7. From the analysis, the specification is able to define not just functional requirements but all other requirements of fitness for use.

In planning for a new product model, an automotive manufacturer identified

FIG. 13.3 Requirements allocation sheet.

over 400 characteristics of fitness for use (see Veraldi, 1985). For each character-istic, (1) marketing research was conducted to learn the current status relative to competition and (2) targets were set, also relative to competition, for the new model. Product development then proceeded.

Sullivan (1986) describes a system of quality function deployment that trans-lates customer requirements into technical requirements for each stage of product development and production. See also Section 6 under the Quality Planning Roadmap.

PLANNING FOR TIME-ORIENTED PERFORMANCE (RELIABILITY)

From time immemorial engineers recognized that a product should have a long service life and that during this life it should give service with few failures. As products became more complex, there were increasing problems with failures over time. Traditional efforts of design, although necessary, were not sufficient to achieve both the functional performance requirements and a low rate of failures with time. What has evolved is a collection of tools called "reliability engineering." Some of the tools are old, some are new.

Definition of Reliability.   Reliability is the probability that an item will perform a required function under stated conditions for a stated period of time.

This definition has four key elements:

1. *The quantification of reliability in terms of a probability.*

2. *A statement defining the required product performance:*   As the function is defined in detail, it becomes more clear which product failures impair the success of the mission and which do not.

3. *A statement of the required operating time between failures:*   (Otherwise, the probability is a meaningless number for time-oriented products.)

4. *A statement defining the environmental conditions in which the equipment must operate:*   Numerous product failures are traceable to a lack of meeting of the minds on what the real environments are to be; e.g., the designer designed the product to operate at 180°C, but in some applications the temperatures rise to 200°C. One of the contributions of the reliability "movement" has been to force all parties to dig deeper in order to discover what the real environment will be.

To achieve a required level of reliability, certain tasks are necessary. The collection of tasks is called the reliability program.

Reliability Program.   An example of the typical tasks in a reliability program for a complex product is given in Table 13.4 [from MIL-STD-785B (1980)]. The Standard explains the degree of applicability by program phase (concept, demonstration and validation, full-scale engineering development, and production). Many of the tasks listed are discussed in this section. (Appendix III, Selected

TABLE 13.4   Reliability Tasks

Reliability program plan
Monitor/control of subcontractors and suppliers
Program reviews
Failure reporting, analysis, and corrective action system (FRACAS)
Failure review board (FRB)
Reliability modeling
Reliability allocations
Reliability predictions
Failure mode, effect, and criticality analysis (FMECA)
Sneak circuit analysis (SCA)
Electronic parts/circuits tolerance analysis
Parts program
Reliability critical items
Effects of functional testing, storage, handling, packaging, transportation, and maintenance
Environmental stress screening (ESS)
Reliability qualification test (RQT) program
Production reliability acceptance test (PRAT) program

Source: MIL-STD-785B, 1980.

Quality Standards, Specifications, and Related Documents, includes reliability documentation.)

The tasks in the reliability program span many company functions. A program requires positive, formal planning if the deeds are to be done and done on time. Moreover, since many departments and individuals are involved, it is useful to have a written list of the tasks to be performed, who is to do them, the timetable, procedures for performing the tasks, and procedure for evaluating the status and control of each task. Often such a written definition is missing. Someone should "make the rounds" of all company functions and help get agreement on tasks and responsibilities. This definition helps to clarify "who is responsible for doing what" and to assure that adequate resources are available.

Before embarking on a discussion of reliability tasks, a remark on the application of the tasks is in order:

1. Many of these tasks are clearly not warranted for simple products. However, products that were originally simple are now becoming more complex. When this is the case, the various reliability tasks should be examined to see which, if any, might be justified to use.

2. These techniques apply both to products that the company markets and to complex manufacturing equipment that a company purchases, e.g., numerically controlled machines in the metalworking industries and processing equipment in the chemical industries.

Quantification of Reliability. A major new tool is the quantification of reliability. The process of reliability quantification involves four phases:

Establishment of reliability requirements or objectives: The process of determining the overall reliability that is needed for the product

Apportionment (or budgeting): The process of allocating the overall reliability objective to the elements which collectively make up the total product

Prediction: The estimation of overall reliability based on prior reliability data of components

Analysis: Identification of the strong and weak portions of the design to serve as a basis for improvements, trade-offs, and similar actions

Fundamental to the quantification process are some statistical concepts that are described in Section 23 under Reliability. The reader is urged to study that discussion to more fully understand the quantification process.

Establishing the Requirements. The definition of reliability as a probability of performing a function for a specified time interval provides one way of stating a reliability requirement. In practice, a reliability requirement is usually stated in simpler language. A summary of common indices (often called figures of merit) is presented in Table 13.5.

Examples of reliability indices and goals are:

1. For a telephone system, the downtime of each switching center should be a maximum of 24 h per 40 years.

2. For an engine manufacturer, 70 percent of the engines produced should pass through the warranty period without generating a claim. The number of failures per failed engine should not exceed 1.

3. For a consumer product manufacturer, the percent failure shall be a maximum

TABLE 13.5 Reliability Figures of Merit

Figure of merit	Meaning
Mean time between failures (MTBF)	Mean time between successive failures of a repairable product
Failure rate	Number of failures per unit time
Mean time to failure (MTTF)	Mean time to failure of a nonrepairable product or mean time to first failure of a repairable product
Mean life	Mean value of life ("life" may be related to major overhaul, wear-out, etc.)
Mean time to first failure (MTFF)	Mean time to first failure of a repairable product
Mean time between maintenance (MTBM)	Mean time between a specified type of maintenance action
Longevity	Wear-out time for a product
Availability	Operating time expressed as a percentage of operating and repair time
System effectiveness	Extent to which a product achieves the requirements of the user
Probability of success	Same as reliability (but often used for "one-shot" or non-time-oriented products)
b_{10} life	Life during which 10% of the population would have failed
b_{50} life	Median life, or life during which 50% of the population would have failed
Repairs/100	Number of repairs per 100 operating hours

of 5.7 percent "dead on arrival," 6.4 percent during the first month, an average of 2.0 percent/month during the first year, and an average of 1.2 percent during the 5-year service life.

4. For a locomotive manufacturer (Emphrain and Hamilton, 1973, p. 6):

Reliability goals: These will be normally expressed as a failure rate in terms of a multiple of warranty periods. For example, a 3 percent failure rate in two warranty periods is expressed as

$$W2 = 3\%$$

Service conditions:

a. Locomotive to have 95 percent availability, and therefore, to have a total operating time of 8350 h/year.

b. Additional details on service conditions included numerical statements on the time spent at each throttle notch, outside ambient temperature, throttle changes per hour, and percent of operating time run at various speeds.

Note that all of these examples quantify reliability.

Setting overall reliability goals requires a meeting of the minds on (1) reliability as a number, (2) the environmental conditions to which the numbers apply, and (3) a definition of successful product performance. This is not easily accomplished. However, the act of requiring designers to define with precision both environmental conditions and successful product performance forces the designer to understand the design in greater depth.

Designers should be alert to the precise wording of the reliability requirements portion of the product specification:

1. For a time-oriented performance, a statement of product reliability purely in percentage is meaningless. For example, a reliability is specified as 95 percent. However, the buyer has in mind mission times of 1.5 h whereas the supplier has in mind mission times of 1.1 h.

2. In some cases, specifications have included a confidence level; e.g., "The MTBF shall be at least 100 h at the 90 percent confidence level." This means that the meantime between failures (MTBF) shall be at least 100 h and *that tests shall be conducted* and analyzed to show that the lower one-sided 90 percent confidence limit is at least 100 h. In such cases, the MTBF needed to meet the demonstration requirement may be many times the MTBF number specified. For further discussion, see Section 23 under Statistical Estimation.

A further critical wording is the definition of what constitutes a failure. This definition can readily be decisive as to whether the product meets the test. It is important to determine and specify any exceptions to the failure definition early, particularly with respect to periodic maintenance, e.g., replacement prior to wearout. In consumer products, the definition of failure is critical to the provisions of the warranty; e.g., was the product serviced in accordance with the provisions of the service manual? [MIL-STD-721C (1981) defines eight types of failures: catastrophic, critical, dependent, independent, intermittent, nonchargeable, nonrelevant, and random.]

Apportionment of Reliability.   This phase of quantification is illustrated in the top two sections of Table 13.6.

In the top section of the table, an overall reliability requirement of 95 percent for 1.45 h is apportioned to the six subsystems of a missile. The second section of the table apportions the budget for the explosive subsystem to the three units within the subsystem. The allocation for the fusing circuitry is 0.998 or, in terms of mean time between failures, 725 h.

Apportionment combines engineering judgment with knowledge of (1) the interrelationships of various subsystems (i.e., is everything in series or are there some redundant elements?), (2) reliability experience of subsystems used on previous products, (3) relative complexity of subsystems, and (4) relative criticality of subsystems. The apportionment process provides numerical objectives for each portion of the design. Kapur and Lamberson (1977) discuss five methods of reliability apportionment.

Reliability Prediction and Analysis.   Inherent in the establishment of reliability requirements is the need to estimate or predict reliability in advance of manufacturing the product. This prediction is a continuing process which takes place at several stages of the progression from design through usage. (See Table 13.7.) At the outset the predictions are "on paper," based on design information, e.g., number of components, plus past failure rate experience. In the final stages, the predictions become measurement based on data from field use of the product.

While the visible result of the prediction procedure is to quantify the reliability numbers, the process of prediction is usually as important as the resulting numbers. This is so because the prediction cannot be made without obtaining rather detailed information on product missions, environments, critical component his-

TABLE 13.6 Establishment of Reliability Objectives

System breakdown

Subsystem	Type of operation	Reliability	Unre-liability	Failure rate per hour	Reliability objective*
Air frame	Continuous	0.997	0.003	0.0021	483
Rocket motor	One-shot	0.995	0.005		1/200 operations
Transmitter	Continuous	0.982	0.018	0.0126	80.5 h
Receiver	Continuous	0.988	0.012	0.0084	121 h
Control system	Continuous	0.993	0.007	0.0049	207 h
Explosive system	One-shot	<u>0.995</u>	<u>0.005</u>		1/200 operations
System		0.95	0.05		

Explosive subsystem breakdown

Unit	Operating mode	Reliability	Unreliability	Reliability objective
Fusing circuitry	Continuous	0.998	0.002	725 h
Safety and arming mechanism	One-shot	0.999	0.001	1/1000 operations
Warhead	One-shot	<u>0.998</u>	<u>0.022</u>	2/1000
Explosive subsystem		0.995	0.005	

Unit breakdown

Fusing circuitry component part classification	Number used, n	Failure rate per part, λ, %/1000 h	Total part failure rate, $n\lambda$, %/1000 h
Transistors	93	0.30	27.90
Diodes	87	0.15	13.05
Film resistors	112	0.04	4.48
Wirewound resistors	29	0.20	5.80
Paper capacitors	63	0.04	2.52
Tantalum capacitors	17	0.50	8.50
Transformers	13	0.20	2.60
Inductors	11	0.14	1.54
Solder joints and wires	512	0.01	<u>5.12</u>
			71.51

$$\text{MTBF} = \frac{1}{\text{failure rate}} = \frac{1}{\Sigma\ n\lambda} = \frac{1}{0.0007151} = 1398 \text{ h}$$

Source: Adapted by F. M. Gryna from G. N. Beaton (1959). "Putting the R&D Reliability Dollar to Work." *Proceedings of the Fifth National Symposium on Reliability and Quality Control.* IEEE, New York, p. 65.
*For a mission time of 1.45 h.

TABLE 13.7 Stages of Reliability Analysis and Prediction*

	1 Start of design	2 During detailed design	3 At final design	4 From system tests	5 From customer usage
Basis	Prediction based on approximate part counts and part failure rates from previous product usage; little knowledge of stress levels, redundancy, etc.	Prediction based on quantities and types of parts, redundancies, stress levels, etc.	Prediction based on types and quantities of parts failure rates for expected stress levels, redundancies, external environments, special maintenance practices, special effects of system complexity, cycling effects, etc.	Measurement based on the results of tests of the complete system. Approximate reliability indexes are calculated from the number of failures and operating time	Same as step 4 except calculations are based on customer usage data
Primary uses	*a.* Evaluate feasibility of meeting a proposed numerical requirement *b.* Help in establishing a reliability goal for design	*a.* Evaluate overall reliability *b.* Define problem areas	*a.* Evaluate reliability *b.* Define problem areas	*a.* Evaluate overall reliability *b.* Define problem areas	*a.* Measure achieved reliability *b.* Define problem areas *c.* Obtain data for future designs

*Note: System tests in steps 4 and/or 5 may reveal problems that result in a revision of the "final" design. Such changes can be evaluated by repeating steps 3 to 5.
Source: From Juran, J. M. and Gryna, F. M. (1980). Quality Planning and Analysis, 2nd ed. McGraw-Hill, New York, p. 179.

tories, etc. Acquiring this information often gives the designer knowledge previously not available. Even if the designer is unable to secure the needed information, this inability nevertheless identifies the areas of ignorance in which the designer is forced to work.

The following steps make up a reliability prediction method which analyzes the design as well as arriving at the reliability numbers (ARINC, 1962):

1. Define the product. The system, subsystems, and units must be precisely defined in terms of their functional configurations and boundaries. This precise definition is aided by preparation of a functional block diagram (Figure 13.4) which shows the subsystems and lower-level products, their interrelation, and the interfaces with other systems. For large systems it may be necessary to prepare block diagrams for several levels of the product hierarchy.

Given a functional block diagram and a well-defined statement of the functional requirements of the product, the conditions which constitute failure or unsatisfactory performance can be defined. The functional block diagram also makes it easier to define the boundaries of each unit and to assure that important items are neither neglected nor considered more than once. For example, a switch used to connect two units must be classified as belonging to one or the other (or as a separate unit).

2. Draw a reliability block diagram. The reliability block diagram (Figure 13.5) is similar to the functional block diagram, but it is modified to emphasize those aspects which influence reliability. The diagram shows, in sequence, those elements which must function for successful operation of each unit. Redundant paths and alternative modes should be clearly shown. Elements which are not essential to successful operation need not be included, e.g., decorative escutcheons. Also, because of the many thousands of individual parts that constitute a complex product, it is necessary to exclude from the calculation those classes of parts which are used in mild applications. The contribution of such parts to product unreliability is relatively small. Examples of items that can generally be disregarded are terminal strips, knobs, chassis, and panels.

3. List factors relevant to reliability. For each critical part, it is necessary to list all factors which are relevant to reliability. These factors include part function, part ratings, internal environments and stresses, expected external environments and stresses, and duty ("on" time) cycle. This detailed information makes it possible to perform a stress analysis which will not only provide information on the appropriate adjustments to standard input data but also serve to uncover weak or questionable areas in the design. Parts with dependent failure probabilities should be grouped together into modules so that the assumptions upon which the prediction is based are satisfied.

4. Select part reliability data. The required part data consist of information on catastrophic failures and on tolerance variations with respect to time under known operating and environmental conditions. Acquiring these data is a major problem for the designer, since there is no single reliability data bank comparable to handbooks such as those which are available for physical properties of materials. Instead, the designer (or supporting technical staff) must either build up a data bank or use reliability data secured from a variety of sources:

Field performance studies conducted under controlled conditions

Specification life tests

Data from parts manufacturers or industry associations

Customers' part-qualification and inspection tests

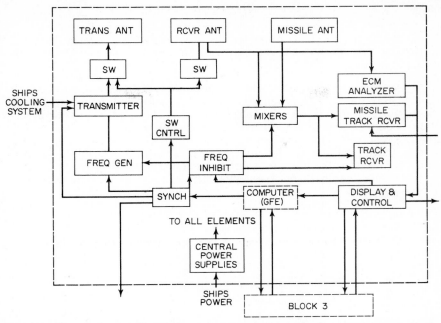

FIG. 13.4 Functional block diagram. *(From Handbook of Reliability Engineering, NAVAIR 00-65-502, courtesy the Commander, Naval Air Systems Command.)*

FIG. 13.5 Reliability block diagram. *(From Handbook of Reliability Engineering, NAVAIR 00-65-502, courtesy the Commander, Naval Air Systems Command.)*

Government agency data banks such as MIL-HDBK-217D, which contains a large amount of failure-rate data together with stress analysis procedures essential to its use

5. Determine appropriate reliability relationships for each part, part class, or module in the product. Basic reliability data such as are acquired in step 4 are in the form of curves or tables (e.g., Table 13.8) which show the relationship of reliability to various stress levels, e.g., failure rates versus temperature (T) under various ratios of operating to rated electrical stress (S). Applying these tables to the specific units, applications, and environments provides the reliability numbers which become the basis of summing up failure rates in step 6, below.

In the absence of basic reliability data, it may be feasible to make reasonably

TABLE 13.8   Base Failure Rates, λ_b, Related to Temperature T and Stress S
MIL-S-19500 transistors, group III, unijunction, in failures per 10^6 h

T, °C	S									
	.1	.2	.3	.4	.5	.6	.7	.8	.9	1.0
0	.0064	.0088	.011	.015	.019	.024	.031	.039	.052	.073
10	.0079	.010	.013	.017	.022	.028	.036	.047	.064	.095
20	.0097	.012	.016	.020	.026	.033	.043	.058	.083	.13
25	.010	.013	.017	.022	.028	.036	.047	.064	.095	.15
30	.011	.015	.019	.024	.031	.039	.052	.073	.11	
40	.013	.017	.022	.028	.036	.047	.064	.095	.15	
50	.016	.020	.026	.033	.043	.058	.083	.13		
55	.017	.022	.028	.036	.047	.064	.095	.15		
60	.019	.024	.031	.039	.052	.073	.11			
65	.020	.026	.033	.043	.058	.083	.13			
70	.022	.028	.036	.047	.064	.095	.15			
75	.024	.031	.039	.052	.073	.11				
80	.026	.033	.043	.058	.083	.13				
85	.028	.036	.047	.064	.095	.15				
90	.031	.039	.052	.073	.11					
95	.033	.043	.058	.083	.13					
100	.036	.047	.064	.095	.15					
105	.039	.052	.073	.11						
110	.043	.058	.083	.13						
115	.047	.064	.095	.15						
120	.052	.073	.11							
125	.058	.083	.13							
130	.064	.095	.15							
135	.073	.11								
140	.083	.13								
145	.095	.15								
150	.11									
155	.13									
160	.15									

Source: MIL-HDBK-217D (1982), p. 5.1.3.3-2.

accurate estimates based on past experience with similar part types. Lacking such experience, it becomes necessary to perform part evaluation tests to secure the data.

6. Determine block and unit failure rates. The failure data of step 5 are added up to obtain failure rates for higher-level product units. (See Table 13.6 and associated discussion.) Pertinent subsystem or assembly correction factors, such as those taking into account the effects of maintenance, can be applied at this point. Block and unit rates are in turn combined to give subsystem and system failure rates.

7. Determine the appropriate reliability unit of measure. This is the choice of reliability index or "figure of merit" as listed in Table 13.5, e.g., MTBF and failure rate.

8. Apply the resulting predictions. The predictions not only indicate the expected reliability of the product, but also point up the weak areas, the extent of improvement needed, and likely opportunities for securing improvement.

An example of a reliability prediction is given in the bottom portion of Table 13.6. In this case, all parts are critical for operation of the fusing circuitry so the failure rates are added up to yield a prediction of the overall failure rate. The reciprocal of the failure is then calculated to yield a mean time between failures of about 1400 h. The 1400 h is greater than the apportionment of 725 h, and the proposed design is therefore acceptable. The prediction technique provides a quantitative evaluation of a design and also identifies design areas having the largest potential for reliability improvement. In this example, the transistors, diodes, and tantalum capacitors account for about 70 percent of the total failure rate.

Reliability predictions and reliability analyses are more effective by making use of software. Such software not only handles the detailed calculations but makes it feasible to identify and assess many alternatives before finalizing a design. The "Directory of Software" published periodically in *Quality Progress* includes a description of software for reliability.

Parts Selection and Control.   Table 13.6 illustrates how system reliability rests on a base of reliability of the component parts.

The vital role played by part reliability has resulted in programs for thorough selection, evaluation, and control of parts. These programs include mainly:

1. *Parts application study:*   The specification and design information supplied by parts manufacturers generally provides guidelines for application. If previous history is available from parts used in similar products, this history becomes an essential input. New applications must be subjected to qualification tests, including overstress, to determine safety factors. The analyses include derating (see below), stress analysis, thermal analysis, and other forms appropriate to each product.

2. *Approved parts list:*   Preliminary component-parts lists are reviewed as early in the design phase as possible to:

Verify that proved parts (i.e., proved in previous usage) are being utilized wherever possible

Verify that unproved or questionable parts are actually capable of meeting reliability or environmental ratings

Compare ratings or qualification test data with anticipated environmental (life) stresses

3. *Critical components list:* A component part is considered "critical" if any of the following conditions apply:

It has a high population in the equipment.

It has a single source of supply.

It must function to special, tight limits.

It has not been proved to the reliability standard, i.e., no test data, insufficient usage data.

The critical components list should be prepared early in the design effort. It is common practice to formalize these lists, showing, for each critical component, the nature of the critical features, the plan to quantify reliability, the plan for improving reliability, etc. The list becomes the basic planning document for (*a*) test programs to qualify parts, (*b*) design guidance in application studies and techniques, and (*c*) design guidance for application of redundant parts, circuits, or subsystems. *⌐ curves not dependent on operating life*

4. *Derating practice:* Derating is the assignment of a product to operate at stress levels below its normal rating; e.g., a capacitor rated at 300 V is used in a 200-V application. For many components, data are available showing failure rate as a function of stress levels. The conservative designer will use such data to achieve reliability by using the parts at low power ratios and low ambient temperatures.

Some companies have established internal policies with respect to derating. Derating is a form of quantifying the factor of safety and hence lends itself to setting guidelines as to the margins to be used. Derating may be considered as a method of determining more scientifically the factor of safety which engineers have long provided on an empirical basis. For example, if the calculated load was 20 tons, the engineers might design the structure to withstand 100 tons as a protection against unanticipated loads, misuse, hidden flaws, deterioration, etc.

Qualitative technique

Failure Mode, Effect, and Criticality Analysis; Fault Tree Analysis. These techniques provide a methodical way to examine a proposed design for possible ways in which failure can occur. In the failure mode, effect, and criticality analysis (FMECA), potential failures are first identified in terms of failure modes. For each mode, the effect on the total system is then studied. Finally, a review is made of the action being taken (or planned) to minimize the probability of failure or to minimize the effect of failure. Figure 13.6 shows a portion of an FMECA for a traveling lawn sprinkler. Each hardware item is listed on a separate line. Note that the failure "mode" is the symptom of the failure, as distinct from the cause of failure, which consists of the proved reasons for the existence of the symptoms. A generalization of the FMECA form is provided in Figure 13.7 (Bajaria, 1983). Dussault (1984) discusses the basic technique (and variations) with a focus on a computerized approach.

Various approaches are used to show the criticality of the failure modes. In Figure 13.7, a risk priority number is calculated as the product of ratings on frequency of occurrence, severity, and likelihood of detection. The risk priority number establishes priorities for further investigations of different failure modes. MIL-STD-1629A (1980) provides a more precise quantification of criticality using data on the probability of mission loss due to the failure mode, the part failure rate, the ratio that a particular failure mode has of the total part failure rate, and the duration of the applicable mission phase.

critical analysis being part of FMECA. identifies critical hardware items and safty problems.

[left margin handwritten:] ⌐ study of the physics of failure to determine how product failed and why
⌐ can vary dramatically due to changes in applications

1 = Very low (<1 in 1000)
2 = Low (3 in 1000)
3 = Medium (5 in 1000)
4 = High (7 in 1000)
5 = Very high (>9 in 1000)

T = Type of failure
P = Probability of occurrence
S = Seriousness of failure to system
H = Hydraulic failure
M = Mechanical failure
W = Wear failure
C = Customer abuse

Product	HRC-1
Date	Jan. 14, 1987
By	S.M.

Component part number	Possible failure	Cause of failure	T	P	S	Effect of failure on product	Alternatives
Worm bearing 4224	Bearing worn	Not aligned with bottom housing	M	1	4	Spray head wobble or slowing down	Improve inspection
Zytel 101		Excessive spray head wobble	M	1	3	DITTO	Improve worm bearing
Bearing stem 4225	Excessive wear	Poor bearing/ material combination	M	5	4	Spray head wobbles and loses power	Change stem material
Brass		Dirty water in bearing area	M	5	4	DITTO	Improve worm seal area
		Excessive spray head wobble	M	2	3	DITTO	Improve operating instructions
Thrust washer 4226	Excessive wear	High water pressure	M	2	5	Spray head will stall out	Inform customer in instructions
Fulton 404		Dirty water in washers	M	5	5	DITTO	Improve worm seal design
Worm 4527	Excessive wear in bearing area	Poor bearing/ material combination	M	5	4	Spray head wobbles and loses power	Change bearing stem material
Brass		Dirty water in bearing area	M	5	4	DITTO	Improve worm seal design
		Excessive spray head wobble	M	2	3	DITTO	Improve operating instructions

FIG. 13.6   Failure mode, effect, and criticality analysis.

Block diagrams which illustrate the operation, interrelationships, and inter-dependencies of functional parts to the system are a useful adjunct to the failure mode, effect, and criticality analysis. These diagrams provide the ability for tracing failure mode-effects throughout all levels of the equipment. Both functional and reliability block diagrams are required to show the functional flow sequence and the series dependence or independence of functions and operations. Raheja (1981) provides examples showing the value of block diagrams in these analyses.

The FMECA can be elaborated to include effects of other matters such as safety, downtime, access to hardware items, maintenance planning, and inspection planning.

Fault tree analysis is another method of studying the potential failures in a system. A fault tree analysis differs from failure mode, effect, and criticality analysis in three respects. First, fault tree analysis studies only those negative outcomes of a product that are considered serious enough to warrant further analysis; FMECA studies all potential modes of failures. Second, the fault tree analysis can analyze situations in which the negative event will not occur unless several subevents first occur. Third, the fault tree analysis does a more explicit job of showing the relationships between events that have an interaction with each other.

In fault tree analysis, the starting point is the list of failure modes (or other undesired events) for which the designer must provide some solution. Each event on the list then becomes a failure mode requiring analysis. The analysis considers

Failure Mode and Effects Analysis

(1) Item _____ (2) Analysis Engineer

_____

Date

_____

(3) Function _____

Mode of Failure	Mechanism and Cause of Failure	Effects of Failure	Frequency of Occurrence 1-10	Degree of Severity 1-10	Chance of Direction 1-10
(4)	(5)	(6)	(7)	(8)	(9)

Risk Priority Number 1-1000	Design Action	Design Validation
(10) = (7) × (8) × (9)	(11)	(12)

Failure Mode and Effects Analysis Form Entry Explanation —

1. Item — Item to which analysis applies.

2. Analysis Engineer — an engineer in charge of design project.

3. Function — Function of the item as user perceives it. This description should be as broad as possible.

4. Mode of Failure — A mode in which the item will fail as perceived by user.

5. Mechanism and Cause of Failure — What caused failure to occur?

6. Effects of Failure — What effects this failure will have on the user or nearby person or nearby property?

7. Frequency of Occurrence (1-10) — How often is this failure expected to occur? This column is subjectively rated on 1 to 10 basis.
   1 — Rare occurrence
   10 — Almost certain occurrence

8. Degree of Severity (1-10) — How severe is the effect of this failure on the user or anything else? This column is subjectively rated on 1 to 10 basis.
   1 — Insignificant loss to user
   10 — Product inoperable or major replacement cost or safety hazard

9. Degree of Detection (1-10) — Can problem be detected by the user before it does the damage? This column too is subjectively rated on 1 to 10 basis.
   1 — Certain detection before failure
   10 — No detection possible before failure

10. Risk Priority Number (1-1000) — Order of problem-solving priority is given by multiplying numbers in columns 7, 8, and 9.

11. Design Action — Action to reduce risk priority number.

12. Design Validation — Method to verify the design motion.

FIG. 13.7 Generalized failure mode, effect, and criticality analysis.

the possible direct causes that could lead to the event. Next, it looks for the origins of these causes. Finally, it looks for ways to avoid these origins and causes. The branching out of origins and causes is what gives the technique the name "fault tree" analysis. The approach is the reverse of failure mode, effect, and criticality analysis, which starts with origins and causes and looks for any resulting bad effects. Fault tree analysis can be useful in studying potential failures for reliability analysis and also potential failures that result in damages or injuries. An example of fault tree analysis will be presented later in this section under Planning for Safety.

Other Analysis Techniques. Other techniques have been developed to aid in analyzing product effectiveness during design. The *Transactions on Reliability* of the Institute of Electrical and Electronics Engineers is a good source of information on such techniques. Two of these techniques, worst-case analysis and sneak-circuit analysis, will be mentioned here. ~~requires that unit Transfer be known in addition to other factors~~

The "worst-case" analysis technique is a detailed electrical analysis often made in conjunction with computer programs. The purpose is to verify the ability of the circuits to perform in an acceptable manner under all anticipated extremes of electrical and physical environments and in the presence of degradation of parts with time and environment. The worst-case approach can be used either by taking all absolute values of the parameters in their extreme condition or by using a probabilistic approach which studies the outcomes for highly probable combinations of parameter values. MIL-STD-785B (1980) provides further discussion.

Another technique is called "sneak-circuit analysis." This is usually a computer-aided technique used to identify latent paths in a circuit which could cause occurrence of unwanted functions or could result in desired functions being inhibited even though all components are functioning properly. In contrast to other analysis techniques, it is not based on failed items. A further description is given in MIL-STD-785B (1980).

The broad area of computer-aided design (CAD) makes use of computers to translate a product's specific requirements into the final physical product. Thus it is useful in doing much of the detailed design and analysis work. Computer-aided design makes it possible for the designer to consider many alternative designs and then select the one that comes closest to having the optimum values. Although this could be done without the use of computers, the time required would be prohibitive. Computer-aided design is now being extended to reliability and other fitness-for-use parameters:

Reliability: Thermal design of equipment for improved reliability at lower operating temperatures (Berger and Jenkins, 1984)

Maintainability: Graphical analysis of work positions, reach, and other human requirements associated with a design (Cahill and Davids, 1984)

Testability: Analysis of overall testing requirements to integrate test planning during the design process (Fennell and Nicolino, 1984)

Mitsuya (1977) discusses the application of an automatic designing and drawing system using a computer and drafting machine for the design of elevator equipment. The application reported improvements in quality due to the standardization of drawings and elimination of mistakes by means of computer checking.

Evaluating Designs by Tests. Although reliability prediction, design review, failure mode, effect, and criticality analysis, and other techniques are valuable as early warning devices, they cannot be a substitute for the ultimate proof, i.e., use of the product by the customer. However, field experience comes too late and must be preceded by a substitute—various forms of testing the product to simulate field use. A summary of types of tests for evaluating a design is given in Table 13.9. Sometimes, a number of tests can be integrated so that one type of test can serve several purposes, e.g., evaluation of both performance and environmental capabilities. Brach and Phaller (1980) describe how an electronics manufacturer reviewed the test programs on a variety of projects and developed an integrated test philosophy (Table 13.10). Stevens (1978) discusses the planning and execution of integrated test programs under operational conditions.

TABLE 13.9 Summary of Tests Used to Evaluate a Design

Type of test	Purpose
Performance	Determine ability of product to meet basic performance requirements
Environmental	Evaluate ability of product to withstand defined environmental levels; determine internal environments generated by product operation; verify environmental levels specified
Stress	Determine levels of stress that a product can withstand in order to determine the safety margin inherent in the design; determine modes of failure that are not associated with time
Reliability	Determine product reliability and compare to requirements; monitor for trends
Maintainability	Determine time required to make repairs and compare to requirements
Life	Determine wear-out time for a product, and failure modes associated with time or operating cycles
Pilot run	Determine if fabrication and assembly processes are capable of meeting design requirements; determine if reliability will be degraded.

Some Problems in Testing. A widely used form of early warning is through construction and test of product models. The model may be a single mechanical or electrical product unit (or part thereof). It may be chemical in nature—all the way from the test tube level to the pilot plant. The test may be a simulation in the laboratory or a large-scale trial lot sent out for field use. All such cases provide some degree of design assurance. They also involve a risk of being led astray. The principal sources of this risk are as follows:

1. *Intended use versus actual use:* The designer typically aims to attain fitness for intended use. However, actual use can differ from the designer's concept due to variations in environments and other conditions of use. In addition some users will misapply or misuse the product.

The solution is for the designer to understand what will be the actual conditions of use and misuse. Field visits will provide this understanding. Alternatively, the design can be reviewed by someone who does have direct knowledge of conditions of use.

2. *Model construction versus subsequent production:* Models are usually built by skilled specialists under the supervision of the designers. The subsequent production is carried out by less skilled factory workers under supervisors who must meet standards of productivity as well as quality. In addition, the factory processes seldom possess the adaptive flexibility available in the model shop.

As before, the solution is for the designer to have enough direct knowledge of the factory conditions and processes to understand how they correlate with model shop conditions. The alternative is for the design to be reviewed by people who do have such understanding.

3. *Variability due to small numbers:* The number of models built is usually small. (Often there is only one.) Yet tests on these small numbers are used to judge the adequacy of the design for making many production units, sometimes running into the thousands and even millions.

The need here is for the designer to understand the extent to which test results on small numbers of models can be relied on to predict the performance of the

TABLE 13.10 Typical Test Program

Test program	Test level*	Purpose	Environment*	Typical test hours
Engineering development tests	SRU/LRU	1. Design verification 2. Design feasibility 3. Overstress test 4. Exploratory environmental tests	Temp. cycle Humidity Vibration	500–1500
	System	1. LRU integration 2. Pre-qual. env. tests 3. Software evaluation 4. System performance verification 5. Maintainability design verification	Temp. cycle Humidity Vibration Lab-bench	1000–3000 ±
Formal environmental qualification	LRU/system	1. Verify design integrity under specified environmental conditions 2. Test for endurance limits of hardware	Temp./alt. Humidity Vibration Salt-fog Dust/sand EMI/EMC Explosive atmosphere	200–300
Preproduction and production tests	SRU/LRU/ system	1. In-line environmental test for quality reliability control 2. Burn-in 3. Acceptance test	Temp. cycle Vibration Bench-lab	1. 25–50 h/syst. 2. Depends on level 3. 10–50 h/syst.
Reliability tests	LRU/system	1. Growth-induced failures caused by wear, design, quality, and workmanship	Temp. cycle Vibration (CERT)	1000 up—depends on program
		2. Qualification-reliability demonstration for spec. compliance	Temp. cycle Vibration MIL-STD-781	Depends on MTBF—test plan, etc.
		3. Acceptance—sample test	Temp. cycle Vibration (CERT) MIL-STD-781	Depends on MTBF—test plan, etc.
		4. Assurance—all equipments test— PRVT	Temp. cycle Vibration (CERT) MIL-STD-781	20–50 h/syst.
Flight test	System	1. Aircraft/system integration 2. Initial R/M assessment 3. Engineering measurement	Aircraft operating environment	100–300

*Note: SRU = shop replaceable unit; LRU = line replaceable unit; EMI = electromagnetic interference; EMC = electromagnetic compatibility; CERT = combined environment reliability test; PRVT = production reliability verification test.
Source: Brach and Phaller, 1980, p. 243.

more numerous production units. This understanding is best derived from statistical quantification of the respective variations and of the "confidence limits" which apply to the numbers of models tested. If the designer is not personally knowledgeable in such matters, the alternative is to enlist the assistance of specialists who do have such knowledge (usually the quality engineers).

4. *Evaluation of test results:* Pressures to release a design for production can result in test plans and evaluations that do not objectively evaluate conformance to performance requirements (let alone complete fitness for use). One organization studied the process of qualifying a new design by having an independent review team analyze a sample of "qualification test" results on designs that had been approved for release. Two conclusions were:

   a. Pressures to release designs caused design approvals that later resulted in field problems. The situation was traced to (*i*) inadequate initial testing or (*ii*) lack of verification of design changes made to correct failures that surfaced on the initial test.

   b. Over 50 percent of the approved test results were rejected because the *test procedure* was unable to evaluate the requirements set by Product Development.

Stern action was taken. All test procedures and test results were submitted to a group independent of Product Development for approval.

Reliability Tests. MIL-STD-785B (1980) identifies four areas of testing:

MTBF correspondes to AQL

1. *Environmental stress screening:* These are tests conducted at lower levels of the product to identify early failures due to weak parts, workmanship defects, and other reasons for nonconformance. Environmental stress tests can also be combined with life testing to help identify weak points in new designs. Bailey and Gilbert (1982) describe a program that combines both stress and life testing.

2. *Reliability development/growth tests:* This testing is performed before the final release of the design to improve product reliability through the identification, analysis, and correction of failures and the verification of the corrective action.

3. *Reliability qualification tests:* These tests are conducted on product which is representative of the approved production configuration. The tests provide assurance that the production articles will meet the formal reliability requirements.

4. *Production reliability acceptance tests:* These tests provide periodic evaluations of reliability of production hardware, particularly when any changes have been made in design, tooling, processes, parts, or other characteristics. MIL-STD-781C (1981) is used as the basis of planning the tests.

Tests for reliability focus on three elements: performance requirements, environmental conditions during use, and time requirements.

Performance requirements are defined uniquely for each product, e.g., the kilowatt output of a generator. During the performance, the product is subjected to stresses, and these stresses vary (e.g., a tractor works in sandy soil on one day and in rocky soil the next day). Hence stress must be viewed as a distribution rather than as a single value. Similarly, strength varies from one unit of product to the next and hence must also be viewed as a distribution. Obtaining the data needed to construct these distributions can be so costly that shortcuts have to be taken, e.g., sampling actual use of the product by typical customers. An alternative is to simulate customer use, e.g., in the company "proving ground." The resulting data disclose the stress levels being encountered. Tests must then be conducted to verify that the product can withstand the expected stress levels for the required time period.

Environmental conditions (e.g., temperature, humidity, vibration) are critical to many products. Here again, the problem is twofold: (a) discovering the expected environmental levels and (b) testing to verify that the product can meet them. By skillful design of test programs, it may be feasible to meet both of these needs simultaneously.

Time requirements are the third element of reliability testing. Testing one item of product to failure, then repairing it and testing again to failure, through several cycles, may provide good information on that particular item. It may also provide useful data on product wear-out, but it will not necessarily reveal the variability that occurs among many items of the same product due to part and production variability. However, testing many items of product for a shorter period of time will produce test data and failure data which do show many effects of part and production variability. Bringing these test data to a state of statistical significance may result in cost problems with both test facilities and "appraisal." In addition, such testing is not necessarily complete; it may still fail to disclose critical early wear-out characteristics of the product.

Interpretation of time-oriented test data is aided greatly by use of the Weibull form of data plotting. (See Section 23 under Predictions with Weibull Distributions.) These plots usually approximate a straight line and simplify the extrapolation process. They are also useful for comparing the results of accelerated testing (see below) with results of testing under normal operating conditions. *This tool is a "must" for the designer.*

Accelerated testing is a common form of securing reliability test data at reduced testing cost. In this form of testing, the products are made to perform at abnormally high levels of stress and/or environments in order to make them fail sooner. (Earlier failures mean less test equipment, lower testing costs, and earlier answers.) Extrapolation is then used to convert the short life under severe conditions into the expected life under normal conditions. Great care is needed to assure that the accelerated test time is properly correlated to normal use time to avoid overstating the expected life. A further problem is that accelerated testing can introduce new failure modes which do not occur during normal product use. Taking such failure modes seriously has sometimes led to major redesigns which provided no benefit from the standpoint of the original product requirements. While the benefits from accelerated testing can be substantial, there are serious risks of being misled. It is obviously essential to apply engineering judgment in such tests.

The accelerated-testing concept can be combined with probability-paper analysis to relate test results with field results. Stanton (1974) describes how this was done for two models of room air conditioners. The field data and data from accelerated tests were plotted on Weibull probability paper as shown in Figure 13.8. As the lines were essentially parallel, it was concluded that the basic mode of failure was the same on the test as in the field. In Figure 13.8 the field data are plotted in *years* of service. The test data are plotted in *tens of days*. The 5-year warranty period is represented by a heavy vertical line. If one follows this line to the point where it intersects the field data line and then horizontally from the field data line to the lines for the accelerated test data, the accelerated time equivalent

FIG. 13.8 Superposed plot of field failure data over test data for two air conditioner models.

to the 5-year period can be read. For example, on one model the cumulative percent failed in 135 days of accelerated testing is equivalent to 5 years of field use. On the other model, the equivalent accelerated test time is 175 days.

Behind all testing is detailed test planning that includes the identification of the key characteristics for testing; deciding on the level of test in terms of going to specification limits or beyond; planning the environment for the test; planning the statistical aspects of the test including sample sizes and other matters; and making provisions for control of the test methods including equipment, calibration, documentation, action in case of failures, and other matters. Stevens (1978) discusses the overall planning of test programs.

Section 23 of this handbook provides the basic tools of statistical methods and Section 26 provides a discussion of the statistical aspects of planning experiments and tests. Nelson (1982) discusses the statistical analysis of life testing. Frank (1982) provides guidelines on maintaining documentation of test data.

Reliability Data Systems.   Reliability data serve several important purposes:

1. To detect current reliability problems and assist in their solution. An example is the use of the data feedback loop shown in Figure 13.9. This loop operates in the conventional way: Failures are detected and reported, analyses are made for causes, remedies are devised and applied.

2. To provide managers with quantitative information on product performance and on the status of problems. This feedback should not be limited to information on current problems; it should include also summaries in the form of executive reports, as discussed in Section 8 under Executive Reports on Quality.

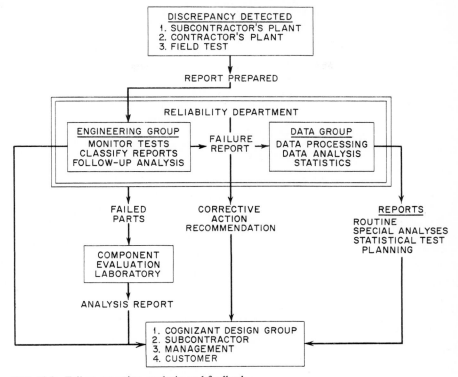

FIG. 13.9   Failure reporting, analysis, and feedback.

3. To assist in reliability improvement programs. (See below, under Reliability Improvement.)

4. To provide failure history and other reference data for use in product changes and in future products. This is the "data bank" concept. It serves the needs of reliability in a manner analogous to that served by handbooks of properties of materials (when one is choosing materials for specific applications).

Reliability Data Banks.   The term "data bank" implies an organized approach to data collection, classification, analysis, summary, and retrieval. Despite the seeming advantages of such an organized approach, it is difficult and costly to execute. In practice, companies make only limited use of the available data. These data originate from:

1. *Engineering, preproduction, production, or special tests (e.g., test track, test kitchen) under the manufacturer's control:*   These tests are usually conducted on the premises, but may include "captive" usage tests, e.g., employee homes, consumer panels, captive sales outlets.

2. *Suppliers and major subcontractors:*   Increasingly these companies are organizing their test data in forms which can be readily used by their customers for product design purposes.

3. *Field performance data, including customer returns:*   While these data have an obvious dramatic effect on practical people, they are suspect in many ways: the sources of the data are notoriously difficult to control; the data are frequently incomplete and of dubious validity; coverage (e.g., the spectrum of environments) is incomplete. For a more extensive discussion, see Section 20 under Quality Complaints: General.

4. *Independent data banks:* These are springing up in recognition of the fact that basic failure data can be used by many companies. For such multiple use, it may be more economic to maintain a central data bank instead of numerous duplicating company data banks. (See below under Public data banks.) In addition, there are laboratories devoted mainly to testing products for safety, and these laboratories develop test data which have wide application.

Acquisition of data is only the first step in creating a working data bank. There must be summaries to permit evaluation of trends and identification of the more important problems. Then the data must be analyzed to assist specialists in finding causes and remedies. See Section 22 under Diagnosis.

5. *Public data banks:* An example is the Government Industry Data Exchange Program (GIDEP), a cooperative activity between the U.S. government and industry. The program provides a means of exchanging technical data in the area of research, design, development, production, and the operational phases of various products. Management and funding of the program is handled by the U.S. government. Participants in the program are expected to contribute information from their own company to the data bank. This then entitles them to access all of the information in the data bank. Participants in GIDEP are presently provided access to four major data interchanges: engineering, reliability-maintainability, metrology, and failure experience.

Special GIDEP services include a system for notifying participants of problem areas (ALERT System); a system which allows a GIDEP participant to query all other GIDEP participants on specific problems (the urgent data request or UDR System); a system for providing rapid responses to participants on queries related to test equipment and measurement (this is the Metrology Information Service, or MIS). Arnitz (1981) provides a description of the GIDEP program. Herrold (1976) discusses the application of GIDEP data to solving reliability problems.

Reliability Improvement. The general approach to quality improvement (Section 22, Quality Improvement) is widely applicable to reliability improvement as far as the economic analysis and the managerial tools are concerned. The differences are in the technological tools used for diagnosis and remedy. Projects can be identified through reliability prediction, design review, failure mode, effect and criticality analysis, and other reliability evaluation techniques.

Action to improve reliability during the design phase is best taken by the designer. The reliability engineer can help by defining areas needing improvement and by assisting in the development of alternatives. The following actions indicate some approaches to improving a design:

1. Review the users' needs to see if the function of the unreliable parts is really necessary to the user. If not, eliminate those parts from the design. Alternatively, look to see if the reliability index (figure of merit) correctly reflects the real needs of the user. For example, availability (see below) is sometimes more meaningful than reliability. If so, a good maintenance program might improve availability and hence ease the reliability problem.

2. Consider trade-offs of reliability for other parameters, e.g., functional performance, or weight. Here again it may be found that the customers' real needs may be better served by such a trade-off.

3. Use redundancy to provide more than one means for accomplishing a given task in such a way that all the means must fail before the system fails. This is discussed in Section 23 under System Reliability.

There are several types of redundancy, a common form being parallel redundancy. A familiar example is the multiengined aircraft, which is so designed that even if one engine fails, the aircraft will still be able to continue on to a safe landing.

Under conditions of independent failures, the overall reliability for parallel redundancy is expressed by the formula

$$P_s = 1 - (1 - P_i)^n$$

where P_s = reliability of the system
P_i = reliability of the individual elements in the redundancy
n = number of identical redundant elements

Figure 13.10 shows some simple examples of series-parallel and parallel-series redundancies and calculates the system reliability versus that prevailing for the case of no redundancy.

4. Review the selection of any parts that are relatively new and unproven. Use standard parts whose reliability has been proven by actual field use. (However, be sure that the conditions of previous use are applicable to the new product.)

5. Use derating to assure that the stresses applied to the parts are lower than the stresses the parts can normally withstand.

6. Use "robust" design methods that enable a product to handle unexpected environments.

7. Control the operating environment to provide conditions that yield lower failure rates. Common examples are (*a*) potting electronic components to protect them against climate and shock, and (*b*) use of cooling systems to keep down ambient temperatures.

8. Specify replacement schedules to remove and replace low-reliability parts before they reach the wear-out stage. In many cases the replacement is made contingent on the results of checkouts or tests which determine whether degradation has reached a prescribed limit.

9. Prescribe screening tests to detect infant-mortality failures and to eliminate substandard components. The tests take various forms—bench tests, "burn in," accelerated life tests. Ekings and Sweetland (1978) discuss how machine

$R_1 = 0.8 \quad R_2 = 0.9$

NO REDUNDANCY:

$R_s = R_1 R_2$
$R_s = (0.8)(0.9) = 0.72$

SERIES-PARALLEL REDUNDANCY:

$R_s = 1 - (1 - R_1 R_2)^2$
$R_s = 1 - [1 - (0.8)(0.9)]^2 = 0.92$

PARALLEL-SERIES REDUNDANCY:

$R_s = [1 - (1 - R_1)^2][1 - (1 - R_2)^2]$
$R_s = [1 - (0.2)^2][1 - (0.1)^2] = 0.95$

FIG. 13.10 Redundancy.

burn-in decision criteria were used in a reliability assurance program for office copier machines.

10. Conduct research and development to attain an improvement in the basic reliability of those components which contribute most of the unreliability. While such improvements avoid the need for subsequent trade-offs, they may require advancing the state of the art and hence an investment of unpredictable size. Research in failure mechanisms has created a body of knowledge called the physics of failure, or reliability physics. *Proceedings of the Annual Meeting on Reliability Physics,* sponsored by the Institute of Electrical and Electronic Engineers, Inc., is an excellent reference.

Although none of the foregoing actions provides a perfect solution, the range of choice is broad. In some instances the designer can arrive at a solution single-handedly. More usually it means collaboration with other company specialists. In still other cases the customer and/or the company management must concur because of the broader considerations involved.

Reliability Growth. A technique for predicting future performance from tests and early field data is the concept of growth curves. The concept assumes that the product involved is one that is undergoing continuous improvements in design and refinements in operating and maintenance procedure. Thus the product performance will improve ("grow") with time. An early reliability growth model is that proposed by Duane (1964):

The Duane reliability growth model is given by:

$$\lambda_t = k(t)^{-b}$$

where λ_t = accumulative failure rate
t = accumulative time
b = slope of the growth curve
k = a constant which depends on equipment complexity, design margins and design factors

Reiff (1978) shows how test data collected during four design phases were used for a reliability growth analysis based on the Duane model.

When such a model has been proven to apply to a class of products, early field data can be plotted on log-log paper and a line drawn using the slope based on previous similar products. The extrapolation of the line then provides a prediction of future performance. This has several uses, including the monitoring of actual progress toward meeting some requirement.

The Duane model can be adapted for measures of use other than time. For example, a manufacturer of duplicating machines uses it to predict failure rates for new products by plotting failure rate versus cumulative number of copies run. Peacord (1975) presents examples of the application of the Duane model. Jayachandran and Moore (1976) describe a simulation study made to compare four growth models. Willard (1979) discusses the approach for developing reliability growth curves for office equipment. MIL-HDBK-189 (1981) discusses reliability growth principles and techniques including 17 growth models.

PLANNING FOR MAINTAINABILITY

Maintainability refers to the ease with which preventive and corrective maintenance on a product can be achieved. ANSI/ASQC Standard A3 (ANSI, 1978) defines maintainability more formally as the ability of an item under stated conditions to be retained in, or restored to, within a given period of time, a specified state in which it can perform its required functions when maintenance is performed under stated conditions and while using prescribed procedures and resources.

Like reliability, maintainability is a fitness-for-use parameter that design engineers have recognized during the creation of new designs. These efforts resulted in many advances, e.g., aluminum siding, maintenance-free batteries, self-lubricating bearings, longer times between oil changes, fewer hours to change an engine on a jet aircraft.

As products have moved from the simple to the complex, the problems of maintainability have increased manyfold. For many electronic military products, the annual maintenance costs are typically several times the original cost of the equipment. As a result of critical needs on military products, some government agencies created specifications for programs of maintainability for contractors. These specifications required the development of goals on maintainability, prediction, and analysis of maintainability during the design process, and demonstration that maintainability goals had been achieved.

The evolution of a maintainability discipline gave rise to the creation of a maintainability specialist. These specialists tried to work with designers to develop maintainability goals and follow through with the analysis, prediction, and demonstration of maintainability. Like the reliability specialist, the maintainability specialist ran into resistance from the designers, and the record of accomplishment was varied.

Maintainability Concepts and Terms.   Users want products that are ready for use when they need them. This fitness-for-use parameter is called "availability." Availability is the ability of an item to perform its designated function when required for use. The availability of a product depends on how often failures occur (reliability), how long it takes to fix any failures (maintainability), and the amount of maintenance support provided. The total time in the operative state (also called uptime) is the sum of the time spent (1) in active use and (2) in the standby state. The total time in the nonoperative state (also called downtime) is the sum of the time spent (3) under active repair, and (4) waiting for spare parts, paperwork, etc. These categories are illustrated in Figure 13.11.

Availability is calculated as the ratio of operating time to operating time plus downtime. However, downtime can be viewed in two ways:

1. *Total downtime:*   This includes the active repair time (diagnosis and repair), preventive maintenance time, and logistics time (time spent waiting for personnel, spare parts, etc.). When total downtime is used, the resulting ratio is called operational availability (A_o).

2. *Active repair time:*   When active repair time is used, the resulting ratio is called "intrinsic availability" (A_i).

Under certain conditions, the availability can be calculated as

$$A_o = \frac{\text{MTBF}}{\text{MTBF} + \text{MDT}} \quad \text{and} \quad A_i = \frac{\text{MTBF}}{\text{MTBF} + \text{MTTR}}$$

where MTBF = mean time between failures $= operating\ time$
      MDT = mean downtime
      MTTR = mean time to repair $= down\ time$

This is known as the "steady-state formula for availability."

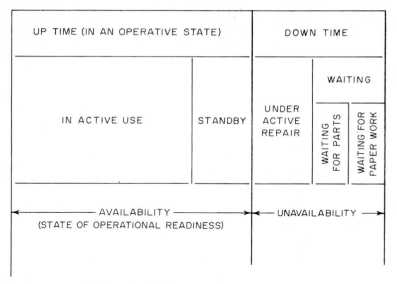

FIG. 13.11   Ingredients of availability.

Garrick and Mulvihill (1974) present data on certain subsystems of a mechanized bulk mail system (see Table 13.11). If estimates of reliability and maintainability can be made during the design process, availability can be evaluated before the design is released for production.

The steady-state formula for availability has the virtue of simplicity. However, the formula has several assumptions that are not always met in the real world. The assumptions are:

1. The product is operating in the constant-failure-rate period of the overall life. Thus, the failure time distribution is exponential.

2. The downtime or repair time distribution is exponential.

3. Attempts to locate system failures do not change the overall system failure rate.

4. No reliability growth occurs. (Such growth might be due to design improvements or through debugging of bad parts.)

5. Preventive maintenance is scheduled outside the time frame included in the availability calculation.

TABLE 13.11   Availability Data for Mail System Equipment

Equipment	MTBF, h	MTTR, h	Availability, %
Sack sorter	90	1.620	98.2
Parcel sorter	160	0.8867	99.4
Conveyor, induction	17,900	1.920	100.0
Deflector, traveling	3,516	3.070	99.9

More precise formulas for calculating availability depend on operational conditions and statistical assumptions. These formulas are discussed by Locks (1973).

Availability analysis has also been applied to developing chemical processes. Such analysis applied the steady-state availability formula to processes involving a series of operations (Cherry et al., 1978).

Maintainability Program Elements. Formal maintainability programs start with the premise that maintainability can be programmed in the same way as parameters such as product performance or reliability. The program consists of three stages:

1. *Program surveillance and control:* This stage consists of defining all of the tasks required in the maintainability program, and monitoring and reviewing those tasks as they are executed.
2. *Design and analysis:* During product design, maintainability goals are set and analyses and predictions are made.
3. *Evaluation and test:* The key element here is a demonstration that maintainability goals have been achieved.

An example of maintainability tasks during a product development program is illustrated in Table 13.12. (MIL-STD-470A, 1983.) The Standard explains the degree of application of each task from the design concept stage to the final operating system development. Many of these tasks are discussed below.

Maintainability Modeling and Allocation. *~ Log normal* There is a trend toward specifying maintainability in quantitative form. A summary of some common figures of merit for maintainability is given in Table 13.13. [MIL-STD-721C (1981) lists 11 different figures of merit based on the mean time concept.]

Wellborn and Lawson (1978) report a case of extensive quantitative maintainability requirements (e.g., mean time between maintenance) for an engine to be furnished to the U.S. Army. In addition to the quantitative requirements there were 15 qualitative requirements, such as "the engine shall be modular."

When product complexity or importance warrants it, a formal model for maintainability can be created. The term "model" here is used to mean a systematic, analytical process that will predict maintainability. The complexity of the model may range from a simple flow or block diagram to a mathematical relationship

TABLE 13.12 MIL-STD-470A (1983) Maintainability Tasks

Maintainability program plan
Monitor/control of subcontractors and suppliers
Program reviews
Data collection, analysis, and corrective action system
Maintainability modeling
Maintainability allocations
Maintainability predictions
Failure modes and effects analysis (FMEA), maintainability information
Maintainability analysis
Maintainability design criteria
Preparation of inputs to detailed maintenance plan and logistics support analysis (LSA)
Maintainability demonstration (MD)

TABLE 13.13 Maintainability Figures of Merit

Figure of merit	Meaning
Mean time to repair (MTTR)	Mean time to correct a failure
Mean time to service	Mean time to perform an act to keep a product in operating condition
Mean preventive maintenance time	Mean time for scheduled preventive maintenance
Repair hours per 100 operating hours	Number of hours required for repairs per 100 product operating hours
Rate of preventive maintenance actions	Number of preventive maintenance actions required per period of operative or calendar hours
Downtime probability	Probability that a failed product is restored to operative condition in a specified downtime
Maintainability index	Score for a product design based on evaluation of defined maintainability features
Rate of maintenance cost	Cost of preventive and corrective maintenance per unit of operating or calendar time

that predicts maintainability as a function of system parameters. A key purpose of the model is to determine the effect of the change in one variable on the cost and/or maintainability performance characteristics. MIL-STD-470A (1983) provides further discussion of maintainability modeling.

Another task in the maintainability program is the allocation of the maintainability goal. The task consists of apportioning the overall maintainability goal to provide designers with goals for individual items and thereby make maintainability a design parameter. The allocation process combines experience on similar products with engineering judgment. An example of the allocation of a mean corrective maintenance time requirement of 0.5 h is given in Table 13.14 (Blanchard and Fabrycky, 1981). Reliability estimates are provided in columns 2 through 5. An assumed maintainability allocation is given in column 6. (Items with a high contribution to total failures are allocated a low maintenance time.) The calculations show an overall time of 0.485. As this is within the 0.5 requirement, the allocation given in column 6 is accepted. MIL-STD-470A (1983) and Blanchard and Fabrycky (1981) provide further discussion on maintainability allocation.

Maintainability Prediction. Maintainability prediction provides a quantitative tool for (1) evaluating a proposed design for maintainability and (2) identifying areas of the design requiring improvement.

Three main approaches can be used:

1. Secure data of past experience on similar equipment, and extrapolate to make predictions on the new design.

2. Break down the maintenance task into elemental tasks needed to carry out maintenance at the various product levels. Then acquire data representing "standard" times to accomplish these tasks. These standards can then be used to build up a predicted total maintainability time in much the same way as reliability is built up from elemental failure rates or as time for manufacturing

TABLE 13.14 Maintainability Allocation for System *XYZ*

1 Item	2 Quantity of items per system (Q)	3 Failure rate (λ) × 1000 h	4 Contribution of total failures $C_f = (Q)(\lambda)$	5 Percent contribution $C_p = C_f/\Sigma C_f \times 100$	6 Average corrective maint. time $\overline{M}ct$, h	7 Contribution of total corrective maint. time $C_t = (C_f)(\overline{M}ct)$
1. Unit *A*	1	0.246	0.246	11%	0.9	0.221
2. Unit *B*	1	1.866	1.866	84%	0.4	0.746
3. Unit *C*	1	0.110	0.110	5%	1.0	0.110
Total			$\Sigma C_f = 2.222$	100%		$\Sigma C_t = 1.077$

$$\overline{M}ct \text{ for system } XYZ = \frac{\Sigma C_t}{\Sigma C_f} = \frac{1.077}{2.222} = 0.485 \text{ h (requirement: 0.5 h)}$$

Source: Blanchard and Fabrycky, 1981, p. 392.

operations is built up from standard elemental times. An example from Blanchard and Fabrycky (1981) is given in Table 13.15.

3. Employ a regression equation that predicts maintainability as a function of key characteristics of the proposed design. Detailed checklists are used to establish a score for the design on each of these characteristics. These scores are inserted into the equation to develop an estimate of the total maintenance time. (Miller, 1971, explains a simpler technique that provides a comparative, rather than absolute, measure of maintainability. Checklists are used to score the design on maintainability characteristics. The total number of points is the measure of maintainability.)

The methodology of maintainability prediction and analysis is going through a period of development. Discussions of advanced techniques can be found in the various issues of the Institute of Electrical and Electronics Engineers publication *Transactions on Reliability.* See particularly the August 1981 issue which was devoted primarily to maintainability.

Failure Mode, Effect, and Criticality Analysis.   The concept of failure mode, effect, and criticality analysis discussed under Reliability can also be applied to evaluating maintainability (Kimble, 1982). The steps are:

1. List the failure modes for the proposed design.
2. For each failure mode, state the effect on other components or on the overall system.
3. For each failure mode, rate the likelihood of occurrence, accessability, detectibility, and labor hours to service or replace the part. The "service value" is the product of these ratings. The higher the number, the more serious is the mode of serviceability or failure. The analysis also takes into account the types of routine servicing required by the design.

Design Aids for Maintainability.   To attain a proper balance between maintainability and other parameters requires that the product designer give consideration to various alternatives and trade-offs, such as the following:

Reliability versus maintainability: For example, given an availability requirement, should the response be an improvement in reliability or in maintainability?

Modular versus nonmodular construction: Modular design requires added design effort but reduces the time required for diagnosis and remedy in the field. The fault need only be localized to the module level, after which the defective module is unplugged and replaced. This concept is being rapidly extended to consumer products such as television sets.

Repair versus throwaway: For some products or modules, the cost of field repair exceeds the cost of making new units in the factory. In such cases, design for throwaway is an economic improvement in maintainability.

Built-in versus external test equipment: Built-in test features reduce diagnostic time but usually at an added investment.

Person versus machine: For example, should the operation/maintenance function be highly engineered with special instrumentation and repair facilities, or should it be left to skilled technicians with general-use equipment?

Beyond such widely prevailing questions, there are numerous design features

TABLE 13.15 Maintainability Prediction Worksheet*

Part category	λ	N	(N)(λ)	Maintenance times, h							(N)(λ)(Mct_i)
				Loc	Iso	Acc	Ali	Che	Int	Mct_i	
Part A	0.161	2	0.322	0.02	0.08	0.14	0.01	0.01	0.11	0.370	0.119
Part B	0.102	4	0.408	0.01	0.05	0.12	0.01	0.02	0.12	0.330	0.134
Part C	0.021	5	0.105	0.03	0.04	0.11	⋯	0.01	0.14	0.330	0.034
Part D	0.084	1	0.084	0.01	0.03	0.10	0.02	0.03	0.11	0.300	0.025
Part E	0.452	9	4.060	0.02	0.04	0.13	0.02	0.03	0.08	0.320	1.299
Part F	0.191	8	1.520	0.01	0.02	0.11	0.01	0.02	0.07	0.240	0.364
Part G	0.022	7	0.154	0.02	0.05	0.15	⋯	0.05	0.15	0.420	0.064
Total			6.653								2.039

*N = quantity of parts; λ = failure rate; Loc = localization; Iso = isolation; Acc = access; Ali = alignment; Che = check-out; Int = interchange; Mct_i = maintenance cycle time. For determination of MMHc, enter worker-hours for maintenance times.

Source: Blanchard and Fabrycky, 1981, p. 405.

which have been identified as contributing to good maintainability. NAVSHIP (1972) has identified design criteria for improved maintainability.

Maintainability Demonstration. For complex equipment, MIL-STD-471A (1983) provides detailed maintainability demonstration procedures. It provides approaches for evaluating maintainability during design by identifying three phases—verification, demonstration, and evaluation. In the verification phase, the objectives are to (1) verify and update the maintainability model that has evolved from a design analysis, (2) correct any design deficiencies with respect to maintainability, and (3) provide assurance that the maintainability requirements can be achieved. In the demonstration phase, tests or analyses are conducted to determine if the formal maintainability requirements have been achieved. Finally, the evaluation phase has three purposes: (1) evaluate the operational, maintenance, and support environment on maintainability parameters, (2) evaluate the correction of any deficiencies that were found in previous phases, and (3) demonstrate maintainability at the depot level.

Demonstration of qualitative requirements consists of evaluating the design using certain design checklists for maintainability. For quantitative maintainability requirements, demonstration consists of conducting certain maintainability tasks, timing them, and comparing the results to the maintainability time requirements.

Maintainability Data Systems. Maintainability data are collected throughout the entire life cycle of a product. The sources of such data include maintainability analyses during design, engineering tests, maintainability demonstration tests, mock-ups, field evaluation of the product, and operational use. Such data are ultimately useful in determining compliance of a product with maintainability requirements and in identifying problem areas requiring corrective action. However, maintainability data have other uses that go beyond determining conformance with specifications. These uses include providing information for spare parts, determining personnel requirements, providing information for technical manuals, test equipment and training, and establishing repair time data for use in prediction on new designs.

Data collection systems for maintainability (and reliability) are essential if designers are to be provided with feedback to help them on future designs. Such feedback is essential during the product development phase of the product life cycle in order to provide insight into areas of the design that may be deficient in maintainability.

PLANNING FOR SAFETY

The wave of new legislation and court decisions of the 1960s and 1970s has greatly intensified emphasis on product safety. Nowhere is this emphasis greater than during product design. The mood of society has been one of putting responsibility for human safety overwhelmingly on manufacturers, and hardly at all on the users of the products.

The Organized Safety Program. Organized, companywide approaches to product safety have taken one of two main roads:

1. *A company product safety committee to coordinate activities of all company* *departments:* This approach is discussed in Section 34 under Product Liability.

2. *A concept of product safety engineering and management which is based in the Product Design Department:* This approach has been fostered by the military agencies (and others) and is discussed below.

Safety Program Objectives. An example of the military approach is seen in MIL-STD-882 (1969) which is frequently specified on government contracts. This standard identifies the following as objectives for safety programs:

Safety should be designed into the product to a degree consistent with mission requirements.

Hazards associated with each product (and its components and units) are to be identified, eliminated, or controlled to an acceptable level.

Control is to be established over hazards that cannot be eliminated, so as to protect personnel, equipment, and property.

Risks involved in the use of new materials, production techniques, or testing techniques are to be minimized.

Safety Tasks. The organized program identifies specific tasks to be performed during the various phases of new-product development. These tasks are principally as follows:

During concept formulation phase: Conduct concept safety studies; perform preliminary hazard analysis; define product safety performance "envelope"; select product safety effectiveness measures, i.e., figure of merit.

During contract definition phase (A:) Prepare a proposed safety plan; update the preliminary hazard analysis; identify which are the safety requirements in the specification; include safety considerations in trade-off studies. It is becoming common practice for safety-sensitive specification requirements to be marked with a special symbol. This symbol then carries through to suppliers, manufacturing processes, test specifications, etc.

During contract definition phase (B): Implement approved contract definition safety plan; complete preliminary hazards analysis; identify safety decisions to be made before the development phase; establish a firm safety plan for the development phase, including a breakdown of safety tasks.

During development phase: Implement program approved in definition phase; provide design criteria and evaluate product design through hazard analysis and safety studies; establish test requirements; participate in program reviews and in trade-off studies.

During subsequent phases: Help maintain safety precautions throughout, including audit of engineering changes.

Quantification of Safety. Generally, quantification of safety has been time-related. Industrial injury rates are quantified on the basis of lost-time accidents per million labor-hours of exposure. (Note that this expresses the frequency of occurrence but does not indicate the severity of the accidents.) Motor vehicle injury rates are on the basis of injuries per 100 million miles. School injury rates are on the basis of injuries per 100 thousand student-days.

Product designers have tended to quantify safety in two ways:

1. *Hazard frequency:*   Hazard is any combination of parts, components, conditions, or changing set of circumstances which present an injury potential. Hazard frequency takes the form of frequency of occurrence of an unsafe event and/or injuries per unit of time, e.g., per million hours of exposure. MIL-STD-882A (1977), *System Safety Program Requirements,* has established categories of probability levels for hazards ranging from "frequent" to "impossible." Such probabilities are sometimes referred to as "risk."

2. *Hazard severity:*   MIL-STD-882A recognizes four levels of severity:

   Category I—Catastrophic: May cause death or system loss

   Category II—Critical: May cause severe injury, severe occupational illness, or minor system damage

   Category III—Marginal: May cause minor injury, minor occupational illness, or minor system damage

   Category IV—Negligible: Will not result in injury, occupational illness, or system damage

General Approach to Safety Analysis.   The steps are:

1.   Review available historical data on safety of similar and predecessor products. These data obviously should include complaints, claims, and lawsuits. In addition, data are available from regulators, independent laboratories, and still other sources.

2.   Study the ways in which the product has actually been used and misused. This study is especially important for products which are used by a wide spectrum of the population, e.g., consumer products or those military products which are used directly by the "foot soldier." Such a wide spectrum of humanity inevitably misuses products or finds uses for which the products were never designed. The ordinary household ladder includes a small platform for holding tools, a can of paint, etc. The platform is "obviously" too flimsy to support the weight of a person. Yet enough people do stand on it and are injured by the resulting fall to suggest that the platform may need to be designed to hold a person's weight.

Products for children (or to which children have access) are a special case because of the inexperience of youngsters and because "logic" becomes academic when injured childern are displayed before a jury. A child's building block has a high reliability. Yet the child may fall and get injured on a corner of the block; the child may throw the block and injure another child. Manufacturers may turn to the use of plastic foam for making the blocks, but now new questions arise: Could a child bite off a piece and choke on it? Would the material be toxic? Obviously, a child is misusing a block when biting off a piece. Yet the standards on electric lamp cords have been revised to minimize the danger to a child who may bite through the insulation.

3.   Assess the likelihood that damage will actually occur. This likelihood is the resultant of several probabilities:

   a. That the product will fail in a way which creates a hazard (this probability may be available through failure-rate analysis)

   b. That the existence of the hazard will result in damage

   c. That despite no failures in the product, it will be misused so as to result in damage

4. Quantify the exposure (time, cycles, etc.) of the product and the users to hazardous conditions.

5. Determine the severity of the effect of hazards on product or user.

While safety analyses are of long standing, the empirical, qualitative approaches of the past are giving way to more formalized, quantitative studies, as discussed below.

Tools of Safety Analysis. Henley (1979) discusses some of the numerous techniques of safety analysis. Only the most complex products, involving detailed human-product interrelationships, will require so wide an array of techniques. Usually a few widely used techniques supply the bulk of the analysis needed.

The most fundamental technique is the hazard analysis. This is similar to the failure mode, effect, and criticality analysis (Figure 13.6). Three forms of hazard analysis can be prepared: the preliminary hazard analysis for use during the conceptual design phase; the operation of procedure hazard analysis for identifying hazards created by operating the system; fault hazard analysis for identifying hazardous conditions as a result of hardware failure. RADC (1983) discusses these several forms of hazard analysis. Hammer (1980) shows a preliminary analysis (Figure 13.12) for a household coffee mill.

The hazard analysis technique presents a thorough and logical analysis of all potential hazards in the system. Like the failure mode, effect, and criticality analysis, the technique is exhaustive but it is also costly and time-consuming.

A second technique is the fault tree analysis. This "top-down" approach starts by supposing that an accident takes place. It then considers the possible direct causes which could lead to this accident. Next, it looks for the origins of these causes. Finally, it looks for ways to avoid these origins and causes. The branching out of origins and causes is what gives the technique the name of "fault tree" analysis. The approach is the reverse of the failure mode, effect, and criticality analysis, which starts with origins and causes and looks for any resulting bad effects.

The general procedure for fault tree analysis consists of the following seven steps as defined by RADC (1983):

1. Define the system, ground rules, and any assumptions to be used in the analysis.

2. Develop a simple block diagram of the system showing inputs, outputs, and interfaces.

3. Define the top event (ultimate failure effect) of interest.

4. Construct the fault tree for the top event using the rules of formal logic.

5. Analyze the completed fault tree.

6. Recommend any corrective actions for design changes.

7. Document the analysis and its results.

Hammer (1980) presents a fault tree analysis for an interlock safety circuit (Figure 13.13).

Fault tree diagrams make use of a standard set of symbols. For example, in Figure 13.13, the spadelike symbol with a straight bottom is an "and gate," meaning the output occurs if all input events below it occur. The spade symbol with the curved bottom is an "or gate," meaning the output occurs if one or more of the input events below it occur.

The basic analysis can be extended by adding estimates of probability of occur-

PRODUCT: Electrically operated rotary coffee mill for household use.

Hazard	Occurrence (Cause) Description	Effect	Probability (with No Safeguard)	Possible Safeguard	Remarks and References
Flying object injury	1. Rotating blade assembly is a device which could come apart at high operating speeds, especially if a hard object is put in mill by mistake. 2. Operating mill without cover could permit beans or ground coffee to be thrown out by centrifugal force.	Parts or fragments of mill thrown out at high speed could injure user. Coffee beans or ground coffee thrown out at high velocity and hitting eye could cause severe damage.	Reasonably probable	1. a. Design to positively secure blade so it will not come off during operation. b. Ensure that stresses due to rotational speeds will not be greater than strength. c. Make case and cover strong enough to hold any parts or fragments thrown off.	Normally, the person operating the mill will be holding it and therefore in close proximity. Flying fragments and parts will therefore have a good probability of hitting someone.
High temperature	Electrical power loss or mechanical motion can create high temperatures.	Burns to personnel who contact a hot surface.	1. Metal surfaces: Reasonably probable 2. Plastic material: Remote	1. a. Keep power and friction losses as low as possible. b. Cool mill if there is still a high source of heat. c. Provide insulation to keep outer surfaces at safe temperature.	

FIG. 13.12 Preliminary hazard analysis—coffee mill.

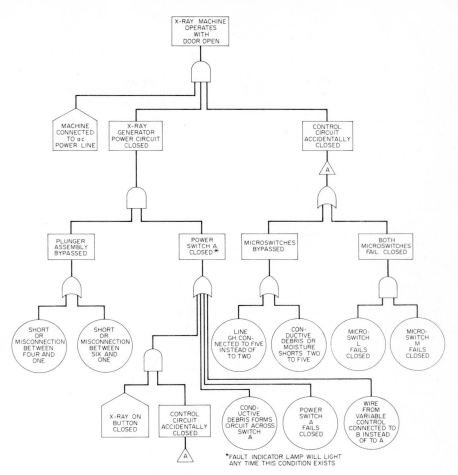

FIG. 13.13 Fault-tree analysis of an interlock safety circuit.

rence to each event on the fault tree. A computer program can then be used to calculate probabilities for various paths and establish priorities for further safety analyses.

Improving Safety through Design. The following are some examples of means used by designers to reduce the hazard levels of products.

   1. *Elimination of hazard:* For example, a pneumatic or hydraulic system might be used instead of an electrical system, where there is a possiblity of fire, explosion, shock, or undesirable heating. Fluidic control systems are being applied more and more for these reasons.

   2. *Hazard-level limitation:* The product can be made intrinsically safe by limiting the energy level of the potential hazard. Electricity may be essential for

a system and cannot be eliminated, but use of solid-state devices—operating at low power levels—can eliminate possibilities of fire, shock, or excessive heating.

3. *Lockouts, lockins, and interlocks:* Isolating transformers in a vault minimizes the possibility of electrocuting personnel. Explosion-proof equipment keeps flame in electrical lines, fittings, and machinery from igniting a flammable environment which surrounds it. Pushbutton switches that must be operated in a specific sequence (if a mishap is to be avoided) can be interlocked.

4. *Fail-safe designs:* These may be fail-passive, fail-operational, or fail-active. A fuse or circuit breaker is a fail-passive device that opens when a dangerous situation occurs, deenergizing and "safing" an electrical system. Admitting water under the disk of a boiler inlet value, instead of over, is a fail-operational arrangement; if the disk separates from the value stem, it is raised by the flowing water so the boiler will continue to operate safely. A destruct system on an air-to-air missile is a fail-active device; if the missile misses its target and does not detonate within a set time, the destruct system blows the missile apart to halt its flight and limit the damage that an armed warhead or entire missile could cause by hitting the ground.

Microprocessors can be incorporated into a design so that single circuit component failures can be detected before the effects produce a hazard to the user. See Section 27 under Computer Integration into Product Design.

While most accidents are caused by failures (of material or personnel), others are the result of hazards inherent in the product; e.g., a color television set may produce an excellent picture and sound but still generate harmful radiation. Minimizing these inherent hazards involves a further list of methods available to the designer:

5. *Monitors:* These are devices which detect dangerous conditions or potential failures so that corrective action can be taken before an accident or failure occurs. Typical examples are temperature and pressure gages, radiation counters, infrared indicators to detect hot spots or flames, and even personnel paired in a buddy-system arrangement to guard each other's well-being in a dangerous situation.

6. *Warnings:* Generally, warnings are made to personnel, but the signals generated by the monitoring systems used for warnings can also be directed to take corrective actions automatically.

7. *Minor loss acceptance:* A restricted amount of product damage may be accepted to assure that major damage is avoided. For example, blowout panels in oil and gas furnaces give way in the event of an explosion and overpressurization from delayed ignition of accumulated fuel vapors. This prevents damage to furnace walls, boiler tubes, and other equipment and structures.

8. *Escape and survival:* Procedures, equipment, and means must be provided to personnel to enable them to leave the scene of an accident to avoid injury, and to survive in the new location. An ejection seat permits escape of a pilot from a disabled aircraft: the parachute is necessary for survival after leaving the aircraft.

9. *Rescue:* Personnel may be incapacitated or trapped in a vehicle or structure where they may be subjected to further injury. It is therefore necessary to provide devices, equipment, and procedures that others can use for their rescue.

10. *Isolation:* Not all hazards can be eliminated. Frequently, control of those hazards which remain is lost, and an accident occurs. It is therefore necessary to provide safeguards to minimize injury or damage that could result. Isolation is not only a means of avoiding accidents, but can also be used to avoid or minimize damaging effects.

Mihalasky (1980) examines the part that human beings play in safety problems. This discussion includes a consideration of the conditions under which machines or human beings are more effective, some of the reasons why human beings make mistakes, and methods to detect and reduce error opportunities involving human beings.

PLANNING FOR HUMAN FACTORS (ERGONOMICS)

As products have become more complex, the interaction of the product with the human being operating the product has assumed increasing importance. The evaluation of the design of a product to assure compatibility with the capabilities of human beings is referred to as "ergonomics" or "human engineering."

The interaction between person and product has two impacts on fitness for use:

1. *The effect that the design has on the ease with which the user can install, operate, and maintain the product:* For example, extensive work has been done applying ergonomics principles to visual display terminals and computer keyboards. This involves the analysis of physical attributes and capabilities to relieve problems of eyestrain, aches and pains, excessive fatigue, and stress (McQuade, 1984).

2. *The effect of the design on the reliability of the performance of the human being using the product:* Some failures of a product are due to mistakes made by the user. Other product failures are due to designs that make human errors more likely. One example concerns the connection for an instrument box on an aircraft. Failures were reported after only 200 to 300 flight hours, but when the "faulty" boxes were returned for repair they operated satisfactorily. Investigation revealed that the boxes would in effect unplug from the plane because of loose connections—an apparent human error. The cause of the loose connection was traced to the position of the boxes in the plane; i.e., it was physically impossible for technicians to apply enough force on the box to lock it firmly in place. The corrective action was a design change to move the location of the boxes. A similar scenario is reported for loose bolts on vehicles. Loose bolts are often viewed as due to improper torquing by an assembly operator. The reason for the improper torquing may be a design that makes it impossible to properly insert a torque tool. Either the design must be changed to gain access or a special tool must be developed.

The early applications of ergonomics were heavily in the aerospace industry. Other applications now include telephones, cameras, sewing machines, and bowling balls. Eastman Kodak Company (1983) has prepared a useful reference that provides principles and guidelines for designing products for human use.

PLANNING FOR MANUFACTURING, INSPECTION, AND TRANSPORTATION

As the product design is the foundation for later steps on the Spiral, planning for these steps should start during product development.

Planning for Manufacturing. All industries are replete with examples illustrating how the lack of thorough consideration of producibility during product development resulted in serious problems during manufacturing.

In one company, a new chemical was developed to provide an economical substitute for another product. Laboratory trials confirmed the savings. Pressure to realize these savings led to a decision to proceed with large-scale manufacture without going through a scaled-up trial or pilot plant. Unfortunately, many problems occurred. An analysis revealed that the "successful" laboratory trials treated some technical factors as insignificant and used oversimplified assumptions. The product was abandoned.

An essential need is to improve the understanding of the relationship of process variables to product results. With such an understanding, designers can then identify in specifications the product characteristics (and their limits) that must be controlled during manufacturing in order to achieve fitness for use. This will be useful to:

1. *Improve the launching of new products:* For example, lighter automobiles require that castings be made with thinner cross sections. In turn, these demands on castings require closer controls on materials and manufacturing processes. However, making such controls effective requires that engineers, supervisors, and workers know which process variables to control and how to control them. In due course, this knowledge is gradually acquired through experience, experiments, and other means. However, during the time of acquiring that knowledge much scrap and rework is endured and often some product recalls are necessary.

2. *Improve the current yield of the manufacuring processes:* Where the relationship is not clearly understood, the costs of scrap, rework, and excessive inspection are high—much higher than the cost of acquiring the new knowledge needed to understand the relationships.

3. *Provide information which can be used to train supervisors and workers:* Job turnover is destroying the old concept of training by experienced supervisors and workers. What is needed is to learn these important relationships, incorporate them into manufacturing planning documents, and train the manufacturing personnel in the use of those relationships.

In understanding the relationship of process variables to product results, experimental design techniques can be useful (see Section 16 under Application of Experimental Design to Optimize Process Variables).

Tolerancing. The selection of tolerances has a dual effect on the economics of quality. The tolerance affects:

1. Fitness for use and hence the saleability of the product
2. Costs of manufacturer (facilities, tooling, productivity) and quality costs (equipment, inspection, scrap, rework, material review, etc.)

Most tolerances are established by methods which, in varying degrees, are less than scientific, The principal methods include:

1. *By precedent:* There is much merit to use of past practice (which has stood the test of time), provided the practice is sound. As will be seen, past practice includes a serious bias toward tight tolerances.

2. *By bargaining:* When proposed tolerances are challenged on the ground of high costs, it is often easier to reach an agreement by bargaining than to undergo the costs of a thorough investigation.

3. *From tolerance systems:* There has been a great deal of standardization of methods of dimensioning and tolerancing, at company, industry, national, and international levels. The published standards become the basis of design and shop practice except for those tolerances which require special consideration. Many companies use preprinted notes on drawings stating, for example, "Unless otherwise specified, all dimensions shown are to be held to ±0.015 in." Even more basic is the approach to always use shop standards and have the designer put tolerances only on characteristics for which shop standards are inadequate. This approach results in realistic tolerances than can be rigidly enforced.

In theory, the designer should, by scientific study, establish the proper balance between the value of precision and the cost of precision. In practice, the designer is unable to do this for each tolerance—there are too many quality characteristics. As a result, only a minority of tolerances are set scientifically. Scientific tools for tolerancing include:

1. *Regression studies:* For example, a thermostat may be required to turn on and shut off a power source at specified low and high temperature values, respectively. A number of thermostat elements are built and tested. The prime recorded data are (*a*) turn on temperature, (*b*) shut off temperature, and (*c*) physical characteristics of the thermostat elements. These data permit scatter diagrams to be prepared and regression equations (see Section 23 under Regression) to be computed to aid in establishing critical component tolerances on a basis which is scientific within the confidence limits for the numbers involved.

In Figure 13.14, the performance limits are located on the vertical axis and extended horizontally until the regression line is intersected. The tolerance limits on the critical dimension can then be read on the horizontal axis. Shainin (1976, 1978) discusses this concept along with the effect of gage variability.

2. *Statistical analysis of development data:* Designers often must set tolerance limits with only a few measurements from the process (or more likely from the development tests conducted under laboratory conditions). In developing a

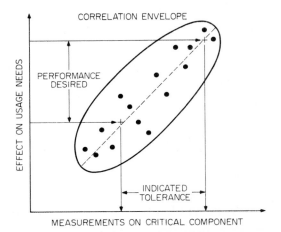

FIG. 13.14 Scatter diagram for setting tolerances.

paint formulation, the following values of gloss were obtained: 76.5, 75.2, 77.5, 78.9, 76.1, 78.3, and 77.7. A group of chemists were asked where they would set a minimum specification limit. Their answer was 75.0—a reasonable answer for those without statistical knowledge. Figure 13.15 shows a plot of the data on normal probability paper (see Section 23 under Predictions with Normal Distributions). If the line is extrapolated to 75.0, the plot predicts that about 11 percent of the population with fall below 75.0—even though all of the sample data exceeds 75.0. Of course, a larger sample size is preferred and further statistical analyses could be made, but the plot provides a simple tool to evaluate a small sample of data.

Another technique for dealing with small samples consists of combining data from different development tests. Suppose the development process investigated several alternative design concepts in order to find a satisfactory design. For each of these concepts, a few tests were run to evaluate the design. Although the different concepts may have yielded much different results on the *average* value, the amount of *variation* about the different average values may be the same. If this is proven statistically to be true, then the data on *variation* within each design can be combined to provide a larger sample size for setting tolerance limits for the chosen design. This approach requires judgment, but it can help when the designer is forced to set limits based on only a few measurements.

FIG. 13.15 Probability plot of development data.

3. *Tolerances for interacting dimensions:* Numerous designs involve "interacting dimensions." An electronic circuit may consist of 11 elements in series; a mechanical assembly may consist of a buildup of 8 elements; a single complex part may include a chain of 10 dimensions, starting from a base line. What these designs have in common is the existence of interaction among these elements or dimensions. Each element of dimension has its own tolerances. However, the variation of the composite (the circuit, the assembly, or the chain) will be related to the variations of the elements according to the laws of probability; i.e., it is unlikely that all the extremes will come together simultaneously.

This unlikelihood makes it possible to establish wider tolerances on elements of such designs without significantly increasing the extent of nonconformance. The scientific approach to this is discussed in Section 23 under Tolerance Limits for Interacting Dimensions. The formula involved requires certain assumptions that have been studied by Bender (1975). He provides suggestions on how to combine "probability and experience" in applying the formula.

4. *Computer simulation of interacting dimensions:* In a series of three papers, Evans (1975) discusses four methods of statistical tolerancing covering both linear and nonlinear cases. One of the methods is a Monte Carlo simulation.

Simulation is one of the most useful of the techniques of operations research and is directly applicable to the problem of statistical tolerancing. It is particularly useful when the component distributions are nonnormal and the relationship between the components and the final result is complex and difficult to analyze with conventional statistical methods.

A simulation is usually made using a computer model. The distribution of each component is defined in terms of the form of the distribution and numerical parameters, e.g., a normal distribution with a mean of 2.000 and standard deviation of 0.004 or an exponential distribution with a mean of 1.000. The relationship between the components and the final result is then expressed in a model equation. This may be a simple or complex combination of component dimensions.

In a Monte Carlo simulation, the computer uses a "random-number generator" to draw values at random from each component distribution and combine them (using the model equation) to obtain a simulated value of the overall result. This process is repeated many times and represents a simulation of what would happen if many assemblies were made at random from components having the characteristics described in the simulation model. The simulated assembly dimensions can then be summarized in a histogram or other form, and used to set assembly tolerances or to evaluate previously defined assembly tolerances. With a simulation model, component distributions can be changed and the effect on the overall result immediately predicted by running additional simulation runs.

Holmes and Michalek (1982) present some examples of the simulation technique as applied in the automotive industry. Rimondi, Tavazza, and Turello (1976) discuss the application to vulcanization and structural problems in rubberlike products.

5. *Concept of position tolerance:* This concept is important where the function and interchangeability of mating parts are vital. It can result in (1) larger tolerances than those possible from conventional tolerancing, and (2) more efficient inspection techniques. Further discussion can be found in Frank (1977) and Shaffer (1982).

6. *Tolerances for nonquantifiable characteristics:* An important subset of quality characteristics are "sensory" features such as surface blemishes, color, and others. These cannot be quantified and measured through conventional technology. If limits on these characteristics are not adequately defined during product development, they will be defined by default by the manufacturing and inspection personnel.

An organized approach to setting sensory standards is discussed in Section 18 under Sensory Qualities.

Peach (1980) discusses a procedure for setting limits of acceptability for characteristics of consumer products.

Unrealistic Tolerances Loosely Enforced. In most companies the accumulated specifications contain an extensive array of unduly tight tolerances, i.e., tolerances not really needed to achieve fitness for use. This accumulation is a natural result of the historical forces to which the design department has been subjected:

1. The designers had clear responsibility for assuring that the product was fit for use and had only vague responsibility for assuring that the product could be made economically.

2. The designer had facilities for testing whether the design would be fit for use, but lacked facilities for testing whether the design could be produced economically.

3. When the resulting tight tolerances created shop troubles, the shop often responded by exceeding the tolerances in order to meet delivery dates. Then, when many of the products performed satisfactorily, the shop drew the conclusion that the designers were needlessly tight. However, there were also cases in which exceeding the tolerances resulted in field failures. From these cases the designers drew the conclusion that the shop could not be trusted fully. One reaction of designers was to set still closer limits in order to neutralize the expected overruns. This game was detected or suspected by the shop, so that the mistrust became mutual.

Recent trends have been in the direction of reducing the biases of both the designers and the shops. However, there remains an accumulation of "unrealistic tolerances loosely enforced" which all concerned would like to convert into a situation of "realistic tolerances rigidly enforced." This conversion cannot be accomplished by the "legitimate" process of making engineering investigations and issuing engineering change orders. There are too many investigations, and the issuance of engineering change orders is too elaborate a process.

The conversion must be restricted to selected tolerances which are creating the bulk of the cost problem. The selection may be made from the "high dollar loss list" of the quality cost studies, the list of products for which 100 percent inspection is being conducted, the list of nonconforming products which has come before the material review board, and the list of changes requested by suppliers.

Once the list of suspect tolerances has been identified, there are a number of ways in use for minimizing the conversion effort:

1. Establish an order of priority for the "vital few" and deal with them through the regular engineering change procedure.

2. For tolerances of less than vital importance, create a "short loop" for changes; i.e., designate a team (e.g., designer and quality control engineer) to make changes without going through full documentation, e.g., marking up local drawings. Later, when some other reason arises for making an engineering change, the incompletely documented cases will be included.

3. Alternatively, if the tolerance is discovered to be too tight, leave the specification unchanged, but revise the sampling plans to accept a wider dispersion of product. In most companies, changes in sampling plans are accomplished with minimal documentation.

4. Adopt the rule that three material review board waivers of the same defect constitutes a permanent waiver.

A broad solution consists of devising a new system of tolerancing and enforcement for all new product lines so that they will be launched on a basis of "realistic tolerances rigidly enforced." (This will mean that there will be two systems of tolerancing and enforcement in the company simultaneously.) Then as the older designs phase out, only the new system will remain in force.

Providing Aids to Designers. Any evolutionary solution to unrealistic tolerances must include ways to minimize the bias of the designers. An essential need is to provide designers with tools which can assist them in understanding the cost consequences of proposed tolerances. Several of these tools are available.

1. *Process capability data:* As data on process capability are worked up and made available for ready reference (see Section 16 under Process Capability: Application), it becomes feasible to train designers in the significance and use of these data.

2. *Data on cost of precision:* A further step is to quantify the actual cost of achieving various levels of precision, e.g., how the cost in dollars increases as the tolerance in millimeters decreases. Surprisingly, the data for preparing tables or charts of these relationships are often already available in the labor standards used to measure production and inspection productivity. What has not been done generally is to convert these data into tables of cost versus precision. For one example, see Section 16, Manufacturing Planning, Table 16.4, and associated discussion.

3. *Seriousness classification:* Generally, the most important characteristics also call for the greatest precision. In consequence, use of seriousness classification of characteristics is also a broad guide to tolerancing. See Section 18 under Seriousness Classification for the methodology employed.

4. *Value analysis:* See the discussion in this section.

5. *Sensory qualities:* See Section 18 under Sensory Qualities.

Rating of Designs for Ease of Manufacture and Other Factors. Phillips (1980) has created a "design quality index" for evaluating proposed designs of an automobile. The numerical value of the index is the sum of the demerits received from checklists of design features which make quality difficult to achieve during manufacture. One checklist covers finish, fit, and function. Typical examples from the checklist along with the number of demerits are given below:

Surface quality: A joint requiring weld, braze, solder, or plastic filler receives one demerit for each 25 mm.

Complexity: Count the number of surface planes, gaps, and joints that have to be matched. If a vertical match is required, this receives one demerit for each feature counted.

Electrical: Each connector not self-ejecting receives one demerit.

The overall quality index is obtained by summing up all of the demerits and subtracting from 145. The result is called the "design quality index."

Fischer (1984) discusses seven principles of designing for assembly. Gager (1986) describes a software system which uses a quantitative approach to analyze a design for efficiency of assembly.

Planning for Inspection and Test.   Complex products increasingly require that planning of inspection and test be done concurrently with design and involve the designer. Jefferson (1974) describes how designers traditionally were asked to create a design and also a factory test specification. A separate department then developed the test. For some designs, test access to the product was difficult. The company now requires the designer to provide an associated debugged test statement (in appropriate automatic test equipment language) which will drive the instrumentation on the shop floor, along with a proven test interface box. In this way, due account is taken of test access, buffering, and measurement capability before designs become too heavily committed. The test statements are evaluated by running formal tests on prototype equipments.

RACD (1982) dicusses approaches for evaluating testability throughout all phases of a major project. Appropriate checklists, design guidelines, and testability engineering techniques are provided.

Designers should identify all quality characteristics in the early design stages and should rate the criticality of characteristics (see below) in order to establish inspection priorities.

Functional and Nonfunctional Characteristics.   The distinction between functional and nonfunctional is set out in Section 18 under Seriousness Classification. The distinctions are clear enough, but industrial practice can intervene to complicate matters. When both kinds of characteristics are published in the same document (as often happens), there is confusion unless it is clearly designated which is which. A major reason for clear designation is the difference in jurisdiction over waivers of nonconformance cases. Generally, the Design Department must be a party to any waiver of functional requirements, but not as to nonfunctional requirements. (Design also has the major voice in deciding what is functional and what is not.)

The trend is toward making clear which characteristics are functional. This is done in any of several ways:

1. Use of separate documents to carry the functional requirements
2. Designation of functional requirements by special code letters
3. Seriousness classifications of characteristics (see Section 18 under Seriousness Classification)

Planning for Packaging, Transportation, and Storage.   Products must be protected from the time they leave the factory to the time they are in the hands of the ultimate user. During that time, the product is exposed to environment in both the transportation mode and the storage mode. Clearly it is important to know what these various environments will be and to plan for them both in the design of the product itself and in the design of the packaging and other protective material used with the product. Planning of the protective material should be done as concurrently as possible with the design of the product. Some of the approaches used to plan for these various environments are discussed in Section 20 on Customer Service under Packaging, Transportation, and Storage.

PLANNING TO MINIMIZE COST

Designing for reliability, maintainability, safety, and other parameters must be done with a simultaneous objective of minimizing cost. Formal techniques to achieve an optimum balance between performance and cost include both quantitative and qualitative approaches. The quantitative approach makes use of a ratio relating performance and cost. Such a ratio tells "what we get for each dollar we spend." The ratio is particularly useful in comparing alternative design approaches for accomplishing a desired function. A comparison of the cost-effectiveness of four alternative designs is shown in Table 13.16. Note that design 3 is the optimum design even though design 4 has higher availability.

Two approaches for achieving a balance between performance and cost, Value Engineering and Design to Cost, are discussed below.

Value Engineering. Value engineering (often called "value analysis") is a technique for evaluating the *design* of a product to assure that the *essential functions* are provided at minimum overall cost to the manufacturer and user. Value engineering tries to assure that the design provides only the essential functions and nothing else that can result in higher costs. Although the aim of value engineering is cost driven, the elimination of nonessential functions can result in improved reliability due to a reduction in product complexity. The steps in a value engineering study are:

1. Collect information on the product.
    a. Define what the customer really wants (e.g., performance, size, weight, appearance, durability, etc.).
    b. Collect design and manufacturing information (e.g., design concepts, preliminary cost estimates, etc.).
    c. Collect cost data and, if appropriate, define the new cost goal to be achieved to meet profitability targets.
    d. Collect information on (*b*) and (*c*) above for competing products.

TABLE 13.16 Cost-Effectiveness Comparison of Alternative Designs

	Design			
	1	2	3	4
Mean time between failures (MTBF)	100	200	500	500
Mean downtime (MDT)	18	18	15	6
Availability	0.847	0.917	0.971	0.988
Life-cycle cost, $	51,000	49,000	50,000	52,000
Number of effective hours	8470	9170	9710	9880
Cost/effective hour, $	6.02	5.34	5.15	5.26

$$\text{Availability} = \frac{\text{MTBF}}{\text{MTBF} + \text{MDT}}$$

Number of effective hours = 10,000 h of life $\times$ availability

2. Define the functions of the product.

    a. Define the total function of the product and then define functions for the lower levels of hardware.

    b. Distinguish between basic and secondary functions.

    c. Define each function in terms of a verb and noun.

    d. Evaluate the relationship between functions.

    e. Determine the current cost of accomplishing each function.

    f. Establish a value target for each function. Possible bases for value are (*i*) the least expensive way of accomplishing the function described by the verb and noun or (*ii*) the estimated cost of accomplishing the same function in a competitor's product.

    g. Analyze the ways competing products accomplish each function.

3. Develop alternative design approaches for accomplishing the function at lower cost.

    a. Establish an atmosphere of open thinking about alternatives and use knowledge from all sources.

    b. Use creative thinking techniques.

    c. Use checklists based on experience within or outside the company.

4. Compare the alternative design approaches and select one for further development and refinement.

    a. Consider using a quantitative rating scheme to compare the alternatives for the various performance factors.

    b. Estimate the cost for each function and compare this to present costs and the target defined in step 2*f.*

    c. Evaluate by comparison of alternatives and search for ways to combine the best ideas from different alternatives.

    d. Estimate the total cost of the selected design approach and determine if this is acceptable for product pricing.

    e. Submit the proposed approach for management approval.

5. Develop the detailed design for the selected design approach.

    a. Use value engineering checklists.

    b. Use knowledge from all sources of information.

    c. Consider using a value engineering team to coordinate the effort.

    d. Prepare a summary report on the old and new designs and submit to management.

    e. Provide for follow-up to determine actual costs.

Some of these steps are illustrated below. Two useful references on concepts and techniques are Miles (1972) and Mudge (1971). Beeck (1985) discusses the interrelation of value engineering and quality.

Tools of Analysis.   The heart of the value engineering approach is the evaluation of function. A product has higher-order functions (the desired function), basic functions, and secondary functions. Allocation of assets should concentrate on the essential functions rather than secondary functions.

The functions can be listed and classified in tabular or graphical form. One graphical tool is the function analysis system technique (FAST) diagram. Figure 13.16 shows a FAST diagram for a truck torsion bar front anchor. The higher-order function on the left-hand side of the diagram is the desired function (in this case, "support vehicle"). Between the two dotted "scope" lines are shown all of the functions required to achieve the higher-order function. The diagram is constructed by working from left to right while asking the question, "How do I achieve the function listed on the left?" In Figure 13.16, the function of "support vehicle" is achieved by "transmit force" which is a basic function. Every FAST diagram has a horizontal critical path of functions going through the center of the diagram. On this path lie the higher-order function, the basic function, required secondary functions, and the "assumed" function. (The assumed function is some activity which is required as input to the basic product itself.)

Required secondary functions appear inside the scope lines but off the critical path. Any function that happens at the same time as a critical path function appears below it and is connected by a vertical line to the critical path function. A function that happens all the time or at the same time as two or more critical path functions is called an "all the time function" and appears in the upper right-hand corner of the diagram (e.g., "fasten parts"). Design objectives or requirements are listed in dotted line boxes above the critical path (e.g., "lab test").

In evaluating the necessity of secondary and basic functions, the diagram is read from right to left while the question is continually asked, "Why do I perform the function to the right of this point?"

A cost analysis revealed that two functions, "fasten parts" and "resist deformation", accounted for 55.5 percent of the total cost. These two functions are not on the critical path of the FAST diagram and thus represent opportunities for cost reduction by redesign.

FIG. 13.16 FAST diagram.

Other Cost-Related Approaches.   Two other approaches are related to the objectives of value analysis—the life cycle cost approach and the design-to-cost (DTC) approach. Life cycle cost is discussed in Section 3 under Life Cycle Costing. In the DTC approach, the starting point is a life cycle cost target and a statement of the overall function desired. No design approach is specified. Alternative design concepts are then developed and evaluated keeping in mind that the cost target must be met. This is in contrast to the conventional approach of creating a design and then estimating the cost of that design.

The DTC approach establishes cost as a parameter equal in importance to technical and field support requirements and delivery schedules. DTC parameters are identified and addressed throughout the product development cycle. The following steps are adapted from MIL-STD-449A (1961):

1. Review technical requirements for feasibility.
2. Translate essential mission requirements into product functions and subfunctions.
3. Define hardware and software characteristics for functions.
4. Evaluate design alternatives for cost.
5. Formulate product requirements.
6. Identify major high-cost elements.
7. Relate high-cost elements to operations, performance, support parameters, and form, fit, and function design characteristics. This requires sensitivity analyses to learn the effect on cost of changes in parameters and characteristics.
8. Perform trade-off analyses to adjust parameters and characteristics to meet DTC targets.
9. Incorporate parameters and characteristics in development specifications and establish firm DTC targets.

To assist in the analyses, computer programs that perform the calculations for life cycle cost are available for specific products (e.g., helicopters, ammunition, and missile systems).

CONFIGURATION MANAGEMENT

Configuration refers to the physical and functional characteristics of a product, including both hardware and software. Ideally, design and development concludes with a design that is "frozen." In practice, design changes are often made after production has started. The collection of activities needed to accomplish these changes is called configuration management. Three elements are involved:

1. *Configuration identification:* This is the process of defining and identifying every element of the product.
2. *Configuration control:* This is a series of actions which manages a design change from the time of the original proposal for change through implementation of approved changes.
3. *Configuration accounting:* This is the process of recording the status of proposed changes and the implementation status of approved changes. Configuration identification and configuration control are discussed below. Configuration accounting is discussed in Section 20 under Configuration Management.

Configuration Identification. A configuration established at a particular point in time is called a base line. The base line is used as a basis of reference from which all future changes are controlled. Configuration identification consists of three levels of base line: (1) the functional base line, which defines the general requirements of an entire product; (2) the allocated base line, which defines the general requirements for a major item in the overall product; and (3) the product base line, which defines the detailed requirements of an item. Additional base lines can be set up if needed.

The base line documents include drawings, specifications, test procedures, standards, and any other information which defines the physical and functional characteristics. In some companies, a configuration base line includes facts such as the following:

1. The physical item conforms to issue 04 of the engineering drawing.

2. The steel was purchased from Feric Steel Furnace on Purchase Order Number 230656, dated 3/27/71, was made on Heat Number WX 37791, and conforms to ASTM 176-61T.

3. The welding was done by operator number 29991 using TIG process 10-721 during April 1981, at which time the operator's license to weld was still in force.

4. The bracket on the item was rejected on April 28, 1981, because the 2.176-in (5.53-cm)-diameter hole was off location (2.719 in instead of 2.705 in $\pm$ 0.010), after which acceptance "as is" was authorized by Engineer Joe Jensen on May 6, 1981.

This broader definition of configuration obviously includes also the identification of the pertinent materials, processes, personnel, etc., which have collectively created the product, plus the data which proves that the resulting product conforms to specifications. Some identification may be marked on the product, but mainly the identification and proof of adequacy are achieved through chains of documentation. The documents consist of engineering drawings, specifications, in-process inspection reports, acceptance inspection and test results, special test results, etc. These inputs are summarized in Figure 13.17 along with some of the resulting outputs.

Configuration Control. This element of configuration management starts at the time of the original proposal for a change and ends with the implementation of approved changes. Configuration control involves the technical evaluation, costing, and determination of which specific products ("serial numbers") will have the change incorporated (called the "effectivity" of the change).

Companies vary widely in their approach to assigning responsibility for configuration control. At one extreme, the real decisions of whether and what to change all rest with the designers, and the "processing" of engineering changes consists solely of assuring that the documentation and products are changed to conform to the intent of the engineers' designs. At the other extreme, processing the engineering change becomes a highly formalized, closely coordinated activity in which the coordinating agency carries a good deal of weight in the decisions of whether and what to change.

The trend has been toward the more formalized, coordinated approach. The reason is that as products have become more complex, the effect of an engineering change has multiplied in complexity and in cost. Since more is at stake and the change for error is multiplied, the companies have made their review structure

Inputs	Documentation system	Outputs and uses
Configuration data		Corrective action loops
Contracts		Discrepancy identification
Product development data	Forms	Failure analysis
Design specifications		Corrective action
Process, other specifications	Procedures	
Engineering changes		Configuration management
	Data recording	Engineering change control
		Traceability
Inspection and test data from:	Data processing	
Receiving inspection	Manual	Improvement programs
Vendor surveillance	Electronic	Quality cost analysis
Process control	Other	Quality improvement
Final inspection, test		
Field performance results	Distribution	Executive reports by time
		Product, responsibility, etc.
	Filing	Vendor performance
Discrepancy data	Retention	In-house performance
Vendor failures	Retrieval	Field performance
Process out of control		Cost results
Scrap rework		Improvement projects
Field complaints, claims		
Warranty charges		Quality assurance to:
Product safety claims		Management
		Customers
		Regulators
		Etc.

FIG. 13.17   Model of documentation system.

more elaborate in order to guard against unneeded or unwise changes and against errors in introducing needed changes.

Special organization machinery is set up to coordinate the engineering changes. This machinery consists of some combination of the following:

1. *A published procedure which defines the role of each department:* Action is taken by the line departments and coordination is done according to the procedure. This approach is sometimes the sole engineering change machinery, e.g., in small companies for noncritical changes or in any company for situations in which there is a continuing procession of many small changes.

2. *A project engineer plus "sign off" by the line departments, usually Design, Manufacture, and Quality Control:* Here the project engineer provides coordination.

3. *A Configuration Control Board set up to review all proposed changes:* The board has representatives from engineering, quality, field engineering, purchasing, manufacturing, and the customer. Usually, the chairman has the authority to make a decision on the change (the decision may be appealed through normal channels). The quality representative may often be in the position of justifying the importance of a change.

4. *A Project Change Administrator who prepares plans, secures approvals, publishes reports, expedites, etc.:* Use of such Administrators tends to be limited to cases where engineering changes are complex and costly.

Classes of Change. A convenient aid for configuration management is to classify the changes as to priority. Companies which use only two classes define them as follows:

Class A changes: These are changes ordered by the customer or changes intended to provide remedies for product safety hazards, deficiencies in field usage, high costs, late deliveries, inadequate field interchangeability, and retrofits in the field.

Class B changes: These are any changes not included in Class A, e.g., minor improvements, phasing out of obsolete products.

In companies using such systems of classifying changes, the class of change is decisive as to:

1. The choice of organization to be used in coordinating the change— e.g., for Class A changes, the combination of committee and administrator may be used, but not for Class B changes.
2. The extent to which the change will be made effective in various categories of product—in field service, in the finished-goods pipeline, in process of manufacture. etc.

Formalized Review Procedure. As the formalized coordination concept takes hold, there evolves a structured review procedure. A sequence of essential tasks is established and forms are designed to require that all changes go through this sequence. Marguglio (1971) presents a thorough discussion of the entire design change control process.

In the formalized reviews, close attention is paid to clear definition of the base line, i.e., the intended design. (During the various phases of product development, there are several design stages.) Unless this base line is clear, the reviews and actions will become confused and will work at cross-purposes.

Once the baseline and the intended changes are clear, the effect of the change is determined. This requires "tracking" the changes through assembly "trees," parts lists, processes, tools, instruments, etc. This tracking must be done through the entire hierarchy of product: system, subsystems, units, components, etc. Increasingly, computers are used to perform most of the tracking in the case of complex products.

As it becomes clear just what aspects of the product are affected, it becomes possible to evaluate the cost and the benefit of the change. For this purpose it is also necessary to secure an inventory of the physical products which will be affected by the change: i.e., how many there are in field use, how many in the pipeline, how many in a semifinished state. There many also be an effect on maintenance support, i.e., on spare parts, repair parts, diagnostic instruments, and repair tools.

Control over this array of information and action is maintained by assigning a project number to each change and establishing for that project the same array of controls as goes with any complex project: list of activities, schedules, cost estimates, cost accounting, status reports, and documentation. This is done over the entire life cycle of the change, from design concept through being made fully effective.

In situations involving sizable, complex inventories, the effectivity of the change likewise becomes complex. If the units of product are serially numbered, then these serial numbers are used to define effectivity, e.g., serial numbers under 450 will undergo no change; serial numbers 451 to 620 will undergo change J only;

serial numbers 621 and over will undergo changes J and K. Where serial numbers are not used, an alternative is to base the effectivity on status of the product in the pipeline, e.g., product already sold will undergo no change; product in finished goods or spare parts inventories will undergo change J; product in process will undergo changes J and K.

Provision is made for countdown, i.e., checking with all affected departments and verifying all critical elements affected.

Marguglio (1971) provides a list of the quality-related factors to be considered during each phase of a change, starting with the change proposal phase and ending with the product verification phase. Berke (1977) discusses methods of monitoring changes during design including the use of a "quality assurance drawing controller." McCarthy (1975) explains how the principles of configuration management can be applied to computer software.

IMPROVING THE EFFECTIVENESS OF PRODUCT DEVELOPMENT

Product development is a "process" which requires the activities of planning, measurement, feedback, and corrective action similar to those required for the manufacturing process, the purchasing process, and other processes. In maximizing the contribution of product development to product quality, the concept of self-control, improving the effectiveness of individual designers, and the role of staff specialists should be examined. These issues are discussed below.

Kano (1984) discussed the use of a "T-typed matrix" for evaluating the capability of an organization to find problems at the early rather than late stages of product development.

Ingram (1984) describes a historical process comprising five steps—historical set-up, grouping and review, creation of a problem log, course analysis, and remedial action.

Gust (1985) describes how the breakthrough sequence for quality improvement (see Section 22, Quality Improvement) was applied to the product development system of a films company.

Concept of Self-Control in Product Development.   Section 17 under Concept of Worker Self-Control presents three criteria which must be met before workers can be held responsible for controlling the quality of their activities. These same criteria are also applicable to product development. Table 13.17 shows a checklist of sample questions to help apply the criteria to product development.

IMPROVING THE EFFECTIVENESS OF INDIVIDUAL DESIGNERS

Implementation of reliability and maintainability techniques is best achieved by bringing designers to a state of self-sufficiency. This is done in two main ways: (1) design experience retention and (2) training.

Design Experience Retention.   All design managers agree that experience is an essential requirement for a good designer. To supplement the designer's own

TABLE 13.17 Self-Control as Applied to Product Development

I. Have designers been provided with the means of knowing what they should be doing?
   A. Do they know the variety of applications for the product?
      1. Do they have complete information on operating environments?
      2. Do they have access to the user to discuss applications?
      3. Do they know the potential field misuses of the product?
   B. Do they have a clear understanding of product requirements on performance, life, warranty period, reliability, maintainability, accessibility, availability, safety, operating costs, and other product features?
      1. Have nonquantitative features been defined in some manner?
      2. Do designers know the level of product sophistication suitable for the user involved?
   C. Are adequate design guidelines, standards, handbooks, and catalogs available?
   D. Do designers understand the interaction of their part of the design with the remainder of the design?
   E. Do they understand the consequences of a failure (or other inadequacy) of their design on: (1) the functioning of the total system? (2) warranty costs? (3) user costs?
   F. Do they know the relative importance of various components and characteristics within components?
   G. Do they know what are the manufacturing process capabilities relative to the design tolerances?
   H. Do they derive tolerances based on functional needs or just use standard tolerances?
   I. Do they know the shop and field costs incurred because of incomplete design specifications or designs requiring change?
II. Have designers been provided with the means for knowing what they are doing?
   A. Do they have the means of testing their design in regard to the following:
      1. Performance, reliability, and other tests?
      2. Tests for unknown design interactions or effects?
      3. Mock-up or pilot run?
   B. Is there an independent review of the design?
   C. Have the detail drawings been checked?
   D. Are designers required to record the analyses for the design?
   E. Do they receive adequate feedback from development tests, manufacturing tests, proving ground tests, acceptance tests, and user experience?
      1. Are the results quantified where possible, including severity and frequency of problems and costs to the manufacturer and user?
      2. Does failure information contain sufficient technical detail on causes?
      3. Have designers visited the user site when appropriate?
   F. Are designers aware of material substitutions, or process changes?
   G. Do they receive notice when their design specifications are not followed in practice?
III. Have designers been provided with the means of regulating the design process?
   A. Are they provided with information on new alternative materials or design approaches? Do they have a means of evaluating these alternatives?
   B. Have they been given performance information on previous designs?
   C. Are the results of research efforts on new products transmitted to designers?
   D. Are designers' approvals required to use products from new suppliers?
   E. Do designers participate in defining the criteria for shipment of products?
   F. May designers propose changes involving trade-offs between functional performance, reliability, and maintainability?
   G. Are designers told of changes to their designs before they are released?
   H. Have causes of design failures been determined by thorough analysis?
   I. Do designers have the authority to follow their designs through the prototype stage and make design changes where needed?
   J. May designers initiate design changes?
   K. Are field reports reviewed with designers before making decisions on design changes?
   L. Do designers understand the procedures and chain of command for changing a design?

experience, it is common to summarize the experience of other designers as well. This "experience retention" is achieved through several widely used tools:

1. *Design Standards Manual:* This book accumulates the departmental standards derived from experience, along with referencing the outside standards which have been adopted. The manual is supplemented by notes, memoranda, and other "standards in the making." In large companies there is an Engineering Standards Department which prepares and maintains these standards manuals.

2. *Checklists:* These lists are a form of "countdown" to be checked out by the designer as he or she proceeds with the project. For example, the checklist on fire hazard would typically include the following:
   - What could cause a break in the fuel line or oil line?
   - What could cause a fuel or oil leak?
   - Could there be a source of ignition?
   - What is combustible?
   - How can a fire be detected?
   - How can the fuel be turned off?
   - What is the escape route for personnel?

3. *Usage and Failure Data Banks:* The performance of the product under conditions of actual use constitutes the most important single source of experience data. A data bank to collect and summarize such information becomes one of the most useful sources of design experience.

4. *Tools for Economic Analysis:* These include charts and tables showing the relationship of cost to precision (see, for example, Section 16, Table 16.4), tables of process capability, and comparative costs of alternative designs.

Training for Designers.   To attain self-sufficiency, designers also need training. In part, this is training to use the design experience retention and, in part, to become proficient in the use of tools which have had their origin in other disciplines. These tools include:

1. *Quantification of reliability:* The basic reliability models, formulas, and procedures are well known and have been organized into standardized training courses. It is comparatively easy to train designers in the use of these basic formulas and procedures (which have wide application). For more complex situations, there must be access to reliability specialists.

2. *Other quantification:* Training courses have been worked up in maintainability and safety, but to a lesser degree. However, enough is available to offer a useful indoctrination to designers.

3. *Design of experiments:* The increased complexity of products and the greater demand for statistical significance in test results has required that test programs be designed in a way which holds costs of testing to a minimum while yielding maximum information. Courses in design of experiments and the associated analysis of the resulting data have been standardized at several levels of sophistication and are widely available.

4. *Process capability:* The concept of process capability as an input in the setting of tolerances is important and can be taught to designers.

5. *Problem-solving methodology:* Quality improvement concepts (see Section 22, Quality Improvement) apply to product development as well as to other

functions on the Spiral. The diagnostic journeys from symptom to cause and cause to remedy are defined and can be taught to designers.

Training courses work best when the student is required to apply the training as part of the course ("learning by doing"). For example, in value engineering seminars, students conduct a value engineering analysis on actual hardware; in quality improvement seminars, students work on a team project while viewing video tapes on problem solving.

Experimentation in training techniques should be encouraged. Crothers (1971) describes using training workshops as a means of conducting audits on activites. In one case, a circuit analysis workshop was held to evaluate the lack of compatibility between circuit analyses performed by designers and those performed by reliability analysts. Ironically, the initial goal of the workshop was to "educate" designers regarding the value of the work from the reliability analysis group. As a result of the workshop, however, it was concluded that the output of the reliability analysts should be changed to present designers with information in a more useful form. This included revising the work on worst-case analysis criteria, thermo analysis goals, and traditional reliability analysis methods using computer aids.

Beyond the specific material presented in formal training courses there is a need for designers to understand more fully the demands which will be made on the product through its life cycle. A Japanese maker of color television sets uses a combination of on-the-job training and classroom training to achieve this goal. Prospective designers are required to undergo training in the following areas:

1. *In the marketplace:* Part of this 3-month training is in the merchant shops, meeting clients, selling the product, and learning of the problems of marketing. In addition, the trainee makes service calls to learn about the conditions of use, the problems of field maintainability, supply of spare parts, etc.

2. *In the factory:* This 9-month training program provides the trainee with knowledge about factory conditions, the factory work stations, the training and outlook of the factory personnel, the capabilities of the processes, etc. In addition, the future designer becomes familiar with the special assembly line used to test out new models.

3. *In statistical methodology:* This 144-h training course enables the designer to become familiar with the mathematical tools. (This training is not given to a new designer, but it is a prerequisite for promotion to the level of "lead designer.")

A designer who possesses the foregoing bodies of knowledge will obviously be more effective than one who lacks them. As an alternative the designer can collaborate with those who do have the knowledge (as in the design review meetings). Failing such collaboration, the designs will be deficient due to the absence of useful knowledge and tools.

Staff Specialist Organization.   A prickly problem in organizing for new-product design is that of using "new" disciplines such as reliability engineering, maintainability engineering, and safety engineering. While the discussion which follows will concentrate on reliability, the principles involved apply generally to all these specialties.

The time required to introduce a new discipline is usually shortened if a new specialty department is created for it and if the head of the specialty understands his or her role. This role is ideally one of analyzing the projects, using the tools of the new specialty, and making the results of the analysis available to the "regular line" departments. All of this must be done in a way that emphasizes that *the responsibility for achieving fitness for use in the product design rests with the line departments—not the staff specialty.*

The track record on the use of specialist departments has been mixed. Usually, the specialist evaluates the design for reliability or maintainability and provides comments to the designer. Unfortunately, these reviews often occur too late. Nothing is more aggravating than to have suggestions made on a design after the design is finalized and manufacturing is waiting for the design to be released. Reliability inputs must be made available early during the design process if they are to be acted upon.

Ultimately, implementation of the new techniques can best be accomplished by training designers to use them as an integral part of the design process. Steps must then be taken by the staff department to gradually transfer the associated responsibilities to the line designers. Jefferson (1974) explains how one company evolved an approach where a designer is required to produce a design, a test specification, a test package, a reliability prediction, and a repair chart. Bajaria (1979, 1980) discusses the relative role of specialists and line designers along with other issues involved in motivating design engineers to use techniques for reliability.

REFERENCES

Advisory Group on Reliability of Electronic Equipment (1957). *Reliability of Military Electronic Equipment.* Office of the Assistant Secretary of Defense (R & D), U. S. Government Printing Office, Washington, DC.

Allen, Martin (1980). "CAD/CAM and the Third Industrial Revolution." Paper presented at the American Society of Mechanical Engineers, 101st Winter Annual Meeting, New York.

ANSI (1978). *Quality Systems Terminology.* American National Standard A-3. Available from American Society for Quality Control, 310 West Wisconsin Avenue, Milwaukee, WI 53202.

ARINC Research Corporation (1962). *Reliability Theory and Practice.* A training program developed by ARINC, Washington, DC.

Arnitz, William E. (1981). "GIDEP Can Improve Productivity through Information Exchange." *Proceedings, Annual Reliability and Maintainability Symposium.* IEEE, New York, pp. 128–131.

Bailey, R. A. and Gilber, R. A. (1982). "Strife Testing." *Quality,* November, pp. 53–55.

Bajaria, H. J. (1979). "Motivating Line Engineers for Reliability, Part I." *ASQC Technical Conference Transactions,* Milwaukee, pp. 767–773.

Bajaria, H. J. (1980). "Motivating Line Engineers for Reliability, Part II." *ASQC Technical Conference Transactions,* Milwaukee, pp. 168–176.

Bajaria, H. J. (1983). *Integration of Reliability, Maintainability and Quality Parameters in Design.* Paper SP-533, Society of Automotive Engineers, Warrendale, PA.

Beeck, W. O. (1985). "Quality and Value Analysis—Engineering, the Ideal Marriage." *Proceedings of the Conference of Quality and Development.* European Organization for Quality Control, Berne, vol. 3, pp. 299–312.

Belbin, R. M. (1970). *Quality Calamities and their Management Implications.* OPN8, British Institute of Management, London.

Bender, Art (1975). "Statistical Tolerancing as it Relates to Quality Control and the Designer." *Automotive Division Newsletter of ASQC,* April, p. 12.

Berger, Robert L. and Jenkins, Larry C. (1984). "Electronic Equipment Thermal Management." *Proceedings, Annual Reliability and Maintainability Symposium.* IEEE, New York, pp. 17–22.

Berke, Howard L. (1977). "To Assure Quality Productivity, Monitor the Design." *ASQC Technical Conference Transactions,* Milwaukee, pp. 590–593.

Blanchard, Benjamin S. and Fabrycky, Wolter J. (1981). *Systems Engineering and Analysis.* Prentice-Hall, Englewood Cliffs, NJ, pp. 391–406.

Brach, J. P., Jr. and Phaller, L. J. (1980). "Integrated Test—A Must for Reliability Achievement." *Proceedings, Annual Reliability and Maintainability Symposium.* IEEE, New York, pp. 242–247.

Burgess, John A. (1985). "Design Reviews for All Seasons." *ASQC Quality Congress Transactions,* Milwaukee, pp. 451–455.

Cahill, Hugh E. and Davids, Richard C. (1984). "Adam—A Computer Aid to Maintainability Design." *Proceedings, Annual Reliability and Maintainability Symposium.* IEEE, New York, pp. 12–16.

Cherry, D. H., Grogan, J. C., Holmes, W. A., and Perris, F. A. (1978). "Availability Analysis for Chemical Plants." *Chemical Engineering Process,* January, pp. 172–185.

Crothers, D. H. (1971). "Workshop Techniques for Programmed Audits." *Proceedings, Annual Symposium on Reliability.* IEEE, New York, pp. 139–144.

Duane, J. T. (1964). "Learning Curve Approach to Reliability Monitoring." *IEEE Transactions on Aerospace,* vol. 2, no. 2, pp. 563–566.

Dussault, Heather B. (1984). "Automated FMEA—Status and Future." *Proceedings, Annual Reliability and Maintainability Symposium.* IEEE, New York, pp. 1–5.

Eastman Kodak Company (1983). *Ergonomic Designs for People at Work,* vol. I, Human Factors Section. Lifetime Learning Publications, Division of Wadsworth Publishing Company, Belmont, CA.

Ekings, J. Douglas and Sweetland, Robert L. (1978). "Burn-In Forever? There Must Be a Better Way." *Proceedings, Annual Reliability and Maintainability Symposium.* IEEE, New York, pp. 286–293.

Emphrain, M., Jr. and Hamilton, A. B. (1973). *Locomotive Reliability.* Paper 73-DGP-14, Diesel and Gas Engine Power Division, American Society of Mechanical Engineers, New York.

Erhardt, C. C. (1980). "Economic Advantages of True Position Tolerancing." *ASQC Technical Conference Transactions,* Milwaukee, pp. 559–564.

Evans, David H. (1975). "Statistical Tolerancing: The State of the Art, Part I: Background; Part II: Methods for Estimating Moments; Part III: Shifts and Drifts." *Journal of Quality Technology,* January, vol. 6, no. 4; April, vol 7, no. 1; October, vol. 7, no. 2.

Fennell, Thomas L. and Nicolino, Thomas A. (1984). Computer Aided Testability." *Proceedings, Annual Reliability and Maintainability Symposium.* IEEE, New York, pp. 6–11.

Fischer, W. Robert (1984). "Design for Assembly." *Proceedings, Annual Reliability and Maintainability Symposium.* IEEE, New York, pp. 409–411.

Frank, Norman C. (1982). "Ten Commandments for Laboratory Notebooks." *Quality Progress,* November, pp. 40–41.

Frank, G. R. (1977). "Tolerance Challenge." *ASQC Technical Conference Transactions,* Milwaukee, pp. 72–78.

Gager, Russ (1986). "Designing for Productivity Saves Millions." *Appliance Manufacturer,* January.

Garrick, B. John and Mulvihill, Robert J. (1974). "Reliability and Maintainability of Mechanized Bulk Mail Systems." *Proceedings, Annual Reliability and Maintainability Symposium.* IEEE, New York.

Goree, Paul F. and Musson, Thomas A. (1984). "DOD/Industry—R&M Case Study Analysis." *Proceedings, Annual Reliability and Maintainability Symposium,* IEEE, New York, pp. 91–98.

Gust, Lawrence J. (1985). "Non-Manufacturing Quality Improvement." *The Juran Report,* No. 4, Winter, pp. 112–120.

Hammel, Lisa (1974). "Five Years and a Large Sum of Money Later, A New Line of Dolls." *The New York Times,* Feb. 18, p. 20.

Hammer, Willie (1980). *Product Safety Management and Engineering.* Prentice-Hall, Englewood Cliffs, NJ.

Hellend, Kris L., Jr. (1978). "Motivating Management on Maintainability." *Proceedings, Annual Reliability and Maintainability Symposium.* IEEE, New York, pp. 32–37.

Henley, Ernest J. (1979). "Analytical Methods in Risk and Safety Assessment." *ASQC Technical Conference Transactions,* Milwaukee, pp. 717–725.

Herrold, George R. (1976). "GIDEP Data Aids Technical Problem Solving." *Proceedings, Annual Reliability and Maintainability Symposium.* IEEE, New York, pp. 46–51.

Hill, John S. and Still, Richard R. (1984). "Adapting Products to LDC Tastes." *Harvard Business Review,* March–April, pp. 92–101.

Holmes, Richard K. and Michalek, Joseph M. (1982). "Optimizing Quality through Variation Simulation." *ASQC Quality Congress Transactions,* Milwaukee, pp. 382–390.

Ingram, Gary E. (1984). "Historical Processes for Quality Project Management." *Project Management Institute Proceedings,* Philadelphia, pp. 1–3.

Jacobs, Richard M. (1967). "Implementing Formal Design Review." *Industrial Quality Control,* February, pp. 398–404.

Jayachandran, Toke and Moore, Louis R. (1976). "A Comparison of Reliability Growth Models." *IEEE Transactions on Reliability,* vol. R-25, no. 1, April, pp. 49–51.

Jefferson, G. R. (1974). "Establishing Quality at the Design and Development Phase." *Joint Conference of the Defense Quality Assurance Board and the Defense Industry Quality Assurance Panel.* University of Kent, Canterbury, England, September, pp. 11–17.

Juran, J. M. and Gryna, Frank M. (1970). *Quality Planning and Analysis,* 1st ed. McGraw-Hill, New York, p. 613.

Juran, J. M. and Gryna, Frank M. (1980). *Quality Planning and Analysis,* 2nd ed. McGraw-Hill, New York, p. 106.

Kano, Noriaki (1984). "Problem Solving in New Product Development—Application of T-Typed Matrix." *World Quality Congress.* European Organization for Quality Control, Berne, pp. 45–55.

Kapur, K. C., and Lamberson, L. R. (1977). *Reliability in Engineering Design.* John Wiley & Sons, New York, pp. 405–423.

Kimble, Roger G. (1982). "Serviceability Analysis." *Proceedings of the Quality in Electronics Conference.* ASQC, Milwaukee, pp. 79–81.

Kogure, Masao and Akao, Yogi (1983). "Quality Function Deployment and CWQC in Japan." *Quality Progress,* October, pp. 25–29.

Lawlor, A. J. (1978). "Quality Assurance in Design and Development." *Quality Assurance,* vol. 4, no. 3, September, pp. 87–91.

Locks, Mitchell O. (1973). *Reliability, Maintainability, and Availability Assesment.* Hayden, Rochelle Park, NJ.

Lowry, Daniel W. (1970). "Maintainability Demonstration Test Performed on a Computer System." *Proceedings, Annual Reliability and Maintainability Symposium.* IEEE, New York.

Marguglio, B. W.(1971). "Quality Factors to be Considered in Implementing Design Changes." *ASQC Technical Conference Transactions,* Milwaukee, pp. 189–191.

McCarthy, Rita (1975). "Configuration Management and Software Reliability." *Transactions of the American Society for Quality Control,* Mikwaukee, pp. 49–55.

McQuade, Walter (1984). "Easing Tensions between Man and Machine." *Fortune,* March, pp. 58–66.

Mihalasky, John (1980). "The Human Factor in Product Safety." *ASQC Technical Conference Transactions,* Milwaukee, pp. 33–40.

MIL-HDBK-189 (1981). *Reliability Growth Management.* U.S. Department of Defense, Naval Publications and Forms Center, Philadelphia.

MIL-HDBK-217D (1982). *Reliability Stress and Failure Data for Electronic Equipment.* U.S. Department of Defense, Naval Publications and Forms Center, Philadelphia.

MIL-STD-449A (1961). *Engineering Management.* Defense Document Distribution Center, Washington, DC.

MIL-STD-470A (1983). *Maintainability Program Requirements for System and Equipment.* U.S. Department of Defense, Naval Publications and Forms Center, Philadelphia.

MIL-STD-471A (1973). *Maintainability Verification/Demonstration/Evaluation.* U.S. Department of Defense, Naval Publications and Forms Center, Philadelphia.

MIL-STD-721C (1981). *Definitions of Terms for Reliability and Maintainability.* U.S. Department of Defense, Naval Publications and Forms Center, Philadelphia.

MIL-STD-785B (1980). *Reliability Program for Systems and Equipment Development and Production.* U.S. Department of Defense, Naval Publications and Forms Center, Philadelphia.

MIL-STD-882 (1969). *Requirements for System Safety Programs for Systems and Associated Subsystems and Equipment.* U.S. Department of Defense, Naval Publications and Forms Center, Philadelphia.

MIL-STD-882A (1977). *System Safety Program Requirements.* U.S. Department of Defense, Naval Publications and Forms Center, Philadelphia.

MIL-STD-1629A (1980). *Procedures for Performing a Failure Mode, Effects and Criticality Analysis.* U.S. Department of Defense, Naval Publications and Forms Center, Philadelphia.

Miles, L. D. (1972). *Techniques of Value Analysis and Engineering,* 2nd ed. McGraw-Hill, New York.

Miller, E. W. (1971). *Maintenance Index—A Design Tool.* SAE Paper 710680, Society of Automotive Engineers, Detroit

Mitsuya, Chikao (1977). "Automatic Designing and Drafting System of Elevators." *Reports of Statistical Applications and Research,* Japanese Union of Scientists and Engineers, vol. 24, no. 2, June, pp. 18–27.

Mudge, A. E. (1971). *Value Engineering.* McGraw-Hill, New York.

NAVSHIP (1972). *Maintainability Design Criteria Handbook for Designers of Shipboard Electronic Equipment.* NAVSHIP Document 0967-312-8010, July, Department of the Navy, Naval Publications and Forms Center, Philadelphia.

Nelson, Wayne (1982). *Applied Life Data Analysis.* John Wiley & Sons, New York.

Peach, Robert W. (1980). "Defining Hard to Define Customer Quality Expectations." *Quality Progress,* December, pp. 14–16.

Peacore, E. J. (1975). "Reliability Developments—AWACS." *Proceedings, Annual Reliability and Maintainability Symposium.* IEEE, New York, pp. 383–389.

Phillips, G. P. (1980). *Design Quality Index.* Internal Document of the Cadillac Motor Car Division, Detroit.

RADC, Rome Air Development Center (1983). *The Evolution and Practical Applications of Failure Modes and Effects Analyses.* Copy can be obtained from the National Technical Information Service, Department of Commerce, 5285 Port Royal Rd., Springfield, VA 22151. The document number is ADA131-358.

RADC, Rome Air Development Center (1982). *RADC Testability Notebook.* Copy can be obtained from the National Technical Information Service, Department of Commerce, 5285 Port Royal Rd., Springfield, VA 22151. The document number is AD-A118881L.

Raheja, Dev (1981). "Failure Mode and Effects Analysis—Uses and Misuses." *ASQC Quality Congress Transactions,* Milwaukee, pp. 374–379.

Reiff, Henry E. (1978). "Practical Application of the Duane Reliability Growth Model." *Automotive Division Newsletter, American Society for Quality Control,* January, pp. 5–7.

Renna, Vincent F. and Howard, Harry P. (1979). "New Product Development—Quality Assurance System Approach." *ASQC Technical Conference Transactions,* Milwaukee, pp. 848–856.

Rimondi, G., Tavazza, G., and Turello, U. (1976). "Numerical Simulation Techniques in the Tolerance Settlement of Product Qualitative Characteristics." *EOQC Quality,* vol. 20, no. 5, pp. 4–8.

Schrader, Lawrence J. (1986). "An Engineering Organization's Cost of Quality Program." *Quality Progress,* January, pp. 29–36.

Shaffer, James (1982). "Project Your Production." *Quality,* April, pp. 33–35.

Shainin, Dorian (1976). *Tool and Manufacturing Engineers Handbook.* Edited by Society of Manufacturing Engineers, McGraw-Hill, New York, pp. 31-6 to 31-10.

Shainin, Dorian (1978). "Test: Tolerances and Measuring—Both Vitally Weak in Q.C." *ASQC Technical Conference Transactions,* Milwaukee, pp. 39–43.

Stanton, Burr (1974). "Consumer Appliance Reliability: Closing the Feedback Loop." *Proceedings, Annual Reliability and Maintainability Symposium.* IEEE, New York, pp. 30–34.

Stevens, Roger T. (1978). *Operational Test and Evaluation: A Systems Engineering Process.* John Wiley & Sons, New York.

Sullivan, L. P. (1986). "Quality Function Deployment." *Quality Progress,* June, pp. 39–50.

Taylor, William R. (1981). "Quality Assured in New Products via Comprehensive Systems Approach." *Industrial Engineering,* March, pp. 28–32.

Veraldi, L. C. (1985). "The Team Taurus Story." Paper presented at MIT conference, Chicago, Aug. 22.

Vinson, William D. and Heany, Donald F. (1977). "Is Quality Out of Control?" *Harvard Business Review,* November–December, pp. 114–122.

Wall Street Journal (1978). "Sweating it Out." November 17, p. 1.

Wellborn, John M. and Lawson, G. W. (1978). "Maintainability by Design." *Proceedings, Annual Reliability and Maintainability Symposium.* IEEE, New York, pp. 478–485.

Willard, Irving E. (1979). "Reliability Growth Curves." *ASQC Technical Conference Transactions,* Milwaukee, pp. 321–328.

Yamada, Katsuyoshi (1977). "Reliability Activities at Toyota Motor Company." *Reports of Statistical Applications and Research,* Japanese Union of Scientists and Engineers, vol. 24, no. 3, September, pp. 22–39.

Zaludova, A. H. (1981). "Some Reflections on Quality Terminology." *EOQC Quality,* vol. 25, no. 1, pp. 3–10.

SECTION 14

SOFTWARE DEVELOPMENT

Patrick J. Fortune, Ph.D.

INTRODUCTION

Over the past 50 years, the computer has had a more significant impact on commercial enterprises than any other single new technology. Starting as extensions of punched card processing that automated a variety of routine financial operations, the breadth of computer applications has expanded significantly. Today, this includes sophisticated monitoring, analysis, and control processing in medicine, defense, and industry as well as a significant expansion of computer usage in what may be termed "business data processing."

In 1972, to mark the 25th anniversary of computing, the Association of Computing Machinery developed a list of computer applications. (See "Perspectives," 1980.) The list numbered 1400, and while already large, it has certainly expanded since then. With the advent of microcomputers, personal computers, and relatively inexpensive software, computer power is within economic reach of essentially all commercial enterprises and a large number of individuals. This can be expected to lead to further growth in the types and complexity of applications.

The economic significance of computer usage is staggering. Within manufacturing companies, annual expenditures on computer-based processing approximate 0.5 to 1.5 percent of revenues. For service companies, which tend to be somewhat more information-intensive than manufacturing companies, this rate rises to 3.0 to 7.0 percent of revenues. Assuming an average of 1 percent among manufacturing companies, the total average annual investment in computer-related information processing among the 500 largest U.S. industrial corporations exceeds $16 billion ("Introduction," 1983). Like the number of applications, the level of investment continues to grow. It is likely that engineering applications are growing faster than traditional commercial applications, due to the increasing complexity of products and the quality and productivity improvement opportunities that computer usage supports. The rapid growth of computer-aided design, computer-aided manufacturing, and computer-based process control are cases in point. It follows that while business data processing has received little attention from formal quality control proponents, expansion to areas more directly related to products and manufacturing processes ensures that this situation will be short-lived.

From a business point of view, cost is the attribute of computer usage that has been and continues to be primary. In the early days of computing, hardware was extremely expensive, so that operating efficiency of both systems and applications programs was crucial. Today, however, system effectiveness and reliability as cost drivers have stepped to the fore. This has occurred for several reasons. First, maximal utilization of hardware is less important as the cost of hardware declines. Second, the applications themselves are involved with processing of data that can be impossible or at least very expensive to repair or replace once corrupted or destroyed. Third, as computers become more involved with designing products, controlling their manufacture, and generally ensuring product quality, the consequences of failures within computer systems can represent costly failures indeed.

This section introduces the concepts of computer system quality in general and the development of computer software quality in particular. (Section 27, Computers and Quality, discusses the application of the computer to various activities within the quality function throughout an organization.) The standard quality assurance terms of "verification," "validation," and "reliability" will be defined with respect to software. Procedures and processes by which quality of software may be realized will be discussed.

Appendix III, Selected Quality Standards, Specifications, and Related Documents, includes documents on software development and software quality assurance.

BASIC CONCEPTS

The central question is: How does one assure that a computer system does what it is supposed to do? To understand the approaches used to achieve such assurance requires an understanding of certain characteristics of computers and computer systems. If we look at a computer system from the point of view of the software, it is clear that all computer systems share certain structural characteristics. In particular, a structure like that in Figure 14.1 is appropriate. Formally, a computer system is defined as an external environment combined with a collection of (often complex) interacting pieces of hardware and software components assembled to solve or address a specific problem. The environment interacts with the hardware and software through a series of inputs and outputs (I/Os).

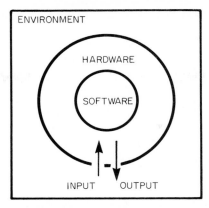

FIG. 14.1   Computer system model.

The environment includes the physical environment and process environment. The physical environment is specified by such parameters as required power, temperature, humidity, etc. The process environment includes all I/O variables with which the computer system must deal. A list of components in typical computer systems is given in Table 14.1. This table serves by example to define the boundaries of the environment and the system. It is noteworthy that the software includes procedures and documentation as well as computer programs. Proper attention to these two areas is critical in assuring system quality.

While the model in Figure 14.1 provides a general view of a computer system, system quality assurance requires a more detailed structure. The implementation of a computer system solution assumes that the system components have been combined into a suitable architecture. By "system architecture," we mean the arrangement of system components comprising the decisions to relegate certain functions to hardware and software and subfunctions to modules. This is illustrated in Figure 14.2.

Based on the above, two issues related to system performance and quality are immediately clear. These might be termed capability and complexity.

"Capability" refers to the fact that we clearly know/understand the problem that we are trying to solve and that we have selected a configuration capable of

TABLE 14.1   System Components*

Hardware	Software
Sensors	Operating systems
Signal conditioners	Telecommunication systems
A/D, D/A converters	Data base management systems
Control actuators	Language processors
Central processors	File systems
Peripheral processors	Application programs
Peripheral devices	Procedures
Timers	Documentation
Annunciator panels	

*This is a partial list.

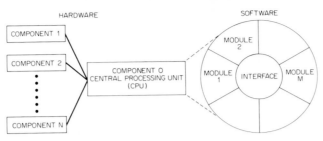

FIG. 14.2 "Internal" computer system structure.

dealing with it. For example, if a parameter to be sensed is represented by a voltage of -5.0 to $+5.0$ V and if it is necessary to measure it with a precision of ± 5 mV, the analog-to-digital (A/D) converter must have at least 10 bits plus sign. That is, from 0 to $+5.0$ V, there are five intervals. Each of these must be divided into 200 parts to get the ± 5-mV precision. Thus, we must be able to represent at least 1000 different values. A 10-bit A/D converter is capable of representing $2^{10} - 1 = 1023$ different values. By adding the sign bit, the range from -5.0 to 0 V is also taken care of. Similarly, if the signal to be processed must be sampled at a rate of 100 times per second, the A/D converter and central processing unit must be capable of supporting this bandwidth. To address this point properly requires that the disciplines of signal processing, computer engineering, computer science, etc., are well understood.

The second factor, system "complexity," refers to the degree of complication of a system or system component as determined by such factors as the size, the number and intricacy of special conditions, the degree of nesting in the software, the types of data structures and languages used, and other system characteristics. [Here, "nesting" refers to the extent to which one module (or segregatable instruction sequence) is contained within or referenced by other modules.] These attributes are determined in part by the problem and in part by the design decisions made in order to arrive at the final solution. Clearly, selection of architecture involves a large number of trade-offs. For example, relegating particular functions to specific software modules leads, in general, to greater simplicity within each module. Thus, it is easier to write the programs that comprise each module, and the quality of those modules will be easier to assure. On the other hand, depending on the problem, the number of module interfaces may increase. Thus, the resultant complexity of the total system may be increased (relative to an alternative architecture), leading to difficulties in assuring quality. As system complexity increases, the problem of ensuring reliability becomes more difficult. Here, "reliability" (numerical) refers to the ability of an item to perform a required function under stated conditions for a stated period of time (ANSI/ASQC A3-1987). (See IEEE, 1983*b*.) Thus, a key thrust in developing high-quality computer systems involves the use of techniques which reduce system complexity.

In the foregoing discussion, hardware and software have been treated in the same manner. It is, however, worthwhile to note some differences, especially as they relate to performance over time in context of the above definition of reliability.

One key difference between hardware and software in relation to quality assurance is that hardware reliability involves not only initial verification and validation but also ongoing indication of failure-free status. Software reliability also involves initial verification and validation. However, the logical components of software are durable. Put another way, software failure results from design/implementation errors only. Since any errors in the software are there until specifically removed and are "encountered" only when the "right" input arises, mean time between failure (MTBF) does not by definition directly apply.

It is possible to construct software reliability models in which MTBF becomes a predicted property of the system. These, however, usually involve the assumption of some probability distribution that describes the probability of encountering a software error between times t_0 and t. To the extent that this assumption is valid, MTBF calculations are straightforward. (See, for example, Sukert, 1977.) Within these models, it is theoretically possible to reduce the software errors to zero at which time the software MTBF approaches infinity. Because of the nonzero probability of hardware failures, the same is not true of hardware.

This difference in durability must be clearly understood as we adapt the usual concepts of verification and validation to software and as policies and procedures are put in place to help assure quality on an ongoing basis. Failure to recognize this can lead to unnecessary, unproductive, and, therefore, overly expensive quality assurance procedures. Worse, it may lead to a failure to address the issues that are truly critical.

Before dealing further with the process of developing quality systems and assuring that quality, the concepts of verification and validation need to be explicitly defined. "Verification" is the process by which a hardware component or software module is shown to meet its specification. Thus, in verification, the specifications (i.e., requirements) are not challenged. "Validation," on the other hand, is the process by which an assembly of hardware components and/or software modules are shown to function properly in a total systems environment (IEEE, 1983b). Here, "function properly" implies that an evaluation of the specification with respect to the problem being addressed is explicit.

Within the set of technologies applied to assuring quality in computer systems, verification and validation attempt to increase system reliability through elimination of errors in elucidation of requirements, as well as elimination of errors in design or implementation. Other techniques are also available as a complement to these. Fault-tolerant and fail-soft design and implementation techniques attempt to introduce mechanisms that permit a system to continue to function properly in spite of the presence of errors, failures, or inputs that are out of range, etc. Hardware and software redundancy are examples of these techniques. Treatment of the fault-tolerant approach will not be included further here.

SYSTEMS ENGINEERING

The problem of determining requirements, implementing a computer-based solution to those requirements, and validating that solution is amenable to an engineering approach. This approach is herein termed "systems engineering." For the purposes of the present discussion, systems engineering may be defined as the systematic, hierarchical approach to the development, operation, maintenance, and retirement of computer systems. Embedded in this definition is the usual association of systems engineering with the process of taking a total (i.e., systems) view of a problem and its solution. From an implementation point of view, systems engineering is supported by a systems engineering process. This process may be defined as the structured series of steps that breaks down a system into its conceptual, functional, and technical operating components so as to reduce complexity and support the effectiveness and efficiency of implementation. This approach clearly applies to any complex problem in general, and to the development of computer systems in particular.

The essence of the systems engineering process is to first separate the problem into digestible subsets and then to distinguish clearly between *what* is to be done within each subset and *how* it is to be done. This ensures that the problem to be solved is clearly defined and that it is broken down into natural units that can be addressed more easily, with solutions implemented more efficiently.

To be sure, the idea of "engineering" a solution to a problem is not novel. Further, to some extent, the systems engineering approach has been applied to the development of computer systems from the outset. This has been particularly true of the hardware parts of a system. Presumably, this is a natural extension of the engineering practices applied to hardware solutions of a mechanical or analog nature to digital computer system engineering. Software, on the other hand, was (and often still is) approached differently, at least partly, because "code" is relatively easy to change. For example, changing a hardware module may involve the use of new parts, significant changes to wiring, changes to board layouts, changes to power requirements, changes to edge connector assignments, etc. A software module can, however, be changed relatively easily by altering a few lines of code, recompiling, linkage editing, and running. Worse, individual machine instructions can be "zapped" or "patched" into stored execution modules with a few manipulations from the system console. In the early days of computer usage, this procedure was seen as an efficient way to develop or fix software. This was partly because early computer applications were not as complex as current and emerging ones and partly because programming as a distinct discipline had not yet developed. In fact, it was felt that as people wrote more programs, the tendency to error would naturally decrease. That a separate discipline of programming was actually required was not recognized clearly until the 1960s; that the development of software systems was actually an engineering process was not recognized until even later.

As computer solutions were applied to more complex problems, the ease of software modification became more of a problem than a boon. This is because the ease of change led to reduced focus on design steps, since the final product could so "easily" be changed. At present levels of complexity, the engineering of the software solution has become critical. Indeed, since a large number of computer applications today are implemented on existing hardware, software is the dominant issue. The remainder of this section deals primarily with the issue of software and software engineering. Conceptually, the extension of the structured approach to problems other than software is direct.

SOFTWARE ENGINEERING

In parallel to the definitions of the previous section, software engineering can be defined as the systematic, hierarchical approach to the development, operation, maintenance, and retirement of computer software. The engineering process used for software development is the structured process that breaks down a system into its conceptual, functional, and technical operating components in order to reduce complexity and support the effectiveness and efficiency of implementation. (Section 27 under Managing Computer Projects discusses the planning, organization, and control of projects to automate manual quality-related activities.)

From a formal point of view, the software engineering process is guided by a software development life cycle (SDLC). For our purposes, an SDLC can be broken down into some six phases.

1. Requirements analysis
2. Preliminary design
3. Detailed design
4. Coding
5. Test and installation
6. Maintenance

Not all formal SDLCs are broken down into six phases; nor do all SDLCs define the phases in precisely the way it is done here. All such SDLCs are, however, functionally equivalent, and in this sense the SDLC discussed here can be considered to be a prototype.

Before proceeding with a discussion of each phase separately, it is worthwhile to look at how the resource requirements in a typical software project breaks down with respect to these phases. For the above prototypical life cycle this breakdown is presented in Table 14.2. The amount of effort spent on maintenance is most striking. The size of the maintenance effort is the main reason why maintenance is explicitly included in the above definitions. It is also why high-quality, cost-effective software by definition must be maintainable and why change control proves to be a critical process. It follows that maintainability must be designed into the system from the beginning, not as an afterthought in the coding phase.

At present, much software development for all types of systems is done by professional systems staffs on behalf of a user group. While this can be expected to change as computers become adapted as tools by the users themselves, it is likely that large data processing, process control, and other real-time systems will continue to involve systems professionals (this includes highly educated and aware users) for the foreseeable future. It is reasonable then to ask what the users' role is in a process such as that outlined above. To be most effective, the group responsible for development of systems should formally include "users" along with systems people. Different people then play different roles in each of the above steps and underlying individual tasks. For example, the requirements definition involves more user time than systems time (say 80 percent versus 20 percent). Coding involves more systems time than user time (say 90 percent versus 10 percent), and testing is approximately a 50-50 proposition. Maintenance involves integration of ongoing user feedback with systems development staff as needed. It follows from this that software is most effectively and efficiently devel-

TABLE 14.2 Typical Resource Requirements for Phases of an SDLC

	Total effort, %	Development effort, %
Requirements definition	3	9
Preliminary design	3	9
Detailed design	5	15
Coding	7	21
Test and installation	15	46
Maintenance	67	

oped by appropriately organized and managed teams of users and systems people. The issue of feedback from users to the development team then makes little sense, since these groups are (or ought to be) synonymous.

In Table 14.2 the relative amount of time (percent of effort) for each of the development phases is also exhibited. If we treat the first three phases as the software design process, we see that testing is the largest consumer of development resources, design second, and coding last. This not only points out the criticality of testing but also illustrates that coding (or programming) is (or ought to be) the least resource-intensive. The use of high-level languages, problem-oriented languages, and specialized packages that permit generation of application programs from libraries and specifications (application generators) are developments in programming technology that help reduce the proportion of time spent on coding. A *well-planned* SDLC is a system engineering development that will ensure that proper resources are dedicated to the upstream processes.

Another perspective on the relative importance of the requirements analysis and design steps is gained from being aware of the incidence of errors in development and the associated costs. Such data are presented in Table 14.3. Here, the logic and syntax errors refer to corresponding types of errors in the programming steps. Design errors not only predominate in number, but also represent an even larger fraction of the total cost of errors. This arises because the later that errors are detected, the greater is the associated cost, due to the need to modify parts of the existing design and the need to change the code in modules outside of those in which the errors actually occurred. It is evident that for software to be cost-effective and reliable, proper effort devoted to the design phases is a necessary condition. The temptation to proceed quickly to coding must be strenuously resisted.

From a management point of view, a cost profile such as that shown in Table 14.3 for any particular software development group will provide the most compelling reason why software quality assurance must be addressed early in the development process. Program managers, quality managers, and others involved in defining projects, estimating costs, and allocating resources must be aware that experience (and to some extent theory) indicates that attempting to assure quality only by inspection of the final product will generally lead to considerably higher costs.

A formal SDLC is most beneficial when applied to large development projects. From a mechanical point of view, small projects or individual programs can utilize a subset of the full SDLC. Conceptually, it is more important that proper attention be paid to the segregation of the design, code, test, and maintenance phases in small projects, or these projects can result in a merry-go-round of continual modification.

A common misconception exists that certain applications, particularly real-time applications, are not appropriate targets for an SDLC, but that a formal

TABLE 14.3   Nature, Number, and Costs of Errors

Error type	Total errors, %	Relative severity	Total cost of error, %
Design	68	2.5	>83
Logic	16	1.0	>8
Syntax	16	1.0	>8

Source: Alberts, 1976, p. 438.

SDLC applies only to "business data processing." Since an SDLC seeks only to partition and structure the steps involved in an engineering approach to systems development, the treatment of real-time systems as an exception is incorrect. To be sure, in the design phases there may have to be an explicit, detailed evaluation of hardware and software timing in order to ensure that an architecture and components are sufficiently *capable*. However, the use of structured systems development techniques serves to mitigate the *complexity* of even real-time systems. In fact, outputs of the various SDLC phases can be tailored to enhance various development steps including emulation, simulation, and design review. The coding and testing phases must readdress any timing requirements noted during design. However, even this can be aided by some of the (graphical) documentation techniques outlined below. Clearly, some of the techniques used in real-time system development do not apply to other types of systems. All types, however, benefit from the spirit and form of the structured approach.

Requirements Analysis.   As its name implies, the requirements analysis (or requirements definition) phase seeks to clearly spell out *what* a system is required to do. Thus, the main thrust is to provide for the effectiveness of the system. Not surprisingly, this phase is the newest and least developed in terms of tools and techniques. The problem (e.g., in a narrative form) here is a difficult one in that the requirements must be first understood and then written down or represented in some other way. Moreover, the representation of the requirements and requirements themselves interact. That is, continued evaluation of the list (i.e., representation) of the requirements in design review steps leads to elucidation of holes and refinement of the requirements themselves. Thus, to be effective, the representation should itself be modular to promote review, understanding, and modification. To support this end, the output of the requirements analysis phase generally consists of five parts:

1. Clear, meaningful statement of the problem scope
2. Explanation of how the problem is presently addressed
3. A statement of deficiencies of the present approach
4. A statement of constraints and added features which, if included, would materially enhance the present system
5. A cost-benefit analysis of the system broken out by system feature

   To illustrate these steps, consider the problem of building a system to track the value of manufacturing process parameters, quality control test results, and measures of product quality. Here, a problem statement will include delineation of the specific process steps to be covered, a listing of the parameters to be collected and tracked, the type of analysis to be done on them, expandability requirements, timing of analysis and feedback, etc. Here, feedback can be intrashift feedback, end-of-shift feedback, or periodic reporting. It is also necessary to describe the current system and its deficiencies (e.g., handles too few parameters, feedback to operations is not sufficiently frequent, analysis is error prone, etc.). The requisite timing, calculation requirements (method, accuracy, and precision), and total parameter list in this case define the added features. The cost-benefit analysis helps to identify whether computerization is necessary or cost-effective. It also provides a basis by which individual features can be dropped or modified to simplify the system and reduce its cost.
   It is clear that at this stage the target system is subject to considerable change before it is actually implemented. Thus, the system must be specified in a manner

that supports the review and the change processes that will occur as the project proceeds.

It is helpful to use graphic techniques such as data flow diagrams (DFD) which show how a data element is created and used, how it must be processed, and where it goes. A data flow diagram consists of four elements: data flows (edges), processing nodes, reference data storage files, and data sources/sinks. An example of a data flow diagram for part of the problem noted above is illustrated in Figure 14.3.

A graphical representation such as this for the requirements of a subset of the monitoring process is easily reviewed and modified. Each process step can be broken down further using similar diagrams. That is, process step 1.1 can be decomposed into 1.11, 1.12, and 1.13; 1.12 can be decomposed into 1.121, 1.122, 1.123, etc. This segregation of function into process steps and decomposition into lower levels of detail as the requirements are developed is referred to as "hierarchical decomposition." Notwithstanding the utility of DFDs, system requirements have historically been represented in a narrative form. This clearly has a number of problems associated with it. One such problem is that the requirements for even a moderate system may take hundreds of pages to describe. Recalling a specific system need and understanding its implications over several pages can be difficult. Resolving ambiguities of the language itself is a further problem. As a partial resolution, both graphical tools and hierarchical decomposition of requirements are useful in the requirements development, the design reviews, and especially in support of system maintenance. The use of graphical tools minimizes ambiguity; hierarchical decomposition facilitates comprehension. The requirements document for a complex system should be partitioned into groups that are meaningful and that are of a sufficiently small size to promote easy understanding and review. These groups are then networked to form the complete requirement. Using the hierarchical numbering approach described above, the requirement is represented in a structured fashion with a progression from less detail (higher level of abstraction) to more detail. Thus, it is not necessary to review a total 100-page specification in one step, but each level is reviewed separately. Since each level of the specification is small (a few pages), self-contained, and concise, it is easier to understand and review. The ease of understanding is a key requirement in reducing the cost of maintenance, since maintaining a system requires educating new staff as well as refreshing the memories of old staff as the need for changes arise. [De Marco (1978) provides an excellent introduction to the various techniques

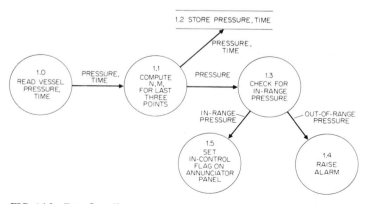

FIG. 14.3   Data flow diagram.

used to express system requirements, including data flow diagrams and structure charts.]

It is noteworthy that the use of a structured specification and an easily understood representation is an aid in promoting the inclusion of users on the systems development team, as discussed earlier. In the above example, a process engineer or quality engineer can easily be involved in both the definition of the requirements and the specification review without being a programmer or without being knowledgable in computer or systems architecture and design. In this way, as the requirements specification documents are used as input to the next SDLC phase (preliminary design), the ultimate user of the system is in a position to certify that what is specified is what is needed.

Preliminary Design.   The preliminary design phase proceeds directly from the requirements definition. Here, the various functions represented in the requirements specifications are assigned to logical modules and these modules are characterized from the external, or user, point of view. That is, they specify how the user will view and interact with the final system. This includes preparation of a dictionary of all critical data, all reports, and all screens. The modules themselves are described by an expression of their input, output, and some description of processing done. To the extent that a system function chart or a data flow diagram has been prepared in the requirements definition, the preliminary design step is a refinement of that diagram and is a further expression of what processing will be done with each element of data.

The data dictionary is one of the most critical parts of the documentation prepared during the preliminary design. Actually, the phrase "data dictionary" presently has two different meanings. The first (not of interest here) is "a piece of software that is used to manage the logical and physical data resource of a group of operational systems." Packages to do this are commercially available. The second meaning (and the one of interest here) is, simply, "a collection of information that describes the data that are important to a system." The data dictionary used in structured design defines the data elements that flow in the system and identifies the processes involved with using or modifying it. Other operational parameters may also be included. For example, the definition of a data element may include its security requirements, its frequency of use, the identification of the update modules that use it, how many bytes in the data, etc. These data attributes evolve as the system is specified in more and more detail. It is evident that the data dictionary and data flow diagrams go hand in hand in describing the structure of a system. The data flow diagram specifies how the data are manipulated from process step to process step, while the data dictionary is a repository of information about the characteristics of that data. This, in turn, helps clarify the process steps.

The system functions are explicitly defined using a function chart technique, e.g., Warnier-Orr diagrams (De Marco, 1978) or an input-process-output (IPO) technique. Warnier-Orr diagrams combine the use of hierarchical data structures and functional requirements (Orr, 1981). The use of IPO techniques is older and less powerful but easier to understand, and will be used here to illustrate the intent. IPO approaches attempt to explicitly add more information to that available in data flow diagrams. Here, the functions are arrayed as blocks that have associated input and output defined. The processing requirements are summarized by brief descriptions within the blocks. Further processing information as well as information on procedures and control is included in the specification either as text associated with each processing block or as appended material [IBM (1974)]. Note that the user's view of data entry and report requirements are automatically provided for, and it follows that user involvement and sign-off are critical here.

The detailed characteristics of the techniques used to represent the preliminary design specification are less important than the use of a structured hierarchical approach in refinement of the system design. The use of an IPO technique is not new, and will be familiar to engineers that have dealt with the development and simulation of manufacturing processes. The important point here is that the same technique can be useful in development of computer systems. Within any given organization, techniques from a variety of alternatives can be chosen to fit that organization's needs at a particular point in time. Where appropriate, structured analysis packages can aid in fostering standard practices throughout an organization. (A review of some of the issues and choices can be found in Colter, 1984.)

One of the key activities undertaken during the preliminary design phase is the search for a commercial application package to solve the problem, instead of in-house-developed software. That is, the system requirements and user view of the system are understood in the later stages of the preliminary design. These requirements can, therefore, be compared to the features of a commercial package to see if the degree of fit is sufficient to justify acquisition. The search for a package also can refine and validate the in-house specification by comparison of that specification to existing systems that purport to fulfill a similar function. Both needed and extraneous functions can be identified in this manner. For example, if the application is relatively common, a reasonable degree of fit of the requirements with the package should be expected. If the degree of fit is (surprisingly) low, the requirements need to be reviewed to see if they are really *requirements.* As a practical matter, many projects tend to confuse "wants" with "needs," so that the system has specified features that are not cost-justified. The candidate packages may be used as foils in ensuring that this does not occur.

Because of the above confusion between needs and wants and the high cost of subsequent life cycle phases, it is often of interest to try to change the business process to enable usage of a "vanilla" package. In this way, needs can be met at the lowest possible costs. In cases where some customization is truly needed to gain business benefit, the customization should be designed as an add-on (e.g., via new report or analysis modules) rather than a modification of the source code in the package. It is worth remembering that the main cost of a system is incurred as maintenance. If an unmodified package can be used, the supplier incurs the cost of maintenance. If add-on modules are used (as opposed to package source code modifications), at least the in-house maintenance costs will be minimized.

In the use of packages, SDLC phases subsequent to preliminary system design are also modified. The extent of modification depends on the degree of fit between package and requirements. For example, coding may be eliminated and in-house (unit) testing reduced.

Detailed Design. The detailed design phase takes the output of the preliminary design phase and converts it to detailed specifications that are sufficient to permit development of physical data bases and files, and coding of the actual programs. The focus of this phase is in the internal design—design, that is, from the computer's point of view.

The data dictionary serves as the basis for construction of the actual data bases and files used within the system. File descriptions, data element length, and security requirements go into detailed descriptions of the file and data base layouts.

When using a formal data base management system (DBMS), construction of the data bases will depend on the DBMS used. The detailed data base specifications involve definitions of relationships among data elements. These may be hierarchical relationships, network relationships, or formal relations. Transactions that add an item, delete an item, or update an item must be identified, and access keys must be specified. Overall properties of the data base structure that affect maintainability and expandability are also taken into account. One such property is normalization. Normalization is a formal approach that examines the data and groups data elements together in a structure that is more adaptable to future changes (see Martin, 1983). Tools to automate the actual normalization process are being developed, and can be expected to greatly aid this process in the future.

The previously developed module specifications are the inputs to this stage. The programming specifications should be developed in a manner that enhances system design review by project participants who are themselves not programmers. There are a number of techniques by which this can be done. One example is the use of pseudocode (see Page-Jones, 1980).

"Pseudocode" is a semiformal language that converts *what* is to be done into *how* the logic will flow in actually doing it. The primitive structures in the pseudolanguage are a balance between the logical constructs required in the programs (IF-THEN-ELSE, DO-WHILE, SEQUENTIAL EXECUTION) and the characteristics of the target programming language to be used in the implementation. The closer the language is to English, the greater is the ease of design review by nonprogrammers, but the more ambiguous the description may be. The closer the pseudolanguage is to the target language, the easier the final programming step is. Besides enhancing the design review steps, the use of pseudolanguages permits the programmer to concentrate separately on the program logic versus the syntax and semantics of the target language. That is, the detailed logic flow is spelled out in pseudocode followed by transliteration of the pseudocode into the target language. There are no generally accepted, standard pseudolanguages, but working examples are readily constructed.

To view the use of pseudocode, consider an example of a module to control temperature in a manufacturing process. Part of the module would be coded in pseudolanguage as follows:

```
READ PROCESS TEMPERATURE:
    COMPARE TO LOW-SET-POINT;
        IF LESS THAN LOW-SET-POINT
            THEN PROCESS HEAT-CYCLE:

    COMPARE TO HI-SET-POINT;
        IF GREATER THAN HI-SET-POINT
            THEN PROCESS COOLING-CYCLE
END;
```

The I/O process and heating-cooling cycles would be specified by other pseudocoded modules. It should be clear from this example that dialects of pseudolanguages are simply definable. The above dialect is useful if the target language is a higher-level language like FORTRAN or even if it is an assembler language. Note that the indentation of pseudocode and resulting source code can help improve structure and understanding.

The use of pseudocode as a specification technique is useful independent of the size of the project. Even if the "project" involves writing a single program, pseudocode will aid in getting the program right the first time. In addition, module pseudocode serves as excellent program documentation.

Design Reviews. During the requirements analysis, the preliminary system design, and the detailed design phases, the process is punctuated by a number of design reviews. These reviews may be conducted among the design team itself (including user personnel) or may include outside reviewers (formal quality reviewers, peer reviewers, etc.). The challenges put to the system in these reviews include what-if scenarios, fault tree analysis, etc. The design review process throughout these phases represents a large part of the static testing (or desk checking) to which the system is subjected. "Static" refers to the fact that the system being tested is not executed on a machine as part of the test process. Nonetheless, the static tests must be formally planned and executed if design errors are to be minimized.

Coding.   The coding, or programming, phase is the first of the two implementation phases. In this phase, the detailed programming specifications are converted to a form executable by a computer. This includes source language development, job control language development, compilation, linkage editing (i.e., linking all modules of the system together into a single load module), and execution. At this point, the design is essentially frozen, but may be changed as errors are discovered. The cost of uncovering design errors at this late point is excessive, as already noted (see Table 14.3).

In addressing the role of the coding process in relation to software quality, the same issues that impacted design will be considered here. Namely, the key way to improve the reliability of the original product as well as its maintainability is to reduce the complexity of the programs. This is done in three ways: First, the programs should be developed from well-written, clear specifications of a properly structured system. Second, the internal structure of the programs should be streamlined and the control should, as much as possible, flow cleanly from start to finish. Third, the language used should be as high a level as possible; that is, it should be as far from machine language and the idiosyncrasies of the hardware as practical, given the problem.

The first point above speaks to the structure of the overall system. By the time the coding phase is reached, this level of structure is largely fixed. The second point, on the other hand, addresses the internal structure of the programs, which, at this point, is only partially set (assuming that well-structured pseudocode is used to produce final program specifications). The approach to programming that incorporates top-down design and top-down control flow implementation and that focuses on the use of explicitly defined data types and on the use of a restricted set of control primitives to improve the structure is called "structured programming." While a rigorous definition would restrict the control primitives to the set DO-WHILE, IF-THEN-ELSE, plus sequential statement execution, for our purposes the definition can be broadened. Within structured programming, we include any approach by which the control flows are simplified via restriction of entry and exit points, segregation of program subfunctions into blocks, and use of a control flow that moves generally from program start to program end. Each of these restrictions helps to reduce complexity, improve clarity, and facilitate maintenance.

To further develop the concept of structured programming (used here very broadly), we can consider some illustrative practices that ought to be followed in programming. For example, all intents should be made explicit. That is, variables ought to be typed explicitly (e.g., REAL, INTEGER, PICTURE, DOUBLE PRECISION, etc.), vector and array sizes ought to be specified explicitly, and legitimate variable ranges should be checked explicitly. Further, variable names should be meaningful. A mnemonic such as PRESSR is more meaningful than X as a variable that represents pressure. All of these points increase the "structure" of the data used within a program.

As a second example, the sections of a program that implement functions within a program should be grouped in explicit program blocks or subroutines. The program blocks should be separated from each other using features of the implementation language (e.g., BEGIN. . . .END in PL/1) or through the use of comments (e.g., in FORTRAN or assembler languages). The use of subroutines will automatically support this functional segregation. The programs themselves should be heavily commented to promote understanding of program intent. As noted earlier, simple techniques (such as indenting source code) further convey structure and promote understanding.

The logical flow in a program should as much as possible be unidirectional with as little branching back to earlier program statements as possible. This implication of structured programming has led to a situation in which GOTO-less programming and structured programming are taken as synonymous. As can be seen from the above, the latter concept is much broader (see also Knuth, 1974, and Dahl et al., 1972).

The techniques of structured programming seek to impact the structure of both data and the program instruction sequences that manipulate that data. Consistent with the general theme of this discussion, the imposition of structure within programs decreases complexity, thereby improves clarity and understanding, and leads to improved quality. It is worth repeating that this is a consequence of the fact that use of structured approaches involves thinking on successively lower levels of abstraction, such that at any point only features relevant to that level are considered. Irrelevant issues then tend not to impact the quality or speed of problem solution. (See Dahl et al., 1972.)

Some programming languages contain features that permit data and logic structure to be more easily implemented than others. It follows then that within some limits, system developers can affect quality by the choice of programming language and programming standards. By definition, the closer a given programming language is to English, the higher level it is said to be. The set of language options available for a particular project is restricted to the set that the selected hardware can support and to a lesser extent by the parameters of the problem itself. Modern hardware tends to support a variety of languages: Assembler language, FORTRAN, and PASCAL is a language sequence (in order of increasing level) available on most hardware today.

In certain applications such as programs that directly control the operation of a device such as a printer disk or communication line, or in cases where high speed is required, low-level (i.e., assembler) languages are often used. More recently, however, optimizing compilers for high-level languages resolves the need for execution speed without recourse to the assembler level. Language extensions such as the Instrument Society of America version of FORTRAN permit device level manipulations within a high-level language.

The current direction of program language development is toward a higher level. The use of languages that are designed to solve a specific class of problems is one approach. These languages are called problem-oriented languages in that the basic verbs or other constructs used are most suited to solving particular types of problems. Report generation (e.g., RAMIS and FOCUS), statistical analysis (SAS), and graphics (SASGRAPH, TELEGRAPH) are examples.

An approach to formally defining the interaction among language level, program volume (i.e., "size"), and complexity to predict the effort required to write a given program in a given language is embedded in the discipline of software science (see Fitzsimmons and Love, 1978, and Halstead, 1977). Mean language levels (λ) computed by comparing implementations of various programs written in these languages have been developed with the following results (Fitzsimmons and Love, 1978, p. 6):

Language	Mean level (λ)
English prose	2.16
PL/1	1.53
ALGOL 68	1.21
FORTRAN	1.14
ASSEMBLER	0.88

Since software science predicts that the effort to create or understand a program (to implement a given algorithm) varies like λ^{-2}, the effort required in creating (understanding) a PL/1 program is 1.8 times less than that for a FORTRAN program and 3.0 times less than that for an assembler language program (Fitzsimmons and Love, 1978). This is because of the reduced complexity of the programming task in these respective languages. Thus, one can conclude that an average programming project will, in general, proceed faster in PL/1 than in FORTRAN or in assembler. Results of using PASCAL would be expected to be similar for these with PL/1. These comparisons assume all alternatives are equally reasonable choices; that is, that no choice is eliminated because of specific problem characteristics. Software science, therefore, quantitatively corroborates the intuition of programmers familiar with these languages. These data illustrate the impact that the proper choice of programming language can have on the simplicity and therefore (presumably) the quality of a system.

Testing.   As pointed out in Table 14.2, the testing phase is the most resource-intensive of all the development phases. As discussed above, static or desk checking takes place during the design phases of the system development cycle. In addition, there is the widely used concept of program testing—or, more correctly, dynamic testing.

In a structured testing approach, dynamic testing is broken down into several subphases such as:

1. Unit testing
2. String testing
3. System testing
4. Stress testing

Unit Testing.   "Unit testing" is targeted toward the testing of each module individually. In this process, the data to be used for exercising the module is selected by a careful examination of the source code for that module. Since the details of program internals are critical in this process, this type of testing is called "white-box" testing.

One of the key success factors in a sound unit test is the extent to which the test data challenge the software. This, in turn, is driven by how well the test data exercise the execution paths of the program. One way of ensuring that unit testing is properly stressful of the program is to ensure that each branch of the program is traversed when executed using the test data as input. Placement of counters in each execution path can facilitate this (see Myers, 1979; and Huang, 1975). Since each well-written program should first check for legitimate inputs, this approach guarantees that at least one point outside the acceptable range, one point on or near the boundary, and one point in the acceptable range execute properly.

By acceptable range, we mean the collection of ranges for each of the program variables (including input and output data) for which the program is supposed to produce good results. An example of an out-of-range condition for an input variable in a subroutine that computes $f(x) = 1/(1 - x)$ is $x = 1$, since $f(x)$ has a discontinuity at $x = 1$.

As programs become complex, the number of branches can become impractically large as a basis for testing. In this case, the test data should be selected by examination of acceptable input ranges and by a consideration of potential internal failure modes. In all cases, one point outside the accepted range for input variables, one point near the boundary, and one point inside is a minimal requirement. Other inside points should be selected based on examination of the program itself.

If a package is used, the source code should be inspected as to structure and comments. However, rerunning the unit test on supplier-provided software may not be worthwhile. It may suffice to audit and validate the testing approaches used by the supplier. Local modifications are then unit-tested, and the linkages to the package are tested during the string and systems test.

String Testing. In the second subphase of testing, "string testing," one begins to put the particular programs together. Since this may involve the use of programs developed by other programmers that have not as yet made their final programs available, stub programs can be useful. "Stub programs" are dummy programs that either generate calls to the tested program or accept or check output from the tested program. As the remainder of the programs become available to the programmers (usually by being added to a project library), the stub programs can be replaced in subsequent testing.

Since unit testing and string testing use a "white-box" approach, most of the testing in these phases is done by the individuals who developed the programs. In addition, since the test data are developed by looking at source code, no explicit evaluation of requirements is performed. Thus, these subphases actually test whether the sets of instructions (i.e., programs) that the programmers put together execute the way the programmers intended. Accordingly, unit test and string test are actually verification techniques. The result of a verified program, however, may differ from what the user intended the system to do. For example, a program to compute a standard deviation can be checked to see if it correctly computes standard deviations. Whether the standard deviation is the correct variable to compute to solve the problem is a separate question. This problem is one of validation and is addressed during system testing.

System Testing. "System testing" refers to testing of the integrated hardware and software *system* to ensure that all *system* requirements are met. Several attributes are implied by this definition. First, data used should be developed from an evaluation of the actual requirements of the system. Second, the data selection and test output evaluation lies more in the end-user domain rather than that of the system developers. In fact, the system test process in many cases is best carried out by members of an organization other than the one that developed the system (Myers, 1979). Third, from the point of view of the code itself, system testing is a "black-box" process. System test data are most appropriately selected by examination of the written systems specifications. The system structure charts, data flow diagrams, data dictionary, etc. developed during the design phases are useful sources. In addition to these approaches, the user documentation is also useful in performing the systems test. During system test execution, user documentation may be particularly useful in understanding ways in which the system may be *misused*. Avoidance of problems that promote misuse is, of course, an implied system requirement. Common examples of problems that promote misuse include output that is difficult to read, error messages that are hard to understand, options that are redundant or unnecessary, and sequences of operations that are cumbersome.

The development of a sound system test is a difficult and creative process for which a consistent general methodology does not appear to exist. One useful alternative to a general methodology is to separate the systems test into test categories and then ensure that no category has been omitted in the test protocol (Myers, 1979). One such category is stress testing. Whether one treats this as an element of system testing or as a separate phase is immaterial as long as it is done.

Stress Testing. By "stress testing," we mean stresses exerted in both volume and time. That is, systems may fail because arrays or files run out of allotted space or the physical capacity of tapes, disks, buffers, etc. are exceeded. Volume testing subjects the system to an amount of data sufficient to test this type of failure mode. Systems may also fail because the volume is nominal, but it arrives in a very short period of time. Short-term buffer capacities may be exceeded, temporary arrays may overflow, etc. This class of error can be a problem in real-time data acquisition and control systems, or collections of batch systems that must turn around within a fixed time period and can have time-based stress failures if the execution time in any given period is too great.

Before leaving the subject of testing, the issue of "debugging" warrants some discussion. Intuitively, the process of debugging is closely related to that of testing. This arises because bugs are often identified through a testing process, and subsequently removed. Testing, as defined herein, is a concept broader than debugging in that the latter concept is usually a "dynamic test" activity only. Further, the limits of testing and debugging need to be clearly recognized inasmuch as, with either approach, one does not show that a piece of software works but actually highlights when and where it does not.

The process of actively showing that software works (as opposed to showing instances in which it does not) is embodied in the concept of "proof of correctness." This technique relies on the development of correctness statements or assertions as statements that must be correct or true if the program is correct (see Anderson, 1979). These assertions can be checked by hand, using flow charts or graphs, or they can actually be inserted in the programs and checked for "truth" during execution. Proof-of-correctness approaches, at the present time, continue to be a subject of research in mathematics and computer science, and it would appear to be sometime before this technique is practically applicable to a broad class of real life problems.

Maintenance. System maintenance includes all the ongoing activities required to ensure that the system continues to function properly even as the problem that the system was designed to address changes over time. Further, notwithstanding careful adherence to a formal SDLC, it is possible for certain errors to remain undetected during all testing work. These errors can remain in the system for long periods of time. Maintenance then also includes fixing such errors as they are discovered.

Since both new requirements and elimination of errors may require either major or minor system modifications, the logic involved in the first five phases of the SDLC should be reapplied as the need for modification is perceived and as the modifications are defined and implemented. In many instances, maintenance activities are routine and the reapplication of the SDLC is done implicitly without the detail described earlier (except for coding and testing of course). In other cases, especially as the system ages, the most economical approach is to redo the entire system. One then proceeds with the full SDLC in detail, including analysis of the cost and benefits of repair versus reconstruction.

MANAGEMENT ISSUES

As with other engineering processes, systems development must be managed properly to ensure quality results. Project organization and staff selection consistent with the requirements of the systems development life cycle are mandatory. One organizational approach that has been used successfully is the concept of a chief–programmer team. The team itself consists of a small group of specialists organized to do a specific project or set of tasks. These specialists are led by an experienced developer/programmer/analyst, etc., and the rest of the team consists of sufficient numbers of other developers/programmers/analysts at appropriate skill levels. The team also has the services of a clerical person (librarian) who assists the rest of the team in job setup, documentation preparation, project time reporting, cost tracking, etc. The key here is to target a *team* toward a particular part of a project. Team members help each other in design reviews, structured walk-throughs, desk checks, and other types of processes that help assure quality. The team approach is useful to the extent that it helps overcome the individual egos that can interfere with project success (Anderson, 1979).

In addition to techniques that focus on software development technology, techniques such as development of software quality assurance units (SQAU) are also being tried. The unit may be an organizational element separate from the systems department or project team. The SQAU is responsible for reviewing the project outputs on a phase-by-phase basis with respect to a formal software quality assurance plan. The plan is actually an outline of documentation requirements relating to both the system product and development process. The scope of the plan covers all issues from system purpose to configuration management and maintenance procedures. (An outline of a prototypical software quality assurance plan may be found in IEEE, 1982.)

Although we have not indicated it directly above, some people may define quality software as that which not only meets functional requirements, but also is implemented on time and on budget. The engineering management techniques of program evaluation and review technique (PERT) and critical path method (CPM) are useful in this connection. However, the use of standard forms-driven SDLCs, project history tracking, and data bases of errors commonly made within a given shop are all useful in preparing accurate estimates to be used with PERT or CPM. In addition, data bases of errors and design lessons learned can be useful in defining training opportunities. Schulmeyer and McManus (1987) discuss concepts and techniques of software quality assurance.

Configuration Management.　The last general area of management interest to be covered here is that of configuration management. The financial impact of configuration management was noted in Table 14.2: 67 percent of the cost of a system is incurred after the system goes into production. It should be clear from the foregoing general discussion that documentation requirements are tailored to each phase of the development life cycle. This includes standards for exposition of clear requirements, concise specifications, unambiguous and uncluttered design descriptions, meaningful program specifications, properly documented source code, and properly prepared test cases, test case results, and user documentation. These items taken together with all other items (hardware and software) that comprise the system may be termed the "system configuration."

Proper control of the quality and cost of system maintenance is supported via the system configuration management plan. This plan provides the outline and detail that defines each configuration end item, and provides definitions of the processes by which these items will be changed, by which the changes will be released, and by which changes are requested, recorded, effected, and audited. (An outline of a configuration management plan may be found in IEEE, 1983*a*. A further discussion of the general management issues overviewed here can be found in Grinath and Vess, 1983.)

The process-of-change management is supported by the use of software libraries. Many computing problems reappear in a number of forms. Mathematical subroutines are a case in point. Once programs that help solve these problems are written and validated, they can be added to a library for use by a number of people within the same organization. The repeated developing and testing of these particular programs is, therefore, avoided. Equally important, however, is the fact that each user has available a valid implementation of an acceptable algorithm for a particular application.

In using in-house developed libraries, it is useful to employ different software classes as approved for problems with different levels of risk. For example, one class may be approved for use at one's own risk and another may be unconditionally certified. Between these two is a continuum of classes. The configuration management process and software quality assurance activity must then support the classification and certification process.

VALIDATION

An essential step in software development is assurance that the computer system does what it is supposed to do. This is important not only from the point of view of developing software engineering techniques but also in ascertaining whether evaluation schemes can be defined to assess software quality in an after-the-fact fashion. As was evident during the above discussion of software engineering, computer systems cannot be validated using simple testing procedures.

To validate a computer system in any meaningful way, one must begin by looking closely at the process by which it was developed. This evaluation must be keyed to an evaluation of the input to and output from each phase of the SDLC. It must, therefore, be conducted on a phase-by-phase basis. To the extent that the process was properly structured, each phase can be examined individually with consideration of how the output of one phase is guaranteed to be consistent with the input of the next.

Source code review plays a special role in the assessment of system validity. Examination of source code for a system of any significant size cannot be done at a level of detail that adds much to the assurance of system quality (beyond that done in unit testing). Rather, the internal quality control process, the nature of the program specifications, and the scope, structure, and output of the various testing phases are more useful targets for examination. To assess the validity of the system in a maintenance environment, the configuration management approach should also be examined.

As indicated above, while the idea of validation "runs" makes little sense, the concept of a "test for record" does. In such a test, the system is executed using the user documentation to determine what steps to take, what the results should be, and how to interpret the output. The test for record differs from a system test in that fewer data are required and the user actually executes the test. Thus the systems test may obviate the need for a test for record. It must be recognized that the result of the test for record is an assessment of how the system can be misused rather than as a testimony of total system validity. As a corollary, and in view of the detailed discussion of the structured testing approach presented above, the full complement of tests (from unit test through systems test) is a far more robust challenge to the system than that associated with a test for record. Further, in absence of the type of analysis and data preparation done in structured testing, there is no way to document the extent to which the data used in the test for record adequately challenges the system. By contrast, audit of the unit test through system test protocols can provide an assessment of the extent of the challenge to which the system was subjected. This audit is therefore a better basis for drawing conclusions with respect to system validity.

There is one exception to the use of the SDLC-based validation process. This exception arises in the large number of instances in which old systems must be evaluated with respect to validity. Here, a structured SDLC may not have been used in systems development, so that many of the procedures discussed above do not directly apply. In this case, top-down analysis can still be performed to permit a validity assessment to be made. To maintain perspective, it is important here to recall what the mission is: Systems validation aims to ensure that the system solves the problem of concern and that it operates at the requisite level of reliability. In order to address these issues with respect to old systems, the structured approach outline throughout this discussion can still be used as a foundation for the type of analysis of system function and performance that must be made.

Although validation of the development process may not be possible for an existing system, system history may obviate the need for certain analysis steps normally done. To illustrate, consider the requirements definition. The purpose of this step is to ensure that the problem is sufficiently well understood and described to permit a solution to be developed. If a system has been operating for some time, the extent to which it solves the problem under consideration ought to be clear. That is, by system performance history, one can *inductively* determine the extent to which the problem is solved. The *deductive* process is used in new development.

If system history shows that some question exists as to the ability of the system to solve the problem, several steps can be taken. First, the requirements as currently (as opposed to originally) defined must be formally understood. Based on these requirements, data for a systems test can be prepared and critical failure modes can be identified and specifically tested for. Second, if the system is expected to require modification over the period of use, the architecture must be understood. Here, the modules and data structures used, mapped to required functions, can also be developed. This provides a basis for determination of the forms of systems modifications necessary to realize given functional changes. Where appropriate, this description can also be used to assess the viability of an existing architecture with respect to adaptability as well as with respect to acceptable operating costs. Based on the results of this analysis, a decision to scrap an old system or parts of it can be made. Note that this is tantamount to the review processes that occur in the preliminary and detailed design steps, and as such increases the level of assurance that the function of the system is clearly understood.

The third step that can be taken involves review of the program specifications and program documentation. The source code can be evaluated with respect to comments and clarity. The program and user documentation should be evaluated to ensure that the function described is consistent with the program specifications. If special concerns arise, the source code can be evaluated in detail by desk checking and unit testing. Data range checks can usually be added to programs relatively easily without impacting the main program flows.

It is worth repeating that some measure of system validity can be inferred from the length of time the system has been in operation without error. Prolonged error-free operation is implicitly equivalent to the desk checking and unit testing that goes on during the structured development process.

Each instance of establishing the validity of an old system must be looked at on a case-by-case basis. The effort expended should be balanced with respect to current knowledge of the system, the cost of additional validation, and the risk associated with system failure. Certain occasions may arise in which it becomes cheaper to rewrite the old system or parts of it than try to revalidate it, especially if risks are high and modifications are expected to be frequent.

Proper validation of an existing system does not depart from the structured approach advocated throughout this discussion. It requires instead that one elucidate the necessary validation requirements assuming that a structured development process had been followed; use system performance history and existing documentation as appropriate to show equivalence between conclusions based on that history and specific validation requirements; and perform the validation steps that are not obviated by consideration of historical performance in some meaningful way.

IMPLICATIONS OF SYSTEM SIZE AND RISK

The foregoing discussion has been concerned mainly with the recommended engineering approach for development of large-scale systems. Actually, the concepts presented apply equally to all types of systems, but the necessary level of documentation and formal control varies with the size and risk associated with the system. For example, systems which control manufacturing processes, process corporate payrolls, or take customer orders on-line have high financial risks associated with failure modes. Accordingly, a great deal of effort is expended in the control of system development, documentation, and maintenance.

Other applications such as reports and analyses written to meet specific departmental needs or other (intact) systems that are small, light-duty, and stand alone do not require a similarly rigorous approach. In fact, these types of applications are often developed exclusively by people who are not professional analysts, designers, or programmers. Alternatively, these systems, especially departmental reports, may be developed using report writer software applied to existing data via an approach known as "prototyping" using a combination of end users and systems professionals. In these instances, the documentation and control required is not as extensive as that for high-risk systems. The level that is required should be determined based on the nature of use, expected lifetime, and attendant risks, and should be judged on a case-by-case basis. Nonetheless, the implication of maintenance costs in large systems should be extrapolated to smaller ones, and requisite documentation, testing, and control practices adopted accordingly.

PROTOTYPING

The general subject of prototyping is one of growing interest. (See Mason and Cary, 1983.) Prototyping is a development process by which part of the requirements definition and preliminary design phases are abbreviated via a trial-and-error approach. The idea here is that much of the cost of system design arises through the iterative process required to communicate users' needs to system developers. In developing a prototype, less time is spent in a formal requirements definition, but enough information is provided to permit a systems developer to get "close" to what the user needs. The system is then implemented using a very high level language in which changes are easy to make. Users are then in a position to review the system and indicate clearly their likes or dislikes. This feedback is converted into a series of required changes. Trade-offs between wants and complexity are easy to identify, and decisions as to what is a true need and what is merely a want become easier to make. Only a few iterations through this process are usually required to arrive at a finished product.

Once the prototype system is in place, the user can exercise it and elucidate the need for further refinement. When the prototype becomes more or less static, a decision can be made to keep it as a prototype or rewrite it in some other programming language. One might wish, for example, to do such rewriting for reasons of operational efficiency. Note that in this case, the final prototype becomes the pseudocode representation of the system specification. Thus, when the rewritten system is delivered, it is what the user needs. Based on the nature of the problem and the tools used, systems development costs and development time may be reduced by 50 percent or more. System quality is assured, since the system delivered is the right one.

CONCLUSION AND SUMMARY

Software engineering is a relatively new discipline and is now one of the key focuses of computer systems engineering. Its birth occurred during the late 1960s to early 1970s and it continues to be developed and refined. Underlying the techniques of development and refinement is the fundamental concept of minimizing complexity by proper structuring of the overall process into phases, as well as structuring the process within each phase. A variety of tools and techniques are available to support the "engineering" content of each phase of the software development life cycle. The tools, techniques, and processes outlined in this discussion constitute the best demonstrated practice for software development defined to date.

High-quality, verified, and validated computer systems result from a well-planned, structured development process using the set of tools, techniques, and controls most appropriate for a given problem in a given organization at a given time. Documentation at each step of the process is critical. The form and substance should be adjusted to the particular phase being documented. Forms-driven methodologies can be of significant help; standards within a given organization help further.

The use of a formal system development life cycle applies (with proper adjustment) to all types of systems projects, including those which rely on package software, maintenance and support projects, and real-time systems projects. The detailed form of an SDLC is less important than its use as a guideline in the development process.

Project management practices, organizational approaches, and configuration management are also applicable. Software quality assurance groups, quality audits, and team building are examples. Validation of the product is intimately tied to validation of the process. As the field of software engineering continues to develop, new tools and techniques will be introduced to improve software quality and reliability. However, the rate at which these are recognized and adopted by organizations as a whole will remain the critical issue.

REFERENCES

Alberts, D. S. (1976). "Economics of Software Quality Assurance." *NCC Conference Proceedings,* vol. 45. National Computer Conference, New York. AFIPS Press, Montvale, NJ.

Anderson, R. D. (1979). *Proving Programs Correct.* John Wiley & Sons, New York.

Beizer, B. (1983). *Software Testing Techniques.* Van Nostrand, New York.

Colter, M. (1984). "A Comparative Examination of Systems Analysis Techniques." *MIS Quarterly,* vol. 8, pp. 51–66.

De Marco, T. (1978). *Structured Analysis and System Specification.* Yourdan Press, New York.

Dahl, O. J., Dijsktra, E. W., and Hoare, C. A. R. (1972). *Structured Programming.* Academic Press, London.

Fitzsimmons, A. and Love, T. (1978). "A Review and Evaluation of Software Science." *Computing Surveys,* vol. 10, pp. 3–17.

Grinath, A. C. and Vess, P. H. (1983). "Making SQA Work: The Development of a Software Quality System." *Quality Progress,* July, pp. 18–23.

Halstead, M. H. (1977). *Elements of Software Science,* North Holland, New York.

"Introduction to the Fortune 500." (1983). *Fortune,* May 2, p. 227.

Huang, J. C. (1975). "An Approach to Program Testing." *Computing Surveys,* vol. 7, pp. 113–128.

IBM (1974). *HIPO—A Design Aid and Documentation Tool.* IBM Publication 6C20–1851, White Plains, NY.

IEEE (1982). *Standard for Software Quality Assurance Plans.* IEEE, Piscataway, NJ.

IEEE (1983*a*). *Standard for Software Configuration Management Plans.* IEEE, Piscataway, NJ.

IEEE (1983*b*). *Standard Glossary of Software Engineering Terminology.* IEEE, Piscataway, NJ.

Knuth, D. E. (1974). "Structured Programming with 6070 Statements." *Computing Surveys,* vol. 6, pp. 261–301.

Martin, J. (1983). *Managing the Data Base Environment.* Prentice-Hall, Englewood Cliffs, NJ.

Mason, R. and Cary, T. (1983). "Prototyping Interactive Information Systems." *Communications of the ACM,* vol. 26, May, pp. 347–354.

Myers, G. J. (1979). *The Art of Software Testing.* Wiley-Interscience, New York.

Orr, K. (1981). *Structured Requirements Definition.* Ken Orr & Associates, Topeka, KS.

Page-Jones, M. (1980). *Practical Guide to Structure Systems Design.* Prentice-Hall, Englewood Cliffs, NJ.

"Perspectives in Business Data Processing." (1980). *Computer,* November, pp. 84–99.

Schulmeyer, G. G. and McManus, J. I. (1987). *Handbook of Software Quality Assurance.* Van Nostrand Reinhold, New York.

Sukert, A. N. (1977). "An Investigation of Software Reliability Models." *1977 Proceedings, Annual Reliability and Maintainability Symposium.* IEEE, New York, pp. 478–484.

Weinberg, G. (1971). *The Psychology of Computer Programming.* Van Nostrand Reinhold, New York.

Zelkowitz, N. V., Shaw, A. C., and Gannon, J. D. (1979). *Principles of Software Engineering and Design.* Prentice-Hall, Englewood Cliffs, NJ.

SECTION 15
SUPPLIER RELATIONS[1]

Frank M. Gryna

---

[1]In the Third Edition, the section on vendor relations was prepared by Robert G. Fitzgibbons and J. M. Juran.

INTRODUCTION

This step on the Spiral of Quality activities concerns the purchase of products (goods or services from suppliers, or "vendors"). Purchases are of two types: (1) those which become a part of the product marketed by the buyer and (2) non-product purchases such as equipment used for plant services, supplies for plant operations, and office supplies and equipment. The concepts discussed in this section apply to all purchases. Juran (1968) presents an overview of supplier relations activities.

Importance of Supplier Quality.   The quality of purchased items has become increasingly important for several reasons:

1. *Amount of purchased product:*   For many original equipment manufacturers, at least half of the materials embodied in their products is purchased from other companies or from divisions of the parent company. Manufacturers of products such as automobiles and office equipment now design the total product, manufacture a chassis or frame, and then purchase and assemble most of the remaining items going into the product.

2. *High costs associated with poor quality supplier items:*   For one home appliance manufacturer, 75 percent of all the warranty claims were traced to purchased items.

3. *Interdependence of buyers and suppliers:*   Some buyers are highly integrated with the facilities of the supplier. For example, a beer producer obtains the beer cans from a supplier whose plant is literally next door to the brewery. A can manufactured by the supplier at 7:00 a.m. is transported to the customer, filled with beer, and shipped by 10:00 a.m.

Other cases of interdependency involve technological skills. The buyer may be completely dependent on the knowledge of the supplier in designing and manufacturing the item. But the supplier is also dependent on the buyer—for complete information on how the supplier product needs to function in the buyer's product.

4. *Other internal factors at the buyer's organization:* One example is inventory reduction. The "just-in-time" inventory concept aims to receive items from suppliers only in the quantity and at the exact time that they are needed for production. Such tight scheduling makes it imperative that the purchased products meet quality requirements. If a portion of the purchased product is defective, then a major disruption may occur at the buyer's plant because of the lack of sufficient backup inventory. Under conventional purchasing, supplier quality problems can be hidden by excess inventory and bringing material in early. Heckel (1984) describes the case of a supplier who sent poor quality material for 4 years. Under the just-in-time concept, the supplier was replaced.

A second example is control of internal costs for the buyer, e.g., incoming inspection costs.

Supplier relations are worthy of review by upper management (see Section 8 under Quality Audits by Upper Managers).

Supplier Relations: Objectives and Activities. The overall objective is to create a relationship with a supplier that assures that the product will meet fitness-for-use needs with a minimum of incoming inspection or corrective action. The primary activities necessary are:

1. Define product and program quality requirements

2. Evaluate alternative suppliers

3. Select suppliers

4. Conduct joint quality planning

5. Cooperate with the supplier during the execution of the contract

6. Obtain proof of conformance to requirements

7. Certify qualified suppliers

8. Conduct quality improvement programs as required

9. Create and utilize supplier quality ratings

The degree that these activities are needed depends on the type of product being purchased, from the simple commodity item to the complex technological marvel. With respect to planning for quality, the spectrum of purchases can be divided into three categories:

1. *Standard materials and hardware.* Examples include fasteners, valves, resistors, simple chemicals, and supplies. For these kinds of purchases, industry specifications have usually been prepared. Generally the supplier relations program for quality is a minimal one.

2. *Minor components and materials:* Examples include gears, bearings, diodes, and relays. The specifications may be unique to each supplier or may be industrywide, or they may be prepared by the buyer. The supplier relations program usually requires some level of each activity previously mentioned.

3. *Major components:* These are often relatively complex items such as electronic assemblies, special purpose chemicals, and mechanical or electrome-

TABLE 15.1   Supplier Relations Activities

Activity	Type of purchase*		
	Standard material and hardware	Minor component	Major component
Definition of requirements	· · ·	M	H
Supplier evaluation	· · ·	M	H
Supplier selection	· · ·	H	H
Joint planning	· · ·	M	H
Cooperation during contract	· · ·	M	H
Proof of conformance	M	H	H
Certification	H	H	H
Quality improvement	· · ·	H	H
Supplier rating	M	H	H

*H = high level of effort; M = moderate level of effort.

chanical assemblies. Design responsibility may reside with either the supplier or the buyer. Such purchases require a complete supplier relations program.

Table 15.1 shows the relative emphasis of the primary activities for the three types of purchases. Simple products require only a minimal quality program. For major components, the consequences of poor supplier quality on the buyer's product justify a complete program. Some highly traditional industries fail to see the need for in-depth quality planning because they view their products as basically simple. Many of these products have now changed and require a higher level of technology; e.g., mechanical products make increasing use of electronics, many paints must be lead-free, and kitchen stoves now use microwave technology. The movement from simplicity to complexity for a product is often gradual, so the need for more intensive quality planning can be overlooked until a disaster occurs. Quality planning in such an environment cannot be done in a vacuum. Other factors must be considered to develop overall strategies for purchasing management. Kraljic (1983) discusses such strategies for several classifications of purchases.

Often it is assumed that supplier relations activities are primarily aimed at external suppliers. In practice, many companies report that their most difficult quality problems rest with suppliers who are "sister divisions" in the same corporation. This section discusses supplier relations both for external and internal suppliers.

SUPPLIER RELATIONS QUALITY POLICY

The general nature of quality policies is set out in Section 5, Quality Policies and Objectives. When supplier relations are studied, the following major problems emerge that require policy decisions:

Basic Relationship between Buyer and Supplier.   The relationship varies from "adversarial" to "teamwork," with several variations in between. In the adversarial relationship the supplier is viewed with suspicion—as someone who tries to sneak a bad product past the receiving inspection activity of the buyer. Low bid price is emphasized, and each party presses for short-term advantages even if this results in terminating the relationship. Mutual suspicion precludes mutual assistance, joint planning, and other forms of close collaboration. In some companies, the adversarial relationship extends to both external and internal suppliers.

In the teamwork relationship, the buyer and the supplier work together as if both were part of the same company. This is a planned, continuing relationship based on mutual confidence, joint planning, mutual visits, and assistance—no secrets. The supplier is regarded as an extension of the buyer's factory.

The 1980s have witnessed some dramatic changes in supplier relations, including some changes of a policy nature. Chief of these was a shift from the prevailing adversarial relationship toward a teamwork relationship. This shift was necessitated by the need to secure quality improvement from suppliers. A company whose product includes a heavy extent of purchased components needs improved quality in those components in order to fully improve their final product. Securing such quality improvement from suppliers is obviously more readily done in a teamwork environment.

To create such a teamwork environment has required some policy changes which many suppliers had long wanted, mainly:

Long-term purchase agreements rather than year to year or batch to batch. The long-term contracts (usually several years) encourage suppliers to invest in improvements. There has, in fact, been a considerable shift to long-term contracts.

Fewer suppliers, thereby increasing the share of market of the survivors. During the period 1980–1985, some large buyers in fact reduced their list of suppliers by about one-third.

In turn, some large buyers have established new or strengthened criteria for judging supplier adequacy:

"Full service," meaning that the supplier is expected to make positive contributions in product design, process design, cost reduction, etc.

Positive programs of quality improvement

Training in quality-related methodology

Miller and Kegaris (1986) describe how the Kodak and Alcoa companies used the teamwork approach to improve the quality of lithoplate materials.

The teamwork relationship gives full recognition to the interdependence of the buyer and the supplier of modern purchases. This interdependence takes three major forms: technological, economic, and managerial. Effective use of the forms is discussed under Joint Quality Planning below. An important element is strong lines of communication between technical specialists to replace the restrictive lines imposed by many companies.

For purchases of moderate to high level of product complexity the teamwork policy is essential to achieve fitness-for-use needs. For purchases of standard materials, the importance of working closely together is at a minimum.

Relative Emphasis of Quality in Purchasing Decisions. The selection of suppliers must assure that the desired product is fit for use, delivered on time, and has low cost. The relative importance of these three criteria is set by the company's middle and upper management. Some companies have traditionally awarded contracts on the basis of the lowest bid price; other companies have traditionally assigned highest priority to quality. Those who select suppliers understand the importance of quality but often are not provided with information which discriminates clearly among suppliers. In such cases it is quite understandable why buyers select suppliers. The tradition of buying primarily by price is an ingrained practice in many companies and will not be changed without a clear policy direction.

One electronics organization separates its purchases into two categories. The first category consists of items in which the quality level has been well established for many suppliers. For this type, purchasing managers are permitted to bargain with suppliers to obtain the lowest price. Items in the second category are more unique, and the quality depends greatly on the suppliers chosen. For these latter purchases, buyers are instructed to award contracts to the supplier who has the highest reputation for quality—even if a premium price must be paid.

Multiple Suppliers versus Single Source.   Multiple sources of supply have advantages: competition can result in better quality, lower costs, better service, and minimum disruption of supply due to strikes or other catastrophes.

A single source of supply also has advantages: the size of contract given to a single source will be larger than with multiple sources, and the supplier may attach more significance to the contract. However, if there are no alternative sources of supply, the monopoly secured by the supplier can have negative effects. With a single source, communications are simplified, and this can foster a team relationship. The most dramatic examples of single source are multidivisional companies in which some divisions are suppliers to others.

The policy decision determines how far the use of multiple suppliers should be carried. During the late 1970s, Toyota Motor Car Company had about 200 suppliers in contrast to large American manufacturers who had many thousands of suppliers.

For those products which require a teamwork relationship, a small number of suppliers provides more time for exchange visits and other forms of technological cooperation.

Internal versus External Suppliers.   Many companies are partly or wholly "integrated," i.e., some divisions are suppliers to others. In such companies it is quite common for the buying divisions to use external suppliers as additional sources of supply. This multiple sourcing provides a comparison of the quality of internal versus external sources.

There are obvious advantages to using the available internal sources: better employee relations, use of existing capacity, financial benefits, etc. However, some managers report that the internal suppliers are the biggest source of supplier quality problems. If such internal problems cannot be resolved, the superiority in quality by external suppliers may become the determining factor when deciding whether to buy from internal or external suppliers.

Long-Term Relationship or Not.   For those types of purchases which require a teamwork relationship, it is important that the supplier be assured of a relatively long-term contract. Otherwise there will be little incentive for that supplier to participate in teamwork. In some companies such a long-term relationship represents a policy change from past practices of annual rebidding of contracts. For an example of the actions taken by a company to promote long-term relationships, see Itoh (1978).

Providing Technical Assistance to Suppliers.   Technical assistance takes multiple forms: provision of training materials; scholarships for training courses; reliability engineering assistance, e.g., in reliability prediction; quality engineering assistance, e.g., in process capability studies; consulting assistance in technology, e.g., metrology. The policy decision is whether to provide such resources or to require the supplier to seek other resources.

Published Quality Policy. A good deal of unwritten supplier quality policy exists in the form of long-standing industry practices, sanctioned by the laws governing sales. There exist also some elements of written policy contained here and there in company supplier relations manuals. (For some examples of published supplier quality policy, see Section 5 under Quality Policies for Functions; Supplier Relations.) As interdependence grows, the need for published policy grows with it. Commonly the resulting published policy is embodied in a supplier relations manual, along with other information of importance and use to suppliers.

On a more comprehensive scale, the U.S. Department of Defense makes wide use of MIL-Q-9858A (1985) as a document to govern quality relations with contractors. This document includes some quality policy matters.

A policy statement specifically oriented to supplier relations is the "Ten Principles for Vendor-Vendee Relationships" evolved by a research committee of the Japanese Union of Scientists and Engineers. In paraphrased form, these principles include:

Mutual respect and cooperation

Prior contractual understanding

Agreed methods of evaluation

Agreed plans for settling disputes

Exchange of essential information

Adequate performance in related functions, e.g., inventory control

Supplier responsible to deliver good product and supporting data

Consumers' interests preeminent

ORGANIZING FOR SUPPLIER RELATIONS

In many companies, a controversial question often arises: Who is responsible for supplier quality? Discussions on so broad a subject are usually futile. Instead, it is better to identify the specific actions and decisions which collectively constitute supplier relations. Then, as these specifics are discussed individually, it is usually easy to agree on most of them. That narrows the area of controversy to a few specific items which require resolution. Table 15.2 shows a typical list, with responsibilities as assigned in one company.

In Table 15.2, most of the effort concerning supplier quality resides in the Quality Department. In an alternative approach, the Purchasing Department carries the ultimate responsibility for supplier quality and executes some of the detailed activities. (This is analogous to shifting the responsibility for quality internally from a Quality Department to the Manufacturing Department.) Under the concept, purchasing managers become familiar with quality requirements, supplier capabilities, and the effects of poor supplier quality. The objectives of such delegation include improvement of supplier selection and unification of responsibility for supplier quality relations.

One aerospace organization decided to place the primary responsibility for

TABLE 15.2   Responsibility Matrix—Supplier Relations

	Participating departments*		
Activity	Product Development	Purchasing	Quality Control
1. Establish a supplier quality policy	X	X	XX
2. Use multiple suppliers for major procurements		XX	
3. Evaluate quality capability of potential suppliers	X	X	XX
4. Specify requirements for suppliers	XX		X
5. Conduct joint quality planning	X		XX
6. Conduct supplier surveillance		X	XX
7. Evaluate delivered product	X		XX
8. Conduct improvement programs	X	X	XX
9. Use supplier quality ratings in selecting suppliers		XX	X

*XX = principal responsibility, X = collateral responsibility.

supplier quality in the Purchasing Department. A published statement listed the following responsibilities for Purchasing:

1. Evaluate the relative capability of suppliers to deliver products that will satisfy quality requirements and utilize the evaluation results as a major factor in procurement.
2. Provide terms and conditions in procurement documents that establish supplier responsibility for compliance with quality requirements and that permit adequate control of supplier performance.
3. Administer procurement contracts and exercise control of supplier performance adequate to assure the delivery of products that satisfy requirements.
4. Provide aggressive follow-up and obtain supplier corrective action when improvement is required.

There are significant resource implications that result from this organizational approach. At a minimum, it requires purchasing personnel to be trained to understand the quality disciplines as they apply to suppliers. It may also require the Purchasing Department to add personnel who are quality specialists. All of this significantly diminishes the role of the Quality Department in supplier matters.

On a related organizational matter, some multiplant organizations are experimenting with the concept of centralized responsibility for supplier quality on a product basis. Under this concept, the responsibility for supplier quality on all purchases of product X is assigned to one of the plants. That plant then becomes a coordinator for all plants who buy product X, and for all the suppliers who supply product X. For example, the plant responsible for procuring product X becomes responsible for specifications, contracts, and quality assurance. The coordinating plant receives inputs from the individual plants and handles all negotiations with suppliers both before and during the contract. This centralized approach is intended to assure that suppliers are presented with consistent requirements from any of the corporation's different plants. It is also intended to provide the buyer with more stature in obtaining resolution of quality problems.

Norquist (1983) describes some of the attitudes of Quality and Purchasing personnel and suggests appropriate responsibilities for each function. For an example of how a team is formed to administer the quality related aspects of major subcontracts, see Ziegler and Diggs (1982). This paper shows specific responsibilities of Engineering, Manufacturing, and Quality department members of a team both during the preaward phase and the post award phase of a subcontract.

PRECONTRACT PLANNING

Precontract planning is largely devoted to securing a mutual understanding sufficient to reach a decision on whether to contract or not. In this exchange the supplier needs to understand the use requirements and specifications of what is to be met; how the system will make use of the purchased component; what the interface requirements are; what the main requirements are for performance, reliability, maintainability, safety, etc.; what the meaning is of key words and phrases. The buyer, in turn, needs to understand just what capabilities the supplier is able to muster to meet all these requirements. Quality surveys can be used to assess prospective suppliers' capabilities.

In the precontract stage there are two types of inputs for specifications.

1. Performance specifications defining what the product is to do, i.e., fitness for use. These specifications are essential.

2. Specifications defining the quality activities the supplier is expected to conduct. Increasingly, buyers are mandating quality systems for suppliers.

The second type of specification is a departure from the traditional practice of the buyer refraining from telling a supplier "how to run the plant." Defining required activities within a supplier's plant is sometimes necessary to assure that a supplier does have the expertise to conduct the full program needed to create a satisfactory product. For some products, government regulations require that a buyer impose certain processing requirements (e.g., keeping special records for traceability; maintaining a locked storeroom as a hold area for nonconforming products) on suppliers. For other products, such as a complex mechanical or electronic subsystem, the overall system requirements may result in a need for a supplier to meet a numerical reliability or maintainability requirement and to conduct certain activities (see Section 13 under Planning for Time-Oriented Performance—Reliability) to assure that such a requirement is met.

Models for Supplier Quality Programs.   Documents defining adequate quality programs exist in several models:

ANSI/ASQC Z-1.15-1979 (1979). *Generic Guidelines for Quality Systems*

MIL-Q-9858A (1985). *Quality Program Requirements*

AQAP-1 (1985). *NATO Quality Control System Requirements for Industry* 3rd ed.

NHB 5300.4 (1B) (1969). *Quality Program Provisions for Aeronautical and Space Systems Contractors*

See Appendix III, Selected Quality Standards, Specifications, and Related Documents, for the sources of these documents. Appendix III also lists additional documents.

Some industrial buyers have prepared documents describing quality program requirements for suppliers (see below). An example is the Q-101 *Quality System Standard* issued by the Ford Motor company (1983). This standard is aimed at defect prevention during the manufacturing phase of the product life cycle. The standard starts with an introduction and a glossary giving definitions for 41 terms. Next, the standard presents requirements that apply to all products:

Advanced Quality planning—control plans
Incoming (subcontracted) products
   Approved materials
   Control of subcontracted products
Manufacturing process capability
   Process potential studies
   Process capability studies
Statistical process control
Ongoing verification and testing
   Inspection and laboratory test instructions
   Measuring and inspecting equipment
   Engineering specification test performance requirements
   Product qualification
   Indication of product status
   Periodic layout inspections
   Repaired products
   Returned product analysis
   Internal audits
   Heat-treated parts and fasteners
Documentation
   Procedures
   Drawing and change control
   Deviation control
   Records
   Changes in manufacturing process
Interface with Ford on quality related matters
   Initial samples and first production shipment approvals
   Requirements for new suppliers
   Requirements for initial samples
   Requirements for first production shipments
Ford supplier quality assurance surveys

There are additional requirements that apply to "control items." Control items are parts which can affect either compliance with government regulations or safe vehicle operations. The additional requirements are:

Preproduction
   Feasibility
   Failure mode and effects analysis (FMEA)
   Control plan
Manufacturing process capability

First production shipment approval
Documentation
    Document identification
    Product identification
    Certification of control items
    Lot traceability
    Process changes
    Heat-treated parts
Critical items

The standard describes the quality system survey, process capability, testing, documentation, approval procedures, and other requirements.

Requirements for a Supplier Reliability Program.   For complex products it may be necessary to identify the reliability engineering activities that a supplier is expected to conduct. One company listed the following required activities:

Validation of reliability requirements received from customer
Preparation of mathematical model for reliability
Apportionment of the reliability requirement to phases of the mission and to elements of the system
Design criteria for reliability
Evaluation of design for reliability
    Reliability estimate
    Design review
Reliability tasks during manufacturing
    Manufacturing and procurement criteria
    Evaluation of manufacturing methods
Reliability activities during shipping, storage, and use
Test program
    Integration of reliability with other tests
    Reliability demonstration plan
Data system
    Requirements for malfunction reports
    Distribution of malfunction reports
    Problem status summary
    Equipment operating time records
Organization for reliability
    Program review and monitoring

The following reliability inputs are also required in proposals submitted to the buyer:

Preliminary estimate of reliability
Reliability features of the equipment

Preliminary analysis showing effects of failures

Design review

Approach to measurement and demonstration of reliability

Preventing degradation of reliability during manufacture and operational use of the product

Integration of reliability efforts with the design efforts

Integration of reliability with the test program

Management philosophy on achieving reliability

Proposed method of reliability program control

Schedule of major reliability tasks

Personnel resources to be assigned

The time spent in precontract planning for quality has several benefits. First, the supplier is made aware of product requirements and program requirements. Conformance to these requirements can then be monitored and problem areas identified before noncomforming product is produced. Second, precontract planning can assure that all suppliers are bidding on the contract on the same basis. If a supplier is not aware of all of the activities necessary, the resources will not be included in the budget and the activities will probably never be performed.

EVALUATING SUPPLIER CAPABILITY

Evaluating supplier capability has two facets:

1. Qualifying the supplier's design through the evaluation of product samples
2. Qualifying the supplier's capability to meet quality requirements on production lots

Qualification of the Supplier Design.   In some purchases, the buyer provides the supplier with a description of the desired function of the product and asks the supplier to create a design and produce the items. The first phases, then, of supplier qualification is an evaluation of the design to assure that it can meet performance and other requirements.

The supplier prepares samples based on the proposed design. The samples are tested either by the buyer or by the supplier who submits the results to the buyer. Numerous performance tests are conducted, often under a variety of environments including temperature, vibration, humidity, and other conditions. Reliability, maintainability, and other parameters of use are also evaluated, but, because of the limited number of samples and test time, to a much lesser degree. For these latter parameters, the supplier can be required to submit other analyses such as a reliability prediction or a failure mode, effect, and criticality analysis (see Section 13 under Planning for Time-Oriented Performance—Reliability).

An important variable in the qualification test of a design is the extent to which the sample is representative of future production. For a new design, the sample items are usually made in an engineering or development shop. In such cases, the results of a qualification test of a design provide little if any information about the ability of the supplier to conform to the design under production conditions. The qualification test results, however, do show whether the supplier understood the basic performance requirements and created a design meeting those requirements.

Qualification of the Supplier Manufacturing Process. Separate steps must be taken to evaluate the ability of the supplier to conform to the design in production quantities. This evaluation of manufacturing capability can take several forms: prior product performance, process capability analysis, and evaluation of the supplier's quality system.

Prior Product Performance. The best predictor of future product quality is the supplier's past quality for the same or similar products. This prior experience can include:

1. *Experience in the buyer's organization with the same supplier:* In many cases, the experience has been codified into a formal rating of the supplier (see below under Supplier Quality Rating).
2. *Experience pooled from multiple plants within the same corporation:* An example of this is the General Motors Source Performance Evaluation and Reporting (SPEAR) system. This is a data bank that pools information on supplier quality surveys, performance reports, and defective material reports.
3. *Data from government data banks:* One example of this is Government Industry Data Exchange Program (GIDEP). The information in the data bank includes engineering evaluation test reports, reliability and maintainability data, metrology data and procedures, and manufacturing test data. Military and other government agencies and industrial organizations make up the primary participants. The program is centrally managed and funded by the U.S. government. The contact is: Director, GIDEP Operations Center, Corona, CA 91720.
4. *Data banks serving a specific industry:* An example is the Coordinating Agency for Supplier Evaluation (CASE). This data bank was set up to reduce redundant surveys of suppliers. Survey data are available to members of the Association (Sheppard, 1977).

Process Capability Analysis. A process capability study is based on measurements collected from the manufacturing process to determine the inherent uniformity of a process, and thereby whether or not the process is capable of meeting the specification. (See Section 16 under Process Capability.) Ford Motor Company requires suppliers to conduct either a process potential study or a process capability study.

The process potential study provides a preliminary assessment of the process. These studies are of short duration and are not intended to measure long-term process capability. Typically a sample of at least 30 units is taken from a production run of at least 300 units. A control chart on average and range is run (see Section 24 under Types of Control Charts; Variables Data). If the chart shows no points out of control and no evidence of trends of an adverse nature, then the data is used to calculate the process potential. The process potential is acceptable if the measured process average ± 4 standard deviations is within the bilateral specifications or on the favorable side of a unilateral specification.

In the process capability study, the control charts are continued from the process potential study until all factors likely to contribute to process variation are reflected in the data. These factors include raw material, personnel, environment, tool wear, and other factors. The study often requires at least 30 days. Again, if the control charts show a state of statistical control, then the capability can be calculated in the manner discussed in Section 16 under Process Capability Management. For a capability study using variables data, Ford requires that the measured process average ± 3 standard deviations be within specification limits. For attributes data, average performance must be at least 99.73 percent conforming to specifications. When this is not met, 100 percent inspection must be used along with a program of analysis to improve the process.

Evaluation of process capability is required by Ford on all "control items" (parts which affect either compliance with government regulations or safety) and other significant product characteristics.

The supplier can also be asked to prepare a failure mode, effect, and criticality analysis. See Section 13 under Failure Mode, Effect, and Criticality Analysis. This analysis is not based on process measurements, but it provides some assurance that the supplier has analyzed the proposed process and identified potential problems.

Evaluation of the Supplier System through a Quality Survey.   A supplier quality survey is based on a plant visit to evaluate a supplier's ability to meet quality requirements on production lots. The usual steps in making a survey are:

1. Assemble available information on prior experience with the supplier. This can help to identify areas to highlight during the survey.
2. Send a presurvey questionnaire to the supplier. The information collected can help to plan the visit itself and save time during the visit. Doing this homework prior to the visit makes it possible to focus the visit on potential problems that may arise during the contract.
3. Organize the survey team. Membership varies and may include specialists from Purchasing, Manufacturing, Engineering, and Quality.
4. Conduct the survey. The survey generally takes one to several days at the supplier's plant. It starts with an opening conference at which the purpose of the survey, the kind of information desired, and a proposed schedule for the visit are discussed. The most usual points of concentration during the survey are:

    a. *Management capabilities:*   These relate mainly to such matters as:
    Policies: Is the supplier willing to be "on the team," i.e., operate on the basis of exchange of visits, no secrets, joint planning, mutual technical assistance, etc.? Does the supplier engage actively in quality improvement and cost reduction?
    Organization: Have the activities essential to attainment of quality been identified and described? Are these activities clearly assigned to the various departments in a logical relationship?
    Personnel: Have the managers, specialists, and work force been trained in modern ways as evidenced by attendance at structured courses and certificates of qualification? Are there clear evidences of high motivation for quality in relation to other parameters (cost, delivery, etc.)?

    b. *Technological capabilities:*   Here the emphasis is on matters such as: the facilities and equipment in the supplier's plant, plus their up-to-dateness and condition; the ability of the process to meet product specifications; the degree of understanding of the relationship between process variables and product results; and the adequacy of the measuring equipment.

    c. *Quality discipline capabilities:*   Here the emphasis is typically on quality-oriented systems and procedures. These include systems for process control, product inspection and test, data recording and summary, documentation, maintenance of equipment, etc. In addition, this part of the survey looks for the existence and completeness of quality manuals as well as provision for audit of conformance to systems and procedures. But systems need to be applied to the specific product. For example, to assure that planning for process control has occurred, a useful technique is to require the supplier to prepare a flow chart showing the proposed inspection stations and process control points for the product.

From the presurvey questionnaire or checklists used during the visit, detailed information can be collected. This can include:

Management: philosophy, quality policies, organization structure, indoctrination, commitment to quality

Design: organization, systems in use, caliber of specifications, orientation to modern technique, attention to reliability, engineering change control, development laboratories

Manufacture: physical facilities, maintenance, special processes, process capability, production capacity, caliber of planning, lot identification and traceability

Purchasing: specifications, supplier relations, procedures

Quality assurance: organization structure, availability of quality control and reliability control and reliability engineers, quality planning (materials, in-process, finished goods, packing, storage, shipping, usage, field service), audit of adherence to plan

Inspection and test: laboratories, special tests, instruments, measurement control

Quality coordination: organization for coordination, order analysis, control over subcontractors, quality cost analysis, corrective action loop, disposition of nonconforming product

Data systems: facilities, procedures, effective use, reports

Personnel: indoctrination, training, motivation

Quality results: performance attained, self-use of product, prestigious customers, prestigious subcontractors

The evaluation of various quality activities can be quantified by a scoring system. For example, in surveys made by the Ford Motor Company, 20 areas of the supplier program are evaluated. Each area is rated on a scale of 0 to 10. A rating of 5 is required for each area and a total of 140 is needed overall.

A scoring system that includes importance weights for activities is illustrated in Table 15.3. This system is used by a manufacturer of electronic assemblies. In this case, the importance weights (W) vary from 1 to 4 and are designed to total to 25 for each of the three areas surveyed. The weights show the relative importance of the various activities in the overall index. The actual ratings (R) of the activities observed are assigned as follows:

10: The specific activity is satisfactory in every respect (or does not apply).

 8: The activity meets minimum requirements, but improvements could be made.

 0: The activity is unsatisfactory.

Scoring schemes can be made simpler (see ASQC, 1976, *Procurement Quality Control—A Handbook of Recommended Practices*), or more complicated as illustrated by a probabilistic approach described by Shilliff and Bodis (1975).

After the survey is completed there is usually a closing conference at which the team presents an oral and sometimes a brief written summary of their observa-

TABLE 15.3   Scoring of a Supplier Quality Survey

Activity	Receiving inspection			Manufacturing			Final inspection		
	$R*$	W	$R \times W$	R	W	$R \times W$	R	W	$R \times W$
1. Quality management	8	3	24	8	3	24	8	3	24
2. Quality planning	8	4	32	8	4	32	10	4	40
3. Inspection equipment	10	3	30	10	3	30	10	3	30
4. Calibration	0	3	0	10	3	30	0	3	0
5. Drawing control	0	3	0	10	2	20	10	2	20
6. Corrective action	10	3	30	8	3	24	8	3	24
7. Handling rejects	10	2	20	8	2	16	10	3	30
8. Storage and shipping	10	1	10	10	1	10	10	1	10
9. Environment	8	1	8	8	1	8	8	1	8
10. Personnel experience	10	2	20	10	3	30	10	2	20
			Area total = 174†			Area total = 224			Area total = 206

*R = rating; W = weight.
†Interpretation of area totals:
   Fully approved: Each of the three area totals is 250.
   Approved: None of the three area totals is less than 200.
   Conditionally approved: No single area total is less than 180.
   Unapproved: One or more of the area totals is less than 180.

tions and conclusions. Some companies require the supplier to sign the written report indicating that it has been presented to the supplier. Later the team prepares a final report summarizing the visit and recommending whether or not the supplier should become an approved source.

Supplier Surveys in Practice.   Supplier surveys have been used extensively for many years, and a large body of experience has been collected. One of the few published studies is that by Brainard (1966). In the study 151 supplier surveys were made and a recommendation made in each case to purchase or not purchase. In all 151 cases the company did purchase from the supplier (even if the recommendation was against such action). The results of the study indicated that in 77 of the 151 cases, the survey correctly predicted the quality of the product as subsequently found at incoming inspection. In the remaining 74 cases, the survey incorrectly predicted the subsequent quality. The study raised doubts as to the predictive value of the surveys, and led to changes in the survey approach.

Collective experience suggests that supplier surveys have both merits and limitations:

Merits.   All surveys provide some extent of objective information. The most obvious concerns the physical facilities—what type, how many, what condition, etc. Where certain essential facilities are not in evidence, e.g., a special type of test equipment, the buyer is alerted as to the extent of delays which might result.

The survey may turn up additional findings of an objective nature—the presence or absence of essential training programs, traceability provisions, data feedbacks, etc. Such findings also give early warnings as to the time and effort required for the supplier to meet the provisions of the contract.

The survey also has the merit of opening up communications between buyer and supplier, and even within the supplier organization. There have been numerous instances in which survey findings have stimulated supplier upper management action on matters which the supplier's own quality manager had been unable to communicate to the top. .

Limitations. Supplier surveys as conducted in the United States have not proved to be useful predictors of future quality performance of suppliers. It is possible that a change in emphasis would improve this. The U.S. emphasis has been on organization, procedures, documentation, etc., whereas the Japanese emphasis has been on the capability of the process, the adequacy of the process controls, the training and qualifications of the work force, etc. (If the survey finds the procedures to be inadequate, they can be changed in a matter of weeks. However, it takes months and even years to remedy inadequate processes or lack of essential training.)

This same U.S. approach has tended to concentrate attention on conformance to procedural specifications rather than on product fitness for use. The procedural emphasis is not on the supplier's general plan of approach, but on specific products or processes.

Multiple Assessment. In the early days of supplier surveys, suppliers were willing to make themselves available for the visit. However, as the number of customers requesting surveys increased, the survey teams became a burden and many suppliers objected to the time required. Repeat surveys of the same supplier are referred to as multiple assessment. Attempts are being made to reduce the amount of multiple assessment. The "assessment" that is referred to is the initial assessment of the supplier to determine capability. It does not refer to monitoring of the supplier during the execution of a contract. Thoday (1983) discusses four elements necessary to reduce the amount of multiple assessment.

1. A standard specification of the element of a quality system
2. Individual assessors who are trained and qualified by a competent body
3. An independent third party to operate a service of supplier assessment
4. The publication of details of the firms who have been successfully appraised

In England, BSI Document BS5750, *Quality Systems,* or BSI *Handbook 22 Quality Assurance* (British Standards Institution, 1979 and 1981), are used to define a quality system. The Institute of Quality Assurance provides training and examinations to qualify assessors. The British Standards Institution (BSI) provides the service of supplier assessment. A register of assessed firms is published by a Stationery Office of the British government.

In the United States, the CASE data bank of supplier surveys (see above under Prior Product Performance) has been effective in reducing multiple assessments.

Third-Party Assessment. This term refers to supplier evaluation by someone other than the supplier or buyer. The forces behind such external audits have been mainly:

1. Large buyers demanding quality assurance beyond that supplied by the supplier
2. Insurance companies demanding independent quality certification as a prerequisite to carrying the risks
3. Government departments engaged in administering regulations oriented to safety, health, and the environment

More recently there has been an added and growing demand for "independent" sources of quality-oriented information relative to consumer economics. An example is the pressure from consumer organizations for independent information to assist consumers in determining which among the competing products offers the best value for the money.

Collectively, these trends in the field of quality bear a striking resemblance to the history of independent audits in the field of finance.

The BSI has created a service of making an independent assessment of the quality program of an organization. The survey is made in comparison to publication BS5750, *Quality Systems,* a 1979 publication that defines the basic elements of a quality program. The BSI provides, on a contract basis, an assessment of a supplier.

Approved Supplier Lists.   A supplier may be listed as "qualified" in two broad respects:

1. Business matters—integrity, financial capability, prompt payment, etc.
2. Product quality (design and manufacturing capability)

The qualification process involves two separate evaluations. The results are often formalized into approved supplier lists—one for business matters in general and one for quality on specific products. Qualification of a supplier on business matters does not automatically qualify the supplier on quality for any product. A "preferred suppliers list" is slightly different, and is discussed below under Certification.

SUPPLIER SELECTION

The selection of suppliers starts with the decision whether to make or buy. This decision requires an analysis of factors such as the skills and facilities needed, plant capacity, ability to meet delivery schedules, expected costs of "make" or "buy," and other matters.

The process of obtaining bids can sometimes reveal excessive design requirements. One electronics company decided to permit purchases externally even though capability was available in-house. Surprisingly, many suppliers submitted bid prices much higher than expected. The suppliers claimed that the prices were necessary in order to meet all requirements. These same requirements had been used internally but the costs had simply been distributed over many products. A review of the requirements revealed that some of them were unnecessary.

At the outset, when there is no prior experience with a supplier, the selection must be pieced together using:

The reputation of the supplier

Information derived from buyers who have had experience with this supplier on similar products

Qualification tests of the supplier's design

Survey of the supplier's manufacturing facility

Information from data banks

Collectively all these inputs still leave doubts as to what will be the subsequent actual performance of the supplier. Many buying companies respond to these doubts by placing new suppliers in a provisional category until the subsequent deliveries remove these doubts. At that time the supplier is placed on a list of approved suppliers. Admittance to this "club" confers on the supplier some useful advantages over other suppliers who are not on the list. These advantages can include a higher share of the available business and longer-term contracts.

Supplier selection is not based solely on quality; it must include consideration of prices, delivery against schedules, and still other parameters. The purchasing manager (or the project manager) has the responsibility for coordinating the competing demands behind these parameters.

Total Cost of a Purchase.   The total cost of purchased products is the purchase price plus the added costs due to scrap, rework, delays, field failures, and other consequences of poor supplier quality. These added costs sometimes exceed greatly the savings due to buying from the lowest bidder. It is easy in such cases to accuse the purchasing managers of buying solely based on the lowest price.

Purchasing managers generally agree that the purchasing decision should be based on all costs—not just the purchase price. However, they point out that they lack data adequate to specify the added quality-related costs; they also point out that they are not in a position to evaluate them. Instead, such evaluation must be made by other departments, e.g., Quality, Accounting.

In theory it is feasible to quantify these added costs by enlarging the accounting system to identify and evaluate all quality-related costs of supplier origin. Many companies have tried this. In practice it is found that these costs follow the Pareto principle of vital few and useful many. For the vital few, it is decidedly worthwhile to evaluate the added costs. For the useful many, the work of tracking the needed data becomes formidable and hence difficult to justify. The way out of this dilemma is to deal with the vital few cases individually and the useful many collectively, e.g., through sampling evaluation.

Some organizations have developed a quality cost index for the vital few cases of procurement. This index is defined as the supplier quality cost plus the purchase price, all divided by the purchase price. The supplier quality cost is the cost associated with quality problems on supplier items. To trace this cost completely would require an extensive record-keeping system. What can be done is to identify the main categories of this cost and to collect actual cost data for those categories. For example, one company identified the categories as:

The cost of processing lot rejections: This can be estimated as the cost of processing the paperwork and handling other matters for each rejected lot.

Cost of complaint investigations: This is the cost involved in resolving quality problems that have arisen on supplier items.

Cost of receiving inspection: This is an estimate of the receiving inspection cost for the particular item and the particular supplier. Depending on the reputation of the supplier, the amount of receiving inspection can vary greatly.

Cost of nonconforming product identified after receiving inspection: This is the cost incurred if a nonconforming product is not identified until later assembly or field use of the product.

The supplier quality cost index can be used to estimate the total cost of future purchases by multiplying the bid price by the index of a similar product from the same supplier. If data on these indices can be given to purchasing managers for the vital few products and suppliers, the managers will be better able to select suppliers on the basis of lowest total cost instead of lowest bid price. ASQC (1980) provides a discussion of this index.

The importance of carefully evaluating the supplier's bid price is emphasized by Itoh (1978). The Toyota Motor Company does not blindly accept an offer based on an unusually low bid. Toyota feels that if the price is unrealistic, serious business problems may arise. That in turn can result in less attention paid to quality matters. Their policy stresses that the supplier should receive a fair price to help maintain a proper quality system and make a fair profit. This helps to develop long-term business relationships with their suppliers.

Products requiring special development efforts may require special types of contracts. Hayes and Romig (1977) discuss seven types of contracts along with the issues involved with respect to quality.

Some organizations keep track of supplier performance and identify certain suppliers as "preferred." Such suppliers have a favored position in source selection and may receive other benefits. The concept is discussed below under Certification.

JOINT QUALITY PLANNING

The finalization and execution of the contract between supplier and buyer requires detailed quality planning covering three elements: economic, technological, and managerial.

Joint Economic Planning. The economic aspects of joint quality planning concentrate on two major approaches:

1. *Buying value rather than conformance to specification:* The technique used is to analyze the value of what is being bought and to try to effect an improvement (see Section 13 under Value Engineering). Applied to supplier quality relations, value engineering looks for excessive costs due to:

   a. *Overspecification for the use to which the product will be put (e.g., special products ordered when a standard product would do:* One example concerns an outboard motor crankshaft seal. A fluoroelastomer costing 20 times as much as the previously used nitrile rubber was chosen for this seal. As a result of a design analysis the metallic seal component was strengthened and a reduced amount of the expensive elastomer was needed to provide the seal. The result was a new design with less cost and no loss in quality (Cooper, 1980).

   b. *Emphasis on original price rather than on cost of use over the life of the product:* For some products, the cost of use can be at least three times the original price.

   c. *Emphasis on conformance to specification, not fitness for use:* A tire manufacturer purchased valves from several suppliers, all of whom met specifications. All valves were fit for use by the ultimate user—the vehicle operator. However, there was an added use for the valves. They were used to inflate and deflate the tires during the vulcanization process. The valves which had the largest hole diameter resulted in the shortest cycle time for the vulcanization process, resulting in higher productivity for the manufacturer of the tires. (Each supplier was permitted to set the hole diameter.)

2. *Optimizing quality costs:* To the purchase price the buyer must add a whole array of quality-related costs: incoming inspection, material review, production delays, downtime, extra inventories, etc. However, the supplier also has a set of costs to be optimized. Both the buyer and seller should put together the data needed to understand their life-cycle costs, or the cost of use, and then work cooperatively toward joint optimization. For example, a heavy-equipment manufacturer bought castings from several suppliers. It was decided to calculate the "total cost of the purchased casting" as the original purchase price

plus incoming inspection costs plus the costs of rejections detected later in assembly. The unit purchase price on a contract given to the lowest bidder was $19.00. The inspection and rejection costs amounted to an additional $2.11. The variation among bid prices was $2.00.

Some buyers require successful performance of the purchased item before payment is authorized. One chemical manufacturer accepts two types of purchase agreements. One is the conventional type in which the buyer performs incoming inspection of the supplier item and then authorizes payment. In the second type of contract, payment is not authorized until the product performs satisfactorily in the buyer's process. Other buyers authorize payment upon initial receipt but later submit a claim to the supplier if the product performs poorly in the buyer's process.

Joint Technological Planning.   The more usual elements of such planning include:

1. *Agreement on the meaning of performance requirements in the specifications:*   Sometimes requirements are inadvertently omitted (e.g., a requirement for edgewise bending of copper strips for the frame size associated with a certain type of motor). In other cases, the need is for clarification on how the product will be used. For example, in investigating cracks on a forged round, it was learned that the supplier was never told that the rounds would receive further forging by upsetting as bars. Given that information, the supplier would have used a higher quality of ingot to prevent the cracks developing (Rau, 1981).

2. *Quantification of reliability and maintainability requirements:*   A supplier was given a contract to provide an air-conditioning system with a mean time between failures of at least 2000 h. As part of joint planning, the supplier was required to submit a detailed reliability program early in the design phase. The program write-up was submitted and included a provision to impose the same 2000-h requirement on each supplier of parts for the system. This revealed a complete lack of understanding by the supplier of the multiplication rule (see Section 23 under Reliability).

3. *Definition of reliability and maintainability tasks to be conducted by the supplier.*

4. *Preparation of a process control plan for the manufacturing process:*   The supplier can be asked to submit a plan summarizing the specific activities that will be conducted during the manufacture of the product. Plans can be required for all products or only for critical items. An example is shown in Figure 15.1.

5. *Definition of special tasks required of the supplier:*   These may include activities to assure that sanitary and other aspects of "good manufacturing practices" are met, special documentation requirements, and special analyses to be prepared for critical items. An example of a special analysis to be submitted by the supplier is the process failure mode effect and criticality analysis (see Section 13 under Failure Mode, Effect, and Criticality Analysis).

6. *Seriousness classification of defects:*   This is intended to help the supplier understand where to concentrate his or her efforts (see Section 18 under Quality Standards).

7. *Establishment of sensory standards:*   This is indicated for those qualities which require use of the human being as an instrument (see Section 18 under Sensory Standards). For example, the federal government was faced with the problem of defining the limits of color on a military uniform. The solution was

PRO FORMA CONTROL PLAN Ongoing

Part Number: ∇E2EB-9A889-BA	Part Name: Switch Assembly—Headlight	Supplier: Able Switch Company

Significant Characteristics:

A. Terminal Blade Thickness   D. Terminal Alignment
B. Terminal Blade Width   E. Continuity—All Circuits(∇)
C. Mounting Bushing Threads   F. Millivolt Drop—Circuit Number 321

	Characteristics Affected	Part Detail	Frequency*	Sample Size*	Analysis Methods	Reaction Program if Out-of-Control Conditions are Encountered***
Incoming Inspection	A	stock thickness	every shipment	· · ·	review control charts provided with each lot	impound lot—contact supplier for resolution
In-Process Inspection						
• Press Area	A	thickness after coining	every 1000 parts	2 pieces	micrometers/X̄ and R chart	correct process
	B	width after stamping	every 10,000 parts	5 pieces	micrometers/median chart	correct process
	C	threads after forming	every 4 hours	75 pieces	tapered ring gage/p chart	correct process
• Assembly Area	D	alignment after staking	hourly	30 pieces	special gage/p chart	correct process
	E	complete assembly	chart hourly	100%	automatic tester/u chart	repair by responsible operator
	F	complete assembly	hourly	20 pieces	automatic tester/X̄ and s chart	correct process
Outgoing Inspection**	C, D, E	complete assembly	each lot	50 pieces	complete visual inspection plus gages and test stand/c chart	reject lot and sort for identified nonconformance

*The frequencies and sample sizes are determined from an initial study of the stability of each process. They are periodically reviewed and updated as required.
**After 6 months production experience, the process control and inspection records will be reviewed with Ford SQA to determine if outgoing inspection can be reduced.
***If any nonconforming products are found in process control samples, 100% inspect all products produced since the last in control point.

SUBMITTED BY: _____   APPROVED BY: _____

Plant Manager—Smalltown Plant   Ford SQA Representative
Able Switch Company

FIG. 15.1 Form Q-101. *(Ford Motor Company, 1983.)*

to prepare physical samples of the lightest and darkest acceptable colors. Standards were sent to the field with the provision of replacing the standards periodically because of color fading.

8. *Standardization of test methods and test conditions between supplier and buyer to assure their compatibility:* A carpet manufacturer complained about yarn weight to the yarn supplier. When the supplier visited the customer to verify the test methods, the mechanics of the methods were found to be alike. An impartial testing lab was hired and the tests at the carpet plant were verified. Finally, the mystery was solved. The supplier was spinning (and measuring) the yarn at bone-dry conditions, but the carpet manufacturer measured it at standard conditions. During this period, $62,000 more was spent for yarn than if it had been purchased at the standard weight.

9. *Establishment of quality levels:* In the past, suppliers were often given "acceptable quality levels" (AQL). The AQL value was an abbreviation of the "operating characteristic" curve that described the risks associated with sampling plans. A typical AQL value might be 2.0 percent. Many suppliers interpreted this to mean that product which included 2 percent defective was to be acceptable. It is best to make clear to the supplier through the contract that all product submitted is expected to meet specifications and that any product which is nonconforming may be returned for replacement.

10. *Establishment of a system of lot identification and traceability:* This concept has long been used in some industries, e.g., heat numbers of steel, lot numbers of pharmaceutical products. More recently, with intensified attention to product reliability, use of this concept has been expanded to simplify localization of trouble, to reduce the volume of product recall, and to fix responsibility. Traceability systems, although demanding some extra effort to preserve the order of manufacture and to identify the product, can be helpful in many ways. For critical products they are usually mandated.

11. *Establishment of a system of timely response to alarm signals resulting from defects:* In many contracts, the buyer and supplier are yoked to a common timetable for completion of the final product. Usually, a separate department called Production Control (or Materials Management, etc.) presides over major aspects of scheduling. However, the upper management properly looks to the people associated with the quality function to set up alarm signals to detect quality failures and to act positively on these signals to avoid deterioration, whether in quality, cost, or delivery.

Joint Managerial Planning. Achieving the economic and technological goals requires use of the conventional management tools of planning. Ideally these should be applied on a joint basis, as though buyer and supplier were all part of the same management team. The more usual elements of this planning include:

Definition of Responsibility: Buyer versus Supplier. When multiple departments of both companies are involved in a joint effort, it becomes important to clear up the assignment of duties between buyer and supplier. The assignments are spelled out partly in the contracts, partly in the supplier relations manual, and partly in the conferences and other communications between the parties.

In modern products some innocent-looking tasks turn out to be quite demanding, e.g., those associated with achieving reliability. These tasks should be clearly defined, and should be clearly assigned as to responsibility, before the contract is signed.

Definition of Responsibility: Within Buyer.   Responsibilities within the buying organization are often more difficult to straighten out than those between buyer and supplier. Table 15.2 shows a typical assignment of some common responsibilities. In practice, this needs to be expanded to cover greater detail.

Documentation and Reporting.   In many contracts the supplier is required to provide documented proof that the product conforms to specification and is fit for use. The buyer can then use these proofs in lieu of incoming inspection of the product.

Achieving compatibility on such reporting requires that a whole array of details be made compatible, details such as designs of forms, code numbers for defects, seriousness classification, data processing systems, terminology, target dates for reports, computer programs, and still other aspects of systems and procedures.

All this compatibility is used for other essential purposes as well, e.g., data feedback, quality certifications, and audits.

Multiple Communication Channels.   The need for multiple forms of joint planning can be met only by setting up multiple channels of communications: designers must communicate directly with designers, quality specialists with quality specialists, etc. These multiple channels are a drastic departure from the single channel (buyer's purchasing department and supplier's sales department) which is the method in common use for purchase of traditional products. The multiple channels also create a risk of confusion unless coordination is provided. One form of such coordination is to provide Purchasing and Sales with copies of all letters, minutes, etc. However, in many cases this is not enough and needs to be supplemented with conferences at which members from the key departments of both companies are present. It is easier to arrive at necessary understandings and trade-offs through such conferences than through multiple isolated channels.

Media for Written Plans.   When the parties reduce their planning to written contracts, there are several ways of putting the quality planning into the official documents:

1. Write the provisions into the purchase order.
2. Incorporate some provisions, e.g., seriousness classification of characteristics, into the product specifications.
3. Prepare a separate quality/reliability specification, and reference this in the purchase orders.
4. Include some quality provisions (e.g., incoming inspection procedures) in a supplier relations manual, and reference this manual in the purchase order.

Of the foregoing methods, numbers 1 and 2 are applicable for specific products, whereas 3 and 4 are more convenient to application to families of products.

Supplier Relations Manual.   Typically, the contents of a supplier relations manual include:

1. A statement or preamble dealing with the company's quality policies and with supplier relations generally.
2. A description of the company's operations and the role played by product quality.

3. The general plan of organization with respect to quality and especially the role of the key supplier relations departments, usually Purchasing and Quality. The duties of specific categories of employees are sometimes set out in detail to help the supplier understand what can be expected from whom.

4. An explanation of the nature of the company's quality specifications, standards, and other means of expressing the product requirements, including seriousness classification.

5. An explanation of the procedures used to evaluate supplier product.

6. Copies of the quality data and report forms used by the buyer.

7. Explanation of the buyer's plan of supplier surveys.

8. Actions expected of the supplier (these may be listed as instructions or as recommendations):

   a. Submission of samples

   b. Preparation of quality plans

   c. Specific inspection and test programs needed

   d. Specific reliability programs needed

   e. Procedure used for disposition of nonconforming material

   f. Records and reports kept

   g. Procedure for making engineering changes effective

9. A glossary of the terms used by the buyer.

Publication of the manual (or a revision) is commonly an occasion for holding seminars for suppliers to explain the manual and to provide other indoctrination.

Joint quality planning may be illustrated by activities in the automobile industry. Every new model of automobile is quite an exercise in teamwork, since both buyer and supplier must meet a severe timetable. The crux of it is a joint venture on several fronts: engineers work directly with engineers; other specialists work directly with their opposite numbers. The manufacturing planning is a joint venture in providing an adequate process, machines, and tools. The quality planning is a joint venture, down to avoiding duplication of gages. The first samples go through a prove-in procedure which includes assembly into prove-out vehicles. Through such joint planning and execution, not only is the preparation intrinsically better done; the personnel of the two companies are brought to work together face to face. The confidence born of such relationships can often outperform the most precisely drawn procedures.

COOPERATION WITH SUPPLIERS DURING EXECUTION OF CONTRACT

The cooperation usually concentrates on the following activities:

Evaluation of Initial Samples of Product. Under many circumstances, it is important that the supplier submit test results of initial samples produced from production tooling. The conditions that warrant such a procedure are:

Purchase of a product from a new supplier

The first shipment of a new product

The first shipment following a change in design, manufacturing process, or manufacturing location

Usually the size of the sample is small (less than 10 units) but submission of an initial sample can provide evidence that the buyer fully understands the specifications.

Evaluation of First Production Shipments. An evaluation of a sample from the first production shipment is also in order before the full shipment is made. The evaluation can be accomplished by having a buyer representative visit the supplier's plant and observe the inspection of a random sample selected from the first production lot. A review can also be made of process capability or process control type data from that lot.

Two-Way Communication. With the end of the planning stage there arises a need for providing continual two-way communication during the execution of the contract. The purpose of this communication is to supply essential information, provide performance data, identify troubles which arise, stimulate corrective action, and improve the ability of the parties to work together. For some special problems in dealing with overseas suppliers, see Doty (1982).

Design Information and Changes. Industry has made great strides in learning how to communicate design information at the beginning of a contract, but the record on communicating design changes is less impressive.

Design changes may take place at the initiative of either the buyer or the supplier. Either way, there is need to treat the supplier like an in-house department in the procedures for processing design changes and in configuration control (see Section 13 under Configuration Management). This need is especially acute for modern products, where design changes can affect products, processes, tools, instruments, stored materials, procedures, etc. Failure to provide adequate design change information to suppliers has been a distinct obstacle to good supplier relations.

Whether the design was originally prepared by the supplier or the buyer, the supplier should be encouraged to make recommendations for changes in the design. Often, the supplier is in a better position to identify needed design changes that can improve overall fitness for use and at the same time reduce costs. Such changes in the design must be submitted to the buyer for approval.

Deviations. During the performance of the contract there will arise instances of nonconformance. These may be on the product itself or on process requirements or procedural requirements. Steps must be established to resolve these deviations. For example, a material review board (see Section 18 under Judgment of Fitness for Use) is one mechanism for assuring proper inputs and decisions on nonconforming product.

Product Unfitness for Use. Cases may be discovered through product testing, material review board decisions, field complaints, service calls, returns, etc. The impact on the manufacturer is direct and severe, since the ability to sell the product is jeopardized. Despite the importance of these feedbacks, the manufacturer may have difficulty in relaying the necessary alarm signals of unfitness for use to the supplier. Some of this difficulty is technological; i.e., there are problems in securing samples to identify the suppliers involved, in acquiring adequate field data, and in working out the data processing needed to separate out the information required by the various suppliers. However, some of the inadequacies in communication have been due to lack of buyer awareness of the usefulness of good feedback to the suppliers.

Corrective Action.   Communications to the supplier on nonconformance must include precise description of the symptoms of the defects. The best description is in the form of samples, but if this is not possible, the supplier should have the opportunity to visit the site of the trouble. There are numerous related questions: What disposition is to be made of the defectives? Who will sort or repair? Who will pay the costs? What were the causes? What steps are needed to avoid a recurrence? These questions are outside the scope of pure defect detection; they require joint discussion among departments within each company and further joint discussions between buyer and supplier. On modern products it is no longer feasible to settle these matters through the single communication link of purchasing agent and sales person. Instead, conferences are held and attended by those who can make the main contribution to the problem at hand.

A final note concerns "positive communication." Buyers usually quickly communicate to suppliers the data defining nonconformance, unfitness for use, and other troubles encountered. In contrast, the supplier is usually not given product data when the situation is trouble-free. When communication is limited to reports of a negative nature, the atmosphere for constructive improvement can also become negative. There is increasing awareness of this problem. Positive communication can include letters of praise, supplier awards, and recognition in supplier ratings. When successfully done, it can help change the supplier's attitude from a defensive one to constructive cooperation on a problem needing quality improvement.

The general approach to quality improvement (see Section 22, Quality Improvement) also applies to suppliers. The Pareto analysis to identify the vital few problems is particularly important as an alternative to broad attempts to tighten up all procedures on a supplier.

Supplier Surveillance.   For many modern products only the supplier has sufficient product knowledge, inspection skills, and facilities to evaluate the final product. In these cases the contract may require the supplier to present (1) a written plan for controlling quality and (2) proof that the plan has been followed.

The contracts permit the buyer to exercise a "surveillance" over all the supplier activities to achieve conformance to specifications and fitness for use. This surveillance includes procedural, process, and product audits, as well as product inspection conducted by the buyer. Surveillance can take place through periodic visits to the supplier's plant. Alternatively, the buyer may maintain a resident auditor at the supplier's plant to provide for a continuing surveillance. This same auditor may also conduct source inspection, although this is not universal. For suppliers who must do considerable design and development, the surveillance may include periodic reviews of the reliability engineering efforts.

The approaches used in a surveillance program (Burgess, 1981) can take a number of forms including:

Program auditing: Here the buyer audits elements of the supplier quality program.

In-process surveillance: This consists of monitoring the manufacturing practices of the supplier.

Witnessing of key events: The events include specific operations, inspections, or tests. An example is the initial sample inspection or the first production lot inspection.

Supplementing receiving inspection: This consists of performing or witnessing specific inspections or tests on critical characteristics.

Acceptance of product: Inspections or tests are performed by the buyer and used as a basis for acceptance.

Troubleshooting: To identify underlying causes, investigations of quality and related problems are conducted.

Supplier surveillance can provide the buyer (and the supplier) with an early warning of problems prior to product nonconformance or unfitness for use. However, surveillance is difficult to administer to the satisfaction of both parties. The buyer emphasis must be on whether or not the product is fit for use rather than on minor product deviations, process deviations, or procedural deviations. Concurrently, the supplier must understand the need for the buyer to insist on a level of documentation that may go beyond the ordinary needs of the supplier. Bruewer and Zaworski (1981) discuss the setting up and functioning of a surveillance program.

Use of On-Site Inspection Personnel.   For important supplier contracts, it is useful for the buyer to have personnel residing at the supplier's plant. On-site capability can improve communications between the two organizations and expedite product acceptance and other decision making. LaBarre (1978) describes one company's field resident program covering the entire United States. The capability does not necessarily have to reside in the buyer's organization. There are now independent services available that will perform many aspects of supplier surveillance for the buyer ("Contract Representative Service," 1981). In another approach the buyer selects someone within the supplier's organization to act as a representative for the buyer. This "certified supplier representative" witnesses inspections and tests and keeps an accurate log of all activities performed. The representative is usually selected from the buyer's organization by a field quality representative who has had contact with personnel in the buyer's organization ("Quality Representative—Certified Vendor Representative," 1981).

EVALUATING DELIVERED PRODUCT

The evaluation of supplier product can assume several forms:

1. *100 percent inspection:*   Every item in the lot is inspected for some or all of the specification requirements.
2. *Sampling inspection:*   A portion of each lot is inspected and a decision made on the entire lot (see Section 25, Acceptance Sampling).
3. *Identity check:*   The lot is examined to determine if the correct product has been received. No inspections for conformance to requirements are made.
4. *No inspection:*   The lot is directly sent to a storeroom or a processing department.
5. *Use of supplier data:*   The supplier provides a copy of the results of outgoing inspection and test at the supplier's plant and this is used in place of incoming

inspection at the buyer's plant. The general concept is explained below under Supplier Certification.

Weaver (1978) discusses an example of how cost reduction efforts at incoming inspection brought about by adverse economic conditions can result in a quality deterioration of purchased product.

Evaluation of Supplier Product by Incoming Inspection. A difficult problem at incoming inspection is distributing the limited inspection resources available over the large number of parts and suppliers. Generally, the resources are not sufficient for 100 percent inspection on all parts or even sampling inspection of all lots, using sample sizes from the conventional sampling tables. Judgments must then be made on how to allocate the inspection effort to part numbers and suppliers. The factors to be considered include:

1. Prior quality history on the part and supplier.
2. Criticality of the part on overall system performance.
3. Criticality on later manufacturing operations.
4. Warranty or use history.
5. Supplier process capability information.
6. Nature of the manufacturing process. For example, a press operation primarily depends on the adequacy of the setup. Information on the first few pieces and last few pieces in a production run is usually sufficient to draw conclusions about the entire run.
7. Product homogeneity. For example, fluid product is homogeneous and reduces the need for large sample sizes.
8. Availability of required inspection skills and equipment.

Often the volume of part numbers and suppliers is so large that judgments on the amount of inspection are made in a cursory manner, resulting in a inefficient distribution of effort at incoming inspection. A balance must be reached between a simple incoming inspection system and one that formally recognizes the factors listed.

At the recommendation of the author, a spare-parts distribution center reviewed its approach to incoming inspection. Inspection ranged from 100 percent to almost no inspection. Special sampling tables had been created because the conventional tables required sample sizes that were judged to be uneconomically large. Prior history of suppliers was documented but only periodically used to determine the amount of inspection. Also, it was felt that all lots should have some inspection and, therefore, the minimum size was one unit.

Seven years of data were readily available (stored in a computer) on lot decisions by supplier and part number, but no continuous system was used to evaluate the data and adjust the amount of inspection. A preliminary analysis revealed:

1. Forty-five percent of the supplier/part number combinations had not had a single lot rejected in 20 or more consecutive lots.
2. Most of the rejected lots were on part numbers with recent lot rejections, i.e., 93 percent of rejected part numbers had four or fewer accepted lots since the last rejected lot.

A system was devised to provide inspection personnel with updated pertinent information to properly allocate inspection effort. History on each supplier/part number combination was compiled using an arbitrary scoring system:

Lot rejection: 20 points

Rejection discovered later: 10 points

Borderline acceptance: 5 points

Dealer complaint: 10 points

Warranty claim: 10 points

The score for a part number was the sum of the points. Each accepted lot resulted in a subtraction of 8 points. Other adjustments restricted the range of the score to 0 to 50.

The sampling tables are now related to the current score, thereby providing inspection personnel with a simple way to reallocate effort on the basis of product history. The system also contains provisions for critical parts in other special situations. Under the new system, 30 percent of inspection hours were saved initially with additional savings expected later. In some cases inspection was eliminated (except for an audit inspection), but in other cases inspection was increased to provide more protection on troublesome part numbers or suppliers.

Allocation of incoming inspection effort is usually done with oversimplified procedures having high or unknown risks. The future need is to develop reasonably simple procedures that incorporate pertinent information, including prior supplier history and the effect of poor product entering the buyer's production process.

Economics of Incoming Inspection. In deciding the amount of incoming inspection, the cost of performing the inspection is compared to the possible damage resulting from no inspection. The approach generally follows that outlined in Section 25 under Sampling Risks and Parameters; Selection of a Numerical Value of The Quality Index. Boudreault (1975) also discusses the concept of the economic aspects of testing.

Use of Supplier Data. Incoming inspection has some drawbacks. These include costs, time delays, added inventories, and the necessity to build up appropriate skills and equipment. An alternative is to eliminate incoming inspection and rely on the inspection already performed by the supplier. The concept is known as audit of decisions or ship to stock, and is discussed below under Supplier Certification.

Use of Histogram Analysis on Supplier Data. A useful tool for learning about a supplier's process and comparing several suppliers' manufacturing product to the same specification is the histogram (see Section 16 under Process Capability: The Concept, and Section 23 under Descriptive Statistics for Summarizing Data). A random sample is selected from a lot, and measurements are made on the selected quality characteristics. The data are charted as frequency histograms. The analysis consists of comparing the histograms to the specification limits.

An application of histograms to evaluating the hardenability of a particular grade of steel from four suppliers is shown in Figure 15.2. The specification was a maximum Rockwell C reading of 43 measured at Jominy position J8. Histo-

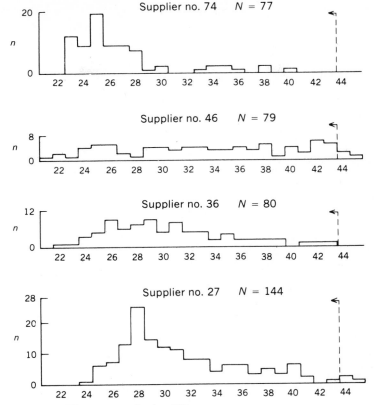

FIG. 15.2 Histograms on hardenability.

grams were also prepared for carbon, manganese, nickel, and chromium content. Analysis revealed:

1. Supplier 46 had a process without any strong central tendency. The histogram on nickel for this supplier was also rectangular in shape, indicating a lack of control of the nickel content and resulting in several heats of steel with excessively high Rockwell values.
2. Supplier 27 had several heats above the maximum, although the process had a central value of about 28. The histograms for manganese, nickel, and chromium showed several values above and apart from the main histogram.
3. Supplier 74 showed much less variability than the others. Analysis of other histograms for this supplier suggested that about half of the original heats of steel had been screened out and used for other applications.

Note how these analyses can be made without visiting the supplier plants, i.e., the "product tells on the process."

The lot plot is a sampling plan that uses histograms to make acceptance and rejection decisions on lots. Section 25 under Variables Sampling discusses this plan.

CERTIFICATION

The terms "certificate" and "certification" have multiple meanings in usage, and these varied meanings have resulted in extensive confusion.

Certificates.   Various forms include the following.

Certificate of Test.   This term is used in the sense of evidence that testing was done. The evidence is embodied in a formal document called a "certificate of test." The document, issued by a test laboratory, states that certain product was tested for certain qualities. The product is identified by description, amount, lot number, etc. Test data are given, along with the conclusion on conformance or nonconformance to specification. The document is signed by a designated official.

The laboratory may be an independent test laboratory or a captive laboratory, i.e., the supplier's laboratory. (There are many situations in which there is recourse to an independent test laboratory.)

The distinguishing characteristic of the certificate of test is the objective evidence it presents—data which are the result of positive, reproducible tests performed to determine the quality of the product.

Certificate of Compliance.   The document asserts that product conforms to specification. A typical wording is: "To whom it may concern: This certifies that to the best of our knowledge the material delivered under this contract is in accord with the terms of the contract." The contract makes no clear identification of the product, makes no statement that tests were conducted, provides no test data. The certificates are often preprinted, including signatures, to serve as an inexpensive way of complying with the wishes of a customer who insists on having them.

Certificates of compliance do not provide any assurance to the buyer that is not already present by the act of shipment. The courts have long held that when the supplier ships the product there is implied certification that the product conforms with the specifications referenced in the purchase contract. *Certificates of test do* provide additional assurance in the form of test data.

Supplier Certification.   "Supplier certification" is the process of evaluating the performance of a supplier, with respect to product quality, with the view of authorizing the supplier to self-certify shipments (if the evaluation concludes that the supplier's performance justifies such authorization).

The process is illustrated by the steps taken by one manufacturer (summarized from information provided by M. E. Noakes of General Motors, Harrison Radiator Division):

1. The buyer invites proposals for self-certification from prospective suppliers. The response from the supplier must include a "failure prevention analysis" along with the supplier's quality plan for the item.
2. The buyer evaluates the failure prevention analysis and the quality plan submitted by the supplier.
3. Conclusions are drawn about supplier capability. This may require a visit to

the supplier's plant. If the capability is acceptable, discussions are held with the supplier to assure that all quality requirements are understood and there is agreement on the quality plan.

4. The supplier starts production and sends a sample shipment along with data to document process capability. If process capability data are not available an estimate of the capability, based on similar processes, must be submitted.

5. The buyer inspects the sample shipment and compares the results to the supplier quality data to determine if the supplier can be relied on to make good product conformance decisions. If the comparison is favorable and if the parts conform to specifications, the supplier is authorized to make a pilot shipment.

6. If the pilot shipment is acceptable, then production shipments are authorized. Data are included with each shipment.

7. After a number of these production shipments have been approved, the supplier becomes "certified" for that item. This means that the supplier is to self-certify all future shipments and keep process data on file for possible review by the buyer. Inspection by the buyer is restricted to sample inspection audits and periodic plant visits to review the supplier's quality program.

Self-certification is sometimes called "audit of decisions" because such is the end result. In conventional inspection of supplier's product (by the buyer) the purpose is to answer the question: Is this lot of product good or not? After supplier self-certification, the buyer's purpose in inspecting the supplier's product is to answer the question: Does the supplier continue to make good decisions? Hence the name "audit of decisions."

Companies that contemplate use of the concept of audit of decisions are always concerned about what to do when the audit check shows an incorrect decision by the supplier's laboratory. Usually, these companies insist that means be set up for tracing the identity and rechecking of all lots not tested by the buyer since the previous audit check. This is quite a sensible requirement and calls for joint planning that will establish clear lot identification and traceability.

Possible differences in supplier and buyer results due to sampling can be analyzed using special evaluation procedures (Office of the Assistant Secretary of Defense, 1960).

Christensen (1975) describes the certification process followed and the savings in receiving inspection costs that were achieved in one company. LaFord and Steers (1979) discuss the steps in a "ship to stock" program for electronics equipment.

Berman (1983) describes a system of international certification for electronic components. Evolved from earlier systems called "Tripartite" (England, France, Germany), and "Cenel" (Europe), this system provides for formal approval of manufacturers, independent test laboratories, and independent distributors. An organization can seek approval in two areas: facilities and specific electronic components. Participating countries have a "national supervising inspectorate" which provides evaluations within that country. When facility approvals are granted, the name of the organization is entered on a list of approved manufacturers, distributors, and test laboratories. When certification is sought for a component, the certification organization observes the testing conducted by the manufacturer. These tests cover both lot-by-lot and periodic testing. Observations of the testing cover test procedures, accuracy and precision of the test equipment, and the range of values for the components being tested. When the tests have been satisfactorily completed, the manufacturer is eligible to ship the components with a "certificate of conformity." The certifying organization conducts periodic surveys during future production. If problems are identified, the manufacturer is instructed to stop using the certificate of conformity until the problem is corrected.

Preferred Supplier Program. The Ford Motor Company has a program called the "Preferred Quality Supplier Program." To become preferred, a supplier must meet the following criteria:

1. Adequacy of the supplier's system to control product quality including the use of statistical process control on selected product characteristics or process parameters that are significant to part function, fit, durability, or appearance (for appearance items only)
2. High success rate on initial sample and first production shipment evaluations
3. Outstanding ongoing performance at the Ford using location
4. An absence of significant field problems
5. The commitment and act of support of the supplier's management to pursuing never-ending improvement in quality
6. The ability and willingness to conduct manufacturing feasibility studies during the design process for parts within the supplier's area of expertise

The main benefit that the supplier receives is a preferred position in new part development programs and in future purchasing decisions. In addition, a preferred supplier is exempt from certain requirements ordinarily required of Ford suppliers (e.g., on-site reviews by Ford of initial samples and first production shipments, submission of quality plans and other documentation to Ford, and routine Ford supplier surveys).

Other Meanings of Certification. The term "certification" is used in other contexts:

Personnel Certification. This refers to the common practice of requiring that supplier (or other) personnel performing critical operations, e.g., those doing welding critical to human safety should first undergo a course of training and pass a qualifying examination. A certificate of qualification is issued as part of the formal procedure.

Lot Certification. This is the process of associating homogeneous lots with certificates of test so that multiple buyers are spared the expense of testing. An old application of this is the use of heat numbers in the metals industry. A more recent application is in centralized testing of electronic parts. Berman (1983) discusses a system for lot testing leading to international certification.

Supplier Accreditation. The term "accreditation" is sometimes used to denote the process of evaluating the overall quality system of a supplier as contrasted to evaluating a specific product (see Mundel, 1972).

IMPROVEMENT OF SUPPLIER QUALITY

The general approach to handling chronic supplier problems follows the approach to quality improvement in Section 22, Quality Improvement. For supplier items certain aspects deserve elaboration.

Stimulating the Supplier to Take Action.   Frequently there have been extensive discussions between the buyer and the supplier (internal or external) on chronic quality problems. Promises are made, but often with no results. What is needed is for the supplier to become convinced of the importance of the problem to the *supplier's organization*. This is often best accomplished with factual information.

One approach is to show the supplier the effect of poor quality on supplier costs and sales income. Specifically, the buyer can show the supplier how to calculate the costs of poor quality within the supplier's organization. (For many suppliers, the number has never been determined.) In addition, the effect on sales income of the buyer and the supplier can be dramatized by presentation of data on competitive quality from the marketplace.

Some buyers take a penalizing approach. In one electronics organization any supplier with a lot acceptance rate of less than 95 percent for the prior quarter is placed on probation. The supplier must submit a corrective action plan within 2 weeks. If 95 percent lot acceptance rate is not achieved within 3 months, the supplier is subject to disqualification and cancellation of all open orders. A supplier with a lot acceptance rate less than 95 percent for the prior two quarters is disqualified. Disqualified suppliers are not given any future business until a satisfactory corrective action plan is submitted and accepted by the buyer. Hopefully, the negative tone of such an approach is balanced by technical assistance offered by the buyer.

Pareto Analysis.   Supplier improvement programs can fail because the vital few problems are not identified and attacked. Instead, the programs consist of broad attempts to tighten up all procedures. The Pareto analysis (see Section 22 under Pareto Concept) can take a number of forms:

1. *Analysis of losses (or nonconformities, lot rejections, etc.) by material number or part number:*   Such analysis serves a useful purpose as applied to catalog numbers involving substantial or frequent purchases.

2. *Analysis of losses by product family:*   This identifies the vital few product families present in small but numerous purchases of common product families, e.g., fasteners, resistors, paints.

3. *Analysis of losses by process:*   That is, classifying the defects or lot rejections in terms of the process to which they relate, e.g., plating, swaging, coil winding, etc.

4. *Analysis by supplier across the entire spectrum of purchases:*   This can help to identify weaknesses in the supplier's managerial approach as contrasted to the technological, which more usually is correlated with products and processes. In one company there were 222 suppliers on the active list. Of these, 38 (or 17 percent) accounted for 53 percent of the lot rejections and 45 percent of the bad parts.

5. *Analysis by cost of the products:*   In one company, 37 percent of the product numbers purchased accounted for only 5 percent of the total dollar volume of purchases, but for a much higher percent of the total incoming inspection cost. The conclusion was that these "useful many" products should be purchased from the best suppliers, even at top prices. The alternative of relying on incoming inspection would be even more costly.

6. *Analysis by system weakness:*   This technique is used to discover major weaknesses in the management system. For example, some studies disclose multiple instances of working to the wrong issue of the specification. In such cases, the

system used for specification revision should be reexamined. If value analysis discovers multiple instances of overspecification, the design procedures for choosing components should be reexamined. These analyses can reveal how the buyer is contributing to his or her own problems.

Bowers (1978) describes an application to printed circuit boards. A study was made of 1092 lots received over 11 months from the five suppliers supplying the boards. Overall, 45.1 percent of the lots were rejected, and this varied, by supplier, from 39.0 percent to 68.8 percent. The cost to process the rejected lots totaled $19,680. A Pareto analysis of the results at receiving inspection is shown in Table 15.4.

Of 27 requirements checked, 7 accounted for 70.4 percent of the defects. For many requirements (e.g., hole size and board dimensions) a large percent of defects were finally accepted as a deviation to the specification. Based on an engineering review, certain specifications were changed. The study was instrumental in alerting management to the size of the supplier problem, defining a main cause, and returning product to suppliers that was not fit for use.

Providing Technical Assistance to the Supplier.   The main supplier quality problems are intercompany in nature and can therefore best be solved by joint analysis and action rather than separately. Each of the parties has experiences and know-how, both in management and technology, which can be of aid in the problem at hand. These aids may consist of:

Access to experts in the technological specialty which underlies the problem

Equipment and instrumentation of a special character

Experience in solving similar problems with other buyers or suppliers

Expertise in problem solving generally

The general approach must be on a project-by-project basis and make use of improvement teams with representatives from both organizations. Miller and Kegarise (1986) describe how it may be necessary to share proprietary information on a "need-to-know" basis.

TABLE 15.4   Pareto Analysis of Incoming Inspection

Requirement	Pareto distribution			Defects accepted under deviation	
	Number of defects	Percent defective	Cumulative percent	Number accepted	Percent accepted
Hole size	165	19.0	19.0	150	90.9
Board dimensions	110	12.7	31.7	96	87.3
Cond. defects	79	9.1	40.8	23	29.1
Cold thickness	69	8.0	48.8	31	44.9
Plating visual	66	7.6	56.4	31	50.8
Cold visual	61	7.0	63.4	27	44.3
PTH thickness	61	7.0	70.4	10	16.4
20 other	257	29.6	100.0	158	61.4
	868			526	60.6

In some cases, supplier problems are due to a design specified by the buyer. Lacking diagnosis based on facts, the buyer initially blames the supplier's manufacturing process. An aura or disagreement then prevails. A manufacturer of electronic components had an incoming rejection rate of 9 percent. Surprisingly, 68 percent of the rejections were classified "use as is." This suggested that the design requirements (set by the buyer) needed either clarification or revision. Investigation revealed this to be the case.

In another case, a rubber drive belt that had been trouble-free for 7 years suddenly experienced problems. The rubber mix used by the supplier was identified as the cause. In order to solve a problem for another client, the supplier had changed the mix. As there was no requirement for the supplier to have a dedicated process for producing the item, the supplier was free to change that process. The proprietary nature of the process and the lack of a teamwork relationship between the organizations complicated the process of achieving improvement.

In another case, a supplier reviewed the inspection process used to evaluate incoming supplier products. Based on an analysis of actual quality results, it was decided to reduce the inspection work force. Some of the inspectors were retrained in problem-solving techniques and assigned to work full time with problem suppliers. Percent defective on incoming product was reduced from 4 percent to 0.5 percent. (These three cases are from the consulting experience of the author.)

Role of Upper Management.   Sometimes upper management must provide the leadership to obtain action from suppliers. One company used this approach in the following manner:

1. Data on failure rate and failure costs were summarized for each supplier. Of the buyer's warranty costs, 75 percent were due to supplier items.

2. A team from the buyer organization met individually with a team from each of the 10 key suppliers. The teams consisted of the president and the heads of Product Engineering, Purchasing, Production, and Quality Assurance from both organizations. The warranty data were presented, the program of quality improvement explained, and a goal set for a 50 percent reduction in warranty costs over a 5-year period. Each supplier was asked to develop a quality improvement program.

3. A quality improvement training session was held for the president and key staff members of the 10 key suppliers. (The outline is presented later in this Section under Training of Suppliers.)

4. Follow-up meetings were held to review the supplier quality improvement plans. Again the participants were the presidents and key staff members.

5. Semiannual followup meetings were held at which the buyer presented the newest data and the suppliers presented the latest data on laboratory test results and other activities to improve quality.

6. A system of supplier recognition awards was set up.

7. Purchasing practices were changed to transfer business to those suppliers who achieved the highest levels of quality and reliability. Sometimes this meant selecting the supplier with the highest bid price, but this was more than offset by a reduction in warranty costs.

The result has been a decline in service calls from 41 calls per 100 products to 13 calls per 100 products and a saving of $16 per unit in the cost of warranty—a significant improvement for the product involved.

SINGLE-SOURCE SUPPLIERS

Some purchased items can be procured from only one source. The reasons are many: another division of the same company makes the item; a customer specifies a supplier; only one supplier exists; the quantity involved is small.

A serious problem arises if a single-source supplier provides poor quality, has been notified, but takes little or no action. The question then is what further steps can be taken to obtain action. Presenting the problem in a form that shows the effect on the supplier is important. With the single-source supplier, the potential effect on future sales is not a strong impetus to spur action. However, showing how to calculate the costs of poor quality in the supplier's organization can help stimulate the supplier to take action.

In addition there are some specific alternatives that can be pursued:

1. Show the supplier what use is made of the product. It may turn out that the supplier can meet the needs of fitness for use despite an inability to conform to specification.

2. Classify the quality characteristics as to their seriousness. This helps the supplier to concentrate efforts on the relatively few critical and major qualities.

3. Provide technical assistance to the supplier, e.g., set up joint quality improvement teams.

4. Provide financial assistance, e.g., to buy an essential machine or instrument.

Beyond the above possibilities for assisting the supplier, there are alternatives for self-solution or for bypassing the supplier:

5. Add an in-house test to sort the good product from the bad.

6. Add an in-house operation to bring the supplier's product into compliance.

7. Make, not buy.

8. Offer the contract to a competing supplier who can solve the problem.

9. Find an alternative design which eliminates the need for what this supplier is supplying.

Finally, there are possibilities for use of broad forms of persuasion:

10. Enlist the support of sister divisions which may be giving profitable business to this supplier.

11. Enlist the support of the (buyer's) client who may also be a client of the supplier.

12. See if the supplier's upper management is responsive to a teamwork policy as a basis for continuity in relationship.

TRAINING OF SUPPLIERS

In many cases, the supplier wishes to improve but is not certain what steps are necessary. The knowledge required by the supplier can be acquired in several ways:

1. *Inviting the supplier to participate in quality training sessions sponsored by the buyer:* Sessions should start with the supplier's upper management. One appliance manufacturer sponsored an 8-hour training course for upper management of the 10 key suppliers. The outline is given in Table 15.5. The training, given by this author, was held after the president's team in the buyer's organization met with each supplier president's team to discuss the significance of the quality problem. Concepts, tools, and techniques were discussed, and each participant was given a copy of a text book.

Training programs can also be sponsored by the buyer for specific elements of the quality disciplines. Examples are courses in statistical quality control techniques, a structured project-by-project approach to quality improvement, use of

TABLE 15.5 Condensed 8-h Training Course

1. Introduction
   a. Fitness for use
   b. Quality function, systems
   c. Quality cost
2. Concept of variability
   a. Basic statistical indices
   b. Patterns of variability
   c. Probability paper
3. Improvement of quality on current products
   a. Distinction between chronic and sporadic problems
   b. Breakthrough sequence for solving problems
   c. Defining the size of the problem and identifying specific projects
   d. Organizing for breakthrough
   e. Distinction between management controllable and operator controllable defects
   f. Diagnosis of management controllable defects
   g. Subspecies of operator controllable defects
4. Prevention of quality problems—product engineering
   a. Quantification of reliability
   b. Selection of tolerances
   c. Formal design review
   d. Failure mode and effects analysis
   e. Reliability testing
   f. Improving reliability during design
   g. Safety analysis
5. Prevention of quality problems—manufacturing
   a. Manufacturing planning for quality
   b. Meeting the criteria for operator control
   c. Process capability evaluation
   d. Failure mode and effects analysis for processes
   e. Selecting tolerance limits for discrete parts
   f. Selecting tolerance limits for interacting dimensions
   g. Concepts of dominance
   h. Process control techniques
   i. Defining responsibility for quality in manufacturing
   j. Process quality audits
6. Role of upper management
   a. Quality policies and objectives
   b. Directing quality improvement
   c. Companywide training for quality
   d. Defining responsibility for quality

reliability techniques during product design, process capability, and other manufacturing planning techniques.

2. *Recommendations to suppliers concerning other training courses:* The buyer can help suppliers by sharing knowledge on the variety of training materials and training courses available in the quality disciplines.

3. *Joint quality improvement teams:* An effective way to learn is to learn by doing. Quality improvement teams formed with members from both organizations can be particularly helpful if the buyer's organization is following a structured approach to quality improvement of chronic problems (see Section 22, Quality Improvement). Not only will problems be solved, but the supplier can benefit generally by applying the improvement process to other products.

SUPPLIER QUALITY RATING

The "rating" of quality of work done by the supplier can take on a variety of forms. "Component rating" shows performance properties of an individual component. "Lot rating" summarizes the quality of incoming lots. "Supplier quality rating" is an overall assessment of supplier quality performance and is used to assist in making decisions of the broadest nature, e.g., whether or not to continue to do business with this supplier. Supplier quality rating has several purposes including:

To provide objective, quantified measures of supplier performance

To aid in arriving at a balanced judgment of supplier performance for all categories of buyer needs

To provide both buyer and supplier with common factual information on overall performance

To minimize the risk of being stampeded by isolated instances of failure

To identify troublesome areas so that corrective action can be concentrated

The extensive literature on supplier quality rating schemes makes clear that differences in products and in purchasing patterns require differences in rating plans. For products whose qualities are clearly identified at incoming inspection, a plan based on summarizing results of incoming inspection is adequate. For purchased components which create substantial excess processing costs, the plan should reflect the existence of these costs. For purchased components which affect the buyer's warranty and service costs, the supplier rating plan should (ideally) reflect these field troubles as well. Dobbins (1980) presents guidelines for developing a plan.

Supplier rating measures and formulas cover the spectrum from the simple to the highly complex. For example, one measure is the ratio of the number of parts accepted to the total number of parts received; a more complex formula includes factors such as the criticality of the nonconformities and the value of the parts.

To create a single numerical quality score is difficult because there are several units of measure, such as:

1. The quality of multiple lots expressed as lots rejected versus lots inspected

2. The quality of multiple parts expressed as percent nonconforming

3. The quality of specific characteristics, expressed in numerous natural units, e.g., ohmic resistance, percent active ingredient, mean time between failures, etc.

4. The economic consequences of bad quality, expressed in dollars

Because these units of measure vary in importance among different companies, the published rating schemes differ markedly in emphasis.

Measures in Use. Supplier quality rating plans are based on one or more of the following measures:

1. *Product percent nonconforming:* This is a ratio of the amount of defective items received to the total number of items received. On a lot-by-lot basis, the formula is number of lots rejected divided by number of lots received; on an individual piece basis, the formula is number of individual pieces rejected divided by the number of individual pieces received. If individual pieces are used, the formula can be adjusted to assign demerits to the different types of defects observed.

2. *Disposition of lots:* This plan summarizes supplier performance by using a weighted analysis of the action taken on lots that were nonconforming. The rating is determined by multiplying the percent of nonconforming lots received (for each of three action categories) by a weighting factor. The products are then totaled and subtracted from 100 percent (see Table 15.6). A rating of 95 through 100 percent is considered excellent, 90 to 94.9 percent is acceptable, and below 90 percent unacceptable (Admiral Corporation, 1976).

3. *Economic analysis:* This type of plan compares suppliers on the total dollar cost for specific purchases. The total dollar cost includes the quoted price plus quality costs associated with defect prevention, detection, and correction. An example of this was given previously in this section under Supplier Selection. Other formulas based on cost define total cost as the quoted price plus quality costs, plus additional cost in connection with deliveries and other matters (Dobbins, 1980).

4. *Composite plan:* Supplier performance is not limited to quality. It includes delivery against schedule, price, and still other performance categories. These multiple needs suggest that supplier rating should include overall supplier performance rather than just supplier quality performance. The purchasing department is a strong advocate of this principle and has valid grounds for this advocacy.

TABLE 15.6 Supplier Rating Example

Action on lots	Number of lots*	% of lots	Weight	% weight
Use "as is"	2	2/50 = 4	1	4
Sort/rework	1	1/50 = 2	5	10
Reject and return	1	1/50 = 2	2	4
Supplier rating = $100 - 18 = 82\%$				18

*Number of lots received during period from supplier: 50

The National Association of Purchasing Management (1967) has recommended several types of supplier rating plans. In one of these plans the three areas of supplier performance are combined into a supplier rating with a weighting that depends on market conditions. For example:

Factor	Unit of measure	Weight
Quality	Percent of lots accepted	40
Price	Low price ÷ net price	35
Service	Percent of promises kept	25

Caplan (1980) describes a supplier rating system based on an evaluation of quality, delivery, and service. The plan uses detailed criteria for each of these three parameters and then combines the data into one overall rating. ASQC (1976) also presents a composite supplier rating formula. This formula reflects incoming inspection results, support documentation, delivery, price, service, and the effect of problems on production and field operations.

Using Supplier Ratings.   It is possible, through the use of arbitrary weightings, to summarize the various types of supplier data into a single index. However, there is no known way of ending up with a single index on which all can agree. If an arbitrary method is used and mandated, the original purpose of supplier rating is lost. Supplier ratings should be used as a servant, not as a master for decision making. The single index hides important details; the decision maker should understand what is hidden. The single index, being numerical, has a pseudoprecision, but the decision maker should not be deceived. The decision maker should understand the fringe around the numbers. The purpose should be kept clearly in mind—product rating (for which the specification is usually the standard) should not be confused with supplier rating (for which other suppliers may be the standard). Supplier rating is an important defect prevention device if it is used in an atmosphere of interdependence betweeen supplier and customer. This means that the customer must:

1. Make the investment of time, effort, and special skills to help the suppliers to improve.

2. Be willing to change the specification when warranted. In some companies, 20 to 40 percent of rejected purchases can be used without any quality compromise. The customer must search for these situations and change the specifications.

Some organizations use a periodic supplier rating to determine the share of future purchases given to each supplier. The rating system and effect on share of market is fully explained to suppliers. The approach has been used successfully by both automotive and appliance manufacturers to highlight the importance of quality to their suppliers.

Finally, in the cases of consistently poor performance by suppliers who seem unable to respond to help, the supplier rating highlights them as candidates to be dropped as suppliers.

SPECIAL BUSINESS PROBLEMS

When an organization purchases products from external sources some special problems arise.

Legal Problems.   The legal basis of supplier relations is the Uniform Commercial Code (UCC). With respect to quality, the legal aspects include such matters as the formalization of product requirements in contracts, matters concerning authorization to ship, separation of goods into separate lots, and inspection and acceptance of goods. Johnson and Webber (1985) discuss legal ramifications of supplier contracts.

One legal aspect is the product warranty. Even if there are no express warranties documented by purchase orders or specifications, the law implies certain warranties based solely on the actions of the parties involved:

1. The warranty of "merchantability," i.e., a warranty that the product is suitable for the general purposes for which products of the same description are used, and that the product is thereby suitable for moving in the channels of trade

2. A warranty of fitness for intended use, in those cases where the supplier knows the specific use the buyer will make of the product

Suppose a product conforms to specification but is not fit for use. Is the supplier responsible for the failure to meet fitness for use? The answer depends on what information is originally conveyed to the supplier. If the supplier is given only a specification, then the supplier is legally responsible only for meeting that specification. However, if the supplier is given knowledge (whether in writing or not) of the fitness needs of the product, then the supplier is responsible for meeting those needs. Hodge (1977) discusses aspects of warranty provisions as they affect quality.

Another issue is liability. Suppose that a supplier component is incorporated in a system, use of the system results in an injury, and the cause of the injury is traced to the supplier component. Who is responsible for damages to the injured person? The injured person has the right (and usually exercises it) to proceed against everyone who is involved, including certainly the manufacturer of the system and the supplier of the component. If damages are awarded, the plaintiff collects from whom he or she chooses. The multiple defendants then contest with each other on how to share the burden.

Another legal matter is the requirement that the buyer select certain suppliers on a contract. For example, on certain military contracts. the prime contractor must select suppliers from four countries (McClure, 1979). Another example is Public Law 95-507 which requires that "small business concerns and small businesses owned and controlled by socially and economically disadvantaged individuals shall have the maximum practicable opportunity to participate in the performance of contracts let by any federal agency." A relatively small supplier may not have the skills and knowledge to conduct a thorough quality program. The implication of the law is that the buyer will need to help such small suppliers so that they do become acceptable suppliers and thereby are able to compete for contracts. Ziegler (1981) discusses the impact of Public Law 95-507 on supplier quality.

Ethical Problems.   In dealing with suppliers, there is a continuing need to establish a relationship that is built on mutual trust and respect and ethical conduct. With respect to quality matters some of the issues that must be faced are:

Suppliers must be completely honest and objective in informing the customer of the quality status of delivered item; e.g., certifications that fail to indicate deviations from specifications will be interpreted as lack of good faith.

Buyers should appraise the supplier's quality and make the supplier aware of this appraisal. Preferably the appraisal should show the comparative quality position of the supplier with respect to other suppliers.

Generally the supplier should on request permit representatives from the buyer to observe inspections or tests performed by the supplier and to review the resulting data.

Both supplier and buyer should respect proprietary information.

Rudelius and Buchholz (1979) discuss the ethical problems involved in purchasing generally.

Counterfeit Product.   Some unscrupulous suppliers knowingly describe product in a false way. Instances of such "counterfeit" product have occurred for both consumer and industrial products.

A supplier manufactures a copy of a product and sells it using the label of a national well-known manufacturer. The product is sold through regular distribution chains at the full price commanded by the well-known manufacturer. The well-known manufacturer is not a party to this and is deprived of the income involved. Such counterfeit product may have poor quality, and damages the reputation of the well-known manufacturer because the buyer is not aware that the product is counterfeit.

In addition, there has been false upgrading of products. For example, a manufacturer produces some off-specification product and sells it to an outside source. The source relabels it to claim full grade quality and then sells the product for full price.

The counterfeiting can take several forms: i.e., upgrading a reliability code, changing a production date code, or even changing an identity number. In some cases the counterfeiting is so well done that only an internal microscopic inspection of the product can detect the situation. Abbott (1977) discusses examples and suggested approaches to taking action.

REFERENCES

American Society for Quality Control (1976). *Procurement Quality Control—A Handbook of Recommended Practices,* 2nd ed. Milwaukee, pp. 65–68.
American Society for Quality Control (1977). *How to Conduct a Supplier Survey.* Milwaukee.
American Society for Quality Control (1980). *Guide for Managing Vendor Quality Costs.* Milwaukee, pp. 9–10.
Abbott, Robert A. (1977). "The Cost of Honest Quality." *Quality Progress,* February, p. 4.
Admiral Corporation (1976). *Supplier Quality Control Manual.* Galesburg, IL.

Berman, Harvey S. (1983). "International Certification for Electronic Components." *Quality Progress,* November, pp. 12–15.

Boudreault, Art (1975). "Component Integrity—A Key Factor in Optimum Design." *Quality,* June, pp. 20–22.

Bowers, Virgil L. (1978). "Procurement Quality Assurance of PC Boards." *ASQC Technical Conference Transactions,* Milwaukee, pp. 62–69.

Brainard, Edgar H. (1966). "Just How Good Are Vendor Surveys?" *Quality Assurance,* August, pp. 22–25.

British Standards Institution (1979). *Quality Systems,* Parts 1–6. BSI Document BS5750, London, England.

British Standards Institution (1981). *Quality Assurance.* BSI Handbook 22, London, England.

Bruewer, Henry F. and Zaworski, Richard A. (1981). "Initiation of a Supplier Surveillance Program." *ASQC Quality Congress Transactions,* Milwaukee, pp. 992–995.

Burgess, J. A. (1981). "Supplier Surveillance." *Quality,* August, pp. Q4–Q7 (reprint).

Caplan, Frank (1980). *The Quality System.* Chilton Book Co., Radnor, PA, pp. 100–108.

Christensen, K. L. (1975). "Certification Program Reduces Costs." *Quality,* August, pp. 14–16.

"Contract Representative Service." (1981). *Quality,* August, p. Q4 (reprint).

Cooper, James (1980). "Total Quality—Design and Conformance." *Quality,* October, pp. 24–25.

Dobbins, Richard K. (1980). "Designing an Effective Procurement Rating System." *ASQC Technical Conference Transactions,* Milwaukee, pp. 488–494.

Doty, Alan L. (1982). "Far East Sourcing." *ASQC Quality Congress Transactions,* Milwaukee, pp. 217–224.

Ford Motor Company (1983). *Q-101 Quality System Standard.* Ford Product Quality Office. Dearborn, MI.

Hayes, Glenn E. and Romig, Harry G. (1977). *Modern Quality Control.* Bruce Publishing Co., Encino, CA, pp. 538–545.

Heckel, Jim (1984). "Purchasing Considerations under the JIT Concept." *Quality,* February, p. 36.

Hodge, Jack H. (1977). "Vendor Relations and Recovery." *ASQC Technical Conference Transactions,* Milwaukee, pp. 214–221.

Itoh, Wasuro (1978). "Upbringing of Component Suppliers Surrounding Toyota." *International Conference on Quality Control.* Japanese Union of Scientists and Engineers, Tokyo, Japan, pp. B1-29 through B1-34.

Johnson, Ross and Webber, Richard (1985). *Buying Quality.* Watts Publications, New York.

Juran, J. M. (1968). "Vendor Relations—An Overview." *Quality Progress,* July, pp. 10–16.

Kraljic, Peter (1983). "Purchasing Must Become Supply Management." *Harvard Business Review,* September–October, pp. 109–117.

LaBarre, Kenneth C. (1978). "Building a Field Resident Quality Program." *Quality Progress,* October, pp. 24–27.

LaFord, Richard J. and Steers, Robert R. (1979). "Receiving Inspection or Ship to Stock, Parts I and II." *ASQC Technical Conference Transactions,* Milwaukee, pp. 69–78.

McClure, J. Y. (1979). "Procurement Quality Control within the Multinational Environment." *ASQC Technical Conference Transactions,* Milwaukee, pp. 643–654.

Miller, G. D. and Kegaris, Ronald J. (1986). "An Alcoa-Kodak Joint Team." *The Juran Report,* no. 6, pp. 29–34.

MIL-Q-9858A (1985). *Quality Program Requirements.* Naval Publications and Forms Center, Philadelphia.

Mundel, August B. (1972). "Vendor-Vendee Accreditation." *ASQC Technical Conference Transactions,* Milwaukee, pp. 408–416.

National Association of Purchasing Agents (1967). *Evaluation of Supplier Performance.* New York.

Norquist, Warren E. (1983). "Improving Quality/Purchasing Teamwork." *ASQC Quality Congress Transactions,* Milwaukee, pp. 136–141.

Office of the Assistant Secretary of Defense (1960). *Statistical Procedures for Determining Validity of Supplier's Attributes Inspection.* Handbook 109, Naval Publications and Forms Center, Philadelphia.

"Quality Representative—Certified Vendor Representative." (1981). *Quality,* August, pp. Q3–Q4 (reprint).

Rau, Sri Y. R. (1981). "Development of Vendor Quality Control." *BHEL Quality Journal* (Bharat Heavy Electricals, Limited, New Delhi), pp. 3–6.

Rudelius, William and Buchholz, Rogene A. (1979). "Ethical Problems of Purchasing Managers." *Harvard Business Review,* March–April, pp. 8–14.

Sheppard, John W. (1977). "CASE Is Now 12 Years Old." *Quality Progress,* November, pp. 38–39.

Shilliff, Karl A. and Bodis, Milan (1975). "How to Pick the Right Vendor." *Quality Progress,* January, pp. 12–14.

Thoday, Wilfred R. (1983). "A Solution to Multiple Assessment." *ASQC Quality Congress Transactions,* Milwaukee, pp. 653–655.

Weaver, Henry (1978). "Quality Deterioration (Economic Marketplace)." *Quality Progress,* February, pp. 28–30.

Ziegler, August H. (1981). "Vendor Quality's New Challenge, Public Law 95-507." *ASQC Quality Congress Transactions,* Milwaukee, pp. 281–286.

Ziegler, August H. and Diggs, James (1982). "An Integrated Approach to Subcontract Support." *ASQC Quality Congress Transactions,* Milwaukee, pp. 947–954.

SECTION 16
MANUFACTURING PLANNING[1]

Frank M. Gryna

---

[1] In the Third Edition, this section was prepared by Donald N. Ekvall and J. M. Juran.

INTRODUCTION

The word "manufacture" as used in this handbook encompasses two areas:

1. *Manufacturing planning:* This is the collection of activities through which the factory is put into a state of readiness to meet quality and other standards. The quality-related aspects of manufacturing planning are discussed in this section.

2. *Production:* This is the execution of the plan; i.e., use of the machines, methods, etc., to make finished products out of purchased materials and components. Quality-related activities of production are covered in Section 17, Production. The role of statistical methods during production is discussed in Section 24, Statistical Process Control. Policy issues are discussed in Section 5 under Quality Policies for Functions

Manufacturing planning begins with the examination of the design concept to identify alternative approaches to manufacture. It ends when all is in readiness for the factory personnel to take over and produce.

Several recent developments make it essential that the quality parameter be an integral part of manufacturing planning:

1. *The increasing complexity of both products and processes:* Many products have become complex because of additional mechanical and electronic design features; many processes must meet "good manufacturing practices" and other forms of government regulation of manufacturing processes.

2. *The emphasis on reduced inventory levels during manufacture:* Under the "just-in-time" (JIT) production system, the concept of large lot sizes is challenged by reducing setup time, redesigning processes, and standardizing jobs. The results can be smaller lot sizes and substantial reductions in inventory. JIT is often run in combination with a production control information system called "kanban" (a card). With the kanban system, cards accompany the work in process and serve to indicate the use of a part in a subsequent operation and the need for production to replace the part. The aim is to have no inventory or buffer stock. If there are disruptions in the system, the causes are investigated and steps taken to reduce the buffer stock even further. Such a system relies on a process that is capable of meeting quality requirements because little or no inventory exists to replace defective product. Thus, JIT is not viable unless product quality is acceptable. Schonberger (1982) explains JIT, kanban, and the impact of these systems on product quality.

3. *Impact of computer-aided manufacture (CAM):* Computer aided manufacturing has the potential of improving the quality of products by providing more consistent equipment operation than is possible with human beings. However, the presence of the human being is an advantage when a process develops special problems. With CAM, the planning for quality must anticipate and make provisions for reacting to such problems.

Putting the factory into a state of readiness for production requires that the planners carry out a series of planning activities such as is shown in Table 16.1. This table shows also the results of the planning and the departments mainly responsible. A major objective of these activities is defect prevention.

RESPONSIBILITY FOR MANUFACTURING PLANNING

A major decision in manufacturing planning for quality is the division of the planning work among major departments. In the mechanical and the electronic industries, the work is usually performed within the manufacturing function by a specialist department (e.g., manufacturing engineering, methods engineering, process engineering). In the process industries, the work is usually divided into two parts. Broad planning (e.g., type of manufacturing process) is done within the research and development function; detailed planning is executed within the manufacturing function. Meal (1984) discusses sequential levels of planning starting at the corporate level and proceeding to the level of plant manager and shop superintendent.

TABLE 16.1 Manufacturing Planning

Planning activity	Planning principally performed by	End result of planning
Review design for clarity of specifications and for producibility; recommend changes	Manufacturing Engineering	Producible design; revised product specification
Choose process for manufacture: operations, sequences	Manufacturing Engineering	Economic, feasible process; process specification
Provide machines and tools capable of meeting tolerances	Manufacturing Engineering and Quality Engineering	Capable machines and tools
Provide instruments with accuracy adequate to control the process	Manufacturing Engineering	Capable instrumentation
Provide manufacturing information: methods, procedures, cautions	Manufacturing Engineering	Operation sheets
Provide system of quality controls: data collection, feedback, adjustment	Quality Engineering and Production	Control stations equipped to provide feedback
Define responsibilities for agreed pattern of quality	Production Supervision	Responsibilities
Select and train Production personnel	Production Supervision	Qualified production workers
Prove adequacy of planning; tryouts, trial lots	Manufacturing Engineering	Proof of adequacy
Provide protection for material during handling and storage	Material Control	Control of material
Provide proper environment	Plant Engineering	Controlled manufacturing conditions
Provide system for disposition of nonconforming product	Quality Engineering	Decision making at proper levels

A further decision in manufacturing planning for quality is the division of planning work among:

Staff planners who operate across departments

Planners within each department

Production supervisors

Production nonsupervisors

The main factors influencing the decision on responsibility are: the complexities of the products being made, the anatomy of the manufacturing process, the technological literacy of the work force, and the managerial philosophy of reliance on systems versus reliance on people.

Some industrialized countries delegate little of the job of manufacturing planning to the departmental supervision or to the work force. In the United States, this situation is largely a residue of the Taylor system of separating manufacturing planning from execution (Taylor, 1947). This system gave rise to separate departments for manufacturing planning.

The Taylor system was proposed early in the twentieth century, at a time when the educational level of the work force was low, while at the same time products and manufacturing technology were becoming more complex. The system was so successful in improving productivity that it was widely adopted in the United States. It took firm root and remains as the dominant approach to manufacturing planning, not only interdepartmentally but departmentally as well.

Times have changed. A major premise of the Taylor system, i.e., technological illiteracy of the work force, is obsolete because of the dramatic increase in the educational levels of the work force. Many companies recognize that extensive job knowledge resides in the work force, and are taking steps to utilize that knowledge. Manufacturing planning should ideally be a collaborative effort in which the work force has the opportunity to contribute input to the planning effort. In the United States, this collaboration is slow-moving because of the widespread adoption of the Taylor system and the vested interests that have been created by that approach.

Some companies are taking dramatic organizational steps to integrate quality matters into manufacturing planning. In one case, a separate quality department was eliminated, and the personnel and their activity were merged within the research and engineering department (Kearney, 1984). A formal "manufacturing plan of control" was established for each operation by analyzing the material and process variables which affected key product properties. This document was prepared by a team of people from Research and Engineering, Manufacturing, and Quality. The responsibility of the team member from Quality was to lead in the development of the plan of quality control.

DESIGN REVIEW

The general approach to design review is discussed in Section 13, under Design Review. The emphasis in that section is on the evaluation of the product design for the adequacy of field performance. Design review must also include an evaluation of producibility to cover the following matters:

1. Clarity of all requirements
2. Relative importance of product characteristics (see below)
3. Effect of tolerances on manufacturing economics (see below)
4. Availability of processes to meet tolerances
5. Tolerance buildup to give excessive clearance or interference
6. Ability to meet special requirements on surface finishes, fits, and other characteristics
7. Identification of special needs for handling, transportation, and storage during manufacture
8. Availability of measurement processes to evaluate requirements
9. Ease of access for measurement
10. Special skills required of manufacturing personnel

Specific criteria should be developed for each of these matters. This review of the *product* design must be supplemented by a review of the *process* design, which is discussed later in this section. These reviews provide an early warning to anticipate the difficulties during manufacture. The manufacturing engineer and the quality engineer, as members of a design review team, have a responsibility to identify these potential troubles and to contribute constructive ideas for possible solutions.

RELATIVE IMPORTANCE OF PRODUCT CHARACTERISTICS

Planners are better able to allocate available time and money where they will do the most good when they are well informed about the relative importance of the diverse characteristics of the product. Two useful techniques are the identification of critical items and the classification of characteristics of the product.

Identification of Critical Items.   Critical items are those features of a product which require a high level of attention to assure that all requirements are achieved. At one company, part of a procedure to identify "quality sensitive parts" uses specific criteria (Table 16.2). For each such part, special planning for quality is undertaken, e.g., supplier involvement before and during the contract, process capability studies, reliability verification, and other activities.

TABLE 16.2   Criteria for Quality-Sensitive Parts

Item	Criteria
Long lead items	25 weeks or longer
Tools and molds	$5000 or greater
Complex items	Multiple/complex operations
Reliability	Parts with predictable high failure rates
Safety items	Potentially hazardous parts
Proprietary items	Company-sensitive technology
Spare parts	Extended volume/special tooling
SMO	Critical processes/materials
New parts	Significant configuration/material changes
Critical specifications	Parts with greater than 20 percent critical design specifications

Source: Private communication.

Classification of Characteristics.   Under this system, the relative importance of individual features or properties of a product are determined and indicated on drawings and other documents. The classification can be simply "functional" or "nonfunctional" or can include several degrees of importance. An example of the latter is a system (Deere and Co., 1983) featuring three classes of seriousness, and criteria based on the impact of the quality characteristic on safety, operating failure, performance, service, and manufacture. (See Table 16.3.) The input data are derived from study of the part and its application, field and test data, reliability design analysis, warranty experience, and past experience on similar designs.

The classifications should be made by personnel with sufficient background in the functioning of the product. For most products, this must include technical

TABLE 16.3 Classification of Characteristics—Definition Product Classification if Characteristic Tolerance Is Increased by Evaluation Criteria*

Class	Safety	Operating failure	Performance	Service	Manufacturing
Critical (C—●)	Condition can create a risk of personal injury (see note below)	Certain failure. Probable failure not readily corrected at point of use.	Critical classification of performance, service, or manufacturing not defined because the characteristic becomes a critical safety or operating failure or a major performance, service, or manufacturing classification.		
Major (M—◐)	Not defined—use next higher classification	Probable failure which can be readily corrected at point of use. Possible failure not readily corrected at point of use.	Cause of substandard performance difficult to locate and/or to correct at point of use	Frequency of repair, cost of repair, time to repair, will be excessive, requiring dealer shop service	Will probably cause disruption of production
Minor (N—○)	Not defined—use next higher classification	Possible failure readily corrected at point of use.	Cause of substandard performance easily located and/or corrected at point of use	Frequency of repair, time to repair will be minimal and readily corrected at point of use	Possibly cause disruption of production
Incidental	The general classification assigned when no higher classification judgment results from application of the evaluation criteria				

*Note: Characteristics classified critical for safety reasons should be reviewed by the Product Safety Committee.
(Courtesy Deere and Company.)

16.7

personnel from the product development function. However, they frequently voice two objections to spending time on classifying characteristics:

1. *"All of the characteristics are critical":*   However, the realities are that the multitude of characteristics inevitably requires setting priorities for manufacturing and inspection efforts. Setting these priorities requires knowledge of the relative importance of characteristics. If this knowledge is not provided by the development engineer, the decisions will by default be made by others who have less background on the design.

2. *"The size of the tolerance range already provides a classification of relative importance":*   One company responds by explaining that the classification is based on the effect of a change in the tolerance range. The design engineer is asked to classify the characteristic assuming that the product variation was twice the stated tolerance. A factor of 2.0 provides a significant enough step for the engineer to form an opinion on the importance of the characteristic.

A classification approach can also be applied to the manufacturing process using the process capability ratio as a criterion (see below under Process Capability: The Concept). Product-process combinations can then be studied to identify high-risk areas, e.g., critical-critical, critical-major, major-critical.

The classification of characteristics often leads to a useful dialogue between Product Development and Manufacturing Planning before the start of production. For example, a characteristic was classified by the designer as "incidental" but required a costly process to meet the tolerance range. After discussions, the design engineer increased the tolerance range and also decided to reclassify the characteristic. The expanded tolerance permitted the substitution of a less costly process. For further discussion of classifying characteristics, see Section 18 under Quality Standards.

Cost of Tolerances.   Discussion of tolerances is an extensive activity during design review. To aid these discussions, it is useful to prepare quantitative data on the cost of holding various tolerances. An example for several levels of surface finish is shown in Table 16.4. The cost varies widely with the precision demanded. Data of this type can sometimes be compiled from industrial engineering studies conducted to set work standards.

TABLE 16.4   Relative Costs of Surface Finishes

Surface symbol designation	Surface roughness, μ in	Approximate cost, %
Cast and other unmachined	500	100
Rough machining	250	250
Ordinary machining	125	500
Fine machining or rough ground	63	1100
Very fine machining or ordinary grinding	32	1800
Fine grinding, shaving, or honing	16	3500
Very fine grinding, shaving, honing, or lapping	6	6000

Source: Martin Marietta Corporation.

INITIAL PLANNING FOR QUALITY

Planning starts with understanding the overall manufacturing process, and correlating process variables with product results.

Process Diagrams.   Understanding the process can be aided by laying out the overall process in a flow or logic diagram. Several types are helpful. Vinson and Heaney (1977) show a quality map (Figure 16.1) that relates customer needs with manufacturing steps for a fluorescent lamp. The map describes some important relationships; i.e., the amount of light depends in part on phosphor surface purity which in turn is affected by five factors. One of these factors, "oven temperature at exhaust," is a process variable that must be closely controlled. If each customer expectation is identified and analyzed, the resulting quality map shows the relationships among customer expectations, raw materials, and the process variables. Although not shown in Figure 16.1 for proprietary reasons, the product and product specifications can in practice be added to the quality map.

Another example is the "process control map" used by a steel manufacturer (Jones and Laughlin Co., 1984). This map (Figure 16.2) has three elements:

Control area: This is a geographic area or a major function.

Control point: This is a function or activity within a control area.

Control element: This is the specific process variable which must be controlled.

A cause-and-effect diagram (see Section 13 under Formulation of Theories) is also helpful in initial planning. Fukuda (1981) describes a system of using cause-and-effect diagrams to transmit new knowledge about a process to all workers. The diagram is posted and, as experience is gained with the process, the engineers and workers attach index cards which contain information on process conditions and technical know-how to prevent defects.

A further type of diagram is a flow diagram showing the paths followed by the materials through their progression into finished product. Planners use such a diagram to divide the flow into logical sections called work stations. For each work station they prepare a formal document listing such items as operations to be performed, sequence of operations, facilities and instruments to be employed, and the process conditions to be maintained. This formal document becomes the plan to be carried out by the production supervision and work force. It serves as the basis for control activities by the inspectors. It also becomes the standard against which the process audits are conducted. An example of a flow diagram for a coating process is shown in Figure 16.3 (Siff, 1984). Venn (1971) discusses the creation of process flowcharts for quality control purposes.

Correlation of Process Variables with Product Results.   A critical aspect of planning during manufacture is to discover, by data collection and analysis, the relationships between process variables or parameters and product results. Such knowledge enables the planner to specify various controls on the variables in order to achieve the specified product results. In Figure 16.3, process variables are shown in a rectangle attached to the circle representing the operation; product characteristics are listed in a rectangle between operations, at the point where conformance can be verified. Some characteristics (e.g., coat weight) are both a process variable and a product characteristic. Determining the optimal settings and

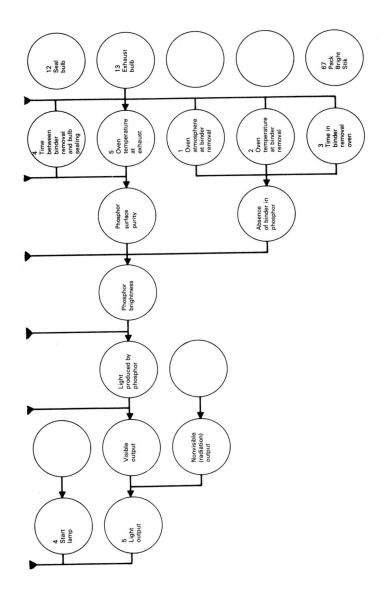

FIG. 16.1 Product design logic.

Control Area ⟶ 1.0.0   Pickle Line

                    1.1.0   Coil Entry
                            111   Coil Identity and Width Verification
                            112   Coil Conditioning

                    1.2.0   Weld Preparation
                            121   Cropping Practice
                            122   Side Guide Board Condition

                    1.3.0   Welding
                            131   Welder Setup
                            132   Weld Inspection

Control Point ⟶ 1.4.0   Wet Pit
                            141   Wet Pit Practices

                    1.5.0   Bliss Mill
                            151   Bliss Mill Rolls
                            152   Bliss Mill Extension

                    1.6.0   Looping
                            161   Looper Section Arms and Rolls
                            162   Looper Section Capacity

                    1.7.0   Pickling
Control Element ⟶ 171   Acid Bath
                            172   Rinsing and Drying

                    1.8.0   Trimming
                            181   Trimmer Knife Setup
                            182   Trim Width Setup

                    1.9.0   Inspection
                            191   Edge Quality Standards
                            192   Surface Quality Standards
                            193   Strip Flatness Standards
                            194   Strip Width Standard

                  1.10.0   Tension Reeling
                         1101   Stamping
                         1102   Surface Oiling
                         1103   Coil Winding

                  1.11.0   Coil Edit
                         1111   Coil Identification and Marking
                         1112   Coil Banding and Edge Sealing Requirements

FIG. 16.2   Process control map.

tolerances for process variables sometimes requires much data collection and analysis. Carpenter (1982) discusses a case which required a statistical analysis of data on 33 parameters in order to pinpoint the key process variables in a copper ore roasting operation.

Many companies have not studied the relationships between process variables and product results. The need is especially acute in those industries where the product goes sequentially through a series of processes and accumulates the effect of many variables. In practice, process engineers conduct only such studies as are sufficient to attain product conformance to specification with competitive yields because:

1. They have no time. The priorities are on bringing new products into production and there is no end to the procession of new products.

2. They lack proficiency in the use of the quality disciplines, notably design of experiments and analysis of variance. Lacking such proficiency, they try to get answers by more intense use of their technological specialty (e.g., organic chemistry, metallurgy), but this is not enough.

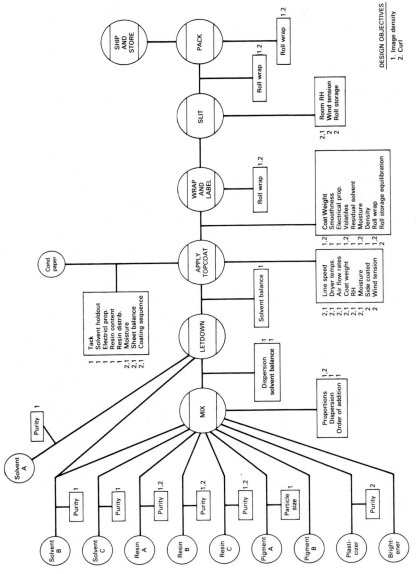

FIG. 16.3 Strategic plan of control. Product and process analysis chart (P-PAC).

The consequences of this lack of knowledge (of the relationship between process variables and product results) can be severe. In the electronic component manufacturing industry some yields are shockingly low and will likely remain that way until the process variables are studied in depth. In all industries the imposition of new quality demands (e.g., reduction in weight of automotive components) can cause a sharp rise in scrap (and hence in costs) because not enough is known about the process variables to adapt promptly to the new demands.

Only upper management can supply the missing essentials, which consist of:

1. The budget for personnel needed full time to assist by analyzing existing data, determining the need for additional studies, designing the experiments, collecting the new data, analyzing, etc.

2. The budget for training in the quality disciplines. The full-time analysts should, of course, have this training in depth. In addition, it is quite helpful for the process engineers to become knowledgeable as well. The necessary training programs are widely available.

The return on these investments is in the form of higher yields, higher productivity, lower costs, and better quality.

Some industries must meet explicit government regulations concerning manufacturing practices, and these must be recognized during manufacturing planning. An example is the good manufacturing practices (GMP) regulations in health-related industries.

Predicting Adequacy of Processes.   The planner should know in advance whether the process will be able to turn out products which are fit for use. One of the necessary ingredients is knowledge of the adequacy of the process.

There are several ways of evaluating adequacy of equipment. In one approach, measurements are made on the process rather than the product. For example, in the manufacture of machine tools it is common to place dial gages, test mandrels, spirit levels, and other instruments in appropriate mountings, in order to measure the trueness of the machine. Also, sterilization chambers are checked with thermocouples to assure that all areas can be brought up to the minimal temperature needed to kill off unwanted organisms. Such measurements are part of the overall evaluation of equipment. However, a complete evaluation requires measurements on the *product* through "process capability studies."

PROCESS CAPABILITY: THE CONCEPT

Process capability is the measured, inherent reproducibility of the product turned out by a process.

Basic Definitions.   Each key word in this definition must itself be clearly defined, since the concept of capability has an enormous extent of application and since nonscientific terms are inadequate for communication within the industrial community.

Process: This refers to some unique combination of machine, tools, methods, materials, *and people* engaged in production. It is often feasible to separate and quantify the effect of the variables entering this combination. Such separation can be illuminating.

Capability: This word is used in the sense of a competence, based on tested performance, to achieve measurable results.

Measured: This refers to the fact that process capability is quantified from data which, in turn, are the results of measurement of work performed by the process.

Inherent reproducibility: This refers to the product uniformity resulting from a process which is in a state of statistical control, i.e., in the absence of time-to-time "drift" or other assignable causes of variation. "Instantaneous reproducibility" is a synonym.

Product: The measurement is made on the product because it is product variation which is the end result.

Machine capability versus process capability: Some practitioners distinguish between these two terms. Machine capability refers to the reproducibility under one set of process conditions (e.g.: one operator, homogeneous raw material, uniform manufacturing practice). Process capability refers to the reproducibility over a long period of time with normal changes in workers, material, and other process conditions.

Process capability as defined above is a measurable property of the process (much as volume in liters is a measurable property of a container). The resulting measure is expressed in terms of 6σ of variation (see below) and is unrelated to the product tolerance; i.e., "the process doesn't know what the tolerance is." However, the capability measurement is compared to the tolerance in order to judge the adequacy of the process.

Process Patterns. The concept of process capability can be better understood by an examination of the usual process patterns encountered. A useful technique for making this examination is to measure a sample, summarize the data in a histogram, and compare the result to the specification limits.

Typical histograms and the usual meaning of each are shown in Figure 16.4. The examination has a three-part focus:

The centering of the histogram: This defines the aim of the process.

Width of the histogram: This defines the variability about the aim.

The shape of the histogram: For most characteristics, a normal or bell-shaped curve is expected. Any significant deviation from the normal pattern has a cause which, once determined, can shed much light on the variability in the process. For example, histograms with two or more peaks reveal that multiple "populations" have been mixed together. These populations may be different mold cavities, different spindles, different heads on a machine, different suppliers, and so forth.

Histograms and chronological plots of process data indicate several reasons why some processes are not capable of holding tolerances. These are:

1. *The inherent variability of the process is too large for the proposed tolerance:* Assuming the process is in statistical control, the only courses of action are to revise the process, to expand the tolerances, or to live with a certain level of defectives.

2. *The process is misdirected:* Here the planner must provide the operating forces with the means to evaluate the extent of misdirection and to make compensating adjustments in the process.

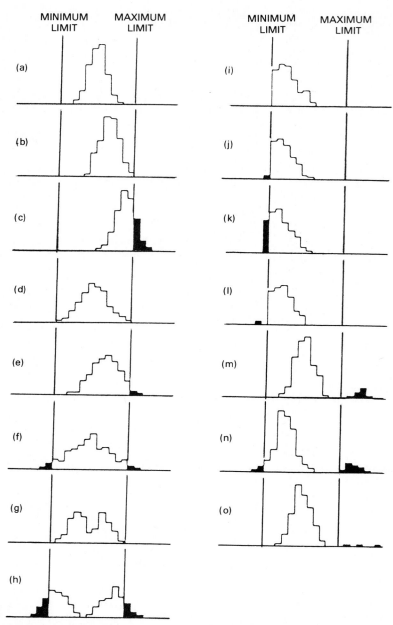

FIG. 16.4 Histogram distribution patterns. *(Adapted from Armstrong, G. R. and Clarke, P. C. (1946). "Frequency Distribution vs. Acceptance Table." Industrial Quality Control. vol. 3, no. 2, September, pp. 22–27.)*

3. *The instrumentation is inadequate.*

4. *There is process drift:* Here the need is to quantify the amount of drift in a given period of time and to provide means for resetting the process to compensate for this drift.

5. *There are cyclical changes in the process:* The need is to identify the underlying cause and either remove it or reduce the effect on the process.

6. *The process is erratic:* Sudden changes can take place in processes. As the capability studies quantify the size of these changes and help to discover the reasons for them, appropriate planning action can be taken:

    a. Temporary phenomena (e.g., cold machine coming up to operating temperature) can be dealt with by scheduling warming periods plus checks at the predicted time of stability.

    b. More enduring phenomena (e.g., change due to new material supply) can be dealt with by specifying setup reverification at the time of introducing such change.

Product Mixture.   A common obstacle to utilizing the inherent capability of a process is that, for reasons of productivity, products from several processes are commingled at the time of manufacture. Examples of this are widespread: multicavity plastic molding, multiple unit film deposition for electronic components, multiple head filling of containers, etc. What these processes have in common is a multiplicity of "machines" mounted on a single frame. The multiple character of these producing sources superimposes a stream-to-stream variation which materially affects the ability of the process to meet the specifications.

In such cases, any conventional sampling of product ends up with data which are a composite of two different sources of variation:

1. The stream-to-stream variation, traceable to differences in the mold cavities, spindles, heads, etc.

2. The within-stream variation, which characterizes a single "pure" process

To quantify the stream-to-stream variation requires that the product from different streams (cavities, spindles, molds, heads) can be segregated. Once segregated, the data for each stream can be treated in the conventional manner. Figure 16.5 is an example of such segregation and quantification for a multiple spindle screw machine. Tarver (1984) presents procedures for process capability studies of multiple stream processes.

Standardized Formula.   The most widely adopted formula for process capability is

$$\text{Process capability} = 6\sigma$$

where σ = the standard deviation of the process under a state of statistical control, i.e., under no drift and no sudden changes.

If the process is centered at the nominal specification and follows a normal probability distribution, 99.73 percent of production will fall within $\pm 3\sigma$ of the nominal specification.

Some industrial processes do operate under a state of statistical control. For such processes, the computed process capability of 6σ can be compared directly to specification tolerances, and judgments of adequacy can be made. However, the majority of industrial processes do exhibit drift and do exhibit sudden

	SPINDLE	APPROXIMATE AVERAGE DIMENSION	APPROXIMATE TOTAL RANGE
	1	3.0	4.2
	2	3.0	3.5
	3	2.5	4.0
	4	2.0	4.8
	5	3.3	4.5
	6	3.3	3.8
COMBINED		3.0	5.5
AVERAGE FOR ALL SPINDLES		3.0	4.1

FIG. 16.5 Separating multiple streams, multiple spindle machine.

changes. These departures from the ideal are a fact of life, and the practitioner must deal with them.

Nevertheless, there is great value in standardizing on a formula for process capability based on a state of statistical control. Under this state, the product variations are the resultant of numerous small variables (rather than being the effect of a single large variable) and hence have the character of random variation. It is most helpful for planners to have such limits in quantified form.

The standardized formula (process capability = 6σ) assumes a normal probability distribution. This is often the case, but it is not universally true. For example, dimensions that are close to a physical limit, such as the amount "out of round" (where a value of zero is desired), tend to show "skewed" distributions. In such cases, $\pm 3\sigma$ does not include 99.73 percent of the population. However, it is possible to use the log normal or Weibull distribution to derive a measure of process capability. This can be most conveniently done by using probability paper (see below).

Relation to Product Tolerance. A major reason for quantifying process capability is to be able to compute the ability of the process to hold product tolerances. For processes which are in a state of statistical control, a comparison of the variation of 6σ to the tolerance limits permits ready calculation of percent defective by conventional statistical theory. (See Section 23, under Continuous Probability Distributions.)

Capability Ratio.   In most processes, not only are there departures from a state of statistical control but the process is not necessarily being operated to secure optimum yields, e.g., the average of the process is not centered between the upper and lower tolerance limits. To allow for these realities, planners try to select processes with the 6σ process capability well within the tolerance width. The two factors are expressed in a capability ratio:

$$\text{Capability ratio} = \frac{\text{tolerance width}}{\text{process capability}}$$

Some companies define the ratio as the reciprocal. Some industries now express defect rates in terms of parts per million. A defect rate of 1 part per million requires a capability ratio (tolerance width over process capability) of about 1.63.

The comparison of process capability to tolerances leads to some broad plans of action:

1. If the process capability is inadequate to meet the tolerance:

   a. Try to shift the job to another process with more adequate capability. If the order already is completed, make provisions for proper assignment when the job occurs again.

   b. Try to improve the capability. This is particularly advisable if the value obtained differs markedly from that of a similar process. The process may require overhauling or the tooling may need to be reviewed. For multispindle machines, the causes for spindle-to-spindle differences may need to be pinpointed. Control chart analysis may be helpful. If the process is in a state of statistical control, a major change such as an overhaul will be required to improve the capability. If the process is not in statistical control, the assignable causes should be identified for the out-of-control points, and removal of these causes can result in improved capability.

   c. Try to get a review of the tolerance. The availability of specific information showing what tolerance can be achieved may soften the engineer's attitude on liberalizing the tolerance.

2. If the process capability is equal to the tolerance, this usually should be treated as in item 1 above, since it means that process must be set exactly at the nominal point and gives no allowance for factors such as tool wear. However, if such factors are negligible or where a small percentage of parts just outside the tolerance can be tolerated, this should be treated as in item 3 below.

3. If the process capability is adequate to meet the tolerance:

   a. If the capability is of the order of two-thirds to three-fourths of the tolerance or less, it is the acceptable situation. The process should produce practically all good work over a long period of time if periodic samples are taken to check the setting of the process.

   b. If the capability is less than one-half of the tolerance, do nothing unless reducing the tolerance will achieve some gain. The ability to tighten the tolerance on one part in an assembly may permit loosening a difficult tolerance on another part. Closer guarantee of tolerances may also have competitive sales advantage.

   c. One hundred percent inspection of the product is not needed and a sampling procedure should be considered.

Kane (1986) discusses the use of a "Performance Index" C_{pk} which reflects the current process mean's proximity to either the upper specification limit USL or lower specification limit LSL. C_{pk} is estimated by:

$$\hat{C}_{pk} = \min \left[\frac{\overline{X} - \text{LSL}}{3s}, \frac{\text{USL} - \overline{X}}{3s} \right]$$

For Kane's example where

$$\text{USL} = 20 \qquad \overline{X} = 16$$

$$\text{LSL} = 8 \qquad s = 2$$

the standard capability ratio is estimated as

$$\frac{\text{USL} - \text{LSL}}{6\sigma} = \frac{20 - 8}{12} = 1.0$$

which implies that, *if* the process were centered between the specification limits (at 14), then only a small proportion (about 0.27 percent) of product would be defective.

However, when we calculate C_{pk}, we obtain

$$\hat{C}_{pk} = \min \left[\frac{16 - 8}{6}, \frac{20 - 16}{6} \right] = 0.67$$

which alerts us that the process mean is *currently* nearer the USL. (Note that if the process were centered at 14, the value of C_{pk} would be 1.0.) An acceptable process will require reducing the standard deviation and/or centering the mean.

There can be circumstances in which product uniformity around a target value is more important than the percent of product that meets specifications. Sullivan (1984) describes a case of two company facilities making the same television set (Figure 16.6). The San Diego plant had no product outside specifications but the

SONY'S case (cited from the Asahi, April 17, 1979):
Color density of TV set
Assumption: repairing cost A = 4 ($)
Loss function:

$$L = \frac{4}{5^2} \sigma^2 = 0.16\sigma^2$$

San Diego: $L = 0.16 \times \left(\frac{10}{\sqrt{12}} \right)^2 = 1.33$

Japan: $L = 0.16 \times \left(\frac{10}{6} \right)^2 = 0.44$

TYPES OF DISTRIBUTION IN THE ASAHI

Factory location	Type of distribution (approx.)	Percent out of spec., %	Standard deviation	Loss per unit, $	Difference in quality, $
San Diego	Uniform	Almost nil	$\frac{10}{\sqrt{12}}$	1.33	- 0.89
Japan	Normal	0.3	$\frac{10}{6}$	0.44	

FIG. 16.6 Uniformity and production quality in Japan and the United States. *(From Sullivan, 1984, p. 19.)*

distribution was virtually rectangular, with a large percent of product close to the specification limits. In contrast, the plant in Japan did have some product outside of specification limits, but the distribution was normal and was concentrated around the target value. Field experience revealed that product near the specification limits generated complaints from customers. This and other reasons led to a higher loss per unit at San Diego even though that plant was superior in meeting the specification.

Sometimes the relationship of process variation to process economics can be evaluated to determine the most profitable target value for a process. Hunter and Kartha (1977) have developed a technique for determining the best target value for a process with a single specification limit that simultaneously produces (1) product conforming to specification, (2) product not conforming but which can be sold at a lower selling price, and (3) product that results in a "giveaway" cost, as when a minimum weight specification is exceeded and product is given away. Nelson (1978) presents an approximating function for the Hunter and Kartha technique.

PROCESS CAPABILITY MEASUREMENT

"Process capability" refers to the variation in a process about some target value. This is illustrated in Figure 16.7. The two processes have equal capabilities because 6σ is the same for the two, as indicated by the widths of the distribution curves. The process aimed at μ_2 is producing defectives because the aim is off center, not because of the inherent variation about the aim (i.e., the capability).

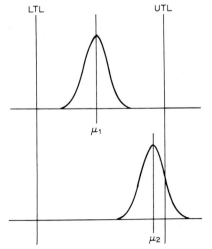

Two categories of techniques are involved:

1. Techniques that measure the present process performance, i.e., what the process is doing

2. Techniques that estimate the inherent process capability, i.e., what the process can do under certain conditions

If a process is in statistical control, then the measure of process performance results also in determining process capability. Several of the techniques described below for determining process performance use the

FIG. 16.7 Processes with equal process capability but different aim.

same calculations as techniques described later for process capability. (The difference involves the assumption of statistical control as explained below.) Mentch (1980) provides a further breakdown of process analysis into four categories and presents methods and examples for each.

Measuring Present Process Performance. Specific tools for this type of study include the frequency distribution and histograms, probability paper, the mini-capability study, plot of individual measurements, and attributes data analysis. It is highly preferable to use variables rather than attributes data, i. e., numerical measurements rather than accept-reject information.

Frequency Distribution and Histogram.   In this type of study, a sample of about 50 consecutive units is taken, during which time no adjustments are made on the machines or tools. The units are all measured, the data are tallied in frequency distribution form, and the standard deviation is calculated and used as an estimate of σ. The characteristic is assumed to follow a normal probability distribution where ± 3 standard deviations includes 99.73 percent of the population. Process performance is then defined as $\pm 3\sigma$ or 6σ.

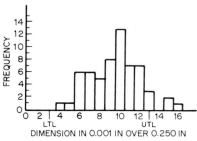

FIG. 16.8   Histogram of measurement.

For example, the histogram for a sample of 60 measurements is shown in Figure 16.8 (machine N-5). Analysis of the 60 measurements yielded:

$$\overline{X} = 9.6 \qquad s = 2.5$$

Computer programs are available to calculate the average and standard deviation, develop and plot the histogram, and make various checks on the assumption of a normal probability distribution. The process capability is calculated $\pm 3(2.5)$ or ± 7.5, or a total of 15.0.

Probability Paper.   Normal probability paper (see Section 23 under Predictions with Normal Distributions) can be used to graphically determine process performance. For example, a sample of 100 measurements on total indicator reading (T.I.R.) was grouped into a frequency distribution of 10 cells. The frequencies were then plotted on normal probability paper (Figure 16.9).The measurements are plotted and are observed to follow a straight line (indicating that the population is normally distributed). The left vertical scale shows the cumulative percent of the population under a value of T.I.R.; the right vertical scale shows the cumulative percent over a value of T.I.R. and also the number of standard deviations from the mean. The upper and lower horizontal grid lines represent $\pm 3\sigma$, respectively. When the plotted line is extended to intersect the grid lines for $\pm 3\sigma$, the values of 0.01 and 0.059 are read, indicating that 99.73 percent of the population will fall between 0.01 and 0.059. The $\pm 3\sigma$ capability is then calculated as 0.059 − 0.01, or 0.058. As the specification range is 0.060, the performance is satisfactory.

By extending the plotted line to intersect the specification limits (shown as vertical lines), the percent of nonconforming product can be predicted. Essentially, zero percent will fall under the lower specification limit or over the upper specification limit.

The mean value can also be quickly estimated from the plot. Enter the vertical axis on the 50 percent line. This line intersects the diagonal at 0.030 on the horizontal scale.

Some examples of probability plots as applied to process analysis are given in Figure 16.10. Weibull probability paper (see Section 23 under Predictions with Weibull Distributions) is available for nonnormal distributions.

Plots of Individual Measurements.   A simple plot of individual measurements, in order of production, can be surprisingly revealing.

FIG. 16.9 Capability analysis on probability paper. *(Adapted from Amsden, Butler, and Amsden, 1986, p. 137.)*

In a classic study of a lathe process for making watch parts, each piece was measured for each of five quality characteristics. The resulting measurements were then plotted in chronological order on a chart which also showed the five sets of tolerances. The study demonstrated that the process was capable of meeting the specification limits. The study also showed that the poor performance (12 percent nonconforming product) was due to the inadequacy of the instruments provided to the work force. Provision of adequate instruments reduced the defect level to 2 percent and made possible a sharp reduction in the amount of gaging done by inspectors (consulting experience of J. M. Juran).

Minicapability Study. This study provides a quick, but highly approximate, estimate of "capability." Ten measurements are taken and the range (maximum-minimum values) is determined. "Capability" (defined as 6σ) is then calculated as twice the range of the sample. The rationale for this simple method is explained later in this section under Determination of Process Capability from a Control Chart Analysis. The method requires that the sample size be 10 and that the characteristic be normally distributed.

Special Studies. Some processes, notably in the process industries, do not readily submit to conventional forms of analysis, and therefore require specially designed studies. Sahrmann (1979) describes a study of the variation of weight of coating applied to a moving web by reverse roll coating. Processes of this type

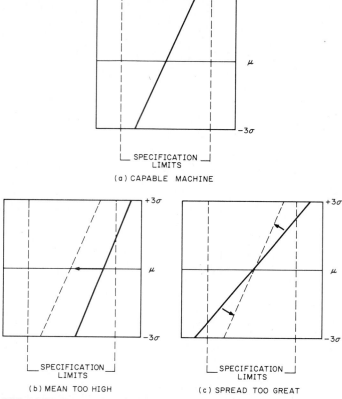

FIG. 16.10 Interpreting the results.

often show a significant amount of cyclical variation with high-low values occurring at regular intervals. (Figure 16.11). Regression analysis and other techniques helped to identify the sources of cyclical variation and measure their relative contribution to overall process variation. This led to a reduction in the total variation, thereby permitting a lower target value. The benefits were reduction in raw material "give-away" and better product uniformity for the customer.

Attributes Data Analyses.   The methods discussed above assume that numerical measurements are available from the process. This is the preferable type of data for a capability study. Sometimes, however, the only data available are in attribute form, i.e., the number defective and the number acceptable. Attributes data require large sample sizes and should be used only where variable measurement is impractical.

Since shifts in the process average are not revealed by attributes data, the sample taken should be randomly selected over as long a time period as possible to assure that the study includes the long-term variability of the process. For attributes data, the Ford Motor Company required a minimum sample size of 250 measurements with none outside of specifications. With this criterion, about 99.73 percent of the products will be within the specified tolerances. In general,

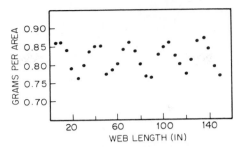

FIG. 16.11 Variations in coating weight applied by reverse roll coating.

where zero products are outside of specification limits the "capability" percentage can be determined as follows:

$$\text{Capability \%} = 100(0.5)^{1/(N+1)}$$

where N is the sample size.

If there are one or more failures to meet specifications, then

$$\text{Capability \%} = 100\left(1 - \frac{F + 0.7}{N}\right)$$

where F is the numbers of failures.

Attributes control charts can also be used in capability studies (Mentch, 1980).

Limitations of Histograms and Probability Paper Analysis. These methods of evaluating process performance do not necessarily evaluate the inherent capability of the process. The data may include measurements from several populations (as in Figure 16.5). There may be time-to-time changes such as solutions becoming dilute or tools becoming worn. Such process conditions result in observed dispersions which are wider than the inherent capability of the process. To evaluate that inherent capability requires use of other, more precise methods of evaluation.

Measuring Inherent Capability. Specific tools for this type of study include the control chart, prediction from data on process elements, computer simulation, and tools for complex processes.

The Control Chart. A control chart is a graphic comparison of process performance data to statistical control limits, not specification limits. The performance data consists of groups of measurements ("rational subgroups") selected in regular sequence of production while preserving the order. The statistical control limits help to evaluate capability by first evaluating whether the process is operating at its minimum inherent variation.

Process variations are traceable to two kinds of causes: (1) random, i.e., due solely to chance, and (2) assignable, i.e., due to specific "findable" causes. Ideally, only random causes should be present in a process, because this represents the minimum possible amount of variation with the given set of process conditions. A process that is operating without assignable causes of variation is said to be "in a state of the statistical control." A control chart analysis should be made and assignable causes eliminated from the process prior to calculating 6σ as a measure of process capability. When this is done, 6σ then represents the inherent process capability. If 6σ is calculated without first making a control chart analysis, the 6σ will probably be inflated. Many control chart analyses reveal the presence of assignable causes even though production people profess that the process is operating with the minimum possible variation. A description of control chart methodology, including formulas and procedures, is given in Section 24, Statistical Process Control.

A state of statistical control is not an end point to process improvement. The use of experimental design techniques makes it possible to reduce process variation even further. A state of statistical control is related to the given set of process conditions including the process variables that are being controlled to yield the product results. The identification and control of other important process variables can result in less product variation. To achieve such improvement requires the use of a variety of techniques. See, for example, Section 26, Design and Analysis of Experiments, and below under Application of Experimental Design to Optimize Process Variables.

For process capability analyses using variables data, a control chart for sample averages and sample ranges is applied. Figure 16.12 shows a control chart for coded T.I.R. readings. Calculations for the control limits are explained in Section 24 under Control Chart for Average and Range. The upper chart, a plot of sample averages of five measurements each, traces the aim of the process. The lower chart, a plot of sample ranges (maximum-minimum in the sample), shows the

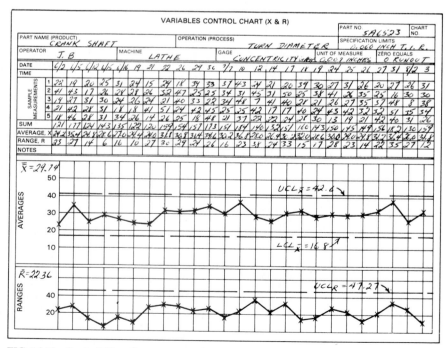

FIG. 16.12   Control Chart for averages and ranges. (*Amsden, Butler, and Amsden, 1986, p. 134.*)

inherent piece to piece variability about the process aim. As both plots fall within the respective statistical control limits, it is concluded that the process is operating in statistical contol. A calculation for process capability then represents the inherent capability.

Determination of Process Capability from a Control Chart Analysis. If, and only if, a process is in statistical control, the following relationship holds:

$$\text{Estimate of } \sigma = s = \frac{\overline{R}}{d_2}$$

Table A in Appendix II provides values of d_2. Knowing the standard deviation, process capability limits can be set at $\pm 3s$ and this used as an estimate of 3σ. (This calculation converts $\overline{R}$ to a standard deviation of *individual* values. Control limits represent 3 standard deviations of samples *averages*.)

For the data of Figure 16.12,

$$s = \frac{\overline{R}}{d_2} = \frac{22.4}{2.326} = 9.63$$

and

$$\pm 3s = \pm 3(9.63) = 28.9 \text{ (or 0.029 in original readings)}$$

or

$$6s = 57.8 \text{ (or 0.058 in original readings)}$$

Note a special case of the $s = \overline{R}/d_2$ calculation. When $n = 10$, $d_2 = 3.078$. Then

$$3s = \frac{3\overline{R}}{3.078} = \text{approximately } 1\overline{R}$$

or the 6σ process is about $2\overline{R}$. If it were necessary to make a quick approximation of process capability, a single sample of 10 could be measured, the range calculated, and process capability estimated at $2R$. (This is described previously under Minicapability Study.) Of course, this loses the advantage of the control chart.

The Assumption of Statistical Control and Its Effect on Process Capability. All statistical predictions assume a stable population. In a statistical sense, a stable population is one which is repeatable, that is, a population that is in a state of statistical control. The statistician rightfully insists that this be the case before predictions can be made. The manufacturing engineer also insists that the process conditions (feeds, speeds, etc.) be fully defined.

In practice, the original control chart analysis will often show the process to be out of statistical control. (It may or may not be meeting product specifications.) However, an investigation may show that the causes cannot be economically eliminated from the process. In theory, a process capability prediction should not be made until the process is in statistical control. However, in practice, some kind of comparison of capability to product tolerances is needed. The danger in delaying the comparison is that the assignable causes may never be eliminated from the process. The resulting indecision will thereby prolong interdepartmental bickering on whether "the tolerance is too tight" or "manufacturing is too careless."

A good way to start is by plotting individual measurements against tolerance limits (see Plots of Individual Measurements above). This may show that the process can meet the product tolerances even with assignable causes present. If a process has assignable causes of variation, but is able to meet the product tolerances, usually no economic problem exists. The statistician can properly point out that a process with assignable variation is unpredictable. This point is well taken; but in establishing priority of quality improvement efforts, processes that are meeting tolerances are seldom given high priority.

If a process is out of control and the causes cannot be economically eliminated, the standard deviation and process capability limits can nevertheless be computed (with the out-of-control points included). These limits will be inflated because the process will not be operating at its best. In addition, the instability of the process means that the prediction is approximate.

It is important to distinguish between a process in a state of statistical control and a process that is meeting specifications. A state of statistical control does *not* necessarily mean that the product from the process conforms to specifications. Statistical control limits on sample averages *cannot* be directly compared to specification limits because the control limits refer to individual units. For some processes which are not in control, the specifications are being met and no action is required; other processes are in control but the specifications are not being met and action is needed. Section 12 under Special Situation of Taking Action When Control Charts Are Used discusses the more usual permutations.

Statistical Prediction of Process Capability from Data on Process Elements. Process capability can sometimes be predicted before any product is manufactured. This may be possible if the process can be divided into elements for which previous data are available. The data are combined statistically to yield an estimate of capability for the new process.

The U.S. Department of Transportation (1982) describes how the approach can be used in ship building:

1. Identify the specific processes that contribute to some final product characteristic.

2. Provide detailed work instructions for executing each of these processes.

3. Obtain data on the mean and variance of each process step from the prior construction of other ships. (As a result of this, tables of data are now available for various work processes.)

4. Statistically predict the result of a final product characteristic on a new product:

   a. Mean value: Add or subtract mean values of the process steps according to the geometry of the dimensions.

   b. Variance: Add the variances of the contributing processes to estimate the variance of the final product characteristic. This is identical to the approach used in the statistical merger of tolerances (see Section 23 under Statistical Method of Relating Tolerances on Interacting Dimensions). Independence of the contributing processes and normality of each of the process characteristics is assumed.

5. Predict the percent of the product outside the specification limits by finding the area under the normal curve (see Section 23 under Predictions with Normal Distributions).

6. If the process is not capable, review the calculations to decide which of the contributing processes must be reduced in variability, and then plan an improvement program.

McCubbin (1971) reports on research to predict capability as a function of manufacturing variables. One mathematical model predicts capability from values of depth of cut, feed, length of cut, material hardness, and dimension size for metal working operations. A second model predicts tool wear as a function of material hardness, depth of cut, and machine dimension.

Computer Simulation of Process Capability.   This technique is useful when (1) several component parts or manufacturing steps contribute to a final result, (2) the distributions are nonnormal, and (3) the relationship between the component and the final result is difficult to analyze with conventional statistical methods. A mathematical model is first created to express the result as a function of the contributing variables. The distribution of each component or each process step is then defined—for example, a normal distribution with a mean of 2.000 and standard deviation of 0.004 or an exponential distribution with a mean of 1.000. Simulated values of the final result are generated by means of a random number generator which draws values at random from each component distribution and combines them in the model. By repeating this process many times, the result is a simulation of what would happen if many products were made at random from components or process steps having the characteristics described in the simulation model. The simulated values can be summarized in a distribution, and the average, standard deviation, and other measures computed. With the simulation model, component distributions can be changed and the effect on the overall result predicted by running additional simulations. In this way, different approaches can be tried before finalizing the manufacturing plans. Michalek and Holmes (1981) apply this technique to analyze manufacturing steps in the automotive industry.

In a communication to the author, Dr. Ronald D. Snee suggests a similar approach for predicting process capability in the process industries. First, a mathematical model is developed which relates the response characteristic (Y) to a set of control variables (X, X_2, $\ldots$,X_p). This would probably require formally designed experiments to identify the control variables, and regression analysis to develop the mathematical model. Next, distributions of each of the control variables are developed from past experience. Finally, a computer simulation is run to generate values of the response Y from values of each of the control variables randomly generated by the simulation. The resultant Y values are summarized in a distribution, and the capability calculated as 6σ.

Measuring Potential Capability of Complex Processes.   As the process becomes complex, the analysis to measure process capability also becomes complex. As noted, the product lots are in reality composed of multiple streams, each of which can exhibit time-to-time drift and other changes. In addition, even at instantaneous time, there are piece-to-piece and within-piece variations.

Several methods of analysis are available to assist the planner in quantifying these components of total variations.

Graphic analysis: An example is the Multi-Vari graph discussed in Section 22 under Test of Theories of Management-Controllable Problems.

Span plan: This is a structured approach to analysis and is likewise discussed in Section 22 under Test of Theories of Management-Controllable Problems.

Design of experiment and analysis of variance: This is a generalized approach, with flexibility to fit any combination of variables. For each such combination, there is prepared a tailor-made "design of experiment" for collecting the data which will permit resolution of the composite variation into its components. The resulting data are analyzed by the technique of "analysis of variance," which provides, in standardized format, the determination of significance of the variables under experiment as well as their interaction. (See Section 26, Design and Analysis of Experiments.)

Response surface methodology: This sophisticated planning device has been increasingly used in the chemical process industries and some others to study the effects of multiple variables on yields or other desired characteristics and to find the combination which optimizes the final result. (See Section 26 under Response Surface Methodology.)

Evolutionary operation (EVOP): This analytical approach is aimed at securing data from manufacturing operations (as distinguished from laboratory or pilot plant experiments). Successive lots are made under process conditions which vary from one lot to another. The EVOP method goes a step further by deliberately creating some variation which will provide needed data without jeopardizing the product. Special analysis techniques then derive the relationships which form the basis of product improvement. (See Section 26 under Evolutionary Operation.)

Application of Experimental Design to Optimize Process Variables ("Off-Line Quality Control"). Taguchi (1978) has developed a method for determining the optimum values of process variables which will minimize the variation in a process while keeping a process mean on target. Phadke et al. (1983) describe an application of this approach to manufacturing planning for integrated circuits. The example concerns the dimensions on the contact window of a large-scale integrated chip. Windows that are not open or are too small result in a loss of contact to the devices, while excessively large windows lead to shorted device features. The steps in window forming and the factors critical in each step are shown in Table 16.5.

Levels of each of the nine critical factors were selected. Six of the factors have three levels each; three of the factors have only two levels each. A full factorial experiment to explore all possible factor-level combinations would require 3 raised to the 6th power times 2 raised to the 3rd power, or 5832 observations. (There were 12 experiments originally planned.) Instead, a fractional factorial design was chosen to investigate 18 combinations (with a total of 34 measurements). Three dimensions were measured on each window. Transformed variables instead of the absolute values were used in the data analysis. The variables selected were the mean and the signal-to-noise ratio (s/n). The signal-to-noise ratio is defined as:

$$s/n = \log_{10}\left(\frac{mean}{standard\ deviation}\right)$$

The problem was to determine the factor levels that yield a maximum signal to noise ratio while keeping the mean on target. Two steps were needed:

1. Determine the factors which have a significant effect on the signal-to-noise ratio. These are the factors that control the process variability and are referred to as control factors. For each control factor, the level chosen is that with the highest signal-to-noise ratio, thus maximizing the overall ratio.

2. Select from the control factors one that has the smallest effect on the signal-to-noise ratio. This factor is called a signal factor. The levels of the factors that are neither control factors nor signal factors are set at the nominal levels prior to the experiment. Finally, the level of the signal factor is set so that the mean response is on target.

TABLE 16.5 Fabrication Steps and Critical Factors in Window Forming

Fabrication step	Critical factors
Apply photo resist	Photo resist viscosity (B) and spin speed (C)
Bake	Bake temperature (D) and bake time (E)
Expose	Mask dimension (A), aperture (F) and exposure time (G)
Develop	Developing time (H)
Plasma etch	Etch time (I)
Remove photo resist	Does not affect window size

The analysis of variance revealed the control factors to be factors A, B, C, F, G, and H. Based on an analysis of the data, and engineering judgment, the signal factor was chosen to be exposure time.

The levels selected for each of the factors are shown in Table 16.6. Using these levels a sample of chips was manufactured. The resulting benefits were:

	Old conditions	Optimum conditions
Standard deviation	0.29	0.14
Visual defects (window per chip)	0.12	0.04

After observing these improvements, the process engineers eliminated a number of in-process checks, thereby reducing the overall time spent by the wafers in photolithography by a factor of 2.

Byrne and Taguchi (1986) discuss a case study where the objective was to maximize the force required to separate a small assembly. The October 1985 issue of the *Journal of Quality Technology* is primarily devoted to papers explaining the Taguchi approach.

TABLE 16.6 Optimum Factor Levels

Label	Factors' names	Standard levels	Optimum levels
A	Mask dimension μm	2.0	2.5
B	Viscosity	204	204
C	Spin speed r/min	3000	4000
D	Bake temperature °C	105	105
E	Bake time, min	30	30
F	Aperture	2	2
G	Exposure, PEP setting	Normal	Normal
H	Developing time, s	45	60
I	Plasma etch time, min	13.2	13.2

Source: Phadke et al., 1983, p. 1303.

Steps in Evaluating Proposed Complex Processes. Bemesderfer (1979) describes an eight-point program for the evaluation of new processes prior to production:

1. Develop a process description using quantitative mathematical equations describing the effects of each process variable on the final quality characteristic. A useful tool for doing this is response surface methodology (see Section 26 under Response/Surface Methodology).

2. Determine the optimum values for each process variable to meet quality requirements. For complex processes, this often requires statistically designed experiments (see Section 26, Design and Analysis of Experiments). Bemesderfer reports an experiment to *(a)* identify the key variables and *(b)* determine optimum machine settings for the drilling of holes using a laser beam. Five process variables were identified, the optimum settings determined, and the results presented in tables giving the "recipe" of settings for various values of hole diameter and material thickness. Each line of the table presents a recipe of the machine settings for drilling a particular size hole.

3. Determine the process capability. Complex processes often involve a variety of operating conditions, and the capability may vary considerably throughout the region of different conditions. The approach to process capability then often involves a formal planned experiment with the data analyzed by analysis of variance (see the previous discussion of the Taguchi method for an example of a specific technique).

4. Determine the capability of the measurement process. This is discussed in Section 18 under Error of Measurement.

5. Evaluate potential side effects. In one situation, a plating process was developed to provide protection against salt air corrosion. The process was defined in the specification, but a corrosion test was not required. After much discussion it was decided to hold up the process until a corrosion test was performed. A suitable test was defined, the parts failed, and the process had to be abandoned.

6. Make sure that each product characteristic has at least one process variable that can be used to adjust it. For example, a fluid temperature control was added to equipment because experiments proved that temperatures affected several product characteristics.

7. Prepare process specifications. The specifications must include one or more variables that can define the process including the means of setting, adjustment, and control.

8. Communicate the process information to production personnel. The means of communicating can run the gamut from manufacturing instructions to a formal course explaining in detail how the process must be run.

Bemesderfer reports that the eight steps have helped to prevent major problems on processes where it was applied, whereas a number of severe problems had been encountered in earlier processes.

Planning for the Process Capability Study. Prior to data collection, the following steps should be taken:

1. Choose the machine(s) to be used to establish capability. If the results of a study on one screw machine are to be used to define capability of all screw

machines of that type, the machine selected must be representative. In addition, a "machine" may actually consist of several machines within it; i.e., a machine with multiple spindles often shows different results for supposedly identical spindles.

2. Define the process conditions. For mechanical processes, examples are machine feeds and speeds, coolant, and cycle time; and for chemical processes, examples are temperature and pressure. Process capability numbers are meaningless unless they are related to a defined set of conditions that will repeat in the future.

3. Select a representative production worker. Where variability depends mainly on the worker, the study may really be one of worker variability.

4. Provide sufficient raw material for an uninterrupted study. A sample of about 50 units is preferred. Smaller samples are sometimes necessary, but they may not clearly show the statistical distribution of the characteristic under study.

5. Provide adequate gauging and a defined measurement method.

6. Make provisions for preserving the order in which the units are made.

7. Use materials or parts which are representative of normal production or shipments during the study.

8. To measure the inherent capability, avoid making adjustments during the study.

9. Measure to a minimum precision of one-tenth the specification tolerance, and use calibrated gauges.

10. Avoid unnecessary interruptions during the study.

11. Observe production under any abnormal conditions which might contribute to product variation.

12. Use tooling that is representative of production conditions.

13. Make sure the process is operating under its normal operating conditions unless the study is also investigating abnormalities (e.g., warmup during startup).

Ford Motor Company (1980) provides further detail on planning a study.

PROCESS CAPABILITY: APPLICATIONS

The most obvious use of process capability data during manufacturing planning is to predict whether the design tolerances can be met with the available processes. In addition there are other uses.

Choice among Alternative Processes. When capability data are available for several alternative processes, it becomes feasible to conduct cost analysis as a means of judging relative cost-effectiveness (see the discussion earlier in this section under Cost of Tolerances). This helps the design engineer to set specifications on a more rational basis; it also helps the manufacturing planner to assign equipment best suited to make particular products. Gibbons (1982) explains the statistical aspects of ranking several processes and identifying the best one.

Purchase of Machinery.   In some industries process capability (in terms of 6σ) is sometimes specified in purchase orders for machinery. The follow-through consists of two phases:

1. A demonstration of capability at the equipment manufacturer's facility. When the equipment is ready for shipment, the manufacturer invites the customer to observe a small production of parts which are used to demonstrate capability. The customer must approve this demonstration before shipment is authorized.

2. A capability demonstration at the customer's facility. This demonstration uses customer personnel and customer operating conditions. Payment is authorized after this final demonstration is approved.

The two phases serve important purposes. The first phase provides some early assurance on capability. It also prevents shipment of equipment with marginal capability. (Equipment, once delivered, tends to move into routine production even if performance is marginal.) The second phase assures that the equipment meets capability requirements under typical operating conditions.

Interrelation of Sequential Processes.   There are numerous situations in which several operation stages are interrelated. In such cases the planner must prepare a virtual product design for each stage of the operation (since the functional design defines only the end product). To prepare these intermediate designs means, for example, specifying how much material to provide for subsequent removal, uniformity of locating surfaces, etc. In such cases, knowledge of the capability of the respective operations greatly facilitates the planning.

Figure 16.13 shows an example of studies of related rough and finishing operations. The data make clear how much material is removed in finishing and what the final uniformity of the product is. With this knowledge and with knowledge of the final product specification, the prior operation can be planned with confidence. (In Figure 16.13, the rough process is more uniform than the finishing process for the charted characteristic. However, the finishing process is performed to

FIG. 16.13   Relation of sequential operations.

achieve high precision on a different characteristic. To do so, it must remove material.)

Other Uses of Capability Data.   Knowledge of process variation provided by capability data can yield still other applications. These include the evaluation of machine setup, establishing control limits, selection of workers, and determining the economic aim of a process. Feigenbaum (1983) discusses these applications.

ERROR-PROOFING THE PROCESS

An important element of manufacturing planning is the concept of designing the process to be error-free through "error-proofing." Where this type of design is economic, it can:

Prevent defects or nonconformities which fallible human beings would otherwise make through inadvertence

Make effective a knack which would otherwise require retraining many workers

Prevent defects or nonconformities resulting from carelessness, indifference, and similar reasons

Bypass complex analysis for causes, by finding a solution even though the cause of defects remains a mystery

Methods of Error-Proofing.   Some of the more usual forms are summarized below.

Fail-Safe Devices   These consist of

1. *Interlocking sequences:*   For example, to ensure that operation A is performed, the subsequent operation B locates from a hole which only operation A creates.
2. *Alarms and cutoffs:*   These are used to signal depletion of material supply, broken threads, or other abnormalities. The alarms are also fail-safe, i.e., they are silent only if all is well. If there is doubt, they sound anyhow.
3. *All-clear signals:*   These are designed to signal only if all remedial steps have been taken.
4. *Foolproof fixtures:*   These serve not only as fixtures but also as instruments to check the quality of work from preceding operations.
5. *Limiting mechanisms:*   For example, a slipping-type torque wrench to prevent overtightening.

Magnification of Senses.   Examples are:

1. Locating indexes and fixtures to outperform human muscle in precision of position
2. Optical magnification to improve visibility
3. Remote-control viewing (closed circuit television) to permit viewing of the process despite distance, heat, fumes, etc.

4. Multiple signals to improve likelihood of recognition and response, e.g., simultaneously ringing of bells and flashing of lights; audiovisual systems

5. Use of pictures in place of numbers (e.g., cards on the hood of a car undergoing assembly, to show pictorially the equipment needed for that car)

Redundancy. This consists of extra work performed purely as a quality safeguard. Examples are:

1. *Multiple-identity codings:* These are intended to prevent product mixups, e.g., color codes or other recognition schemes on drug labels, tool steel, aluminum sheet, etc.

2. *Redundant actions and approvals:* For example, the drug industry requires that formulation of recipes be prepared and approved by two registered pharmacists working independently.

3. *Audit review and checking procedures:* These are widely used to assure that the plans are being followed.

4. *Design for verification:* The product may include specially designed provision for verification (holes for viewing, coupons for test, etc). It also includes the rapidly growing use of nuclear tracers.

5. *Multiple test stations:* For example, a can-filling line may provide checks for empty cans through height gages, weighing scales, and air jets (for blowing empties off the conveyer).

Countdowns. These are arranged by structuring sensing and information procedures to parallel the operating procedures so that the operational steps are checked against the sensing and informational needs. A dramatic example is the elaborate countdown for the launching of a space vehicle. Surgical operations require countdowns, accounting for all materials and tools used (sponges, surgical instruments, etc.). A useful principle is to use an active rather than passive form of countdown. For example, a welder counts all welds *aloud* in progressing from spot to spot. When the count reaches 17 the last weld has been made—just as called for by the specification.

A useful principle in errorproofing is that of providing feedback to the worker, i.e., *the performance of the work conveys a message to the worker.* For example, a worker at a control panel pushes a switch and receives three feedbacks: the *feel* of the shape of the switch handle; the *sound* of an audible click signaling that the switch went all the way; the *sight* of a visual illumination of a specific color and shape.

In a classic study, Nakajo and Kume (1985) discuss five fundamental principles of errorproofing developed from an analysis of about 1000 examples collected mainly from assembly lines. The principles are elimination, replacement, facilitation, detection, and mitigation (see Table 16.7).

Error-Prone Systems. Beyond the errorproofing of individual operations, there may be need to errorproof entire systems which are error-prone. In one classic example, a naval vessel was almost lost due to conflict in standards for hydraulic versus electrical systems. A hydraulic valve increases energy when turned counterclockwise; an electrical valve does the opposite. A technician who had been upgraded from the hydraulics section of the ship to the electronics section became confused during an emergency and reverted back to the hydraulic standard, causing a near disaster.

Identifying such error-prone systems is seldom done from ordinary analysis.

TABLE 16.7 Summary of Errorproofing Principles

Principle	Objective	Example
Elimination	Eliminate the possibility of error	Redesign the process or product so that the task is no longer necessary
Replacement	Substitute a more reliable process for the worker	Use robotics (e.g., in welding or painting)
Facilitation	Make the work easier to perform	Color code parts
Detection	Detect the error before further processing	Develop computer software which notifies the worker when a wrong type of keyboard entry is made (e.g., alpha versus numeric)
Mitigation	Minimize the effect of the error	Utilize fuses for overloaded circuits

More usually, it requires a feedback from actual problems encountered, so that some analyst can find a common cause. At the least, the planner should keep informed on the failures which are occurring and on the causes and remedies. To an important degree, the new ideas for planning have their origin in remedies found during troubleshooting and especially during breakthroughs.

OTHER ELEMENTS OF EQUIPMENT AND WORK METHODS PLANNING

Planning for equipment goes beyond making a process capability study. Other factors include providing for process adjustments and for preventive maintenance.

Providing for Adjustments to Processes. Many processes require periodic adjustments. Manufacturing planners should (1) identify the process variables that must be monitored for possible adjustment, (2) provide rules for determining when an adjustment is necessary, (3) provide instructions for determining the amount of adjustment, and (4) provide a convenient physical means for making the adjustment.

Each product characteristic should have a process variable that can be used to adjust it. As corollaries to this principle, Bemesderfer (1979) proposes:

1. A single process variable should correspond to a single characteristic.
2. The degree of adjustment required during the process for a given change in the characteristic should be constant.
3. The range of possible adjustments must be consistent with the range of application need.
4. The setting accuracy must be consistent with the product tolerance requirements.
5. The controlling accuracy, once the process is set, must be consistent with the product tolerance requirements.

To the degree that these aims cannot be achieved, the process will be difficult for a worker to control.

Preventive Maintenance. Maintenance of equipment is generally recognized as essential, but pressures for production can result in delaying the scheduled preventive maintenance. Sometimes the delay is indefinite, the equipment breaks down, and the maintenance becomes corrective instead of preventive.

The planning should determine how often preventive maintenance is necessary, what form it should take, and how processes should be audited to assure that preventive maintenance schedules are followed.

In the event of objections to the proposed plan for preventive maintenance on the grounds of high cost, data on the cost of poor quality from the process can help to justify the maintenance plan.

PLANNING OF PERSONNEL REQUIREMENTS

This planning should identify the skills required during manufacturing and should provide criteria for selecting and training personnel to assure that those skills are provided. If the skills required are simple, the selection and training of personnel can be handled in ordinary ways; if the skills are complex, special approaches are needed. Examples of the latter include the skills required for welding, heat treatment wire bonding for integrated circuits, and other processes.

Critical processes often justify a program to formally "certify" workers. The certification program consists first of training workers in the specific skills required and then requiring them to demonstrate those skills in the manufacture of product. If the demonstration is satisfactory the worker becomes certified for that skill, e.g., welding. Periodic recertification is often required. Certification programs for workers are typically conducted by companies but are sometimes conducted by labor unions.

The training of workers should include thorough communication of any special process requirements or procedures. For simple processes the training can be done in conventional ways; for complex processes special approaches may be necessary. Bemesderfer (1979) describes how a 20-h course on an electrochemical machining process was given to a group of managers, professional personnel, and production workers as part of their training for using the process.

PLANNING FOR PROTECTION AND TRACEABILITY OF MATERIAL

The processing, transportation, and storage of product from raw materials through finished goods are potential sources of degradation of quality. Caplan (1980) discusses the prevention activities needed during receipt of purchased material, production operations, and post production. These include tasks to protect product from handling damage, environmental effects, transportation damage, and deterioration. In addition, nonconforming product should be segregated from good product throughout all phases. Finally, provision should be made for traceability.

Traceability.   The process design must provide for "traceability," i.e., the ability to preserve the identify of the product and its origins. Traceability is needed principally to:

1. Assure that only materials and components of adequate quality enter the final product, e.g., sterility in drug materials, adequate metallurgical composition and heat treatment in structural components.
2. Provide obvious identification to avoid mixup of products which otherwise look alike (these cases abound).
3. Permit recall of suspected product on a precise basis. Many of the huge recalls of automobiles in the 1960s were the result of inadequate traceability. The defective cars were only a small fraction of the total recalled.
4. Localize causes of failure and take remedial action at minimal cost.

There are still other uses of traceability—in inventory control, scheduling, etc. Some of these uses also affect quality. For example, use of materials on a first-in, first-out basis reduces the risk of quality deterioration due to perishable materials.

Batch Control.   The materials entering a batch are measured out in accordance with the recipe or formula. A lot number is assigned and a set of batch documents bearing that lot number is created. The "genealogy" of the input materials is recorded in the batch documents, as are the processing data and the product test data. For complex or critical products (e.g., aerospace vehicles, drugs) the batch documents may become a formidable collection. When the finished product is packaged, the lot number is imprinted on the individual containers and on the mass containers, i.e., cartons, drums, skids, etc. Subsequently, when the product is sold, it may be necessary to maintain a record of customers' names through the entire distribution chain.

Continuous Production, Low Unit Value.   In this form there is no natural lot, since materials of various genealogical origins keep entering the process at irregular intervals. In consequence, the designation for traceability becomes a *date code* and is based on the calendar dates of the occurrence of some cardinal event, e.g., packaging, final test, final assembly. The choice of time span is arbitrary, e.g., a week's production. (This arbitrary amount of production may still be called a "lot.") See Section 18, under The Nature of Lots of Product.

The documentation system for this arbitrary lot is quite similar to that used for the batch. Provision is made to record the history of the input materials, the process conditions prevailing during fabrication, and the test results. Due to the inherent nature of continuous production, traceability is now incomplete, since cutoff dates for introduction of new material batches or for process changes cannot be identified with precision. In consequence, any subsequent recalls or investigations must provide for this margin of error.

For some products, it may be feasible to show the date code (lot number) directly on the product. More usually, for reasons of cost (and available space), the date code appears only on the containers.

Continuous Production, High Unit Value.   In this form, the distinguishing feature is the unique designation of each unit of product by serial number. The documentation is then keyed to individual serial number or blocks of numbers.

The serial number is widely used in the manufacture of consumer goods as well as industrial equipment. Household appliances and home entertainment electronics use serial numbers, and the system of guarantees is keyed to these. Larger units (e.g., motor vehicles) may employ serial numbers for major subsystems (e.g., engines) as well as for the vehicle itself.

Traceability requires the coding of products. Among the methods in use are dating of products, "bar-code" symbols which appear as parallel bars and spaces on packages and which are read by computers, and laser coding which marks a code into virtually any material.

Attaining complete traceability for complex products (made of many materials and components and employing numerous processes) can be a formidable job, involving extensive paperwork, records, bonded stock rooms, physical markings on the products, etc. Yet this is actually done for many products in the drug, aerospace, and nuclear industries.

In commercial products complete traceability is limited to safety-oriented qualities and to those components which are decisive in achieving overall fitness for use. For example, in one semiconductor product line the component chiefly responsible for final product quality was the semiconducting wafer. The company therefore structured the traceability system around the wafer lot numbers. The finished products were then coded with the wafer lot number rather than with a weekly dating code, which might involve the same code number for products made from multiple wafer lots (Staffiery, 1975).

Caplan (1980, pp. 118–120) identifies five techniques used in a material tracking program which has much in common with traceability. See also the discussion in Section 20 under Configuration Management.

PLANNING OF PROCESS ENVIRONMENT

For simple products the necessary process environment can be achieved by good housekeeping. Without adequate housekeeping there can be catastrophies, e.g., mating parts abnormally wearing because of foreign material in a lubricant, or fumes during processing causing discoloration of products.

Complex products are more sensitive to environmental conditions that can cause contamination of product by chlorides, acids, shop grit, microscopic skin particles, nonvolatile residues, fibers from work sheet papers, and other conditions. For example, some companies must control airborne particles such that products are free from particles that are larger than 20 millionths of an inch. Also, rigid control of temperature and humidity in electronics manufacture can be critical in order to control electrostatic discharge (Downer, 1983).

The techniques of assuring a clean environment include a cleaning of air, selection of tools, flooring, containers, paper and paint, special clothing for personnel, and other methods. For example, in the control of electrostatic discharge, simple tools such as pliers and side cutters can be a problem if they are not equipped with plastic handles.

The control of environmental conditions is often referred to as a "clean-room" program. Harrington (1981) recommends that the following items be included in a clean-room specification for an electronics plant:

1. Contamination level
2. Temperature range
3. Humidity level

4. Pressure differential—positive pressure out of the clean room
5. Dressing area adjacent to the clean room with sink, disposal
6. Ceiling tile
7. Types of paper used in the room

Harrington further recommends that the certification procedure for a clean room include:

1. Complete air flow measurments
2. Leak testing of all filters
3. Measurement of temperature and humidity throughout the area
4. Differential pressure measurements
5. Initial janitorial cleaning accomplished according to a separate specification
6. Complete particle count measurements conducted in all areas, to numerical requirements
7. Deviations corrected and verified by measurement
8. Complete data recorded for all of the above steps

The pharmaceutical and other industries must meet stringent government regulations ("good manufacturing practice") to control the manufacturing environment.

Marguglio (1981) discusses the role of the quality function in compliance with environmental program requirements.

OVERALL REVIEW OF MANUFACTURING PLANNING

Review of the proposed process can most effectively be accomplished through preproduction trials and runs. Techniques such as failure mode, effect, and criticality analysis can provide an even earlier warning before any product is made. Checklists for review of proposed processes can also be useful. These approaches are discussed below.

Preproduction Trials. Because the manufacturing plan starts as a mental concept, it will be "scaled up" many orders of magnitude if it goes into large-scale production. There is great risk in going directly into production from the conceptual plan primarily because of the risk of quality failures. To reduce this risk, companies make use of trial production lots (called "pilot plant production," "preproduction," etc.) to discover deficiencies in the planning and to remedy them before going into full-scale production. In some industries this concept is formalized into regular phases of scaling up.

The scaling up of production is actually a continuation of the scaling up which takes place from product design concept to prototype or model construction and test. The adequacy of the full-scale manufacturing plan cannot be judged from the record of models made in the model shop. In the model shop the basic purpose is to prove engineering feasibility; in the production shop the purpose is to meet standards of quality, cost, and delivery. The model-shop machinery, tools, personnel, supervision, motivation, etc., are all different from the corresponding situations in the production shop.

Tool Tryout At the work-station level, as new tools are completed, they are subjected to a tryout procedure which, in most companies, is highly formalized. The tryout consists of producing enough product from the new tool to demonstrate that it can meet quality standards under shop conditions.

These formalized tryouts conclude with the execution of a formal document backed up by supporting data, which always include the quality data. The release of the tool for full-scale production is contingent on the approval of this tryout document.

Limited Trial Lots. Beyond the tryouts at individual work stations, there is need for collective tryouts. These require trial production lots, which must be scheduled for the prime purpose of proving in the manufacturing process. The trial lot is usually made in the regular production shop and provides an extensive preview of the problems which will be encountered in large-scale production. In the process industries the equivalent intermediate scaling up is the "pilot plant." It is widely used to provide the essential information (on quality, costs, productivity, etc.) needed to determine whether and how to go into full-scale production.

Software Verification. Software used with a process requires a tryout just like new tools—with the same degree of formality and approval process.

Experimental Lots. The trial lot concept provides opportunities for planners to test out alternatives, and they often combine the concept of experimentation with that of proving in the nonexperimental portion of the trial.

Attainment of good process yields is one of the most important purposes of experimental lots. These experiments can make use of all the techniques discussed in Section 26, Design and Analysis of Experiments, and in the various statistical sections.

Preproduction Runs. Ideally, product lots should be put through the entire system, with the deficiencies found and corrected before going into full-scale production. In practice, companies usually make some compromises with this ideal approach. The "preproduction" may be merely the first of the regular production, but with special provision for prompt feedback and correction of errors as found. Alternatively, the preproduction may be limited to those features of product and process design which are so new that prior experience cannot reliably provide a basis for good risk taking. While some companies do adhere to a strict rule of proving in the product and process through preproduction lots, the more usual approach is one of flexibility, in which the use of preproduction lots depends on:

1. The extent to which the product embodies new or untested quality features
2. The extent to which the design of the manufacturing process embodies new or untried machines, tools, etc.
3. The amount and value of product which will be out in the field before there is conclusive evidence of the extent of process, product, and use difficulties

These trials sometimes include "production validation tests" to ensure that the full-scale process can meet the design intent. Figure 16.14 shows an example from Ford Motor Company (1972).

Failure Mode, Effect, and Criticality Analysis for Processes. A failure mode, effect, and criticality analysis is useful in analyzing the proposed design of a product (see Section 13 under Failure Mode, Effect, and Criticality Analysis).

PRODUCTION VALIDATION PLAN AND REPORT   #3

SYSTEM __1.00 Body__   ASSEMBLY __Door Latch-Diab.__   PROGRAM __1.14-21812-A__   PAGE __1__ OF __3__

SUBSYSTEM __1.14 Locks Handles & Mechs.__   COMP __N/A__   DES LEVEL __AA__   DES. ENGR. __S. Martin__   CONC'R __W.R.__

TEST NAME SOURCE	ACCEPTANCE CRITERIA	TEST RESULTS	DES.	S/SIZE		REL. ACCEP. CRIT.		TIMING		REMARKS
				REQ.	TEST	REQ.	ACTUAL	SCH.	ACTUAL	
Life Cycle ES-Diab-652181 AB	35,000 cycles minimum at 650# rebound and 250#	21 completed 120,000 cycles	AA	21	21	$P_{.90} = .90$	$P_{.90} = .90$	7-15-71	7-20-71	
Static Strength FMVSS (ES)	Prim. Sec. longitude 3000 2250 transverse 4000 2700	-3σ greater than min. strength req'd (see Problem Plots)	AA	60	60	-3σ> req't.	-3σ> req't.	7-24-71	7-20-71	
Corrosion Resistance (ES) 48-hour salt spray	Operating efforts must not increase 25% over drawing specifications	+ 3σ less than max. effort allowed (see Problem Plots)	AA	40	40	+3σ< req't.	+3σ< req't.	7-30-71	8-15-71	

FIG. 16.14   Product validation plan and report.

16.43

The same technique can dissect the potential failure modes and their effects on a proposed process. Ishiyama (1977) discusses the application of the failure mode and effects analysis technique to both product design and manufacturing processes in the automobile industry.

The fault tree analysis technique is also useful in analyzing a design (see Section 13 under Fault Tree Analysis). Proposed manufacturing processes can be analyzed with this same technique. Raheja (1982) discusses this approach. Fault tree analysis can help to identify areas of a process that require errorproofing.

Checklist for Review of Manufacturing Planning. The review of manufacturing planning for quality should be made in accordance with previously defined criteria. An example for a complex electronics manufacturing facility is discussed below (Harrington, 1981).

The review takes place at four stages or levels. At Level I, a product is being considered for capitalization. Parts from the process will not be shipped to customers. Qualification at this level requires the following:

1. Controlled engineering documents.
2. The process plan must demonstrate good manufacturing and quality practices including:
   a. The development pilot line description and process instructions must be released and the change level controlled.
   b. All changes in process activity and documentation must be reviewed by Quality Assurance.
   c. Quality must certify the functional level tester for each component and subassembly.
   d. Inspectors from the Quality Department must verify the results of all final functional tests on a piece-by-piece basis.
   e. An evaluation by Quality Assurance indicates that there are no major problems that cannot be resolved.

Level II is also a development pilot line qualification, but the parts may later be classified as customer shippable. Level II certification requires:

1. All engineering documents must be formally released and controlled.
2. The following additional process controls beyond Level I are required:
   a. Manufacturing is to avoid any large dollar commitment on tool design and procurement negotiation because the parts design is still under review.
   b. Formal release process routings are available and controlled.
   c. Each operation must be certified by Quality Assurance.
   d. Critical development manufacturing tools and test equipment must be certified.
   e. Certain components used will be classified as customer shippable.
   f. Development level product standards must be identified and controlled.
   g. Incoming components and materials must be processed through receiving inspection.
   h. An in-process quality assurance audit plan must be available.

3. A series of qualification lots must be processed through the development pilot line with the following preconditions:

   a. All supporting documents must have completed the sign-off cycle.

   b. Operators must be trained.

   c. Yield targets must be established and documented.

   d. Lot size must be large enough to get an adequate evaluation of process yields.

   e. Equipment must be calibrated.

   f. Head and disk development level standards must be used with supporting documentation.

   g. Purchased parts must be inspected to specification.

In a Level III situation a manufacturing production facility is set up to produce mass quantities. The requirements here are shown in Figure 16.15. A qualification lot is also required.

Whereas Level III qualifies a single production line, Level IV qualifies a complete manufacturing facility. The qualification consists of process certification, qualification lots, and evaluation of "technical exposures" (conditions that could impact on performance).

The requirements for process certification include:

1. Documentation, including engineering software, maintenance procedures, quality program plan, and inspection specification and training requirements

2. Test/process equipment, equipment accepted by maintenance, long-term precision drift evaluations completed, extremes of settings evaluated, manufacturing training program implemented, equipment certification and correlation

3. Process capability studies completed, process variation analysis completed, process controls totally implemented, in-process audit inspection and control program implemented, quality reporting system implemented, process compatibility assessment completed

4. Process yields progressing, process quality goals being achieved, first customer ship performance target levels being measured, reliability and environmental testing performed, outgoing quality levels being met

A Level IV qualification lot is processed with requirements similar to those under Level III, and the results at the two levels are compared.

Finally, an independent audit is made of the quality and manufacturing programs to identify any outstanding issues related to product performance, process variation, manufacturability assessment, and process stability.

Role of Quality Assurance in Review of Manufacturing Planning. Bell (1983) describes the role of a quality assurance function in reviewing the quality-related aspects of manufacturing planning for an electronics manufacturing facility. Prior to instituting a formal system of review, 7 percent of the manufacturing planning was defective (based on a page count of planning documentation). Some of the problems were essentially documentation errors, but other errors could result in defective product. A 40-h training program for reviewers was developed to make the reviews effective (Table 16.8).

LIII PROCESS CERTIFICATION CHECKLIST

ACTIVITY

I. DOCUMENTATION

1. All Development documents released to Manufacturing
2. All Manufacturing documents released
3. All Quality documents released
4. Manufacturing training requirements released
5. Four-way signoff in practice
6. Software documented
7. Test equipment and tool prints complete
8. Workmanship standards released
9. Outgoing quality levels documented
10. Critical components list complete
11. Quality inspector training requirements released
12. Stress test specifications released
13. Process compatibility plan complete
14. Quality plan updated
15. Rework procedures complete
16. In-process quality defect targets established

LIII PROCESS CERTIFICATION CHECK LIST

ACTIVITY

II. TESTS/PROCESS EQUIPMENT

1. Equipment evaluated by Manufacturing engineer and Test engineer
2. Quality certified equipment
3. Calibration intervals established
4. Maintenance and calibration program in place and working
5. Equipment testing to specifications
6. Safety approval on all major equipment
7. Products standards supported by the products standard lab
8. Added control over art effects standards
9. Receiving inspection tool and certified
10. Test equipment software level control
11. Process that manufactures special tools is certified

III. MANUFACTURING OPERATIONS

1. Qualified operators and inspectors used to mfg. product
2. Operators are following the documentation
3. Adequacy of the manufacturing procedures and documents have been evaluated by Quality Assurance

LIII PROCESS CE

ACTIVITY

III. MANUFACTURING OPERATIONS Contin.

4. Tools were built to print
5. Brass tag tools and equipment are on the recall cycle
6. Only mfg. tools & equipment used on the mfg. floor
7. Nonconforming materials controls in place
8. Class room operating to specification
9. Hard tooling requirements and documented & understood
10. Controls over water, air, temperature, humidity, etc., are adequate
11. Shipping containers & packaging containers have been evaluated
12. Adequate controls over materials used in mfg. are in place
13. Mfg. data system is adequate to report defects and yields
14. Quality engineering, process inspection, and control program implemented
15. Mfg. process is stable
16. Clean controls in place
17. Quality Assurance failure analysis system working
18. Added controls over experiment and sent-ahead orders

FIG. 16.15 Process certification checklist.

As a result of the review activity, the errors in manufacturing planning dropped to 3 percent and defects due to poor planning were eliminated.

An important but often missing element in manufacturing planning is the input of line production personnel. A steel company (Jones and Laughlin Company, 1984) obtains this input through a formal meeting in which manufacturing personnel review the preliminary draft of a process control standards handbook. The meeting, which is held off site, is chaired by a department superintendent. Included on the agenda are a videotape presentation on the review process, small group discussions on the proposed process, and preparation of revisions.

See also Section 8 under Quality Audit by Upper Managers.

RTIFICATION CHECKLIST

LIII PROCESS CERTIFICATION CHECKLIST			
ACTIVITY	COMMENTS	VERIFIED BY:	DATE
IV. PRODUCT			
1. No Q. level components used			
2. Traceability system in place			
3. Incoming parts controlled and purchased from approved vendors			
4. Product meeting performance specification			
5. Product meeting quality and yield levels			

FIG. 16.15   *(Continued)*

Use of a "Lessons Learned" System in Reviewing Plans.

As applied to manufacturing planning, this system captures and documents past problems in a readily retrievable form to use in the review of plans for a new process. The documentation of each lesson includes key words, a problem description, actions taken along with results, and references for further details.

Sources of problems include production activities, complaints, product holds and recalls, and test results which reveal cause-effect relationships or identify important product or process parameters. Criteria are defined for deciding if a problem should be entered in the system.

To use the system, the planner reviews the key word index and selects those

TABLE 16.8   Quality Planning Review

1st Day	*3rd Day (cont.)*
Introduction	Tool order to engineering drawing
Background—purpose	verification
Government requirements	Manufacturing aids
Division requirements	Other
Planning manual—overview	Special requirements
Types of planning (planning levels)	Controlled components
Planning formats	Traceability
Content of complete planning package	Lot-date codes
	Serialization
2nd Day	
Configuration verification	*4th Day*
Drawing change	Detailed review—continued: visual aids
Specification change	Verification of clarity
Parts list—alternative parts	Compliance with engineering design
Planning change control	Adequacy for level of personnel
Traceability—history jackets	Nonambiguous
Verification of change	Traceability of specific operations
Effect on next use application	Control—change authority
Manufacturing change orders	Planning change requests
	How initiated
3rd Day	When planning changes required
Detailed review techniques	Effect of shop liaison requests
Specific operations	Quality assurance role
Logical sequence	
Adequacy	*5th Day*
Sequence of inspection operations	Planning review documentation
No. of inspection operations (too	Need for objective evidence
many/too few)	Data collection
Test requirements	Reporting/charting
Customer requirements	Trend evaluation
Customer inspection/witness	Review/feedback to planning
Referenced items	department
Workmanship standards	Corrective action
Manufacturing process standards	Effectiveness evaluation
Equipment operation instructions	Post review audits
Test procedures	Final critique
Tooling/fixtures	

words which seem relevant. Next, the data base is searched for entries with the selected key words, and the references are obtained from the listed originators.

Werner and Zetzsche (1982) discuss the concept of an "experience-return flow-store" as a means of using past experiences in starting up and operating large chemical plants. The technique uses catalogs and notched cards to document about 50,000 items of information.

PLANNING PROCESS CONTROLS

The process specification, procedures, and instruction sheets prepared by the planners are the software of manufacturing planning. Their purpose is to inform the production people how to set up, run, and regulate the processes so that the result will be good product. Conversely, the production people should follow these plans. Otherwise, good product might not be the result.

Many companies institute process controls to provide assurance that the plans will in fact be followed. There are several kinds of these controls, and they are established by some combination of manufacturing engineers, quality engineers, production supervisors, and workers. The precise combination varies widely from company to company.

Process control is based on the feedback loop as discussed in Section 6 under The Feedback Loop. The steps for planning manufacturing process controls follow closely the universal approach for use of the feedback loop.

Control Criteria.   While execution of the control plan is typically delegated to the work force, it is common to impose criteria to be met before the process is allowed to run. These criteria are imposed in three main areas:

1. *Setup criteria:*   For some processes the start of production must await meeting setup criteria (e.g., five pieces in a row must test "good"). In critical cases this form of early warning assurance may require that a supervisor or inspector independently approve the setup.

2. *Running criteria:*   For many processes there is need to check the running periodically to decide whether the process should continue to run or should stop for readjustment. The criteria here relate to such things as frequency of check, size of sample, manner of sample selection, tests to be made, tolerances to be met.

3. *Equipment maintenance criteria:*   In some processes the equipment itself must be closely controlled if quality is to be maintained. This type of control is preventive in nature and is quite different in concept from repair of equipment breakdowns. This preventive form of equipment maintenance includes a carefully drawn set of criteria which define the essential performance characteristics of the equipment. Then, on a scheduled basis (strictly adhered to), the equipment is checked against these criteria. In the United States this aspect of equipment maintenance is not well developed, and there is need to take positive steps to strengthen it.

Relation to Product Controls.   Process controls are sometimes confused with product controls but there is a clear difference. Process controls are associated with the decision: Should the process run or stop? Product controls are associated with the decision: Does the product conform to specification? Usually both of these decisions require input derived from sampling and measuring the product. (It is seldom feasible to measure the process directly.) However, the method of selecting the samples is often different. Production usually makes the "process run or stop" decision and tends to sample in ways which tell the most about the process. Inspection usually (in the United States) makes the product conformance decision and tends to sample in ways which tell the most about the product.

This difference in sampling can easily result in different conclusions on the "same" product. Production commonly does its sampling on a scheduled basis and at a time when the product is still traceable to specific streams of the process. Inspection often does its sampling on a random basis and at a time when traceability has begun to blur.

Despite the different purposes being served, it is feasible for the two departments to do joint planning. Usually they are able to establish their respective controls so that both purposes are well served and so that the respective data reinforce each other.

Control Systems and the Concept of Dominance.   Specific systems for controlling characteristics can be related to the underlying factors that dominate a process. The main categories of dominance include those discussed below.

1. *Setup-dominant:*   Such processes have high reproducibility and stability for the entire length of the batch to be made. Hence the control system emphasizes verification of the setup before production proceeds. Examples of such processes are drilling, labeling, heat sealing, printing, and presswork.

2. *Time-dominant:*   Such a process is subject to progressive change with time (wear of tools, depletion of reagent, machine heating up). The associated control system will feature a schedule of process checks with feedback to enable the worker to make compensatory changes. Screw machining, volume filling, wood carding, and papermaking are examples of time-dominant processes.

3. *Component-dominant:*   Here the quality of the input materials and components is the most influential. The control system is strongly oriented toward supplier relations along with incoming inspection and sorting of inferior lots. Many assembly operations and food formulation processes are component-dominant.

4. *Worker-dominant:*   For such processes quality depends mainly on the skill and knack possessed by the production worker. The control system emphasizes such features as training courses and certification for workers, errorproofing, and worker and quality rating. Workers are dominant in processes such as welding, painting, and order picking.

5. *Information-dominant:*   These are usually processes in which the job information undergoes frequent change. Hence the control system places emphasis on the accuracy and up-to-dateness of the information provided to the worker (and everyone else). Examples include order editing and "travelers" used in job shops.

The different types of dominance differ also in the tools used for process control. Table 16.9 lists the forms of process dominance along with the usual tools used for process control. Additonal discussion of control tools as related to precess dominance is included in Section 17 under Ability to Regulate.

Evaluation of Proposed Control Tools.   Proposed control tools need to be evaluated for both deficiencies and excesses. One health care manufacturer uses "process failure analysis" to analyze proposed control tools. A flowchart is first prepared to identify the elements of the manufacturing system and the output. Possible failure mechanisms are listed and the control system is analyzed in terms of:

1. *The failure:*   probability of occurrence, criticality, effects, etc.
2. *The measurement:*   method, frequency, documentation, etc.
3. *The standard of comparison:*   selection, limits, etc.
4. *The feedback:*   method, content, speed

The proposed control for each failure mechanism is analyzed and classified as deficient, appropriate, or excessive.

TABLE 16.9 Control Tools for Forms of Process Dominance

Setup-dominant	Time-dominant	Component-dominant	Worker-dominant	Information-dominant
Inspection of process conditions	Periodic inspection	Supplier rating	Acceptance inspection	Computer generated information
First piece inspection	$\overline{X}$ chart	Incoming inspection	p chart	"Active" checking of documentation
Lot plot	Median chart	Prior operation control	c chart	Barcodes and electronic entry
Precontrol	$\overline{X}$ and R chart	Acceptance inspection	Operator scoring	Process audits
Narrow limit gaging	Precontrol	Mockup evaluation	Recertification of workers	
Attribute visual inspection	Narrow-limit gaging		Process audits	
	p chart			
	Process variables check			
	Automatic recording			
	Process audits			

16.51

PLANNING FOR EVALUATION OF PRODUCT

The planning must recognize the need for formal evaluation of product to determine its suitability for the marketplace. Three activities are involved:

1. Measuring the product for conformance to specifications
2. Taking action on the nonconforming product
3. Communicating information on the disposition of nonconforming product

These activities are discussed in Section 18 under Inspection and Test. However, these activities impinge on the manufacturing planning process. For example, several alternatives are possible for determining conformance, i.e., to have it done by production workers, by an independent inspection force, or by a combination of both. Second, the disposition of nonconforming product involves participation by production personnel, in such forms as segregation of product in the shop, and documentation. Finally, the communication of the decisions should include feedback to Production.

QUALITY INFORMATION EQUIPMENT

The term "quality information equipment" (QIE), as used here, designates the physical apparatus which makes measurements of products and processes, processes the information, and feeds the information back for decision making.
The development cycle for the QIE must plan for product effectiveness parameters including:

1. Reliability
2. Maintainability (calibration, repair, preventive maintenance, and so forth)
3. Accuracy and precision
4. Human factors aspects (ease of use, errorproofing to prevent errors)
5. Interfaces of the QIE with the product being measured to assure swift, sure connections and disconnect
6. Design of the QIE to withstand use environments
7. Safety
8. Skill levels available versus requirements of the QIE
9. Modes on input and output
10. Procedures for formal evaluation of the QIE (e.g., acceptance tests of hardware and software)
11. Operating instructions and training of personnel
12. Tie-in of the QIE with the overall data processing system

The extensive interdepartmental effect of QIE makes it evident that the planner must follow the QIE project through to the end. The design must meet exacting, complex criteria; the construction must be responsive to that design. Most important, the design must then be proved out in trials conducted under actual use conditions.
The evolution of the automated process (see below) and the numerically controlled machine has required corresponding evolution in QIE.

AUTOMATED MANUFACTURING

In many manufacturing facilities, the computer is leading the march to automation. Several terms have become important:

Computer-integrated manufacturing (CIM):   This is the process of applying the computer in a planned fashion from design through manufacturing and shipping of the product. CIM has a broad scope.

Computer-aided manufacturing (CAM):   This is the process in which the computer is used to plan and control the work of specific equipment.

Computer-aided design (CAD):   This is the process by which the computer assists in the creation or modification of a design.

Some useful references are available. The June 1984 issue of *Quality Progress* describes the "factory of the future." An introductory book by Harrington (1979) discusses conventional manufacturing, CAD, CAM, application of the computer to scheduling and control, and other topics. Krouse (1982) provides an introduction to some of the technologies of CAD/CAM including geometric modeling, finite analysis, machine tool controls, and artificial intelligence. Goldhar and Jelinek (1983) explain how CAM can automate not only high-volume operations on a few products but also low-volume requirments on many products. Wilson (1983) describes an automated manufacturing planning system for aircraft production and how quality assurance inputs are integrated in the planning. Section 27 under New-Process Quality discusses the role of the computer in process planning and control.

Benefits to Product Quality.   Automation may provide as large an increase in factory productivity as did the introduction of electric power. Product quality will benefit in several ways:

1. Automation can eliminate some of the monotonous or fatiguing tasks that cause errors by human beings. For example, when a manual seam welding operation was turned over to a robot, the scrap rate plunged from 15 percent to zero (Kegg, 1985).

2. Process variation can be reduced by the automatic monitoring and continuous adjustment of process variables.

3. An important source of process troubles can be reduced, i.e., the number of machine setups.

4. Machines can not only automatically measure product, but can record, summarize, and display the data for line production operators and staff personnel. Feedback to the worker can be immediate, thus providing an early warning of impending troubles.

5. With cellular manufacture (see below), tracing a part to its origin is simplified, and this facilitates accountability for quality.

6. With CAD, the quality engineer can provide inputs early in the design stage. When a design is placed in the computer, the quality engineer can review that design over and over again and keep abreast of design changes.

Achieving these benefits requires a spectrum of concepts and techniques. Three of these are discussed below: the key functions of CIM, group technology, and flexible manufacturing systems.

Key Functions of Computer Integrated Manufacturing. To integrate the computer from design through shipping involves a network of functions and associated computer systems. Willis and Sullivan (1984) describe this in terms of eight functions (Table 16.10). Such a CIM system rests on a foundation of data bases covering both manufacturing data and product data.

Group Technology. Group technology is the process of examining all items manufactured by a company to identify those with sufficient similarity that a common design or manufacturing plan can be used. The aim is to reduce the number of new designs or new manufacturing plans. In addition to the savings in resources, group technology can improve both the quality of design and the quality of conformance by using proven designs and manufacturing plans. Gunn (1982, p. 121) reports that in many companies "only 20 percent of the parts initially thought to require new designs actually need them; of the remaining new

TABLE 16.10   Eight Key CIMS Functions

Function	Description	Typical hardware
1. Design and drafting (CAD/CAM)	Automated design and drafting of products and computer-aided manufacturing	Minicomputer, mainframe
2. Production scheduling and control	Master scheduling coupled with material management and requirements planning from procurement to shipment	Host mainframe
3. Process automation	Direct numerical control of processes, inspection and testing; utilization of robotics, flexible manufacturing systems, and other automated equipment to perform certain processes and direct shop floor activities	Programmable controller, minicomputer, mainframe
4. Process control	Sensing of equipment activities and reporting of conditions that require operator intervention	Programmable controller
5. Material handling and storage	Automated storage and retrieval of finished and purchased parts based on picking schedules and requisitions	Minicomputer
6. Maintenance scheduling and control	Preventive maintenance scheduling and reporting of equipment downtime by cause; spare parts inventory management and usage reporting	Host mainframe
7. Distribution management	Order processing, sales reporting, and invoicing coupled with warehousing and transportation	Host mainframe
8. Finance and accounting	Reporting of operating results, forecasting of future results, and analysis of costs	Host mainframe

Source: Willis and Sullivan, 1984, p. 32.

parts 40 percent could be built from an existing design and the other 40 percent could be created by modifying an existing design."

Each item is coded according to a variety of characteristics such as shape, material, tolerances, finish, and required production operations. After coding, parts with similar characteristics are sorted into groups. Phillipp (1982) shows an example of an 18-digit coding system:

Form	4 digits
Dimensions	4 digits
Tolerances	2 digits
Material	2 digits
Machine	2 digits
Process	2 digits
Inspection	2 digits

The process planner for a new part can retrieve a list of old parts that have some of the same characteristics. Planning for the new part can then simply specify the process for an old part with any differences noted.

Location of the production machines can also benefit from the group technology concept. Machines are grouped according to the parts they make and can be sorted into cells of machines, each cell producing one or several part families (thus "cellular manufacture").

Flexible Manufacturing System.   A flexible manufacturing system (FMS) is a group of several computer controlled machine tools linked by a materials handling system and a mainframe computer to completely process a group of parts. The FMS can be programmed to suit varying production requirements and can be reprogrammed to accommodate design changes or new parts. This is in contrast to a fixed automation system which follows a preordained sequence.

Kegg (1984) summarizes the evolution of a flexible system in six steps:

1. The basic elements are a machine and an operator. Adjustments to the process are continually made by the operator.

2. Electronic intelligence is added in the form of computer control. This involves programming ("numerically controlling") the machine tools. A complicated series of operations can be repeated with the push of a single button.

3. Automatic devices for tool changing and workpiece loading and unloading are added.

4. Sensing devices are added to the machine that allow adjustments to be made automatically. Batch operations can then be performed continuously without human intervention.

5. The work cell is linked with other areas of the plant which supply workpieces, tooling, and other materials and information. The operator becomes a manager of a computer controlled system.

6. Finally, integration of all of the functions from design and manufacturing planning to inventory control, scheduling, and shop floor control is achieved by having all of the systems communicate with each other automatically.

Typically, the individual machines are robots or other types of numerically controlled machine tools, each of which is run by a microcomputer. Several of these numerically controlled tools are linked by a minicomputer and then several of these minicomputers tie into the mainframe computer. Gunn (1982, p. 128) shows an example of a flexible manufacturing system.

Quality Planning for Automated Processes.   Planning for automated processes requires special precautions:

1. Changes in the product design may be necessary to facilitate automated manufacture. For example, robots have difficulty picking up a randomly oriented part in a bin, but a redesign of the part may solve the problem.
2. Automated manufacturing equipment is complex and has the reliability and maintainability problems of most complex products. Design planning and evaluation tools (see Section 13, Product Development) should be a part of the design process for automated equipment.
3. All software must be thoroughly tested (see Section 14, Software Development). In a survey of problems with numerically controlled tapes, Flavell (1983) classified the reasons for changes in the computer programs (Table 16.11). Note that 24.1 percent of the changes were due to programming technique or program errors.

TABLE 16.11   Analysis of Problems with Numerical Control Programs

Reason for program change	Percentage of changes
Dimensional error	19.4
Programming technique	18.1
Tooling problems	12.1
Speeds and feeds	9.1
Setup problems	8.4
Machine function errors	7.8
Stock allowance	7.7
Miscellaneous program errors	6.0
Engineering change	3.5
Routing change	2.5
Miscellaneous	4.7
Total	100.0

4. Knowledge of process capability, precise setup of equipment, and preventive maintenance are essential.
5. When feasible, on-line automatic inspection should be integrated with the operation. With manual operation of a process, the worker can observe a defect and take action. Automated processes can have mechanical, programming, or other problems that can create a disaster if not detected early.
6. Special provisions are necessary for measurement. This includes the need for rugged gages, cleaning of the measured and measuring surfaces, reliability of gages, and adherence to calibration schedules.
7. Some personnel will have greater responsiblity under automated manufacture. This is particularly so as we give minicomputers and microcomputers to workers for data entry and process control. All of this means training.

The potential benefits of the automated factory will require significant time and resources for planning.

REFERENCES

Amsden, R. T., Butler, H. E., and Amsden, D. M. (1986). *SPC Simplified; Practical Steps to Quality.* UNIPUB, Whiteplains, NY.

Bell, L. Ferris (1983). "Quality Verification of Manufacturing Planning." *ASQC Quality Congress Transactions,* Milwaukee, pp. 70–75.

Bemesderfer, John L. (1979). "Approving a Process for Production." *Journal of Quality Technology,* vol. 11, no. 1, pp. 1–12.

Byrne, Diane M. and Taguchi, Shin (1986). "The Taguchi Approach to Parameter Design." *ASQC Quality Congress Transactions,* Milwaukee, pp. 168–177.

Caplan, Frank (1980). *The Quality System.* Chilton Book Company, Radnor, PA.

Carpenter, Ben H. (1982). "Control of Copper Ore Roasting Exit Gas Quality." *ASQC Quality Congress Transactions,* Milwaukee, pp. 748–755.

Caswell, A. R. and Zimmer, J. D. (1979). "Flow Chart Analysis of Pharmaceutical Products." *ASQC Technical Conference Transactions,* Milwaukee, pp. 161–167.

Deere and Company (1983). *Classification of Characteristics.* John Deere Standard JDE-D46, Moline, IL.

Downer, Winston C. (1983). "Management's Commitment to QA Includes ESD Control." *ASQC Quality Congress Transactions,* Milwaukee, pp. 76–81.

Feigenbaum, Armand V. (1983). *Total Quality Control,* 3rd ed. McGraw-Hill, New York.

Flavell, Norman L. (1983). "Error Rate of First Run NC Programs." *20th Annual Meeting and Technical Conference,* Numerical Control Society, Cincinnati, pp. 34–46.

Ford Motor Company (1972). *Reliability Methods—Manufacturing Planning for Reliability—Module XX.* Dearborn, MI, p. 11.

Ford Motor Company (1980). *Study and Analysis of Machine, Equipment and Process Capability.* Manufacturing Procedure VII-b-3, Dearborn, MI.

Ford Motor Company (1980). *Machine Capability Studies.* Booklet 80-01-250, Dearborn, MI.

Fukuda, Ryuji (1981). "Introduction to the CEDAC." *Quality Progress,* November, pp. 14–19.

Gibbons, Jean D. (1982). "Methods for Selecting the Best Process." *Journal of Quality Technology,* vol. 14, no. 2, pp. 80–88.

Goldhar, Joel D. and Jelinek, Mariann (1983). "Plan for Economies of Scope." *Harvard Business Review,* November–December, pp. 141–148.

Gunn, Thomas G. (1982). "The Mechanization of Design and Manufacturing," *Scientific American,* September, p. 121.

Harrington, H. James (1981). *Process Qualification—Manufacturing's Insurance Policy.* IBM Technical Report 02.901, San Jose, CA.

Harrington, Joseph, Jr. (1979). *Computer Integrated Manufacturing.* Robert E. Krieger, Huntington, NY.

Hunter, William G. and Kartha, C. P. (1977). "Determining the Most Profitable Target Value for a Production Process." *Journal of Quality Technology,* vol. 9, no. 4, October, pp. 176–181.

Ishiyama, Takayuki (1977). "On System for Applying FMEA, An Outline of Its Application." *Reports of Statistical Applications and Research,* Japanese Union of Scientists and Engineers, vol. 24, no. 3, pp. 40–50.

Jones and Laughlin Company (1984). *The Integrated Quality System: How to Develop a Process Control Map of Key Control Variables.* Pittsburgh.

Kane, Victor E. (1986). "Process Capability Indices." *Journal of Quality Technology,* vol. 18, no. 1, January, pp. 41–52.

Kaneko, Hiromi (1977). "Plant Reliability Improvement." *Reports of Statistical Applications and Research,* Japanese Union of Scientists and Engineers, vol. 24, no. 3, pp. 68–77.

Kearney, Francis J. (1984). "Management of Product Quality without A Quality Department." *ASQC Quality Congress Transactions,* Milwaukee, pp. 249–252.

Kegg, Richard L. (1985). "Quality and Productivity in Manufacturing Systems." *Annals of the CIRP* (International Association for Production Research), Rivis, vol. 34, no. 2, pp. 531–534.

Kegg, Richard L. (1984). "Quality and Productivity in Manufacturing Systems." *Second Bi-Annual Machine Tool Technical Conference.* National Machine Tool Builders Association, Gaithersburg, MD, pp. 9-71 to 9-86.

Kinnucan, Paul (1983). "Flexible Systems Invade the Factory." *High Technology,* July, pp. 32–42.

Krouse, John (1982). *What Every Engineer Should Know about Computer-Aided Design and Computer-Aided Manufacturing.* Marcel Dekker, New York.

Marguglio, B. W. (1981). "Environmental Compliance and Universal Quality Assurance." *Quality Progress,* September, pp. 14–18.

McCubbin, Robert E. (1971). "Machine Tool Information System." *ASQC Technical Conference Transactions,* Milwaukee, pp. 235–243.

Meal, Harlan C. (1984). "Putting Production Decisions Where They Belong." *Harvard Business Review,* March-April, pp. 102–111.

Mentch, C. C. (1980). "Manufacturing Process Quality Optimization Studies." *Journal of Quality Technology,* vol. 12, no. 3, pp. 119–129.

Michalek, Joseph M. and Holmes, Richard K. (1981). *Quality Engineering Techniques in Product Design/Process.* Society of Automotive Engineers Paper 810392, Detroit.

Nakajo, Takeshi and Kume, Hitoshi (1985). "The Principles of Foolproofing and Their Application in Manufacturing." *Reports of Statistical Application Research,* Union of Japanese Scientists and Engineers, vol. 32, no. 2, June, pp. 10–29.

Nelson, Lloyd S. (1978). "Best Target Value for a Production Process." *Journal of Quality Technology,* vol. 10, no. 2, April, pp. 88–89.

Phadke, M. S., Kackar, R. R., Speeny, D. V., and Grieco, M. J. (1983). "Off-Line Quality Control in Integrated Circuit Fabrication Using Experimental Design." *The Bell System Technical Journal,* vol. 62, no. 5, pp. 1273–1309.

Phillipp, Thomas J. (1982). "Quality System Concepts in the CAD/CAM Era." *ASQC Quality Congress Transactions,* Milwaukee, pp. 569–573.

Raheja, Dev (1982). "Fault Tree Analysis—How Are We Doing?" *ASQC Quality Congress Transactions,* Milwaukee, pp. 355–359.

Remboldt, Ulrich, Seth, Mahesh K., and Weinstein, Jeremy (1977). *Computers in Manufacturing.* Marcel Dekker, New York.

Sahrmann, Herman (1979). "Set-Up Assurance through Time Series Analysis." *Journal of Quality Technology,* vol. 11, no. 7, pp. 105–115.

Schonberger, Richard J. (1982). *Japanese Manufacturing Techniques.* Free Press, New York.

Siff, Walter C. (1984). "The Strategic Plan of Control—A Tool for Participative Management." *ASQC Quality Congress Transactions,* Milwaukee, pp.384–390.

Staffiery, Richard A. (1975). "A Semiconductor Traceability Plan That Avoids Confusion." *Quality Management and Engineering,* April, pp. 20, 21.

Sullivan, L. P. (1984). "Reducing Variability: A New Approach to Quality." *Quality Progress,* July, pp. 15–21.

Taguchi, G. (1978). "Off-Line and On-Line Quality Control Systems." *International Conference on Quality Control,* Japanese Union of Scientists and Engineers, Tokyo, pp. B4-1 through B4-5.

Tarver, Mae-G. (1984). "Multistation Process Capability—Filling Equipment." *ASQC Quality Congress Transactions,* Milwaukee, pp. 281–288.

Taylor, F. W. (1947). *Scientific Management.* Harper & Brothers, New York.

U.S. Department of Transportation (1982). "Process Analysis via Accuracy Control." *The National Ship Building Research Program,* Washington, DC.

Venn, B. (1971). "Standardization of Flow Charts for Process Quality Control Systems." *EOQC Quality,* vol. 25, no. 2, pp. 35–39.

Vinson, William D. and Heany, Donald F. (1977). "Is Quality Out of Control?" *Harvard Business Review,* vol. 55, no. 6, November-December, pp. 114–122.

Werner, G. W. and Zetzsche, E. (1982). "Working Methods and Means of Quality and Reliability Assurance in Large Industrial Plants." *EOQC Quality,* vo. 26, no. 5, pp. 8–13.

Willis, Roger G. and Sullivan, Kevin H. (1984). "CIMS in Perspective: Costs, Benefits, Timing, Payback Periods Are Outlined." *Industrial Engineering,* February, vol. 16, no. 2, pp. 23–36.

Wilson, Lawrence A. (1983). "Generative Quality Assurance Planning." *ASQC Quality Congress Transactions,* Milwaukee, pp. 95–100.

SECTION 17
PRODUCTION[1]

Frank M. Gryna

---

[1]In the Third Edition, the section on production was prepared by J. M. Juran.

17.1

NATURE OF PRODUCTION

"Production," as the term is used here, designates the activity of running the processes, machines, and tools, and of performing the associated mental and manual operations to make products from basic materials and components. Production is part of the broader activity of manufacture, which includes also manufacturing planning; see Section 16, Manufacturing Planning. As the term is commonly used, production involves the use of manufacturing "processes" to change the physical raw material into products. Other areas of an organization also make use of a variety of "processes" which do not involve the changing of a raw material. Many of these other processes are discussed in Section 21, Administrative and Support Operations.

Statistical techniques useful in process control are discussed in Section 24, Statistical Process Control; behavioral aspects on the production floor and throughout an organization are covered in Section 10, Managing Human Performance. Policy issues are discussed in Section 5 under Quality Policies for Functions.

Scope of Activity.   Production as an activity must be distinguished from the capitalized word "Production," meaning a department of that name. The Production Department is often given duties beyond those of performing direct production activities. These added duties vary widely from one company to another, depending on product and process complexity, volume of production, management philosophy, training of supervisors, and national tradition.

Company response to these factors has resulted in divergent forms of organization. At one extreme the department called Production has wide responsibilities for manufacturing planning, machine maintenance, and product inspection. At the other extreme, the department has a narrow scope of activity—that of executing the plans which others have prepared. Competitive forces of the 1980s have fostered some useful experiments in organizing and conducting production operations. From these experiments are emerging new approaches that would have been considered heretical just a decade earlier. Stone and Guith (1985) describe an example for an automobile plant.

QUALITY RESPONSIBILITIES ON THE FACTORY FLOOR

"Responsibility" is never clear unless it is stated in terms of decisions or actions. A question in the form, "Who is responsible for approving setups?" admits of an unequivocal answer.

The factory floor is the scene of myriad decisions which affect quality. Several categories of these decisions are so highly repetitive that companies should make crystal clear who is to make which decisions.

Principal Decision and Action Categories.   The most frequent categories are the following:

Setup Approval.   The "setup" consists of assembling the proper machines, tools, instruments, and material and adjusting them so that the resulting product will conform to specification. This setup is prepared either by the production worker or by a setup specialist. Once the setup has been prepared, a decision must be made: "Should this process be allowed to commence production?" This decision is known as "setup approval."

Running Approval.   Once the process is running, there is need for periodic checks to see if the process is still producing product which conforms to specification. The decision to be made is: "Should the process continue to run or should it stop?" This decision is known as "running approval."

Product Approval.   As product is completed, there is a periodic need to decide whether the product conforms to specification. This decision is called "product approval," as contrasted with the preceding two decisions, which together constitute process approval.

Decision on Fitness for Use.   As a result of the product approval procedure, some nonconforming product may be found. A further decision is then necessary on the disposition of the nonconforming product.

Pattern of Departmental Responsibilities.   In the United States, the *departmental* assignment for making these decisions has usually been as follows:

Decision	*Usually assigned to*
Setup approval	Production, but sometimes jointly with Inspection
Running approval	Production
Product approval	Inspection
Fitness-for-use decision	Committee of representatives from various departments

There is also the further question of how these departmental responsibilities are to be assigned to the categories of job classes on the factory floor. To answer this question, it is convenient to make use of a responsibility matrix to reach agreement on who should make which decisions.

Pattern of Individual Responsibilities.   Unless the managers decide who may make what decisions, the people on the work floor must work out among themselves who is to decide what. Some of these local agreements are an unpleasant surprise to managers once they are discovered.

Managers can quite readily work out an agreed pattern of decision making by using a responsibility matrix. Cognizant supervisors meet to discuss the problem. At this meeting the blank matrix is first drawn on the blackboard. The members then agree on what decisions and actions they will talk about. These are listed in the left-hand column to become the headings for the horizontal rows of the matrix. Next, the members agree on who is available on the factory floor to make these decisions. These potential decision makers become the headings for the vertical columns of the matrix.

Next, the matrix is reproduced and a copy is given to each conferee to indicate who should make which decision and take which action. These filled-in copies (sometimes executed anonymously) are collected and all the marks are transferred to the blackboard to show the composite belief of the membership.

The summary enables the members to identify their collective agreements and the extent of their differences. These differences can be talked out until agreement is complete. This agreement can then be reduced to a written procedure, formally approved and published.

An example of the results of this approach is given in Table 17.1. Inputs were collected on five decisions—the four already mentioned and an additional decision on product sorting. The beliefs on current responsibility came from four

TABLE 17.1 Divergence of Views on Responsibility

Plant	W*	S	I	E	W	S	I	E
	Setup acceptance				Running acceptance			
A	1	4	2	0	5	1	2	0
B	4	2	7	0	7	4	3	0
C	0	0	1	7	2	1	5	0
D	3	0	5	0	2	1	7	2
	Conformance				Fitness for use			
A	1	5	2	0	1	3	4	0
B	3	5	7	0	2	6	6	1
C	0	1	6	1	0	2	4	2
D	3	1	5	2	2	1	10	0
	Sorting							
A	0	4	3	0				
B	4	2	6	0				
C	0	1	4	0				
D	0	0	5	4				

*W = worker; S = supervisor; I = inspector; E = engineer.

plants (A, B, C, D) within the company. Lack of agreement on who was responsible for the decisions was a clear conclusion from the study. Disagreement existed within every plant on each of the five decisions. Clarification was essential.

Managers often ask, "Is there a right way to organize?" The answer is no. The pattern of responsibility must be designed to fit the local conditions. In one department it is convenient to assign to the same person the jobs of setup and operate; in another department setup is best done by a special setup person. In one department the process is so stable that the original setup will endure for the length of the lot; in another department the setup requires check and readjust during the life of the lot. There are differences in the extent of training, the level of morale, etc., of the work force. The permutations of these and other differences make each department unique and require a made-to-measure design of responsibility for decision making.

It is instructive to study the approach to responsibility for quality on the production floor in Japan. Here a heavy emphasis is placed on having many decisions and actions under the control of the production workers themselves. Schonberger (1982) discusses the emphasis on responsibility of the workers in Japan. See also Section 35F, Quality in Japan.

CONCEPT OF CONTROLLABILITY; SELF-CONTROL

Creating a state of self-control for a human being requires that we meet several essential criteria. We must provide people with a means for:

1. Knowing what they are supposed to do

2. Knowing what they are actually doing

3. Regulating the process

May (1978) divides the criteria into seven categories, all of which are incorporated and discussed below for the three criteria stated.

The three basic criteria for self-control make possible a separation of defects into categories of "controllability," of which the most important are:

1. *Worker-controllable:* A defect or nonconformity is worker-controllable if all three criteria for self-control have been met.

2. *Management-controllable:* A defect or nonconformity is management-controllable if one or more of the criteria for self-control have not been met.

The theory behind these categories is that only the management can provide the means for meeting the criteria for self-control. Hence any failure to meet these criteria is a failure of management, and the resulting defects are therefore beyond the control of the workers. This theory is not 100 percent sound. Workers commonly have the duty to call management's attention to deficiencies in the system of control, and sometimes they do not do so. (Sometimes they do, and it is management who fails to act.) However, the theory is much more right than wrong.

Whether the defects or nonconformities in a plant are mainly management-controllable or worker-controllable is a fact of the highest order of importance. To reduce the former requires a program in which the main contributions must come from the managers, supervisors, and technical specialists. To reduce the latter requires a different kind of program in which much of the contribution comes from the workers. The great difference between these two kinds of programs suggests that managers should quantify their knowledge of the state of controllability before embarking on major programs.

An example of controllability study is given in Table 17.2. A diagnostic team was set up to study scrap and rework reports in six machine shop departments for 17 working days. The defect cause was entered on each report by a quality engineer who was assigned to collect the data. When the cause was not apparent,

TABLE 17.2   Controllability Study in a Machine Shop, %

Management-controllable	
Inadequate training	15
Machine inadequate	8
Machine maintenance	8
Other process problems	8
Materials handling	7
Tool, fixture, gage (TFG) maintenance	6
TFG inadequate	5
Wrong material	3
Operation run out of sequence	3
Miscellaneous	5
Total	68
Worker-controllable	
Failure to check work	11
Improperly operated	11
Other (e.g., piece mislocated)	10
Total	32

the team reviewed the defect and, when necessary, contacted other specialists (who had been alerted by management about the priority of the project) to identify the cause. The purpose of the study was to resolve a lack of agreement on the causes of chronically high scrap and rework. It did the job. The study was decisive in obtaining agreement on the focus of the improvement program. In less than 1 year over $2 million was saved and important strides were made in reducing production backlogs.

Controllability can also be evaluated by posing specific questions for each of the three criteria of self-control. (Typical questions that can be posed are presented below.) Although this approach does not yield a quantitative evaluation of management-controllable and worker-controllable defects, it does show whether the defects are primarily management-controllable or worker-controllable.

In the experience of the editors, defects are about 80 percent management-controllable. This figure does not vary much from industry to industry, but varies greatly among processes. Other investigators, in Japan, Sweden, the Netherlands, and Czechoslovakia, have reached similar conclusions.

While the available quantitative studies make clear that defects are mainly management-controllable, many industrial managers do not know this, or are unable to accept the data. Their long-standing beliefs are that most defects are the result of worker carelessness, indifference, and even sabotage. Such managers are easily persuaded to embark on worker-motivation schemes which, under the usual state of facts, aim at a small minority of the problems and hence are doomed to achieve minor results at best. The issue is not whether quality problems *in industry* are management-controllable. The need is to determine the answer *in a given plant*. This cannot be answered authoritatively by opinion, but requires solid facts, preferably through a controllability study of actual defects, as in Table 17.2.

The concept of self-control draws attention to the importance of manufacturing planning. Manufacturing planning for quality (see Section 16) is the means of *prevention* of both management- and worker-controllable defects on the manufacturing floor.

The three main criteria for self-control are discussed below.

KNOWLEDGE OF "SUPPOSED TO DO"

This knowledge commonly consists of the following:

1. The product standard, which may be a written specification, a product sample, or other definition of the end result to be attained

2. The process standard, which may be a written process specification, written process instructions, an oral instruction, or other definition of "means to an end"

3. A definition of responsibility, i.e., what decisions to make and what actions to take (discussed earlier in this section)

Product Specifications.   The ideal source of knowledge is the use required by the user. In most situations this is translated into a product specification. In developing these product specifications, some essential precautions must be observed.

Provide Unequivocal Information.   Two obstacles to proper knowledge can exist:

1. The specification may be vague. For example, when fiberglass tanks are transported in vehicles, the surface of the supporting cradles should be smooth. It

was recognized that weld spatter would be deposited on the cradle surface, so an operation was specifed to scrape the surface "smooth." However, there was no definition of "how smooth," and many rejections resulted.

2. There may be conflicting specifications. The supervisor's "black book" has had a long, durable career. Changes in specifications may fail to be communicated, especially when there is a constant parade of changes. In one instance, an inspector rejected product which lacked an angle cut needed for clearance in assembly. It was discovered that the inspector was using drawing revision D, the production floor had used revision B, and the design office had issued revision E just 3 days before.

Provide Information on Seriousness. All specifications contain multiple characteristics, and these are not equally important. When workers are informed of the vital few characteristics, their emphasis is better placed.

Explain the "Why." Explanation of the purposes served by the product and by the specification enlarges the knowledge of "supposed to do" and provides motivation through the resulting feeling of participation.

For example, a specification on weight called for a nominal value of 40.0 g with a tolerance of $\pm$ 0.5 g. Although the total tolerance of 1.0 was being met, most of the tolerance range was being used up, and this created some problems later in assembly. A process capability study showed that the process capability was 0.10 g—far better than the tolerance of 1.0 g. But why was most of the tolerance range being used? Discussion revealed that (1) workers had not been told of the impact of inconsistent weights on later assembly, and (2) workers had not been instructed on centering the process to the nominal specification value.

Provide Standards. In those cases where the specification cannot be quantitative, physical or photographic standards should be provided. There is an extensive array of needs here, especially on widely prevailing characteristics such as product appearance. (For years, enormous numbers of electrical connections were soldered in the absence of clear standards for an acceptable soldered connection.) If these standards are not provided by the managers and engineers, then, by default, the standards will be set by the inspectors and workers.

Train the Workers. The general aspects of worker training for quality are discussed in Section 11, Training for Quality. Beyond this general training are the special training needs of specific jobs. For example, some welding operations affect human safety. It is common practice to require that workers undergo a training program, including welding of specimen pieces, to qualify for the job. A qualification examination is then held, including test of the specimen pieces. Workers who pass the examination are given a license to perform the operation for a stated interval of time. In some cases the license remains in effect until there is evidence of poor work or until the worker becomes inactive for several months. In such cases, requalification is required.

Process Specifications. Work methods and process conditions (e.g., temperature, pressure, time cycles) must be unequivocally clear.

Howell (1981) states that six factors are important in developing a statement of a work method:

1. Provide only the information needed to accomplish the task.
2. Make sure abbreviations are understood.
3. Do not make written instructions too wordy.

4. Use photographs and visual aids, where possible.

5. Make sure assembly instructions are consistent with the specified engineering configuration.

6. Make sure that on-the-job instructions are consistent with formal training program instruction.

LTV Steel		**INTEGRATED PROCESS CONTROL**			
Plant __Indiana Harbor__		**Standard Procedures** **Process Control**		File No __716-2.2.2__	
Dept __No. 3 Sheet Mill__				Date Orig. Issue __3/83__	

Control Area	Control Point	Control Element	No	Revision No __`1__
Tandem Mill	Rolling	Rolling Solutions	2.2.2	Date Revised __9/83__

Control Task
To maintain rolling solution characteristics at the proper levels.

Responsible for Control
Solution Attendant

Process Standard
- Oil concentration must be 2.5% to 3.5%
- Solution temperature must be 110°F - 120°F
- SAP value must be above 120
- Iron fines must be less that 600 ppm

Reason for Control
- To provide the correct lubricity between work rolls and strip for reduced roll wear and control of strip temperature. This helps control strip flatness and avoids friction scratches.

Measurement	Routine Reporting of Data	Control Chart	Yes	No
Tools/Equipment - Standard chem. test set-up	Form/Form No. -		X	
Frequency - Twice/turn	Solution Attendant's Report	Type - X & Moving Range		
By - Solution Attendant	By - Solution Attendant	By - Solution Att.		

Corrective Action
- Solution concentration approaching limits - add rolling oil or water.
- Solution temp. approaching limits - adjust temperature control.
- SAP reading between 100 & 120, skim solution tank and add new oil. SAP reading below 100, retest immediately and contact Operating Supervisor. If retest below 100, shutdown mill and switch to alternative solution tank.
- Iron fines approaching limit, skim tank for 2 hours and add 100 gallons oil. Retest after 30 minutes second time, repeat procedure if still near or above limit.

Operating Procedure

See attached sheet

Disposition of Non-Compliant Product
Identify coil(s) for special surface evaluation. Notify Metallurgical Supervisor.

Review Procedure
Once per turn the Operating Supervisor will:
- Check Solution Attendant's Report
- Visually check temperature of solution

Developed By: _Robert Goedken_
IPC Coordinator

Richard H. Berry

Approved: _DT Zid_
Department Superintendent/Manager

Dale H. Dick Jr.
Manager - Quality Control

R. Voth
General Superintendent/ Plant Manager

FIG. 17.1 Process Control standard procedure. *(From LTV Steel pamphlet, Integrated Process Control.)*

A steel manufacturer uses a highly structured system of identifying key process variables, defining process control standards, communicating the information to the work force, monitoring performance, and accomplishing diagnosis when problems arise. The process specification is a collection of process control standard procedures (Figure 17.1.) A procedure is developed for controlling each of the key process variables (variables that must be controlled in order to meet specification limits on the product). The procedure answers the following questions:

1. What the process standards are
2. Why control is needed
3. Who is responsible for control
4. How to measure
5. When to measure
6. How to report routine data
7. Who is responsible for data reporting
8. How to audit
9. Who is responsible for audit
10. What to do with product out of compliance
11. Who developed the standard

Often, detailed process instructions are not known until workers have become experienced with the process. Updating of process instructions based on job experience can be conveniently accomplished by posting a cause-and-effect diagram in the production department and attaching index cards to the diagram (Fukuda, 1981). Each card states additional process instructions based on recent experience.

Confusion of Process Control Tolerances with Product Accept Tolerances. Process control tolerances apply to characteristics of the process; product acceptance tolerances apply to characteristics of the product. Table 17.3 distinguishes between these two kinds of tolerances.

In some operations the units of measure for the process are dramatically different from those used on the product. For example, in hardening of steel, the process variables are bath temperature, cycle time, etc. In contrast, the product is measured in terms of grain size, degrees of hardness, etc. In such a case the responsibility of the hardening furnace worker is clearly one of meeting the process tolerances, not the product tolerances.

In other operations, the units of measure for process and product are identical. A common example is the millimeter or inch used as a unit of measure in metal cutting. This is used both for controlling the process and accepting the product.

Confusion of Mandatory with Advisory Process Tolerances. Many process specifications contain two different kinds of tolerances:

1. *Mandatory tolerances:* These are specified to assure fitness for use, make the product more marketable, achieve high reliability, etc.
2. *Advisory tolerances:* These are specified for the convenience of production, e.g., to help reduce the amount of cut and try in running the process. For example, the process for cooking fish sticks (for frozen food marketing) includes requirements that (*a*) the cooking cycle shall be x degrees for y minutes and

TABLE 17.3   Distinction between Tolerances

	Process control	Product acceptance
Purpose of the tolerances:	To provide a basis for making decisions on the process	To provide a basis for making decisions on the product
Tolerances published in:	Process specification	Product specification
Specification usually issued by:	Process Engineering Department	Product Design Department
Tolerances concern:	Process conditions	Product qualities
Instrumentation is usually:	An integral part of the process	Not an integral part of the process
Usual measurement to discover compliance is by:	Production Department for advisory tolerances; Inspection Department for mandatory tolerances*	Inspection Department
Decisions on whether there is compliance made usually by:	Production Department for advisory tolerances, Inspection Department for mandatory tolerances	Inspection Department
Deviation from specification usually authorized by:	Production Department for advisory tolerances, Process Engineering Department for mandatory tolerances	Inspection Department for nonfunctional tolerances, Product Design Department for functional tolerances

*Advisory tolerances are supplied to workers for manufacturing convenience. Mandatory process tolerances must be met as a means of supplying essential product qualities, i.e., long life, safety, etc., when there is no immediate economic test for the product quality.

also that (b) the cooked product shall have a golden brown color. The latter is regarded as mandatory for marketing the product; the former is advisory. For most input materials (fish), the specified temperature and time will produce the proper color. However, the materials vary, and Production is authorized to vary the cooking cycle to suit.

Some process specifications contain many tolerances without designating which are mandatory and which are advisory. Lacking this knowledge, Production tends to regard them all as advisory, whereas Inspection tends to regard them all as mandatory. The answer, "of course," is to designate which is which. The problem is to induce busy technical departments to take the time to do the designating. Where they are unable to take the time, the quality manager may be driven to make his or her own determination.

Confusion When Control Charts Are Introduced into a Process.   Control charts are discussed in Section 24, Statistical Process Control. To the quality specialists, control charts serve as a sensitive device for detecting process changes. To the production force the charts are complex and confusing. Table 17.4 shows the initial impact on the production worker.

TABLE 17.4 Operator Action Table

Type of information or decision needed	Sources of worker's information or decision		After introduction of control charts
	Before introduction of control charts; worker responsible for meeting:		
	Process specification	Product specification	
1. Information on what the process should be doing	Direct from process specification	Direct from product specification	From the control chart
2. Information on what the process actually is doing	From process instruments or inspectors	From measurements on the product	From the control chart
3. Decision on whether "is doing" differs from "should be doing" by an amount great enough to warrant process adjustment	From worker experience	From worker experience	From the control chart
4. Decision on extent of process adjustment needed	From worker experience	From worker experience	From worker experience

Since the earliest applications (and into the 1980s), some pertinent questions were raised about the status of the control chart:

1. What is the official status of the control chart? Is it merely an informal suggestion by the quality engineer, or is it a "legitimate" impersonal boss, like the specification, the collective bargaining agreement, etc.? Workers react to nonconforming product because specification limits have been law in the shop. Workers do not react in the same way to control charts, because legitimacy has not been fully established.

2. Is the control to be used in addition to or instead of the specification?

3. If "in addition to," what of the cases where there is conflict; e.g., control chart requires more frequent adjustment, process is not capable, etc.?

4. If the control chart is to be used instead of the specification, why is this not legitimized; i.e., why is there no formal order relieving the worker of the responsibility for meeting specifications?

Unless these questions are answered, confusion will result and the charts will be doomed to the grave of a file cabinet.

Checklist.   The above discussion covers the first criterion of self-control: people must have the means for knowing what they are supposed to do. To evaluate adherence to this criterion, a checklist of questions can be created, including the following:

1. Are there written product specifications, process specifications, and work instructions? If written in more than one place, do they all agree? Are they legible? Are they conveniently accessible to the worker?

2. Does the specification define the relative importance of different quality characteristics? Are advisory tolerances on a process distinguished from mandatory tolerances on a product? If control charts or other control techniques are to be used, is it clear how these relate to product specifications?

3. Are standards for visual defects displayed in the work area?

4. Are the written specifications given to the worker the same as the criteria used by inspectors? Are deviations from the specification often allowed?

5. Does the worker know how the product is used?

6. Has the worker been adequately trained to understand the specification and perform the steps needed to meet the specification? Has the worker been evaluated by test or other means to see if he or she is qualified?

7. Does the worker know the effect on future operations and product performance if the specification is not met?

8. Does the worker receive specification changes automatically and promptly?

9. Does the worker know what to do with defective raw material and defective finished product?

10. Have responsibilities in terms of decisions and actions been clearly defined?

KNOWLEDGE OF "IS DOING"

This is the second criterion for self-control. For self-control, people must have the means of knowing whether their performance conforms to standard. This conformance applies to:

1. The product in the form of specifications on product characteristics
2. The process in the form of specifications on process variables

The knowledge is secured from three primary sources: measurements inherent in the process, measurements by production workers, and measurements by inspectors.

Measurement Inherent in the Process. Many processes are engineered to include much instrumentation. The resulting information provides a feedback to enable the worker to close the loop. Even where the feedback is into an automated system, the data are usually available to human workers acting as monitors.

Measurements by Workers. Where the worker is to use the instruments, it is necessary to provide training in how to measure, what sampling criteria to use, how to record, how to chart, and what kinds of corrective action to take. The difficulty of motivating the workers to follow these instructions is so widespread a problem that many companies go to great lengths to minimize the need for worker action by providing instruments which require little or no human effort to measure, record, and control.

When these instruments are provided to workers, it is also necessary to ensure that these instruments are compatible with those used by inspectors and in other operations later in the progression of events.

On one construction project, the "form setters" were provided with carpenter levels and rulers to set the height of forms prior to the pouring of concrete. The inspectors were provided with a complex optical instrument. The differences in measurement led to many disputes.

Control of the process is strengthened if the worker is provided with the type of gage that provides numerical measurements on a characteristic rather than providing accept-reject information.

A problem arises when the measurement necessary to control a process must be made in a laboratory off the production floor. The time required to send a sample to the laboratory, to have the analysis made, and to have the data relayed back to production can result in a delay to proper control of a process. One solution is the development of auxiliary measuring devices that can be used on the production floor by the worker and thereby provide immediate feedback. An example comes from a process used to control the concentration of chloride in a corn product derivative. Traditionally the raw material undergoes centrifuging, a sample of the product is sent to a laboratory for analysis, the test results are forwarded to Production, and any necessary changes are then made in the centrifugal loads. (Chloride level, for the most part, is dependent on the load size of crystallized liquor being spun in the centrifugals.) Under the new setup, the worker takes a spot sample at the surge bin, and analyzes the product for parts per million chloride on an ion analyzer, and thereby directly regulates the process. Total time between processing a batch and obtaining a measurement plunges from 90 to 20 min. As a result, the amount of inferior product due to delayed process adjustment is greatly reduced.

Parker (1981) describes how the use of on-line gages overcame problems in obtaining adequate sampling of product at a paper mill.

Measurements by Inspectors.   When Inspection makes measurements which are to serve as a basis for action by Production, the division of work is as follows:

Activity	Usually performed by
Measure the product or process	Inspection
Record and publish the data	Inspection
Analyze the data for significance	Both
Decide on a course of action	Production
Take the action	Production

Where this form persists for any length of time, it is common for the responsibility for achievement of quality to pass from Production to Inspection. Once this has happened, it is a long road back.

Methods of Closing the Feedback Loop.   The choice of ways of closing the loop is influenced partly by technology, but more often by the prevailing pattern of human relations.

Loop Closed by Inspector.   At one extreme, the inspector is under orders to stop the process when there is evidence of failure to conform. This form is used in cases where the management has become unwilling to entrust the production workers with the responsibility for closing the loop.

Personal Feedback to Workers.   In this form the inspector tells the worker of the results of measurement, and advises on the change needed. In some companies it is virtually mandatory for the workers to act on this advice. Usually, however, the worker decides whether to take the advice or not.

Personal Feedback to Supervisor.   In some companies the rule is that the inspector may not communicate directly with the worker but, instead, must take feedback to the supervisor.

Where the worker is in a state of self-control, feedback through the supervisor slows up the signal and may distort it as well. Usually it is better to communicate directly with the workers, provided that the feedback avoids the implication of being an order.

Impersonal Feedback.   One way of directing the feedback to the worker without implying an order is through depersonalizing the feedback. A special reporting format is needed for this purpose (e.g., charts, signal lights) as discussed under Timeliness of Feedback (see below).

In some cases it is feasible to provide feedback of deeds rather than data. Numerous applications of closed-circuit television are used to permit observation of processes which are distant or which are conducted in an environment hostile to human comfort, e.g., heat, fumes, noise.

The opportunity to view the deeds has the added advantage of being a "real-time" feedback; i.e., the deeds and the signals are simultaneous. The response of workers to such realities tends to be more wholehearted than their response to after-the-fact data.

Timeliness of Feedback.   Once defects are discovered, prompt feedback is needed to avoid continuing production of defects. Depending on the process, various ways have been devised for providing this prompt feedback.

Multiple Machines.   Where the process consists of numerous machines all producing independently (e.g., textile looms, lathes), signals are designed to identify those machines which are in need of attention. For example, signal lamps may be mounted to each machine. Green lights show that the product from those machines is under control. A red light signals that the machine is in trouble. These signals are turned on and off by Inspection. There are numerous other forms of such signals at machines: colored tags, swiveling red hands, etc. Denissoff (1980) describes a process control system that classifies each process into one of four levels of quality performance. Color codes are used for identification. Different process control approaches are used for the four levels.

Large Assembly Lines.   One form of feedback has been the large chart mounted in the assembly area so as to be widely visible. The chart is a matrix with vertical columns representing hours of the shift and horizontal rows representing various assembly defects. The results of inspection are posted hourly, so that any one square of the matrix shows how many instances of that type of defect were found in that hour. These feedbacks can be provided by instantaneous electronic readout.

Criteria for Good Feedback to Workers.   The needs of production workers (as distinguished from supervisors or technical specialists) require that the data feedback read at a glance, deal only with the few important defects, deal only with worker-controllable defects, provide prompt information about symptom and cause, and provide enough information to guide corrective actions. Criteria of good feedback are:

1. *Read at a glance:*   The pace of events on the factory floor is swift. Workers should be able to review the feedback in stride.

Where the worker needs information about process performance over time, charts can provide an excellent form of feedback, provided they are designed to be consistent with the assigned responsibility of the worker (Table 17.5). It is useful to use visual displays to highlight recurrent problems. A problem described as "outer hopper switch installed backwards" displayed on a wall chart in large block letters has much more impact than the same message buried away as a marginal note in a work folder. Carlisle (1981) describes the effectiveness of such a system.

2. *Deal only with the few important defects:* Overwhelming workers with data on all defects will result in diverting attention from the vital few.

3. *Deal only with worker-controllable defects:* Any other course provides a basis for argument which will be unfruitful.

4. *Provide prompt information about symptom and cause:* Timeliness is a basic test of good feedback; the closer the system is to "real time" signaling, the better.

5. *Provide enough information to guide corrective action:* The signal should be in terms which make it easy to decide on remedial action.

Feedback Related to Worker Action. The worker needs to know what kind of *process* change to make to respond to a *product* deviation. Sources of the knowledge are:

1. From the process specification (see Figure 17.1 under "corrective action")

2. From cut-and-try experience by the worker

3. From the fact that the units of measure for product and process are identical

Lacking all these, the workers can only cut and try further or stop the process and sound the alarm.

Sometimes it is feasible for the data feedback to be converted into a form which makes easier the worker's decision about what action to take on the process.

For example, a copper cap had six critical dimensions. It was easy to measure the dimensions and to discover the nature of product deviation. However, it was difficult to translate the product data into process changes. To simplify this translation, use was made of a position-dimension (*P-D*) diagram. The six measurements were first "corrected" (i.e., coded) by subtracting the thinnest from all the

TABLE 17.5 Worker Responsibility versus Chart Design

Responsibility of the worker is to	Chart should be designed to show
1. Make individual units of product meet a product specification	The measurements of individual units of product compared to product specification limits
2. Hold process conditions to the requirements of a process specification	The measurements of the process conditions compared with the process specification limits
3. Hold averages and ranges to specified statistical control limits	The averages and ranges compared to the statistical control limits
4. Hold percent nonconforming below some prescribed level	Actual percent nonconforming compared to the limiting level

others. These corrected data were then plotted on a *P-D* diagram as shown in Figure 17.2. Such diagrams provided a way of analyzing the tool setup.

Feedback to Supervisors.   Beyond the need for feedback at the work stations, there is need to provide supervisors with short-term summaries. These take several forms.

Matrix Summary.   A common form of matrix is workers versus defects; i.e., the vertical columns are headed by worker names and the horizontal rows by the names of defect types. The matrix makes clear which defect types predominate, which workers have the most defects, and what the interaction is. Other matrices include machine number versus defect type, defect type versus calendar week, etc.

When the summary is published, it is usual to circle the matrix cells to highlight the vital few situations which call for attention.

FIG. 17.2   Method of drawing *P-D* diagram.

An elaboration of the matrix is to split the cell diagonally, permitting the entry of two numbers, e.g., number defective and number produced.

Pareto Analysis.   Some companies prefer to minimize the detail and provide information on the total defects for the day plus a list of the top three (or so) defects encountered, and how many of each.

In some industries, a "chart room" displays performance by product and by department, against goals.

Computer Data Analysis and Reporting.   Production volume and complexity are important factors in determining the role of the computer. Burgess (1982) describes a simple manual reporting system for a low-volume, labor-intensive operation. Blumenthal (1978) discusses a system of greater complexity that is useful for moderate- to high-volume operations. Section 27, Computers and Quality, explains the role of computers in analyzing and reporting data during production and other phases of the product life cycle.

Automated Quality Information.   Some situations justify the mechanization of both the recording of data and the analysis of data. Direct feedback can even include printing of summaries at typewriters located in the offices of the supervisors involved. Fisher (1983) describes a system (Figure 17.3) for using a minicomputer to control the net weight in a food-filling operation. The quality station has a cathode ray tube (CRT) and a scale; the supervisor's office has a CRT and a hard copy machine; a modem connects corporate headquarters with each plant's computer setup.

As weight data are obtained and entered at the weight station, the computer forms the data into samples (five weights in each sample), and when the final net weight in each sample is obtained, the CRT instantly displays an average and range control chart. Touch another key and a histogram is the output. All graphs and charts are in real time and are updated automatically after each subgroup. Although the computer is graphing only subgroup averages and ranges, it is internally checking each individual reading against a minimum allowable value. If this value is not met, the CRT locks out until the worker acknowledges the low reading. In addition, a terminal in the supervisor's office beeps in response to an out-

FIG. 17.3   Gerber computerized net weight system.

of-control situation. This beeping continues until the supervisor clears the terminal, signalling recognition of the problem. The system enables the supervisor to monitor the line without leaving the office.

Entry of data through the use of computer terminals on production floors is now common. Kassarda (1980) describes the versatility of these shop floor terminals. Many varieties of software are now available for analyzing, processing, and presenting quality information collected on the production floor. See Section 24 under Software for Statistical Process Control.

Checklist. A checklist to evaluate the second criterion of self-control includes questions such as:

1. Are gages provided to the worker? Do they provide numerical measurements rather than sort good from bad? Are they precise enough? Are they regularly checked for accuracy?
2. Is the worker told how often to sample work? Is sufficient time allowed?
3. Is the worker told how to evaluate measurements to decide when to adjust the process and when to leave it alone?
4. Is there a check to see that the worker does follow instructions on sampling work and making process adjustments?
5. Are inspection results provided to the worker, and are these results reviewed by the supervisor with the worker?

ABILITY TO REGULATE

This is the third criterion for self-control. Regulating the process depends on a number of management-controllable factors, including:

1. *The process must be capable of meeting the tolerances:* (see Section 16 under Process Capability).

2. *The process must be responsive to the regulatory action in a predictable cause-and-effect relationship:* In a process for making polythelyne film, the workers were required to meet multiple product parameters. The equipment had various regulatory devices, each of which could vary performance with respect to one or more parameters. However, the workers could not "dial in" a predetermined list of settings which would meet all parameters. Instead, it was necessary to cut and try in order to meet all parameters simultaneously. During the period of cut and try, the machine produced nonconforming product to an extent which interfered with meeting standards for productivity and delivery. The workers were unable to predict how long the cut-and-try process would go on before full conformance was achieved. In consequence it became the practice to stop "cut and try" after a reasonable amount of time, and to let the process run, whether in conformance or not.

3. *The worker must be trained in how to use the regulating mechanisms and procedures:* This training should cover the entire spectrum of action—under what conditions to act, what kind and extent of changes to make, how to use the regulating devices, and why these things need to be done.

Of three qualified workers on a food process, only one operated the process every week and became proficient. The other two workers were used when the primary worker was on vacation or was ill, and thus they never became proficient.

Continuous training of the relief people was considered uneconomical, and agreements with the union prohibited their use except under the situations cited above. This problem is management-controllable; i.e., additional training or a change in union agreements is necessary.

4. *The act of adjustment should not be personally distasteful to the worker, e.g., should not require undue physical exertion:* In a plant making glass bottles, one adjustment mechanism was located next to a furnace area. During the summer months this area was so hot that workers tended to keep out as much as possible.

When the regulation consists of varying the human component of the operation, the question of process capability arises in a new form: Does the worker have the capability to regulate? This important question is discussed in Section 22 under Technique Errors, which includes some examples of discovering worker "knack."

Process Control Tools. Section 16, under Planning Process Controls, discusses how manufacturing planning should include the development of specific process control tools. The tools selected are often related to one of five forms of dominance in a process.

Setup-Dominant Operations. When the setup is the dominant cause of poor quality, the process setup should be formally approved before production starts. The evaluation of a process setup can vary from a first-piece inspection for a simple mechanical operation to an evaluation of a pilot plant for a complex chemical process. (See Section 16 under Overall Review of Manufacturing Planning).

Setup acceptance criteria have historically been based on rule-of-thumb methods, exemplified by first-piece inspection. Here the process is set up and the first piece produced is inspected. If acceptable, the setup is approved and production begins. Unfortunately, one measurement provides little information on the *centering* of the process and no information on the variation of the process.

A limited sample of measurements can lead to incorrect decisions. One error can be to disapprove a correct setup; another error can be to approve an incorrect setup. The risks associated with these errors can be controlled by using tools such as lot plot, variables sampling plans, attributes sampling plans (see Section 25, Acceptance Sampling), PRE-Control (see Section 24, under PRE-Control), and tests of hypotheses (see Section 23 under Tests of Hypotheses).

Cyclical variation presents a further complication. Sahrmann (1979) discusses the evaluation of setups for a coating weight process that exhibits significant cyclical variation.

Time-Dominant Operations. Time-dominant processes undergo a continuing time-to-time change (e.g., depletion of reagents, wear of tools, heat buildup) of such magnitude that nonconforming product will eventually be made. To prevent this, provision must be made for a periodic check and adjustment. This is often called "patrol inspection," of which there are numerous forms:

1. Preserve the order of manufacture. For example, the machine discharges its production into a small container called a "pan." The production worker periodically empties the entire pan into one of three larger containers:

   a. A "junk" box if the parts are junk.

   b. A "doubtful" box if the parts are questionable or are mixed good and bad.

   c. A "tray" if the parts are presumably good. The patrol inspector periodically checks product in the tray—either the most recent pieces or a random sample. Based on this check, the product in the tray goes to the junk box, the doubtful box, or a "good" box. The good box goes on to the next operation. Only the inspector may dispose of the tray, and only the inspector may place any product in the good box. The doubtful box is gone over by a sorter, who makes the final disposition.

2. This method is similar to that described in item 1 above, but the inspection data from the last few pieces are posted to a control chart (see Section 24, Statistical Process Control). If the process remains in control, all product made since the last check is accepted.

3. The accumulated product is sampled at random using a standard sampling plan, and acceptance is based on the sampling criteria (see Section 25, Acceptance Sampling).

4. The process variables are checked against a process specification, and product is. accepted provided the process conforms to specification. This method is usually restricted to cases in which there is to be a direct check on the product at later stages. Checks of process variables can be supplemented with checks on other process conditions (see Systems Audit later in this section).

Worker-Dominant Operations. When the worker is the dominant cause, feedback can be presented to supervisors and workers using the methods discussed earlier in this section.

Performance can also be presented in control-chart form using one of the following indices:

1. *Percent nonconforming:* This method is used in attributes cases when the product is either good or bad.

2. *Number of nonconformities:* This method is used for more elaborate products in which multiple errors can occur on a single unit of product, e.g., a television set or a large roll of woven carpeting.

3. *Nonconformities per opportunity:* Each job is given a rating, prior to production based on its complexity, or on the "number of opportunities for a nonconformity." In electronics assembly work, for example, the rating is the sum of all components, solder connections, hardware insertions, etc., for the operations to be performed by a given worker. The worker's error rate is then the actual number of nonconformities found in a sample divided by the total number of opportunities for a nonconformity (i.e., units inspected times opportunities per unit for the job). This denominator more nearly puts all workers on the same basis, so that fair comparisons can be made between them.

4. *Nonconformities per characteristic:* For mechanical parts or assemblies, "opportunities for a nonconformity" may more conveniently be defined as the total number of quality characteristics for a given operation. This is used as the denominator. Such a scoring method is readily adapted to cumulative "pyramiding" for higher-management reporting.

Control charts for fraction nonconforming or number of nonconformities are often plotted without statistical control limits. When such charts are installed on a worker-dominant process, a dramatic and quick improvement in quality sometimes occurs. There can be several reasons for such an improvement. First, the chart may demonstrate management's concern about quality and thereby bring increased worker vigilance on the process. Second, the chart may provide the worker with useful time-related information that was not available before.

Another technique for worker-dominated processes is the system audit (discussed later in this chapter).

Component-Dominant Operations. In component-dominant operations, the prime cause of poor quality is in the input materials to the operations. Defects may occur in epidemics (a lot of wrong material or out-of-specification material) or they may occur at random (a lot containing partially defective material). Assembly and subassembly, many chemical and food-processing operations, and packaging operations are typical examples.

Means of worker regulation are usually limited to notifying supervisors of the incoming materials' problems, and screening out the defective material.

Information-Dominant Operations. In information-dominant processes, the main cause of poor quality is in the data, instructions, and other forms of information provided to supervisors and workers. Such information may relate either to the product or to the process. Problems are often associated with products or processes that are subject to frequent changes, e.g., job shop operations (see Section 32, Job Shop Industries).

As in component-dominant operations, the worker has limited means of direct regulation. Problem areas, however, can be brought to the attention of supervision or reported through other corrective action channels such as Engineering Change Requests.

Special Situation of Taking Action When Control Charts Are Used. Limits on statistical control charts are different from engineering specification limits. In some situations, a process is not in statistical control, but may not require action since the product tolerances are being easily met; in other situations a process is in statistical control but the product tolerances are not being met. Table 17.6 shows the more usual permutations encountered and provides suggestions on the type of action to be taken.

Checklist. A checklist to evaluate the third criterion of self-control typically includes such questions as the following:

1. Has the quality capability of the process been measured to include both inherent variability and variability due to time? Is the capability periodically checked?
2. Has the worker been told how often to reset the process or how to evaluate measurements to decide when the process should be reset?
3. Is there a process adjustment that the worker can make to eliminate defects? Under what conditions should the worker adjust the process? When should the worker shut down the machine and seek more help? Whose help?
4. Have the worker actions which cause defects, and the necessary preventive action, been given to the worker, preferably in the written form?
5. Is there an adequate preventive maintenance program on the process?
6. Is there a hidden "knack" possessed by some workers that needs to be discovered and transmitted to all workers?

QUALITY AND PRODUCTION FLOOR CULTURE

Meeting the criteria of self-regulation is necessary but not sufficient. Even if all three criteria are initially met (they rarely are), two problems remain:

1. Worker errors may occur. The causes of some of those errors can be corrected

TABLE 17.6 Action to Be Taken

	Product meets tolerances		Product does not meet tolerances	
	Process variation small relative to tolerances*	Process variation large relative to tolerances*	Process variation small relative to tolerances	Process variation large relative to tolerances
Process is in control.	Consider cost reduction through less precise process; consider value to designer of tighter tolerances.	Generally no action.	Process is "misdirected" to wrong average. Generally easy to correct permanently.	Process may be misdirected and also too scattered. Correct misdirection. Consider economics of more precise process versus wider tolerances versus sorting the product.
Process is out of control.	Process is erratic and unpredictable. Investigate causes of lack of control. Decision to correct based on economics of corrective action.		Process is misdirected or erratic or both. Correct misdirection. Discover cause for lack of control. Consider economics of more precise process versus wider tolerances versus sorting the product.	

*As a rule of thumb, a process variation (sometimes called natural tolerance = 6σ) less than a third of tolerance is small; more than two-thirds of tolerance is large.

by the workers themselves (see Section 22, under Test of Theories of Worker-Controllable Problems).

2. Conditions change and result in violations of the criteria of self-control: e.g., a specification becomes obsolete, a gage is out of calibration, equipment deteriorates due to a reduction in preventive maintenance.

To handle these problems, production management and the work force must be determined to remove the causes by directly taking action or by having others take action. Such determination requires a strong quality ethic on the production floor. For some companies, this entails a revolution.

An important step is to determine if the production floor culture does foster quality. Examples are legion to suggest that not only is a positive culture on qualtiy lacking, but negative actions are often taken in order to achieve other objectives such as production quotas. Worse yet, such actions are hidden from management, such as in the following three ways.

1. *Not reporting the nonconforming product:*   Examples include burying nonconforming paint in the ground, storing defective tires in railroad cars that are kept in transit, and disguising nonconforming parts as spare parts and shipping them with a finished vehicle. A variation is to "delay reporting" nonconforming items, i.e., report only the allowable percent of nonconforming needles in a given week and hold back any excess until a "good week" occurs.

2. *Finessing the inspector:*   One form of this approach is for the worker to ignore the fact that defectives are occurring and wait until a patrol inspector discovers the situation. In another ploy, the worker purposely creates a minor defect and makes an obvious correction in order to draw attention away from another defect, e.g., roughs up a surface and smooths it over, hoping that an inspector will overlook some rivets that are out of line (possibly reducing the strength).

3. *Charging rework operations as part of basic manufacturing costs.*

To survive in a culture that stresses production quotas or other priorities, people devise ways to meet these priorities. Clearly, a culture having the symptoms described above needs significant change. Two steps are required:

1. *Acertain the culture for quality on the production floor:*   Some of the conditions described can be discovered with special data collection and analysis. Also, a carefully planned attitude survey on quality for various levels of production supervision and workers can be a sobering and revealing study. See Section 9 under Summary of Quality Status.

2. *Take the steps necessary to change the culture:*   The road will be lengthy and difficult. A change in culture must be led by upper management. (Often enough the supervisors and managers have known about the goings-on and done nothing, or have even set bad examples.) Before that happens, management must understand (*a*) the extent of the problem and (*b*) that the conditions of the past have changed and new conditions demand a new culture. Section 10 under Management's Role discusses the role of management in creating the proper culture.

SELF-INSPECTION

Once product has been produced, there arises the question: Does this product conform to specification? In the United States, the responsibility for making this decision has generally rested with full-time inspectors who are members of a separate Inspection Department. These inspectors measure the product and decide whether it conforms to specification.

Under the concept of self-inspection, the worker who made the product also measures the product and decides whether it conforms to specification.

Note that the worker is *not* given the responsibility for determining the disposition of any nonconforming product. Also, self-inspection does *not* involve transfer of full-time inspectors to the Production Department. It involves abolishing the jobs of full-time inspectors and having the inspection done on a part-time basis by the production workers. Provision is made for an audit (see below under Audit of Decisions).

Self-inspection has decided advantages over the traditional delegation of inspection to a separate department:

1. Production workers are made to feel more responsible for the quality of their work.

2. Feedback on performance is immediate, thereby facilitating process adjustments. Traditional inspection also has the psychological disadvantage of using an "outsider" to report the defects to a worker.

3. The costs of a separate Inspection Department can be reduced.

4. The job enlargement that takes place by adding inspection to the production activity of the worker helps to reduce the monotony and boredom that are inherent in many jobs.

5. Elimination of a specific station for inspecting all products reduces the total manufacturing cycle time.

Criteria for Self-Inspection.   Before self-inspection can be adopted, some essential criteria must be met:

1. Quality must be the number 1 priority within an organization. If this is not clear, the worker may succumb to schedule and cost pressures and classify, as acceptable, products that should be rejected.

2. Mutual confidence is necessary. Managers must have sufficient confidence in the work force to be willing to entrust to them the responsibility of deciding whether the product conforms to specification. In turn, workers must have enough confidence in the management to be willing to accept this responsibility.

3. The criteria for self-control must be met. Failure to eliminate the management-controllable causes of defects suggest that management does not view quality as a high priority, and this may bias the workers during inspections.

4. Workers must be trained to understand the specifications and perform the inspection.

5. Specifications must be unequivocally clear.

6. Workers should understand the use that will be made of their products (internally and externally) in order to grasp the importance of a conformance decision.

7. The process must be of a nature which permits assignment of clear responsibility for decision making. An easy case for application is the worker running a lathe, since there is clear responsibility for making both the product and the product-conformance decision. In contrast, the long assembly line or the

numerous steps in a chemical process make it difficult to assign clear responsibility. Application to such multistep processes is best deferred until experience is gained with simple processes.

Whittingham (1982) describes the operation of self-inspection at an electronics plant. A "keypoint card" placed at the work station shows what inspections must be made, including the frequency interval and the method of inspection. Feedback to supervisors from an audit inspection summarizes the defects missed by each worker.

Cautions to Be Observed under Self-Inspection.   Note the following:

1. Training costs can be high, particularly with high turnover. It may take months for a worker to perform confidently the inspection of a complex electronic product.
2. The time needed for inspection may significantly reduce the time for doing productive work.
3. There may be potential conflicts in interpretation of specifications between workers and auditors.
4. Union agreements may require strict job specialization.
5. Workers may feel that the added responsibility of inspection requires additional compensation (and they may be correct).
6. There must be agreement on who is to perform any reinspection of a lot if an audit sample discovers nonconformities. (A "clean-up" to go back over prior lots can involve products already shipped to the customer.)
7. Some regulators oppose such delegations to the work force.
8. The reasons for instituting self-inspection must be explained to everyone so that the change is not interpreted as lowering the priority on quality.

Sequence for Instituting Self-Inspection Concept.   If workers are to be given the product-conformance decision, it is necessary to decide whether the responsibility should be given to all workers or only to those who have demonstrated their ability to make good decisions. The latter approach is highly preferable and should proceed as follows:

1. Train the workers in how to make product-conformance decisions.
2. Set up the necessary system of product indentification and preserving the order to assure that product decisions can be traced readily back to the worker who made them.
3. Institute a trial period during which workers make conformance decisions while duplicate decision making is done by inspectors. The purpose of this duplication is to discover, through data, which workers consistently make good product-conformance decisions.
4. Issue "licenses" (for making product-conformance decisions) only to those workers who demonstrate their competence. (This is analogous to qualification for certain manufacturing skills such as welding.)
5. For the licensed workers, institute an audit of decisions (see below). For the workers who do not qualify, retain the regular inspection.
6. Based on the results of the audits, continue or suspend the licenses.
7. Periodically conduct new trials in an effort to qualify the unlicensed workers.

Audit of Decisions.   During the trial period the inspection is conducted for two purposes:

1. Product approval, lot by lot
2. Comparison of inspector results with worker results

As the comparison establishes validity of the worker's decisions, the duplicate inspections are reduced in frequency until their prime purpose is to determine whether the worker continues to make good decisions. (Hence the name "audit of decisions.") At this stage any knowledge of the product is incidental. If an audit reveals that wrong decisions were made by the workers, then the product evaluated since the last audit is suspect and must be investigated.

Results of Self-Inspection.   Castagna (1983) reports results of applying the self-inspection concept at a rework facility for military aircraft. The number of in-process nonconformities decreased 31.8 percent in 1 year.

In a coning operation of textile yarn, the traditional method of inspection often resulted in finished cones sitting for several days in the inspection department, thereby delaying any feedback to production. Under the self-inspection, the worker received immediate feedback and could more promptly get machines repaired and setups improved. Overall, the program reduced nonconformities from 8 to 3 percent. An audit inspection of the products that were classified by the workers as "good" showed that virtually all of them were correctly classified. In this company workers can also classify product as "doubtful." In one analysis, worker inspections classified 3 percent of the product as doubtful, after which an independent inspector reviewed the doubtful product and classified 2 percent as acceptable, and 1 percent as nonconforming.

Wittingham (1982) and Noonan (1984) describe self-inspection in the electronics industry, including some unusual approaches to the audit inspection. Sanders (1974) discusses the ingredients for success and the results achieved at an aircraft plant. Kolinka (1984) traces the evolution of self-inspection for a computer manufacturer.

AUDIT OF PRODUCTION QUALITY

A quality audit is an independent evaluation of various aspects of quality performance for the purpose of providing information to those in need of assurance with respect to that performance. A full discussion of quality audit is given in Section 9 generally. See also Section 8 under Quality Audits by Upper Managers.

Application to manufacturing has been extensive and includes both audit of activities (systems audits) and audit of product (product audit).

Systems Audit.   Systems audits can be conducted for any activity that can affect final product quality.

The audit (as contrasted to a broad survey) is usually made on a specific activity, such as the system for calibrating measuring equipment. The checklists presented earlier in this section for the three criteria of self-control can suggest useful specific subjects for audits. Priority should be assigned to subjects that affect fitness for use. Adherence to existing procedures is often emphasized, but systems audits often uncover situations of inadequate or nonexistent procedures.

Dedhia (1985) describes an audit system for an electronics manufacturer. The audit consists of 14 subsystems each having an audit checklist (see Figure 17.4). Routine audits are performed by quality audit personnel on a scheduled basis. For selected activities, annual audits are conducted by a team from manufacturing, quality engineering, test engineering, purchasing, and other disciplines. The system includes a numerical audit rating based on classifying each discrepancy as major or minor. A rating below 90 percent requires an immediate corrective action response. A discussion of systems audit for an assembly manufacturer is given by Zeccardi and Radigan (1976). Freund and Trulli (1982) describe a comprehensive approach that incorporates flowcharts, cause-and-effect diagrams, and detailed check sheets.

Who Performs the Audits.   There are several categories of personnel to whom systems audits may be delegated:

Production Management.   In this situation, the middle or upper Production managers undertake the audit of execution versus plan. Because most production activities are highly visible, skilled observers can learn much from shop tours. Generally, Production managers possess these skills and, in addition, put a high value on direct observation.

The strength of these audits is that the managers believe and respond to their own senses more vigorously than to an auditor's report. The weaknesses are that the managers lack the time and skills to be thorough auditors. They seldom get fully into the data and documentation or into other matters not evident from shop observation. The fact that they are busy people limits the completeness of the audit and even the adherence to the audit schedule. There is also a risk that they will overreact to the shop observations. Finally, they do not document their findings adequately, so that for long-range solutions the follow-up can be poor.

Inspectors.   Some inspections are conducted not to measure the product but to observe the process (see, for example, the patrol beat, Section 18 under Inspection at Inspection Stations; Patrol Inspection). Such observations are themselves a review of execution versus plan. It is often feasible to extend these patrol inspections to review other aspects of execution.

The advantages of using inspectors are the economy of avoiding a separate auditor and the regularity inherent in use of patrol inspectors. The disadvantages arise from the fact that the patrol inspector is not sufficiently detached and not sufficiently "independent." Findings are less likely to come to the attention of the middle or upper supervision than those of the independent auditor who is on the scene only occasionally.

Independent Auditors.   For critical work the auditing should preferably be done by those who are not a part of the Inspection Department. Usually such auditors review the practices of inspectors as well as production workers.

The independent audit tends to be more completely planned than an audit by Production management or by inspectors. In addition, the entire concept of the independent audit has the support of upper management, which receives the audit reports for review.

Special Audit Teams.   Some organizations create a team of supervisory, professional, and production workers to audit the process. Wirkus (1982) describes a program in which the department supervisor, an area manufacturing engineer, a quality control engineer, workers, and inspectors form a team to perform audits. Ashby and Hines (1982) discuss a concept of auditing as applied to "quality clusters" or areas of activity on a production floor. Here the audit team includes production supervision, a statistical quality engineer, and cluster auditors.

The audit of decisions discussed previously requires a regular examination of

Audit Type	Audit Type	Audit Type

1. Equipment/tester/tools control
Calibration control/schedule
Monitoring activity
Certification status
Maintenance status
Data integrity/verification
Standards check
Availability of tools
Startup/shutdown procedure
Correlation verification
 	
2. Operator
Qualification status
Compliance with procedure
Output (quality) verification/operator capability
Data recording verification
Rework verification
Observation for conformance to procedures
Product handling
Workmanship
 	
3. Documentation
• Line documents (availability, readability, accessibility, document content, level)
  MPI
  PCN
• Document adherence
• Quality documents
  Inspection instructions
  Inspection tools
  Applicable test procedures
• Routings/flow chart/traveller
• Maintenance documents
• Training documents
• Experimental procedures
• Records/log books
• Off-specs
	4. Parts/Assembly
	Conformance to spec.
	EC level
	Handling/packaging/storage/shipping
	Data availability
	Scrap/M.E. hold/MRB parts (nonconforming parts)
	Traceability
	Inprocess product
	Finished product
	Nonconforming product control and disposition
	
	5. Process Control Status
	Process control instructions/actions
	Control chart status
	Check corrective actions
	Verify manufacturing data
	
	6. Environment
	Cleanliness of the work area
	Particle count verification
	Humidity recording
	Temperature recording
	General housekeeping (safety, etc.)
	
	7. Calibration/standards audits
	Calibration evidence
	Overdue for calibration
	Monitor standards
	
	8. Chemicals/materials control
	Shelf life labeling
	Receiving inspection status
	Handling/storage
	Shelf life
	Nonconforming chemicals/materials control and disposition
	Relationship to work instructions
		9. Software system
		Software control
		Data integrity/verification
		
		10. Q.A. Self-Audits
		Inspection data verification
		Housekeeping
		Inspector training/qualification
		
		11. Production Control Crib
		• Finished product control
		  Storage/handling
		  Receiving inspection status
		  EC level
		• Raw material control
		  Storage/handling
		  Receiving inspection status
		  EC level
		
		12. Rework
		• Procedures
		• Product quality
		• Product disposition
		
		13. System Audit
		• General administration
		• Product development
		• Product qualification
		• Functional testing
		• Field performance
		• Personnel training
		
		14. MRB Audit

FIG. 17.4 Audit checklist guidelines. *(Adapted from Dedhia, 1985, pp. 170–172.)*

product conformance along with the associated documentation. This cannot readily be done by the independent auditors who are on the scene so infrequently. Instead it is assigned to a special category of auditor created at the time of delegating conformance decisions to production workers.

Product Audit.   This form of audit provides information on the extent of product conformance to specification and fitness for use. See Section 9 under Product Audit.

TROUBLESHOOTING

Factory quality troubles exist in two different forms: chronic and sporadic.

Chronic troubles go on and on because no way has ever been found to eliminate them. For example, a factory process has for years operated at 10 percent nonconforming. No one has succeeded in reducing this level, so the factory has learned to live with it.

Sporadic troubles are the result of some sudden adverse change. For example, a process which is usually at 10 percent nonconforming suddenly goes to 25 percent. Such a change sets off a number of alarm signals which demand prompt action to restore the status quo (to go back to the usual 10 percent).

"Troubleshooting" (also "firefighting") is the process of dealing with the sporadic and restoring quality to the original level. Section 22, Quality Improvement, discusses a structured approach for dealing with chronic problems.

Responsibility for Troubleshooting.   Production personnel have quite a clear responsibility for restoring the status quo. Sometimes this responsibility is specifically written out. In other cases it is implied from the more basic responsibility of meeting the goals for quality, productivity, schedule, etc. Those goals cannot be met unless the sporadic trouble is eliminated.

To carry out this responsibility requries that Production:

Discover the cause (make the journey from symptom to cause).

Remove the cause. This action also makes the journey from cause to remedy— i.e., removing the cause will result in restoring the status quo.

Diagnosing the cause requires a problem-solving process of the kind described in Section 22 under Troubleshooting. This process focuses on *discovering what has changed.* Production personnel, by virtue of extensive presence on the factory floor, can contribute valuable theories of causes and can in addition evaluate the likely validity of theories.

While Production Department responsibility for troubleshooting is fairly clear, the ability to carry out this responsibility varies. The main variables are:

The complexity of the adverse change

The extent to which Production personnel are trained in the tools of diagnosis

A complex adverse change can require an extent of data collection and analysis which goes beyond the training and experience of Production personnel. That same complexity can also require extensive time for data collection and analysis—time which is not available to Production supervisors.

In such complex cases a team approach may be needed. The team is usually drawn from the following:

Production personnel to supply theories and authorize data collection

Technicians to carry out data collection

Diagnosticians to design the data plan and to analyze the subsequent data

"Outsiders" as the needs arise

The responsibility for creating such a team rests with Production.

The ideal approach is to train Production personnel to become self-sufficient in troubleshooting. If nonsupervisors are trained to do troubleshooting within their own work areas, the supervisors will have more time to participate on the cross-functional project teams that are typically needed for chronic troubles. The training needed is common to that needed by Production personnel for dealing with quality problems generally. The problem-solving training provided to quality circles is useful (see Section 11 under Training for Nonsupervisors).

TRAINING OF PRODUCTION PERSONNEL

The general subject of training for quality is treated in Section 11, and includes those aspects of training which relate to production.

The training required for Production supervisors and other personnel depends on the responsibilities assigned (see the discussion earlier in this section). Major areas of training are:

1. *Job skills:*   This is the minimal training. Such training must include provisions for updating, as knowledge on "special knacks" or other process information becomes available. Critical skills such as welding should have formal skills testing to certify that personnel can apply their training to make product that meet specifications. Passing these tests becomes a requirement for this job. Instances of falsification of tests have occurred, and steps must be taken to ensure valid results.

2. *Problem-solving tools:*   Depending on the responsibilities assigned to Production, training in problem solving may be needed. A notable example is the training provided to quality circles (data collection, cause-and-effect diagrams, Pareto analysis, histograms and other graphic techniques, etc.).

3. *Process control tools:*   Increasingly, production workers are receiving training in statistical control charts and other analysis techniques for routine control of a process.

4. *Importance of meeting specifications:*   It is useful periodically to reinforce the importance of meeting all specifications. In one chemical company, visits are made by workers to customer sites. Immediately after each visit, the workers hold a "reflections meeting" to discuss their observations and to decide how to get the message to the rest of the work force.

Training given in order to change the practices of personnel must unequivocally answer the question, "What do you want me to do differently?"

REFERENCES

Asby, Carl C. III and Hines, James E. (1982). "Quality Clusters, a New Concept in Quality Control." *Proceedings, Quality in Electronics Conference.* ASQC, Milwaukee, pp. 89–94.

Blumenthal, Irvin R. (1978). "Fabrication Information System." *ASQC Technical Conference Transactions,* Milwaukee, pp. 661–668.

Burgess, John A. (1982). "Measuring In-Process Quality Performance," *ASQC Quality Congress Transactions,* Milwaukee, pp. 70–76.

Carlisle, Rodney (1981). "Shirt-Sleeve Quality." *Quality,* March, pp. 48–49.

Castagna, Edward (1983). "Well Done." *Quality,* March, pp. 50–51.

Dedhia, Navin S. (1985). "Process Audit System Effectiveness." *European Organization for Quality Control Annual Conference, 1985.* EOQC, Berne, Switzerland, pp. 159–173.

Denissoff, Basile A. (1980). "Process Control Management." *Quality Process,* June, pp. 14–16.

Emmons, Sidney L. (1977). "Auditing for Profit and Productivity." *ASQC Technical Conference Transactions,* Milwaukee, pp. 206–212.

Fisher, James R. (1983). "Computer Assisted Net Weight Control." *Quality Progress,* June, pp. 22–25.

Freund, R. A. and Trulli, H. B. (1982). "Quality Assurance Review Technique." *Quality Assurance,* vol. 8, no. 1, March, pp. 17–22.

Fukuda, Ryuji (1981). "Quality Control Factor in Methods Engineering." *ASQC Quality Congress Transactions,* Milwaukee, pp. 268–273.

Howell, Vincent W. (1981). "Quality Control Factor in Methods Engineering." *ASQC Quality Congress Transactions,* Milwaukee, pp. 268–273.

Kassarda, John B. (1980). " Shop Floor Control Must Be Able to Provide Real-Time Status and Control." *Industrial Engineering,* pp. 74–78, 96.

Kolinka, Edward (1984). "Zero Inspectors—Is It Attainable?" *ASQC Quality Congress Transactions,* Milwaukee, pp. 152–156.

May, E. (1978). "Operator Participation in Quality Control, Also Called Self-Control." *Proceedings, International Convention on QC Circle,* Tokyo, pp. A4-17 through A4-22.

Noonan, Martin (1984). "Operator Quality Control." *EOQC Quality,* November, pp. 7–11.

Parker, H. V. (1981). "A Paper Mill Solves a Quality Control Problem with Process Control Data." *Quality Progress,* March, pp. 18–22.

Sahrmann, Herman (1979). "Set-Up Assurance through Time Series Analysis." *Journal of Quality Technology,* July, pp. 105–115.

Sanders, George (1974). "Total Process Control." *Quality Progress,* January, pp. 22–25.

Schonberger, Richard J. (1982). "Production Workers Bear Major Quality Responsibility in Japanese Industry." *Industrial Engineering,* December, pp. 34–40.

Stone, Herbert D. and Guith, T. A. (1984). "Buick City: Strategy for Quality and Productivity." *Quality Progress,* April, pp. 34–38.

Whittingham, P. R. B. (1982). "Practical Operator Control." *Quality Assurance,* December, pp. 99–102.

Wirkus, Stephen R. (1982). "Quality Awareness—Control Where It Counts." *ASQC Quality Congress Transactions,* Milwaukee, pp. 225–229.

Zeccardi, J. J. and Radigan, R. A. (1976). "Auditing Systems which Affect Product Quality: Increasing the Management Visibility of Quality Systems Performance." *ASQC Technical Conference Transactions,* Milwaukee, pp. 323–329.

SECTION 18

INSPECTION AND TEST[1]

Joseph J. Zeccardi

---

[1]In the Third Edition, the section on Inspection and Test was prepared by J. M. Juran and Hardy M. Cook, Jr.; the section on Measurement was prepared by J. M. Juran.

18.1

INTRODUCTION

The word "inspection" has so many meanings that precise definition must precede any critical discussion. As used in this handbook, "inspection" always involves evaluating the quality of some characteristic in relation to a standard. This evaluation may be described as the "inspection act" and consists of the following actions applied to each quality characteristic (Juran, 1945, p. 23):

1. Interpretation of the specification
2. Measurement of the quality of the characteristic
3. Comparing 1 with 2
4. Judging conformance
5. Disposing of conforming cases
6. Disposing of nonconforming cases
7. Recording the data obtained

Every key word in the foregoing is itself subject to much variation. The word "specification" is used in the generic sense as the *standard* for the characteristic. It may consist of a written description, a drawing, a photograph, a physical sample, an oral instruction, a hazy memory.

The term "measurement" is used in the generic sense of *evaluation,* and it has its own dialect:

When the measurement is done	*The word commonly used to describe it is*
By the unaided human being	Inspection (this is a second meaning for the word used in the title of this section)
With the aid of mechanical measuring instruments	Gaging or calipering
With the aid of electronic measuring instruments	Testing
With the aid of chemical or metallurgical measuring instruments	Testing or assaying

The main purpose of inspection is to determine whether products conform to specification. This purpose is often called "acceptance inspection," or "product acceptance." However, there are other purposes as well, the more important being listed in Table 18.1. The present section is concerned primarily with acceptance inspection, but it deals also with those purposes of inspection which are closely allied to acceptance inspection, e.g., rating of accuracy of inspectors.

The persons engaged full time in inspection work commonly carry the title "inspector." (The title is sometimes used to describe persons not concerned with industrial products, processes, or services, e.g., safety inspectors, health inspectors, etc. These categories are outside the scope of this section.) Other titles include "tester, " "gager," "chemist," "metallurgist," "technician." Persons engaged only part time in inspection commonly carry a job title which reflects their major activities, e.g., "machine operator," "adjuster," etc.

Since the 1960s there has been a worldwide trend toward returning some of the responsibility for product acceptance to production operators. Details of this

TABLE 18.1 The Purposes of Inspection* (*Continued*)

Purpose	Usually called	Distinguishing features
a. To distinguish good lots from bad lots.	Acceptance sampling or sampling inspection; also called:	Prime purpose is to classify lots of product as to whether they are acceptable or nonacceptable. Results of the sampling are used to make this classification. Data from sampling usually made available to producing department.
	Supplier (or incoming) inspection	If done by purchaser on material bought from another company.
	Process inspection	If done between departments of the same company.
	Final inspection	If done by seller prior to shipment of finished goods to the customer.
b. To distinguish good pieces from bad pieces.	Detail inspection, 100% inspection, or sorting; also called:	Prime purpose is to sort the product between good pieces and bad. Any data are incidental but are usually made available to producer.
	Classification	If process is inadequate to meet tolerances.
c. To determine if the process is changing. See Section 24.	Control sampling	If process is adequate, but shop difficulties have created defects "needlessly." Prime purpose is to see if the process is changing. Usually done through Shewhart control charts which compare averages of samples to statistical limit lines. Detects the entrance of significant causes of variation. Any classification of product is incidental.
d. To determine if the process is approaching the specification limits. See Section 24.	PRE-Control	Prime purpose is to see if the trend of change within the process is such that there is danger of producing defective

18.5

TABLE 18.1 The Purposes of Inspection* (*Continued*)

Purpose	Usually called	Distinguishing features
e. To rate the quality of product. See Section 9, under Product Auditing.	Product auditing or quality rating	product. Usually done through charts which compare measurements on individual units of product to narrowed specification limits. Prime purpose is to "photograph" the quality of product. Usually the seriousness of defects is recognized by assigning demerits or weights depending on the severity of defects. Results are usually charted as demerits per unit of product.
f. To rate the accuracy of inspectors. See in this section, under Measure of Inspector Accuracy.	Accuracy inspection, or overinspection, or accuracy rating, or check inspection	Prime purpose is to measure the effectiveness of inspectors in finding defects. Comparison is made between (1) defects found by the inspector and, (2) defects which should have been found by the inspector. The ratio of (1) to (2) is the accuracy of the inspector.
g. To measure the precision of the measuring instrument. See in this section, under Error of Measurement.		Prime purpose is to measure the ability of the instrument to reproduce its own readings under like conditions. Usually involves repeat checks by the same instrument on the same unit of product. May involve checks by more than one instrument on the same unit of product.
h. To secure product-design information.	Qualification testing	Prime purpose is to judge the service capability of the product. Sometimes involves tests of increased severity.
i. To measure process capability. See Section 16, under Process Capability Measurement.	Process-capability measurement	Quantifies inherent variation of process.

*Inspection includes, in all instances (1) interpretation of the specification, (2) measurement of the product, and (3) comparison of (1) with (2). Inspection also includes additional elements depending on the purpose (as noted).

18.6

are discussed in Section 11, under Self-Inspection. See also Sears (1982) for a discussion on how this trend will provide the inspection function the opportunity to improve its effectiveness through more specialized testing.

Appendix III, Selected Quality Standards, Specifications, and Related Documents, includes documents on inspection and test methods.

INSPECTION AND TEST PLANNING

As products have grown complex and the job of making them has been divided among many departments, the job of inspection has also become complex and divided. Most inspection is now done by inspectors who lack full understanding of fitness for use. For this more complex work, it has been found necessary to engage in formal inspection planning, i.e., preparing a written plan of what to inspect for and how to do it (see also American Society for Quality Control and American National Standards Institute, 1984).

The approach to inspection planning follows closely the principles of quality planning as set out in Section 6. Application of these principles to the inspection job has been extensively studied, and good tools are available to facilitate inspection planning.

Who Plans? It depends on the work situation. Table 18.2 lists some usual inspection and test activities and the identity of the usual planner. The unifying concept within Table 18.2 is that inspection planning can be done by anyone who understands the fitness for use of the product being inspected.

Where planning is done by a staff planner, it is usual to require that his or her proposal be accepted by the inspection supervision before the plan becomes effective. The staff planner also is assigned a scope of responsibility to work within. This scope determines which aspects of inspection planning are to be covered: inspecton instructions, instrumentation, cost estimates, space and workplace design, documentation, etc. In large organizations the planning is sometimes divided among specialists rather than being assigned by project.

TABLE 18.2   Who Does the Inspection Planning?

Products requiring inspection and test planning	Inspector	Usual planner	
		Inspection supervisor	Quality control staff planner
Components completed within single department, small series production	X		
Components completed within single department, large series production		X	
Simple components and services, purchased or in-house (casting, plating)		X	
Complex units, small series production (machine tools)		X	
Components produced by progression through multiple departments			X
Subsystem test, interdependent units			X

The Flow Diagram.   The more complex the product, the greater the need to prepare a flow diagram showing the various materials, components, and processes which collectively or sequentially turn out the final product. Figure 6.5 (in Section 6) is an example of a flow diagram prepared to aid inspection planning.

To prepare the flow diagram, the planner visits the various locations, interviews the key people, observes the activities, and records findings. The planner simplifies the picture by good use of symbols. The most usual symbols are:

○ OPERATION   D DELAY
⇨ TRANSPORTATION   ▽ STORAGE
☐ INSPECTION   ◍ COMBINED ACTIVITY

In addition, the planner prepares proposals for improvement, sends copies of the diagram to all concerned, and then is ready to convene them for discussion of the diagram and the proposals.

Inspection Stations.   Selection of inspection stations follows closely the criteria for selection of control stations set out in Section 6. Applied to inspection, the stations are usually placed:

At movement of goods between companies, usually called "supplier inspection"

Before starting a costly or irreversible operation, usually called "setup inspection"

At movement of goods between departments, usually called "process inspection"

Upon completion of the product, usually called "finished goods inspection"

For complex products, such as missile systems, acceptance may require tests of mechanical compatibility, electrical mating, vehicle performance under specified environmental conditions, and final configuration. These are usually called "systems tests."

These general rules do not decide all questions of inspection stations. Complex supplier relations may require an inspection station at the supplier's plant. Some process operations may require a "station" in which the inspector patrols a large area. Other process operations may be sufficiently well in hand so that no inspection stations are used between departments; instead, there is a station after completion of all operations. In assembly lines, inspection stations may be located on the line as well as at the end of the line. (See Section 30, under In-Line Assembly Inspection.) In still other situations, there may be an added station after packing or at the customer's premises.

For each inspection station, instruct the inspector what to inspect for and how to do it:

Just what the mission of that inspection station is, i.e., which qualities to check

How to determine whether a unit of product conforms to standard or not

How to determine whether a lot of product is acceptable or not ("lot criteria")

What to do with conforming and nonconforming products

What records to make

While these categories of instruction are quite similar from one job to another, the degree of detail varies enormously.

In allocating the inspection work among the various inspection stations, the planner should be alert to the presence of "self-policing" operations. Some oversize parts will not enter tools or fixtures for further processing, or cannot be assembled. Some parts are subjected to greater stresses during manufacture than during usage. Some electrical circuit tests identify deficient components. Oil-pressure tests identify some undersize parts. [Refer to Trippi (1975) for a discussion on the optimal allocation of inspection resources; Ballou and Pazer (1982) for the optimal placement of inspection stations; and Eppen and Hurst (1974) for the optimal location of inspection stations in multistage production processes.]

List of Characteristics.   For each inspection station, the planner lists the quality characteristics to be checked. To determine these, the planner considers the various sources of pertinent product information:

The needs of fitness for use

The product and process specifications as published by the engineers

The customer's order, which references the product specification but may call for modifications

The pertinent industry standards, shop standards, and other general use sources

The presence of such multiple sources of information poses a question which should be faced squarely: Should the job of finding, interpreting, and reconciling these sources be left to the inspector, or should the planner do it? The answer will depend on the situation, but it should be clear.

Interpretation of the Specification.   The specification information is seldom sufficient for the inspector to meet the realities to be faced. The inspection planner can help to bridge this gap in several ways:

1. *Clear up the meaning of the words used:*   Terminology for describing sensory qualities is often confusing. In one company, the term "beauty defects" was used generally to describe blemishes on the product. Some of these blemishes (scratches in the focal plane of an optical instrument) made the product unfit for service. Other blemishes, though nonfunctional, could be seen by the customers and were objectionable for esthetic reasons. Still other nonfunctional blemishes could be seen by the company inspectors but not by consumers. However, because the multiple meanings of the term "beauty defect" had not been clarified, the inspectors rejected all blemishes. Data analysis showed that most of the blemishes were both nonfunctional and nonoffensive to customers. Hence, new terminology was created to make the distinctions needed to describe the effect of blemishes. The clarification of terminology improved yields and opened the way to improvement in manufacturing processes as well. [Based on the consulting experience of J. M. Juran. For some added examples, see Juran (1952).]

2. *Provide supplemental information:*   Make it available on matters for which the specification is vague or silent, e.g., workmanship. Usually this can be done for entire commodity or component classes, with minimum individual analysis. The greatest needs for supplemental standards arise in new and rapidly changing technology; in such cases it is common to find that vague standards are provided to the inspectors. Vague standards create confusion among departments as well as among companies. Refer to Miller (1975) for a discussion on specifying test methods and specifications.

3. *Classify the characteristics for seriousness:* This will help place the emphasis on the most important features of the product. (See Seriousness Classification, later in this section.) In the case of process characteristics, make use of the Concept of Dominance, as discussed in Section 16.

4. *Provide samples, photographs, or other reference aids:* This will help explain the meaning of the specification. The greatest single need is for visual standards (see below).

5. *Review clarity of specifications in general:* Periodically, the inspection planners should take time out from product-by-product planning to review with the specification writers the recurring, chronic problems of interpretation. Such reviews have historically been the means for making major strides in clarifying specifications, e.g., serious classification of characteristics; quantifying widely used characteristics such as torque required to turn knobs; standardization of surface finishes; sample reference file, etc.

Written Inspection Instructions.   The final results of inspection planning are reduced to writing in one of several ways:

Inspection and Test Procedure.   This is a tailor-made plan for a specific component or product type. It always lists the characteristics to be checked, the method of check (e.g., visual, gage, etc.), and the instruments to be used. It may, in addition, include the seriousness classification of characteristics; tolerances and other piece criteria; list of applicable standards; sequence of inspection operations; frequency of inspection; sample size, allowable number of defects, and other lot criteria; and inspection stamps to be applied.

Inspection and test procedures are very widely used in industry. In companies making complex systems or undergoing frequent design changes, these procedures become very numerous and consume extensive staff manpower to prepare them.

For some simple examples of inspection and test procedures, see Figure 13.11 and Table 29.1, in Sections 13 and 29, respectively.

Patrol Beat.   For many types of process inspection, the inspection stations require less than the full time of an inspector—often much less. A usual practice is to collect such stations into a "patrol beat" so designed that it will occupy the full time of one person. Table 18.3 is an example of such a patrol beat.

Patrol beats usually involve multiple production and inspection departmental areas. In addition, the inspection findings are reported to several departments for information and action, e.g., Production, Inspection, Quality Control.

In consequence, the planner should assure that these and other departments affected participate in the design of the patrol beat.

"Work sampling" is a useful concept in patrol inspection. Under this concept, the inspectors make *random* visits to the inspection stations. The resulting data are analyzed and become the basis for supervisory action. [Refer to Cooper (1977) for further discussion.]

Finished Goods Acceptance Procedure.   There are actually a number of levels of "finished goods": materials, parts, components, subassemblies, assembled units, subsystems, systems. Each of these can be a completed product to some company or department, and thereby "finished goods" acceptance is performed at all these levels. System tests are most elaborate, not merely because of the problems of mating subsystems but because of the many complex environmental tests needed for modern apparatus.

The acceptance procedure should certainly provide inspection for new defects created by the progression of the product into higher levels of assembly and finishing operations. In addition, acceptance testing may be designed to provide redundancy against failure to detect defects missed at earlier stages of progression.

Much of the previous and current inspection literature uses the term "defect" to mean a deviation from the specification of a particular quality characteristic. Clearly a deviation from a specification does not automatically mean a product is unfit for use (see later in this section under Three Decisions). Thus, some recent terminology has used the term "nonconforming" to describe a deviation from a specification. For simplicity, the terms "defect" and "defective" will be used in this section.

The planner should be especially alert to discover duplications between what is done at final inspection and elsewhere. When field troubles show up as a result of ineffective controls prior to final inspection, field engineers and higher management all may be indifferent to the niceties of inspection stations and may urge multiple checks as a temporary measure. These bits of work can take firm root, accumulate, and endure beyond the reasons which gave them birth. The planner is in a good position to discover such out-of-date duplications and to root them out.

In conveyor assembly and test lines, the planning is usually for an entire inspection and test *team*. Sometimes the team is housed in a separate test area, the product being conveyed in and out. In other cases, the team is largely stationed on the main assembly line, the inspection stations being located amid production stations.

Planning of such team activities requires close collaboration among the industrial neighbors involved in the common work flow. It also requires a balancing of the work load among the team members through ingenious design of test equipment, handling equipment, and work assignments.

Nonproduction Operations. The planner should be alert to the need for locating inspection stations at such operations as material handling, storage, packing, and shipping. The fact that the departments doing these operations are not a part of production is of no consequence if product quality is affected.

Aspects which may require inspection planning include:

Internal handling: Use of correct containers and other handling facilities; product protection against corrosion, contamination, etc.

Internal storage: Adequate identity and traceability

Packing: Product identification, lot numbers, traceability; protection against adverse environments; protection against damage due to handling, shipping and unpacking; presence of incidental small parts and information circulars

Shipping: Care in loading; special markings required by customers

Once the planner has prepared the procedure, the interested departmental supervisors can be convened to reach agreement on who is to carry out that part of the inspection plan.

Inspection Data Planning. The planner also determines the data-recording needs for each inspection station. In many cases, the standard inspection report forms will meet the recording needs. For finished products, a special test document is usually provided. In addition, the planner makes provision for any special recording needed for frequency distribution, control charts, certification, traceability, etc. (See also Feedback of Inspection Data, below.)

TABLE 18.3 Patrol Beat

No.	Test	Sampling		Testing	How results are used
		Where	Frequency	Where	
Acid manufacturing process					
1	% SO_2 gas test TAPPI 603 M-45	From gas line off coolers	Once every two hours	Acid plant	This test is used for checking the automatic Leeds and Northrup SO_2 recorders.
2	Temperature of gas, strong tower and weak tower M & O method		Once per hour	Acid plant	The acid maker controls the temperature of the gas, the strong tower, and the weak tower to regulate the speed of the gas absorption in the acid-making process.

3	Acid test, total, free, and combined SO_2 TAPPI 640 M-45	From strong and weak towers	Once per hour	Acid plant	This test tells the acid maker how much lime rock to use. The amount of water and gas going to the towers is adjusted with this information.
4	Baumé on acid in strong tower and acid in weak tower M & O method	From strong tower and weak tower	Once per hour	Acid plant	The acid maker controls the strength of his acid in the towers with these test results. They tell the concentration of the acid.
Digester cooking process					
5	Chip moisture M & O method	Sample taken in chip bin	Once per cook	Chip room	The cook adjusts the volume of the chips put in the digesters with this information.

Source: Carter, C. W. (1958). "Audit Testing," *Industrial Quality Control*, March, pp. 8–11.

Extent of Planning. The concept of separating inspection planning from execution has great value if properly applied. If planning is underapplied, there is increased risk of catastrophic product failure. If overapplied, the result is excess cost and much internal friction. Striking a sound balance requires periodic reappraisal of the major forces in contention as well as analysis of the conventional alarm signals, e.g., rising staff costs, abrasion between departments. In addition, the changing job situations influence the extent of formal planning needed, notably (1) the education, experience, and training of the work force; (2) the stability of the processes; and (3) the severity of the product requirements.

Recognition of Profound Changes. Planners should be on the alert to identify revolutionary changes in quality criteria and to provide correspondingly revolutionary procedures dealing with these changes. To cite several examples:

1. Assembly of nuclear reactors and space vehicles requires a level of care far beyond that exercised in conventional assembly. The Enrico Fermi reactor at Lagoona Beach, MI, was badly damaged in October 1966, evidently because of a foreign object blocking the flow of sodium coolant. Pumps in nuclear reactors have been badly damaged by a loose nut being pumped through the system. Complex missiles have failed in their mission because of comparatively simple defects on mechanical components. In such situations the penalties for undetected defects rise so high that elaborate countdowns and checkouts must be instituted.

2. When the U.S. Navy undertook procurement of materials and components to build nuclear submarines, it encountered a widespread failure to adhere to specifications and sharply criticized the contractors for the nonconformances. Actually, the contractors were doing what they had always done—shipping nonconforming products which experience had shown to be fit for use. The big change was that the new species of submarines required rigid compliance with specifications which had been unrealistic in respect to previous applications. In addition, there was a clash between two cultures: (*a*) the contractors, who took too long to discover that loose enforcement had no place in the nuclear submarine program, and (*b*) a new breed of Navy engineers, who were unaware that loose enforcement had long been used to neutralize the effect of unrealistic specifications. [See also Juran (1969) and Ramaswamy (1981).]

3. Soon after the Motor Vehicle Safety Act of 1966 became law, the government regulators found that a significant number of vehicle components failed to comply to standards which "industry itself" (i.e., committees of industry engineers) had set before there was legislation on the subject. Here the two cultures involved (industry regulation and government regulation) represented different levels of enforcement, the one based on fitness for use and the other based on the concept that each instance of nonconformance now constituted a "federal case."

These cases of "massive change" can be multiplied widely. Failure to recognize their existence sets the stage for a shocking, expensive confrontation which damages many innocent people as well as the guilty (see also Paul, 1982).

Errorproofing. The planner faces two responsibilities related to inspection error: (1) avoiding built-in sources of error and (2) providing positive means of foolproofing the inspection against error. See, for a detailed discussion, Inadvertent Inspector Errors, under Inspector Errors, below.

Overplanning. In some companies, the writing of inspection plans is extensively done. New customer orders, new product designs, new process changes, new regulations, etc., are all occasions for scrutiny by the quality engineers, who issue inspection plans accordingly. As this goes to extremes, the cost of planning rises, and the excess formality increases the training time for inspectors, the attention to trivia, the documentation, and the control effort generally. Error rates tend to increase, with adverse effects on inspection costs and inspector morale.

Dealing with excess planning costs takes several forms. One is to do the planning by computer or by other means of mechanizing much of what the engineers otherwise do manually.

A second approach is to minimize the amount of tailor-made planning by extending the use of inspection and test manuals which have broad application. See Inspection Manual, below.

A third approach is to delegate some of the planning itself to the inspection supervisors and the inspectors. To do this usually requires preparation of a manual on inspection planning plus training the inspection force to do the planning for all except the vital few characteristics, which are reserved for the staff planners.

Still another device is to agree, case by case, on the amount of detailed planning needed.

Human, Machine, and System. A major decision in all planning is the extent to which tasks will be assigned to people versus machines, and the related decision regarding delegation of tasks to people versus systems.

Machines are superior for doing deeds which can be clearly defined and which require exacting attention to repetitive detail. (Contrary to popular belief, machines cannot think for humans; rather, humans must do the thinking for the machines. Thereafter, the machines follow the prescribed programs.)

Table 18.4 is a list contrasting intellectual activities, and proposes a division between person and machine as applied to inspection and test. (See also Thompson and Reynolds, 1964.)

The study of the interrelationship of people, machines, and system masquerades under a variety of names: human factors; biomechanics; human engineering; ergonomics; industrial psychology. Industrial managers, including quality managers, are commonly amateurs in the understanding of human capacities and especially human behavior. The behavioral scientists are the "professionals," but the subject is as yet hardly a science. In addition, communication between the practicing managers and the behavioral scientists is severely limited by differences in dialect and, especially, cultural background.

INSPECTION MANUAL

This manual elaborates the work of the Inspection Department and includes much information of general interest to all company departments with respect to inspection practice. (The inspection manual is a part of the overall quality manual. See Section 6.) It consists of:

1. A manual of inspection procedures common to all products and processes
2. Supplemental manuals for specific products and processes

TABLE 18.4   Assignment to Machines versus People

Lower intellectual activities	Higher intellectual activities
1. Things that can be expressed exactly.	Things that cannot be expressed exactly.
2. Decisions that can be made in advance.	Decisions that cannot be made in advance.
3. Arithmetic, algebraic, and chesslike symbolic logic.	Pattern recognition, judgment, creativity, foresight, leadership, and such thinking.
4. Highly repetitive and, therefore, menial.	Random, having many degrees of freedom, never exactly the same.
5. Can be reduced to logic and, therefore, programmed exactly into a machine.	Cannot be programmed exactly but can use heuristic approximations as an aid.
6. Those a small machine can handle completely, faster, and more positively.	A machine cannot handle completely and it becomes excessively large and uneconomical in attempting to do so.
7. Design and programming require a high level of intelligence but, once done, the mental activity need not be repeated.	This problem is never exactly the same and it must be reconsidered, that is, rethought out for each new decision.
8. Involves decisions as to what is right or wrong. The person guesses and the machine monitors to prevent him or her from making a mistake. It does this positively enough for use in safety systems.	People use the display which is driven by the machine and possibly a separate computer to assist them in making the choice type of decisions as to what is best, using the most advanced mathematical techniques.
9. Requires a high degree of orderliness.	Takes care of matters which cannot be arranged into any sort of orderly procedures.
10. Includes the decisions which must be made rapidly by the machine in periods of congestions and in emergencies.	Involves situations that develop more slowly, that will, sooner or later, require a considered decision.

Inspection Procedures Manual.   The contents of this manual are quite similar from one company to another and consist typically of:

The statement of legitimacy and purpose, approved by the responsible manager.

The table of contents of the manual.

The organization section, including inspection organization charts, job descriptions, and statements of responsibilities.

The general concept of inspection as used in the company.

The plan for seriousness classification of defects. (The actual classifications of defects are in the supplemental product manuals.)

The standard plans for sampling inspection: bulk sampling, tables for random sampling, continuous sampling, narrow-limit sampling.

The standard plans for use of control charts.

Supplier inspection procedures.

In-process inspection procedures.

Finished goods inspection procedures.

Measurement control procedures, including the schedule of checking intervals for general-use equipment.

Copies of all the inspection forms used and instructions for data recording and documentation.

Product identification procedure.

Procedure for issuance and control of inspection stamps.

Feedback of data to Production; procedure for corrective action.

Procedure for dealing with nonconforming material.

Index and glossary.

Product and Process Inspection Manuals.   These specialized supplemental manuals, though dealing with a variety of products, are organized under similar outlines, typically:

The materials section, which includes material specification

The process section which includes:

    Process specifications

    Formulation control criteria

    Patrol beats and associated criteria

The product section, which includes:

    Product specifications and associated technical data

    Product samples where feasible, e.g., textile swatches, color samples

    Lists of defects, classified for seriousness

    Sample sizes, frequencies, AQLs, and acceptance criteria

The test section, which includes test specifications—both internal and industrial standards

THREE DECISIONS

A major purpose of inspection is to determine the disposition of a product based on its quality. This disposition involves three cardinal decisions (Juran and Gryna, 1980):

Conformance decision	To judge whether the product conforms to specification
Fitness-for-use decision	To decide whether nonconforming product is fit for use
Communication decision	To decide what to communicate to outsiders and insiders

The Conformance Decision.   Except in small companies, the number of conformance decisions made per year is simply huge. There is no possibility for the supervisory body to become involved in the details of so many decisions. Hence the work is so organized that the inspectors or production workers can make these decisions. To this end they are trained to understand the products, the standards, and the instruments. Once trained, they are given the job of making the inspections and of judging conformance. (In many cases the delegation is to automated instruments.)

Associated with the conformance decision is the disposition of conforming product; the inspector is authorized to identify the product ("stamp it up") as an acceptable product. This identification then serves to inform the packers, shippers, etc., that the product should proceed to its next destination (further processing, storeroom, customer). Strictly speaking, this decision to "ship" is made not by the inspectors but by the management. With some exceptions, a product that conforms to specification is also fit for use. Hence the company procedures (which are established by the managers) provide that conforming products should be shipped as a regular practice.

The Fitness-for-Use Decision.   In the case of nonconforming products, a new question arises: Is this nonconforming product fit for use or unfit? In some cases the answer is obvious—the nonconformance is so severe as to make the product clearly unfit. Hence it is scrapped or, if economically repairable, brought to a state of conformance. However, in many cases the answer as to fitness for use is not obvious. In such cases, if enough is at stake, a study is made to determine fitness for use. This study involves securing inputs such as those shown in Table 18.5.

Once all the information has been collected and analyzed, the fitness-for-use decision can be made. If the amount at stake is small, this decision will be delegated to a staff specialist, to the quality manager, or to some continuing decision-making committee such as a Material Review Board. If the amount at stake is large, the decision will usually be made by a team of upper managers.

The Communication Decision.   Inspection serves not only to make decisions on the product, but also to generate data which provide essential information for a wide variety of purposes, such as those listed in Table 18.1. The conformance and fitness-for-use decisions likewise are a source of essential information, although some of this is not well communicated.

Data on nonconforming products are usually communicated to the producing departments to aid them in preventing a recurrence. In more elaborate data collection systems there may be periodic summaries to identify "repeaters" or "top 10," which then become the subject of special studies.

TABLE 18.5   Inputs Required for Fitness-for-Use Decision

Input	Usual sources
Who will be the user?	Marketing
How will the nonconforming product be used?	Marketing, client
Are there risks to human safety or structural integrity?	Product research and design
What is the urgency?	Marketing, client
What are the company's and the users' economics?	All departments, client
What are the users' measures of fitness for use?	Market research, marketing, client

When nonconforming products are sent out as fit for use, there arises the need for two additional categories of communication:

1. *Communication to "outsiders":*   They (usually customers) have a right and a need to know. All too often, the manufacturing companies neglect to inform their customers when shipping nonconforming products. This may be as a result of bad experience, i.e., some customers will seize on such nonconformances to secure a price discount despite the fact that use of the product will not add to their costs. More usually, the neglect indicates a failure even to face the question of what to communicate. A major factor here is the design of the forms used to record the decisions. With rare exceptions, these forms lack provisions which force those involved to make recommendations and decisions on (*a*) whether to inform the outsiders, and (*b*) what to communicate to them.

2. *Communication to insiders:*   When nonconforming goods are shipped as fit for use, the reasons are not always communicated to the inspectors and especially not to the production workers. The resulting vacuum of knowledge has been known to breed some bad practices. When the same type of nonconformance has been shipped several times, an inspector may conclude (in the absence of knowing why) that it is just a waste of time to report such nonconformances in the first place. Yet in some future case, the special reasons (which were the basis of the decision to ship the nonconforming goods) may not be present. In like manner, a production worker may conclude that it is a waste of time to exert all that effort to avoid some nonconformance which will be shipped anyway. Such reactions by well-meaning employees can be minimized if the company faces squarely the question: what shall we communicate to the insiders?

PRODUCT CONFORMANCE

The principal decision making assigned to inspectors is to determine whether product conforms to standard. (See also Three Decisions, discussed above, and under Feedback to Production below, for a discussion of decision making to determine whether the process conforms to standard.) When the words "product" and "standard" are examined closely, it becomes evident that some careful distinctions be made.

The Nature of Product.   "Product" takes multiple forms. When submitted to Inspection for decision on conformance to standard, product may consist either of (*a*) single elements of product or (*b*) lots of product. Single elements exhibit one of two main forms:

Discrete Units of Product.   These are separate entities such as bolts, teacups, refrigerators. The term "discrete" refers to the fact that the product is made, tested, and used as a separate unit. The approach to these activities is simplified through prior knowledge of how the product will be used.

Specimens from a Coalesced Mass.   These are samples from batches, such as a melt of steel or from continuous processes such as petroleum refining. These situations lack the common base of knowledge of the discrete units, since the product is made as a coalesced mass, tested as a specimen, and used in numerous forms not fully predictable at the time of test.

The Nature of Lots of Product. Usually the product submitted for decision on conformance to standard consists of a "lot." The true lot is an aggregation of product made under a common system of causes. When this ideal is met, the lot possesses an *inherent uniformity derived from the common system of causes.* The extent to which the lot conforms to this ideal greatly influences the approach to the product conformance decision and especially the kind and extent of sampling.

In its simplest form, the true lot emerges from one machine run by one operator processing one material batch, all under a state of statistical control, e.g., a single formulation of a drug product or a run of screw machine parts turned from one piece of rod on one machine. A great deal of industrial production consists of true lots.

However, a great deal of other production consists of product mixtures which, in varying degrees, fall short of the ideal lot definition. Product made from several material batches, or on several machines, or by several operators, may be dumped into a common container. In shop language, this mixture is a "lot," but in precise language it is only a mixture. In continuous processes or in conveyor production, the process may well be common and constant, but the input materials may not be.

For precise and economic product conformance decisions, it is most helpful to "preserve the order." This means that product is kept segregated in true lots or at least identified as to common cause. In addition, for those processes which exhibit a time-to-time variation or "drift" (e.g., the solution gradually becomes dilute, the tool gradually wears), preserving the order includes preserving the time sequence during which various portions of the lot were made. Any loss of order of manufacture becomes also a loss of some prior knowledge as to inherent uniformity. (See Section 17, under Product and Process Relationship, for a discussion of preserving the order as an important aid to process regulation.)

Some products are naturally fluid and develop a homogeneity through this fluidity. Homogeneity from this new cause can also qualify the product as a true lot, with important implications for the sampling process.

When several true lots are combined for the purposes of acceptance, the combination is known as a "grand lot" (a term believed to have been first used by L. E. Simon). Such mixtures are very common, e.g., product from multiple cavities of molding operations or from multiple spindles of screw machine operations.

The two categories of single elements of product (discrete units and specimens) have their counterparts in two categories of lots:

The Lot as a Collection of Discrete Units. Here the lot consists of numerous bolts, teacups, or refrigerators, each one of which is governed by the product specification. In batch production, the lot is usually determined by the obvious boundaries of the batch. In continuous production, the lot is usually defined as an arbitrary amount of production, or as the amount produced during an arbitrary time span, e.g., a shift, a week.

The Lot as a Coalesced Mass. Here the lot may also consist of a batch, e.g., the melt of steel. In continuous production, the lot is again based on some arbitrary selection, e.g., 1 ton, a day's production.

Product Conformance Criteria. Table 18.6 shows the criteria used for judging product conformance to standard, both for product elements and for lots, whether of discrete units or coalesced. It is evident that there are profound differences which affect decisions on how to inspect and which even affect the way of thinking about inspection.

Criteria for Discrete Units. Table 18.6 shows that criteria for judging conformance of discrete units to standard are contained in the product specifications and in the supplemental interpretations provided by the inspection planning (see Interpretation of the Specification, above). Inspection planners are greatly aided in setting these criteria because of the consistency inherent in the discrete unit concept—it is made, tested, and used as a unit. Knowledge of product usage is obtainable and can be put to work in developing added criteria for judging conformance.

Criteria for Specimens. Coalesced products usually lack the consistency among manufacture, test, and usage which characterizes discrete units of product. Quite often it is not known, at the time of testing the specimen, what the future use of the product will be. As a result, criteria for judging the conformance of a specimen to its specification must include much discussion and common consent among the parties of interest. This is precisely what has happened, and a great deal has been done to evolve industry standards which define the specimen and prescribe how to test it.

Criteria for Lots (Collections of Discrete Units). For these lots, the lot criteria consist of rules for lot formation, sample sizes, and allowable number of defects. These criteria are not provided in the design specifications. In consequence, they are provided as part of the inspection planning process.

Criteria for Lots (Coalesced). For some of these products the lot criteria are set up in a manner similar to that used for lots of discrete units, treating each specimen as though it were a discrete unit of product. Coalesced products exhibit *defects* but not defective units *(defectives)*. Discrete units of products can exhibit either defects or defectives.

Increasingly, the lot criteria are being established by setting limits on the product mass in the form of (1) plus and minus tolerances on the average and (2) a maximum on the standard deviation. When the lot limits are in this form, the data on the various specimens are pooled together on a variables basis to permit judgement of conformance.

Sampling Criteria for Lots. Two major considerations guide the sampling plans to be established for lot acceptance:

1. The extent of knowledge available from sources other than sampling the lot. This is discussed below, under How Much Inspection?

2. The statistical principles governing sampling. These are discussed in Section 25.

HOW MUCH INSPECTION? EFFECT OF PRIOR KNOWLEDGE

The usual starting point is an awareness that product conformance decisions must be based on product knowledge and that this product knowledge is available from multiple sources:

Prior Conformance Decisions on the Same Lot. In some cases, the concept of "audit of decisions" has been put to work so that suppliers, independent lab-

TABLE 18.6 Criteria for Judging Conformance of Product in Units and Lots

Aspects of conformance	Product consists of discrete units		Product consists of a coalesced mass	
	Individual unit of product	Lot = collection of discrete units	Specimen from mass	Lot = coalesced mass
Usual name of subject matter of inspection:	Part, unit, component, assembly, product, etc.	Lot	Specimen	Lot, mass
Standard usually consists of:	Product specification, plus supplemental criteria in inspection plan	Sampling plan	Material specification	Sampling plan
Standard usually published by:	Product Design Department and Inspection Planning	Quality Control Department	Product Design Department	Product Design or Quality Control Department
Standard usually expressed in terms of:	Natural units of measure	Percent defective	Natural units of measure	Percent conforming

Tolerance usually expressed as:	Maximum and minimum measurements	Allowable defects in sample	Maximum and minimum measurements	Maximum and minimum on averages; maximum on dispersion
Information on conformance usually derived from:	Measuring instruments	Sampling data plus prior knowledge of process (capability, order of manufacture, etc.)	Measuring instruments	Sampling data; inherent fluidity; prior knowledge of process
Criteria for judging conformance are:	Measurement versus tolerance	Actual defects versus allowable evidence of process behavior	Measurement versus tolerance	Averages and dispersion versus tolerances; prior data

18.23

oratories, workers, etc., have been qualified as able to give reliable product conformance decisions and in addition have accepted this very lot. In such cases, no further product inspection is necessary (beyond that inherent in "audit of decisions"). See, in this connection, Section 15, under Audit of Decisions; also Section 17, under Self-Inspection.

Prior Knowledge of the Process.   To illustrate, a press operation stamps out 10,000 pieces. If the first and last pieces contain certain specified holes of correct size and location, it follows that the intervening 9998 pieces also carry holes of correct size and in correct locations. Such is the inherent nature of the press dies. In statistical language, the sample size is two pieces and the number of allowable defects is zero. Yet despite the tiny sample size, this is a sound way to do the inspection for these characteristics in the example given.

The press example is rather simple. In more complex cases there is need to measure process capability and to arrange specially to take the samples with knowledge of the order of production. One organized form of this is the conventional control chart method used for process control (see Section 24 generally). For product conformance, the approach is less well organized (see, however, Section 25, under Bayesian Procedures).

Prior knowledge of the "process" as used here includes knowledge of the qualifications of the suppliers, workers, etc., who run the process. Workers who have qualified for licenses require less rigorous inspection of their work than operators who have not qualified. Suppliers who have established a record of good deliveries need not be checked as severely as suppliers who lack such a record.

Product Fluidity.   When the product is a fluid, this fluidity contributes to homogeneity. The extent of this homogeneity can be established by taking multiple specimens and computing the dispersion (another form of study of process capability). The presence of uniformity through fluidity greatly reduces the need for random sampling and thereby greatly reduces the sample sizes.

Even when the product is a solid, the inspection planner should be alert to the possibility that it possesses homogeneity through former fluidity. For example, a centrifugal casting process was used to cast metal cylinders which were then destroyed during testing for strength. However, it was then found that the dispersion of several strength tests all made on one ring was not different from the ring-to-ring dispersion. This discovery made it possible to reduce the amount of product destroyed during test.

Prior Successful Usage.   Where product, though nonconforming, has nevertheless been successfully used, this fact is a proper consideration in the question of how much inspection.

Cost Impact.   When it is important to allocate limited testing resources to those parts which cost the most to replace, unique testing strategies can be designed that utilize past test, line, and field history. (See Wambach and Anthony, 1977, for a discussion of this application for reliability critical parts.)

Product Inspection.   To the extent that the foregoing sources of knowledge are not adequate to make product-acceptance decisions, the gap must be filled by inspection and test of the product.

Securing the Prior Knowledge.   The "prior knowledge" does not automatically come to the inspection planner or the inspector. Some of this knowledge is already in existence as a by-product of other activities and hence can be had for the procedural cost of retrieval. Other knowledge is not in existence, and must be created by additional effort. However, this added effort is usually a one-time study, whereas the benefits then go on and on.

HOW MUCH INSPECTION? THE ALTERNATIVES

It is evident that a determination of "How much inspection?" should be made only after there has been an evaluation of the other inputs to product knowledge. This evaluation can then dictate any of several levels of inspection:

No Inspection.   There is already adequate evidence that the product conforms, and hence no further inspection is needed.

Small Samples.   There is a high degree of prior knowledge, requiring only small *stratified* samples so chosen as to verify the continuing validity of this prior knowledge, e.g., control charts, audit of decisions, preserving the order. In the absence of prior knowledge, such small sample sizes would be absurd, i.e., lots 20 or 30 percent defective could easily escape detection. See Section 25, under Sampling Plans Based on Prior Information, for the statistical approaches; and see also Babcombe (1970) for a discussion on quality control for small lots.

Large Samples.   Where there is little or no prior knowledge and no product fluidity, the main source of product knowledge becomes product inspection through *random* sampling. The amount of this inspection can be determined "scientifically" once the tolerable level of defects in accepted product has been clearly defined. However, choice of these levels—using the sampling parameters AQL (acceptable quality level), AOQL (average outgoing quality level), etc.—is largely arbitrary and is usually determined by negotiation. In theory, the sampling parameters can be determined from economic considerations, i.e., the cost of detecting unsatisfactory lots versus the cost of failing to detect them. In practice, the "cost of detecting" is fairly easy to determine, but the cost of "failing to detect" is difficult to determine. For intangibles such as customer goodwill, there is no way known to make the determination with any useful precision.

ONE HUNDRED PERCENT INSPECTION

This alternative is usually used for final test of critical or complex products. In very critical cases, it is used to provide redundancy against the unreliability of 100 percent inspection. In these cases the amount may be 200 percent or over. In cases where "zero defects" is the objective or requirement, 100 percent automated inspection is required (see Nygaard, 1981, and the discussion on machine-vision systems later in this section). In some cases, 100 percent inspection is required to satisfy legal or political requirements (see Walsh, 1974). In other cases 100 percent inspection is the most cost-effective approach. (See Walsh et al., 1976 and 1978, for examples where 100 percent inspection is the cost-effective alternative in high-volume production and in testing hardness of finished steel wheels.)

One hundred percent inspection may also be used when process capability is inherently too poor to meet product specifications. Sampling is of no avail in such cases, since the accepted lots are usually no better than the rejected lots, i.e., the difference is merely the result of statistical variations in the respective samples. This does not apply in cases where the process is highly erratic so that some lots are truly conforming and others are not merely the result of statistical accidents. For such processes, sampling can be a useful way to separate the conforming lots from the nonconforming ones.

Whatever the motivation for selecting the 100 percent alternative, effective implementation goes beyond choosing the inspection methodology or test equipment. Physical arrangements and personnel procedures must be changed. In many cases, attitudes of in-house and vendor personnel must be changed through reeducation. (See Walsh et al., 1979b.)

With the advent of computer-based testing, 100 percent inspection is becoming more practical (see Schweber, 1982). However, it is not clear that it is cost-effective in all cases, even if the technology is readily available (see Walsh et al., 1979a). This is especially true if the total costs of quality are considered. (See Gunter, 1983.)

OTHER TYPES OF CONFORMANCE INSPECTION

Faced with the objective to minimize (inspection) costs and achieve maximum (quality) control, management must be sensitive to nontraditional types of conformance decision-making inspection.

Simulation. With the advancement of the digital computer, system-simulation techniques are used as an alternative to the experimental or analytical approach (see Wang et al., 1981). Examples of application:

Receiving inspection simulation

Printed circuit board assembly inspection simulation

Camera subassembly and final inspection simulation

Management by Exception. This employs the principle of *no inspection* described in How Much Inspection? above. The variation, described by Moburg (1968) employs the Pareto concept to focus the major conformance-decision resources on the "relatively few" lots that had rejects in them. This approach is also feasible within the lot with the advent of new automated technology. (See Keller et al., 1975, for a discussion of exception inspection through automated video techniques.)

Automated Inspection. The first large-scale applications of automated testing were very likely done by the Western Electric Company during the 1920s. Current developments in the microcomputer, artifical intelligence (AI), integrated computer-aided manufacturing (ICAM), robotics, and software are making automated inspection practical and cost-effective. (See "An Outlook for 3D Vision," 1984, and "ASD's Quality Assurance Program Rates in Top 10," 1984; also the discussion on 100 percent inspection above, and that on Machine Vision, in Human Factors in Inspection, below.)

Automated inspection and testing are used to reduce costs, improve precision, shorten time intervals, alleviate labor shortages, and avoid inspection monotony among other advantages. In some industries the labor problems now seem insoluble in the absence of automated inspection. Already in widespread use, automated inspection is still expanding, with no end in sight.

The economics of automation involve a substantial investment in special equipment to secure a reduction in operating costs. The crux of justifying the investment lies in the amount of repetitive work the equipment will be called on to perform. This estimate of the anticipated volume of testing should therefore be checked out with great care.

A common starting point in discovering opportunities for automated inspection is to make a Pareto analysis of the kinds of inspections and tests being conducted. The vital few types are identified. Estimates are then made of the personnel, costs, and other current problems associated with these tests. The economics of automation are then estimated, and the comparable figures are an aid in deciding on the feasibility of successful conversion.

For complex equipments involving depot storage and field maintenance, the question of use of automated testing is itself highly complex and requires a tailor-made study of some magnitude.

Technologically, the "machine" poses many problems. It is less adaptable than the human being it replaces, so some changes may need to be made in the product to offset this rigidity. For example, the machine may hold the units to be tested by grasping certain surfaces whose dimensions were previously unimportant. Now these surfaces may need to be held to close dimensions because the machine is not as adaptable as the human inspector. Alternatively, the product design may need to be changed to provide for adequate location.

Beyond the work of original design, construction, and prove-in, the machine must be set up specially for each job. (See generally Section 16, under Quality Information Equipment.) However, modular construction, master test pieces, and taped programs have considerable reduced setup time while improving reproducibility. Reliability has generally been high, and use of printed circuit cards and other modular components has so reduced the "mean time to repair" that downtime is generally below 5 percent for well-designed machines.

Automated gaging and testing is extensively used in the mechanical industries. It is also widely used in the electronics industries, especially for electronic components (see Section 29, under Automated Test and Data Processing), where the problem of making connections to the automated test equipment is so severe that the original product design must provide specially for this.

In the chemical industries, the corresponding development has been the "autoanalyzer." This has already made possible some extensive cost reductions and solutions of otherwise forbidding problems of recruitment of laboratory technicians.

The autoanalyzer makes use of some equipment common to all tests—sensors, transducers, recorders, and computers. However, each type of analysis has its unique procedure for converting the material under test into a form suitable for sensing.

The advent of numerically controlled (NC) machines has required development of new inspection techniques which likewise use the NC principle. Since the machine is controlled by a tape, the validity of that tape is critical. One form of inspection control is through certifying the tapes. Once certified, the tapes become an important stabilizer in the process capability of the NC machine. (See "Tape Controlled Machines," 1970.)

Inspection of NC product can make use of the properties of the machines by substituting a stylus for the cutter. The measurements made by the stylus can be checked against the master tape. A further approach is to use coordinate-measuring machines, also tape-controlled, to check the NC-produced components. Still another approach is to make and measure a full-scale picture. (See Kirwan, 1972, Woods and Zeiss, 1981, and Karabatsos, 1983.)

Computer-Aided Inspection.   The marriage of computers and inspectors takes the form of (*a*) providing information and/or (*b*) providing assistance to enhance the conformance decision for almost any inspection situation. This is especially applicable to inspecting precision machine parts and assembly inspection (see Holmes, 1974, and Linn, 1981, for further discussion). The selective use of computer-aided inspection (CAI) techniques can minimize the more mental, repetitive inspection tasks and direct the human resource (the inspector) to preventative quality control.

Voice Entry.   Antother unique enhancement of computer-aided technology is the voice-data-entry system (VDES), which has at least these practical benefits (see "Voice Entry System Gives Quality Inspectors a Hand," 1973):

1. Saves money
2. Eliminates manual entry
3. Reduces labor requirements
4. Speeds management information
5. Has instant response time
6. Accepts all speakers
7. Permits on-line, real-time control
8. Has flexible and expandable capabilities
9. Allows remote control
10. Accepts off-line telephone input
11. Has verification-correction capability

INSPECTION AT INSPECTION STATIONS

Inspection stations are usually staffed by full-time inspectors responsible to the Inspection Department. This is by no means universal. Some final inspection stations are staffed by full-time inspectors responsible to Production. Many process inspection stations are staffed by Production workers whose principal job is production.

Incoming Inspection.   The extent of inspection of products received from suppliers depends largely on the extent of prior planning for supplier quality control (see Section 15, under Joint Quality Planning). In the extreme case of using surveillance and audit of decisions (see Section 15, under Audit of Decision), there is virtually no incoming inspection except for identity. At the other extreme, many "conventional" products are bought under an arrangement which relies primarily on incoming inspection for control of supplier quality.

The inspectors and their facilities are housed in the receiving area to provide ready collaboration with other supplier-related activities, i.e., materials receiving, weighing, counting, storage. Depending on the physical bulk and tonnage of product, entire shipments or just samples are brought to the inspection floor. The documentation routines provide the inspectors with copies of the purchase orders and specifications, which are filed by supplier name.

Inspection planning is conventional, as discussed under Inspection Planning, above. However, there is usually a lack of prior knowledge of process capability, order of manufacture, etc. In consequence, the sampling plans involve random and (often) large samples, employing standard random inspection tables (see generally Section 25, Acceptance Sampling). Randomness becomes a severe problem in the case of large shipments, whether bulk or not. However, special arrangements can be made with the supplier. (See Section 15, under Joint Quality Planning: Joint Technolgoical Planning.) Setting AQLs has been a troublesome problem to such an extent that some industry standards have been worked up. In the absence of such standards, the AQLs are established based on precedent, past performance, or just arbitrarily. Then, as instances of rejection arise, the negotiations with vendors result in adjustment of the AQLs.

Data feedback to vendors follows conventional feedback practice. (In this connection, see also Section 15, under Two-Way Communication; Deviations.)

Process Inspection.   This commonly serves two purposes simultaneously:

1. To provide data for making decisions on the *product;* i.e., does the product conform to specification?
2. To provide data for making decisions on the *process;* i.e., should the process run or stop?

Because of the interrelation between process and product variables, process inspection involves observation of process variables as well as inspection of the product. These observations and inspections are made by both Production and Inspection personnel. The resulting interplay is discussed in Section 17, Production of Quality, under Product and Process Relationship.

Product acceptance of work in process may be done in any of several stages or by a combination of them. These stages include:

Setup Inspection.   Some processes are inherently so stable that if the setup is correct, the entire lot will be correct, within certain limits of lot size. For such processes the setup approval can also be used as the lot approval. Where a good deal is at stake, it is usual to formalize the setup inspection and to require that the process may not run until the inspector has formally approved the setup, e.g., by signing off, by stamping the first pieces, etc. (See Garfinkel and Clodfelter, 1984.) Some of the setup criteria make use of narrow limit or PRE-control techniques as discussed in Section 24.

Patrol Inspection.   For processes which will not remain stable for the duration of the lot, it is usual to provide for periodic sampling to be conducted during the progression of the lot, making use of various techniques described in Section 24. The numerous plans in use consist mainly of variations of the following four types:

1. Preserve the order of manufacture under an arrangement such as is depicted in Figure 18.1. In this example, the machine discharges its production into a small container called a "pan." The production operator periodically empties the pan into one of three larger containers:
    a. Into the junk box if the parts are junk
    b. Into the reject box if the parts are questionable or are mixed good and bad
    c. Into the "tray" if the parts are presumably good

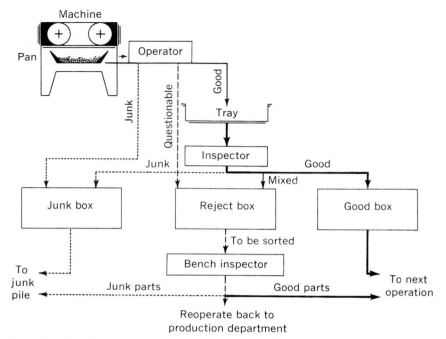

FIG. 18.1 Patrol inspection plan based on preserving the order.

The patrol inspector comes to the machine and checks the last few pieces being made. (He or she may also sample the tray.) Based on this check, the tray is disposed of in one of three ways:

    a. Into the junk box if the parts are junk.

    b. Into the reject box if the parts are questionable or are mixed good or bad.

    c. Into the "good" box if the parts are acceptable. The good box goes on to the next operation.

Only the inspector may dispose of the tray, and only the inspector may place any product in the good box.

The reject box is gone over by a sorter, who makes three dispositions:

    a. Junk to junk department

    b. Reoperate back to production department

    c. Good parts on to next operation

    2. This method is similar to the first, but the inspeciton data from the last few pieces are posted to a control chart. If the process remains in control, all product made since the last check is accepted.

    3. The accumulated product (e.g., in the tray of Figure 18.1) is sampled at random using some standard sampling plan, and acceptance is based on the sampling criteria.

    4. The process variables are checked against a process specification, and the product is accepted provided the process conforms to specification. This method is usually restricted to cases in which there is to be a direct check on the product at later stages.

Tollgate Inspection.   This is a lot-by-lot product acceptance procedure. Commonly it is done after a production department has concluded its operations. Sometimes the product is moved physically to an inspection area, where it waits its turn to be inspected. Sampling is at random, using standard sampling tables.

Tollgate inspection reduces congestion at the machines and clarifies departmental responsibility. The price paid is in added material handling, added floor space, loss of order of production, and greater difficulty in fixing individual responsibility.

Finished Goods Inspection.   Most finished products are tested 100 percent for minimal simulation of use. Tests are often automated, as are the data recordings. Testing may be done either at inspection stations on the production line or in separate inspection areas.

JUDGMENT OF FITNESS FOR USE

Knowledge of *conformance to specification* is needed to:

Provide protection to the user when usage experience is not yet available

Provide working criteria to those who lack knowledge of fitness for use

Create an atmosphere of law and order

Protect innocents from unwarranted blame

In contrast, *knowledge of fitness* for use is needed to:

Protect the user

Preserve marketability of the product

Avoid excesses of perfectionism

A trained inspector, if provided with the specification, the product, and the instruments, can readily judge conformance to the specification. However, possession of these facilities is not enough to enable him or her to judge fitness for use. This second judgment requires added knowledge, as discussed below.

When inspection determines that the product conforms to specification, the product is routinely assumed to be fit for use; i.e., if the answer to the conformance question is yes, the fitness-for use is not even raised. (There are occasional exceptions to this. Field reports of unfitness for use are enough to hold up deliveries even if the product under test conforms to specification.) The routines are structured to ship the product accordingly. It is only when product fails to conform to specification that there arises the second question: Is the (nonconforming) product fit for use?

What is significant is that much nonconforming product is actually fit for use and that this fact is known to many people in middle and lower management. Unless the authorized routines provide for legitimate ways for dealing with this practical problem, the unauthorized ways will take over, with unpredictable results. Where the Quality Department is poorly supported, there will be unauthorized shipment of nonconforming product, including some which is unfit for use. Where the Quality Department is well supported, there may be unnecessary waste due to failure to accept nonconforming product which is fit for use.

The hazards of delegation by default have led many companies to establish an organized approach for review of nonconforming products. The most popular form of this organized approach is the Material Review Board.

Methods of Decision Making on Fitness for Use.   There have been several methods for providing answers to this:

1. Assume that all nonconforming product is unfit for use. Under this assumption, all nonconforming lots are scrapped, repaired, sorted, etc., but not shipped as is. A great deal of waste has resulted from this assumption, since many designs are unrealistically strict and many nonconforming products are in fact fit for use.

2. Create an agency for decision making, e.g., a Material Review Board, and give this agency the responsibility to determine fitness for use of all nonconforming product. This arrangement is fairly practical if there is very little nonconforming material, but tends to require an elaborate apparatus for disposing of numerous small matters (as well as for the vital few cases where the elaborate appartus is clearly warranted).

3. Create a system of multiple delegation for making decisions on fitness for use. Under such a system, the "vital few" decisions are reserved to a formal Material Review Board. The remaining decisions are delegated to other people. This is the emerging solution.

Material Review Board.   The basic function of a Material Review Board (MRB) is to (*a*) review material that does not conform to standard, (*b*) determine what its disposition should be, and (*c*) drive the development of effective corrective action to prevent recurrence.

The MRB is a broad-based reviewing agency whose membership usually consists minimally of representatives from:

Engineering: The cognizant designer is often the representative.

Quality Assurance: The representative is often from Quality Control Engineering.

Customers: The representative may be from the customer's organization (e.g., the government inspector) or from Marketing.

Bond (1983) discusses board composition, philosophy, and problem documentation.

In some companies, the role of the Material Review Board is solely one of judging fitness for use of nonconforming products. Such was the scope of the boards when they were first set up (by the military procurement services). However, other companies broaden the scope of the MRB so that it includes:

Decision on disposition of unfit lots internally—by scrap, repair, sorting, etc.; fixing responsibility for the losses incurred

Periodic analysis of the accumulated waiver investigations to identify quality improvement projects

As MRBs conduct their affairs, they tend to work out some delegations of the more routine cases to individual members to act without taking up the time of the full Board. The main form of this delegation is in fact finding, which is usually delegated to the Quality Engineer. However, there may be added delegations, e.g., to the Product Designer for memorandum or marked print waivers in certain cases; to the Quality Engineer for guiding internal disposition of product, etc.

The MRB works to a formal agenda and keeps minutes of its deliberations and actions. A universal rule is that acceptance of nonconforming material requires *unanimous concurrence* of all members of the MRB.

Multiple Delegation. In some companies the delegation for decision making is based on a system of classification to separate the "vital few" nonconformances from the rest. One such system involves classifying defects (and/or quality characteristics) into categories of seriousness. (See Seriousness Classification, below.) If such classification is available it simplifies the problem of delegating the fitness-for-use decision. The vital few cases are decided by the upper managers. The less serious cases are delegated to lower levels.

Another such system is based on classifying quality characteristics as to whether they are functional or nonfunctional. (The term "nonfunctional" is not to be confused with appearance or other esthetic qualities. For some products, esthetic qualities are quite essential to fitness for use.) Where such classification is available, it becomes feasible to assign decisions on functional characteristics to the upper levels of the organizations, leaving the rest to the lower levels.

With multiple delegation in a large company, uncertainty can arise as to placement of authority. The way out of such vagueness is to establish a table of delegation which fits the unique situation of the company. Table 18.7 shows an example of such a table of delegation for a specific company.

TABLE 18.7 Responsibility for Making Decisions on Fitness for Use*

Effect of nonconformance is on:	Amount of product or money at stake is:	
	Small	Large
Internal economics only	Department head directly involved; quality engineer	Plant managers involved; quality manager
Economic relations with Supplier	Supplier; purchasing agent; quality engineer	Supplier, manager
Economic relations with client	Client; salesperson; quality engineer	Client; for Marketing, Manufacturing, Technical, Quality
Field performance of the product	Product designer; salesperson; quality engineer	Client; managers for Technical, Manufacturing, Marketing Quality
Risk of damage to society or of nonconformance to government regulations	Product design manager; compliance officer; lawyer; quality manager	General manager and team of upper managers

*For those industries whose quality mission is really one of conformance to specification (e.g., atomic energy, space), the real decision maker on fitness for use is the client or the government regulator.

Organized Material Reviews.   In any case, decision making on nonconforming products should be done on an organized basis, through recognized, legitimate channels. Lacking an organized approach there arises a "delegation by default." In one company (consulting experience of J. M. Juran) there existed five sources of waivers in actual use by inspection:

1. Written authority from Engineering
2. Written authority from Sales
3. Long-standing practice for which there existed no written authority
4. Measurement variations added to product tolerances
5. Inspector judgment on sensory qualities not clearly defined in the specifications

Steps Preceding Review.   Some elements of the preparation for review of non-conforming material are virtually alike for all companies:

1. The inspector prepares a nonconformance report identifying the product involved, the nature of the defects, and related factual data. These reports are serially numbered (for some examples of the documentation, see Section 19).
2. The inspector "red-tags" the product, thereby creating an automatic "hold for disposition." Often the product is moved to a special "hold area" to get it out of the regular stream of production.
3. An investigator (often a Quality Engineer) is assigned to collect information pertinent to disposition of the impounded material. This information includes:
   Value of the product
   Cost of scrap, repair. or sort
   Possibility of use in various ways: "as is," with modifications, through concessions to customer, etc.
4. Based on the analysis and on the prevailing pattern of delegation of authority, the investigator takes or recommends action. One of these recommendations may be to accept the material as fit for use.
5. To recommend acceptance "as is" despite nonconformance, the investigator prepares a formal waiver request to a reviewing agency.

Inputs for Fitness-for-Use Decisions.   Factual answers to several questions are useful in arriving at fitness-for-use decisions:

1. *Who will be the user?*   A technologically sophisticated user may be able to deal successfully with the nonconformance; a consumer may not. A nearby user may have easy access to field service; a distant or international user may lack such easy access.
2. *How will this product be used?*   For many materials and standard products the specifications are broad enough to cover a variety of possible uses, and it is not known at the time of manufacture just what will be the actual use to which the product will be put. For example, sheet steel may be cut up to service as decorative plates or as structural members; the television receiver may be stationed at a comfortable range or at an extreme range; chemical intermediates may be employed in numerous formulas.
3. *Are there risks to human safety or to structural integrity?*   Where such risks are significant, all else is academic.

4. *What is the urgency?* For some applications, clients cannot wait, because the product in question is critical to putting some broader system into operation. Hence they may demand delivery now, and make repairs in the field. Thus for the review process, facts are needed on:

   a. The schedule requirements for the part(s) or material

   b. The lead time to replace or rework the part(s) or material

5. *What are the company's and the user's economics?* For some nonconformances the economics of repair are so forbidding that the product must be used as is, although at a price discount. In some industries, e.g., textiles, the price structure formalizes this concept by use of a separate grade—"seconds." Among the facts needed for the review of the economics are:

   a. The minimum rework required to make the part(s) or material usable, and the cost of this rework

   b. The cost of scrapping and replacing the part(s) or material

6. *What are the users' measures of fitness for use?* These may differ significantly from those available to the manufacturer. For example, a manufacturer of abrasive cloth used a laboratory test to judge the ability of the cloth to polish metal; a major client evaluated the cost per 1000 pieces polished.

These and other inputs may be needed at several levels of fitness for use, i.e., the effects on the economics of subsequent processors, the marketability requirements of the merchants, and the qualities that determine fitness for the ultimate user, and the qualities that influence field maintenance.

The job of securing such inputs is often assigned to a staff specialist, e.g., a quality engineer. This person "makes the rounds," contacting the various departments which are able to provide pertinent information. There may be need to contact the customer, and even to conduct an actual tryout.

Effect of Multiple Product Usage. Fitness for use is often complicated by the multiple usage for the products under investigation. For the coalesced products, multiple forms of usage are widespread. In consequence, the study of fitness for use involves an inquiry as to how this impounded lot will be used. The resulting waiver may very well be restricted, e.g., for this specific customer or application only.

Product in discrete units likewise involves multiple usages, and the same principles hold. Sometime the technological usage may be identical, but the circumstances of usage create the difference. An example is seen in many kinds of interchangeable components. These serve a multiplicity of uses:

1. To be shipped to original equipment manufacturers (OEM) to be assembled into apparatus

2. To be shipped to OEM to be sold or used by them as spare parts

3. To be assembled into apparatus by the component maker itself

4. To be shipped, through intermediate merchants, to repair shops who use the components as spare parts for repair of products in the hands of the general public

At the time these components are made, it is seldom known to which of these destinations they will be shipped. However, when the OEM customer orders (1) and (2) are filled, the practice is to follow strict product acceptance procedures, since the OEM customer has great economic importance, backed up by competent engineers and inspectors who in turn operate out of well-equipped laboratories.

In contrast, components used for purposes 3 and 4 may include those which failed to make the OEM grade. In the company's own assembly department, the operators often have tools which permit them to adjust for nonconforming components. Failing this, they put the poor parts aside and use others. In the case of spare parts to be sold to the general public (through merchants and repair shops), there are opportunities for abuses due to the technological ignorance of everyone involved, and some of these abuses take place. (See generally Juran, 1970.) Some highly ethical companies flatly require that nonconforming components be used only in their own assembly areas and never be shipped out as spare parts.

Disposition of Unfit Product.   Product which is unfit for use is disposed of in a number of ways: scrap, sort, rework, return to supplier, sell at a discount, etc. Mainly these alternatives involve internal economics within the manufacturing company, and hence they can be quantified sufficiently to arrive at a logical economic balance. However, no matter what the disposition is, money is lost, schedules are disrupted, and people are blamed. In such an atmosphere it is important to establish rules of conduct which minimize the costs, disruptions, and human abrasion.

When purchased products are involved, the rule should be to find that disposition which creates the minimum total loss to the parties. Adherence to this rule reduces the amount at stake so that there is less to argue about. In turn, this makes it easier to bargain how to share this loss. It is also well to write the purchase contract in a way which makes clear how to handle the various elements of cost which arise because of unfit product.

For self-made products, the rule should still be the same—to find that disposition which results in the minimum total loss. On the face of it this should be obvious, e.g., any sorting of product should be done by that department which can do it at the lowest total cost to the company. However, this logic can be frustrated by other considerations, e.g., labor shortages or cultural resistance.

A major obstacle to "logical" solutions is the presence of an atmosphere of "blame" in the company, e.g., an official requirement that responsibility for errors should be discovered and allocated (often with associated "charging" of the departments responsible). In such an atmosphere the disposition of unfit products is hampered at every turn by the reluctance of supervisors to agree to actions which might be construed as admissions of guilt.

A policy of charging back all cases of error pays a high price for dubious results. The price is not only the cost of analysis but also—and even greater—the effect on supervisory time and morale. The other extreme of regarding everything as indeterminate is no better. The middle ground is to concentrate the analysis on the chronic, vital few defects which go on and on, since these account for the bulk of the losses. For the sporadic "useful many" errors, analysis to fix blame is seldom warranted. The local supervision is in the best position to study these and to find ways to minimize their recurrence.

For the vital few errors there remains a question of transfer of charges to the department responsible once responsibility is clear. As a matter of good accounting practice, the department responsible should be charged. However, much depends on how the budgets were prepared in the first place. If charging is to be inaugurated, the setting up of future budgets should take this into account. In addition, a look should be taken to assure that the costs of analysis and accounting are low in relation to the amounts at stake.

An undue atmosphere of blame can infect the nonsupervisory levels as well.

Here the effect is often to conceal the evidence of defects by hiding the scrap, scrapping products which may be repairable, "forgetting" to execute the scrap or repair tickets, etc. See, in this connection, Section 22 under Test of Theories of Worker-Controllable Problems.

Disposition of unfit product by sorting may involve external as well as internal economics. Several sorting situations are common:

1. The product in question is processed further within the same company, e.g., resistors wired into circuits. In such cases it is usually feasible to evaluate:

   a. The cost of finding a defect through inspection. This is approximately equal to the inspection cost per unit divided by the fraction defective.

   b. The cost of not finding a defect, i.e., the added costs incurred by further processing until the defect is found in later testing. This can be estimated.

Under these circumstances (and assuming 100 percent accuracy of sorting) it is economic to sort the product when the fraction defective is more than the ratio of *a* to *b* (see Taguchi, 1970).

2. The product in question goes to the user. Here it is still feasible to evaluate the cost of finding a defect. However, it is now more difficult to estimate the cost of not finding a defect and virtually impossible to estimate the intangible damage done to goodwill. Nevertheless, when the cost of finding a defect is *compared* to the *value of the product,* managers seem to be able to make a practical judgment. Commonly, managers will conclude that they are not willing to spend as much to find a defect as the sales value of the product.

For example, a line of consumer products sells for $5 each. A major defect has an incidence of one per thousand. The cost of testing to find the defect is $10 per thousand, so it costs $10 to find one defect. Most managers would not be willing to spend $10 to find a defective $5 product.

3. The product in question contains defects which are known to be a safety or health hazard. The cost of finding the defect can still be figured, but the managers make their decision almost exclusively on the fact that the hazard is present. (There is risk of civil and criminal lawsuits.) Somehow the hazard will be eliminated or neutralized.

Physical Control of the Product. The majority of companies apply rigid controls to movement of finished goods. Inspection approval is required before goods enter the (locked) finished goods storeroom (or are shipped to a customer). Packers, counters, and storekeepers are under strict orders to assure that inspection approval is present before finished goods move on to their destination. To a lesser degree, similar controls apply to finished components entering the assembly storeroom.

Control of nonconforming product is likewise rigid. The containers are red-tagged and usually are moved out of the stream of production to avoid mixups.

For parts, components, and intermediate products moving between Production departments, the practice varies widely. At one extreme, physical control is entirely in the hands of production people until the final product is presented to Inspection for acceptance as finished goods. At the other extreme, movement from any Production department is always to an Inspection area (before dispatch to the next Production department) and then only after an Inspection-approved "move ticket" has been executed.

A further form of inspection control is through approval stamps applied directly to the product during various stages of operation and especially at final test. Some stamps are coded to show the condition of the product. Stamps commonly identify the inspector to establish traceability as well as to fix responsibility.

For complex apparatus a dossier is invariably prepared to collect the history of the product, the inspection log books, calibration curves, and other matters of significance. Copies of pertinent results go to the customer as well. Seals or locks may be used to minimize unauthorized tampering with the product.

The need for elaborate control systems is obvious when a mixup could be catastrophic (e.g., for pharmaceuticals). However, some companies use these elaborate systems largely because the managers do not trust the work force. Such mistrust is always mutual, and the long-range solution lies in resolving this mistrust, not in retaining elaborate systems.

Another source of elaboration of system is the human drive for self-sufficiency in floor space, equipment, etc. This drive can be accentuated by departmental loyalties and interdepartmental conflicts. Managers should be alert to distinguish cases requiring elaborate systems due to the nature of the product from those created by human beings for reasons of status, departmental loyalty, etc. For example, creation of separate Inspection areas can greatly increase the total time interval for manufacture, the process inventory, and the amount of paperwork. As far as possible, the inspector should be brought to the product rather than the other way around. This principle is illustrated by patrol inspectors, assembly line inspectors, resident inspectors at supplier plants, etc. It has been applied to conveyorized production by establishing inspection stations at the conveyor. It has even been applied where, for reasons of identity and certification, a physical fence separates the Production and Inspection departments; i.e., a conveyor moves the product into and out of the inspection cage through windows cut for the purpose.

A similar principle is used where strict certification of inspected parts is essential. The only entrance to the fenced-in storeroom is through a fenced-in inspection area.

QUALITY STANDARDS

The cornerstone of quality control is the specfication. Specifications embody the minimum and maximum values. (See also Bader, 1980.) However, they are usually *incomplete.* They tend to ignore *visual quality characteristics,* or they treat characteristics labeled as *workmanship* superficially. (Refer to the discussion of visual quality characteristics below; and see also Dodds, 1967, and Alaimo, 1969, for further discussion on workmanship standards.)

Seriousness Classification.   Some quality characteristics and defects are very important to fitness for use; others are not. The village craftsperson and the small-shop proprietor, with their firsthand knowledge of fitness for use, are able to concentrate their efforts on the most important qualities. In modern, large, complex organizations, the workmen, inspectors, and many of the supervisors lack complete knowledge of fitness for use and thereby are not fully clear on where to place their emphasis and how to make their decisions.

For example, one company studying the fabrication and inspection of machine parts classified the quality characteristics into four classes. Table 18.8 shows the effect of this classification on product tolerances and on the number of dimensions checked. The inspection time was reduced from 215 to 120 min. In addition, there were greater savings through lower rework costs, lower tooling costs, and lower engineering costs for disposition of nonconforming product. (See also Allen, 1959.)

To provide such missing knowledge on a broad scale, there has evolved a concept of formal seriousness classification, both for quality characteristics and for defects. The quality characteristics list comes from the specifications; the list of defects comes from evidences of failures during use (e.g., service reports) and from evidence of nonconformance during manufacture (e.g., inspection reports). When these two lists are classified for seriousness, the former is used mainly for quality planning while the latter is used mainly for inspection planning and for product auditing. (See Section 8; also El Gabry, 1972.)

These two lists differ in their content, though the overlap is often great. A single quality characteristic, e.g., shaft diameter 1.000 ± 0.001, gives rise to two defects, oversize and undersize. These defects may be assigned different degrees of seriousness depending on the extent of nonconformance. Some extensive defect lists, e.g., the list for glass bottles, have little resemblance to the list of characteristics set out in the specifications.

Some companies use the same system of classification both for characteristics and defects. However, there is enough uniqueness about each of the two lists to suggest that adoption of a single system should be preceded by a positive examination of the nature of the two lists. For example, the effect of seriousness classification on design decisions can be quite different from the effect on inspection decisions, as is evident from Table 18.8.

Formal systems of seriousness classification were originally evolved to serve specialized purposes. (The Bell System pioneered by developing a system to permit rating of quality of finished product. The U.S. Armed Services developed systems to simplify the administration of acceptance of goods purchased from contractors.) However, as the systems came into being, they were found to have application in the entire progression of product from design through usage: in quality specification, manufacturing planning, supplier relations, tooling, produc-

TABLE 18.8 Results of Seriousness Classification of Characteristics

Characteristic classification	Effect of classification on design tolerance	Effect of classification on amount of inspection	Number of dimensions checked	
			Before classification	After classification
Critical	None.	None.	154	154
Major	None.	None.	110	110
Minor A	Tolerance was increased by a specified amount (doubled, etc.) provided the part assembled satisfactorily.	Inspection was made normally, but to wider tolerances.	66	15
Minor B	Tolerance was ignored provided the part assembled satisfactorily.	Inspection was eliminated.	352	0
Total			682	279

tion, salvage, product auditing, and executing reporting. Vital qualities could now be identified with greater confidence, and it also became feasible to delegate class decisions and actions on a broad scale. For example, all class C defects could be assigned a common sampling plan, thereby avoiding the need for publishing numerous individual plans.

The multiple uses of seriousness classification systems make it desirable that the job of developing such a system be guided by an interdepartmental committee which has the responsibility for drafting a plan, modifying it, and recommending it for adoption. Such a committee has a series of tasks:

1. Determining the number of strata or classes of seriousness to use
2. Defining each class
3. Classifying each defect into one of the classes

Number of Levels or Strata.   In theory, the number may be large, e.g., a defect may have any weight from 1000 down to 1. In practice, such a large number of weights is too complex to administer. The actual plans in use consist of only several classes. While choice of the actual number of classes is arbitrary, extensive experience has shown that three or four classes suffice for a wide variety of situations.

Definitions for the Classes.   These will differ with the nature of the product, process, etc. However, plans in existence tend to show striking similarity in definition, the result in part of the influence of the Bell System classification plan (see also Dodge, 1928, and Dodge and Torrey, 1956). Not only was this pioneering plan uncommonly well reasoned out; the men who devised it were later consultants to some of the U.S. Armed Services during World War II, and their thinking influenced the classification plans adopted by these services. These plans, in turn, influenced the plans adopted by the contractors to the armed services.

The standard definitions adopted by the Bell System (see also Dodge and Torrey, 1956) are shown in Table 18.9. Study of these definitions discloses that there is an inner pattern common to the basic definitions (Table 18.10).

A composite of definitions used in food industry companies is shown in Table 18.11. It is evident that there are industry-to-industry differences in products, markets, etc., which require a tailor-made wording for each industry. In addition, the lists are not static. The growth of government regulation has further influenced the definition, as has the problem of repairs and guarantees for long-life products.

It is also evident that the classifications must simultaneously take into account multiple considerations such as functional performance, user awareness, and financial loss. For example, the effects and awareness of a radio receiver's defects may be as follows:

Defect	Effect on functional performance	Consumer awareness
Open circuit in power supply	Set is inoperative	Fully aware
Short circuit in resistor	Excess power consumption	Seldom aware
Poor exterior finish	No effect	Usually aware
Poor dress or internal wiring	No effect	Seldom aware

TABLE 18.9 Serious Classification of Defects (Bell System)

Class A—very serious (demerit value, 100)

a. Will surely cause an operating failure of the unit in service which cannot be readily corrected in the field, e.g., open relay winding; or
b. Will surely cause intermittent operating trouble, difficult to locate in the field, e.g., loose connection; or
c. Will render unit totally unfit for service, e.g., dial finger wheel does not return to normal after operation; or
d. Liable to cause personal injury or property damage under normal conditions of use, e.g., exposed part has sharp edges.

Class B—serious (demerit value, 50)

a. Will probably cause an operating failure of the unit in service which cannot be readily corrected in the field, e.g., protective finish missing from coaxial plug; or
b. Will surely cause an operating failure of the unit in service which can be readily corrected in the field, e.g., relay contact does not make; or
c. Will surely cause trouble of a nature less serious than an operating failure, such as substandard performance, e.g., protector block does not operate at specified voltage; or
d. Will surely involve increased maintenance or decreased life, e.g., single contact disk missing.
e. Will cause a major increase in installation effort by the customer, e.g., mounting holes in wrong location; or
f. Defects of appearance or finish that are extreme in intensity, e.g., finish does not match finish on other parts—requires refinishing.

Class C—moderately serious (demerit value, 10)

a. May possibly cause an operating failure of the unit in service, e.g., contact follow less than minimum; or
b. Likely to cause trouble of a nature less serious than an operating failure, such as substandard performance, e.g., ringer does operate within specified limits; or
c. Likely to involve increased maintenance or decreased life, e.g., dirty contact; or
d. Will cause a minor increase in installation effort by the customer, e.g., mounting bracket distorted; or
e. Major defects of appearance, finish, or workmanship, e.g., finish conspicuously scratched, designation omitted or illegible.

Class D—not serious (demerit value, 1)

a. Will not affect operation, maintenance, or life of the unit in service (including minor deviations from engineering requirements), e.g., sleeving too short; or
b. Minor defects of appearance, finish, or workmanship, e.g., slightly scratched finish.

Classifying the Defects.   This essential task is time-consuming, since there are always many defects to be classified. If the class definitions have been well drawn, the task becomes much easier.

During classifying, much confusion is cleared up. It is found that the seriousness of important visual defects depends not so much on whether the inspector can see it as on whether the consumer can see it. It is found that some words describing defects must be subdivided; i.e., a "stain" may be placed in two or

TABLE 18.10 Inner Pattern—Seriousness Classification System

Defect class	Demerit weight	Cause personal injury	Cause operating failure	Cause intermittent operating trouble difficult to locate in field	Cause substandard performance	Involve increased maintenance or decreased life	Cause increase in installation effort by customer	Appearance, finish, or workmanship defects
A	100	Liable to	Will surely*	Will surely				
B	50		Will surely† Will probably		Will surely	Will surely	Major increase	
C	10		May possibly		Likely to	Likely to	Minor increase	Major
D	1		Will not		Will not	Will not		Minor

*Not readily corrected in the field.
†Readily corrected in the field.

TABLE 18.11 Composite Definitions for Seriousness Classification in Food Industry

Defect	Effect on consumer safety	Effect on usage	Consumer relations	Loss to company	Effect on conformance to government relations
Critical	Will surely cause personal injury or illness	Will render the product totally unfit for use	Will offend consumer's sensibilities because of odor, appearance, etc.	Will lose customers and will result in losses greater than value of product	Fails to conform to regulations for purity, toxicity, identification
Major A	Very unlikely to cause personal injury or illness	May render the product unfit for use and may cause rejection by the user	Will likely be noticed by consumer, and will likely reduce product salability	May lose customers and may result in losses greater than the value of the product; will substantially reduce production yields	Fails to conform to regulations on weight, volume, or batch control
Major B	Will not cause injury or illness	Will make the product more difficult to use, e.g., removal from package, or will require improvisation by the user; affects appearance, neatness	May be noticed by some consumers, and may be an annoyance if noticed	Unlikely to lose customers; may require product replacement; may result in loss equal to product value	Minor nonconformance to regulations on weight, volume, or batch control, e.g., completeness of documentation
Minor	Will not cause injury or illness	Will not affect usability of the product; may affect appearance, neatness	Unlikely to be noticed by consumers, and of little concern if noticed	Unlikely to result in loss	Conforms fully to regulations

three classes depending on severity and location. In many ways, the work of classifying defects is rewarding through clearing away misconceptions and through giving a fresh view to all who participate.

Classification of Characteristics.   In some companies the formal "seriousness" classification is not of defects but of characteristics in the specifications. The classification may be in any of several alternatives:

1. *Functional or nonfunctional:*   Where a single set of drawings carries both functional ("end use") requirements and nonfunctional ("means to an end") requirements, it is important to make clear which is which. (This is not to be confused with mechanical, chemical, or electrical functioning. In products such as jewelry or textiles, the most important functional requirement is *appearance*.) The purposes served by these two classes are generally alike throughout industry:

Functional requirements are intended to	*Nonfunctional requirements are intended to*
Ensure performance for intended use	Inform the shop as to method of manufacture
Ensure long, useful life	Reduce cost of manufacture
Minimize accident hazards	Facilitate manufacture
Protect life or property	Provide interchangeability in the shop
Provide interchangeability in the field	Provide information to toolmakers
Provide competitive sales advantage	

"Which is which" becomes important because it directs the priorities of process design and many aspects of economics of manufacture, as well as the jurisdiction over waivers.

When the engineers make this classification, they commonly add a designation such as E (for Engineering) to the functional characteristics. All others are then assumed to be nonfunctional.

A comparable situation prevails in process specifications, where the need is to distinguish mandatory from advisory requirements, which correspond roughly to functional and nonfunctional requirements as applied to the product. However, the process specifications seldom make this distinction. (For further discussion, see Section 17, in Process Specifications, under Knowledge of "Supposed to Do.")

2. *Seriousness classification:*   When this method is used, it parallels closely the classification into critical, major, and minor as used for classification of defects. (The contention is often raised that the tolerances on the specifications are an automatic form of seriousness classification, i.e., anything with assigned tolerances must be met and is "therefore" critical. An alternative contention is that the closeness of the tolerances is a key to seriousness classification, i.e., the narrowest tolerances are assigned to the most critical characteristics. When these contentions are examined more closely, they are found to contain too many exceptions to serve as firm rules for classifications.)

The resulting classifications then become a supplement to the specification or are shown on the drawings themselves by some code designation, for example:
Critical—   ⊕
Major A—   ⊙
Major B—   ○
Minor—not marked

One large automotive company differentiates between regulatory and nonregulatory critical characteristics by the use of two different symbols.

3. *Segregation of functional requirements:* Place in a separate document, such as an "engineering specification" or a "test specification."

4. *Shop practice tolerances versus special tolerances:* This method is based on preparation of a shop practice manual which sets out general use tolerances derived from the process capability of general use machines and tools. Once published, these shop practice tolerances govern all characteristics not specially toleranced.

Who Classifies?　For defect classification, an interdepartmental committee is the ideal choice. This provides each department with the benefits derived from the process of active review, and it also produces a better final result (sometimes the committee goes further and establishes a plan for product rating, including demerit weights for each class; see Section 8, under Product Auditing). However, some companies assign a staff specialist to prepare a proposed classification, which is then reviewed by all interested departments. The specialist is usually a quality control engineer.

When the classification is limited to specified characteristics, e.g., functional versus nonfunctional, the designer usually prepares the draft.

SENSORY QUALITIES

"Sensory qualities" are those for which we lack technological measuring instruments and for which the senses of human beings must be used as measuring instruments. (For some special purposes, e.g., tests of toxicity, the test panel may consist of animals.) Sensory qualities may involve:

Technological performance of the product, e.g., adhesion of a protective coating; friction of a sliding fit

Esthetic characteristics of consumer products, e.g., taste of food, odor of perfume, appearance of carpets, noise of room air conditioners

In common with other qualities, sensor qualities require:

1. Discovery of which characteristics, and in what degree, are required to meet the needs of fitness for use

2. Design of products which will possess these characteristics

3. Establishment of product and process standards, and of tests which will simulate fitness for use

4. Judgment of conformance to the product and process standards

This multiplicity of tasks requires a corresponding multiplicity in type of sensory test panel used, choice of test design, etc. It is easy to become confused, since the conventional terminology does not reflect the great differences needed in the approaches. Table 18.12 lists some of the main problems requiring use of sensory testing and shows the resulting differences in subject matter of test, choice of test panel, environment, statistical design, etc.

Discovery of Sensory Characteristics Required for Fitness for Use. For technological sensory qualities, this determination is made using mainly the conventional methods of product development, laboratory testing, field tryouts, etc., as discussed in Section 13. Commonly it is feasible to set up, in the laboratory, test criteria which simulate field usage. Such simulation greatly simplifies discovery of the needed characteristics of the product.

Esthetic sensory qualities present a more difficult problem and pose several questions as to fitness for use:

> Do consumers like or dislike the esthetic quality in question, and to what degree? (The term "consumer" commonly applies to the user of products made for sale and use by individuals, as distinguished from enterprises. More broadly, most commercial products are also "used" by individuals, e.g., the operator running a lathe, the programmer running a computer, the employee using the cafeteria. The collective views of these industrial users become an important input to decisions on esthetic qualities for commerical products.)

> Of two or more competing products (exhibiting the same sensory quality), which do consumers prefer?

> At what threshold level of an esthetic quality do consumers notice its presence?

On the face of it, manufacturing company employees (managers, sales persons, engineers, inspectors) are qualified to answer these questions, since they are also members of the consuming public. However, in practice, these employees exhibit strong biases due to close association with the product, vested departmental interests, and undue sensitivity arising from intimate knowledge. Some costly instances of marketing failure and of perfectionism have been directly traceable to biased judgments of consumer preference made by company employees. The safe course is to secure answers to these questions not from company employees but from consumers (or potential consumers) in the marketplace. The cost of the market research may restrict this approach to the important qualities. (The very question of which are the important qualities is likewise best answered by consumers in the marketplace.)

The upper half of Table 18.12 deals with these same three questions and notes that to get objective answers, we:

> Employ panel members who are representative of consumers in the marketplace. The resulting data are more likely to predict actual market response to the product.

> Avoid training of the panelists. The potential and actual consumers represent a mixture of people in varying degrees of product knowledge.

> Conduct the study under conditions of regular use, not in a laboratory environment. Only in this way can the data reflect the future results of actual usage.

Consumer Likes and Dislikes. One approach to prediction of consumer acceptance of a new product is to secure data on consumer likes or dislikes. For example, a food company may be interested in securing market reaction to a new ingredient (e.g., passion fruit). A new food formulation containing the ingredient under test is submitted to numerous users. Their responses are secured on a "hedonic" scale, e.g., (1) like very much, (2) like, (3) neither like nor dislike, (4) dislike, (5) dislike very much.

The consumer panel may consist of a "standing panel" of several hundred families to whom samples are sent "free." (Such panels are usually contacted not

TABLE 18.12 Uses of Sensory Tests

Problem	Products under test— what is being measured	Panel selected from	Criteria for selection of panel members	Prior training of panel members	Test environment desired	Type of test	Results of test
To discover consumer likes and dislikes	Experimental products containing new or changed qualities	Potential consumers	Should be representative of consumers in the market	None	Conditions of regular use of the product	Quality evaluation	Rating of product on a "hedonic scale" of how well liked
To discover consumer preferences	Two (or more) different products, for the same quality	Consumers	Should be representative of consumers in the market	None	Conditions of regular use of the product	Preference test	Percent and degree of preference of product A versus product B
To discover consumer sensitivity	A controlled selection of products varying across the range under study	Consumers	Should be representative of consumers in the market	None	Conditions of regular use of the product	Special	Basis for decision on product tolerances
To discover effect, on a sensory quality, of material and process changes (for design of products and processes)	A controlled selection of products varying across the range under study	Laboratory or other company personnel	Proved ability to discriminate with respect to the quality under study	Experience with testing and with qualities under test	Controlled laboratory conditions	Various	Relationship of material and process variables to effect on quality characteristic under study
Process regulation	Samples of intermediate or finished product	Quality control laboratory or other company personnel	Proved ability to discriminate	Experience with testing and with qualities under test	Controlled laboratory conditions	Duo-trio, triangle, etc.	Basis for decision on whether to change process
Product (batch or lot) acceptance	Finished products	Quality control laboratory	Proved ability to discriminate	Experience with testing and with qualities under test	Controlled laboratory conditions	Duo-trio, triangle, etc.	Basis for decision on acceptance of product

by the food company but by an intermediate research company, so as to avoid any associations with the name of the food company.) The "payment" is in data on the extent to which the family (adults, children, pets) liked or disliked the product. Alternatively, the panel may consist of other groups, e.g., passersby at a booth rented in a department store.

The data on the hedonic scale are summarized in conventional ways. As experience is gained in the response patterns to such tests, the decisions on whether to proceed further with the new product can be made with greater and greater confidence.

Consumer Preference Testing. The aim of this test is to discover consumer preferences, e.g., our product versus competitors' products, new designs versus current designs, etc. In competitive markets, such preference tests can give useful guides to decisions on product marketability, pricing, etc.

For preference testing, the submission to the consumer panel always consists of two or more samples. The responses may be "forced choice," i.e., prefer A or prefer B. Another form involves degrees of preference, e.g., strongly prefer A, prefer A, no preference, prefer B, strongly prefer B.

Figure 3.2 (in Section 3, Quality and Income) is an example showing the results of consumer preference testing of 41 products plotted against share of market. The great concentration of data along the horizontal axis suggests strongly that products with consumer preference test results of less than 30 percent are unable to survive in a competitive market, all other things being equal.

Consumer Sensitivity Testing. In this form of test, the purpose is to discover the "threshold" level at which consumers can detect the presence of sensory qualities. The qualities under test may be "desirable." For example, if an expensive ingredient is used in a product blend, it is very useful to know the threshold concentration level which ensures consumer recognition of the ingredient. The qualities under test may also be "undesirable." For example, a product exhibits varying degrees of visual blemish. It is very useful to know the threshold degree of defectiveness which makes the consumer respond negatively to the product.

In consumer-sensitivity testing, a graduated set of samples is prepared, each exhibiting a progressively greater extent of the quality or deficiency under investigation. These samples are submitted to a consumer panel as part of an organized study.

For example, in two companies—one making sterling silverware and the other making costume jewelry—studies were conducted to discover consumer sensitivity to visual defects. In both companies, a committee of key people (from Marketing, Design, Manufacture, and Quality) structured a plan of study as follows:

1. An assortment of product was chosen to reflect the principal visual defects, the principal products in the product line, and the principal price levels.
2. These samples were inspected in the factory by the regular inspectors to determine the severity of the defects as judged by the frequency with which the inspectors rejected the various units of product.
3. The assortment of products was then shown to a number of consumer panels chosen from those segments of the buying public which constituted important customer classes, e.g., suburban women, college students, etc. These panels reviewed the products under conditions which simulated use of the product, e.g., silverware in place settings on a dining room table. The consumers were instructed (by printed card) somewhat as follows: "Assume you have previously bought these products and they have been delivered to you. Naturally,

you will want to look them over to see that the merchandise is satisfactory. Will you be good enough to look it over, and if you see anything which is objectionable to you, will you please point it out to us?"

The resulting data showed that the consumer panels were highly sensitive to some defects. For such defects the strict visual standards were retained. For certain other defects the consumer sensitivity was far less than factor-inspector sensitivity. For such defects the standards were relaxed. In still other instances, some operations had deliberately been omitted, but the consumers proved to be insensitive to the effect of the omission. As a result, the operations were abolished.

Consumer-sensitivity testing is an extension of the principle that "the consumer is right." This principle may be subdivided as follows:

1. The consumer is right as to qualities he or she can sense. As to such qualities, the manufacturer is justified in taking action to make such qualities acceptable to the consumer.
2. The consumer is also right as to qualities he or she *cannot* sense. The manufacturer is not justified in adding costs to create an esthetic effect not sensed by the consumer.
3. Where, for a given quality, the customer is sensitive to a limited level but not beyond, the manufacturer should take action to make the quality to that level but not beyond.

The intermediate marketing chain sometimes interferes with these principles. Sales clerks are proficient in emphasizing product differences, whether important or not. In turn, dealers are alert to seize on such differences to wring concessions out of competing manufacturers. A frequent result is that all manufacturers are driven to adopt wasteful standards, resulting in a needlessly high cost, e.g., finishes on nonworking or nonvisible surfaces. Elimination of such perfectionism commonly requires that the manufacturer secure data direct from consumers and then use the data to convince the distribution chain. These same data may be needed to convince other nonconsumers who exhibit perfectionist tendencies: upper management, designers, salespeople, inspectors, etc.

Visual Quality Characteristics. These are a special category of sensory qualities. (Visual inspection remains the largest single form of inspection activity.) For these characteristics, the written specifications seldom describe completely what is wanted, and often inspectors are left to make their own interpretation. In such cases, inspectors are really making two judgments simultaneously:

1. What is the meaning of this visual characteristic of the specification, e.g., what is the standard?
2. Does this unit of product conform to the standard?

Where inspectors understand fitness for use, they are qualified to make both these judgments. If a particular inspector lacks this knowledge, he or she is qualified only to make judgment 2, no matter how long on the job. Extensive experience has shown that inspectors who lack this knowledge differ widely when setting standards and, in addition, do not remain consistent. (As an example, from the consulting experience of J. M. Juran, in an optical company, study of the methods used by 18 different inspectors, engineers, etc., disclosed the existence of six methods of counting the number of "fringes of irregularity.")

Several methods are available to planners to clarify the standard for visual characteristics.

Visual Inspection Standards.   The most elementary form of visual standard is the limit sample—a unit of product showing the worst condition acceptable. In using this standard the inspector is aided in two ways:

1. The Sample conveys a more precise meaning than does a written specification.
2. The inspection is now made by comparison, which is well known to give more consistent results than judgment in the absence of comparison.

A more elaborate form of visual standards involves preparation of an exhibit of samples of varying degrees of defects, ranging from clearly defective to clearly acceptable. See, for an example involving solder connections, Leek (1975 and 1976), who describes how the companies Martin Marietta and Northrup support series or "ranges" to provide manufacturing latitude in processing material, while at the same time identifying minimum and maximum limits on visual attributes. This exhibit is used to secure the collective judgments of all who have a stake in the standard—consumers, supervisors, engineers, inspectors. Based on these judgments, standards are agreed on and limit samples are chosen. (It is also feasible to estimate, by sampling, what would be the yield of the process, and thereby the cost of defects, for any one of the various degrees of defectiveness.)

In products sold for esthetic appeal, appearance becomes a major element of fitness for use and commonly a major element of cost as well. In such cases, an exhibit of samples of various degrees of defects intermingled with perfect units of product becomes a means of measuring consumer sensitivity (or insensitivity) to various defects. Use of consumer panels to judge such mixtures of product invariably confirms some previous concepts but also denies some long-standing beliefs held by the managers as well as by the inspectors.

In the sterling silverware case, above, consumers were quite sensitive to several types of defect—they held out 22 percent of the defects present. However, for the bulk of defects, the consumers were quite insensitive and found only 3 percent of such defects. The salespeople generally found twice as many defects as consumers but still considerable less than factory inspectors.

A further use of samples of various defects is to establish *grades* of defects. The concept of different grades is vital when a plant makes products which, while outwardly similar, are used in widely different applications, e.g., ball bearings used for precision instruments and those used for roller skates, lenses for precision apparatus and lenses for simple magnifiers, sterling silverware and plated silverware. Unless the grades are well defined and spelled out in authoritative form, the risk is that the inspectors will apply one standard to all grades.

Once limit samples have been agreed on, there remains a problem of providing working standards to the inspection force. Sometimes it is feasible to select duplicates for inspection use while retaining the official standard sample in the laboratory. An alternative is to prepare photographs (sometimes stereoscopic) of the approved standards and to distribute these photographs instead. (See also Schilling, 1982.)

Standardizing the Conditions of Inspection.   Visual inspection results are greatly influenced by the type, color, and intensity of illumination, by the angle of viewing, by the viewing distance, etc. Standardizing these conditions is a long step in the direction of securing uniform inspection results.

In the case of esthetic visual qualities, the guiding rule for conditions of inspection is to simulate the conditions of use, but with a factor of safety.

Establish a "fading distance." In some products the variety of visual defects is so great and the range of severity so wide that the creation of visual standards becomes prohibitively complex. An alternative approach is to standardize the conditions of inspection and then to establish a *fading distance* for each broad defect class. The definition for a defect becomes "anything which can be seen at the fading distance." [This technique appears to have been evolved in 1951 by N. O. Langenborg of St. Regis Paper Company. See also Riley (1979).]

Design of Products to Achieve Sensory Effects. The approach to this product design parallels closely the general approach set out in Section 13, Product Development. What is special is the absence of agreed units of measure and of instruments which can measure in terms of those units. Lacking these tools, the methods of sensory testing must be applied to the new designs, using both laboratory panels and consumer panels. Experiments involving substitution of materials, changes in process, reformulation, etc., all require sensory evaluations if cause and effect relationships are to be established. The laboratory panels provide the judgment on which these relationships can be based. The consumer panels are used to confirm the acceptability of the design in the marketplace.

The fourth row of Table 18.12 traces the use of sensory testing to discover the effect of material and process changes on sensory qualities. It is seen that the testing is done by a laboratory panel, specially selected and trained and working under controlled laboratory conditions.

Providing Standards for Sensory Qualities. Once the laboratory and consumer panels have provided the technological and marketing data, respectively, there remains a problem of setting standards to serve as a future basis for judging conformance. Setting these standards can be done by an organized approach which also considers factory yields and economics. This organized approach includes the following:

1. Definition of various levels of sensory quality along a "scale of measurement," i.e., a hedonic scale or a degree of defect severity as judged by panels.

2. Estimation of cost of meeting these various levels based on studies of process yields, need for added refinements in the process, etc.

3. Consideration of the effect of the various levels on product marketability based on consumer-sensitivity data, competitive product analysis, etc. (See Figure 18.2.)

4. Decision on the level to be adopted as the standard. This decision should be made with full participation of all departments in interest.

5. Executive approval of the standards. This approval should be formalized. The signature of the responsible executive(s) should appear on the approved samples (or on the document evidencing the approval). This formality serves to clear the air on decision making as well as to identify the samples unmistakably. These standards take any of numerous forms: physical samples of product for visual comparison, feel, texture, etc.; photographs; sound recordings; formulation of taste and smell; and still others.

6. Duplication of the standard for shop use. For *stable* products, the sensory standard can be filed like any other master reference standard. Duplicates can be prepared for everyday use, and these duplicates can be checked against the master under a scheduled maintenance plan. For *unstable* products, new masters must regularly be prepared, at intervals shorter than the rate of deterioration. Sometimes special storage or preservatives can help to stabilize the master.

FIG. 18.2 Summary for executive decision on sensory standards.

Judgment of Conformance to Sensory Standards.   The lowest two rows in Table 18.12 elaborate this problem. It is evident that there are conformance problems both as to process regulation and as to product acceptance. Laboratory panels are used throughout, under controlled laboratory conditions, employing various types of sensory tests and making use of the approved standards for reference purposes.

Panels for Sensory Testing.   Panels are composed of two very different populations, and these must not be confused.

Consumer Panels.   These serve to provide information on fitness for use in its various aspects (consumer likes and dislikes, preferences, sensitivity). The prime qualification for such a panel is to be representative of the consumers in the market. Since this precludes prior selection for ability to discriminate, it follows that a proportion of the panel members will lack the ability to make discriminations (e.g., color blindness). Training is also precluded because it introduces bias. Controlled test environments are also precluded; the conditions must be those of normal usage. These restrictions combine to make consumer panels numerically large. Often they run to hundreds of people. As a corollary, the time to conduct a test is lengthy—it can readily run to weeks and even months.

Laboratory Panels. These serve to judge conformance to standards and to provide product and process research data. Here the need is to make prompt, low-cost judgments. Selection of panel members for this purpose is based on tested ability to discriminate, and this ability is then sharpened by training. The work of these panels is carried out under controlled laboratory conditions, hence the name "laboratory panels." These features make it possible for small panels to provide prompt, low-cost data of measurable precision.

Selection of Laboratory Panels. In this selection it is first necessary to distinguish the candidate's (1) inherent ability to sense from (2) the ability to translate what is sensed into a judgment. For example, in color classification, the distinguishing terms are color blindness and color ignorance. Ability to sense differs in humans, and this difference is discoverable by selection tests; i.e., tests for visual acuity, taste perception, etc. If the candidate lacks the ability to sense, it is normally not feasible nor economic to awaken this ability. If, however, the candidate has the sensory ability, then he or she can be trained to use this ability to render judgments.

The overwhelming source of laboratory panelists is company employees. The company makes clear its needs for panelists and invites employees to volunteer to be tested for qualification. Responses are generally good, so that there is little difficulty in selecting and training enough panelists to provide for attrition in existing panels. The job of panelist is almost always a part-time job and consitutes a welcome change from the regular job (bottling line or whatever).

Tests used for screening prospective panelists are designed to discover (1) *sensitivity*, i.e., ability to detect the stimulus under study, and (2) *consistency*, i.e., ability to reproduce results on repeated testing. (For an early, pioneering study, see Helm and Trolle, 1946.) The paper reports extensive studies made at Carlsberg Breweries, Copenhagen, Denmark, and shows results for various categories of personnel. [See also Louis (1981) for a later discussion on testing by Jos. Schlitz Brewing Company.] These tests make use of various statistical designs as discussed in Sensory Tests: Design and Analysis, below. To execute these designs, test samples are prepared to possess known concentrations or degrees of the characteristics under study. (For products made as discrete units, the examination may be based on a preselected lot of graded samples. For coalesced products, special samples, in varying degrees of concentration, are commonly prepared.) The ability of the prospective panelist to judge the samples correctly is the decisive element in the panel-selection process. (For many years, industries such as brewing, food, and candy had put their confidence in a taste "expert." When, in due course, these experts were tested under statistical designs, some of the companies underwent a good deal of shock.)

Environment for Laboratory Panels. The laboratory panels conduct their work under controlled laboratory conditions to minimize the effect of extraneous variables, reduce the sample sizes needed, and increase the precision of results. See, for example, Figure 18.3, which shows the environment of a taste-test panel. In such an environment, unwanted variables can be stratified or randomized, design of experiments can be scientific, and cost of experimentation can be held to a minimum for a given precision.

Of course, laboratory testing is not conclusive as to consumer acceptability, which is properly determined by actual use by consumers (hence "kitchen-tested," "road-tested," etc.); it is still only an approximation. Simulated service

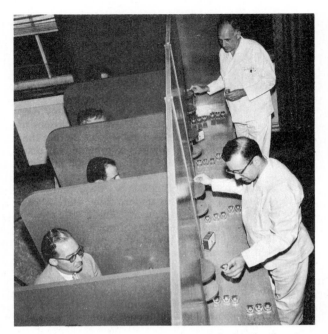

FIG. 18.3 Sensory test panel. *(Courtesy Schenley Distillers, Inc., Cincinnati, OH.)*

testing is an approximation further removed. Materials test data (to predict *potential* service results) are an approximation still further removed.

Selecting Inspectors for Sensory Tests. It is important for the inspector to have a *feel* for the end use of the product. He or she can then not only categorize the material or product but make more intelligent decisions in borderline circumstances (Chebookjian, 1980). However, four elements are needed to conduct a sensory or *cosmetic* inspection program in order to avoid too much product being rejected. They are documented cosmetic criteria, proper viewing and lighting conditions, methods to monitor inspection results, and formal training for inspectors who have decision-making authority (Davidson, 1982). The above four elements are most effective if those inspectors are selected who have the highest abilities to discriminate sensory characteristics. Evaluation techniques are rooted in common statistical methods (see Geidel, 1978), and they range from geometrical methods (Ohta and Kase, 1980) to the use of the *indifference zone approach* (Shimoda and Miyazaki, 1981).

Sensory Tests: Design and Analysis. There are numerous designs of sensory tests, some of them quite complex. Some of the basic forms are described below.

Tests for Differences or Similarities. These include:

1. *The paired-comparison test:* Product is submitted to members of a panel in pairs of samples. One sample is identified to each panelist as the standard or

"control"; the other is the test sample. The panelist is asked to judge and record the difference on a scale of differences (such as no difference, slight difference; pronounced difference). Some of the pairs have no difference; i.e., both are "controls."

2. *The triangle test:*   The panelist is asked to identify the odd sample in a group of three, two of which are alike. He or she may also be asked to estimate the degree of difference and to describe the difference between the odd sample and the two like samples.

3. *The duo-trio test:*   The panelist is asked to identify which of two samples is like the "control" to which she or he has previously been subjected. For example, in liquor manufacture, the aim is to make each batch indistinguishable in taste from past batches. The duo-trio test is used as a product-acceptance test. Each panelist tastes the "control," which he or she is told comes from previous product. Then each panelist tastes the two remaining samples, one of which is "control" and the other the batch under test. However, the panelists are not told which is which. If the data make clear that the panel cannot distinguish the new batch from the control, the batch is accepted. Otherwise, it is reblended.

4. *Ranking test:*   Coded samples are submitted to each panelist, who is asked to rank them in the order of concentration.

Tests for Quality Description.   The panelist is asked to judge the absence, presence, or intensity of various suspected quality characteristics in the sample. A usual form is "profile" testing, in which the characteristics to be judged are listed in advance and the panelist is used as an instrument for qualitative and quantitative analysis, i.e., to "prepare a profile."

Descriptive tests are also used to identify the seeming nature of unknown qualities ("it smells like lilac").

Tests for Quality Preference or Acceptance.   These are aimed at judging marketability and therefore make use of consumer panels. The most usual forms are:

1. Hedonic scale tests, which rank the product anywhere between limits, e.g., from "like very much" down to "dislike very much."

2. "Home use" testing done by a "standing" panel of consumers to whom products and instructions are delivered. The panel sends its data in return. Emphasis is on *use* testing at the point of use.

3. "Store testing" done by a sample of the stream of people flowing through a store. Data are recorded by a trained observer. Emphasis is on *preference* testing at the point of *sale.* (See Brandt, 1963.)

Analysis of sensory test data is mainly by conventional statistical significance tests. [See generally Section 23 under Tests of Hypotheses. However, a specialized literature has also evolved. Methods for dealing with paired comparisons were prepared by Scheffe (1952).] An early use of the duo-trio test was by Peryam (1950), who used 2.26 as the boundary for significance, in accordance with the formula:

$$\sigma_p = \left(\frac{pq}{n}\right)^{1/2}$$

TABLE 18.13 Rating Table for Sensory Testing

Total judgments	Number correct	Percent correct	SE distance from 50% (σ_p rating)	Percent area between 50% and this point	Percent area beyond this point
20	10	50.0	0.0	0.0	50.0
20	11	55.0	0.4	15.6	34.4
20	12	60.0	0.9	31.6	18.4
20	13	65.0	1.3	40.3	9.7
20	14	70.0	1.8	46.4	3.6
20	15	75.0	2.2	48.6	1.4
20	16	80.0	2.7	49.7	0.3
20	17	85.0	3.1	49.9	0.1
20	18	90.0	3.6	50.0—	Very small
20	19	95.0	4.0	50.0—	Very small
20	20	100.0	4.5	50.0—	Very small
30	18	60.0	1.1	36.4	13.6
30	19	63.3	1.5	43.3	6.7
30	20	66.7	1.8	46.4	3.6
30	21	70.0	2.2	48.6	1.4
30	22	73.3	2.6	49.6	0.4
30	23	76.7	2.9	49.8	0.2
30	24	80.0	3.3	50.0—	Very small

where p = fraction correct identification of the unknown with standard
q = fraction incorrect = $(1 - p)$
n = number of samples in the series

At this level of significance, the probability is 0.014 that the lot is actually at standard despite the ratings of the panelists to the contrary. Peryam's table for sample sizes of 20 and 30 is reproduced as Table 18.13.

A comparison of operating characteristic curves for the pair, duo-trio, and triangle tests is provided by Fortuin and Van Beek (1960).

Creating New Instruments to Measure Sensory Qualities. Many sensory qualities formerly judged by human perception are now measured by instruments. This development of new instrumentation goes on apace, using essentially the following approach (based on a procedure set out by Dr. Amihud Kramer, 1952; see also Hains, 1978):

1. Define precisely what is meant by the quality characteristic under discussion. This must be done with participation of all interested parties.
2. Discover, through analytical study, the subcharacteristics, and define them in a way which permits, in theory, measurement by some inanimate instrument.
3. Search the literature to become informed on methods already in existence or under development for measuring these subcharacteristics. This search will disclose a number of such possible measurement methods.
4. Choose or create product samples which vary widely for the subcharacteristics. Test a limited number (10 to 50) of samples with each of the various

measurement methods, and correlate these tests with evaluation by panels of human testers. The human evaluation here aims not to measure personal preferences but to rate the degree to which the samples possess the variable under study. Hence the main requirement of the panel is that it be able to discriminate the subcharacteristics under study. Discard those measurement methods which lack precision or which fail to reflect human evaluation.

5. For the remaining, more promising measurement methods, conduct tests on a larger number of samples (100 to 1000) also chosen to reflect the entire range of quality variation. In addition, conduct tests of duplicate samples using evaluation by human test panels.

6. Correlate the results of measurement against the human test panel evaluation; select that method which gives a high, outstanding correlation. (Multiple correlation methods may be necessary.)

7. Improve and simplify the selected measurement method through further test and correlation.

8. Establish a scale of grades through use of a human sensory test panel. At this stage, the prime purpose of the human test panel is *to state preferences* along the scale of measure. Hence the main requirement of this panel is that it be representative of the producers and users of the product.

9. Weigh the various subcharacteristics in accordance with their rated performance (see also Montville, 1983, and Papadopoulos, 1983).

10. Develop the sampling procedures needed to apply the resulting method of measurement.

MEASUREMENT—AN INTRODUCTION

Conduct of the quality function depends heavily on quantification of product and process characteristics. This quantification is done through a systematic approach involving:

1. Definition of standardized units called "units of measure" which permit conversion of abstractions (e.g., length, mass) into a form capable of being quantified (e.g., meter, kilogram).

2. *Instruments* which are calibrated in terms of these standardized units of measure.

3. Use of these instruments to quantify or *measure* the extent to which the product or process possesses the characteristic under study. This process of quantification is called "measurement."

The word "measurement" has multiple meanings, these being principally:

1. The *process* of quantification, e.g., "the measurement was done in the laboratory"

2. The resulting number, e.g., "the measurement fell within the tolerances"

Measurement rests on a highly organized, scientific base called "metrology," i.e., the science of measurement. This science underlies the entire systematic approach through which we quantify quality characteristics.

UNITS OF MEASURE

The concept of quantifying bigness and smallness is thousands of years old. At first, units of measure were in terms of parts of the human body. For example, the ancient Egyptian unit of measure for length was the royal cubit, which was defined as the length of the forearm of the reigning pharaoh.

With the expansion of commerce, and especially of international commerce, the metrologists evolved systems of international units of measure, the chief systems being the metric and the English. The metric system is entirely based on decimal notation and primarily uses units of measure which scientists developed in the nineteenth and twentieth centuries. The English system is only partially based on decimal notation, and includes units of measure which antedate the industrial revolution.

Metrication. The existence of multiple systems of measurement is a serious handicap to international commerce. During the twentieth century there has been extensive adoption of the metric system by countries previously using the English or other systems. At the beginning of the 1970s, all industrialized countries with the single exception of the United States had either adopted the metric system or had decided to do so. In the United States, resistance to the metric system arises from a heavy investment in the English system coupled with a low ratio of volume of international trade to total size of the economy. However, those industries which are strongly exposed to international trade have largely adopted dual systems or have converted to metric. On purely technological grounds, the metric system is widely regarded as preferable to the English. (For further discussion see Sharp, 1976, and Darby, 1970.)

Despite the lack of a positive national plan for converting to metric, the United States is in a slow conversion process. The gradual conversion, if continued, will likely become virtually complete in about a century, whereas a planned program would reduce the conversion time to a decade or two. (For further discussion, see De Simone, 1971.)

Conversion costs in specific cases vary widely. Dual reading scales for instruments or dual reading dials for machines may involve less than $100 per instance. In contrast, new digital readout systems for machine tools may run to several thousand dollars per axis (Blaufuss, 1972).

Aside from conversion of machine tools, instruments, and small tools, there are other costs (De Simone, 1972):

Revision of specifications, standards, and other documentation

Provision of dual sets of spare parts during the conversion process

Retraining of personnel

SI System. More recently there has been evolved a fully coherent international system, the Système International d'Unités (SI). This SI system consists of:

1. Seven fundamental units of measure—for length, mass, time, electric current, temperature, light intensity, and amount of substance
2. Two supplemental units for plane and solid angles
3. A long list of units derived from 1 and 2
4. A standardized terminology for multiples and subdivisions of all units of measure

TABLE 18.14 SI System Units of Measure

Characteristic	Unit of measure	Symbol	Formula
Fundamental units			
Length	Meter	m	
Mass	Kilogram	kg	
Time	second	s	
Electric current	ampere	A	
Thermodynamic temperature	Kelvin	K	
Luminous intensity	candela	cd	
Amount of substance	Mole	mol	
Supplementary units			
Plane angle	radian	rad	
Solid angle	steradian	sr	
Derived units			
Area	square meter	m^2	
Volume	cubic meter	m^3	
Frequency	hertz	Hz	(s^{-1})
Density	kilogram per cubic meter	kg/m^3	
Velocity	meter per second	m/s	
Angular velocity	radian per second	rad/s	
Acceleration	meter per second squared	m/s^2	
Angular acceleration	radian per second squared	rad/s^2	
Force	newton	N	(kg/ms)
Pressure	newton per sq meter	N/m^2	
Kinematic viscosity	sq meter per second	m^2/s	
Dynamic viscosity	newton-second per sq meter	$N \cdot s/m^2$	
Work, energy, quantity of heat	joule	J	(N/m)
Power	watt	W	(J/s)
Electric charge	coulomb	C	(A/s)
Voltage, potential difference, electromotive force	volt	V	(W/A)
Electric field strength	volt per meter	V/m	
Electric resistance	ohm	Ω	(V/A)
Electric capacitance	farad	F	(A/s/V)
Magnetic flux	weber	Wb	(V/s)
Inductance	henry	H	(V/s/A)
Magnetic flux density	tesla	T	(Wb/m^2)
Magnetic field strength	ampere per meter	A/m	
Magnetomotive force	ampere	A	
Luminous flux	lumen	lm	(cd/sr)
Luminance	candela per sq meter	cd/m^2	
Illumination	lux	lx	(lm/m^2)

Table 18.14 lists the fundamental, supplemental, and derived units of the SI system along with the symbols used and the derivation formulas. (See Griffin, 1980, and McNish, 1966.) Table 18.15 lists the terms used for multiples and subdivisions of these units of measure. (See also "SI—Systeme International Rationale," 1972.)

TABLE 18.15 SI System Multiples and Subdivisions

Multiple or subdivision	Prefix	Symbol
$1\,000\,000\,000\,000 = 10^{12}$	tera	T
$1\,000\,000\,000 = 10^9$	giga	G
$1\,000\,000 = 10^6$	mega	M
$1\,000 = 10^3$	kilo	k
$100 = 10^2$	hecto*	h
$10 = 10^1$	deca*	da
$0.1 = 10^{-1}$	deci*	d
$0.01 = 10^{-2}$	centi*	c
$0.001 = 10^{-3}$	milli	m
$0.000\,001 = 10^{-6}$	micro	μ
$0.000\,000\,001 = 10^{-9}$	nano	n
$0.000\,000\,000\,001 = 10^{-12}$	pico	p
$0.000\,000\,000\,000\,001 = 10^{-15}$	femto	f
$0.000\,000\,000\,000\,000\,001 = 10^{-18}$	atto	a

*Use is discouraged.

The SI system is fully compatible with the metric system, though it supersedes some earlier units (e.g., liter, calorie). The SI system is not fully compatible with the English system of feet, pounds, etc., though conversion factors are, of course, available.

Nonmeasurable Characteristics. For many characteristics there are as yet no agreed units of measure. Nevertheless, useful evaluations can be made of such characteristics by:

1. *Sensory testing:* Here no instrument is available for sensing, and the sensing is done by human sense organs (taste, feel, smell, etc.). For a full discussion, see Section 18, under Sensory Qualities.
2. *Instrument testing:* An example is the "nondestructive" testing performed to detect weaknesses in metal components (see below, under Nondestructive Testing).

Development of new units of measure and of new sensing instruments is a continuing process. All today's units of measure were evolved to replace qualitative evaluations. Presumably all today's qualitative evaluations will, at some time in the future, be susceptible of measurement using agreed units of measure.

MEASUREMENT STANDARDS

The seven fundamental units of the International System (SI) are defined as shown in Table 18.16. It is seen that except for the kilogram, all units are defined in terms of natural phenomena. (The kilogram is defined as the mass of a specific object.)

Primary Reference Standards. In all industrialized countries there exists a national bureau of standards whose functions include construction and maintenance of "primary reference standards." These standards consist of copies of the

TABLE 18.16 Definitions of Fundamental Units of the SI System

Unit	Definition
Meter, m	1/650 763.73 Wavelengths in vacuo of the unperturbed transition 2_{p10}—$5d_5$ in ^{86}Kr
Kilogram, kg	Mass of the international kilogram at Sevres, France
Second, s	1/31 556 925 974 7 of the tropical year at 12^h ET, 0 January 1900, supplementarily defined in 1964 in terms of the cesium F, 4; M, 0 to F, 3; M, 0, transition, the frequency assigned being 9 192 631 770 Hz
Kelvin, K	Defined in the thermodynamic scale by assigning 273.16 K to the triple point of water (freezing point, 273.15 K = 0°C)
Ampere, A	The constant current which, if maintained in two straight parallel conductors of infinite length, of negligible circular sections, and placed 1 m apart in a vacuum, will produce between these conductors a force equal to 2×10^{-7} mks unit of force per meter of length.
Candela, cd	1/60 of the intensity of 1 cm^2 of a perfect radiator at the temperature of freezing platinum.
Mole, mol	An amount of substance whose weight in grams numerically equals the molecular formula weight.

International Kilogram plus measuring systems which are responsive to the definitions of the fundamental units (Table 18.16 and to the derived units of Table 18.14).

In addition, professional societies, (e.g., American Society for Testing and Materials) have evolved standardized test methods for measuring many hundreds of quality characteristics not listed in Table 18.13. These standard test methods describe the test conditions, equipment, procedure, etc., to be followed. The various national bureaus of standards, as well as other laboratories, then develop primary reference standards which embody the units of measure corresponding to these standard test methods.

Primary reference standards have a distinct legal status, since commercial contracts usually require that "measuring and test equipment shall be calibrated . . . utilizing reference standards . . . whose calibration is certified as being traceable to the National Bureau of Standards." (This wording is from MIL-STD-45662, *Military Specification—Calibration System Requirements.*) In practice it is not feasible for the U.S. National Bureau of Standards to calibrate and certify the accuracy of the enormous volume of test equipment in use in the shops and test laboratories. Instead, resort is had to a hierarchy of secondary standards and laboratories, along with a system of documented certification of accuracy.

Hierarchy of Standards. The primary reference standards are the apex of an entire hierarchy of reference standards (Figure 18.4). At the base of the hierarchy there stands the huge array of "test equipment" (the terminology varies; for a discussion, see Section 16, under Quality Information Equipment), i.e., instruments used by laboratory technicians, workers and inspectors to control processes and products. These instruments are calibrated against "working standards" which are used solely to calibrate these laboratory and shop instruments. In turn, the working standards are related to the primary reference standards through one or more intermediate secondary reference standards or "transfer standards." Each

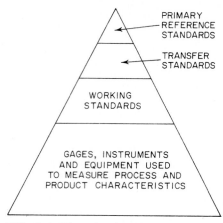

FIG. 18.4   Hierarchy of standards.

of these levels in the hierarchy serves to "transfer" accuracy of measurement to the next lower level in the hierarchy.

Within the hierarchy of standards there are differences both in the physical construction of the standards and in their precision. The primary reference standards are used by a relatively few highly skilled metrologists, and their skills are a vital contribution to the high precision attained by these standards. As we progress down the hierarchy, the number of technicians increases with each level, until at the base there are millions of workers, inspectors, and technicians using test equipment to control product and process. Because of the wide variation in the training, skills, and dedication among these millions, the design and construction of test equipment must feature ruggedness, stability, and foolproofing so as to minimize errors contributed by the human beings using the equipment.

Precision of measurement differs widely among the various levels of the hierarchy of standards. At the level of primary reference standards, the precision is determined by the state of the art. For example, Figure 18.5 shows the precision

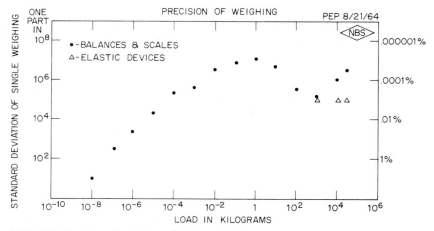

FIG. 18.5   Precision of weighing.

attained by the U.S. National Bureau of Standards when weighing loads across the spectrum of 10^{-10} to 10^6 (National Bureau of Standards, 1965).

At the base of the hierarchy, the precision of measurement is determined by the needs of fitness for use as reflected by the product and process tolerances. While some specialists urge that the test equipment be able to "divide the tolerance into tenths," this ideal is by no means always attained in practice. However, the tolerances themselves have been drastically tightened over the centuries, and this tightening has generally paralleled the advances made in the state of the art. For example, accuracy of measurement of a meter of length has progressed from an error of 1000 per million (at the end of the fifteenth century) to an error of 0.001 per million late in the twentieth century (see Loxham, 1967).

Allocation of measurement errors among the working and transfer standards has been widely discussed but has not been well standardized. The precision gap between primary reference standards and product test equipment may be anywhere from one to several orders of magnitude. This gap must then be allocated among the number of levels of standards and laboratories (transfer plus working) prevailing in any given situation. (Some models have been worked out to show the interrelation among the cost of developing greater precision in the primary reference standard, cost of attaining precision at each level of transfer laboratory, and number of laboratories at each level. See, for example, Crow, 1966.) When this problem of allocation was first faced, there was a tendency to conclude that each level should have a precision 10 times greater than the level it was checking. More recently, there has been growing awareness of how multiple levels of precision combine: i.e., their composite is better represented by the square root of the sum of the squares rather than by the arithmetic sum. This new awareness has caused many practitioners to accept a ratio of 5 to 1 rather than 10 to 1 for precision of working standards to product tolerances. This same ratio has also been tolerated among transfer standards as well.

ERROR OF MEASUREMENT

Product and process conformance are determined by measurements made by the test equipment at the bottom of the hierarchy of standards. Obviously, any error in these measurements has a direct bearing on the ability to judge conformance. On examination, the nature of measurement error is quite complex; even the terminology is confused. A clear understanding of the meaning of the measurements requires a minimal degree of understanding of the nature of measurement error. The starting point is to understand the nature of accuracy and precision. Figure 18.6 shows the meanings of these terms, by example and by analogy. See, in this connection, ASTM 177-71 (listed in Appendix III) on use of the terms "precision" and "accuracy" as applied to measurement of the properties of materials. See also Mathur, 1974, for a discussion on the influence of measurement variation in mass production of parts.

Accuracy. Suppose that we make numerous measurements on a single unit of product and that we then compute the average of these measurements. The extent to which this average agrees with the "true" value of that unit of product is called the accuracy of the instrument or measurement system which was employed. The difference between the average and the true value is called the "error" (also "systematic error," "bias," or "inaccuracy") and is the extent to which the instrument is out of calibration. The error can be positive or negative. The "correction" needed to put the instrument in calibration is of the same magnitude as the error

Measurements on One Unit of Product by Three Instruments

Readings					Frequency Distribution of Readings	Target Analogy

Instrument A

.014	.015	.015	.017	.015
.015	.016	.014	.016	.015
.016	.016	.015	.016	.016
.017	.017	.016	.014	.016
.015	.015	.016	.014	.017

.017 ⎡ IIII
.016 ⎣ HHH IIII   AVE.
.015 ⎣ HHH III
.014 ⎣ IIII
.013 ⎣   ERROR
.012 ⎣
.011 ⎣   TRUE VALUE
.010 ⎣

Precise, but Not Accurate

Instrument B

.009	.011	.008	.007	.011
.009	.011	.009	.016	.012
.008	.012	.014	.008	.011
.010	.013	.014	.011	.012
.010	.013	.015	.010	.013

.016 ⎡ I
.015 ⎣ I
.014 ⎣ II
.013 ⎣ III
.012 ⎣ III
.011 ⎣ HHH   AVE.
.010 ⎣ HHH   TRUE
.009 ⎣ III   ERROR   VALUE
.008 ⎣ III
.007 ⎣ I

Accurate, but Not Precise

Instrument C

.009	.010	.010	.010	.009
.009	.010	.011	.011	.010
.009	.009	.011	.011	.009
.010	.011	.010	.011	.010
.010	.009	.011	.010	.010

.011 ⎡ HHH II
.010 ⎣ HHH HHH I   AVE.
.009 ⎣ HHH II   TRUE VALUE

Accurate and Precise

FIG. 18.6 Accuracy and precision.

but opposite in sign. The instrument is still considered "accurate" if the error is less than the "tolerance" or maximum error allowable for that grade of instrument.

Accuracy and error are quantified as a difference between (1) the average of multiple measurements and (2) the true value. As will be seen, each of these is surrounded by a fringe of doubt. In consequence, the expression of accuracy must show the extent of these doubts if the full meaning of the numbers is to be conveyed.

Precision. Irrespective of accuracy of calibration, an instrument will not give identical readings even when making a series of measurements on one single unit of product. Instead, the measurements scatter about the average, as exemplified in Figure 18.6. The ability of the instrument to reproduce its own measurements is called its "precision," and this varies inversely with the dispersion of the multiple ("replicated") measurements.

Experience has shown that any measurement system has an inherent dispersion which is itself reproducible, measurable, and therefore (once known) predictable. This inherent precision of measurement parallels the inherent process capability of a machine tool. (The parallel extends to the requirement that the system be in a state of statistical control.)

Quantification of precision is in terms of the standard deviation of replicated measurements, and is expressed by σ, the statistical symbol for standard deviation of a population.

Normally, recalibration can improve the accuracy of an instrument by reducing its error. However, recalibration normally does not improve the precision of the instrument, as this precision remains relatively constant over the working range. See Gantt (1959) for a discussion on the relation of instrument precision to product tolerance, using the ratio "repeatability."

Sources of Error. Systematic error and dispersion of measurements have their origin in several well-known components of measurement error. (In some industries, e.g., chemical process, the measurement problems are so severe that development of valid test procedures is a major step in the launching of a new product or process.)

Within-Operator Variation. The same operator, inspector, or technician, even when using the same measuring system on the same unit of product, will nevertheless come up with a dispersion of readings. This variation is usually referred to as "within-operator" variation.

Between-Operators Variation. When two operators use the same measuring system on the same products, they will usually exhibit differences traceable to differences in operator technique. These differences are called "between-operators" variation and can be exhibited both as systematic error and as differences in dispersion.

Materials Variation. In many cases it is not feasible to conduct replicated tests on the same "unit of product"; i.e., the product is changed or destroyed by testing. In other cases, the standard itself is consumable (e.g., hardness test blocks), so that material variation affects the standard as well. In these cases, where replicate testing is not feasible, the variations due to operator, equipment, and test method are composited with the materials variation. Sometimes it is feasible to resolve these composites into their components and sometimes it is not. A further complication is the case of perishable materials, which may require use of calibrations which relate time elapsed to degradation suffered.

Test Equipment Variation. Instruments are subject to numerous sources of error, both within a single instrument and between instruments: nonlinearity, hysteresis (e.g., gear backlash), drift due to temperature rise, sensitivity to extraneous "noise" (e.g., magnetic, thermal, electrical fields). Each technology is subject to its own unique array of troubles. These instrument troubles are multiplied by the "fixturing" troubles of connecting the instruments into the larger test equipment units and of connecting the test specimens for tests. These fixturing troubles include such problems as making good electrical connections, fastening mechanical linkages, locating probes precisely, etc.

Test Procedure Variation. In those cases where more than one test procedure is available to conduct measurement, it is essential to determine the relative variations, since these are one of the criteria for judging the adequacy of the procedure.

Between-Laboratories Variation. This is a major problem both within companies and between companies. Some major programs must await resolution of this problem before they can be concluded, e.g., industry standardization of materials, test equipment, and test procedures. In like manner, variation between vendor and buyer laboratories may be at the root of a major quality problem. So extensive is the need to reduce between-laboratories variation that standard procedures have been evolved for the purpose (see under Interlaboratory Test Programs).

Composite Errors.   The observed measurements are, of course, a resultant of the contributing variations. Generally this resultant or composite is related to the component variables in accordance with the formula:

$$\sigma_{obs}^2 = \sigma_w^2 + \sigma_b^2 + \sigma_m^2 + \sigma_e^2 + \sigma_p^2 + \text{etc.}$$

where σ_{obs} is the standard deviation of the observed measurements and where σ_w, σ_b, σ_m, σ_e, σ_p, etc., are the standard deviations reflecting the size of the variables which affect precision, i.e., within operator, between operators, material used, test equipment, test procedure, etc., respectively.

This relationship is valid provided the variables are independent of each other, which they often are. Where two or more of the variables are interrelated, then the equation must be modified. If for example, variables A and B are interrelated, then:

$$\sigma_T^2 = \sigma_A^2 + \sigma_B^2 + \rho_{AB}\sigma_A\sigma_B$$

where σ_T^2 = total variance
$\quad\ \sigma_A^2$ = variance of A
$\quad\ \sigma_B^2$ = variance of B
$\quad\ \rho_{AB}$ = the correlation coefficient (ρ) of A and B

In many cases it is feasible to quantify the effect of some component sources of variation by simple designs of experiment. When an instrument measures a series of different units of product, the resulting observations will have a scatter which is a composite of (1) the variation in the system of measurement and (2) the variation in the product itself. This relationship can be expressed as:

$$\sigma_{obs} = \sqrt{\sigma_{prod}^2 + \sigma_{meas}^2}$$

where σ_{obs} = σ of the observed data
$\quad\ \sigma_{prod}$ = σ of the product
$\quad\ \sigma_{meas}$ = σ of the measuring method

Now solving for σ_{prod},

$$\sigma_{prod} = \sqrt{\sigma_{obs}^2 - \sigma_{meas}^2}$$

It is readily seen that if σ_{meas} is less than one-tenth σ_{obs}, then the effect upon σ_{prod} will be less than 1 percent. This is the basis of the rule of thumb that the instrument should be able to divide the tolerance into about 10 parts.

To illustrate, in one shop the validity of a new type of instrument was questioned on the ground that it lacked adequate precision. The observed variation σ_{obs} was 11 (coded). An experiment was conducted by having the instrument make replicate checks on the same units of product. The σ_{means} was figured out to be 2. Then, since

$$\sigma_{prod}^2 = \sigma_{obs}^2 - \sigma_{meas}^2$$

$$\sigma_{prod} = \sqrt{121 - 4} = \sqrt{117} = 10.8$$

This was convincing proof that the instrument variation did not significantly inflate the product variation.

In another instance, involving the efficiency of an air-cooling mechanism, the observed variation σ_{obs} was 23, and the variation on retests, σ_{meas}, was 16. Thereupon

$$\sigma_{prod} = \sqrt{23^2 - 16^2} = \sqrt{529 - 256} = \sqrt{273} = 16 +$$

This showed that the measurement variation was as great as the product variation. Further study disclosed that the measurement variation could be resolved into

Variable	σ of that variable	σ^2
A	14	196
B	5	25
All other	7+	52
		273

It became clear that real progress could be made only by improving variable A, and the engineers took steps accordingly.

To quantify the individual components of variation requires still more elaborate analysis, usually through a special design of experiment (see Section 26, Design and Analysis of Experiments). (See also McCaslin and Grusko, 1976, for a discussion on an attribute gage study procedure; and Ezer, 1979, for statistical models for testing vial-to-vial variation in medical laboratories.)

Statement of Error.   In publishing results it is necessary to make clear the extent of error in those results. Lacking clear conventions or statements, those who review the results simply do not know how to evaluate the validity of the data presented. To make clear the extent of error present in the data, metrologists have adopted some guidelines which are ever more widely used.

Effect of Reference Standards.   Accuracy of an instrument is expressed as the difference between T, the "true" value, and $\overline{X}_m$, the average of the replicated measurements. The reference standard used is *assumed* to be the true value, but of course this is not fully valid, i.e., the standards laboratory is able to make only a close approximation. In theory, the true value cannot be attained. However, the extent of error can be ascertained through the use of replication and other statistical devices. As long as the systematic error of the standard is small in relation to the error of the instrument under calibration (the usual situation), the error of the standard is ignored. If there is some need to refer to the error of the standard, the published measurements may include a reference to the standard in a form similar to "as maintained at the National Bureau of Standards."

Effect of Significant Systematic Error.   When the systematic error is large enough to require explanation, the approved forms of explanation consist of sentences appended to the data, stating (for example), "This value is accurate within $\pm x$ units," or "This value is accurate within $\pm y$ percent." [See National Bureau of Standards (1966).]

If necessary, these statements may be further qualified by stating the conditions under which they are valid, e.g., temperature range.

It is a mistake to show a result in the form "$a \pm b$" with no further explanation. Such a form fails to make clear whether "b" is a measure of systematic error or is an expression of standard deviation of replicate measurements or an expression of probable error, etc.

Effect of Imprecision.   The quantification of precision is through the standard error (standard deviation), which is the major method in use for measuring dispersion. In publishing the standard error of a set of data, care must be taken to clear up what are otherwise confusions in the interpretation:

1. Does the standard error apply to individual observations or to the average of the observations? Unless otherwise stated, it should be the practice to relate the published standard error to the published average, citing the number of observations in the average.

2. If uncertainty is expressed as a multiple of the standard error, how many multiples are used? An approved form of expression is: " . . . with an overall uncertainty of ±4.5 km/s derived from a standard error of 1.5 km/s."

3. Is the standard error based solely on the data presented or on a broader history of data? To clarify this requires still more intricate wording, since a dispersion based solely on the current data is itself uncertain. (See Eisenhart, 1968.)

Effect of Combined Systematic Error and Imprecision. In these cases the expression of the published result must make clear that both types of error are present and significant. Eisenhart (1968) recommends a phraseology such as " . . . with an overall uncertainty of ±3 percent based on a standard error of 0.5 percent and an allowance of ±1.5 percent for systematic error."

Errors Negligible. Results may also be published in such a way that the significant figures themselves reflect the extent of the uncertainty. For example, in the statement, "The resistance is 3942.1 Ω, correct to five significant figures," the conventional meaning is that the "true" value lies between the stated value ±0.05 Ω.

Effect of Measurement Error on Acceptance Decisions. Two types of errors can occur in the classification of a product: (1) a nonconforming unit can be accepted (the consumer's risk) and (2) a conforming unit can be rejected (the producer's risk). In a classic paper Eagle (1954) shows the effect of precision on each of these errors (for variable measurement). McCaslin and Gruska (1976) discuss measurement error for attributes gages. These and other investigations have concluded that measurement error can be a serious problem. Greb (1976) presents a contrasting view and discusses the conditions that must occur before the problem becomes serious.

Programs to Reduce Error. As noted above in Sources of Error, there are a number of sources of variation which combine to produce the composite error. Each major variation is in turn a composite of multiple subvariations. Reducing the overall error usually involves two related programs:

1. Quantifying the components of error. These components are not equally important; they follow the Pareto principle, so that one or a very few are of greater influence than all the rest put together. Through statistical design of experiment, it is feasible to quantify the main components contributing to error. This statistical design follows the basic approach set out in Section 26, and the reader is referred to that section for a full discussion. (See also Schumacher, 1981, for a discussion on "random errors" and "systematic errors," and Abernethy et al., 1979, for a tutorial on measurement error.)

2. Finding ways to reduce the major variations through improved technique or new technology. While the major variable is usually "worker technique," this finding usually concludes also that the test has not been sufficiently engineered and that new technology is needed to minimize the variations due to worker technique (see Pipkin and Ritter, 1983).

This overall approach has much in common with that discussed in detail in Section 22 for improving quality generally.

Interlaboratory Test Programs. The most complex problem of reducing error is that involving multiple laboratories. In such cases, the approach used may be an interlaboratory test program, which is also used for some other important purposes such as:

Development of a new test method

Comparison of results of alternative test methods

Standardization of samples

Resolution of conflicts

Solution. Several hundred independent, commercial scientific inspection/test laboratories are in operation in the United States. A very useful guide to the available services is provided by the American Council of Independent Laboratories (Karasek, 1975). Selecting a capable laboratory is the most effective way to reduce the probability of error (see also Tustin, 1980).

So extensive is the need for interlaboratory test programs that the approach has been subjected to some standardization and control.

Techniques. A number of tools and techniques for monitoring laboratories have been evaluated. A general use standard is available from ASTM (1963) and a discussion of techniques from ASQC (1978).

Accreditation. Numerous accreditation programs of commercial testing laboratories have been developed to assure the accuracy of test/inspection results (see Hyer, 1979). Many accreditation programs are more familiarly known under terms such as laboratory approval, acceptance, recognition, listing, authorization, certification, endorsement, or registration programs.

Quality Assurance. Programs defining quality assurance standards for testing laboratories have also been developed and are available from ASTM (1984). See Provost and Elder (1983) for a discussion of cost-effective laboratory quality control; see also Schumacher (1976) for a discussion of methods for measuring compliance with calibration requirements.

MEASUREMENT TECHNOLOGY

While measurement technology is beyond the scope of this handbook, it is useful to note some of the aspects of this technology as they affect measurement generally. To this end, a brief look will be taken at trends in technology with respect to (1) measurement of length and (2) nondestructive testing. This is a small sample indeed.

Measurement of Length. Except for visual inspection, measurement of length is the oldest form of measurement and occupies more laboratory and inspection time than measurement for any other quality. Yet this old form of measurement has undergone several revolutions during the twentieth century alone. These revolutions include:

Obsolescence of Fixed-Limit Gages. Early in the century, product tolerances for metal cutting were generally of the order of 0.005 to 0.010 in, or about 0.10 to 0.25 mm. With such tolerances, the fixed-limit gages, despite their error of "feel" and despite the purely "good or bad" information they provided, were an adequate, inexpensive, and swift means for product inspection. In consequence, the preponderance of gages were of the fixed-limit type. While "variable" gages were available (i.e., dial gages, verniers, etc.), the fixed-limit gages dominated gage usage and the gage budgets. Still more precise measurement forms were also available, but these were usually carried out in the precision laboratories rather than on the shop floor.

Within several decades, the usual tolerances for metal cutting had been reduced by an order of magnitude or more, making the fixed-limit gage largely obsolete due to (1) the high error of "feel" in relation to the new level of tolerances and (2) the inadequacy of "good or bad" information for purposes of process control.

New Technological Principles.   The early methods for measuring length all employed mechanical principles. To measure the numerous special configurations, e.g., inside diameters, depths, tapers, etc., many special tools were evolved: surface plates, scales, verniers, micrometers, dial mechanisms, amplification linkages, gage blocks. These were brought to higher and higher levels of mechanical precision. Finally, the economics of continuing to improve precision through extension of mechanical principles reached its limit and it became necessary to use other principles, mainly electronic, pneumatic, and optical.

Electronic Measurement.   A usual form is built around a balanced Wheatstone bridge circuit. The gaging head or probe is used as a comparator, first resting on a known buildup of gage blocks and then on the specimen. The difference in vertical positions of this gaging head actuates a linear-variable-differential transformer which in turn unbalances the Wheatstone bridge. The amount of unbalance can be amplified by various orders of magnitude and then read on the scale, which is calibrated in units of length. Amplifications can exceed $5000\times$.

Pneumatic Measurement.   The pneumatic family of instruments operates on the principle that the volume of air flowing through a gap varies with the size of the gap. In some configurations this variation is virtually linear and hence permits ready calibration. The amplification factor of these systems is surprisingly high, extending comfortably to over $10,000\times$; i.e., a product variation of 0.001 in (0.0254 mm) would show up on the scale as 10 in (or 254 mm).

Optical Measurement.   There are various ways of using optical magnification for measuring length. The most precise makes use of the well-known phenomenon of "interference fringes," resulting when waves of light in the visible spectrum are alternately in and out of phase. A count of these fringes becomes a count of wavelengths of light. These distances are tiny—there are over a million wavelengths of visible light in each meter. The resulting precision permits magnifications of over a million in measuring with interference fringes. So precise is the method of using optical interference that the length of the meter, once defined as the length of a certain metal bar housed in the International Bureau of Weights and Measures (Paris), is now defined as 1,650,763.73 wavelengths of the orange-red line in the spectrum of krypton-86.

Still other means are available for measuring length: time (see Robinson, 1983), laser beams, holography, radiation, ultrasonics, eddy current, etc. (also see Abbe and O'Brian, 1972). In addition, research laboratories continue to work out new principles or new applications of old principles.

Nondestructive Testing. This broad term describes testing done to (1) detect flaws in materials and components and (2) measure physical properties such as dimensions, hardness, conductivity, composition, magnetic and elastic constants.

This testing is done without impairing the subsequent usefulness of the product, hence the name "nondestructive testing," or NDT. (Visual inspection is the oldest form of NDT.)

There is no single technique that will effectively do all the jobs required for nondestructive examination; rather each method supplements or complements the other. There are about a dozen basic technological principles which underlie the principal NDT methods (see Buckrop, 1976). These basic methods—along with their applications, advantages, and limitations—are set out in Table 18.17. Variations in technique have multiplied the dozen basic methods several times over, and this proliferation continues. (See Turner, 1974, for a discussion on emerging techniques.)

The versatility of NDT systems may be seen from Table 18.18 which shows the kinds of purposes or functions served by NDT systems in a great variety of test situations.

A likely moving force in the growing use of NDT is the need for greater assurance on matters of product safety, product liability, and government regulation. These forces stimulate not only testing but also formality of test programs. (ASTM has numerous standards on nondestructive testing, and the field is very active.) Increasingly there are demands for certification of test equipment and of the technicians who conduct the tests; i.e., the tests are not accepted as valid unless the technicians are formally qualified to conduct the tests and interpret the results.

In addition, the technology is itself tending to become "professionalized." Here and there an engineer specialist is designated as nondestructive-test engineer. An American Society for Nondestructive Testing has been in existence since 1941. Under the auspices of the society there was prepared the *Nondestructive Testing Handbook* (McMaster, 1959).

Section 27 under Computer-Aided Inspection (particularly Table 27.8) shows potential applications for automating various types of inspection.

Emergence of New Functions Associated with Measurement. The early gages were designed to classify product into good or bad. The hierarchy of standards and of laboratories served to assure that these classifying gages did an accurate job of classifying. Since then, the emphasis on defect prevention and on quality planning has demanded that the shop test equipment be usable for additional functions, mainly:

1. *Indicating:* The gages must show the "reading" along a scale of measurement. (The dial gage was the symbol of the indicating instrument until the advent of electronic readouts.) These readings become the feedback to operators for process control and to inspectors for product conformance decisions.

2. *Regulating:* In some applications it is economic to feed the measurements directly into the process so that the gage closes the loop to make the process self-regulating. See Section 16, under Automatic Process Regulation.

3. *Recording:* Increasingly, the burden of recording measurement data is being shifted from workers and inspectors to instruments specially designed to record data. These records are not merely a series of readings expressed in numbers. They include charts showing the data in time progression and related to tolerances or to control limits.

TABLE 18.17 Nondestructive Testing Comparison Table

Type	Applications	Advantages	Limitations
Eddy current	Checks for variation in wall thickness, conductivity, metallurgical properties, coating thickness, detection of incorrect material, seams, pits, porosity, surface finish, discontinuities.	Adapts to high-speed testing without probe contact. Excellent sensitivity to such defects as pinhole leakers, stitching, and hook cracks. Operates in poor optical environment and in presence of nonconductive contaminants.	Used only in conjunction with conductive materials. Alloy and hardness dependent and affected by temperature and magnetic fields. Cannot give absolute measurement, only qualitative comparison. Sensitivity of ID defects dependent on total wall thickness and depth of defect in terms of percent of wall thickness.
X-ray	Detects internal defects in welds, slag inclusion, penetration, lack of bond, thickness variations, cavities, metal inclusions, cracks, foreign particles.	Shows size and nature of hidden flaws or discontinuities in different thicknesses of metal. Gives permanent graphic record of defects. Radiation source can be turned off when not in use. Short time exposure. Unaffected by temperature changes or contaminants.	Has higher initial cost than gamma ray, requires power source, and has radiation hazard. Results not immediately known—requires trained technicians. Not sensitive to defects less than 2% thickness of total metal. Size and weight are generally larger than gamma. Depends on alloy uniformity.
Gamma ray	Detects interior flaws, cracks, seams, porosity, holes, inclusions, weld defects. Checks for thickness variations, integrity of assemblies.	Shows size and nature of hidden flaws or discontinuities in different thicknesses of metal. Needs no electrical power source nor oil or water cooling. Provides permanent record. Lower initial cost than x-ray.	Energy cannot be adjusted. Isotope must be chosen to meet sensitivity requirements and thickness of material. Sensitivity is not as great as x-ray. Trained technicians are needed. Results not immediately known.
Magnetic particle test	Detects surface and subsurface flaws that result from fatigue, thermal stresses, gas pockets,	Offers positive and simple method for finding cracklike defects at or close to the surface. Method is flexible	Limited to ferromagnetic material. No indications apparent for cracks parallel to the magnetic field, so

Method	Detects / Applications	Characteristics	Limitations
	lack of fusion, slag inclusions, corrosion and grinding in ferromagnetic material. Locates cracks, seams, porosity, holes, inclusions.	and economical. Portable equipment is available. Immediate results.	magnetism in two directions is needed to find all discontinuities. Surfaces must be clean and dry.
Penetrant dye	Detects all defects open to the surface. (Cracks, seams, porosity, laps, cold shuts, leaks, weld defects, fatigue cracks, processing cracks.) Used in production dip tanks or with portable units.	Detects minute cracks and leaks. Dye penetrant appears as a deep red glow on white background. Fluorescent penetrant shows under ultraviolet. Simple to apply. Accurate, fast, low initial cost and per-test cost.	Limited to surface defects. Surface must be free from oil and grease. A semidarkened area is necessary for ultraviolet inspection.
Ultrasonic: Resonance	Gages thickness of materials with relatively smooth and parallel or concentric surfaces and some moderately rough corroded surfaces.	Displays instantly size, location, orientation and degree of flaw. Accuracy not affected by temperature or pressure—2% of thickness on rough surfaces, and up to 1% on smooth surfaces. Portable units enable field testing.	Must use a couplant (oil, grease, water, glycerine) or pressure to introduce the sound into the material under test. Rough surfaces and complex geometries complicate tests. Requires trained technicians.
Pulse echo	Locates case inclusions, internal ruptures, flaws, cracks, etc. Thickness gaging.		
Capacitive	Metallic or nonmetallic thickness and displacement gages. Dynamic vibration and high-speed inspection.	Good for both metals and nonmetals and temperature stable. Calibration relatively easy and has short response time. Readily adaptable to various configurations.	Does not work in liquid environments, and metal parts must be grounded to system.
Fiber optical	Displacement, flaw detection, and overall dimensions.	High speed and not affected by type of material or magnetic fields.	Dependent on surface optical properties and affected by ambient light. Subject to contamination.

TABLE 18.18 Functional and Situational Applications of Nondestructive Testing

Type of situation to be tested	Function or purpose of the nondestructive testing											
	Analysis	Detection*	Examination	Evaluation	Imaging	Identification	Inspection, checking	Location*	Maintenance (preventive)	Measurement*	Searching*	Testing*
Bonded areas	…	…	…	…	…	…	X					
Brazed areas	…	…	…	…	…	…	X					
Casting defects	…	…	…	…	…	…	…	X				
Cracks	…	…	…	…	…	…	…	X				
Defects, general	…	X	…	…	…	…	X	X				
Equipment	…	…	…	X	…	…	X					
Fabricating discontinuities	…	…	…	…	…	…	…	X				
Failure	X	…	…	…	…	…	…					
Fluid flow	…	…	…	…	X	…	…	X				
Foreign objects	…	X	…	…	X	…	…	X				
General	X	X	X	X	X	X	X	X	X	X	X	
Inclusions in castings	…	…	…	…	…	…	…	X				X

18.74

Internal parts of
hardware
systems

Internal organs,
etc., of animals

Laminar defects

Material types

Particles

Ruptures, internal

Stress—internal,
residual,
vibration

Surfaces—external,
internal, hidden

Thickness, general

Wall thickness:
corrosion wall
thinning

Welds

Weld defects

*Functions followed with an asterisk often can be performed on an automatic or semiautomatic basis instead of manually.

Source: Courtesy Lloyd B. Wilson.

18.75

4. *Computing, summarizing, and reporting:* A further step is to feed the data into computers. Some of these computers are used to figure averages and standard deviations. Others summarize data and prepare reports for supervisory and managerial review. These new and multiple functions have given rise to the name "quality information equipment" to emphasize that the dominant role is to provide information. For further discussion, especially as to the planning aspects, see Section 16, under Quality Information Equipment. See generally Section 27 (also Guest, 1981).

Collectively, these and related new functions associated with measurement have revolutionized the nature of the equipment and thereby the problems of keeping everything in calibration. It is no longer enough to assure that the mechanism which senses length remains in calibration. In addition, the entire train of attachments which indicate control, record, compute, etc., must likewise remain in calibration. All this has greatly expanded the role of the metrologists and their supporting technicians (also see Hunter, 1980).

CALIBRATION CONTROL

Measurement standards deteriorate in accuracy (and in precision) during use, and, to a lesser degree, during storage. To maintain accuracy requires a continuing system of calibration control. The elements of this system are well known and are set out below.

(The terminology associated with "calibration control" is not yet standardized. To put an instrument into a state of accuracy requires first that it be tested to see if it is within its calibration limits. This test is often referred to as "checking" the instrument. If, upon check, the instrument is found to be out of calibration, then a rectification or adjustment must be made. This adjustment is called variously "calibration," "recalibration," or "reconditioning." In some dialects, the word "calibration" is used to designate the combination of checking the instrument and adjusting it to bring it within its tolerances for accuracy.)

While the same system can be applied to all levels of standards, as well as to test equipment, there are some significant differences in detail of application. Transfer standards are exclusively under the control of standards laboratories staffed by technicians whose major interest is maintaining the accuracy of calibration. In contrast, test equipment and, to some extent, working standards are in the hands of those production, inspection, and test personnel whose major interest is product and process control. This difference in outlook affects the response of these people to the demands of the control system and requires appropriate safeguards in the design and administration of the system.

New-Equipment Control.   The control system regularly receives new elements in the form of additional standards, new units of test equipment, and expendable materials. These elements should be of proved accuracy before they are allowed to enter the system. The approach varies depending on the nature of the new item:

1. *Purchased precision standards:* These include high-accuracy gage blocks, standard cells, etc. Control is based on the supplier's calibration data and on his or her certification that the calibration is traceable to the National Bureau of Standards. Where such purchased standards represent the highest level of accuracy in the buyer's company, any subsequent recalibration must be performed by an outside laboratory, i.e., the supplier, an independent laboratory, or the National Bureau of Standards.

2. *Purchased working standards:*   These are subjected to "incoming inspection" by the buying company unless the demonstrated performance of the supplier merits use of "audit of decisions" (see Section 15).

3. *New test equipment:*   This equipment is intended for use in checking products and processes. However, it usually embodies measuring instruments of various sorts and may well include working standards as well, i.e., test pieces ("masters" for in-place check of calibration). Such new test equipment should be checked out for calibration before being put into use. (Refer to Figure 18.7, from Meckley, 1955; in addition, there are various usage criteria, as discussed in Section 16, under Quality Information Equipment.)

4. *Test materials:*   These include consumable standards as well as expandable supplies such as reagents or photographic film. Variability in such materials can directly affect the associated measurements and calibrations.

FIG. 18.7 Flow diagram for gage control. Daily: Repair orders and inspection reports sent to Gage Record Section by areas 1, 2, 3, 4, and 5. Weekly: Lists sent to gage control for periodic inspection of instruments in areas 1, 2, 3, 4, and 6. Area 5 is handled by electrical maintenance. (*From Meckley, 1955.*)

For example, a manufacturer of sandpaper needed a uniform material on which to test the abrasive qualities of the sandpaper. He investigated the possibility of using plastic blocks and found that the plastics manufacturer was using the same sandpaper as a means of testing the toughness of the plastic.

For some of these materials, the suppliers can provide data on variability. For the rest, it is necessary to discover the variability through analysis, as discussed above under Error of Measurement.

Inventory and Classification. A systematic approach to calibration control starts with a physical inventory of all standards, instruments, and test equipment. (Where tooling is used as one of the means of product inspection, such tooling is commonly included within the list of items to be systematically controlled for accuracy.)

For each item which is to enter the system, a record card is made out. This card shows the historical origin of the item, its assigned serial number, the checking schedule, and related information. The card also provides space to record the results of checking and the repairs needed (see also Woods, 1978).

The physical test equipment is also marked with an assigned serial number for identification and traceability in the system.

Calibration Schedules. These are established by class of equipment and are varied to reflect precision, nature, and extent of use and still other factors. At the outset, these schedules are established by judgment and bargaining. Later, as data become available on the results of checking, it becomes feasible to change the schedules in the interest of greater effectiveness and economy.

The broad intent of calibration schedules is to detect deterioration beyond tolerable levels of accuracy. This deterioration takes place primarily through usage and secondarily through the passing of time. As a result, the calibration schedules describe the extent of usage or of elapsed time in several ways:

1. *Elapsed calendar time:* This method is in widest use. It establishes a fixed calendar time, e.g., 3 months, as a checking interval. At the end of the 3 months, steps are taken to check the equipment in accordance with schedule.

2. *Actual amount of usage:* This is based on counting the actual usage, e.g., number of units of product checked by the equipment. The count may be made (*a*) manually, by the inspectors, (*b*) through automatic counters installed in the equipment, or (*c*) by programming the computers to show the amount of testing performed based on production schedules.

3. *Metering of actual operating hours:* For electrical equipments it is feasible to meter the actual time that the equipment is drawing power. A simple device for this purpose is a direct reading coulometer (Figure 18.8). The heart of this device is a capillary tube filled with two columns of mercury separated by an electrolyte. Passage of direct currents results in transfer of mercury from one column to the other. The electrolytic gap moves as a result and serves as an indicator to measure cumulative current (and hence cumulative hours of use) on a calibrated scale (see Marwell, 1966).

4. *Test accuracy ratio (TAR) control.* This is a systems approach that analyzes the degree to which interrelated parameters are identified and controlled within a *traceability cone.* Minimum TARs for each traceable parameter are measured and controlled. (See also Tobey, 1979.)

FIG. 18.8   Coulometer for recording instrument usage.

Adherence to Schedule.   This vital detail makes or breaks the entire system of calibration control.

Generally, the transfer standards and most working standards pose no problem of adherence to schedule, since they are in the custody of a few standards laboratories and a relatively few associated technicians. In contrast, the test equipment (and some working standards) are widely scattered over numerous locations and are in the custody of thousands of workers, inspectors, and testers. Some of these individuals can be relied on to see that the checking schedule is followed, but many cannot.

In part, the problem is one of lack of knowledge of when the recalibration is due. The shop personnel require the aid of a memory system if they are to know which piece of equipment is due to be checked that day. They may recall what the checking intervals for each class of equipment are, but they cannot recall what the date of the last calibration was.

Some systems for adherence to schedule make use of ingenious color codes or labels which mark on each unit of equipment the date it was put back into service. (These codes are often extended to identify the grades of the standards themselves, whether primary, secondary, etc.) For large units, the expiration date is entered on a maintenance card which is attached to the unit. Such dates are an aid to the personnel for adhering to the checking schedule.

However, an added problem is that of motivation. The numerous users of test equipment are quite concerned with recalibration when trouble is encountered but less concerned when things seem to be going smoothly. In these latter cases, interruptions for calibration can even be a nuisance.

The solution is to give responsibility (for adherence to schedule) to the standards laboratory rather than to the production, inspection, and test personnel. When this proposal is made to practicing managers, they seldom accept it purely on grounds of theory of organization. However, when it is proposed that a sample of instruments be taken at random and checked for calibration (as a test of the existing "system" of calibration control), these same managers are quite willing to conduct such a test. The resulting disclosure of the actual state of calibration of the sample (of 25 to 100 instruments) is then decisive in convincing the managers of the need for a revision in the system of adherence to schedule. Under this assignment, the laboratory organizes a plan of checking which will keep up with the scheduled load. (See also Gebhardt, 1982.)

In administering the checking plan, manual record cards may be used to identify the calibration dates. For example, in the time-interval system, the record card carries a calendar printed at the top. A "flag" is clipped to the card at the place representing the recalibration date. On that date, all cards so marked will have moved to the front of the pack. Alternatively, the system may use a computer to provide a runoff showing which standards and equipments are due to be checked in the forthcoming week.

Calibration Practice.   To assure accuracy and to establish traceability, control laboratories have evolved some widely used procedures.

Individual responsibility is established by requiring that all concerned sign for their actions. The equipment record cards carry these signatures, as do the labels on the equipment.

Dates are recorded for all actions in view of the role of elapsed time in the calibration procedures.

Manuals of practice are established, including tolerances for accuracy, and methods to be used in calibration. In some types of test, these methods must be spelled out in detail, e.g., temperature or humidity controls, time cycle, human technique, etc. (Witness the detail of some of the ASTM standards on test method.)

Training programs are established for personnel, including (in some cases) formal qualification certificates to attest to proficiency.

Equipment is tamperproofed through sealing the adjusting screws. (The seals are then imprinted with the stamp of the laboratory.) In like manner, panels and drawers of test equipments are lock-wired, and the wires are lead-sealed together. (The laboratory takes no responsibility when seals are broken, and the company takes stern measures against tampering with the seals.)

As a means of assisting enforcement, quality assurance audits are conducted to review the calibration control procedures.

Record and Analysis of Results.   It is most useful to keep a record of the results of checking calibration and of the extent of work done to restore accuracy. Typically such a record lists:

Observed deficiencies in the equipment

Causes of out-of-calibration conditions

Repair time and recalibration time

Periodic analysis of these data then becomes the basis for:

1. Reducing checking for equipment shown to be stable
2. Redesigning equipment to eliminate causes of repetitive failure

Organization for Calibration Control. In small companies, the control laboratory carries out the multiple functions of:

1. Establishment of a system for maintaining calibration of standards and test equipment
2. Issuance, calibration, and custody in accordance with the established system

As the company grows, the standards laboratory decentralizes, partly for reasons of geography and partly for specialization in technology.

When multiple plants are located in different cities, the need for some geographical decentralization is obvious. Even in single large plants, the problems of checking test equipment may be simplified through decentralization, including the concept of mobile laboratories. For mechanical work, these take the form of the traveling gage cart equipped with surface plates, master gages, and accessories as well as an inventory of working gages. (See "Portable Gage Lab Provides Flexibility and Minimizes Downtime," 1971).

In addition, the cart carries a file drawer of gage records to aid in adhering to checking schedules. An extension of the mobile gage cart is the truck or van which is equipped as a mechanical or electrical laboratory and travels from factory to factory within the same metropolitan area.

Still another form of decentralization is the "in-place" calibration. Under this concept, a working "master" is provided to simulate product or process conditions of various kinds. The test equipment must "pass an examination" by properly classifying the masters. These masters are kept physically at the test station until they are recalled for recalibration of their own accuracy.

Physical design of the laboratory workplace has been greatly complicated by the proliferation of many varieties of specialized testing: ultrasonic, x-ray, vibration, shock, acceleration, heat, humidity, etc. The details of these designs are beyond the scope of this handbook. The practitioner must consult with the available experts: equipment manufacturers, researchers, metrologists, and still others. This must be a continuing process, since there is continuing progress in development of new tests and standards.

HUMAN FACTORS IN INSPECTION

A myriad of factors can influence inspector behavior; they are summarized by Baker (1975), as shown in Table 18.19. One factor, visual acuity or sight, is the dominant sense in human beings, and great reliance is placed upon it in inspection tasks. The effectiveness of the use of sight depends largely on eye movements which bring the images of significant features of the material being inspected to the most sensitive part of the retina. However, experience and studies have shown that the other factors in Table 18.19 have an interrelated effect on the effectiveness, productivity, reliability, and accuracy of the inspector. (See Megaw, 1978, for related studies carried out in a textile factory.)

A detailed discussion of inspector errors below follows the discussion on human factors; however, it appears appropriate to first discuss the techniques and measurements developed to improve the reliability of the inspection function.

Machine Vision. The term "machine vision," or noncontact inspection, is applied to a wide range of electrooptical sensing techniques, from relatively sim-

TABLE 18.19   Variables Influencing Inspector Behavior

---

1. Individual abilities
   a. Visual activity
   b. General intelligence and comprehension
   c. Method of inspection
2. Task
   a. Defect probability
   b. Fault type
   c. Number of faults occurring simultaneously
   d. Time allowed for inspection
   e. Frequency of rest periods
   f. Illumination
   g. Time of day
   h. Objectivity of conformance standards
   i. Inspection station layout
3. Organizational and social
   a. Training
   b. Peer standards
   c. Management standards
   d. Knowledge of operator or group producing the item
   e. Proximity of inspectors
   f. Reinspection versus immediate shipping procedures

Source: Baker, 1975, p. 62.

ple triangulation and profiling to three-dimensional object recognition and bin picking, techniques based on sophisticated computerized image-analysis routines still under development. The applications are broad, ranging from relatively simple detection and measuring tasks to full-blown robot control. (See Schaffer, 1984, for a comprehensive report on machine-vision techniques.) The machine-vision industry is expected to grow by more than 50 percent a year through 1987, and annual industry sales are expected to reach $1 billion before 1990 and $10 to $20 billion by the turn of the century. Current machine-vision applications are summarized in Table 18.20.

The incentive to introduce machine-based systems, e.g., robots, is obvious—to eliminate human error. (See Spow, 1984, for a discussion of robots in an automatic assembly application.) The key influences behind the growth of the machine-vision industry also include inspector capability, inspector productivity, and inspection costs. (See also Nelson, 1984, for a review of machine-vision equipment, some designed to eliminate process contamination, in addition to human error.) Table 18.21 discusses these factors as they relate to inspecting printed circuit boards. [See Ken, 1984, for a detailed discussion of automated optical inspection (AOI) of printed circuit boards (PCB); also Denker, 1984, for a detailed discussion on justifying investments in automatic visual PCB testing.]

Vision-based systems—human or machine—involve an inspection procedure: the examination of a scene. The examination, in turn, can lead to recognition of an object or feature, to a quality decision, or to the control of a complex mechanism (Schaffer, 1984).

When the human inspector is involved, human judgment and perception have an influence on the quality assessment process. These result in two problems:

Vigilance Problem.   In highly repetitive subjective inspection (e.g., inspecting parts on an automated paint line), the process of perceiving can become numbed

TABLE 18.20   Machine-Vision Applications

1. Inspection
   a. Dimensional accuracy
   b. Hole location and accuracy
   c. Component verification
   d. Component defects
   e. Surface flaws
   f. Surface-contour accuracy
2. Part identification
   a. Part sorting
   b. Palletizing
   c. Character recognition
   d. Inventory monitoring
   e. Conveyer picking (overlap, no overlap)
   f. Bin picking
3. Guidance and control
   a. Seam-weld tracking
   b. Part positioning
   c. Processing/machining
   d. Fastening/assembly
   e. Collision avoidance

or hypnotized by the sheer monotony of repetition. In some way the scanning process and the model became disconnected, and the observer sees only what he or she expects to see, but does not see anything not actively expected. According to Thomas (1978) this happens in spite of the apparent activity of the perceptual scanning apparatus. This is called a "vigilance" problem. The known remedies are:

Break up the benumbing rhythm with pauses.

Introduce greater variety into the job.

Increase the noticeability of the faults through enhancing.

Provide background and context cues.

Arrange for frequent job rotation.

Vigilance becomes a big problem when faults are obvious and therefore serious, but infrequent and unpredictable.

TABLE 18.21   Selected Example of Factors and Effect of AOI on Printed Circuit Board

Manufacturing inspection costs	Inspection accounts for up to 30 percent of the manufacturing costs of complex double-sided and multilayer boards.
Inspection capability	Human inspection capability decreases well before 5 mil because of fatigue.
Inspection productivity	AOI reduces the number of inspections from 30 to 7 per shift while obtaining a 1 percent yield improvement and fivefold increase in inspection speeds.

Drift Problem.   The second problem characteristic of the human vision-based system, discussed by Thomas (1978), is that subjective standards appear to drift over time. Thus products which would have been rejected at one time are accepted at another.

Continuous experiences of either exceptionally high-quality or low-quality product will modify the inspector's model, leading him or her to raise or lower standards. The inspector is also influenced by the comments and actions of colleagues.

INSPECTOR ERRORS

The inspector, as the human element in the inspection process, contributes importantly to inspection errors. Inspection errors due to the inspector, called "inspector errors," are discussed here. We have previously discussed the reliability of the human inspector under human factors (as opposed to noncontract machine inspection or machine-vision system). Other sources of inspection error, e.g., vague specifications, lack of standards, inaccurate instruments, etc., are discussed elsewhere in this handbook. (*Note:* The problem of human error is common to operators, inspectors, and anyone else. For an extensive discussion of problems of worker error, see Section 22, under Test of Theories of Worker-Controllable Problems, et seq.)

Inspector errors are of several categories:

Technique errors

Inadvertent errors

Conscious errors

Each of these categories has its own unique causes and remedies. Collectively, these inspector errors result in a performance of about 80 percent accuracy in finding defects, i.e., inspectors find about 80 percent of the defects actually present in the product and miss the remaining 20 percent. [*Note by the editor (Juran):* Numerous studies in various countries have yielded the 80 to 20 ratio as a broad measure of quantified inspector accuracy. For example, Konz et al. (1981) found that inspectors were only catching about 80 percent of the defects in glass subassemblies.]

However, little is known about the relative importance of each category of inspector error (e.g., lack of technique, inadvertence, conscious). For further discussion, see Tawara (1980).

Technique Errors.   Into this category are grouped several subcategories: lack of capacity for the job, e.g., color blindness; lack of knowledge due to insufficient education or job training; lack of "skill," whether due to lack of natural aptitude or to ignorance of the knack for doing the job. Technique errors can be identified in any of several ways:

Check Inspection.   A check inspector reexamines work performed by the inspector, both the accepted and rejected product. Figure 18.9 shows an example of the results of such check inspection of the work of several inspectors. It is evident that inspectors C and F operate to loose standards while inspector B operates to tight standards. Inspector E shows poor discrimination in both directions.

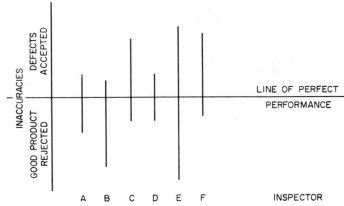

FIG. 18.9 Analysis of inspection errors.

Round-Robin Inspections. In this analysis, the same product is independently inspected by multiple inspectors. The resulting data, when arrayed in a matrix (usually with defect type along one axis and the inspectors along the other axis), shows the defects found by each inspector in relation to the inspectors as a group.

Repeat Inspections. In this method, the inspector repeats his or her own inspection of the product without knowledge of his or her own prior results. The analysis of the resulting data discloses the extent of the consistency or lack of consistency of the inspector's judgments.

Standard Sample Array. In this method the inspector takes an "examination" by inspecting a prefabricated mixture of product consisting of good units plus various kinds of defects. The standard sample array is known by various names, including "job sample." For added discussion, refer to Harris and Chaney (1969). All units were previously carefully graded by a team of experts and numbered for ready analysis of results. The inspector's score and his pattern of errors all point to the need, if any, for further training or other remedial steps. (In effect, the check inspection is conducted before the inspection.)

For example, in a company making glass bottles, an attempt was made to correlate process variables with the frequency and type of defects found by inspectors stationed at the cold end of the annealing lehr. The experiment failed because inspector variability from shift to shift exceeded product variability. This also threw suspicion on the accuracy of the inspection performed by the final product sorters at the end of the line. A standard sample array of 500 bottles was created and was used to examine the inspectors. (The examinations were conducted in the Training Department, on a miniature lehr.) The suspicions turned out to be well founded. (*Note:* Consulting experience of J. M. Juran.)

Remedies for Technique Errors. The need is to provide the missing skill or know-how and to answer the inspector's proper question, "What should I do different than I am doing now?" Unless the inspector is in a position to discover the answer for her- or himself, the answer must be provided by management. If no answer is provided, there will be no change in performance.

The various methods of analysis discussed above all can provide some clues which suggest the type of remedial action needed. In particular, use can be made of the concept of finding the "knack," as discussed in Section 10, under Technique Errors. Under this concept, the data on inspector performance are analyzed to discover which inspectors give consistently superior performances and which inferior. Next, a study is made of the work methods used by both types of inspectors to identify the differences in methods. Analysis of these differences often discovers what is the secret know-how (knack) being used to get the superior performance (or what is the secret ignorance which results in poor performance). Finally the knack can be transferred to all inspectors through retraining (Czaja and Drury, 1981, and Cooper, 1980) or through being embodied in the technology (Kusch, 1979).

Where the technique errors are the result of lack of job capacity, the foregoing may be of no avail, and the need may be to foolproof the operation (see below) or to reassign the inspector to a job for which he or she does have adequate job capacity.

Certification of Inspectors. In critical inspections involving inspector judgment (e.g., interpreting x-rays of critical welds), it is increasingly the practice to require that the inspector be formally certified as qualified to do this job. (See Gibson, 1983, for a further discussion of inspector qualifications in offshore industries.) The qualification process follows a well-standardized series of steps:

A formal training program on how to do the job

A formal examination, including a demonstration of successful performance of the job

A formal certificate attesting to the success in the examination

A license to do the job for some designated period of time

A program of audit to review performance and to serve as a basis for renewing the license

In some companies, this concept of certification has been based on the "escape rate," i.e., the extent to which defects escape detection, as determined by subsequent check inspection. (See Measure of Inspector Accuracy, below.) When this concept is used, a limited "license" (e.g., 2 months) is given to the inspector, subject to renewal if check inspection results continue to be favorable.

Inadvertent Inspector Errors. These errors are characterized by the fact that at the time the error is made, the inspector is not even aware he is making an error. Also, the best intentions are present—the inspector wants not to make any errors. The term "inadvertent" or "unavoidable" is used to connote the fact that the human being is simply unable to achieve perfection, no matter how good his intentions. (This topic is closely related to inadvertent worker errors. For added discussion, see Section 10, under Inadvertent Errors.)

The theory of inadvertence has wavered up and down. For years it was the sincere belief of many inspection supervisors that when product was inspected 100 percent, the inspectors would find all the defects. Numerous unpublished and published studies have since demonstrated that human inspectors do not find all defects present. By and large, the human inspector finds about 80 percent of the defects present and misses the remaining 20 percent.

While the 80 to 20 ratio is widely accepted, there are numerous aspects which are not fully researched, i.e., how this ratio changes with percent defective in the product, with types of inspection (visual, mechanical gaging, electrical testing), with product complexity, with amount of time allotted for inspection, etc. For a discussion from the viewpoint of human factors plus some supporting data (e.g., that increased product complexity results in increased inspector error), see Harris and Chaney (1969, pp. 77–85).

Inspection fallibility can easily be demonstrated in the industrial classroom. The following sentence has been used thousands of times:

> FEDERAL FUSES ARE THE RESULTS OF YEARS
> OF SCIENTIFIC STUDY COMBINED WITH
> THE EXPERIENCE OF YEARS

The sentence is flashed before the audience for 30 s or for a full minute. Each member is asked to count and record the number of times the letter F appears. When the record slips are collected and tallied, the result is invariable. Of the F's present, only about 80 percent have actually been found.

The existence of so extensive an error rate has stimulated action on several fronts:

1. *To discover why inspectors make these errors:* To date, the researches have not been adequate to provide conclusive answers, so that the industrial psychologists are not agreed on what the main causes are.

2. *To measure the extent of the errors:* Techniques for this are now available. See Measure of Inspector Accuracy, below.

3. *To reduce the extent of these errors:* There is a wide assortment of remedies, as discussed below.

Remedies for Inadvertent Inspector Errors. In the absence of convincing knowledge of the causes of these errors, managers have resorted to a variety of remedies, all involving job changes in some form. These remedies include:

Error-Proofing. There are several forms of error-proofing which are widely applicable to inspection work: redundancy, countdowns, and fail-safe methods. These are discussed in detail in Section 16, under Error-Proofing the Process. See also Inspection Planning, above.

Automation. This is really a replacement of the repetitive inspection by an automation which makes no inadvertent (or other) errors once the setup is correct and stable. The economics of automation and the state of technology impose severe limits on the application of this remedy. See Automated Inspection, above.

Sense Multipliers. Use can be made of optical magnifiers, sound amplifiers, and other devices to magnify the ability of the unaided human being to sense the defects. Development of a new instrument to do the sensing is the ultimate form of this multiplication. Evidently there is an optimum to the level of magnification, and this optimum can be discovered by experimentation. (For some industrial studies, see Harris and Chaney, 1969, pp. 124–126 and 137–142.)

Conversion to Comparison. In many types of inspection, inspectors must judge products against their memories of the standard. When such inspectors are provided with a physical standard against which to make direct comparison, their accuracy improves noticeably. For example, in the optical industry, scratches are graded by width, and tolerances for scratches vary depending on the function of the product element (lens, prism, etc.). To aid the inspectors, plates are prepared exhibiting several scratches of different measured width, so that the inspectors can compare the product to a physical standard.

Standards for comparison are in wide use: colored plastic chips, textile swatches, forging specimens, units of product exemplifying pits and other visual blemishes, etc. Sometimes photographs are used in lieu of product. There are also special optical instruments which permit dividing the field of view to permit comparison of product with standard.

In some cases it is feasible to line up units of product in a way which makes any irregularities become highly conspicuous, e.g., lining up the holes in a row. (The childhood row of tin soldiers makes it obvious which one has the broken arm.) Some practitioners advocate inspecting units of product in pairs, to utilize the comparison principle. See Shainin (1972) for further discussion.

Templates.   These are a combination gage, magnifier, and mask. An example is the cardboard template placed over terminal boards. Holes in the template mate with the projecting terminals and serve as a gage for size. Any extra or misplaced terminal will prevent the template from seating properly. Missing terminals become evident because the associated hole is empty.

Masks.   These are used to blot out the inspector's view of characteristics for which she is not responsible so she can concentrate on her real responsibility. Some psychologists contend that when the number of characteristics to be inspected rises to large numbers, the inspector error rate also rises.

Overlay.   These are visual aids in the form of transparent sheets on which guidelines or tolerance lines are drawn. The inspector's task of judging the size or location of product elements is greatly simplified by such guidelines, since they present the inspector with an easy comparison for judging sizes and locations.

Checklists.   These may be as simple as a grocery shopping list used to verify that you purchased all the items you originally planned to buy. On the other extreme a checklist may consist of the countdown for the lofting of a new space shuttle. (See Walsmann, 1981, for a discussion of the purpose, advantages, and drawbacks as well as the development and implementation of various checklists.)

Reorganization of Work.   One of the theories of cause of inadvertent inspector errors is fatigue, due to inability to maintain concentration for long periods of time. Responses to this theory have been to break up these long periods in any of several ways: rest periods; rotation to other inspection operations, several times a day; job enlargement, e.g., a wider assortment of duties, greater responsibility. Some behavioral scientists urge reorganization of work on the broader ground of motivation theory, and they offer data to support this theory (see generally Harris and Chaney, 1969, pp. 201–229). However, to date, there is no conclusive evidence that in Western culture, reorganization of work (to provide greater participation, etc.) will give measurably superior results in work accomplishments. (See, in this connection, Section 10, under Processing System Design.)

Product Redesign.   In some instances the product design is such that inspection access is difficult or that needless burdens are placed on inspectors. In such cases, product redesign can help to reduce inspector errors as well as operator errors.

For some examples, see Section 16, under Error-Proofing the Process. (See also Smith and Duvier, 1984.)

Errorless Proofreading.   Beyond the techniques described in Section 16, under Error-Proofing the Process, there are special problems of error-proofing in inspection work. A major form of this is proofreading of text of a highly critical nature, i.e., critical to human safety and health. In such cases the low tolerance for error has driven many companies to use redundant checking, despite which some errors still get through.

A closer look makes it clear that proofreading is of two very different kinds:

1. *Passive proofreading:*   Here the proofreader takes no overt action. For example, he silently reads the copy while someone else reads the master aloud. Alternatively, he silently reads both documents and compares them. In such cases it is quite possible for extraneous matters to intrude on him and dominate his attention temporarily.

2. *Active proofreading:*   Here the proofreader must taken an overt action, e.g., she reads aloud, performs a calculation, etc. Such positive actions dominate her attention and minimize the chance of error.

For a second example, in blood donor centers it is usual to centrifuge the whole blood, remove the plasma, and then return the red blood cells to the donor. This return demands absolute assurance that the cells are being returned to that donor and to no one else. The system in use involves piping both the donation and the return through tubing on which there are repeats of 10-digit numbers. The tubing is cut when the donation goes to the centrifuge. Prior to return of the cells, two technicians check to compare the two 10-digit numbers on the two ends of the cut tubing. One technician actively reads the number on the tubing end attached to the donor. The other technician passively listens while comparing the number he or she hears with the number seen on the end of the tubing which is attached to the bag of blood cells.

It is feasible to make both technicians "active." For example, each is required to tap out on a keyboard the number he or she sees. These signals go to a computer which compares to the two numbers and signals either a go-ahead or an alarm. This same principle of comparing two independent active sets of signals can be extended to any problem in proofreading.

While the foregoing are listed as remedies for inadvertent inspector errors, most of them can also be used to reduce errors due to lack of skill or errors of a willful nature.

Procedural Errors.   Aside from inadvertent failures to find defects, there are inadvertent errors in shipment of uninspected product or even shipment of rejected product. These errors are usually the result of loose shipping procedures. For example, a container full of uninspected product may inadvertently be moved in with the inspected product; a container full of defectives may inadvertently be moved into the shipping area.

Such errors can be reduced by error-proofing the identification and shipping routines:

1. The inspector must *mark the product* at the time of inspection. Sometimes the inspector places the good in one box and the bad in another, or places the good lengthwise and the bad crosswise. Lacking the markings, there is always the

risk that between shifts, during rest periods, etc., the unmarked product will go to the wrong destination.

2. The product markings should be so distinctive that the product "screams its identity" to packers and shippers. Bar codes should be used where appropriate.

3. The colors used for markers which identify good product should be used for no other purpose. These markers should be attached only when the inspector finds there remains nothing to be done but ship the product.

4. Issuance of markers used to identify good product should be restricted to specially chosen personnel.(These markers are a form of company seal.) For products of substantial value, serial numbers may be used as a further control.

5. The markers should provide inspector identity. In some companies the system of identification includes the operators and packers.

6. Shipping personnel should be held responsible for any shipment of goods failing to bear an inspector's approval.

Conscious Inspector Errors: Management-Initiated.   The distinguishing features of the willful inspector error are that the inspector knows he or she is committing the error and intends to keep it up. These willful errors may be initiated by management, by the inspector, or by a combination of both. However, with few exceptions, the major notorious quality errors and blunders have been traceable to the decisions of managers and engineers rather than to those of the inspectors at the bottom of the hierarchy. Management-initiated errors take several forms, all resulting in willful inspector errors:

Conflicting Management Priorities.   Management's priorities for its multiple standards (quality, cost, delivery, etc.) vary with the state of the economic cycle. When the state of management priorities is such that conformance to quality standards is subordinated to the need for meeting other standards, the inspectors' actions are inevitably affected, since they also are given multiple standards to meet.

Management Enforcement of Specifications.   When management fails to act on evidence of nonconformance and on cause of defects, the inspectors properly judge management's real interest in quality from these deeds rather than from the propaganda. For example, if the supervision or the Material Review Board consistently accepts a chronic nonconformance condition as fit for use, the inspectors tend to quit reporting these defects, since they will be accepted anyhow.

Management Apathy.   When management makes no firm response to suggestions on quality or to inspector complaints about vague information, inadequate instruments, etc., the inspectors again conclude that management's real interests are elsewhere. In consequence, the inspectors do the best they can with information and facilities which they believe to be deficient.

Management Fraud.   Periodically a company manager attempts to deceive customers (or the regulators, etc.) through fictitious or deceitful records on quality. Seldom can a manager acting alone perpetrate such a fraud. The manager requires confederates who submit themselves to orders, usually in a way which makes clear to them the real character of what is going on. An inspector who is a willing accomplice (e.g., for a bribe) shares in the legal responsibility. However, the inspector may also be a most reluctant accomplice, e.g., an immediate superior gives orders to prepare nonfactual reports or to take actions clearly contrary to regulations. In such cases the inspector cannot escape taking some kind of risk, i.e., participation in a conspiracy versus the threat of reprisal if he or she fails to participate.

These management-initiated errors parallel closely those associated with conscious worker errors. See Section 22, under Test of Theories of Worker-Controllable Problems.

Conscious Inspector Errors: Inspector-Initiated. These errors likewise take multiple forms, and some take place for "good" reasons. It is important to understand the distinctions among these forms, since any misunderstandings are a breeding ground for poor industrial relations.

Inspector Fraud. The inspector is subjected to a variety of pressures. The most rudimentary forms are those by production supervisors and operators pleading for a "break." Sometimes this extends to a collusion where piecework payments are involved, both for quality and for quantity certification. At higher levels are cases in which an inspector is exposed to suppliers who have a good deal at stake in the lot of product in question. Even a situation in which inspectors dealing directly with production supervisors who outrank them involve substantial pressures to which inspectors should not be subjected.

Another form of inspector fraud consists of reporting false results solely to improve the outward evidence of his or her own efficiency or to make life more convenient. For example, Figure 18.10 shows the results reported by an inspector after taking a sample of n pieces from each of 49 lots. There is a large predominance of three defects per lot reported in the sample (exactly the maximum allowable number). The reason was found to be the inspector's reluctance to do the paperwork involved in a lot rejection.

In the example of Figure 18.11, the inspector was to take a sample of 100 pieces from each lot, with no defects allowable. If one or more pieces were defective, an added sample of 165 pieces was to be taken, with a total of three defects allowed in the combined sample of 265. It is seen that the inspector reported defects in virtually every first sample of 100 pieces.

**MAX. ALLOWABLE NO

FIG. 18.10 Inspector error made for personal convenience.

However, no defects were reported in most of the second (larger) samples. It was found that the inspector could improve personal efficiency by taking second samples, since the time allowance for taking the second samples was liberal. Inspector fraud can be minimized by:

1. Filling inspection jobs only with persons of proved integrity
2. Restricting the down-the-line inspector to the job of fact finding, and reserving to the inspection supervision the job of negotiating and bargaining with other supervisors or executives

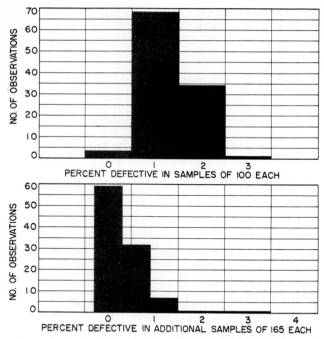

FIG. 18.11   Inspector error made to improve personal efficiency.

3. Rotating inspectors and workers to have both employee categories evaluate first hand the consequence of actions and decisions

4. Including inspectors in customer presentations or visits.

5. Conducting regular check inspections and periodic independent audits to detect fraud

6. Taking prompt action when fraud is discovered

Inspector Shortcuts.   These may be unauthorized omissions of operations which the inspector has reason to believe are of dubious usefulness; e.g., accidental omissions had failed to give evidence of trouble. In some cases there is a shared blame, i.e., management has imposed a highly disagreeable task. For example, in a company making "tin cans," one inspection involved cutting up a can with hand-held tin shears, submerging the pieces in chloroform to remove the enamel, and measuring the thickness of the bare pieces with a micrometer. The cutting process was tedious and the chloroform was irritating to the skin, so the inspectors avoided the operation as much as possible. When better cutting tools and a different solvent were provided, the problem became minimal.

Flinching.   This is the tendency of inspectors to falsify the results of inspection of borderline product. Flinching is actually widespread among all persons who report on performance versus goals, and especially when it is their own performance. Figure 18.12 shows a frequency distribution of measurement on volume efficiency of electronic receivers. There is an "excess" of readings at the specification maximum of 30, and there are no readings at all at 31, 32, or 33. Retest showed that the inspector recorded these "slightly over" units of product as 30.

FIG. 18.12 How inspector flinches at design limit.

By this flinching, the inspector, in effect, changed the specification maximum from 30 to 33. This is a serious error (Juran, 1935).

Flinching during variables measurements is easy to detect by check inspection, which is also conducted on a variables basis. Analysis of the inspector's variables data will likewise detect flinching (as in the above example).

The remedy for flinching is an atmosphere of respect for the facts as the ethical foundation of the Inspection Department. The main means for achieving this are examples set by the Inspection supervisors.

One way *not* to deal with flinching is to criticize the inspector on the basis that the pattern of readings does not follow the laws of chance. Such criticism can be interpreted as being aimed at the symptom (the unnatural pattern of reading) rather than the disease (recording fictitious instead of factual readings). The risk is that inspectors will try to meet such criticisms by trying to make the false results look more natural, hence eliminating the symptom but not the disease.

Flinching also takes place during attribute inspection. Numerous studies have shown that inspector errors in rejecting good product outnumber the errors of accepting bad product. In part this arises because the good product outnumbers the bad and hence affords greater opportunity for error. But it also arises in part from the fact that acceptance of defects often comes dramatically to the attention of higher management, whereas rejection of good product seldom does so.

These same studies show that when check inspection is introduced and check is made both of product rejected and product accepted, the rejection of good product is reduced without affecting the acceptance of bad product.

Another form of flinching is to modify the inspection results to conform to the results which the inspector expects. For example, a visual inspection was being performed following a specified lapping operation.

An experiment to omit the lapping operations, conducted without inspector awareness of omission of the operation, resulted in rejection of less than a third of unlapped product.

FIG. 18.13   Rounding off. The needle is in the same location on both charts. The charts are likely to be read as 31 and 32, left and right, respectively.

In some cases, flinching by inspectors is actually management-initiated through manager pressures which seem to the inspectors to leave no alternative. In one company, the inspectors making hardness tests were discovered to be flinching to an astonishing degree. This practice had been going on for years. It developed that the manufacturing vice president had designed this hardening process himself when he was the process engineer. At the time, he had deluded himself as to its capabilities and thereby had been the author of this long-standing practice (Juran, early consulting experience).

Rounding Off.   The process of dispensing with unneeded accuracy is generally referred to as "rounding off." Inspectors commonly round off their meter readings to the nearest scale division, as shown in Figure 18.13. The effect of rounding off is seen in the "picket fence" frequency distribution of Figure 18.12.

Rounding off is easy to detect from analysis of inspection data. A good analyst can, from the data alone, reconstruct the pattern of scale markings of an instrument without ever having seen the scale itself.

Rounding off is often a good thing, since it avoids undue attention to individual readings. But sometimes the need for precision on individual readings is great enough that rounding off should not be practiced. The planner and inspection supervisor should be on the alert to identify situations in which rounding off is not tolerable, and they should provide accordingly.

Instruments and gages should be properly selected for the application. (Churchill, 1956, gives a quantitative discussion on scale interval length and pointer clearance.) One practice is to require "readings to be recorded to the nearest. . . . "

Measures of Inspector Accuracy.   The collective effect of inspector errors, from all causes, is so extensive that there is need for measuring the extent of errors and for use of the data in controlling the effectiveness of inspectors. If this measurement is made only occasionally, use can be made of standard sample arrays (see above, under Technique Errors) and cross-check among inspectors, as well as check inspection. If the measurement is to be conducted regularly so as to discover trends in performance, then check inspection is necessary.

In conventional check inspection, a second inspector, i.e., a check inspector, reviews the decisions of the inspector by reexamining the product after it has been inspected. For an early example, refer to Taylor (1911). The best practice is to reexamine the rejected product as well as the accepted product.

Inspector errors may consist of accepting defective units of product or rejecting good units of product. If, in addition, the check inspection reviews the procedure followed by the inspector, other errors may be found, e.g., use of wrong issue of the specification, wrong instrument, improper filling out of documents, etc.

The conventional use of check inspection data to quantify inspector accuracy is to count the errors, to assign weights, and to use the composite of errors as an index of accuracy (of inaccuracy, usually). (See, for example, Gilman, 1963.) In some schemes, the errors discovered in later operations or in customer complaints are included in the data. The composite of errors may be expressed in terms of percent defective (found to exist in the inspected product) or in terms of demerits per unit. (Refer to Weaver, 1975, which reports on a study of inspector accuracy during the production process, based on accept/reject decisions involving the product currently produced.) Either way, the scoring system is open to the objection that the inspector's accuracy depends, to an important degree, on the quality of the product submitted to him by the process; i.e., the more defects submitted the greater is the chance of missing some.

A plan for measuring inspectors' accuracy in a way which is independent of incoming quality is that evolved in 1928 by J. M. Juran and C. A. Melsheimer. (See Juran, 1935, for the original published description of this plan.) Under this plan the check inspector, as usual, reexamines the inspected product, both the accepted and the rejected units.

In addition, the check inspector secures the inspector's own data on the original makeup of the lot, i.e., total units, total good, total defective. From these data, the following formulas emerge as applied to a single lot which has been check inspected:

$$\text{Accuracy of inspector} = \text{percent of defects correctly identified}$$

$$= \frac{d - k}{d - k + b}$$

where d = defects reported by the inspector
k = number of defects reported by the inspector, but determined by the check inspector not to be defects
$d - k$ = true defects found by the inspector
b = defects missed by the inspector, as determined by check inspection
$d - k + b$ = true defects originally in the product

Figure 18.14 illustrates how the percentage of accuracy is determined. The number of defects reported by the inspector, d, is 45. Of these, 5 were found by the check inspector to be good; that is, $k = 5$. Hence $d - k$ is 40, the true number of defects found by the inspector. However, the inspector missed 10 defects; that is, $b = 10$. Hence the original number of defects, $d - k + b$ is 50, that is, the 40 found by the inspector plus the 10 missed. Hence,

$$\text{Percentage of accuracy} = \frac{d - k}{d - k + b} = \frac{45 - 5}{45 - 5 + 10} = 80\%$$

In application of the plan, periodic check inspection is made of the inspector's work. Data on d, k, and b are accumulated over a period of months to summarize the inspector's accuracy, as for example:

Job no.	Total pieces	d	b	k
3	1000	10	0	0
19	50	3	1	0
42	150	5	1	0
48	5000	10	4	0
Total		200	30	0

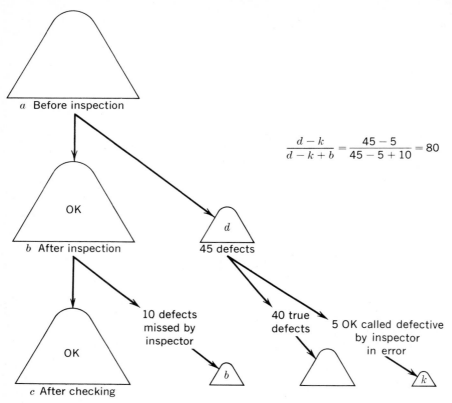

$$\frac{d - k}{d - k + b} = \frac{45 - 5}{45 - 5 + 10} = 80$$

a Before inspection

b After inspection

d 45 defects

10 defects missed by inspector

40 true defects

5 OK called defective by inspector in error

c After checking

FIG. 18.14 Process for determining accuracy of inspectors.

The totals give, for percent accuracy:

$$\frac{d}{d + b} = \frac{200}{230} = 87\%$$

As is evident, the plan lends itself to simple cumulation of data. However, some compromise is made with theory to avoid undue emphasis on any one lot checked. Over a 6-month period, where the cumulative checks may reach 50 or more, the need for such compromise or weighting is diminished.

The check inspector also makes errors. However, these have only a secondary effect on the inspector's accuracy. In the above example, if the check inspector were only 90 percent accurate, only 27 of the 30 defects missed by the inspector would be found. The inspector's accuracy would become:

$$\frac{200}{227} = 88.1\% \text{ instead of } 87.0\%$$

In some situations, k is small and may be ignored. However, in other situations, notably for sensory qualities, the inspector may have a bias for rejecting borderline work. In such cases, it is feasible to use, as an added measure, the inspector's accuracy due to rejection of good pieces. This has been termed "waste." Under the terminology used here:

$$\text{Waste} = \text{percent of good pieces rejected} = \frac{k}{n - d - b + k}$$

where n = total pieces inspected.

The "percent accuracy" is also equal to the percent of material correctly inspected. This feature permits use of the plan in the pay formula of the inspector.

Some investigators have developed variations on the foregoing measures of inspector accuracy as applied to visual inspection. These include measures based on probability theory (Wang, 1975), and the on use of signal-detection theory in the analysis of industrial inspection (Ainsworth, 1980).

The proportion of correct decisions made by the inspector is an intuitively good index of the inspector's efficiency when the costs of rejecting a good item and accepting a bad item are equal.

The two measures for evaluating inspector's efficiency, introduced by Wang (1975) are:

$$N_\alpha = \frac{\text{number of true defects detected by the inspector}}{\text{number of true defects}}$$

$$N_\beta = \frac{\text{number of true defects detected by the inspector}}{\text{number of all defects detected by the inspector}}$$

If the two costs are not equal, the theory of signal detectability (TSD) provides a better measure for analyzing an inspector's performance. However, the use of TSD requires assumptions about normal and equal variant population distributions, and the probability density functions for the "good" and "defective" populations must be calculated. See Johnson and Funke (1980) for a discussion of the advantages and disadvantages of a number of human performance measures, including Wang's (1975) approach.

In the application of any plan to check the accuracy of inspectors, it is essential that the checks be at random. Neither the inspector nor the check inspector should know the schedule in advance. Random dice, cards from a pack, etc., should be used. It is also essential that the responsibility be clear. The inspector who has accepted defects under orders or through inaccurate instruments, etc., cannot be held responsible for the results.

FEEDBACK OF INSPECTION DATA

Inspection generates data in profusion, and these data are widely used. Virtually all sections of this handbook involve some degree of reliance on inspection data, and for some sections this reliance is extensive. Table 18.22 lists the sections which make such extensive use of inspection data, along with the principal purpose served. In addition, Sections 23 through 26 deal with methods of data analysis; and Section 27 deals with use of computers.

Feedback to Production. This is the most extensive inspection feedback judged by volume of data and by worker-hours consumed. The feedbacks serve mainly as alarm signals to identify out-of-control processes and to urge corrective action. In addition, to assist Production in problem identification, summaries are prepared by department, process, product, operator, etc., using the Pareto prin-

TABLE 18.22 Uses of Inspection Data

Section number and title	Inspection data used extensively
4 Quality Costs	As inputs to quality cost estimates
16 Manufacturing Planning	For process capability determination
15 Supplier Relations	As feedback to suppliers
17 Production	As feedback to production
18 Inspection and Test	To judge product instrument conformance
19 Marketing	To provide "feedforward" for customer relations
20 Customer Service	To improve field service
22 Quality Improvement	To remedy chronic defects
10 Managing Human Performance	To improve human performance
13 Product Development	To identify and certify products
8 Upper Management and Quality	To prepare executive reports on quality

ciple to focus on the vital few problems. The detailed methods, along with the nature of Inspection relations with Production, are discussed in Section 17, under Inspection Feedback to Production, as is the problem of corrective action.

Data Feedback to Management. A second extensive use of inspection data is to provide company managers with the summaries and analyses needed as part of the system of managerial control of the quality function. See Section 8 for details, including discussion of means for auditing the system of data feedback.

Feedback to Inspection. An often neglected use of inspector data is feedback to the inspector(s). Quality information feedback and the visual display of inspector data has both a positive human factors impact in reducing inspector error and an effect on improving inspector productivity (Coleman, 1982).

Data "Feedforward" to the Market. A fourth major use of inspection data is to identify the product, provide certificates of analysis, and otherwise to provide product information to consumers, marketers, regulators, etc. A great deal of this is on a "to whom it may concern" basis through use of product markings, tags, certificates, circulars, instructions, cautions, etc.

Data System. To provide data to meet these and other needs (Table 18.22), planners evolve a whole system of documentation such as is elaborated in Section 13. Briefly, this system provides:

Record forms and data sheets to secure the basic data.

A system of defect codes to simplify data recording and subsequent data processing.

Provision for data processing, whether manually or by computer (Section 27). (See also Wurster, 1980.)

ORGANIZATION FOR INSPECTION AND TEST

Prior to the industrial revolution, manufacturing industries consisted largely of small shops, each dominated by a master. The master trained the apprentices and supervised their work in various ways, including a form of quality control. This consisted of process surveillance and product inspection conducted until such time as the apprentice demonstrated the capability of repeatedly turning out quality products.

Emergence of the Inspector.   As the shops grew larger, they outgrew the ability of the master to direct all affairs personally. Therefore specialized departments were created and assistants appointed to supervise these departments. One of these assistants, the shop supervisor, took over supervision of the workers and continued the tradition of personally exercising the quality controls.

In due course the number of workers grew to an extent that exceeded the capacity of the shop foreman to exercise the quality controls. This problem was solved by creating the post of inspector and delegating to the inspector the job of judging fitness for use or conformance to specification. The earliest form of this was probably in the large construction projects of antiquity. Figure 18.15 shows an inspector using a string to measure the flatness of stone blocks while a worker is engaged in dressing the stone. The date is 1450 B.C.

FIG. 18.15 Ancient construction inspector. *(From C. Singer et al., A History of Technology, Oxford University Press, 1957, vol. 1, fig. 313.)*

The industrial revolution resulted in the growth of large manufacturing companies which included multiple production shops (foundry, lathe, etc.). The tradition of shop inspectors reporting to the foreman was carried over, so that the organization for inspection resembled that shown in Figure 18.16.

FIG. 18.16 Organization for inspection, early factories.

The supervisors of those shops had virtually no technical education. Their job knowledge was derived from long association with materials, processes, and products which had remained largely static over the years. When World War I required these shops to take on products new to them, many foremen were in deep trouble. They knew from experience how far they safely could go in overruling their inspectors on the old products. But in regard to the new products, this experience was of little help; in addition, the foremen lacked the technical education which might have qualified them to make a swift transition. In consequence, there were many serious quality failures and scandals.

Emergence of the Central Inspection Department.   Following these catastrophes, and under the urging of the Taylor System advocates, the companies now accepted the advice of those who had long been calling for making the inspectors independent of the production foremen. The companies took the inspectors away from the production foremen and made them responsible to full-time inspection foremen instead. Then, to provide adequate supervision for these inspectors, a new office, that of chief inspector, was created. Figure 18.17 shows the resulting organization form in contrast to the prior form (Figure 18.16).

FIG. 18.17   Creation of central inspection department.

(*Note:* Frederick W. Taylor and his school of "Scientific Management" advocated creation of specialized departments to conduct various activities—manufacturing planning, cost accounting, maintenance, inspection, etc., previously responsible to the foreman. See Section 10, under Role of Motivation: The Taylor System.)

Inspection Department Structure.   The early inspection departments generally took a form similar to that shown in Figure 18.18. In due course, further developments followed, as discussed below.

Purchased Material Inspection.   All inspectors engaged in this work were brought together in a single organization section for some logical, compelling reasons. Incoming material was received at a central receiving station, requiring also a centralized inspection station. The purchasing routines could better be enforced by a single supplier inspection section. The problems of dealing with suppliers

FIG. 18.18 Early central inspection department.

were special, requiring a standard supplier inspection procedure. To a very high degree, these reasons still prevail, though new concepts of supplier relations are now needed to deal with modern subcontracting. (See generally Section 15.)

Process Inspection.   The process inspectors were widely dispersed among the production processing departments. The first centralizing step was to make these inspectors responsible to a chief process inspector while remaining geographically dispersed. As the plants grew, multiple process inspection departments were organized to parallel the associated production departments, as shown in Figure 18.19.

Finished Goods Inspection.   This is also called "final inspection," "test," etc. While this has long been a separate department, there have been variations in the manner of connecting this activity into the overall organization chart.

In the mechanical and electronic industries, the usual pattern has been to make finished goods inspection responsible to the chief inspector (Figure 18.18). An alternative form has been a separation of the functional testing from the remain-

FIG. 18.19 Organization of process inspection in large plants.

ing inspection (visual, gaging, etc.). Under such an arrangement, the testing is made responsible to the Technical Department, while the remaining inspection reports to the chief inspector (Figure 18.20). Generally, the more critical the product in terms of human safety, the more likely it is that the functional testing reports to upper management, either directly or through some channel other than Manufacture.

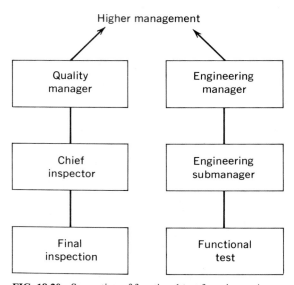

FIG. 18.20   Separation of functional test from inspection.

In the process industries, there has long been a separation of critical testing (for safety, structural integrity, and functional performance) from the inspection for esthetic and noncritical qualities. The critical testing was the responsibility of the laboratory, which reported to the technical manager. The noncritical inspection was performed by inspectors responsible to Production (Figure 18.21). To a high degree, this arrangement has persisted. In most process industries, the inspectors (for noncritical properties) are brought together in a separate department which reports to a production manager. However, in some process industries these inspectors remain dispersed organizationally and are responsible to the departmental production foremen.

In multiproduct plants there are alternatives for organizing the process and final inspection. One form is to create separate hierarchies for process and final inspectors (Figure 18.22). Another form is to create product hierarchies, each of which includes both process and final inspectors (Figure 18.23). The choice depends largely on the extent to which the processes are unique to particular products. The plan of Figure 18.23 permits better coordination if the processes are largely unique to the associated products.

Creation of the central Inspection Department also created a new organizational problem: To whom should the chief inspector report? This problem is discussed in Section 7, under Evolution of the Quality Control Hierarchy.

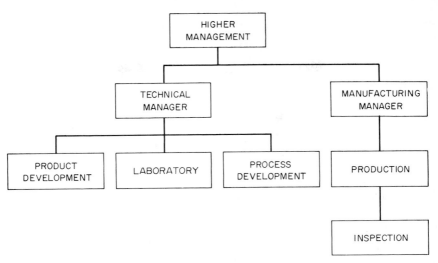

FIG. 18.21   Organization form, process industries, single plant.

Evolution of Inspection Support Activities.   The formation of central inspection departments enabled the new chief inspectors to tend to some matters which had previously received scant attention. These included the following:

Metrology.   Laboratories were created for calibrating, protecting, storing, issuing, and otherwise regulating the precision of measuring instruments. In addition, new skills were evolved for design of better instruments and test equipment and for planning instrumentation as part of the design of the production process and of the inspection stations. See generally Sections 16 and 18.

FIG. 18.22   Inspection organized by function.

FIG. 18.23   Inspection organized by product.

Inspection Planning.   The full-time inspection supervisors evolved the concept of planning the inspection job. Inspection methods sheets were designed to list the inspection operations to be performed, sample sizes, allowable defects, instruments, standards, and other criteria needed by the inspectors. See Inspection Planning, above.

Inspector Selection, Training.   The full-time inspection supervisors felt keenly the need for well-selected, trained inspection personnel and began to evolve the means for reaching this goal. See generally Section 10.

Salvage.   The ministerial work associated with disposition of nonconforming product was gradually assigned to the chief inspector. It includes identification, segregation, custody, documentation, and still other activities. It may involve sorting the product and planning repairs or other salvage forms.

Noninspection Operations Performed by Inspectors.   In many companies there are forces which try to confine work assignments to strict jurisdictional lines; i.e., inspectors should do nothing but inspection work. (A common spur to strict enforcement of jurisdictional boundaries is management pressure on departmental budgets.) However, the increasing complexity of the quality function has weakened these boundaries. The trends appear in several forms including the counting, weighing, and packing of product.

Some assignment of noninspection work to inspectors has been on economic grounds, i.e., since the inspector handles the product anyhow, why require still another person to rehandle the product just to count it? Many other examples exist. It is evident that the planning of inspection work must be done with flexible concepts of jurisdiction. Failing this, the rigid enforcement of jurisdictional lines will lead to absurd duplications of work.

INSPECTION DEPARTMENT MANAGEMENT

Managing the Inspection Department is usually accomplished through a hierarchy of supervisors whose duties have much in common. A typical list of these common duties includes the following:

Participate in inspection planning; approve all manuals and procedures to be used by the inspectors

Approve product and process standards supplemental to engineering specifications

Prepare the departmental budget for personnel, facilities, and supplies

Participate in design of the inspection workplace, in choice of facilities and instruments, and in design of work methods; approve the final design

Recruit and train inspectors; assign work to the inspectors; supervise and evaluate their performance; motivate inspectors to meet standards of quality and efficiency

Collaborate with other departments in investigation and solution of quality problems and in other interdepartmental activities

Review the condition of products found to be nonconforming; participate in the studies leading to disposition

Review the condition of processes for which there is evidence of nonconformance to specification; collaborate in the steps needed to restore control

Prepare and approve necessary documentation on quality

Develop the potentialities of subordinates

Keep informed on new industrial developments in facilities, instrumentation, inspection methods and practices; adapt for company use as appropriate

These duties vary in detail with the specialties of the various inspection departments. The chief inspector (or equivalent title) carries, in addition, the broader duties of participating in discussion of numerous higher-level quality problems.

Laboratory Management.   This activity involves several special problems in inspection management.

Interlaboratory Comparisons.   Despite extensive standardization of test methods, it is still necessary to conduct periodic interlaboratory comparisons among companies, between division and plant laboratories, between central and branch laboratories, etc. (See also Section 26 under Planning Interlaboratory Tests for methods of graphical diagnosis, especially Youden two sample plots in Figure 26.20.)

Decentralizing the Laboratory.   It is usually not feasible to centralize all test facilities in one laboratory. The usual forms of decentralizing are:

1. *Branch laboratories:*   Branch laboratories serve to simplify the transport of samples and to provide more prompt feedback of the resulting data. The branch laboratory may consist of:
   a. A laboratory staffed full time by Inspection but located physically amid the production areas which require test service.

    b. A traveling laboratory which moves from department to department according to a schedule. A common form is the gage cart or other traveling metrology laboratory used to maintain accuracy of measuring instruments.

    c. A laboratory staffed part time by Production to provide prompt service without the need for requisitions and other paperwork. Such laboratories, restricted to routine testing, are located on the Production floor.

2. *Independent laboratories:* These can be a useful adjunct to the company's laboratory for reasons of cost, scarce facilities, peak loads, specialized personnel, customer relations, and still other considerations. Inspection managers are well advised to keep informed on the services offered by independent laboratories and to use these as the occasion warrants. (See Maass, 1970, for a discussion of pros and cons.)

Multiple Laboratory Functions.   In many companies the Inspection laboratory is the company's sole facility for making such tests. In consequence, the laboratory will be asked to make tests for a variety of purposes:

    As a service to Production, which uses the data to make process control decisions

    As a service to research, which lacks a facility for making such tests

    As a basis for product conformance decisions, for which the laboratory itself has the responsibility

In such cases the laboratory is "selling" test results to multiple clients, including itself. Numerous questions of schedule priority, cost allocation, etc., arise and require that the laboratory managers make these allocations by balancing the interests of all clients rather than on the basis of departmental biases. (See Burgess, 1983, for further elaboration.)

Inspection by Production Departments.   There are three varieties of this, and care must be taken to identify which one is the subject under discussion:

1. Inspection conducted part time by production operators to determine whether the process should run or stop. This is a widespread form of process control and is discussed in Section 17 under Concept of Controllability.

2. Inspection conducted part time by production workers to make decisions on product conformance. This is discussed in Section 17, under Self-Inspection.

3. Inspection (product acceptance) conducted by full-time inspectors who report not to the Inspection Department but to the Production Department. This will now be discussed.

    Most chief inspectors take a dim view of any arrangement in which full-time inspectors engaged in product acceptance report to anyone other than the Inspection Department. The usual reasons advanced emphasize the needs for professional inspection planning, special recruitment and training for inspectors, establishing a career pattern, unbiased judgment, etc. The real reason may be cultural resistance, but the asserted reasons have validity. However, use of modern staff concepts makes it possible to meet most of the objections by use of a well-known formula for delegation:

Activity	Responsibility assigned to	
	Production	Quality Control
Prepare and approve the inspection plan	X	X
Execute the plan	X	
Audit to see that the execution follows the plan		X

The contents of the "audit" vary depending on circumstances. For example, if the inspectors (in Production) sort or test the product 100 percent, a check inspection may be set up to follow this (Figure 18.24).

FIG. 18.24   Organization for sorting by production, with subsequent acceptance sampling.

Short-term economics are not noticeably affected by transferring full-time inspectors from Inspection to Production or vice versa. After the change, the same people perform the same duties as before. The really big effect on short-term economics is to abolish full-time inspectors by instituting "product acceptance by operators," as described in Section 17 under that heading.

The "laborpower" aspects of Inspection Department management (e.g., inspector selection, training, compensation) are discussed in Section 10, as are motivational aspects. (See also Gittler, 1973, and Carter and Carter, 1983.)

INSPECTION PERSONNEL MANAGEMENT

The effective management of Inspection personnel is an important factor in controlling the frequency and impact of inspector errors, and in improving inspector productivity (both topics discussed in this section). To be effective, management must address the following areas (see Gittler, 1973):

- Select and keep good inspectors
- Determine who is a good inspector and who is a poor one
- Know whether or not an inspector or group of inspectors are performing their jobs to expected standards
- Measure the impact inspectors have on the product and on costs

Inspection personnel must also be managed in a manner that maintains credibility with the total company (See Jaehn, 1982). There are three areas of opportunity for inspection to maintain credibility:

1. Provide adequate instructions
2. Assure the integrity of the quality measurement system
3. Monitor performance and audit compliance to the specified procedures

PRODUCTIVITY IN INSPECTION AND TEST

As the costs of quality are managed down, the ability to produce more or serve more frequently increases, resulting in increased productivity. It is also true that as internal costs or appraisal costs are decreased, the productivity of inspectors and the inspection process improves.

Loss Productivity Factors.   One of the objectives of the Quality Management Department is to optimize the effectiveness of the Inspection Department by removing any factors which decrease productivity. Some of these factors are internal while others are external to the quality function. (See Thomas, 1977, and Minor, 1981, for further discussion on factors.) Some of these factors have been discussed under other topics in this section. They include:

Employee selection

Clear information/direction

Physical layout

Efficient tools/instruments

Proper training

Effective information feedback

Motivation and incentives

Appropriate compensation and recognition

Adequate supervision

Measuring Inspectors' Productivity.   Productivity is the measure of the effectiveness of the utilization (conversion process) of allocated resources (input) to accomplish specific goals and results (output). The inspection process is also a traditional conversion process. Where inputs (items to be inspected), subject to an inspection conversion (accept/reject), result in an output (data). Therefore, the inspection process can be measured for the productivity of the inspection process and the impact of the inspector. (See Goldbeck, 1981, and Ulla, 1982 for discussion and examples.) Traditionally, the measurement or productivity metric is: units per worker-hour for month x.

BUDGETING FOR INSPECTION

An invariable responsibility of inspection supervisors is to run the department at minimal cost. This they do through the common sequence of (1) establishing efficient methods, (2) setting standards for quality and quantity of work, (3) selecting and training inspectors to be able to meet these standards, and (4) motivating them to do so. This responsibility for cost control is usually formalized into the company's system of budgetary control (see also Section 4, Quality Costs).

The inspection budget deals with the first two elements of the above sequence. These may be restated as (1) inspection cost reduction and (2) setting standards of inspection cost performance. Both these activities are concerned with doing deeds, though these deeds must be translated into the common language of money to meet the needs of management budgetary review.

Inspection Cost Reduction.   Because a budget becomes the goal to be met, it should reflect good practice, not poor practice. For this reason, inspection cost reduction should precede setting standards. There are several approaches available to achieve inspection cost reduction:

Defect Prevention.   High defect levels are the most widespread single reason for high inspection costs. In consequence, a usual prerequisite for major reductions of inspection costs is to reduce the major reasons for these costs, i.e., high defect levels. (See generally Section 22.) After the causes of defects have been identified and removed, inspection costs can be reduced. The reduction in costs takes several forms including:

1. Use sampling instead of sorting (see generally Section 25).
2. Transfer inspection to the production operators while retaining an audit. (See Section 17 under Self-Inspection.)
3. Use test data from suppliers to abolish incoming inspection. Assurance is provided by an audit. (See Section 15 under Audit of Decisions.)

Census of Inspection Costs.   In this census, all inspection work is identified, whether done by employees of Inspection departments, of Production departments, of Laboratory departments, etc. The decisive feature for entering the census is not the titles of the people or the names of the departments to whom they report, but the deeds they perform; i.e., do they examine product, compare the results to a specification, and make judgments of conformance?

Commonly the census is conducted to determine, for each department involved:

The number of equivalent full-time inspectors, and their pay

The type of work they do (sorting, sampling, etc.)., the job grade, and the approach to selection and training of inspectors

Other costs, e.g., facilities, supplies

The inspection plans used, the acceptance criteria, the procedures and other routines

The methods of supervision, both in setting up the inspection plan and in seeing that the execution follows the plan

The measures of performance for accuracy and efficiency

The census is not merely a questionnaire; it includes visits to all the areas to see the manner of conducting the work. Work sampling is used to help identify the nature of the jobs being done. The census may well be part of the study of quality costs, as discussed in Section 4.

The summary of the census shows the total inspection cost, which is an index of the importance of the problem in relation to other management problems. The summary also shows where these costs are concentrated, suggesting the choice of areas for more detailed study.

Contract Inspection.   Service organizations, serving both private and industrial sectors, are growing in numbers and influence. (See Karabatsos, 1983, and Garfinkel and Clodfelter, 1984.) Their greatest benefit is cost savings, and therefore they provide a cost management option. Typical services offered:

Failure analysis/product liability

Materials evaluation—metallurgy

Microscopy

Nondestructive testing

Analytical laboratories

High reliability component testing

Nuclear plant inspections

Supplier surveillance

Machine/instrument calibration

First-article inspection

Statistical services

Personnel training

Consulting services

The forms of these service organizations range from "job shops" (Wood, 1979) to organizations that provide part-time inspectors ("Where Quality Control Is a Part Time Job," 1979).

Industrial Engineering Studies.   These have wide application to inspection work. (See Williams, 1981, for a detailed plan for in-depth evaluation of all phases of the quality control operation.)

Methods study can be used to improve the design of workplaces. Work standards can be applied to repetitive jobs. Work simplification can be used to analyze principal operations. One plan is as follows (Barry, 1959):

1. Choose one of the more troublesome inspection operations for study.
2. Consider eliminating the operation entirely.
3. Failing this, break the job down as follows:
    a. List the work elements.
    b. List the equipment used.
    c. Prepare flow diagrams and workplace sketches.
    d. Discuss the job with the inspector to get his or her ideas.
    e. Question every detail (a checklist of 33 questions is provided).
4. Prepare a new method as the result of the study.
5. Install the new method and follow up.

Work sampling is a further industrial engineering tool available for study of the nature and content of inspection jobs (Kay, 1972).

Quality Engineering Studies.   These aim at a wide variety of improvements:

1. Coordinated inspection planning is used to minimize duplication of work between Inspection and Production, or between inspection departments. Also, it may be easier to transport inspectors to the Production Department rather than move the product from Production to the Inspection Department.
2. Automated testing is developed to replace highly repetitive manual testing.
3. Sampling is used to replace detail inspection.
4. Sampling costs are reduced by use of other available knowledge about product conformance, process capability, and the sequence of manufacture (see How Much Inspection? above).

5. Economic inspection intervals are established in proportion to the potential for loss from out-of-control manufacturing processes (see "A Management Standard for Economical Inspection," 1976).

6. Documentation is reduced. One manager reduced the documentation for good product (the great majority of all orders) by imprinting the production order with a stamp which provided space for the minimal data needed for approved lots. The conventional documentation was retained for defective material. Other records of inspection can be designed for maximum utility (see Stalker, 1980), and ink stamps for efficiency (see "Inspection Can Make an Impression with a Saving," 1976).

7. Documentation is turned over to noninspectors so that the inspector can concentrate on product inspection. One form of this is to assign a separate individual to collect the papers needed by the inspector and to deliver this package to the inspector.

8. Perfectionism is reduced by studying the cost of finding a defect compared to the cost of (*a*) not finding it, (*b*) the selling price of a unit, or (*c*) the cost of a service call.

Interdepartmental Studies. While means are available for reducing inspection costs by purely departmental study and action, the main opportunities are through joint study with other departments. The principal forms of this study consist of:

1. Defect prevention to reduce the need for inspection (see above).

2. Collaboration with Production to determine process capability and to preserve the order of manufacture so that the information needed for decisions on conformance is not restricted to the data derived from inspection and test (see How Much Inspection? above; also Section 17, under Product and Process Relationship).

3. Collaboration with Production to transfer the inspection to production operators and to regulate this through audit of decisions (see Section 17, under Product Acceptance by Operators).

4. Challenging the standards, especially on sensory qualities. One approach is described above under Providing Standards for Sensory Qualities.

The Budgetary Process. The Inspection budget is only one of numerous departmental budgets. These must all be prepared under a common format, and in a common language, to permit summary and review at higher and higher levels until finally approved by top management. Because the common language is money, all the deeds must be restated in terms of money to make these summaries and reviews possible.

The common budgetary format is devised by the company's finance and accounting specialists. This format features several universals employed in the budgetary process.

Cost Centers. These are logical subdivisions of inspection activity, chosen to fix responsibility and to provide a basis for collecting data on actual costs. The cost centers usually follow organization boundaries, since responsibility becomes very clear thereby.

Activity Index. Most inspection costs vary with the amount of plant activity. Sound budgeting requires that there be discovered, for each cost center, an activity index, i.e., an expression of the relationship between plant activity and budgeted inspection costs. For different kinds of inspection, the budget will vary in different ways:

Type of inspection	*Budget varies with*
Receiving inspection	Number of lots
	Value of purchased goods
Process inspection	Hours of direct production labor
	Dollars of direct production labor
	Number of projects serviced
Final inspection	Units of product inspected
	Value of product inspected
	Hours of direct production labor
	Dollars of direct production labor
Test laboratory	Number of requisitions (sometimes there is a standard time for each type of test)
Instrument laboratory	Number of active instruments in use

There are added variables which affect budgeting in all activities and which may be of major effect in some activities. These variables include:

1. *Lot size:* Inspection costs per lot do not vary greatly with lot size. However, variation in lot size can cause great variation in inspection cost per unit of product or per dollar value of product.
2. *Product mix:* Budgeting is often done on the basis of a historical product mix. When this mix changes, the costs may change either way.
3. *Flow of material:* The most exaggerated form of this takes place when much or even most of the product is presented for inspection in the last few days of the month.

Historical Standards. A budget for cost control is a standard for expenditures. This standard may be established in a number of ways, the most prevalent being the historical standard; i.e., we will be guided by how much we used to spend.

An example of evolution of an historical standard is seen in Figure 18.25. In this example, it had been determined that the best activity index was direct shop labor costs. Data for the last 18 months were plotted in Figure 18.25, resulting in a correlation scatter of inspection labor costs to direct shop labor costs. A line fitted to the points resulted in the relationship of a budget of $8.80 inspection labor per every $100 of direct shop labor. Costs of the supervisory and clerical force were regarded as "constant" over a wide range of activity and these were added to the variable costs shown in Figure 18.25.

On a more sophisticated level, one company identified 11 "factors" which influence the extent of inspection needed, e.g., type of product, identity of customer, degree of "black-box" subcontracting, etc. For each factor, there were several degrees or levels of influence. From a study of eight prior projects, weights were assigned to each degree of each factor. These weights were then used to analyze new contract proposals to arrive at an estimate of the inspection personnel levels needed (see Hutter, 1966).

Standards for Projects. Another form of standard is "the plan"; i.e., spending in accordance with a prearranged plan for a project. This device is most common

FIG. 18.25   Ratio of inspection labor costs to shop labor costs.

when the company has secured a contract based on a bid price and now faces the problem of holding its various components of cost within the respective components of the bid.

Seldom does a company use only one form of standard for costs. The cost centers are unlike, and it is common to find different forms of cost standards used in different cost centers. Moreover, there is a measure of judgment exercised in any event. None of the methods of setting standards are precise enough to be used automatically as a basis for judging future performance.

Measure of Actual Costs.   The establishment of cost centers, activity indexes, and standards provides a measure of what costs should be. It remains to establish means for measuring what costs actually are. This requires added tools:

An adequate timekeeping system: Inspectors must be provided with account numbers and forms for charging their time to proper account numbers.

A system for computing expenses: In like manner, there must be account numbers, requisitions, and other means for charging supplies and services to the proper accounts.

Data-processing systems: Means must be available (manual or otherwise) for processing the basic time and expense data into prompt summaries and reports for the various cost centers.

A budget office: Coordination of the activities of budgeting and reporting requires that administration of the system be a separate responsibility, clearly assigned to specific persons.

When a company embarks for the first time on formal budgeting, it is well to go through a trial period for "debugging." During the trial period, minds are open for constructive change. Lacking a trial period, minds may close and the entire project may face defeat.

Review of Cost Performance. Reports on costs versus budgets are prepared and distributed by the budget office on a regular schedule, usually weekly or monthly. Supervisory review is concentrated on significant departure from standard. This review is often conducted as a scheduled group review of performance against budget, since there is much interrelation between causes in one department and effects in another. At these review sessions, alternative courses of action are proposed and considered.

The very act of systematically reviewing performance and questioning variances is a main factor in holding costs to standard. If variances are sure to be questioned, supervisors do their utmost to prevent variances in the first place. If there is laxity in the review, performance will soon become lax as well.

Other Cost-Control Devices. Whether inspection is budgeted or not, there are available various special tools for controlling inspection costs. These special tools use physical units rather than money. Some of these tools do not require use of the company's financial accounting system, though the clerks of the Accounting Department may process the special data prepared.

For example, it is usually feasible to establish a ratio indicating the number of inspection hours required as compared with the number of productive machine hours (or operator hours) spent producing the product. This ratio can then be built into the form of a variable budget. Within normal variations in volume of operation, as production hours change, inspection hours will change in the same proportion.

In some companies, data are available through history, or through industrial-engineering study, of expected inspection costs. The simplest form is associated with products made in discrete units—so many coils, condensers, tubes. Here the data are in terms of inspection hours per 100 units, or per 100 lb, and future estimates can be based on knowledge of the future production schedule.

Slightly more complicated is the case where there is a line of product sufficiently varied so that the hours per 100 differ somewhat for the different types in the line. Inspection for the 1A gadget may require 13.2 per 100 as against 14.7 h for the 2A gadget and 16.8 h for the 3A gadget. Here, knowledge of the detailed production schedule or "mix" will permit an estimate. If details are not known, an estimate can still be made if there is no reason to believe that the mix has changed as compared with previous history.

This ratio of hours to hours or to units has the advantage of simplicity and ease of preparation. The main disadvantage is that only labor costs are considered, with the effect of other expenses, facility improvements, and other realities omitted.

A less precise measure is the ratio of inspectors to production workers. Beyond the deficiencies of the hours-to-hours measure, this ratio fails to consider inequalities in hours worked, absenteeism, overtime, etc.

SUMMARY

The foregoing brief look at inspection, test, and measurement systems and technologies makes it clear that revolutionary changes have been extensive. The growth of new technology can properly be called explosive. Technological breakthroughs in semiconductors, microprocessors, and computers are making 100 percent inspection and noncontact (visual) inspection applications practical and cost effective.

The growth in components and systems areas will require a much heavier demand for test and measurement instrumentation at all levels: R & D, production, manufacturing, quality control, calibration, maintenance, and so forth. It is estimated that by the end of this decade the measurement manufacturing industry will serve a market worth almost $5000 million in the United States and about $8400 million in the Free World. Refer to Figure 18.26. (See also "Test and Measurement," 1984.)

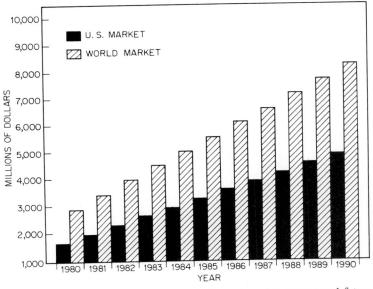

FIG. 18.26 The test and measurement equipment market, current and future estimated.

Developments such as these make clear that much effort is needed, on a continuing basis, to keep inspection and test departments, their laboratories and equipment, and above all, their personnel up to date with current developments and in a state of preparation for future developments.

Acknowledgment. The author gratefully acknowledges the assistance of Lloyd B. Wilson, then Measurement Consultant, Sperry Gyroscope Division, Sperry Rand Corporation, in preparing the material on measurements used in both the Third and current Editions.

REFERENCES

Abbe, R. C. and O'Brian, M. (1972). "A Brief Report on Non-Contact Gaging." *Quality Management and Engineering,* May, pp. 16–19.
Abernethy, R. B. et al. (1979). "Tutorial, Test Measurement Accuracy." *ISA,* ISBN 87664-453-3, pp. 1–11.

Ainsworth, L. (1980). "The Use of Signal-Detection Theory in the Analysis of Industrial Inspection." *Quality Assurance,* vol. 6, no. 3, September, pp. 63–68.

Alaimo, A. P. (1969). "A Total Inspection System." *ASQC Technical Conference Transactions,* Los Angeles, pp. 71–78.

Allen, P. E. (1959). "Evaluating Inspection Costs." *ASQC National Convention Transactions,* pp. 585–596.

"A Management Standard for Economical Inspection" (1976). *Quality,* vol. 15, no. 1, January, pp. 28–30.

American Society for Quality Control (1978). *Chemical Division Technical Supplement, Interlaboratory Testing Techniques,* Milwaukee.

American Society for Quality Control and American National Standards Institute (1984). *Guide to Inspection Planning.* ANSI/ASQC Publication E-2, Milwaukee.

American Society for Testing and Materials (1984). *Standard Guide for Establishing a Quality Assurance Program for Analytical Chemistry Laboratories.* ASTM Publication C1009-83, Annual Book of ASTM Standards, vol. 12.01, Philadelphia.

American Society for Testing and Materials (1963). *Manual for Conducting an Interlaboratory Study of a Test Method.* ASTM Special Technical Publication 335, Philadelphia.

"An Outlook for 3D Vision" (1984). *American Machinist, Quality Assurance,* November, p. 59.

"ASD's Quality Assurance Program Rates in Top 10" (1984). *Assembly Engineering, Newsline,* August, p. 6.

Babcombe, P. (1970). "Quality Control for the Very Small Batch." *Quality Engineer,* vol. 34, no. 1, January-February, pp. 19–22.

Bader, M. E. (1980). "Quality Assurance and Quality Control. Part 1: Specifications." *Chemical Engineering,* vol. 83, no. 3, Feb. 11, pp. 92–96.

Baker, E. M. (1975). "Signal Detection Theory Analysis of Quality Control Inspector Performance." *Journal of Quality Technology,* vol. 7, no. 2, April, pp. 62–71.

Ballou, D. P. and Pazer, H. L. (1982). "The Impact of Inspector Fallibility on the Inspection Policy in Serial Production Systems." *Management Science,* vol. 28, no. 4, April, pp. 387–399.

Barry, E. N. (1959). "Work Simplification Applied to Inspection." *Industrial Quality Control,* May, pp. 56–58; also June, pp. 19–20.

Blaufuss, Jo (1972). "Metric Memo." *Quality Management and Engineering,* June, p. 40.

Bond, T. P. (1983). "Basics of an MRB." *Quality,* November, p. 48.

Brandt, D. A. (1963). "When the Swallows Come Home." *ASQC Transactions of the Fifth Annual All-Day Conference, Akron-Canton Section.*

Buckrop, R. L. (1976). "Nondestructive Testing Overview." *Quality Progress,* June, pp. 26–29.

Burgess, J. A. (1983). "Quality Assurance in Testing." *Quality,* January, pp. 36–37.

Carter, C. L. and Carter, G. M. (1983). "A Motivation Program for Inspectors." *ASQC Quality Congress Transactions,* Boston, pp. 525–528.

Chebookjian, S. L. (1980). "The Inspector Is Human." *ASQC Technical Conference Transactions,* Milwaukee, p. 365.

Churchill, A. V. (1956). "The Effect of Scale Interval Length and Pointer Clearance on Speed and Accuracy of Interpolation." *Journal of Applied Psychology,* vol 40, December, pp. 358–361.

Coleman, L. R. (1982). "Detailed Defect Reporting—A Key to Productivity." *ASQC Quality Congress Transactions,* Detroit, pp. 574–579.

Cooper, J. E. (1977). "Patrol Inspection: Guide to Productivity & Profit." *ASQC Technical Conference Transactions,* Philadelphia, pp. 50–52.

Cooper, J. E. (1980). "The Care and Training of Your Inspectors." *ASQC Technical Conference Transactions,* Milwaukee, pp. 674–676.

Crow, E. L. (1966). "Optimum Allocation of Calibration Errors." *Industrial Quality Control,* November, pp. 215–219.

Czaja, S. J. and Drury, C. G. (1981). "Training Programs for Inspectors." *Human Factors,* vol. 23, no. 4, pp. 473–484.

Darby, G. R. (1970). "The Metric System—Practical Implementation." *Quality Engineer,* vol. 34, no. 4, July–August, pp. 8–10.

Davidson, D. (1982). "The Eye of the Beholder." *Quality,* vol. 21, no. 4, April, pp. 38–39.

De Simone, Daniel V. (1971). *A Metric America: A Decision Whose Time Has Come.* National Bureau of Standards Special Publication 345, July, Washington, DC; SD Catalog No. 13.10:345.

De Simone, Daniel V. (1972). "Moving to Metric Makes Dollars and Sense." *Harvard Business Review,* January–February, pp. 100–111.

Denker, S. P. (1984). "Justifying Your Investment in Automatic Visual PCB Testing." *Circuits Manufacturing,* October, pp. 56, 58, 60, 62.

Dodds, L. B. (1967). "Workmanships." *ASQC Technical Conference Transactions,* Chicago, pp. 249–252.

Dodge, H. F. (1928). *A Method of Rating Manufactured Product.* Reprint B-315, May, Bell Telephone Laboratories.

Dodge, H. F. and Torrey, M. N. (1956). "A Check Inspection and Demerit Rating Plan." *Industrial Quality Control,* vol. 13, no. 1, July, pp. 5–12.

Eagle, A. R. (1954). "A Method for Handling Errors in Testing and Measuring." *Industrial Quality Control,* March, pp. 10–14.

Eisenhart, C. (1968). "Expression of the Uncertainties of Final Results." *Science,* June 14, pp. 1201–1204.

El Gabry, A. A. (1972). "Inter-Relation of Quality Characteristics." *ASQC Technical Conference Transactions,* Chicago, pp. 422–428.

Eppen, G. D. and Hurst, E. G., Jr. (1974). "Optimal Location of Inspection Stations in a Multistage Production Process." *Management Science,* vol. 20, no. 8, April, pp. 1194–1200.

Ezer, S. (1979). "Statistical Models for Proficiency Testing." *ASQC Technical Conference Transactions,* Houston, pp. 448–457.

Fagan, M. E. (1976). "Design and Code Inspections to Reduce Errors in Program Development." *IBM Systems Journal.* Also Chapter 7 in Yourdon, Edward (ed.). *Writings of the Revolution,* pp. 123–148.

Fortuin, G. J. and Van Beek, A. (1960). "A Flavor Trial." *Statistical Nederlandica,* vol. 14, no. 2, pp. 175–185 (in Dutch).

Gantt, J. S. (1959). "Let's Take the Guesswork out of Inspection." *American Machinist,* March 9, 1959, pp. 1–6.

Garfinkel, D. and Clodfelter, S. (1984). "Contract Inspection Comes into Its Own." *American Machinist,* October, pp. 90–92.

Gebhardt, C. (1982). "Color Me Calibrated." *Quality,* March, pp. 62–63.

Geidel, H. (1978). "Statistical Evaluation of Sensory Tests." *Qualitat und Zuverlassigkeit,* vol. 23, no. 7, July, pp. 176–178 (in German).

Gibson, J. D. (1983). "How Do You Recognize a Qualified Inspector?" *Quality Assurance for the Offshore Industry (London),* April, pp. 55–56.

Gilman, J. R. (1963). "Quality Reports to Management." *Industrial Quality Control,* May, pp. 15–17. [In this demerit scheme of check inspecting the work of inspectors (who are paid by piece work), the accuracy is expressed in a form equivalent to the number of demerits found per lot checked.]

Gittler, H. (1973). "Why Not Put Inspectors on Incentive?" *Quality Management and Engineering,* December, pp. 22–24.

Goldbeck, J. M. (1981). "Measuring Inspector's Productivity." *ASQC Quality Congress Transactions,* San Francisco, pp. 343–347.

Greb, D. J. (1976). "Does Bad Test Equipment Accept Bad Product?—A Quantitative Analysis." *ASQC Technical Conference Transactions,* Milwaukee, pp. 389–391.

Griffin, R. J. (1980). "Aerospace and Defense Metric System Impact." *ASQC Technical Conference Transactions,* Atlanta, pp. 606–609.

Guest, R. (1981). "Gauging: The Next Five Years" *Quality Assurance,* vol. 7, no. 4, December, pp. 113–115.

Gunter, B. (1983). "The Fallacy of 100% Inspection." *ASQC Statistical Division Newsletter,* vol. 5, no. 1, September, pp. 1–2.

Hains, R. W. (1978). "Measurement of Subjective Variables." *ASQC Technical Conference Transactions,* Chicago, pp. 237–244.

Harris, D. H. and Chaney, F. B. (1969). *Human Factors in Quality Assurance.* John Wiley & Sons, New York, pp. 107–113.

Helm, E. and Trolle, B. (1946). "Selection of a Test Panel." *Wallerstein Laboratories Communications,* vol. 9, no. 28, pp. 181–194.

Holmes, H. (1974). "Computer Assisted Inspection." *The Quality Engineer,* vol. 38, no. 9, September, pp. 211–213.

Hunter, J. S. (1980). "The National System of Scientific Measurement." *Science,* vol. 210, Nov. 21, pp. 869–874.

Hutter, R. G. (1966). "Inspection Manpower Planning." *Industrial Quality Control,* April, pp. 521–523.

Hyer, C. W. (1979). *Principal Aspects of U.S. Laboratory Accreditation Program.* The Marley Organization, Ridgefield, CT, Jan. 24.

"Inspection Can Make an Impression with a Saving" (1975). *Quality,* vol. 15, no. 9, September, p. 37.

Jaehm, A. H. (1982). "Maintaining the Credibility of Your Quality Control Department." *TAPPI,* vol. 65, no. 5, May, p. 187.

Johnson, S. L. and Funke, D. J. (1980). "An Analysis of Human Reliability Measure in Visual Inspection." *Journal of Quality Technology,* vol. 12, no. 2, April, pp. 71–74.

Juran, J. M. (1935). "Inspector's Errors in Quality Control." *Mechanical Engineering,* vol. 59, no. 10, October, pp. 643–644.

Juran, J. M. (1945). *Management of Inspection and Quality Control.* Harper & Brothers, New York.

Juran, J. M. (1952). "Is Your Product Too Fussy?" *Factory Management and Maintenance,* vol. 110, no. 8, August, pp. 125–128.

Juran, J. M. (1969). "Mobilizing for the 1970s." *Quality Progress,* August.

Juran, J. M. (1970). "Consumerism and Product Quality." *Quality Progress,* July.

Juran, J. M. and Gryna, F. M., Jr. (1980). *Quality Planning and Analysis from Product Development through Use.* McGraw-Hill, New York, pp. 357, 360–361.

Karabatsos, N. (1983a). "Serving Quality." *Quality,* vol. 22, no. 9, September, pp. 65–68.

Karabatsos, N. (1983b). "Update on Coordinate Measuring Machines." *Quality,* vol. 22, no. 12, December, pp. 23–28, 30, 32, 34.

Karasek, F. W. (1975). "Analytical Service Laboratories." *Research/Development,* vol. 26, no. 4, April, pp. 32, 34, 36.

Kay, T. G. (1972). "Timeless Work Sampling." *Journal of Industrial Engineering,* vol. 4, no. 6, June, pp. 30–33.

Keller, T. A. et al. (1975). "Inspection by Exception through Automated Video Techniques." *ASQC Technical Conference Transactions,* San Diego, pp. 1–7.

Ken, J. (1984). "The (Artificial) Eyes Have It." *Electronic Business,* Sept. 1, pp. 154–162.

Kirwan, M. S. (1972). "Guaranteed Accurate Numerical Tapes." *Mechanical Engineering,* August, pp. 13–17.

Konz, S., Peterson, G., and Joshi, A. (1981). "Reducing Inspector Errors." *Quality Progress,* vol. 14, no. 7, July, pp. 24–26.

Kramer, A. (1952). "The Problem of Developing Grades and Standards of Quality." *Food Drug Cosmetic Law Journal,* January, pp. 23–30.

Kusch, J. (1979). "Robots and Their Advantage in Inspection." *Proceedings, Society of Photo-Optical Instrumentation Engineers,* vol. 170, *Optics in Quality Assurance, II,* pp. 40–42.

Leek, J. W. (1975). "See It as It Really Is." *ASQC Technical Conference Transactions,* San Diego, pp. 41–43.

Leek, J. W. (1976). "Benefits from Visual Standards." *Quality Progress,* December, pp. 16–18.

Linn, R. D. (1981). "Computer Aided Inspection—Its Time Has Come." *ASQC Quality Congress Transactions,* San Francisco, pp. 599–602.

Louis, A. M. (1981). "Schlitz's Crafty Taste Test." *Fortune,* Jan. 26, 1981, pp. 32–34.

Loxham, J. (1967). "From Science to Technology." *Quality Engineer,* January–February, pp. 16–26.

Maass, R. A. (1970). "The Independent Test Lab." *Quality Assurance,* Part I: April, pp. 24–29; also Part II: May, pp. 43–46.

Marwell, E. M. (1966). "Calibration by Use." *Instruments and Control Systems,* January.

Mathur, C. P. (1974). "The Influence of Measurement Variation in Mass Production of Precision Parts." *Q.R. Journal,* January, pp. 1–5.

McCaslin, J. A. and Gruska, G. F. (1976). "Analysis of Attribute Gage Systems." *ASQC Technical Conference Transactions,* Toronto, pp. 392–400.

McMaster, R. C. (1959). *Nondestructive Testing Handbook.* Ronald Press, New York.

Measurements and Calibrations. Technical Note 252, U.S. Government Printing Office, Washington, DC, p. 4.

Meckley, D. G., III (1955). "How to Set Up a Gaging Policy and Procedure. *American Machinist,* vol. 99, no. 6, Mar. 14, p. 133.

Megaw, E. D. (1978). "Eye Movements in Visual Inspection Tasks." *Quality Assurance,* vol. 4, no. 4, December, pp. 121–125.

Miller, E. M. (1975). "Test Methods and Specification Requirements." *ASQC Technical Conference Transactions,* San Diego, pp. 229–230.

Minor, G. W. (1981). "An Approach to Inspector Productivity." *ASQC Quality Congress Transactions,* San Francisco, pp. 975–979.

Moburg, K. W. (1968). "Defect Management by Exception." *ASQC Technical Conference Transactions,* Philadelphia, pp. 685–690.

Montville, V. L. (1983). "Color Control from Start to Finish." *Quality,* March, pp. 36–38.

National Bureau of Standards (1965). *Accuracy in Measurements and Calibrations.* NBS Technical Note 262, U.S. Government Printing Office, Washington, DC, p. 4.

National Bureau of Standards (1966). "Expression of the Uncertainties of Final Results." Chapter 23 in *Experimental Statistics.* NBS Handbook 91, U.S. Government Printing Office, Washington, DC.

Nelson, A. V. (1984). "Machine Vision: Tomorrow's Inspections with Today's Equipment." *Evaluation Engineer,* vol. 23, no. 9, October, pp. 21, 24, 26, 29, 30, 34, 37.

Nygaard, G. M. (1981). "Why 100 Percent Inspection?" *Quality,* October, pp. 38–39.

Ohta, H. and Kase, S. (1980). "Evaluation of Inspectors in Sensory Tests—Qualification by Geometrical Methods and Classification by Bayesian Diagnosis Rule." *Journal of Quality Technology,* vol. 12, no. 1, January, pp. 19–24.

Papadopoulos, N. (1983). "Instrumental Color Control—Where to Start." *Quality,* December, pp. 44–46.

Paul, B. (1982). "Chance of Deadly Bridge Collapse Growing as Quality Deteriorates, Safety Critics Say." *Wall Street Journal,* Dec. 29.

Peacox, E. F. (1970). "Rating Inspectors and Evaluating Inspection." *ASQC Technical Conference Transactions,* Pittsburg, pp. 263–271.

Peryam, D. R. (1950). "Quality Control in the Production of Blended Whesday." *Industrial Quality Control,* vol. 7, no. 3, November, pp. 17–21.

Pipkin, F. M. and Ritter, R. C. (1983). "Precision Measurements and Fundamental Constants." *Science,* vol. 219, Feb. 25, pp. 913–921.

"Portable Gage Lab Provides Flexibility and Minimizes Downtime" (1971). *Quality Management and Engineering,* November, p. 23.

Provost, L. P. and Elder, R. S. (1983). "Cost-Effective Laboratory Quality Control." *ASQC Quality Congress Transactions,* Boston, pp. 496–502.

Ramaswamy, C. V. (1981). "How Good Are You as a Fabrication Inspector?" *BHEL,* January, pp. 8–10.

Riley, F. D. (1979). "Visual Inspection—Time and Distance Method." *ASQC Technical Conference Transactions,* Houston, pp. 483–490.

Robinson, A. L. (1983). "Using Time to Measure Length." *Science,* vol. 220, June 24, p. 1367.

Schaffer, G. (1984). "Machine Vision: A Sense for CIM." *American Machinist,* Special Report 767, June, pp. 101–120.

Scheffe, H. (1952). "An Analysis of Variance for Paired Comparisons." *Journal of the American Statistical Association,* vol. 47, pp. 381–400.

Schumacher, R. B. F. (1976). "Quality Control in a Calibration Laboratory." *Quality Progress,* Part I: vol. 9, no. 1, January, pp. 25–28; Part II; vol. 9, no. 2, February, pp. 16–20.

Schumacher, R. B. F. (1981). "Systematic Measurement Errors." *Journal of Quality Technology,* vol. 13, no. 1, January, pp. 10–24.

Schweber, W. (1982). "Programming for Control—Computerizing Measurement and Control." *Quality,* March, pp. 38–42.

Sears, J. A. (1982). "Changing Role of the Quality Inspection Function." *ASQC Quality Congress Transactions,* Detroit, pp. 506–512.

Shainin, D. (1972). "Unusual Practices for Defect Control." *Quality Management and Engineering,* February, pp. 8, 9, 30.

Sharp, D. B. (1976). "Inching toward the Metric System." *ASQC Technical Conference Transactions,* Toronto, pp. 381–388.

Shimoda, Y. and Miyazaki, H. (1981). "The Selection of Inspectors for Sensory Tests." *ASQC Quality Congress Transactions,* San Francisco, pp. 884–891.

"SI—Systeme International Rationale" (1972). *Quality Progress,* January, pp. 15–18.

Smith, J. R. and Duvier, H., III (1984). "Effect of Inspector Error on Inspection Strategies." *ASQC Quality Congress Transactions,* Chicago, pp. 146–151.

Spow, E. E. (1984). "Automatic Assembly." *Tooling and Production,* October, pp. 46–47.

Stalker, A. H. (1980). "The Inspection Record." *Quality,* vol. 19, no. 8, August, p. 33.

Taguchi, G. (1970). "Quality Assurance and Design of Inspection During Production—2." *Reports of Statistical Applications and Research,* Japanese Union of Scientists and Engineers, vol. 17, no. 1.

"Tape Controlled Machines at Sunstrand Aviation" (1970). *Quality Assurance,* June, pp. 30–34.

Tawara, N. (1980). "A Case Study on Measuring Inspection Performance for Inspection Job Design." *International Journal of Production Research,* vol. 18, no. 3, May–June, pp. 343–353.

Taylor, F. W. (1911). *Principles of Scientific Management.* Harper & Brothers, New York, pp. 80–96 for a discussion on inspection of ball bearings.

"Test and Measurement" (1984). *Microwave System News,* vol. 14, Nov. 12, pp. 108–188.

Thomas, J. H. (1977). "Productivity in the Quality Control Department." *ASQC Inspection Division Newsletter,* vol. 8, no. 3, March, pp. 2–3.

Thomas, L. (1978). "Human Judgement and Perceiving the Complexity of Quality." *Quality Assurance,* vol. 4, no. 4, December, pp. 116–120.

Thompson, H. A. and Reynolds, E. A. (1964). "Inspection and Testing as a Problem in Man–Machine Systems Control Engineering." *Industrial Quality Control,* July, pp. 21–23.

Tobey, D. (1979). "Metrology = Calibration." *ASQC Technical Conference Transactions,* Houston, pp. 513–520.

Trippi, R. R. (1975). "The Warehouse Location Formulation as a Special Type of Inspection Problem." *Management Science,* vol. 21, no. 9, May, pp. 986–988.

Turner, R. E. (1974). "Today and Tomorrow for NDT." *"Quality Management and Engineering,"* December, pp. 36–41.

Tustin, W. (1980). "Selecting a Testing Laboratory." *Quality,* June, pp. 24–26.

Ulla, F. M. (1982). "Productivity Measurements of Inspectors." *ASQC Quality Congress Transactions,* Detroit, pp. 108–117.

"Voice Entry System Gives Quality Inspectors a Hand" (1973). *Quality Progress,* vol. 6, no. 7, July, pp. 12–14.

Walsh, L. (1974). "Back to One Hundred Percent Inspection??" Editorial Comment, *Quality Management and Engineering,* March, p. 9.

Walsh, L. et al. (1976). "100% Inspection at Production Line Rates." *Quality,* November, pp. 30–31.

Walsh, L. et al. (1978). "Steel Wheel Maker Tests Hardness 100%." *Quality,* November, p. 37.

Walsh, L. et al. (1979a). "Can 100% Testing Be Eliminated?" *Quality,* May, pp. 42–43.

Walsh, L. et al. (1979b). "100% Inspection Plus." *Quality,* September, pp. 102, 104.

Walsmann, M. R. (1981). "The Check List—A Powerful Inspection Tool." *ASQC Technical Conference Transactions,* pp. 348–351.

Wambach, G. W. and Raymond, A. S. (1977). "The Optimum Sampling Plan." *ASQC Technical Conference Transactions,* Philadelphia, pp. 574–578.

Wang, S. C. (1975). "Human Reliability in Visual Inspection." *Quality,* September, pp. 24–25.

Wang, S. H. S. et al. (1981). "A System Simulation for Inspection Planning." *ASQC Quality Congress Transactions,* San Francisco, pp. 769–776.

Weaver, L. A. (1975). "Inspection Accuracy Sampling Plans." *ASQC Technical Conference Transactions,* San Diego, pp. 34–39.

"Where Quality Control is a Part Time Job" (1979). *Business Week,* Nov. 26, p. 44F.

Williams, C. D. (1981). "How You Can Optimize the QC Function in Your Firm." *Inspection Engineering,* March, pp. 48, 50–51.

Wood, N. (1979). "Contract Inspection Service." *Quality,* vol. 18, no. 5, May, pp. 13–14.

Woods, K. C. (1978). "Calibration System for Measuring and Testing Equipment." *Quality Progress,* March, pp. 20–21.

Woods, D. G. and Zeiss, C. (1981). "Coordinate Measuring and Finite Metrology." *ASQC Quality Congress Transactions,* San Francisco, pp. 232–237.

Wurster (ed.) (1980). "A Data Acquisition Overview." *Quality,* May, pp. 47–51.

SECTION 19
MARKETING[1]

Frank M. Gryna

INTRODUCTION

This step on the Spiral of Progress (see Figure 2.2 in Section 2) concerns the process of persuading customers to buy products for reasons related to product quality. This process is part of a broader marketing activity which impacts all steps on the Spiral. Some of this activity takes place before production of the product. (See Section 3, Quality and Income; also Section 12, Field Intelligence.) Still other

---

[1]In the Third Edition, this section was prepared by J. M. Juran.

marketing activity takes place after sale to customers. (See Section 20, Customer Service.) Some policy matters with respect to marketing are discussed in Section 5, Quality Policies and Objectives.

Advertising of Quality.   The process of disseminating commercial information is called "advertising." The purpose of advertising is to enlarge the sales income of the advertiser, either through (1) product advertising, which aims to induce people to buy the product, or (2) institutional advertising, which aims to create a favorable image of the company. An important adjunct to these purposes is to provide information to the customer to help in making purchasing decisions.

The concept of product advertising is that human beings harbor powerful drives, needs, and wants and that through application of relatively small stimuli, these drives can be converted into decisions to buy. Under this concept, the advertiser is then faced with the dual problems of:

1. Discovering and presenting the stimuli which can best translate these human forces into action to buy. These stimuli are appeals to animal senses and to emotions.

2. Demonstrating that the product is superior to other products for meeting the human wants. This demonstration takes the form of communicating information on quality or fitness for use and is mainly an appeal to logic and reason.

In practice, many advertisements contain appeals to both emotion and reason. However, centuries of advertising have demonstrated that when human beings are buying for their own needs, appeals to emotion generate more action than appeals to reason.

Emotional Stimuli.   These are widely used to advertise consumer products and, to a degree, industrial products as well. As they appeal to emotion, their effects are subjective and not susceptible of objective verification. They take numerous forms:

Attention getters of all sorts—singing, dancing, humor, unorthodox behavior

Product names, package colors, surrounding decor, etc., which are believed to induce a favorable response from potential buyers

A vision of the well-being which, by implication, results from purchase of the product—health, safety, comfort, social success

An aura of company competence: the record of innovation "firsts" of the company; the prizes its products have won in competitions

A display of "seals" from so-called "independent" laboratories

Asserted secret ingredients, or ingredients bearing a fanciful name for which there is no standard definition

Pseudoscientific explanations: cartoons depicting aches, pains, and their implied disappearance; staged laboratories and "scientists"

Challenges to competitors to meet performance or reliability levels

Emphasis on a high price as an indicator of better quality

Such stimuli, however, do not constitute objective evidence of fitness for use. Some of the facts stated (e.g., a list of company innovations in products generally) may warrant broad inferences about the specific product being advertised. But any idea that advertisers should replace emotional stimuli with objective evidence runs into some hard realities as applied to consumers:

1. The great majority of quality characteristics cannot be sensed by the consumer.

2. The great majority of factual explanations of the technological properties of products cannot be understood by the consumer.

The advertising managers have concluded, with much justification, that the emotional stimuli are an essential element of advertising of consumer products and a useful adjunct to the advertising of commercial products.

Objective Evidence. Advertising based on objective product and quality data is widely used for industrial products and, to some degree, for consumer products as well. These objective presentations likewise take numerous forms:

Laboratory and inspection test results: tensile strength, frequency distribution, Weibull plots, safety ratings, tar and nicotine content

Usage data: mean time between failures of 10,000 h; fuel consumption of 35 mi/gal; cost per unit product, e.g., copies from a copier machine; lower frequency of adjustments, replacements, service

Listing of features possessed by the product (often to show that competitors lack these features)

Warranty provided (see below under Warranty of Quality)

Demonstrations of product usage by a series of still pictures or on television

Evidence of user satisfaction: testimonials from named users; data on share of market, e.g., "more than all other makes combined"

Results of tests by independent test laboratories: marks or certifications from such independent laboratories

Advertising which compares product features with those of competitors has a long history. However such advertising has traditionally avoided naming the competitors in question. More recently there has been a dramatic increase in the frequency of naming the competitors. Some of these advertisements have stimulated competitors to complain to government regulators who then demand objective proof of the claims made in the advertisement. Alternatively, the competitors file legal actions to recover damages. In the face of such threats, advertisers are well advised to assure that the claims made in the advertising are based on objective test data. (See "Should an Ad Identify Brand X?" 1979.)

The benefits and problems of comparative advertising are being studied, and advertising specialists are divided on the subject. (See Wilkie and Farris, 1975.)

Despite the excesses and abuses of advertising, the movement has brought extensive benefits to consumers. The urge to develop quality reputations has stimulated manufacturers to develop product quality and quality controls to levels which can back up the advertising.

Use of distinctive packaging has improved packaging generally and has greatly simplified distribution (but at the cost of disposal of the packages). Even the propaganda, being competitive, has contributed materially to the education of consumers.

In many countries the public is skeptical about the truthfulness of advertising. One survey (Schutz and Casey, 1981) revealed that over half of those sampled believed "most" or "all" mail and telephone advertising to be misleading; 38 percent felt the same about television advertising. In another survey ("America's Search for Quality," 1983), only 6 percent of the respondents viewed advertising as the most trustworthy source of consumer information. (For a discussion of quality and the media, see Taylor, 1981.)

Puffing.   The practice of exaggerating the properties of the advertised product is known as "puffing," i.e., a self-serving exaggerated praise. Expressions like "none better," "your best buy," etc., are examples of puffing.

Puffing and caveat emptor (let the buyer beware) are now largely obsolete for industrial products and are becoming obsolete for many consumer products. (See Juran, 1970.)

The increased scrutiny of advertising (by consumer organizations, government regulators, and competitors) has stimulated the growth of internal controls. In many companies the advertising copy is reviewed by cognizant functions (e.g., legal, product development, quality) as a check on the validity of the claims. Of special importance is the potential use of the advertisement in a product liability suit. A pertinent question to raise during a review is, "How would this phrase sound in court?"

Government Regulation of Advertising.

The obsolescence of caveat emptor makes necessary a considerable change in advertising practice. Some manufacturers and merchants have already taken major steps in the direction of strict objectivity. Most of them have not, however, and this has led to demands for increasing government regulation. Examples of claims made in advertisements that have been challenged by government regulators include:

Products are superior to other brands (effectiveness of aspirin, taste of wine, on-time performance of airlines).

Specialists prefer brand X (technicians prefer a certain microwave oven, clerks are unable to assist consumers on loss of certain brands of traveler's checks).

A product contains preferred ingredients ("natural" ingredients of beer, soups with more solid ingredients).

A product promotes health (a remedy prevents colds or sore throats, a bread builds strong bodies).

Faulty performance of a product requires the replacement of a certain component (the failure of a car to start requires the replacement of the spark plugs).

An important byproduct of regulation of advertising is the fact that the government is empowered to act against the offender. In the absence of regulation, the deceived buyer must proceed directly against the advertiser, a costly, time-consuming procedure.

Some proponents of advertising contend that advertised brands tend to be of higher quality. The evidence is not strong. One study (Rotfeld and Rotzoll, 1976) examined 13 categories of consumer products for the relationship between advertising expenditures and product quality. The conclusion: No broad generalizations can be made.

Assistance to Customers in Product Selection.

Sale of manufactured products takes place through a chain of intermediate, independent merchants. (A small minority of manufacturing companies sell directly to the consumer, either through captive retail shops or through door-to-door selling by salespeople who are manufacturing-company employees.) Depending on the nature of the product and the identity of the customer, the merchant's influence on quality varies widely. To sell technological products to industrial companies requires a high level of knowledge of the product, including some capacity to provide technical assistance. At the other extreme is self-service. The selling is done by display of the product plus prior propaganda. Between these extremes are numerous situations in which the tools and the techniques of selling play an important role in the customer's decision of which competing product to buy or whether to buy at all.

Industrial Products.   The concept of technical service involves the use of technically trained intermediaries between the company and its clients. The "applications engineer" is knowledgeable in the performance capabilities of the company's products. By studying the client's needs, the engineer assists the client in choosing that product design which best suits the application. Alternatively the applications engineer proposes design modifications to adapt standard designs to the client's special needs. By having knowledge in both fields (the capabilities of the designs and the needs of the users), the engineer is helpful in bringing the two together.

For some materials and components there are hundreds or thousands of potential applications. It is impractical to establish separate product types or specifications for each application. The applications engineering concept makes it possible to offer a limited number of standard product types and yet serve a wide spectrum of applications.

It is useful for the customer to be aware of alternative products or product models that can satisfy customer needs. Sometimes the customer can become overwhelmed with information on the array of alternatives. A useful technique in these cases is multiattribute rating. (See Section 12 under Competitive Evaluations by Field Studies.) By showing how to identify quality and other important attributes, establish a relative importance rating, and score the alternatives, an applications engineer can help a customer reach a decision.

A different approach applies in situations where the industrial customer modifies the product or combines it with other products before reselling it. Many industrial customers are, in a sense, intermediaries, i.e., distributors and/or processors of the products they buy. In such capacities they may benefit by assistance from the prior manufacturer (or supplier) in making the ultimate user aware of the virtues of both the intermediate and the final product. A cooperative effort is inherent in such cases, and it can lead to increased sales for both. An important element of such arrangements is explanation of the quality features. Such explanation is usually best done by the manufacturer of those features rather than by subsequent processors. (See Fuss, 1973.)

Consumer Products.   Decision making on the selection of consumer products involves many links in the marketing chain, and is often less structured than that for industrial products.

The manufacturer of branded products faces the problem of carrying the influence of the product brand through the entire merchant chain right to the point of sale. A major tool for doing this is a good reputation, derived from prior performance of the products, for providing predictable fitness for use. Additionally, the manufacturer propagandizes the product directly to consumers through advertising and brand labeling (see under Advertising of Quality and under Labeling, respectively, in this section). Tools to aid the merchant and salespeople in selling the product, e.g., product information literature, samples, demonstration kits, prepared sales training aids, etc., can also be provided. Some manufacturers do a superlative job of aiding merchants and customers through such means. Particularly when the product possesses superior fitness for use, the manufacturer finds ways to sensitize the salespeople to this fact so that the prospective customer can, in turn, be sensitized.

In one example (van Leer, 1976), a manufacturer of latex material wished to convince consumers that latex paint outlasted oil-based paint. The latex manufacturer developed a scrubber device to demonstrate the latex property, then provided the device to paint manufacturers (the customers for the latex). The paint manufacturers demonstrated the scrubber to paint store clerks for use with customers.

In many competitive situations, there is no clear superiority in fitness for use. What is decisive in selling products in such cases is the marketing tools: prior reputation, attractive packaging, appealing propaganda, personable salespeople. In such cases, appeals to emotion prevail over appeals to precise reasoning. Since the manufacturer is competing with other manufacturers for the attention and support of the merchant and salespeople, some of the manufacturer's energies must be directed to "selling" these salespeople. In part, the manufacturer does this through favorable contract terms. In part, the manufacturer uses tools similar to those used in selling the product to the customer: prior reputation, attractive packaging, appealing propaganda, personable salespeople.

Consumer information on quality is available to merchants and consumers from several sources—manufacturers, private organizations, and government agencies. (See Section 3 under Degrees of User Knowledge.)

THE SALES CONTRACT

The sales contract often contains provisions on quality. For consumer products, these provisions may simply be a statement of the product warranty. (A discussion of warranties is provided later in this section.)

For industrial products, the sales contract may contain extensive provisions on quality such as:

1. Requirements on the product.
    a. Performance requirements. This may include highly detailed performance specifications on the product.
    b. Specific technical requirements, e.g., composition of raw material.
    c. Requirements on the "level" of quality of delivered product, e.g., number of defects per million, percent defective, mean time between failures.
2. Requirements on execution of the contract. For critical products these requirements may include:
    a. A quality plan prepared by the manufacturer to itemize the specific activities that will be conducted from design through field use.
    b. Reliability analyses (e.g., reliability predictions, failure mode, effect, and criticality analyses) and test data (e.g., inspection results, reliability test data).
    c. Product design and manufacture in accordance with other industry or government specifications; e.g., a product must comply to the specifications of the Occupational Safety and Health Administration (OSHA).
    d. Prior customer notification of changes in material or in the method of manufacture.

e. Purchase from specified suppliers of certain components going into the final product.

f. Formal approval, by the customer, of specified documentation. For example, a customer may reserve final approval of product designs before they are released for manufacturing. In another example, a purchaser of machine tools may require that a demonstration of process capability be made at the supplier's plant before the machine tool can be shipped.

g. Special warranties, such as reliability improvement, may be required along with standard warranty provisions.

Increasingly, contracts are being written on industrial products to permit certain actions by customers if a specified quality level is not met. For example, one purchaser of electronic parts reserves the right to cancel the remaining production under a contract if the quality level does not meet the requirement. Such provisions reflect the desire of industrial purchasers to eliminate incoming inspection, so that the product can be shipped directly to the manufacturing line.

Incentive Provisions on Quality and Reliability. Manufacturers and customers of military products have experimented with contract provisions to provide monetary incentives and penalties based on product performance. An early application involved the airplane. The Wright brothers made their first sale to the Signal Corps under an incentive penalty contract. The contract called for payment of $25,000 for a "flying machine" that would achieve 40 mi/h, with a payment of $5000 extra if the machine did 2 mi/h more. If it did 2 mi/h less, the payment would be reduced by $5000. The Wrights collected the incentive (*Newsweek,* June 9, 1969).

In a more recent example involving a medium range air-to-air missile (Wood, 1982), four parameters were identified as the ones most essential for mission success. The parameters and the approach to incentives were:

Parameter	*Incentive approach*
Storage reliability	Based on tests conducted; missile has been in storage
Captive carry reliability	Reliability demonstration program
Missile on aircraft test	Award fee panel evaluates progress on mission dependability, costs, and program milestones
Free flight reliability	Award panel evaluates progress on mission dependability, costs, and program milestones

ROLE OF THE MARKETING DEPARTMENT DURING THE LAUNCHING OF NEW PRODUCTS

A key factor in launching new products is the fit of the product with market needs. The importance of field intelligence to identify market needs is discussed in Section 12.

Even with superior field intelligence and product development, the final test of the new product can be made only in the marketplace. Before mass producing and distributing the product on a nationwide basis, many companies use the concept of a "test market." In a test market, the product is sold on a limited basis for the purpose of:

1. Measuring the potential sales performance in order to decide whether or not to go ahead with full-scale marketing
2. Identifying weaknesses in the product
3. Identifying weaknesses in the marketing plan (product name, packaging, advertisements)

Conducting a test market can be expensive, and generally this step is taken only after pretesting has shown that the product will likely be a winner in the marketplace.

As in the collection of field intelligence prior to the start of product development, it is essential that a team of people from marketing, product development, manufacturing, and other departments decide what questions need to be answered by the test market. After such agreement, the marketing department (with the aid of others, if necessary) collects the information in the marketplace. The mechanisms for collecting the information can include questionnaires, phone calls, focus groups, and other marketing research techniques (see Section 12 under Some Simple Tools for Collecting Field Intelligence).

The decision of whether or not to use a test market requires a comparison of the costs and risks. The costs include not only the expenses for data collection but also the income lost by delaying a full-scale market introduction. The key risk is introducing a product that fails. Even though prior marketing research has been conducted, weaknesses in a new product are sometimes not revealed until the product lives in the marketplace environment. Examples of product weaknesses that did not show up until the marketplace are (Klompmaker et al., 1976):

1. Because packages would not stack, the scouring pads fell off the shelf.
2. A dog food discolored on the store shelves.
3. Because of insufficient glue, over half of the packages came apart during transit.

Use of test marketing can help to prevent such disasters.

The process of launching new products is an example of an activity that is worthy of review by upper management (See Section 8 under Quality Audits by Upper Managers).

WARRANTY OF QUALITY

A warranty is a form of assurance that products are fit for use or, if defective, that the customer will receive some extent of compensation. From a legal point of view, there are several types of warranties:

Implied Warranties. Warranties by the seller may be implied from actions, under the provisions of the Uniform Commercial Code (which governs contracts of sale in virtually all states of the United States). Under these provisions, the seller, by the mere act of sale, makes two implied warranties:

1. A general warranty of fitness for use ("merchantability" is the legal term) for the purposes for which such products are customarily used

2. An added special warranty of fitness for the special uses to which the user will put it, provided the seller knows these special conditions

Express Warranties.   Here the seller goes beyond the mere act of sale and makes some representations about the product, i.e., properties it possesses (or lacks). The representations may take various forms: oral promises to the buyer; display of a sample of the product; descriptions of the product in specifications, catalogs, and circulars; claims made in advertising; markings on the product itself; or written statements of guarantee.

Written guarantees can be especially helpful to the parties by making clear what otherwise is usually not well understood. When stated clearly, these written guarantees serve two basic, useful purposes:

1. They protect the buyer by spelling out the seller's obligations to the buyer.

2. They protect the seller by spelling out the limit of the seller's obligation.

The discussion which follows under the various "Warranty" headings deals with matters of money but not with human health and safety. For the latter, see Section 34 under Product Liability.

Warranty: Industrial Products.   Parties to a sale of industrial products are knowledgeable in contract relations and they tend to draft a purchase contract to embody their known needs and to cover contingencies experienced under previous contract arrangements. The resulting written contracts reflect mutual agreement on various pertinent matters including the warranty.

Warranties on industrial products are created uniquely for each product or type of product. For many commodity items, the warranty calls for compliance to specifications, and the warranty extends to survive "acceptance" of the item by the customer. Usually, no time period is specified. For other industrial products, the warranty often includes a time period and special provisions covering consequential damages. In some cases the warranty concept is extended to place predictable limits on users' costs. For example, a manufacturer of electrical generating equipment warrants to its industrial clients that the cost of power generated will be no higher than the cost of purchased power. If it is higher, the manufacturer agrees to pay the difference.

Warranty: Consumer Products.   In contrast to the tailor-made warranties which are written into large industrial contracts, warranties for consumer products are relatively standardized. Usually printed on good quality paper with an artwork border, these warranties look like, and are, legal certificates. A preamble is included stating the good intentions and care supplied by the manufacturer. Specific statements of the manufacturer's written responsibility then follow.

Consumer product warranties are either "full" or "limited." The term "full warranty" refers to the consumer's rights, not to the portion of the physical product that is covered by the warranty; i.e., it does not have to cover the entire product. A full warranty means:

1. The manufacturer will fix or replace any defective product free of charge.

2. The warranty is not limited in time.

3. The warranty does not exclude or limit payment for consequential damages (see below).

4. If the manufacturer has been unable to make an adequate repair, the consumer may choose between a refund and a replacement.

5. The manufacturer cannot impose unreasonable duties on the consumer. For example, the warranty cannot require the consumer to ship a piano to the factory (one manufacturer listed such a condition).

6. The manufacturer is not responsible if the damage to the product was caused by unreasonable use.

The full warranty also provides that not only the original purchaser but any subsequent owners of the product during the warranty period are entitled to make claims.

A limited warranty is a warranty that does not meet the requirements for a full warranty. Typically, the limited warranty may exclude labor costs, may require the purchaser to pay for transportation charges, and may also be limited to the original purchaser of the product. As a practical matter, most warranties on consumer products are limited warranties and must be so labeled.

Duration of Warranty.   This is always spelled out and may be nonuniform as to different features of the product. For example, a 1-year warranty on a product may include a 5-year warranty on certain components, while holding the warranty on finish to 30 days. Here is an actual wording:

> *During the first year* after purchase we provide home service (parts and labor) to repair any defect except surface finishes, which are guaranteed for thirty days. *During the second year* we provide replacement parts; labor is extra. *During the third, fourth, and fifth years* we provide replacement parts to repair the washer transmission; labor is extra.

A short warranty period has a subtle disadvantage for the manufacturer. Important field intelligence on the frequency and type of problems after the warranty period is not routinely collected.

Sometimes the manufacturer extends the original warranty. In one example, a heat pump experienced field failures after the warranty period. A government agency concluded that at the time of sale, the pumps had a defect resulting in the field problems. The agency obtained a "restitution for defects" by having the manufacturer agree to extend the warranty period and pay for the repairs. In another example, an automobile manufacturer extended the car warranty to cover rust problems but allegedly provided the coverage only to favored customers. A consumer group then accused the manufacturer of having a "secret" warranty program.

An example of a lengthy warranty is the 10-year warranty on homes. Originally started in Great Britain, the system was set up in the United States by the National Association of Home Builders. It is a voluntary program for builders and provides for the builder to pay for claims during the early portion of the warranty. Claims made during the remainder of the 10-year period are covered by an insurance policy paid for by the builder. The state of New Jersey has a requirement for a 10-year warranty. A few warranties have an unlimited duration. Examples include hand tools, pens, and the stainless steel tub in an automatic washing machine.

Disclaimers.   Warranties also list various conditions under which the warranty is *not* to apply, e.g., use of a home laundry machine for commercial duty, or service by unauthorized personnel. There may be specific disclaimers on incidental damage, e.g., food spoiled during nonoperation of a freezer. Some disclaimers are probably of no legal effect; they are usually ruled by the courts to be contrary to public policy. Other disclaimers are probably unnecessary because they only restate the manufacturers' legal rights. However, some manufacturers use these disclaimers to discourage lawsuits or related actions.

Consumer Reactions to Warranty Provisions.   Some consumers are not satisfied with warranties, and the dissatisfaction takes several forms:

1. The warranty provisions are too complicated.
2. The length of the warranty period is too short. A typical warranty on a consumer appliance provides 1 year of free parts and labor although such appliances have an expected life of 10 years or longer. Thus the consumer usually pays more for repairs than does the manufacturer. Some research on washing machines shows that the consumer's cost for repairs is 2 to 7 times greater than that of the manufacturer's (Gryna, 1971).
3. Inadequate repairs are made during the warranty period and later.

Consequential Damage.   Users' costs associated with product failures can go well beyond the cost of parts and service labor. Additional costs can include:

Productivity losses (e.g., idle direct labor)

Extra capacity maintained because of expected failures (e.g., equipment, labor)

Damages caused by a failed item (e.g., injuries to personnel, damage to other items)

Lost income (e.g., profit on lost production, penalties due to missed schedules)

Although they can be quite substantial, consequential damage costs are seldom as well tracked as warranty period costs. (For a discussion and application of these additional costs, see Gryna, 1972 and 1977.)

Consequential, pyramiding costs are normally not implied in the warranties and are borne by the seller only if the contract says so. Some sellers try to protect themselves further by writing a disclaimer into the warranty.

There *are* instances in which contracts will specifically provide payment for consequential damage. For example, if hard castings cause tool breakage and shutdown of an automatic transfer line, the foundry pays for the broken tools and the downtime. If breaks in paper rolls require a new setup on rotary printing presses, the paper company pays for the downtime. If breaks in beams of yarn cause downtime on textile machinery, the yarn maker pays for the downtime.

Generally disclaimers in matters of injury to human beings are held by the courts to be contrary to public policy, and hence are not enforced. However, disclaimers on consequential money damages not involving human safety are generally upheld.

The service industry provides an unusual example of redress given consumers. For long-time customers who are members of a special club, a major hotel chain guarantees reservations made for a room. If the hotel is unable to honor the reservation, the hotel:

1. Finds a nearby hotel room for the guest and pays for the room
2. Gives free additional nights at any one of its hotels in the future
3. Gives the consumer $200 as a form of atonement for the inconvenience caused

GOVERNMENT REGULATION OF WARRANTIES

The Magnuson-Moss Warranty Act of 1974 was created to provide minimum warranty protection for consumer products. As originally written, it applied to consumer products which cost more than $5.00. But in implementing the act, the Federal Trade Commission adopted regulations covering only those products that cost more than $15.00.

Under the act, the warranty must be available to the consumer in written form before the sale and must contain the following information:

1. The persons who are entitled to make use of the warranty. It must be clear whether the warranty applies only to the original customer or to any subsequent owners of the product during the period of the warranty.
2. A description of the products covered by the warranty and of any product excluded from the warranty.
3. A statement detailing the items or services that will be paid for if the product does not meet the warranty.
4. The duration of the warranty and the time that the warranty begins.
5. An explanation of how to obtain warranty service and information about the handling of disputes.
6. Limitations on the duration of the warranties and any exclusions such as consequential damages.
7. A statement that the consumer has rights both under the warranty and additional rights that may vary from state to state.
8. A statement declaring the warranty to be full or limited.

The act provides basic guidelines to be implemented by the Federal Trade Commission. (For futher discussion, see Lusk et al., 1982, pp. 1063–1065.)

BUSINESS OPPORTUNITIES THROUGH WARRANTIES

Because the warranty period covers only a portion of the product life, users must contend with any service needs that arise during the remainder of the item's life. Recognizing this as a business opportunity, manufacturers are responding in several ways:

Product Redesign.   If the manufacturer can create a design with few problems for the user throughout the complete product life, a competitive advantage will be gained. Though the product may have a higher initial cost, there are customers who are willing to pay the price to obtain higher reliability. Some manufacturers of both consumer and industrial products have clearly aimed at this market segment and have created a market penetration with a premium-priced product. Ironically, the warranty period maintained is the same as that of competitors with lower-priced products. Some dealers do, however, extend the duration of the warranty because the product is relatively failure-free.

Competition in Warranties.   With such products as automobiles and appliances, the warranty can serve as a competitive tool. The competition usually centers around the duration of the warranty period and the extent of coverage (e.g., parts only, or parts and labor).

Extended Warranties. For some products, the customer is offered, at extra cost, an extended warranty which covers the cost of repairs after the conventional warranty period. This is similar to a service contract. But there is a legal distinction between warranties and service contracts. A warranty is provided by the manufacturer at the time of purchase at no cost beyond the purchase price. A service contract is provided either by the original manufacturer or by some other party, at any time during the life of the product but a fee is charged for this. Extended warranties and service contracts can be a source of income for the organization offering them. The value of these contracts from the viewpoint of the customer varies with the amount and kind of use. For some customers, those who encounter frequent repairs due to heavy use, the agreements are a worthwhile investment. However, studies made on appliances and automobiles have concluded that the cost of the agreement is often larger than the probable cost of repairs. (See "Are Repair Contracts Worth It?" 1981; and "The Trouble with Auto Warranties," 1979.) An extended warranty or service contract is really a form of insurance. For some customers it is worth the cost; for others, it is not.

Reliability Improvement Warranties. In a reliability improvement warranty, the manufacturer agrees to perform repair services on products at a previously established price for a stated period of time. The objectives are threefold:

1. Minimize the total life cycle cost for the customer.
2. Provide an incentive for the manufacturer to initially build in high reliability and to improve the reliability over time.
3. Encourage cooperation between the manufacturer and the customer to improve reliability.

A summary of some of the benefits and risks is given in Table 19.1.
From the manufacturer's point of view, a reliability improvement warranty

TABLE 19.1 Benefits and Risks of Reliability Improvement Warranties

Benefits	
Manufacturer	Customer
Potential source of profits	Potential source of cost savings
Improve sales of future products	Can foster reliability improvements at no cost to customer
Obtain field reliability data and intelligence on reliability problems and needs	Provides assurance of specified level of reliability in field
Fosters cooperation with customer	Fosters cooperation with manufacturer
Risks	
Difficulties of estimating future repair costs (number of failures, inflation, etc.)	Total cost may be higher than with conventional contracting
Product may encounter unexpected environments, misuse, etc.	Dependence on manufacturer for support of product
May result in reduction in income from spare parts	Seller may optimize design to meet seller's needs

provides an additional opportunity for profit. The manufacturer proposes a fixed price for the repair services based on an estimate of the number of repairs and unit repair costs. The manufacturer agrees to make all repairs for the period of the contract but receives the fixed price regardless of the actual number of repairs. Types of repairs for which the manufacturer is responsible are defined in the contract. Thus, if the actual number of repairs is less than that predicted, the manufacturer makes an additional profit; if the number of repairs is more than that predicted, the manufacturer does not gain the extra profit and may incur a loss. Under the concept, the manufacturer can propose changes to improve product reliability on a "no-cost" basis to the customer. Such changes, if approved and implemented, benefit the customer in terms of higher reliability and benefit the manufacturer in the form of lower repair costs. As the manufacturer performs the repairs, important field intelligence is collected about product failures for use with both the present and future products. All such proposals, of course, must compete against those from other manufacturers.

From the customer's point of view, the incentive given to the manufacturer to improve reliability tends to assure a higher level of reliability. Part of the contract can also contain a requirement on mean time between failures. If the requirement is not met, the manufacturer must provide sufficient spare parts to the customer to meet the mean time between failures. Thus, the customer has assurance that a specified mean time between failures will be met. (For a discussion from the viewpoint of the buyer, see Markowitz, 1975; the seller viewpoints are presented by Rosenthal, 1975.)

Experience with such contracts indicates that they are applicable only in certain situations. Some formal application criteria have been developed (see Balaban, 1978).

The overall results of reliability improvement contracting are encouraging and may provide a means of going further into life cycle costing.

LABELING

The term "labeling" refers to actions taken by manufacturers, or merchants, to provide users with information about the product. An early example goes back to about 1400 B.C. Inscriptions on wine jars included the year of pressing, the geographical area, the owner of the vineyard, and the chief vintner. Of 22 inscribed jars, one included the phrase "wine of good quality" ("The Pharaoh's Wine Cellar," 1978). As labeling has evolved it has taken multiple, overlapping forms.

Product Labeling. This refers to information about the inherent nature of the product, e.g., the net weight of the package contents, the ingredients used, instructions for operation and maintenance, and warnings of danger. The information is often placed on a small tag or label, hence the term "labeling," However, the information may also be placed directly on the product, the wrapper, the container, an accompanying circular, or a manual, etc.

For most products, the extent of product labeling is determined by the manufacturer. In consequence, the "labels" (meaning any of the means to convey the information) are a mixture of product information and advertising. However, there are statutes on the books requiring that the product actually conform to the label. Generally there is good adherence to these statutes as applied to the intrinsic properties of the product. Proper labeling is essential in connection with minimizing product liability risks. (See "Lucid Labeling Lessens Liability," 1978.)

For some products, certain labeling is required by law. For example, all food packages are required by law to state the net contents and the list of ingredients. All poisonous products are required by law to be so labeled.

The Fair Packaging and Labeling Act (administered by the Federal Trade Commission) includes general provisions as to the identity of the product, identity of manufacturer (or distributor), quantity of the contents, terminology, etc. In addition, there are provisions specific to certain products. Still other provisions relate to pricing practices and promotions (Federal Trade Commission). A recent addition to the labels of many grocery products is the "bar code." Each prepackaged item for sale is coded with a set of vertical lines that represent numbers or letters. When the checkout clerk passes a wand across the code, both the price and quantity of the product are automatically entered into the cash register. This simplifies checkout procedures, reduces pricing errors, and simplifies inventory control. The bar coding concept seems destined to be extended to many kinds of products (see "Bar Codes in Industry," 1983).

On occasion, the material included on labels leads to disputes. For example, a label described a new product as "potato chips." Competing manufacturers objected. They felt that the product did not conform to the dictionary definition of a potato chip, i.e., a thin slice of raw potato, fried crisp and then salted. Instead the new "potato chip" was first dehydrated, then turned into a mush, and finally pressed and fried. A regulatory agency ruled that the manufacturer's new product could be referred to as potato chips. Subsequently, competitors came out with similar products and even packaged them in a look-alike container. ("Pringle's vs. the Real Thing," 1975.)

Product Grading. A second form of product information is *grade* or quality of design. For manufactured products, the grade designations are based on various contrasting intrinsic qualities, which are usually measurable. When individual units of product involve substantial prices, the grade distinctions are often made in the form of model names or numbers to simplify user recognition. When the units of the product are low in price, the grading may be done in broad classes. For example, one large merchant company uses three grade designations (good, better, best) to designate differences in quality for the same functional use.

Some grade designations have led to controversies. All automobile tires sold in the United States were required, by government regulation, to have grades assigned in three performance areas—traction, heat resistance, and tread life. The grades were intended to help consumers to compare types and brands of tires. Disputes developed about the validity of the three areas as measures of performance, and it was decided to delete the grading on tread life. (For discussion, see "U.S. Punctures Tire Grading," 1983, and Endres, 1979.) The disputes occurred not only between the regulators and manufacturers but among the manufacturers themselves.

Brand Labeling. Many companies try to build a quality reputation around a distinctive name or brand. Efforts are exerted to assure that products sold under this brand name are of sufficient quality to earn a good reputation. Use of advertising is made to promote both familiarity and confidence in the brand name. The concept dates back to Rōman pottery manufacturers in 35 B.C., and the process, application of a brand name to products, is known as brand labeling. Varied forms of such labeling are in use.

Manufacturer's Brands. Many manufacturers market their products under their own name, which then also becomes the brand name. Other companies market the products under noncompany names (e.g., Maxwell House Coffee marketed by General Foods Corporation) or under fanciful names chosen to arrest public attention and cling to memory. In any case, the product advertising and promotion is built around the brand name.

Manufacturers protect the integrity of their branded products through conventional systems of quality controls, as described throughout this handbook.

In some cases, use of the manufacturer's brand is complicated because of intermediate manufacturers. For example, the major chemical companies have created certain materials, e.g., synthetic fibers, with special properties useful to consumers. These materials are given brand names, and these brands are propagandized by advertising aimed at consumers, including guarantees which the chemical companies make *direct to these consumers.* However, the chemical companies sell these materials not to consumers, but to the first links in the chain of yarn makers, cloth weavers, fabricators of end products (e.g., garments, blankets, carpets), retailers, and consumers. (The same applies to some industrial products, e.g., polypropylene pipe.) Hence the chemical companies conduct these sales under a license arrangement which requires that the subsequent fabricators adhere to certain essential quality standards. The terms of the license permit the chemical companies to establish controls which will safeguard the brand names.

Brand names may be so valuable that they invite the production of counterfeit merchandise. Here a manufacturer produces an item, illegally attaches a label with a brand name of another manufacturer, then sells the product for the brand-name price. Examples have been reported on consumer goods such as clothing, luggage, and beverages (see "A Crackdown on Fake Brand Name Products," 1978). If a brand name commands great respect in the marketplace, competitors may choose a similar name. Again there are disputes (see "Corporate Shoot-Outs over Brand Names," 1978). For example, a manufacturer of beer created a product that was lower in calories than the standard beer. The brand name chosen was "Lite." Because "Lite" was a success, competitors introduced similar products and included the words "light beer" on the label. A suit against the competitors for use of the term "light" was filed by the manufacturer of "Lite." The courts ruled that the competitors were allowed to describe their beer as "light beer." Even though the word was spelled differently, the manufacturer of "Lite" would not be given a trademark on a commonly used word. Other commonly used words, "aspirin" and "cellophane," for example, were originally regarded as brand names but have become part of the language and can be used by all manufacturers.

A recent development is the concept of "generic" products. Here merchants contract with the manufacturer to produce merchandise without a brand name. It is claimed that these products provide equivalent quality at a lower price than the branded products because the generic products do not incur such costs as product development, advertising, and promotion. The concept has been widely applied to consumer goods such as foods.

Merchants' Brands.   Merchants sell products both under manufacturers' brands and under their own brands. In the latter case, the merchant's source of supply is either a captive (owned) manufacturing source or a product bought from an independent manufacturer, who agrees to apply the merchant's brand to the product. Such products are known as "private label." Often these products are bought under functional specifications, leaving it to the manufacturer to prepare the detailed design.

Large merchants who market extensively under their private label make use of the tools of quality control to protect their label. Qualification testing of new designs is extensively used, as is supplier surveillance. Regular inspection for lot acceptance is highly selective, depending on the nature of the product and the record of the supplier. In addition, effort is exerted to use information on product failures and on user dissatisfaction to take remedial steps, both as to product and supplier.

Franchise and Chain Brands. Some large manufacturing and service organizations operate on a basis of a "chain" of numerous local markets, plants, restaurants, motels, etc. Some of these local units may be owned by the chain; others may be franchised under an agreement which permits them to use the brand name. The use of this brand name greatly aids the marketing efforts of the local unit.

In such chain operations the company regulations or the franchise agreements spell out the criteria under which the brand name may be used. In addition, there is provision for inspection and surveillance by a designated laboratory. This laboratory may be a corporate quality control service or even a subsidiary.

Industry Association Brands. These are the creations of industry associations. Under the concept, a number of manufacturers collectively agree on a brand which includes minimum product quality standards. The brand is then promoted by the association to achieve public knowledge and acceptance. Manufacturers who meet the standards may then use the brand and gain the marketing value it provides.

The product known as Harris Tweed is defined as "made from 100 percent pure virgin wool produced in Scotland, spun, dyed, and finished in the Outer Hebrides, and handwoven by the islanders at their own home" (Thomas, 1966). Inspection is by the Harris Tweed Association, which authorizes use of the brand.

Once more there are cases of disputes. For centuries, natives working in limestone caves in the town of Roquefort, France, have produced a cheese, and the townspeople have formed a trade group called the "Community of Roquefort." A cheese made in Italy and Hungary was marketed as "imported Roquefort cheese" in 1966 in the United States. The people from Roquefort, France, appealed to the American courts, claiming that the use of the term "Roquefort" should be restricted to cheese made in that region. The courts agreed. The judge concluded that the cheese in France was made in accordance with "ingredients, technology, and environment that no region could duplicate. Geography is one of those ingredients" ("Corporate Shoot-Outs over Brand Names," 1978).

Certification Labeling. "Certification" as used here is a form of product assurance centered around a formal document or certificate. The certificate always represents the product as either conforming to specification or as fit for use. It may or may not include test data, and it may be issued either by the manufacturer or by a separate testing service. For a detailed discussion of these differences, see Section 15 under Certification. Certification is not to be confused with conventional testing services by independent laboratories. Such laboratories provide test services to a company under a variety of conditions: The company lacks a certain instrument; the company's laboratory is momentarily overloaded; the company wants to conduct a check on its own accuracy.

In those cases where a manufacturer is "licensed" to apply an independent mark (by a government regulator or by an independent laboratory), the application of the mark is likewise a form of certification, the mark being a shorthand form of certificate; e.g., the "UL" mark for Underwriters' Laboratories, Inc., or the "©" which is the shorthand statement of "copyrighted."

It should be noted than an independent laboratory which certifies products as fit for use (or as conforming to standard) assumes some legal responsibilities. A user who relies on such certification and is damaged has the right to proceed against the independent laboratory as well as against some of the other parties directly involved.

THE MERCHANT AND QUALITY

Quality Activities.   The giant merchant companies are extensively involved in all aspects of product quality. They have technical departments to establish specifications and to conduct product qualification tests. Their central purchasing departments carry out supplier selection and qualification. Their quality control departments carry out supplier surveillance and incoming inspection as required by the merchandise managers. (For a discussion of one program, see Koch, 1974.)

The small merchant (retailer) lacks technical or quality control departments. However, he or she carries out some activities which do influence quality: unpacking, handling, display, repacking, transportation. These activities afford some opportunities to find defective product, and, even more, to create new quality problems due to product damage, confusion in identity, and misplacement of components. Storage is a further source of risk, e.g., proper stock rotation (perishable products) or proper environment (temperature of frozen foods).

Much can be done by manufacturers to minimize these risks through product design or systems redesign. As to the residue of risk, the manufacturer can provide clear information on how to care for the product, establish standards to be observed, and offer assistance in training the merchant's personnel.

In addition, manufacturers are well advised to institute audits to determine how well the merchant chain conforms to standards in matters of product quality. These audits can provide a vital input to manufacturers in their efforts to attain fitness for use. At the retail store level, the large merchant also carries out these activities. See also, in this connection, the related discussions in Section 20 on merchant roles in product repairs and the handling of complaints.

REFERENCES

"A Crackdown on Fake Brand Name Products" (1978). *Business Week,* Oct. 23, pp. 53–54.

"America's Search for Quality" (1983). Whirlpool Corporation, Benton Harbor, MI.

"Are Repair Contracts Worth It?" (1981). *New York Times,* Dec. 26, p. 28.

Balaban, Harold S. (1978). "Reliability Improvement by Profit Incentive." *Quality,* November, pp. 22–28.

"Bar Codes in Industry" (1983). *Quality,* October, pp. 14–15.

"Corporate Shoot-Outs over Brand Names" (1978). *New York Times,* Jan. 22, p. 2.

Endres, David A. (1979). "Whatever Became of Performance and Safety Labeling?" *Quality Progress,* November, pp. 34–37.

Fuss, Normam H., Jr. (1973). "Pull through Marketing for Industrial Marketers." *Management Review,* April, pp. 9–18.

Gryna, Frank M. (1971). "Three Creators of Consumer Quality Problems." *ASQC Technical Conference Transactions,* Milwaukee, pp. 303–308.

Gryna, Frank M. (1977). "Quality Costs: User vs Manufacturer." *Quality Progress,* June, pp. 10–13.

Gryna, Frank M. (1972). "User Quality Costs." *Quality Progress,* November, pp. 18–21.

Juran, J. M. (1970). "Consumerism and Product Quality." *Quality Progress,* July, pp. 18–27.

Klompmaker, Jay E., Hughes, G. David, and Haley, Russell I. (1976). "Test Marketing in New Product Development." *Harvard Business Review,* May–June, pp. 128–138.

Koch, Richard A. (1974). "Consumer Product Reliability—The Role of the Retailer." *Proceedings, Annual Reliability and Maintainability Symposium.* IEEE, New York, pp. 27–29.

Lusk, Harold F., Hewitt, Charles M., Donnell, John D., and Barnes, A. James (1982). *Business Law and the Regulatory Environment: Concepts and Cases.* Richard D. Irwin, Homewood, IL.

"Lucid Labeling Lessens Liability" (1978). *Quality,* February, pp. 18–20.

Markowitz, Oscar (1975). "Failure Free Warranty/Reliability Improvement Warranty, Buyer Viewpoints." *ASQC Technical Conference Transactions,* Milwaukee, pp. 18–97.

"Pharaoh's Wine Cellar, The" (1978). *Scientific American,* March, p. 74.

"Pringle's vs the Real Thing" (1975). *New York Times,* November 30, pp. 8, 9.

Rosenthal, Sanford T. (1975). "Failure Free Warranty/Reliability Improvement Warranty—Seller Viewpoints." *ASQC Technical Conference Transactions,* Milwaukee, pp. 80–86.

Rotfeld, Herbert J. and Rotzoll, Kim B. (1976). "Advertising and Product Quality: Are Heavily Advertised Products Better?" *Journal of Consumer Affairs,* Summer, pp. 33–47.

Schutz, Howard G. and Casey, Marianne (1981). "Consumer Perceptions of Advertising as Misleading." *Journal of Consumer Affairs,* Winter, pp. 340–357.

"Should an Ad Identify Brand X?" (1979). *Media and Advertising,* Sept. 24, pp. 156–161.

Taylor, Ervin F. (1981). "Product Quality and the Media," *ASQC Quality Congress Transactions,* Milwaukee, pp. 825–830.

Thomas, Veronica (1966). "The Wizard of Plockropool." *Atlantic Monthly,* July, pp. 124–126.

"Trouble with Auto Warranties, The" (1979). *Consumer Reports,* October, pp. 598–601.

"US Punctures Tire Grading" (1983). *Consumer Reports,* April, p. 166.

van Leer, R. Karl (1976). "Industrial Marketing with a Flair." *Harvard Business Review,* November–December, pp. 117–124.

Wilkie, William L. and Farris, Paul W. (1975). "Comparison Advertising: Problems and Potential." *Journal of Marketing,* vol. 39, October, pp. 7–15.

Wood, Buddy B. (1982). "Development of the Reliability Program for the Advanced Medium Range Air to Air Missile (AMRAAM)." *Proceedings, Annual Reliability and Maintainability Symposium.* IEEE, New York, pp. 510–514.

SECTION 20
CUSTOMER SERVICE[1]

Frank M. Gryna

---

[1]In the Third Edition, the section on Field Performance was prepared by J. M. Juran and Robert W. Peach.

INTRODUCTION

This step on the Spiral for attaining quality concerns activities after a sale is made. Discussions in several other sections of this handbook are closely related. Section 3 discusses the broad aspects of quality and sales income; Section 5 discusses some policy issues concerning customer service; Section 9 identifies some areas of audit; Section 12 covers the marketing research needed to gather field intelligence on user needs; Section 19 examines the quality issues in marketing to achieve a sale.

The act of final product acceptance may be regarded as terminating the manufacturing phase. Following this act, and before customer use of the product, a number of preuse phases take place: packing, shipping, receiving, and storage. Finally, there are the use phases: installation, checkout, operation, and maintenance.

As product complexity grows, the extent of field problems increases. Field factors cause 20 to 30 percent of problems concerning fitness for use on long life products of moderate to high complexity.

Those who do quality planning for service activities can learn much from the experience of formalizing quality planning in design and manufacturing. Those who perform service activities that affect quality often believe that their current activities are sufficient to provide a quality service. In cases where service is in fact deficient, there is often need to revise the service plan as it relates to the topics discussed below. Such planning must show, explicitly, what to do differently. Generalities are unacceptable.

The degree of excellence provided in customer service clearly affects the buyer's choice on the next purchasing decision. To maintain satisfied customers, sellers must achieve a constructive relationship with buyers. Levitt (1983) offers suggestions on how sellers can maintain a useful interaction with buyers throughout the service phase of the product life cycle.

PACKAGING, TRANSPORT, AND STORAGE

One major department store found that more customer complaints were caused by store activities in packaging, storage, and delivering the product than were caused by the original manufacturing.

All products are subject to deterioration in quality due to damage during the activities following manufacture, inspection, and test. Some of the deterioration is due to inherent instability, e.g., progressive biological activity, evaporation of solvents, crystallization of metals. Control of the environment can accelerate or retard the effects of such instability. Proper quality planning and control can go far to minimize damage and ensure that the product conforms closely to that which left the factory test station.

The Sequence of Activities for Packaging. Packaging requires a sequence of activities similar to those used to achieve fitness for use for the product itself. These activities include package design and the purchasing, manufacturing, and testing of packaging materials.

Package Design. Designing the package and the product simultaneously is the ideal approach. Sometimes a minor alteration in product design can strengthen the product and thereby eliminate the need for extensive packaging materials.

This simultaneous approach requires that packaging design start during the product design stage rather than after manufacture begins. If little or no product information is available to the packaging engineer, the result may be a package that either underprotects or overprotects the product. Design of packaging calls for laboratory testing (e.g., impact, vibration, compression, and drop tests) and field testing of materials.

Especially for products that undergo numerous or critical handlings, it becomes important to look at handling and packaging from a systems viewpoint as opposed to numerous department viewpoints. The extent of handling during production, packaging, and transportation can be surprising. In one survey reported by Amrine (1975) handling costs were 22 percent of manufacturing costs. Some estimates run as high as 60 to 80 percent. A system review can identify opportunities to improve the overall handling by methods such as:

1. Modifying supplier packaging. Some electronic components are blister-packaged in a way that allows testing without unpacking.
2. Starting unitized and other containerization at early operations or even at the supplier's location. For example, the drug industry has evolved unitized packaging of dosages in which the identity of the dose (and even its own environment) are designed into the unit package and carry through to the patient.
3. Designing racks, trays, bins, tote boxes, etc., to provide optimal service to all companies and departments involved rather than to require added handling and repacking for some.

The systems concept includes the adaptation of the product and the package to each other. Fiedler (1978) described how a company that analyzed the interaction of their cartons (products) and cases (packages) determined the combined maximum compression resistance. The analysis led to a design that saved $50,000 annually in materials while increasing the compression resistance of the product/package system.

Purchasing, Manufacturing, and Testing of Packaging Materials. The techniques described in other sections of this handbook for manufacturing and test of the product apply equally to the packaging material. In many cases, the packaging material is obtained for a supplier, and thus the elements of a supplier quality program are applicable.

1. Suppliers are asked to submit samples of product which is intended to meet the design requirements.
2. The samples are tested and evaluated against requirements. If necessary, the production capabilities of the supplier are evaluated through the use of supplier surveys.
3. Contracts are awarded to suppliers. (Sometimes packaging costs more than the product itself.)
4. Initial production samples are obtained from the suppliers and evaluated.
5. Means are set up for periodically monitoring the quality of product received from suppliers.

The variety of packaging has grown to such an extent as to stimulate attempts at standardization (see Canut, 1975).

Transportation.   Handling and transport introduce many perils to the product. Some are fully predictable: climatic temperature, humidity, vibration, and shock. Others are the result of ignorance, carelessness, blunder, and even sabotage. For some of these perils the product is in greater danger from handling and transport than from use. Fiedler (1978) recommends a seven-step program for protecting a product during transportation:

1. Define the packaging objectives.
2. Determine the method of shipment. Most manufacturers' products are handled by just a few modes of shipment. The packaging engineer can examine the vital few modes and determine the typical environmental hazards. For example, in truck shipment the hazards include loading, moving, and storing pallets, movement of the truck, and mechanical or manual handling when the load is broken into smaller quantities.
3. Conduct tests to learn how the product will react to the transportation hazards. Tests can be run to simulate shock, vibration, and other transport damage. (The stresses are measured in terms of cycles per second, "g levels" of deceleration, pulse shapes, and still other quantified measures.) The experience gained finds its way into specifications for packaging and vehicle loading.
4. Analyze the test data to decide if the product can withstand the predicted environmental hazards.
5. Decide on a course of action. Choose a packaging material or some other course of action (e.g., modify the product or change the distribution methods).
6. Select a packaging material.
7. Combine the package with the product, and together subject them to final testing. This can be done by trial shipment or simulated laboratory testing.

Damage claims on products amount to about $4 billion per year (Fiedler, 1978). Methods of prevention are clearly justified.

Storage.   Immense quantities of raw materials, components, and finished products are constantly in storage, awaiting further processing, sale, or use. To minimize deterioration and degradation, actions can be taken beyond those discussed above.

1. Establish the "shelf life" of the product based on laboratory and field data.
2. Establish standards to place limits on time in storage.
3. Date the product conspicuously to make it easy to identify the age of the product in stock.
4. Design the package and control the environment to minimize expected and unexpected degradation.

A common weakness in these programs is the failure to "date" the product conspicuously. Sometimes this failure is due to technical reasons or marketing decisions. These reasons are obsolete. Conspicuous dating on outer cartons as well as on unit packages aid in traceability as well as in stock rotation and in establishing the ages of inventories.

Where product is deliberately stockpiled for use at some unknown time, special controls are needed, notably periodic reevaluations of actual quality of the stored products. The effects of long-term storage on system reliability can become a serious matter. In one study (based on over one million hours of storage data), the expected failure rates of four classes of complex systems were determined for a 5-year period. In two of the four systems, less than 20 percent of the product was expected to be available for operation after 5 years of storage (see Cherkasky,

1970). The major factors that affected the nonoperating failure rate were the parts count, parts class, parts screening, temperature stress, parts application, mechanical stress during fabrication, humidity effects, electrical stress, variation of operating environment, check-out capability, nature of duty cycle, time between check-outs, built-in test equipment, reliability scoring, and radiation effects.

Provision for Audit. The manufacturer whose brand name is identified with the product is inevitably regarded by the user as responsible for any failures, no matter how caused. Consequently, such manufacturers are faced with the need for auditing specification conformance in packaging, transport, and storage.

The general approach to auditing is set out in Section 9 under Planning and Performing Audits. Application of this general approach to the operations of packaging, transport, and storage runs into some special problems, especially with the activities conducted by independent carriers and merchants. Common interest in reducing claims and improving customer relations is usually adequate to assure good collaboration.

INSTALLATION

Before the packaged product is put into use, it undergoes additional processing during distribution, assembly, installation and checkout, etc. These operations are as much a part of the product's progression as are design or manufacture. Thus, they demand corresponding controls.

Processing during Distribution. The distribution process carries out operations such as breaking bulk, readjusting, adding reagents, touching up finishes, repackaging, etc. Errors can be made in any of these activities, and thus planning should be embodied in specifications with provisions for an independent audit. Some of the causes of errors are "unusual," e.g., international problems of language or culture; small retailers lacking in technological skills. For such cases the need is for a systems redesign which eliminates the necessity for technological skills or even for the operations. These problems can be at their worst when the operations are to be performed by the ultimate user. (See below, under Installation by User.) Serious errors can also occur in the filling of orders.

On-Site Installation by Specialists. This is the assembly setup which is conducted at the user's premises to put the product in a state of readiness to operate plus installation "in place" at the site. Some products such as an elevator involve a complex erection; products such as a word processor may require special hookups with utilities; a simple consumer product may only need plugging in to an outlet.

On-site installation may require:

1. Special facilities to house the product (plus its auxiliary equipment), including means for controlling the environment.
2. Special tools and instruments. All too often these are not as completely engineered as are the corresponding facilities in the factory.
3. Special instructions. These are increasingly needed for complex products. The opportunities for errors and omissions are now so numerous that the instructions are needed for errorproofing as well as for information. There is still need

for reliance on skilled installers to carry out these instructions and to meet those job problems which differ from one user location to another.

Installation by User.   Often products are installed by users—either a consumer or an employee of the client. Even with clear, well-illustrated instructions, there remain a distressing number of users who are seemingly unable to follow them. (A manufacturer of kitchen faucets provides an audio recording describing how the installation should be made.)

Richardson (1981) discusses some of the issues involved in designing for customer setup on computers and terminals:

1. The setup must be simple enough to be accomplished by inexperienced people without using *any* tools.
2. The instructions must be errorproof. Photographs and exploded drawings are superior to wordy descriptions.
3. The design and manufacturing of the product should be such to prevent connections from becoming loose during shipment.
4. Customer education and telephone hotlines should be provided.
5. Translation of written instructions into foreign languages must be verified to assure that the translation is clear.
6. Each step of the instructions should contain only one task and if possible provide positive feedback (e.g., an indicator light) upon successful completion of the task.
7. When the product is available with options, instructions become more complicated to write because they must address the different combinations of features possible. One approach may be to modularize the instructions.
8. Additional testing is needed to reduce susceptibility to shipping damage on customer setup products.

USE

Some field problems can be traced to improper operation of the product. LaSala and Siegel (1983) describe several studies made to quantify the extent and effect of human error on product reliability and maintainability. In one study, about 50 percent of the failures in major systems were due to human errors. The errors were sorted into five types: procedural, incorrect diagnosis, misinterpretation of communications, inadequate support of environment, and insufficient attention or caution.

As products become increasingly complex, the problem of human error during operation of the equipment becomes more critical to address.

Manufacturers have done much to prepare an operating manual or other instructions for proper use and maintenance. These manuals are rudimentary for simple products and grow to elaborate handbooks for complex products. An intermediate example is the "owners' manual" for owners of automobiles.

Of special importance are the safety warnings that must be included with many products. It is not sufficient to include these warnings in the operating instructions. They must be placed in a prominent location to assure that the user will see them. The warnings must take into account the problems of multiple languages including braille, and the messages on these notices should be user tested for complete understanding. Sometimes, changes in a product design can eliminate the safety hazard altogether. If this is not possible, the publication of the warning becomes critical.

While installation and use by specialists tends to become rather professional, use by consumers is characterized by much ignorance in several ways:

1. *Failure to allow sufficient time for training and learning the operation of new complex products:* The recent advances in word-processing equipment provide an example. The amazing capabilities of such equipment can only be realized when the personnel are thoroughly trained and given sufficient time to practice. The capabilities of the equipment have tended to overshadow the importance of learning time and practice.

2. *Failure to use available information:* For example, a vacuum cleaner rotary brush encounters an obstruction and stops rotating. The owner's manual states clearly what to do: remove the obstruction and reset the little red button. The user does not know this, because the owner's manual is lost, or it is simpler to have the unit serviced.

3. *Use under environments never contemplated:* For example, a householder finds an automobile door locked frozen on a subzero day. A portable hair drier is used to thaw out the lock. The drier fails because it was not designed to operate in subzero temperatures.

4. *Application of stresses never contemplated:* For example, a householder stands on a washing machine to paint the overhead ceiling.

5. *Failure to maintain:* Consumers are notoriously lax in following prescribed schedules for lubrication, cleaning, replacement of expendables, etc.

Of paramount importance is the need for the manufacturer to find out the actual use which takes place. As this knowledge becomes available—through field observation, complaint analysis, etc.—the manufacturer has a wide variety of options for improving use: consumer education, product redesign, systems redesign, etc.

In many cases, the prevention of human errors during use requires changes in the product design. In one study of a printing press (LaSala and Siegel, 1983), the distribution of operating problems was as follows:

Difficulty in extracting a component	71 percent
Difficulty in positioning a component	14 percent
Extended inspection	6 percent
Difficulty in grasping a component	5 percent
Adjusting/greasing	4 percent

An analysis concluded that most of the problems could have been anticipated and prevented during product design.

Interaction of the worker and the product is important. Factors involved can be the anatomical dimensions of the worker; placement on products of push buttons and switches; physical loads imposed on the worker by the product; monotony or other psychological effects of the product operation; environmental effects produced by the product, such as noise and vibration; and workplace design, such as lighting and space.

Collectively, such matters are called "ergonomics" and need to be considered during the product design (see Section 13 under Planning for Human Factors: Ergonomics).

As human performance always will be less than perfect, methodology has been developed to quantify it. Meister (1978) discusses various nethods.

Configuration Management. Configuration refers to the physical and functional characteristics of a product, including both hardware and software. Ideally, a complex product is thoroughly evaluated and changes are made during design and development so that the design (configuration) released to production is "frozen." In practice, additional changes are made after production has started. If there are many changes, and if most of them are to be made to units already in the field, the customer is confronted with a maze of questions:

1. Can or should all units in the field receive the change from an engineering point of view?
2. What are the maintenance problems involved in making the change in the field (personnel, facilities, time, etc.)?
3. How should changes in operating and maintenance instructions be made?
4. What should be done with spare parts that become obsolete by the change?
5. Will the change require any retraining of workers or other personnel?

The collection of activities needed to accomplish these changes is called configuration management. A program usually has three elements:

1. *Configuration identification:* This is the process of defining and identifying every element of the product, and is discussed in Section 13 under Configuration Identification.
2. *Configuration control:* This series of actions manages the design change from the time of the original proposal for change through the implementation of approved changes. This is also discussed in Section 13 under Configuration Control.
3. *Configuration accounting:* This is the process of recording the status of proposed changes and the implementation status of approved changes. From an engineering point of view, every change must be compatible with existing hardware. In deciding which units will receive the change, the "configuration" of each unit of hardware must be recorded and reviewed. As changes may continually be made, a large but necessary, formal accounting-type system is required. The major role of verifying that the changes have been made and documentation completed is usually performed by the Quality Department.

One important adjunct to configuration management is "product traceability." This is discussed later in this section under Product Recall.

FIELD SERVICE

Many field service activities are bound up with field quality performance. The activities include:

1. Operation of owned repair service centers and franchising of independent repair shops.
2. Administration of service contracts with users. (These contracts are discussed in Section 19 under Business Opportunities through Warranties.)

3. Training of merchants, maintenance and repair personnel, users, and others with respect to quality.

4. Technical assistance throughout all phases of customer relations.

The scorecard on adequacy of services for consumer products is not strong. In a survey sponsored by the Whirlpool Corporation (1983), 998 consumers were asked how satisfied they were with customer service in general. (The survey did not address itself to Whirlpool's service.) The responses showed that 18 percent reported being "just barely satisfied" or worse; 17 percent believed that service had deteriorated in recent years.

It is valuable to analyze the factors that influence customer perception of quality after the purchase of the product. Takeuchi and Quelch (1983) show these factors for three points in time: before the purchase, at the point of purchase, and after the purchase (see Table 20.1). Note that some of the service factors that are important after the purchase are dependent on the design of the product.

Repair Service Centers. Service shop performance in the United States has been severely criticized for several reasons: incompetent mechanics, lack of prompt response, high prices, and dishonesty. Manufacturers and merchants have, to a degree, responded to these criticisms by:

1. Increasing the use of owned repair shops versus independents.

2. Reducing the list of independent shops to whom they referred user complaints.

3. Extending the use of franchise agreements and imposing standards for adequacy of repair work.

4. Extending the use of audit, in franchised shops as well as in owned shops.

5. Improving the inherent effectiveness of the service shop through improved engineering and management: design of superior facilities, diagnostic instruments, and repair tools; establishment of good systems for maintaining inventories of spare parts; training of mechanics and other personnel, etc.

6. Providing guarantees on service work. For example, a major automobile manufacturer has advertised a lifetime guarantee on the repair service provided.

It is difficult to provide up-to-date, technically superior service and high productivity in the form of small, independent shops. A revolution may be required

TABLE 20.1   Factors Influencing Customer Perception of Quality*

Before purchase	At point of purchase	After purchase
Company's brand name and image	Performance specifications	Ease of installation and use
Previous experience	Comments of salespeople	Handling of repairs, claims, warranty
Opinions of friends	Warranty provisions	Spare parts availability
Store reputation	Service and repair policies	Service effectiveness
Published test results	Support programs	Reliability
Advertised price for performance	Quoted price for performance	Comparative performance

*Not necessarily in order of importance.
Source: Takeuchi and Quelch, 1983, p. 142.

to create chains of service shops. This would enable the local manager to do a superlative job by having the resources of the chain providing basic support. The situation resembles the progressive replacement of the corner grocery store with chain food stores. The Center for Policy Alternatives (1974) has conducted research on the productivity of providing service on consumer durable products such as television sets and refrigerators. Of the service agencies, 76 percent were one-person operations. One of the conclusions from the research was that it would be difficult to obtain a substantial improvement in productivity in these operations.

Maintenance.   Maintenance includes:

Scheduled inspections, tests, and overhauls

Scheduled servicing, e.g., cleaning, lubrication, replacement of consumables

Unscheduled servicing, i.e., diagnosis of failures, and repairs to remedy the failures.

Scheduled Inspection and Test.   These scheduled activities are planned by service and quality control specialists. The planned approach is similar to that discussed in Section 18, under Inspection Planning.

Scheduled Servicing.   This is also planned by specialists as to timetables and work to be performed. It includes replacement of components either on a planned basis or as dictated by the findings of the scheduled inspections. In addition, it includes cleaning, adjustment, lubrication, replacement of filters, etc. It may include a check-out of operation following the servicing.

An important development is the concept of "reliability centered mainte-nance," also called "on condition maintenance." This concept grew out of an analysis of engine maintenance made by commercial airlines and is described by Nowlan and Heap (1978). Four types of preventive maintenance tasks are identified:

On condition tasks: Inspect an item at specified intervals to find and correct potential failures.

Scheduled rework tasks: Rework an item before a specified age to reduce the likelihood of failure.

Scheduled discard tasks: Discard an item before a specified age to reduce the likelihood of failure.

Scheduled failure-finding tasks: Inspect a hidden function item at specified intervals to find an actual failure that was not evident to the operating crew.

Research was conducted on previous maintenance practices to establish pat-terns of operating age and reliability. Surprisingly, for 89 percent of the items there was no decrease in reliability with age and therefore reliability could not be improved by imposing an age limitation on the items. Such a finding was signif-icant because traditional maintenance concepts required that an item be replaced after it had accumulated x hours of operation.

This led to a new approach:

1. Identify those items whose failure is significant at the airplane level.

2. For each significant item, evaluate the consequences of a failure. Four types of consequences are identified: safety, economic (operational and nonopera-tional) and hidden failure. For each of these consequences, the appropriateness

of an on condition, rework, or discard maintenance task is considered. If none of these three tasks meets defined criteria for applicability and effectiveness and if a failed item would be evident, then the conclusion is that the item would not benefit from scheduled maintenance. If the item has a hidden function, and a failure would not be evident, then a scheduled failure-finding maintenance task must be performed.

3. When appropriate information or experience is not available, then a "default strategy" is employed. This strategy gives a conservative initial decision on maintenance that is revised as additional information becomes available.

The concept of "reliability centered maintenance" can result in significantly lower maintenance costs. One airline reported 66,000 maintenance hours on major structural inspections on a plane before establishing an initial inspection interval of 20,000 h. Traditional maintenance policies on a smaller and less complex plane required 54 million maintenance hours before the same interval (Nowlan, 1980).

An extensive form of scheduled servicing is the "overhaul," which requires removing the unit from service while major scheduled servicing is performed (or scheduling the overhaul during some shutdown). As products have become more complex, the overhaul of a product comes closer to requiring the same kinds of manufacturing skills and controls as were present in the original manufacture of the product. Some manufacturers provide technical assistance to dealers to develop quality programs for repairs and overhaul services. One such program (Caterpillar Tractor Factory, 1978) identifies the following areas that must be explicitly planned for by the dealer:

1. Identification of critical rebuild operations

2. Inspection and approval of these operations

3. Formal specifications for critical rebuild operations

4. Tools and gauges for accurate measurement

5. Systems for identifying the responsibility of service persons and recording their performance during critical repair procedures

6. Calibration schedules to ensure the accuracy of tools and gauges

7. Reporting systems to provide dealer management with progress reports on service quality levels

One agency that was responsible for reconditioning electronic gear encountered a basic issue: Should the reconditioning be done to the original product specifications? For many applications, the original specifications were unnecessarily strict. Making judgments in matters like this requires knowledge of the costs involved and the fitness-for-use needs.

Unscheduled Servicing. This category includes diagnosis and repair of the numerous failures which put users out of service and for which they demand prompt restoration.

For simple products, a product malfunction can often be corrected by replacing the defective unit. As products become more complex, the process of finding and correcting becomes more difficult. The usual steps are shown in Figure 20.1 (Juran and Gryna, 1980).

Training. The principles of training discussed in Section 11 are fully applicable to the training of maintenance personnel and are in fact applied in large manufacturing companies.

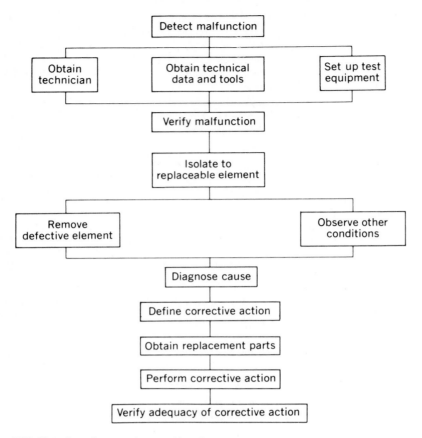

FIG. 20.1   Steps in correcting a malfunction.

Manufacturers have gone far to help small service centers by establishing training courses which the technicians may attend. Even more widespread is the preparation of special service manuals for use by service centers. These manuals provide well-designed aids for diagnosis and repair, including:

Exploded views and diagrams to show the structure of the product

Lists of parts used for various products

Color codes for wiring, and components to simplify diagnosis and repair

Detailed instruction for repair, i.e., sequence of operations, tools to be used, etc.

Multinational companies prepare these manuals in various languages. Some industries (e.g., automobile repairs) now use the concept of formal certification of technicians.

Spare Parts.   Spare parts provisioning has two major aspects: providing adequate quantities, and assuring the quality of the spare parts. Rosenthal (1983)

describes a program for provision of spare parts for a family of personal computers:

1. A maintenance strategy was based on the assumption that customers would install and maintain the computers themselves.

2. Design engineers were given specific requirements. For example, the system had to be able to self-diagnose faults down to the spare parts level. The user then had to be able to remove the part and install the replacement without being concerned about compatibility or the need for adjustments.

3. Manufacturing had to be able to produce the spare parts at high-quality levels.

4. The packaging, stocking, and distribution of the spare parts had to be properly executed, because customers were performing more of the maintenance themselves. This meant that spares had to be available to customers at many locations. That in turn increased the transportation and handling by individuals unfamiliar with electronic components and thereby increased the risks of damage.

A further problem that arises with spare parts concerns the completeness of testing. For some electronic products, the system does not provide for full interchangeability or compatibility of the subsystems. Hence the practice is to assemble the system and test it as a system before shipment, even if this means reassembly and retesting in the field. For such products, when subsystems are shipped out as spares, those subsystems have not undergone a system assembly and system test. There is no easy solution. Of course the fundamental solution is a system design which does provide full interchangeability.

Assuring the Adequacy of Maintenance Services. Maintenance itself can be a cause of failures in the field. Horn and Hall (1983) discuss techniques for estimating the extent of the maintenance contribution to field failures and also techniques for identifying maintenance-induced failures and their causes. On some Air Force activities, maintenance-induced failures varied from 2 to 48 percent of the total failures, depending on the type of equipment. Das, Hendry, and Hong (1980) have developed quantitative relationships for estimating the effect of imperfect repair on reliability.

Quality control of repair work is a troublesome problem for the service center. The great majority of shops are small, and the tradition has been self-inspection by the mechanic, with only sporadic review by the service manager. Some organizations establish standards of performance for service centers and provide audit and certification to assure that these standards are met. The Chevrolet Division of General Motors identifies 22 areas that are essential to total service satisfaction (e.g., quality, facilities, personnel, etc.). For each of these 22 areas, specific "evaluators" help to determine if the dealer conforms to the standards. The quality parameter has 15 evaluators, e.g., "inspection procedures are available." Technical assistance is provided by Chevrolet to enable the dealers to achieve certification. Certification involves both a review of the dealer's procedures and facilities and formal feedback from customers on the performance of the dealer. The program also provides for periodic recertification of the dealers.

Service Improvement. Good service is a moving target due to continuing changes in the marketplace. To keep up with competition requires continuing improvement of service. Because improvement takes place project by project, it is necessary to agree on specific needed improvements and then to organize to carry out the resulting improvement projects.

TABLE 20.2   Alternative Strategies for a Tractor

Key	Strategy
A	Improve fill rate for parts from 91% to 95%
B	Improve mean time between failures from 350 to 450 h
C	Develop and install microprocessor-based diagnostic capability in each tractor
D	Provide faster parts service using parts vans
E	Redesign tractor to permit faster modular exchange of electrical and hydraulic components
F	Provide users with tractors on loan during serious failures
G	Redesign tractor for modular exchange of electrical, hydraulic, and engine-driven train components
H	Redesign tractor as in strategy E and provide loaners
I	Redesign tractor as in strategy G and provide loaners
J	Redesign tractor as in strategy C; provide loaners and built-in diagnostics

Source: Lele and Karmarkar, 1983, p. 130.

An example of an approach to such improvement is seen in Lele and Karmar-kar (1983). They use the term "support strategies"in the sense of nominations for service improvement projects. In their definition, the term "strategy" means a collection of activities used to satisfy customer service needs. A strategy can vary from one market segment to another and can change with conditions in the marketplace. A company must choose a strategy, evaluate their own and competitors' relative positions and determine when customer needs or competitive pressures require that the strategy be changed. For example, Table 20.2 shows 10 alternative strategies for an industrial tractor.

These alternative strategies were identified after investigations revealed that customers were concerned about the downtime per product failure and the total downtime. A computer simulation was run to duplicate the effect of using a strategy (or combination of strategies) in terms of downtime and operational availability. The life cycle cost of each alternative was also calculated. Additional information resulting from the simulation included the effects of improving part availability, built-in diagnostics, making loans of equipment and modular exchange. The simulation showed that there were three stages, each requiring different strategies: from 50 to 30 h of downtime, from 30 to 20 h, and 20 to 10 h. Management decided to:

1. Improve the reliability of the existing design
2. Introduce equipment on loan (strategy F) in the mid-1980s, or earlier if competitive pressures demanded it
3. Change the design to allow progressive modularization of key components
4. Switch to a combination of modular exchange and loans (strategies H and I) in the late 1980s

The simulation provided conclusions that ordinarily would not be available until many months of experience had been accumulated.

QUALITY COMPLAINTS: GENERAL

As used in this handbook, the term "complaint" is an assertion of the quality deficiency. The complaint may concern the product or it may concern other activities such as incorrect invoicing or shipment of incorrect goods. In the discussion which follows, the term "complaint" refers to the product.

Underreported Complaints.   For the most part, complaints are underreported. This is particularly true for products of low unit price, where the time and effort required to complain are large in relation to the amount at stake. Underreporting also happens for other reasons:

Shortages of Goods.   During times of shortage, merchants and users take what they can get.

Contract Limitations.   Goods sold under a limited time warranty will generate no complaints at all during the great majority of their service life.

Futility.   Users who are unable to get redress finally stop complaining to the manufacturer. Instead, they complain to their friends and become sales advocates for competitor's products.
  Research performed by Andreasen and Best (1977) revealed that consumers complained about only 42.3 percent of nonprice problems. During the research, consumers were also asked questions going beyond their voiced complaints. One of the conclusions from this "probe" was that consumers do not complain about the design of products or the design of a service. The consumer tends to complain about product breakage or failure, but apparently thinks that nothing can be done about the design of the product.

Overreported Complaints

User Mistake.   Perhaps a third of the service calls made during the warranty period find nothing wrong with the product; the consumer misused the product, misread the instructions, or mislaid the instructions. In an unusual case involving a "walkie-talkie" communication set, a large number of sets that were returned as "inoperative" were found to operate perfectly. Investigation revealed that most users expected certain sounds to be audible when the set was turned on. However, the set had been designed to be free of such sounds. The quietness was interpreted by users as a defect.

Returned Spare Parts.   Sometimes a maintenance technician who is diagnosing a product failure misjudges the cause. A suspect component is replaced but the failure remains in evidence. Now the technician has a surplus component, and returns it as "defective." In some cases, from 35 to 85 percent of the components returned as defective are in fact good product.
  Some servicing policies resulted in a bias of data. Under a new policy, a manufacturer refused to pay charges for a component replaced during the warranty period unless the failure was verified by the manufacturer. Suddenly, the manufacturer received a large proportion of failed components that were destroyed. This made it impossible to perform a failed parts analysis to determine the cause. An investigation revealed that dealers applied a voltage across the electronic components to destroy the component and thereby assure payment of the claim.

Subterfuge.   Some sales organizations follow a practice of leaving muiltiple models with prospective buyers who can not make up their minds. Those models which are not purchased are then returned for credit as defective. A similar situation exists when a buyer receives a product in perfect operating condition, then decides that the product is undesirable for other reasons. The sales force accepts the returned product and may classify it as defective in order to expedite acceptance of the return by the company. Companies who encourage this practice as a sales device are well aware that the complaint rate is inflated. In companies where such practices are sanctioned, it is easy for managers to be misled by the reports.

SIGNIFICANCE OF FIELD COMPLAINTS

In many product lines the levels of warranty charges, complaints, and returns are low, e.g., under 1 percent of sales. Some managers of such product lines conclude that their product has a high quality reputation in the marketplace. They reason that if no one is dissatisfied, then everyone must be satisfied. The fallacy is a subtle one: product dissatisfaction and product satisfaction are not opposites. Product satisfaction is why clients buy the product. Product dissatisfaction has its origin in product failures. Customers buy products because of a positive attitude that they have toward the product. Complaints and other measures of dissatisfaction do shed some useful light on field performance but such data must be supplemented by marketing research to draw conclusions about customer satisfaction. (See Section 12, Field Intelligence.)

Field complaints are a poor measure of product performance. Some users complain despite the fact that the product is fit for use. Other users do not complain, despite the fact that the product is not fit for use. In addition, there are some broad influences which affect entire classes of products and users:

1. *The economic climate:* Complaints fall in a seller's market and rise in a buyer's market, even for the same product. A manufacturer of photographic film noticed that when silver prices rose complaints also rose. A manufacturer of pet food learned that when postal rates increase, there is a temporary drop in complaints on small unit price packages. Also, the degree of competition appears to influence complaints. A company having an essential monopoly tends to hear fewer complaints, apparently because people view the complaint process as futile.

2. *The age, affluence, technological skills, etc., of users:* For example, complaints on breakfast foods usually involve more complaints on the toys that are included with the package than on the food itself. To the child, the toy is a high priority. There seems to be conflicting research on the influence of economic status on complaints. Some studies have found that persons of an affluent background tend to be the most active complainers. Other studies have found that this is not as important as the product involved or the nature of the problem. (See Andreasen and Best, 1977).

TARP (1976) conducted research on complaint-handling procedures used by consumers. The results included:

32 percent of the households questioned were able to recall consumer problems in the past year.

As household income increases, the propensity to have a consumer problem increases significantly.

Over age 25, as age increases, the propensity to have a consumer problem also increases.

Race, region of the country, and urban versus rural status were not associated with significant differences in the proportion of households with problems.

3. *The unit price of the product:*   Complaint rates are strongly influenced by the unit price of the product. Figure 20.2 shows graphically that the complaint rate can understate by several orders of magnitude the extent of product inadequacy.

Numerous approaches are effective for determining the ratio of complaints to defects:

1. Company employees are given the product and asked to keep detailed records of performance. The employee data is then compared to complaints received from regular customers.
2. Create an arrangement with one or several large users of the product to buy their data. This requires an agreed-upon plan of data recording.
3. Use results from product audit. (See Section 9 under Product Audit.) Product audits can be made internally before the product is shipped, or externally through a sampling of dealers paid for conducting the audit. To establish a complaint ratio, the audit results can be compared to the regular complaints received from customers. One example involves some glassware selling at a unit price of $2.00. The results of a product audit in the warehouse on breakage was 7 percent defective. This compared to a regular customer complaint rate on breakage of 1.5 percent. The ratio of complaints to actual failures then was 0.2 (1.5 percent divided by 7.0 percent).

Effect of Time on the Complaint Rate.   For long-life products, time to first failure is a major variable determining the complaint rate. Products which "wear out," i.e., fail in "old age" after giving an acceptable service life, do not generate complaints. In contrast, "infant mortality" failures are highly complaint-prone. Intermediate random failures decrease in complaint rate as the extent of failure-free operation increases. (For an elaboration of the concept of infant mortality,

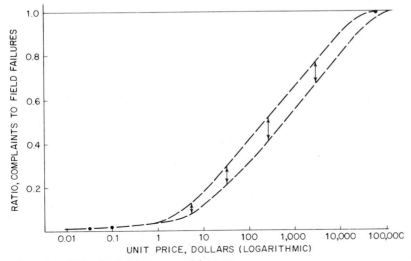

FIG. 20.2   Effect of unit price on complaint rate.

random failures, and wear-out, see Section 23 under Failure Patterns for Complex Products.)

The great importance of time to first failure requires that the product be "dated." The most useful date is that of the product's start into active service. If it cannot be secured conveniently, it can be approximated from the date of manufacture or from the date of sale. With ingenuity, it is possible to secure one of these dates at nominal cost.

Date of manufacture is marked on the product through a coded serial number or other means.

As the date of sale is difficult to record for 100 percent of the product, sampling techniques are generally used. For example, if the product is serially numbered, arrangements can be worked out with selected dealers to record the date of sale on enough product to establish the interval between date of manufacture and date of sale.

Date of actually going into service is normally available only for large units of product, in which case the date is secured from the attending service person or from the guarantee contract. For smaller units of product, resort must be had to sampling methods.

The analysis of field data from product which is dated is discussed below under Data Analysis Techniques.

Collectively, the above influences make the complaint rate a poor index of product quality especially for low-price products. However, the complaint rate is an index of user dissatisfaction, and this alone is enough to require that the complaint rate be measured and watched closely.

Effect of Word-of-Mouth Transmission by Consumers. In addition to recorded complaints received by companies, there is transmission of information by consumers through conversations with friends. Research by the Coca-Cola Company (1981) included the following findings:

Consumers who felt their complaint had not been satisfactorily resolved told a median of 9 to 10 people about their negative experience.

Consumers who were completely satisfied with the response from the Company told a median of 4 to 5 people about their positive experience.

More than 12 percent of the complainants told more than 20 people about the response they received from the Company.

The research further established the effect of the process on the purchase of future products:

Nearly 10 percent of those consumers who were completely satisfied with the response from the Company now buy more products of the Company.

More than 30 percent of the consumers who felt their complaints had not been satisfactorily resolved said they no longer buy the products of the Company; nearly 45 percent of these dissatisfied complainants claim they now buy products of the Company less often.

Research reported by Goodman and Yates (1982) discusses the relationship between complaining and making a decision to repurchase the offending product or service. As might be expected, a decision to repurchase depends on the financial loss and the resolution of the complaint (see Table 20.3).

Field Failures versus Factory Rejects. It is illuminating to compare the list of principal field failures with the list of principal factory rejects. For example, in

TABLE 20.3 Percent Repurchase Based on Handling of Complaints

	Potential financial loss	
	$1 to $5	More than $100
Complaint satisfactorily resolved	70.0%	54.3%
Complaint unsatisfactorily resolved	46.2	19.0
Did not complain	36.8	9.5

a company making rubber products, there was a drop in the sales of a major product type. The sales force blamed the drop on poor quality, whereupon the president ordered an improvement in quality. The factory complied by tightening up on quality standards, resulting in higher shop rejections (and higher costs) for dirt, discoloration, and other factory defects. Actually, the field problems were different, as listed in Table 20.4. The factory "improvement" had no significant effect on the real quality problems of the user.

TABLE 20.4 Field Returns and Factory Rejections

Principal reasons for field returns	Percent of all field returns	Principal factory defects	Percent of all factory rejections
Product has odor	78	Dirt	46
Product crumbles	15	Discoloration	22
Product tears in use	6	Nicked	12
All other	1	All other	20

In another example, in a line of ophthalmic products, a continuing product audit regularly disclosed 65 percent of outgoing product to have minor appearance faults. But there had never been a field return for these faults. Instead, 81 percent of the field returns were for breakage, for which the product audit had no systematic test.

Comparison of the two lists can help to identify:

1. Lack of audit tests for potential field failures
2. Unjustified perfectionism in audit standards

PROCESSING OF COMPLAINTS

In small companies involved in few field complaints, there is little need for a systematic approach to complaint analysis. As the number of complaints increases, the need for a systematic approach increases. In some large companies, lack of an organized approach has been a serious obstacle to sound customer relations.

Sources of Complaints: Registration. Complaints flow in to the manufacturer from a wide variety of sources: consumers, merchants, service shops, industrial users, regulators, consumer advocates, stockholders, etc. The channels of communication are also diverse: letters, telephone calls, personal visits, newspapers accounts. The complaints may also be addressed to various departments in the company: Sales, Service, Quality, any manager (especially the president), etc. Some companies have established a 24-h "hotline" telephone service to answer inquiries from customers.

To avoid confusion it is useful to set up a "registration desk" and to instruct all concerned to send a copy of the complaint to the desk, which will:

Register all complaints, no matter by whom received.

Assign a serial number to permit tracing progress.

Route the complaint to that department best qualified to conduct the analysis.

Assist in identifying complaint cases requiring fundamental study.

Follow up to assure that adequate analyses and dispositions are made.

Assist in summarized reporting.

The registration desk may be located in any of several departments—Complaint Bureau, Quality, Sales, or Service—depending on the organizational structure of the company.

All complaints require an immediate acknowledgment, whether or not a full response can be given at that time. The form of acknowledging a complaint and preparing further written follow-up with the customer is also important. One insurance company conducted an image study of its operations and learned that many customers felt that written communications from the company were stilted, legalistic, and difficult to understand. The company then established a unit with the responsibility for putting all correspondence into simple language.

Programs of Action. Complaints require several different programs of action:

1. *Satisfying the complainant:* As this program is oriented to the complainant, it is needed in virtually every case of complaint.
2. *Identifying those "vital few" serious complaints:* Studies must be made in depth to discover the basic causes.
3. *Analysis in depth to discover the basic causes of the complaint:* This action is oriented to the product and is especially needed in those vital few cases which are responsible for the bulk of the failures.
4. *Further analysis:* To discover and apply remedies for the basic causes.
5. *Preventing a recurrence of isolated complaints:* Isolated complaints are brought to the attention of those who are suspected of having caused them. It becomes their responsibility to take action to prevent a recurrence.

Satisfying the Complainant. Typically, the manufacturer must meet three needs of the complainant:

1. *Restoration of service:* The complainant is lacking service and needs a repair or replacement. Action must be prompt, and often the need is acute.
2. *Claim adjustment:* Often the complainant is out of pocket because of the failure, and wants compensation.
3. *Restoration of goodwill:* Even after service is restored and the claim is paid, there remains a residue of irritation due to annoyance and frustration. A proper complaint adjustment includes added effort to calm the ruffled feelings of the complainant. Some automobile dealers have a program of periodically calling a sample of customers to verify that a repair has been satisfactory.

Even with procedures set up to handle complaints, the response record is far from perfect. In a national survey of consumers, TARP (1976) found the following:

30 percent of the households who contacted a first source felt that the second source had to be contacted in order to resolve their problem.

27 percent of those who contacted a second source found it necessary to contact a third source.

Some organizations have set up a consumer affairs office as part of the corporate organization to assure adequate resolution of complaints. One automobile company has experimented with an approach that involves third-party arbitration. The consumer first contacts the local dealer to register the complaint. If the response is not satisfactory, the consumer then contacts the zone office of the manufacturer. If the consumer is still dissatisfied, then an arbitrator from the Better Business Bureau can be requested, with the understanding that the findings of the arbitrator are binding on both the manufacturer and the consumer. In the appliance industry the Major Appliance Consumer Action Panel (MACAP) is a recourse available to consumers who feel that a complaint has not been answered adequately. The panel consists of a group of people from the areas of law, economics, engineering, minority representation, education, and communications. Although the recommendations of the panel are not binding on the manufacturer they are regarded with great credibility.

Identifying the "Vital Few."   Figure 20.3 is a flow diagram showing how one large company selects problems for resolution and then solves the selected problems. As the causes and remedies may involve many departments, a "corrective action group" is often formed with representatives from Design, Manufacturing, Purchasing, Quality, and Field Service. The group jointly analyzes the data to select the vital few problems, conducts an initial investigation to prepare a thorough problem statement, and assigns responsibility for determining a remedy.

The group meets regularly to review all new complaints and to review progress on current problems. A problem agenda is sent out by the chairperson several days ahead of the meeting date. Minutes of the meetings, including a problem-status log, are formally recorded, and actions to be taken are documented and distributed to all concerned. This log summarizes each problem before the committee. It also shows the scheduled start and completion of activity, assigns responsibility, and lists action taken. It gives Project Management an indication of major problems and the status of corrective efforts. Additional effort may then be placed on troublesome areas as deemed necessary.

Discovery of Causes.   The process starts with a review of the individual and summarized field data in order to select potential problems. Techniques such as defect matrices and Pareto analyses (see Section 22 under Diagnosis) are directly applicable to field data.

Some organizations have created extensive data collection and summarization systems for repairs made in the field. A manufacturer of heavy equipment has a computer terminal system that transmits details on every repair made at dealerships throughout the country to the manufacturer. The data are continuously updated and eight different summaries provided using a Pareto ranking of defect types by serial number, model, component, part, and dealer.

This system has reduced the data collection time, because the old manual system required complex warranty forms which not only took a long time to complete but required additional time for transmission and recording into the system.

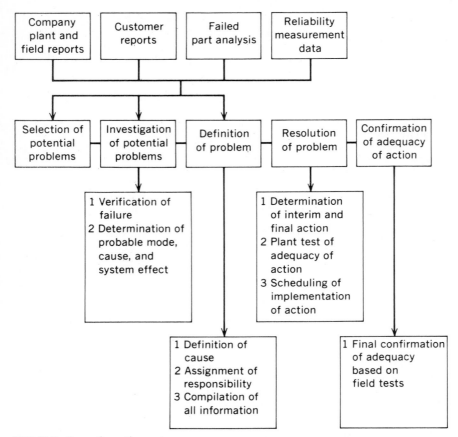

FIG. 20.3 Corrective action system.

Problem identification occurs much faster because of the Pareto analyses that are available and continually updated. Under this system, the manufacturer knows what some of the major problems are before they are apparent to all of the dealers. In many cases, the corrective action can be developed before a problem becomes widespread. The system also makes it easier to identify problems by generic part type even though individual part numbers may not have a high frequency of occurrence.

The investigation of problems often involves obtaining the physical part that failed and conducting a failed parts analysis by disassembly and/or additional laboratory tests. (One of the confusing aspects of failure analysis is that often the "failed" part works perfectly.) When a problem is determined to be real and of significant enough consequence to require follow-up, then a detailed failure analysis may be needed. Dobbins (1977) provides an excellent checklist for a failure analysis program.

Some industries have taken the progressive step of establishing special instrumentation and data systems needed to correlate product and operating variables with field failures and even incipient field failures. A large manufacturer of synthetic fibers collaborated with a textile mill to evolve a correlation of yarn breaks with causes. This was done through:

1. Equipping the process with scanners and working up a process history of each package of yarn (about 1000 lb)
2. Securing the history of the field performance of these packages, including capture of the broken yarns, through the field service personnel
3. Correlating textile mill results with chemical process variables

The resulting correlations permitted remedial steps to be taken much earlier than they could have been by accumulating failure data in the absence of planned causation data.

Instrumentation for field failure analysis is increasingly specially designed. For example, the application of computerized diagnostic tools has been applied in a wide variety of products ranging from aircraft engines and automobiles to telephone subscriber lines. Also, the application of fiber optic concepts has been applied to analysis of bearing failures (Philips and Hirschfeld, 1980).

In some cases it is necessary to study the mechanism of failure under field conditions. In one example, a bus company spent 6 months on laboratory analyses to learn the causes of failure of alternators, with no conclusions. Then an engineer noticed that the alternators were located in an area of the bus that was prone to corrosion due to the environment. It had been assumed that the alternators were in an engine compartment where the effect of corrosion would be minimal. The study concluded that the alternators were failing due to corrosion that came from the salt spray on the roads. This had not been clear from the laboratory analysis.

In some industries the problems of failure analysis are so demanding that special failure analysis laboratories and organizations are created to do the job. Such laboratories must sometimes be equipped with special facilities and a variety of technical skills. The equipment, skills, and time for failure analysis are often underestimated.

Discovery of Remedies. The complaint bureau or other investigative body can establish the cause of the product deficiency, but it cannot provide a remedy. Instead, based on the analysis for cause, the matter is referred to that department which can remedy the known cause, e.g., Design or Manufacture.

However, the investigative bureau should be a party to the tryout of the remedy to verify that the design change (or whatever) provides a "fix" which is effective under operating conditions. In addition, provisions must be made for proper disposition of shop and field inventories which have been under "hold" pending the discovery of a remedy.

Preventing Recurrence of Isolated Complaints. Under the Pareto principle, a few types of failures account for the bulk of the field performance problems. It is these "vital few" which deserve and usually receive the bulk of the investigative effort. On purely economic grounds, this discrimination against the remaining defects is fully warranted. For many of them the cure may cost more than the disease. However, for some products and applications, infrequent defects cannot be ignored merely because they are infrequent. The most obvious examples are defects which are critical to the safety of human beings. A single instance of such a defect dictates that it becomes part of the "vital few" for investigation.

In some situations, the collective volume of symptoms occurring at a low frequency overwhelms those occurring at a higher frequency. For example, on one product about 75 percent of all warranty claims involved defects occurring at a low frequency. This 75 percent overshadowed the amount of defect reduction achieved by identifying and correcting the high-frequency defects.

Isolated complaints are usually the result of inadvertent mistakes, carelessness, errors in judgment, unusual environmental conditions, etc. The error has usually taken place weeks or even months before the failure takes place, so that the fundamental cause is difficult to establish, whether by a trained investigator from a central bureau or by a departmental supervisor. A useful approach to diagnosis of isolated complaints is discussed in Section 22 under Troubleshooting.

DATA ANALYSIS TECHNIQUES

Quality-related data on field performance includes not only complaints but also basic performance data on the pattern of failures over time, data on repair frequency and repair time, data on repair costs, and still other useful field data. The analyses of such data range from simple summaries to complex statistical analyses. These analyses are used to provide measures of field performance, to help determine causes of problems, and to predict the rate at which future problems will occur. The following paragraphs describe some analytical and graphical approaches, starting with the simple and proceeding to the complex.

Basic Time-Related Plotting Techniques. A simple plot of data over time (e.g., number of premature removals of an aircraft engine) is a useful way to start. The data for individual months are plotted, and then a moving average of the data is updated each month to indicate an underlying trend.

Another useful technique is cumulative complaint analysis. This requires that the product be "dated" to show when it was made, sold, or installed. The various dates are useful in disposing of complaints and claims for product of a slowly perishable character (candy, photographic film, etc.). They also can help in predicting the failure rate of various product designs.

An example of the cumulative data analysis technique involves women's clothing. Certain articles were tearing in service, and some were being returned. When the products made during one specific month were code dated, the cumulative returns reached 2 percent within 2 years after the date of manufacture. The resulting cumulative curve is shown on Figure 20.4. This 2 percent was regarded as tolerable. (At the unit price level of the product, it was likely that about 20 percent of the product was actually tearing in service.)

Meanwhile, the research department evolved a new product which possessed new, useful sales features that were unrelated to the problem of tearing. This new product then went into full-scale production 14 months after the "specific month" noted above. The cumulative returns for the new product are also charted on Figure 20.4. Note that by use of a horizontal time scale based on "months following manufacture," the two curves both start at the origin and hence can readily be compared with each other. By such analysis the company could be informed within the first few months of the life of the new design that the new design had, as to the problem of tearing, made the situation much worse.

Johnson (1975) describes the cumulative analysis approach as applied to data on tractors.

A technique for predicting future performance is the concept of growth curves. The concept assumes that the product involved is one that is undergoing continuous improvements in design and manufacturing, and refinements in field pro-

FIG. 20.4 Comparison of cumulative returns for two designs, by month, following month of manufacture.

cedures. Thus the product performance will improve ("grow") with time. The concept is discussed in Section 13 under Reliability Growth.

Use of Probability Paper for Predicting Complaint Level. Weibull probability paper (see Section 23) can be used to analyze early field data on warranty claims. Through such analysis it is possible to predict what will be the cumulative claims at the end of the warranty period.

Repair information on an electrical subassembly is collected (Ford, 1972). The cumulative repairs per 100 units is interpreted as a cumulative failure rate in percent. These data are summarized from a large number of warranty reports.

The Weibull plot is shown in Figure 20.5. The 8 months of data have been plotted and a line drawn through the points. This line has been extended, and it predicts the repair rate at the end of the 12-month warranty period to be 2.6 repairs per 100 units.

Note that this Weibull paper includes a scale for estimating the Weibull slope or shape parameter (see Section 23). The slope can be found by drawing a line parallel to the line of best fit and through the point circled on the vertical scale. Here, the slope is read as 0.7. This defines the shape of the failure distribution and can aid in problem definition.

For slopes < 1, the distribution is exponential and generally means that the failures are early failures due to manufacturing or assembly deficiencies.

For slopes > 1, the distribution is skewed or approximately normal and generally means that the failures are due to wear-out or fatigue, especially for higher slopes.

FIG. 20.5 Warranty data plot.

Extrapolation beyond the limits of actual data is always questionable. However, when extrapolated performance has been confirmed by actual performance on similar product lines, the approach may be justified. Although the approach suggested here is not rigorous, it is a major step beyond intuitive decisions.

A special case of analysis involves units in the field that have been placed in service at different dates. Some of the units have failed after having accumulated various lengths of time in service. Other units are still in operation, also with various accumulations of time in service. This type of data can be handled with "hazard plotting paper" for the Weibull or other distributions. King (1971) describes the mechanics of analysis and the application to service and warranty problems. An associated problem involves changes in the size of a warranty population. This occurs in any time interval in which the number of product units entering the warranty period differs. Alternative methods for handling this situation are discussed by Nelson (1982).

Effect of Time Lag. Differences between usage dates, dates of sale, and dates of manufacture can create important errors in judging performance trends and in correlating cause (design and manufacturing variables) with effect (failure during usage).

For industrial apparatus, dates of installation can usually be obtained, but the lag time between the date that a failure occurs and the date that is reported to the manufacturer can be large.

For consumer products, Powell (1970) found a time lag between date of manufacture and receipt of failure reports of 6 to 32 weeks, as shown in Table 20.5.

Delays distort the reported failure rate when based purely on date of manufacture or date of sale. For a new model, the reports will, at the outset, greatly understate the failure rates, since the shipments are substantial whereas the reported failures are few due to the time lag. In contrast, when the failure reports all come in weeks or months later, the reported rate will exaggerate the actual failure rate of the units. To eliminate these exaggerations, practitioners have evolved methods for correcting failure rate data based on quantifying the time lag. (See Powell, 1970.)

A related problem is the movement of sold products into and out of the guarantee period. One measure of failure rate is the number of failures (reported during the guarantee period) per 100 units under guarantee. There are difficulties with this measure because failure rates (and hence guarantee charges) are not uniform over the guarantee period, plus the fact that the population of units covered by the guarantee period is rarely spread evenly, month by month, over the guarantee period. Sandholm (1965) and Robertson (1969) describe approaches for handling such data.

TABLE 20.5 Distribution of Time Lag

	Time elapsed, weeks	
Status	During this state	Cumulative
In manufacturer's inventory	1–12	1–12
In transit to dealer	1–2	2–14
In dealer inventory	1–8	3–22
In use	1–4	4–26
Undergoing service	1–3	5–29
Being reported	1–3	6–32

IMPROVING FIELD FEEDBACK

Improving the quality and promptness of field feedback requires a variety of actions:

1. *Provide personnel with well-designed data sheets:* This is intended to facilitate easy, accurate recording. The design of forms is not a matter that can be left to amateurs.

An important basic form is the service report. This fundamental document is originated for each service call made or each failure reported. Such forms should be designed not only to record basic information for warranty payment and analysis purposes, but also to provide information for diagnosis of the cause. Among the items that should be included are identification of the product (model number, system, assembly, subassembly, component, and part); the geographical location at which the failure occurred; operating time on the product; description of the symptom; immediate action taken to place the product back in operating condition; action taken on the failed item; and total amount of downtime, broken down into diagnosis, obtaining a replacement part, installing the replacement part, adjusting, and checking out the system.

Some open space should be left on the form for additional items of information required in the future.

2. *Provide incentives to encourage adequate feedback:* Payment on a warranty failure can be withheld until the information describing the failure is complete and in the form desired by the company.

3. *Provide a glossary of terms to improve communication and a mnemonic code number to simplify the data entry and analysis:* Words have different meanings to different people. For example, a steel company received a number of complaints of "bad coating" on wire. The company interpreted this to mean that their steel was bad and that the coating had become flakey. After much futile discussion it was finally discovered that the customer's meaning of "bad coating" was that the coating had oxidized. In another example, "fit of doors" meant dimensional problems to an automobile manufacturer. The customers meant that unless the doors were pushed shut with great effort they did not close completely. A glossary provides a written list of key words along with definitions. Personnel are then trained to use these definitions.

4. *Provide training in the how and why:* Show how the data are used. Service personnel view their primary job as repair and maintenance of a product, and not one of filling out forms and doing other paperwork. Also, many of them believe that no use is made of their reports. In order to be encouraged to provide adequate feedback, they need to be reminded how the data will be used.

5. *Conduct audits of the data feedback process:* This is intended to discover deficiencies and to demonstrate management's concern for good data. A sample of the routine reports provided can be evaluated in terms of the adequacy of information provided ("adequate, marginal, and unsatisfactory"). A summary can be given to the field personnel along with examples of both good and bad reports.

6. *Make use of modern technology to collect the field information:* An electronics company recently developed and provided each repair person with a simple recording system so that they could dictate the details of the repair instead of filling out a form. In another example, dealers selling earth-moving equipment now have computer terminals to report back daily to the factory every service operation performed.

7. *Make use of modern methods of analysis to provide managers with valid* *summaries for decision making:* McClure (1976) describes an automated data system that makes use of quality assurance indicators covering both in-plant and field performance. This information is made continuously available through computer terminals not only for the manufacturer but also for the customer. Both groups have identical access to outputs of the system. This provides a demonstration of the contractor's integrity in disclosing performance information and saves time in responding to customer requests for information.

8. *Minimize the number of data relay stations:* Each adds delay and possible noise to the signals.

9. *Make use of the sample concept:* A sample of data with precise, detailed information is more valuable than a large quantity of superficial information.

10. *Obtain the operations log:* Normally the log, which is kept on certain kinds of systems, includes records of significant phenomena observed, stoppages encountered, action taken to restore operations, proposals for improvement, and other information deemed necessary to provide a complete history.

11. *Buy the data:* It may be better to purchase the data from a customer who is keeping detailed records.

12. *Make use of the concept of controlled usage:* Here the product is used by employees or some other special group, and they provide detailed feedback on the performance of the product. In turn these users are either paid for their services or receive use of the product free of charge.

With the best of data systems it may be necessary to provide for supplementary data collection. Takeuchi and Quelch (1983) list the elements of "customer-driven" quality programs for a mail-order firm and an earth-moving equipment manufacturer (see Table 20.6). Note that in each case provisions are made for

TABLE 20.6 Customer-Driven Quality Programs

Mail-order apparel company	Equipment manufacturer
Conducting regular customer satisfaction surveys and sample group interviews to track customer and noncustomer perceptions of the quality of its own and its competitors' products and services	Conducting two customer satisfaction surveys following each purchase, one after 300 h of product use and the second after 500 h of use
Tracking on its computer all customer inquiries and complaints and updating the file daily	Maintaining a centrally managed list of product problems as identified by customers from around the world
Guaranteeing all its products to be 100% satisfactory and providing a full cash refund, if requested, on any returns	Analyzing warranty and service reports submitted by dealers, as part of a product improvement program
Asking customers to fill out a short, coded questionnaire and explain their reasons for returning the merchandise	Asking dealers to conduct a quality audit as soon as the products are received and to attribute defects to either assembly errors or shipping damages
Performing extensive field tests on any new outdoor equipment before listing it in the company's catalogs	Guaranteeing 48-h delivery of any part to any customer in the world
Even stocking extra buttons for most of the apparel items carried years ago, just in case a customer needs one	Encouraging dealers to establish side businesses in rebuilding parts to reduce costs and increase the speed of repairs

obtaining special field intelligence from customers. Smith (1979) describes the routine data system and supplementary information collected by an automobile manufacturer.

EXECUTIVE REPORTS ON FIELD PERFORMANCE

In the absence of regular reports on field performance upper managers can be stampeded by individual, isolated cases, so that they misdirect company resources for the improvement of field performance. This makes it essential that the executive instrument panel include information on the overall status on field performance.

The general concept of executive reports on quality is discussed in Section 8 under Executive Reports on Quality. The application of the concept to field performance is discussed below.

Control Subjects and Units of Measure.   For field performance, the most widely used control subjects and units of measure are those shown in Table 20.7.

Beyond the control subjects listed in Table 20.7, the executive reports may include:

Breakdown of important control subjects by subcategories such as product type, subsystems, department responsibile, etc.

Lists of vital few problems and status of solution

TABLE 20.7   Control Subjects and Units of Measure for Field Performance

Control subject	Units of measure in use
Complaints	Total number of complaints
	Number of complaints per $1 million of sales
	Number of complaints per million units of product
	Value of material under complaint per $100 of sales for such products
Returns	Value of material returned per $100 of sales
Claims	Cost of claims paid
	Cost of claims per $1 million of sales
Failures	Mean time between failures (MTBF)
	Mean usage between failures, e.g., cycles, miles
	Mean time between repair calls
	Failures per 1000 units under warranty
Shipments	Amount of product shipped that did not meet specifications
Maintainability	Mean time to repair (MTTR)
	Mean downtime
	Number of repeat service calls for same complaint
Service cost	Ratio of maintenance hours to operating hours
	Repair cost per unit under warranty
	Cost per service call

Additional control subjects or added detail demanded by the special nature of the company's product

A composite index which reflects the collective effect of a variety of control subjects

Status information about the Complaint Bureau (or Service Department, etc.): complaints received, closed, on hand; time required to close complaints; important unresolved cases in order of age; productivity of complaint analysis

Complaint indices of various types are the most frequently used forms of field performance measure. Sasaki et al. (1978) performed a research on the complaint indices being used by companies in Japan. Twenty types of complaint indices were identified. The four must commonly used were:

1. The number of complaints
2. The loss in money by complaints
3. Comparison of the number of complaints for each product type
4. The number of complaints compared to the amount of production

The absolute number of complaints can be misleading because of the difference in seriousness of different defects. McRobb (1982) reports on comparing five measures to summarize customer perceived quality levels. A composite complaint measure was selected for reporting to management. Three categories of complaints were identified and weighting factors were assigned based on seriousness.

In one application of this system, two models of product were compared. The general impression throughout the factory was that the two models were about equal on quality. When the complaint data were summarized and a composite quality index was prepared, the index for the first model was 3000; the index for the second model was 500.

This example illustrated that the prevailing method of judging market acceptability could lead to erroneous results.

Failures as Seen By the User. Usually, the manufacturer measures repair costs only during the warranty period. The user is concerned with repair costs for the entire service life. Also, the user is concerned with various added costs caused by failures but which are divided into five categories:

R = repair cost
E = effectiveness loss (e.g., idle labor)
C = extra capacity required because of product downtime
D = damages caused by failure
I = lost income (e.g., profit)

If the categories applicable for a specific product are measured each year over the life (n) of the product and if i is the yearly interest rate, the total user failure cost (C_f) is:

$$\sum_{j=1}^{n} \frac{1}{(1 + i)^j} (R_j + E_j + C_j + D_j + I_j)$$

This model collects all the costs associated with failures over the product life and takes into account the time value of money (Gryna, 1977).

Users' costs are enormous. Studies of life cycle costs show that for consumer products the costs of failures often exceed the purchase price; for military products the *annual* maintenance cost may exceed the purchase price (see Section 13 under Planning for Maintainability). The manufacturer who is unaware of these costs may be unwittingly losing sales. In addition, the manufacturer remains unaware of the business opportunities that such knowledge would reveal.

PRODUCT RECALLS

"Product recall" is a term used to describe the actions taken due to deficiencies in products which have already been shipped to users. The actions may consist of corrections made in the field. The actions may also consist of removing the product from the field.

The most highly publicized recalls are those which pose a threat to human safety or health. Other important recalls are those which involve extensive economic loss to users.

Recalled products have spanned a broad spectrum including automobiles, toys, computers, appliances, food, and medical devices. The reasons for recall range from minor to serious. In food products, the deficiency may be as minor as a deterioration in flavor or as serious as a highly toxic contamination. In electronics, defects may range from calculators that do not work to harmful radiation emitted from television sets.

When a recall must be made the costs involved can be considerable. Jacobs and Mundel (1975) have identified the cost elements of a product recall.

For a recall to be effective it is essential that the procedures for the recall be in place before there is any need for the recall. In this sense a recall plan is similar to a will—it evokes little interest but it is necessary that the document be completed before the event takes place. Unless the recall procedures are ready for use when the recall decision is made, valuable time is lost in making the recall.

ASQC (1981) lists the key steps for implementing and evaluating a recall:

1. Initial activities to implement a recall
   a. Establishment of a management control center
   b. Description of the product, features, problem
   c. Identification of products
   d. Definition of product groups to be recalled
   e. Data on population of products
   f. Planning and designing reporting forms
   g. Estimating, ordering, and distributing replacement parts
2. Release of recall information
   a. Preparation of notification information
   b. Special news releases
   c. Notification to customers and users
   d. Internal employee information
   e. Timing
3. Field Response
   a. Response from the field
   b. Collection of internal and field cost information

    c. Parts usage traceability

    d. Field data reporting

        i. Periodic reporting

        ii. Summary reports

4. Monitoring activity

    a. Audit of field corrective action

    b. Data verification and correlation

5. Management evaluation, program completion

    a. Project review on periodic basis

    b. Success level evaluation

The quantity of product that must be recalled can be minimized if the suspect product units can be identified separately from other production. This separation is simplified if a system of "traceability" has been established. Once a recall is required, it is of critical importance not only to know where to locate the product in general, but also to be able to identify the specific suspect units quickly.

The factors to be considered in setting up a traceability program have been summarized by ASQC (1981) as follows:

1. *Product category:* A unique designation such as a part name or part number is required.

2. *Product life:* The longer the product life, the greater the number of similar items that are present in the field. Also, as modifications are made in design or manufacturing, the traceability plan must be able to identify which units of product embody which changes.

3. *Unit cost:* The greater the unit cost, the greater the incentive to recall only the most important problem items.

4. *Recall or modify in the field:* If the product is repairable, then a decision must be made whether to (*a*) bring the product in from the field and have it corrected by the manufacturer; (*b*) send a manufacturer's representative to the field to correct the problem; or (*c*) provide the user with parts and instructions to make the necessary modification.

5. *Product complexity:* If a design consists of many components, then a decision must be made to determine how far down the product hierarchy to extend the traceability.

6. *Level of downstream traceability:* This refers to the reason for recall. For each failure mode, it must be decided what level of traceability is needed to segregate the suspect items from the total product population. For example, if a recall results from a manufacturing problem, then the manufacturing date, facility, lot identification, etc., may be required.

7. *Documents providing traceability:* An analysis of the failure modes will indicate the types of information necessary.

8. *Type of identification:* The cost of identification should be consistent with the product price. For expensive products, serial numbers are often used; for lower priced products, dates are used.

9. *Should identification be coded or uncoded?* An uncoded identification may have an adverse effect on sales, but it makes it easier to identify the defective product and thereby to finish the recall sooner.

10. *Method of identification:* This includes tags, name plates, ink stamps, and other means.

Consideration must also be given to the need for the traceability program extending back through the vendor's organization. This is sometimes called second-tier traceability. Jacobs and Mundel (1975) discuss the elements of a program for the supplier's organization.

Even with thorough recall programs, it has not been possible to recover all of the products that are in the field. Some consumers simply do not return the product even if they are aware of the recall. Much depends on the cost of the product and other factors. Evaluating the effectiveness of the recall is part of the overall recall process.

The U.S. Consumer Product Safety Commission (1978) studied the effectiveness of some recalls. Half of the 245 recall cases studied resulted in 80 percent or more of the suspected products being examined and corrected where necessary. Seven variables were identified as having strong relationships with recall effectiveness: product price, product life, number of units, time in distribution, percent of unit in consumers' hands, recall action, and level of direct consumer notification.

For example, it was estimated that recalls will probably be less than 50 percent effective when any of the following conditions occur: the product price is less than \$25; the average life is less than 6 years; the number of units is over 10,000; over two-thirds of the total units have been purchased by consumers.

One study (Food and Drug Administration, 1978) evaluated the effectiveness of seven methods of contacting customers. The conclusion was that mail with telephone follow-up was the most efficient method.

REFERENCES

American Society for Quality Control (1981). *Product Recall Planning Guide.* Milwaukee.

Andreasen, Alan R. and Best, Arthur (1977). "Consumers Complain—Does Business Respond?" *Harvard Business Review,* July–August, pp. 124–132.

Amrine, Harold, Ritchey, John A., and Hulley, Oliver S. (1975). *Manufacturing Organization and Management,* 3rd ed. Prentice-Hall, Englewood Cliffs, NJ.

Canut, Luis Sicre (1975). "Standardization of Packaging—A Survey with Examples from Western Europe." *EOQC Quality,* vol. XIX, no. 1, pp. 10–15.

Caterpillar Tractor Company (1978). *Service Quality Guide.* Peoria, IL.

The Center for Policy Alternatives, Massachusetts Institute of Technology and Charles Stark Draper Laboratory, Inc. (1974). *The Productivity of Servicing Consumer Durable Products.* Report 74-4, Cambridge, MA.

Cherkasky, Stanley M. (1970). "Long-Term Storage and System Reliability." *Proceedings, Annual Reliability and Maintainability, Symposium.* IEEE, New York, pp. 120–127.

Coca-Cola Company (1981). *Measuring the Grapevine-Consumer Response and Word of Mouth.* Atlanta, GA.

Das, S., Hendry, A., and Hong, S. (1980). "The Impact of Imperfect Repair on System Reliability." *Proceedings, Annual Reliability and Maintainability Symposium.* IEEE, New York, pp. 393–402.

Dobbins, Richard K. (1977). "A Dollars and Cents Approach to Failure Analysis." *ASQC Technical Conference Transactions,* Milwaukee, pp. 230–235.

Duane, J. T. (1964). "Learning Curve Approach to Reliability Monitoring." *IEEE Transactions on Aerospace,* vol. 2, no. 2, pp. 563–566.

Fiedler, Robert M. (1978). "Portal to Portal Product Protection." *Quality,* May, pp. 12–14.

Food and Drug Administration (1978). *Checking the Effectiveness of Recalls—A Cost-Effectiveness Study.* Publication PB-277 174, Washington, DC.

Ford Motor Company (1972). *Reliability Methods, Module No. XII.* Dearborn, MI, pp. 11–13.

Goodman, John and Yates, Jane (1982). "Economic Aspects of Quality Controlled Decisions—Development of a Market-Driven Quality Assurance System." *ASQC Conference on Statistical Control in Good Manufacturing Practice,* New Brunswick, NJ, Oct. 5. ASQC, Milwaukee, pp. 1–19.

Gryna, Frank M., Jr. (1977). "Quality Costs: User vs. Manufacturer." *Quality Progress,* June pp. 10–15.

Horn, Roy L. and Hall, Fred M. (1983). "Maintenance-Centered Reliability." *Proceedings, Annual Reliability and Maintainability Symposium.* IEEE, New York, pp. 197–204.

Jacobs, R. M. and Mundel, A. B. (1975). "Quality Tasks in Product Recall." *Quality Progress,* June, pp. 16–19.

Jayachandran, Toke and Moore, Louis R. (1976). "A Comparison of Reliability Growth Models." *IEEE Transactions on Reliability,* vol. R-25, no. 1, pp. 49–51.

Johnson, D. A. (1975). "Product Problem Control through Warranty Analysis—Ford's Approach." *ASQC Automotive Division Second Annual Agricultural, Industrial, and Construction Equipment Conference.* ASQC, Milwaukee.

Juran, J. M. and Gryna, Frank M. (1980). *Quality Planning and Analysis,* 2nd ed. McGraw-Hill, New York, p. 474.

King, James R. (1971). *Probability Charts for Decision Making.* Industrial Press, New York.

LaSala, Kenneth P. and Siegel, Arthur I. (1983). "Improved R & M in Productivity by Designs for People." *Proceedings Annual Reliability and Maintainability Symposium.* IEEE, New York, pp. 494–500.

Lele, Milind and Karmarkar, Uday S. (1983). "Good Product Support is Smart Marketing." *Harvard Business Review,* November–December, pp. 124–132.

Levitt, Theodore (1983). "After the Sale is Over." *Harvard Business Review,* September–October, pp. 87–93.

McClure, J. Y. (1976). "The Role of Automated Data in Maintaining Optimum Customer Relations."*ASQC Technical Conference Transactions,* Milwaukee, pp. 375–380.

McRobb, R. M. (1982). "Customer-Perceived Quality Levels." *ASQC Quality Congress Transactions,* Milwaukee, pp. 428–432.

Meister, David (1978). "Subjective Data in Human Reliability Estimated." *Proceedings, Annual Reliability and Maintainability Symposium.* IEEE, New York, pp. 380–384.

Nelson, Wayne (1982). *Applied Life Data Analysis.* John Wiley & Sons, New York.

Nowlan, F. S. (1980). "Reliability Centered Maintenance." *Symposium on Design to Cost and Life Cycle Cost.* North Atlantic Treaty Organization, Amsterdam, Netherlands.

Nowlan, F. Stanley and Heap, Howard F. (1978). *Reliability Centered Maintenance.* Document ADA066579, Defense Documentation Center, Alexandria, VA.

Peacore, E. J. (1975). "Reliability Developments—AWACS." *Proceedings, Annual Reliability and Maintainability Symposium.* IEEE, New York, pp. 383–389.

Phillips, G. J. and Hirschfeld, Fritz (1980). "Rotating Machinery Bearing Analysis." *Mechanical Engineering,* July, pp. 28–33.

Powell, Richard F. (1970). "Analyzing and Interpreting Field Failure Data." *Proceedings, Annual Symposium on Reliability and Maintainability.* IEEE, New York, pp. 94–100.

Richardson, Hugh W. (1981). "Designing for Customer Setup." *Quality,* October, pp. 62–65.

Robertson, James A. (1969). "Analyzing Field Failure." *Quality Progress,* January, pp. 12–13.

Rosenthal, Robert (1983). "Spare Part Quality Assurance." *Quality Progress,* May, pp. 24–27.

Sandholm, L. (1965). "Improving Quality Assurance." *Proceedings, IXth EOQC Conference, European Organization for Quality Control,* Rotterdam, pp. 186–203.

Sasaki, Osamu, Ohfuju, Tadashi, and Naoi, Tomoyoshi (1978). "The Quality Complaint

Index Being Used by Companies in Japan." *Proceedings of the International Conference on Quality Control,* Tokyo, pp. C1-17, C1-22.

Smith, R. P. (1979). "Research and Other Data in the Monitoring of Product Quality." *Journal of the Market Research Society, Great Britain,* vol. 21, no. 3, pp. 189–205.

Takeuchi, Hirotaka and Quelch, John A. (1983). "Quality is More than Making a Good Product." *Harvard Business Review,* July–August, pp. 139–145.

TARP (Technical Assistance Research Programs) (1976). *A National Survey of the Complaint/Handling Procedures Used by Consumers.* TARP, Washington, DC.

U.S. Consumer Product Safety Commission (1978). *Recall Effectiveness Study.* May, Washington, DC.

Whirlpool Corporation (1983). *America's Search for Quality.* Benton Harbor, MI, pp. 7–9.

SECTION 21

ADMINISTRATIVE AND SUPPORT OPERATIONS[1]

Frank M. Gryna

---

[1]In the Third Edition, the section on support operations was prepared by S. P. Zobel.

INTRODUCTION

The quality function involves numerous activities through which we achieve fitness for use. Those activities which directly influence the nature of the product (e.g., design, purchase of materials, fabrication, inspection) have received much attention from the quality "movement." However, there are other activities which, though indirectly influencing quality of product, have largely escaped the attention of the quality movement. This section examines the ways in which the quality concepts can be applied to these activities.

The literature has not created a generic term which can embrace all of these activities. In this handbook, the term "administrative and support operations" will be used to designate these activities. Administrative activities encompass operations required for the organization to complete its overall mission. Examples include finance (billing, accounts payable, accounts receivable, corporate accounting, etc.), personnel (recruiting, training, etc.), security, data processing and computers, plant engineering (preventive maintenance, building services, new construction, etc.), legal, general publications, and other activities. Support activities are those indirect activities which have some effect on the product itself, e.g., shipping, receiving, material, in-process and finished goods storage, traffic, product publications, advertising, and order filling.

Historical Perspective. The manufacturing company's mission is to produce a product which is fit for use, can create a market, and can thereby generate the company's income. Awareness of the interrelation between fitness for use and income has led the companies to the familiar product quality controls. These controls have been most highly developed on those aspects of product progression which are obvious to the user, i.e., materials, processes, products. The effect of the administrative and support operations on fitness for use has been less obvious, and may account for the underdevelopment of quality controls in these "indirect" activities.

This split in emphasis extends to the study of the performance of the human beings as well. Traditionally, the most intense studies of quality performance and of motivation for quality have been devoted to those people who have an obvious connection with the physical product, i.e., the inspectors and the production operators. Extension of this study to the "indirect" personnel has been a comparatively recent phenomenon. The number (and variety) of these personnel is considerable. Improvement of their contribution to the company's overall quality mission is a major opportunity which in most companies is still waiting to be realized. Taking action on the opportunity requires a better understanding of the effect on fitness for use.

People readily understand the importance of quality in manufacturing, research and development, and other technologically oriented functions. With the increased emphasis on a companywide approach to quality, personnel in administrative and support operations are wondering what quality means in their activities and "what they must do that is different." In administrative activities, the situation is not as clear. Some errors (e.g., a mistake in billing a customer for a product) can have a direct effect on the customer even though the error may not affect the physical product. Other errors (e.g., an error in a company newspaper or an error in the security activity) do not necessarily affect the product or the customer. For support operations, one can point to the effect that errors have on the product provided to the customer. For example, an error in the filling of orders for spare parts can result in the customer receiving the wrong spare parts.

However, errors in any activity usually must be corrected, and the corrective action requires additional effort analogous to rework in manufacturing. Even if no correction is made, the consequences of the errors represent a loss to someone.

The boundary line between "direct" and other quality activities has undergone considerable change in the twentieth century. The Chief Inspectors who emerged in the reorganizations following World War I tended to regard inspection, test, and metrology as the core quality activities. The rise of the Quality Engineer expanded this core through the concept of organized quality planning and defect prevention. The rise of the Reliability Engineer expanded the core further to include some vital activities inherent in the launching of new designs. In some industries (e.g., drug, food) the core now includes product packaging and storage. In all regulated industries the core now includes much of the documentation activity.

These changes underscore the dynamic nature of the boundary between direct quality activities and administrative and support quality activities. However, the direction of change has been essentially one way. The core has kept increasing, so that the administrative and support quality activities of today are all candidates to become the direct quality activities of tomorrow. At the same time, the growing complexity of industry has been creating new support activities which require new plans and controls to make them effective in control of quality.

The support activities are not unique to manufacturing industries. The service industries (see Section 33) likewise employ a wide array of administrative and support quality activities, many of which are identical to those used in the manufacturing industries. The tasks, the operations, and the tools are largely alike; what is different is the application and the emphasis.

Error Rates in Administrative and Support Activities. The potential for errors exists in *all* activities. A study made in an electronics organization identified these examples:

Fifty percent of time cards were in error.

Forty percent of all travel reservations made in one month were changed; two of them were changed nine times.

Ten percent of performance appraisals that were sampled in one month were returned because of lack of signatures.

Ten to fifteen percent of employee profiles required phone call follow up by the salary administration function.

Twenty to thirty percent of consignments to suppliers were in error.

Little work has been done to quantify the extent and cost of errors in support operations or administrative operations. It is the author's belief that the cost of poor quality for these activities is as great as the cost of poor quality directly associated with the product.

Relation to Other Sections of this Handbook. The sections on Field Intelligence, Supplier Relations, Marketing, and Customer Service discuss topics that are related to administrative and support operations. In addition, the section on Service Industries provides an additional reference because those industries use many administrative type activities. Finally, the concepts of quality planning, quality control, and quality improvement are discussed throughout this handbook, mainly as applied to the direct activities in an organization. These same three concepts apply fully to the administrative and support functions.

Defining Quality Responsibilities for Administrative and Support Activities. The concept of fitness for use can be a starting point in defining these responsibilities. At the outset, it is essential to identify the *users* or customers of the outputs. Table 21.1 shows examples of possible users for several support activities. Note that users can be internal as well as external to the company.

A further aid in defining quality responsibilities is the concept of the the three roles of each organization (see Section 6 under The Triple Role Concept). Every administrative and support activity plays the roles of user, processor, and supplier. Table 21.2 applies the concept to the personnel, finance, and warehouse and shipping. The entries in the table provide examples of activities pertinent to the three roles.

One of the units of IBM Corporation uses a "department activity analysis" which focuses on the following questions (IBM, 1984):

1. What functions or tasks does my department perform?
2. What are the key external interfaces (input/output)?
3. Have the requirements across those interfaces been clearly established?

TABLE 21.1   Examples of Multiple Users of Support Activities

Warehouse and shipping function	Finance function	Personnel function
Production withdraws raw material.	*Customers* receive invoices.	*Applicant* receives company information.
Production stores finished product.	*Suppliers* receive payments.	*Managers* receive information for hiring process.
Suppliers require documentation on deliveries.	*Employees* receive salary payments.	*Employees* receive training.
Purchasing Department requires documentation on receipts.	*Middle managers* receive cost reports.	*Government agencies* receive information on employees.
Finance Department requires documentation for invoices.	*Upper managers* receive financial reports and budgetary information.	*Outside agencies* receive information for recruiting.
	Stockholders receive financial information.	
	Government agencies receive financial information on the company and employees.	

TABLE 21.2 Examples of Triple Roles of Customer/User, Processor, and Supplier

Customer/user	Processor	Supplier
Personnel (recruitment) function		
Receive requisitions from interested customers	Review, critique job descriptions	Supply recruits to internal customers
Receive job descriptions	Publish information on job openings	Provide associated documentation
Receive feedback from interviews	Interview, screen job applicants	Provide induction to recruits when hired
	Conduct checks on references	
Finance (financial data) function		
Receive basic data from various sources	Establish data processing system	Publish reports
Receive feedbacks from published reports	Process data into summaries	Disseminate to internal and external customers
	Analyze data, prepare reports	
Warehouse and shipping function		
Acquire equipment needed to conduct operations	Store goods	Ship goods to destinations
Receive goods from production areas	Select goods to fill orders	Provide shipping documents, inventory data
	Package, ship	
Receive requisitions, customers' orders to be filled	Maintain inventory status	Respond to inquiries, feedback
Receive feedback from customers	Maintain equipment	

4. Have measurements been established to verify and track the quality of input, activity, output?

Three steps are used in the analysis:

1. List all major activities. For example, the list for one finance department is:
   a. Inventory analysis and review.
   b. Supplier sourcing decisions.
   c. Equipment justifications.
   d. Payroll processing.

   e. Pay adjustments.
   f. Banking activities.
   g. Billing.
   h. Variance report.
   i. Supplier payment.
   j. Special checks.
   k. Acceptance/rejection invoices.
   l. Rejected purchase report.
2. For *each* activity (Figure 21.1):
   a. List the inputs—What? From where?
   b. Analyze the work—Why do it? What is the value? Suppose it is not done?
   c. List the outputs—What? Who receives them?
3. For each activity (Figure 21.2):
   a. Meet with the supplier and agree on the requirements.
   b. Meet with the customer and agree on the requirements.
   c. Define the measurements that will evaluate output against requirements.

Of course, the supplier and customer may be internal or external to the company.
   Melan (1985) discusses techniques of process management in service and administrative operations at IBM. See also Section 10 under Team Performance: A Processing System Viewpoint.

Activity:	Dept.	Date:	Prepared By:

Input

What:
From:

Value Added — Work Accomplished in Dept.

Why Do:
Value Added:
Impact If Not Done:

Output

What:
To:

FIG. 21.1 Activity analysis for input and output (one sheet for each major activity).

Activity:	Dept.	Date:	Prepared By:

What are the input requirements that you and your supplier have agreed to?
-
-
-
-

What are the output requirements that you and your customer have agreed to?
-
-
-
-

What are the quality measurements that will show if your output meets requirements?
-
-
-
-

FIG. 21.2   Supplier and customer analysis.

QUALITY PLANNING FOR ADMINISTRATIVE AND SUPPORT ACTIVITIES

The general approach to quality planning (see Section 6, Companywide Planning for Quality) applies fully to quality planning for administrative and support activities.

Identify the Customers.   The starting point is to identify the customers or users of the service provided by the administrative or support activities. This identification is aided by constructing a flow diagram to show the progression of the activities and thereby to see who is impacted. Figure 21.3 is an example of such a flow diagram (International Paper Company, 1984).

External Customers.   Those who are impacted, but are not within the same company as the administrative and support departments, are external customers. External customers include:

1. *Clients:*   They buy products (goods and services); they receive products and product information; they receive invoices; they receive requests for feedback of data.
2. *Regulatory agencies:*   They monitor products and product information; they issue regulations and receive requests for interpretation.
3. *The public:*   Members of the public may be impacted due to the effect of products on human safety, health, or on the environment.
4. *The community:*   It may be impacted by numerous practices relative to: employee relations; neighborhood noise, odors, congestion; participation in community affairs; payment of community taxes.

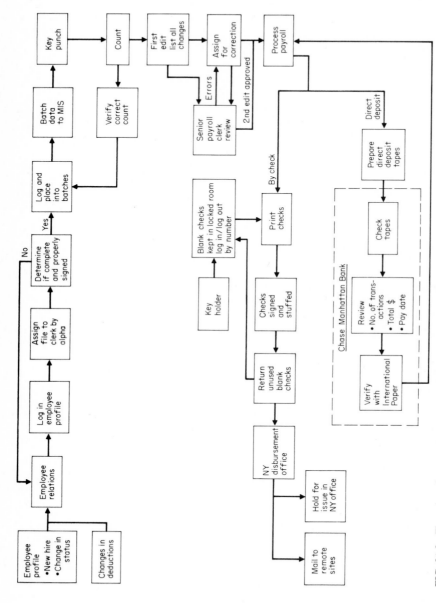

FIG. 21.3 Flow chart for payroll changes. *(Courtesy International Paper Co.)*

Internal Customers. Within any company, each internal department supplies products to other internal departments. For example:

Supplying departments	Major products	Some internal customers
Finance	Financial statements	Managers
Employment	Recruits	All departments
Order editing	Edited orders	Operations
Office services	Office space, supplies, maintenance	All office departments
Legal	Legal advice	All departments

Vital Few Customers. Customers are not equally important. Their importance follows the Pareto principle: a relative few of the customers absorb most of the impact. The planning process requires that these vital few customers be identified so that their needs will become known and met.

Discover the Needs of Customers. Customer needs consist primarily of (*a*) product satisfaction and (*b*) freedom from product dissatisfaction. While such are the primary needs, discovery of those needs requires some looking below the surface.

Stated Needs and Real Needs. Customer's stated needs often differ from the real needs. For example, an internal department asks the finance office for a change in some cost standard. The real reason may be to avoid criticism for cost overruns.

Difference in Perceptions. Customers' perceptions often differ from those of suppliers. For example, a personnel office perceives the need to train the work force in some specialty. However, the line managers do not perceive such training as helping their departments meet departmental goals. In like manner, a budget office may propose a new procedure which will reduce the amount of work in the budget office. However, the line departments may resist the proposal because their work is increased.

Cultural Needs. The needs of customers, especially internal customers, go beyond products and processes. They include needs for job security, self-respect, respect of others, continuity of habit patterns, and still other elements of what is broadly called cultural values. While such needs are real they are seldom stated openly. Instead they are stated in disguised form.

A widespread example is "turf," i.e., the "ownership" of some area of responsibility, expertise, etc. Such ownership confers status; a threat to the ownership is a threat to that status.

Strategies for Determining Customer Needs. To learn about customer needs in adequate detail, suppliers make use of multiple strategies.

Be a Customer. Here the supplier carries out some activities similar to those carried out by customers. For example, some departments, e.g., office service, supply service to themselves as well as to other departments. A second form of "be a customer" is to provide the supplier personnel with training—to assign them to conducting the activities carried out by customers.

Communicate with Customers. This is the most widely used form of discovering customers' needs. Some of it is initiated by customers who have endured product dissatisfactions. Some is initiated by suppliers who are conducting researches on product satisfaction. In too many companies the emphasis on external customers is so dominant that the needs of internal customers suffer from inattention.

Simulation. Simulation is a further way of identifying needs of customers, in administrative and support activities as well as in model shops and pilot plants. A well-known example is training in simulated environments. In selected cases the concept offers cost-effective ways of reducing risks. However, the concept is itself subject to risks. Chief of these is the "two worlds" phenomenon—the world of the laboratory and the world of operations. These two worlds can differ widely in their mission, scale of operations, technology, and personnel. These differences demand that any extrapolation from laboratory findings be based on inputs from both worlds.

Tools for Determining Customer Needs. The principal tools include

The flow diagram: See above, under Identify the Customers.

The spreadsheet: In cases involving many customers and needs it is useful to organize the information in the form of a spreadsheet (table, matrix). Then, as the planning progresses further, additional entries are made. The spreadsheet provides an orderly means for assuring that essential tasks are carried out. For examples of a planning spreadsheet, see Section 13, Figures 13.2 and 13.3.

Marketing research: The tools of marketing research are used especially to determine customer needs for product performance. This applies to internal customers as well as to external customers. For a discussion of marketing research as applied to quality, see Section 12, under Some Simple Tools for Collecting Field Intelligence and under Competitive Evaluations.

Translation of Customer Needs. Customer needs may be stated in any of several languages:

The customer's language

The supplier's language

A common language

When customer needs are stated in the customer's language it becomes necessary to translate such needs into either the supplier's language or a common language. This necessity applies to internal customers as well as to external customers.

Beyond sheer differences in language, translation may be required due to vague terminology and to local dialects peculiar to specific functions, companies, industries, and countries. The remedies include a glossary of meanings of key terms; physical samples; use of special departments to provide translation, e.g., Order Editing; standardization; and establishment of measurement. (See below.)

Establish Measurement. A major aid for determining customer needs is some means of expressing those needs in numbers, i.e., measurement. If such means can be made available they will also be major aids throughout the entire quality planning process.

Units of Measure and Sensors. To "say it in numbers" requires a system of measurement consisting of

A unit of measure: A defined amount of some quality features which permits evaluation of that feature in numbers

A sensor: A method or instrument which can carry out the evaluation, and state the findings in numbers, in terms of the unit of measure

In the case of physical goods, the unit of measure is often technological in nature—millimeters, grams, amperes, hours. The associated sensors are technological instruments—calipers, scales, ammeters, clocks. For products from administrative and support activities, the units of measure are often statistical and financial in nature—percent of on-time deliveries, percent errors in billing (or transportation, warehousing, etc). The associated sensors are the basic documents—clock cards, material requisitions, etc.—as well as the data systems which summarize the information for use by the various customers. Figure 6.10 in Section 6 depicts how the various units of measure constitute a sort of pyramid of measure.

For added discussion of units of measure, see Section 18.

Human Sensing. Human sensing takes place at all levels of the hierarchy of measurement. At the basic data level human beings must decide: which accounts should be charged with these hours of time; which of several tasks has top priority. At higher levels, similar questions arise with respect to use of summaries, indexes, etc. In addition, human sensing is subject to various sources of error. A discussion of Evaluation of Performance later in this section includes a listing of some of the common types of error along with the usual remedial steps.

Product Development. In administrative and support activities, "products" consist mainly of services of various kinds. Typical examples for various functions are as follows:

Function	*Products*
Controller	Budget, controls, financial reports
Personnel	Courses, employment candidates
Purchasing	Supplier list, purchase contracts
Materials handling	Packaging, transport, storage

The purpose of these products is to meet customer needs. The building block of product design is the *product feature.* Each specific customer need is met through development of some product feature which responds to that specific need. (See Section 13 for discussion of product development tasks.)

Optimize Product Design. Application of product development tasks to administrative and support activities requires extensive collaboration with customers. These customers are primarily internal customers, so that there is great need for participation. Such participation is needed to assure that the products meet the needs of the customers and that the product designs will optimize company performance, not departmental performance. For elaboration see Section 6 under Optimizing Product Design.

Process Development. The purpose of this step in the planning sequence is to provide a process which is capable of producing the product features. In administrative and support activities, such processes are called systems, procedures, routines, etc. Specific process features must correspond to specific product features, just as specific product features must correspond to specific customer needs.

Section 16, Manufacturing Planning, deals with process development as applied to production of goods. The same concepts are fully applicable to the administrative and support activities for producing services. A major difference is the greater impact of the latter on internal customers. This difference in turn requires that developers of processes for producing administrative and support services establish close collaboration with the line departments to assure product fitness for use and optimal cost performance.

Process Capability. An essential requirement of any process is that it should be capable of meeting the product goals under operating conditions. To a degree this capability can be quantified sufficiently to be used in the planning process. This concept of process capability is widely used in administrative and support activities as well as in manufacturing processes. Examples include the following:

Function	Subject of process capability information
Purchasing	Credit worthiness of suppliers
Certification of suppliers as to quality	Product quality of suppliers
Sales potential of various territories	Marketing
Certification of workers as to qualification to perform critical tasks	Personnel

Transfer to Operations. This final step in the planning process is often carried out with formality since there is a shift of responsibility from the planning forces to the operating forces. Prior to this shift of responsibility, steps should have been taken to:

Prove Process Capability. The process should be able to meet the product goals under operating conditions. This proof may be established in various ways: quantify process capability as discussed in Section 16 under Process Capability Measurements; conduct pilot tests under operating conditions; conduct tests under simulated operating conditions.

In one company (IBM, 1984) process capability was approached through a concept of certifying "key business processes." In one area, key processes included contract management, billing, accounts receivable, order entry, backlog, sales compensation, software, spare parts, inventory, payment generation, accounting, and materials management.

To apply the certification concept, an "owner" is designated for each key business process. For a functional process, the functional manager is the owner. For a cross-functional process, the manager of one of the key functions is designated as owner.

The key processes are then "rated" on a scale of 1 (best) to 5 for several features: control of the process, adequacy of quality management, and progress on quality improvement. Criteria are established for each level of rating, and the owner of the process is made responsible for bringing the process up to the targeted levels of rating.

Latzko (1985) presents a procedure for quantifying capability in administrative activities using attribute data on error rates. Dmytrow (1985) shows the role of control charts in evaluating capability for data collection and review processes.

Prove Process Controllability.   Here the purpose is to establish that the operating forces have been put into a state of self-control with respect to the process. Such a state of self-control requires providing the operating forces with:

1. Means of knowing what are the product and process goals
2. Means of evaluating actual performance and comparing actual to goals
3. Means to take action on the difference

Table 21.3 consists of a list of questions which are pertinent to determining whether a state of self-control has been established. The list makes clear that a good deal of thought and analysis can be involved in attaining such a state.

Transfer Know-How.   The minimal information transfer consists of the product and process specification plus the associated procedures manuals. However the planners invariably possess additional know-how which can be of value to the operating forces. Transfer of this added know-how requires special steps to be taken: briefing meetings; on-the-job training in which the planners participate as instructors; formal training courses. A widespread example of transfer of such additional know-how has been in the area of introducing word processors into administrative and support activities.

TABLE 21.3   Questions for Analyzing Self-Control

---

1. Have personnel been provided with the means of knowing what they are supposed to do?
   a. Have written policies, guidelines or procedures been developed?
   b. Have quality standards been developed?
   c. Do personnel have ready access to *a* and *b*?
   d. Do they fully understand *a* and *b* and use them?
   e. Do they know whom to consult to interpret *a* and *b*?
   f. Do they know how the results of their activity will be used?
   g. Do they know the consequences to the user of a failure to meet the requirements in *a* and *b*?
   h. Are changes in *a* and *b* transmitted rapidly to personnel affected?
   i. Do personnel know what to do when inputs to them contain errors or omissions?
2. Have personnel been provided with the means of knowing what they are doing?
   a. Are personnel provided with some means of evaluating the adequacy and completeness of their work, e.g., quality standards, checklists, etc.?
   b. Are they told how often to sample their work? Is time allowed to do the checking?
   c. Are they required to record the results of checking of their work?
   d. Is there any independent check of the work?
   e. Are personnel provided with feedback on the quality of their work?
   f. Are there provisions for periodically checking the accuracy of records prepared by support and administrative personnel?
   g. Do supervisors have a record of performance of individual personnel?
3. Have personnel been provided with the means of regulating their work?
   a. Has the quality capability of the activity been evaluated in quantitative terms and compared to the goal?
   b. Do personnel have criteria for defining when their activity requires correction?
   c. Do personnel know what to do when the criteria for action are exceeded?
   d. Have the actions which cause errors been diagnosed and told to personnel?
   e. Have the actions which prevent errors been diagnosed and told to personnel?

QUALITY CONTROL FOR ADMINISTRATIVE AND SUPPORT ACTIVITIES

As used in this handbook, quality control consists essentially of:

Evaluating actual quality performance

Comparing actual performance to quality goals

Taking action on the difference

Quality control has long been practiced in administrative and support activities. In fact, the bulk of the literature in this area deals with quality control and the associated statistical tools.

The Feedback Loop. The conceptual approach behind quality control is the feedback loop. Many sections of the handbook discuss application of the feedback loop to specific functional areas. In addition, some sections deal with the general-use tools through which the feedback loop is applied, e.g., Section 24 on Statistical Process Control. To avoid duplication, this Section 21 will give some examples of application of elements of the feedback loop to administrative and support activities, along with examples of use of specific tools.

Control Subjects. Each feedback loop is centered on a control subject which is a goal of some sort, e.g., a product goal, a process goal. For example, in the personnel recruitment area, control subjects consist of such matters as:

Adequacy of job descriptions

Effectiveness of interviews

Effectiveness of reference checks

Time required to complete the recruitment

Quality of applicants

Yield of the recruitment process

Performance of persons after hiring

Accuracy of documentation

Evaluation of Performance. Conceptually, evaluation for administrative and support activities is identical with that used for product-related activities. However, the units of measure and the associated sensors are mainly financial and statistical rather than technological. In addition, evaluation for these activities tends to require human sensing to a significant degree. Because of error-proneness of human sensing, special precautions should be taken, as set out in Table 21.4.

The administrative and support departments have made extensive use of measures of performance. Mainly these have related to cost and productivity but there are measures of quality as well. The two most widely used have been:

1. *Error rate:* Here the measure consists of a fraction in which the numerator is the number of errors, and the denominator is the number of opportunities for error. Through data summaries this fraction can be applied at any level of organization.

2. *Promptness of service:* The usual units of measure have been either (*a*) time required to provide service, or (*b*) percent of delivery promises met. (To a recipient of service, promptness is a major quality requirement.)

TABLE 21.4 Human Error Types and Remedies

Error types	Remedies
Misinterpretation	Precise definition; glossary Check lists Examples
Inadvertent errors	Aptitude testing Reorganization of work to reduce fatigue and monotony Fail-safe designs Redundancy Foolproofing (error-proofing) Automation, robotics
Lack of technique	Discovery of knack of successful workers Revision of technology to incorporate the knack Retraining
Conscious errors: coloration, bias, futility	Design review of data collection plan Remove atmosphere of blame Act on reports, or give explanation for no action Depersonalize the orders Establish accountability Provide balanced emphasis on goals Conduct quality audits Create competition, incentives Reassign the work

There is considerable need for development of further units of measure in the administrative and support area. Generally the approach is to ask those who will be impacted to propose nominations on how to measure quality. Reports are then prepared and published in response to the nominations. Those reports which seem to be useful are retained and improved. The rest are discarded.

QUALITY IMPROVEMENT IN ADMINISTRATIVE AND SUPPORT ACTIVITIES

The general approach to quality improvement is set out in Section 22, Quality Improvement. This approach is fully applicable to administrative and support activities.

Historically, most quality improvement was directed at product-related activities. However, with the emergence of the quality crisis in the late 1970s, many companies began to expand their efforts to improve quality. This expansion was at first limited to product-related activities. It has since been extended to include administrative and support activities as well. This trend seems to be irreversible.

Two examples of application can be seen in the materials handling function.

1. An apparatus manufacturer used a large amount of steel. Because of a shortage of covered storage space, much steel was stored in an uncovered yard. Before

being placed in open storage, the steel was treated with a rust preservative. However, there was much rusting since the materials handlers had no way of applying a first-in, first-out method of stock rotation. The support department (Materials Management) met all criticisms with a demand for more covered storage space. However, a quality improvement project uncovered an alternative solution by periodically changing the color of the rust preservative to enable the materials handlers to rotate the stock.

2. A team study of causes of poor customer service established that a prime cause was loss of product identification which in turn was caused by the pulling off, in transit, of the tickets which were wired to the pans. Following tryout of several alternatives, this long-standing method was replaced by use of self-adhesive clear plastic envelopes.

The action needed is an application of the breakthrough sequence (see Section 22 under The Universal Sequence for Breakthrough). It is particularly important to establish proof of the need for quality improvement. A useful starting point is to estimate the cost of poor quality in the administrative and support activities. Higgins and Dice (1984) describe a computer-assisted technique for analyzing and quantifying the time spent in administrative activities. Such analysis can help to estimate the cost of poor quality.

Tools of Diagnosis. Reported case examples of quality improvement in administrative and support areas show that the tools of diagnosis are identical with those used in product-oriented quality improvement projects.

Pareto Analysis. The Pareto concept is discussed in Section 22 under The Project Concept. Table 21.5 shows an analysis of the time spent performing various tasks in a finance function (Witterick, 1983). The Pareto analysis shows that of the 15 tasks, the top four account for 48 percent of the total time spent. (These tasks then become candidates for automation.) Surprisingly, the traditional function of typing consumed the least amount of personal time.

Another application of the Pareto concept comes from a study of paperwork problems in a receiving department. The Pareto analysis appears in graphic form

TABLE 21.5   Functional Analysis

Task	Percent of personal time	Cumulative percent
Forms and invoices	19	19
Planning	11	30
Writing	9	39
Arithmetic	9	48
Informal discussion	8	56
Reading	8	64
Local telephone calls	6	70
Data entry	5	75
Filing	5	80
Remote telephone calls	5	85
Formal meetings	5	90
Systems activity	4	94
Word processing	3	97
Photocopying	2	99
Typing	1	100

FIG. 21.4 Pareto chart. *(Courtesy General Motors.)*

in Figure 21.4 (General Motors, 1984). Missing bill of lading and packing slips are the main symptoms.

Cause-and-Effect Diagram. The cause-and-effect diagram is described in Section 22 under Generation of Theories. Figure 21.5 shows the cause-and-effect diagram for the problem of analyzing delays in filling open personnel requisitions. This diagram helped to raise a question about the time taken by hiring managers to review and return resumés. Data collection and dissection of the process

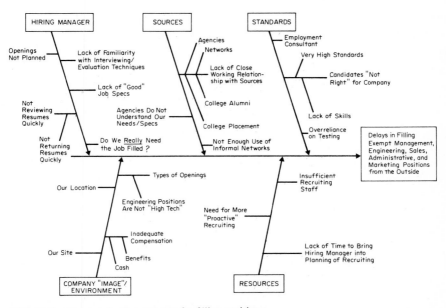

FIG. 21.5 Cause-and-effect diagram for filling positions.

FIG. 21.6 Cause-and-effect diagram for transportation damage. *(Courtesy General Motors.)*

answered the question. Also, the diagram made clear that the process included a variety of inputs and the existence of subjective elements such as standards, applicant's perception of the company image, and the organizational environment or climate.

Another example (General Motors, 1984) of a cause-and-effect diagram is related to the transportation of product from the plant to the customer (Figure 21.6). The problem was damage to taillights during transportation of 1-ton trucks. Of course the theories shown in the diagram remain to be tested through data collection and analysis.

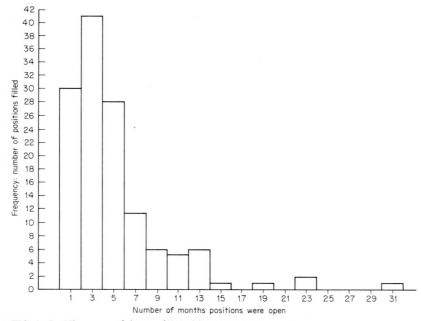

FIG. 21.7 Histogram of time to fill positions. *(From Leonard, p. 13.)*

Frequency Distribution and Histogram. Section 23 under Descriptive Statistics for Summarizing Data discusses the Frequency Distribution and Histogram. In an application to a personnel function, data collected on the time required to fill open personnel requisitions were summarized in a histogram (Figure 21.7). Analysis showed that the average time was about 5 months, the range was about 30 months, and 75 percent of the 132 filled positions were filled within 6 months or less.

Dissection of a Process. Dissection of a process into steps is presented in Section 22 under Product and Process Dissection. Applying this concept to the study of the time required to fill personnel requisitions resulted in some surprises. In Figure 21.8, a sample of data for 24 hires is analyzed by breaking the total processing

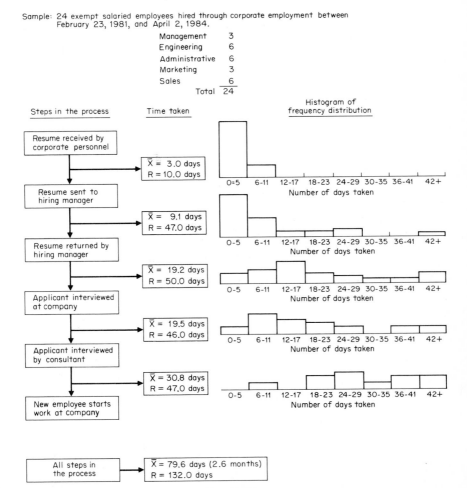

FIG. 21.8 Dissection of process for filling positions. *(From Leonard, p. 15.)*

time down into its component steps. This dissection of the total time led to several important conclusions:

1. Of the total time to fill requisitions (an average of 5.02 months), more than half (2.6 months) is spent moving the successful applicant through the *internal* company process of interviewing and decision making. Thus, to reduce the overall time to fill positions, two problems had to be addressed—the time to find the right resumé or person, and the time to move that person through the rest of the process.

2. The 30.8 days average time between the consultant interview and a new employee starting work is misleading. This number includes time over which the company had no control, i.e., the notice that people give to a former employer before leaving, and vacation time between jobs.

3. Some people take significantly longer than others to make it through the process.

Dissection of the problem into steps and the quantification at each step provided constructive information to replace the unsubstantiated beliefs, some of which turned out to be false.

Statistical Control Chart.   Section 24, Statistical Process Control, explains the concept of the control chart. Baker and Artinian (1985) describe how control charts analyzed a system for auditing freight bills and making payments to the external carrier. Audits of freight bills revealed many errors which then caused delays in making payments. As one part of a study, data were collected on the time from receipt of a freight invoice to issuance of the check to the carrier. An average and range chart (Figure 21.9) showed the system to be in statistical con-

FIG. 21.9   Control charts for time required to process bills. *(Courtesy Baker and Artinian, 1985.)*

trol but at a level that was too high—an average of about 14 days. (When combined with mail delays and other factors, some carriers would wait for at least 35 days for payment.)

With the knowledge that the process was in statistical control, attention was directed to analyzing the system itself. Using a cause-and-effect diagram, the major reasons for rejection of freight bills were identified. Further analysis resulted in changes in the steps to audit bills and make payments. Results were dramatic: Bills rejected were reduced from 34 percent to under 1 percent; time required to process bills dropped from an average of 15 days to 6 days with an associated reduction in variation (Figure 21.9).

McCabe (1985) presents applications of control charts to employee communications, employee medical examinations, purchase orders, and office rearrangements. Control charts as an aid in improving the quality of data collection and review for price index preparation is discussed by Dmytrow (1985).

Sampling.   Sampling is widely employed in administrative and support activities. The resulting data are used in all managerial processes, quality planning, control, and improvement. Great strides have been made in conducting sampling in accordance with valid statistical methodology as discussed in Sections 23, 24, and 25 of this handbook.

Glasser (1985) provides a detailed discussion of statistical sampling concepts applied to paperwork operations. The American Institute of Certified Public Accountants (1986) provides step-by-step procedures for financial auditing.

Reliability Engineering Tools.   A collection of reliability engineering tools, both quantitative and qualitative, is presented in this handbook. (See Section 13 under Planning for Time-Oriented Performance and Section 23 under Reliability.) These tools were originally developed to evaluate reliability during design and to measure reliability during use by the customer.

A major application to administrative and support activities is in the area of facilities maintenance. Nowlan and Heap (1978) present an uncommonly comprehensive discussion of use of reliability models and other tools to improve quality and productivity in aircraft maintenance. The concepts are applicable to maintenance of any type of product or facility.

Another application is in purchase of facilities. Administrative and support areas are purchasers and users of a variety of equipment including plant facilities, materials handling equipment, computers, and office equipment. Many of these items are relatively complex and involve a considerable investment. Opportunities exist to apply reliability engineering methods during the selection, specification, and usage phases for these equipments.

ORGANIZING THE ADMINISTRATIVE AND SUPPORT QUALITY ACTIVITIES

Administrative and support quality activities are carried out by a variety of company departments, outside suppliers, and after-sales service companies. These organizations pursue their departmental or company goals, including quality goals. However, they are often handicapped in meeting their goals because of limitations in organization structure. A widespread such limitation relates to participation in broad quality planning.

Participation in Planning. Administrative and support activities do conduct departmental planning for their assigned functions. However, because of their seeming detachment from the "mainstream" of product-oriented operations, there is often a failure to plan for the interaction of administrative and support activities with the activities of other departments. For example, during the launching of a new product the Customer Service Department may be brought into the picture only after the product and process have been designed, and production has commenced. In such cases the failure to provide Customer Service with participation in the planning will result in a failure to provide early warning of problems ahead. The resulting quality problems become after-the-fact crises.

An organized approach to orchestration can consist of:

1. Identification of those aspects of the work of administrative and support operations which significantly affect product quality. This identification can logically be done by a study team which includes the support department and the Quality Department.

2. Coordination of these significant operations through a well-known table of delegation:

Activity	Role of support organization	Role of quality department
Quality planning	X	X
Execution of plan	X	
Audit of execution versus plan		X

Such an approach retains for the administrative and support activities their jurisdiction over their day-to-day operations. Orchestration is provided through the joint planning and through the audit.

Provision for Diagnosis. The administrative and support departments commonly lack specialists in problem analysis. Hence, this analysis must be done by the supervision or by outside staff specialists. A progressive step is to enlist the service of the quality staff specialists for diagnosis of chronic quality troubles.

REFERENCES

American Institute of Certified Public Accountants (1986). *Codification of Statements on Auditing Standards.* AICPA, New York.

Baker, Edward M. and Artinian, Harry L. (1985). "The Deming Philosophy of Continuing Improvement in a Service Organization: The Case of Windsor Export Supply." *Quality Progress,* June, pp. 61–69.

Dmytrow, Eric D. (1985). "Process Capability in the Service Sector." *The Juran Report,* no. 5, summer, pp. 31–37.

General Motors Corporation (1984). Internal document of Truck and Bus Division.

Glasser, Gerald J. (1985). "Quality Audits of Paperwork Operations—The First Step toward Quality Control." *Journal of Quality Technology,* vol. 17, no. 2, April, pp. 100–107.

Higgins, Brian K. and Dice, Christopher, M. (1984). "Quantifying White Collar Functions." *National Productivity Review,* summer, pp. 288–302.

IBM Corporation (1984). *IBM FSD Owego Excellence Plus Manual.* Owego, NY, pp. VIII–9 to 15.

International Paper Company (1984). *Quality Management Concepts,* section on CTQ Flow Charting. IPCO, New York.

Latzko, William J. (1985). "Process Capability in Administrative Applications." *ASQC Quality Congress Transactions,* Milwaukee, pp. 168–173.

McCabe, William J. (1985). "A Service Organization Improved Quality and Cut Costs at the Same Time." *Quality Progress,* June, pp. 85–89.

Melan, E. H. (1985). "Process Management in Service and Administrative Operations." *Quality Progress,* June, pp. 52–59.

Nowlan, F. Stanley and Heap, Howard F. (1978). *Reliability-Centered Maintenance.* Catalog no. ADA 066579, National Technical Information Service, Springfield, VA 22161.

Witterick, Leonard W. (1983). "Juran Training in the Financial Area." *The Juran Report,* no. 2, November, pp. 82–86.

SECTION 22
QUALITY IMPROVEMENT[1]

Frank M. Gryna

---

[1]In the Third Edition, the section on Quality Improvement was prepared by J. M. Juran.

INTRODUCTION

"Improvement" as used in this section is the attainment of a new level of performance that is superior to any previous level. This superiority is attained by applying the breakthrough concept to problems of quality.

Other sections of the handbook provide important supplementary material for this section. For example, see all of the sections presenting statistical concepts (particularly Section 23, Basic Statistical Methods); Section 10, Managing Human Performance (especially discussions of the human aspects of achieving change); and Section 6, Companywide Planning for Quality, on the elements of the feedback loop that is basic to the control process. Elaboration of the role of upper management in quality improvement is covered in Section 5 under Policies on Improvement and in Section 8 under Participation by Upper Management and also under Quality Audits by Upper Managers.

Quality improvement encompasses both improving fitness for use and reducing the level of defects or errors. Both of these activities apply to all customers—internal and external. Improving fitness for use can have some important benefits:

Better quality for the users

Higher market share for the manufacturer

Premium price for the manufacturer

Status in the marketplace for the manufacturer

Reducing the level of defects and errors also provides multiple benefits:

Lower costs and fewer irritations for users

Dramatically lower costs for the manufacturer

Improved productivity; more useable product is produced with the same resources

Reduction in inventories to assist the just-in-time concept

These benefits are further supplemented by improved teamwork resulting from the project team concept and opportunities for worker participation on improvement projects.

Despite these obvious benefits, most organizations have traditionally conducted their affairs with limited priority on improvement. During periods of economic growth, products are saleable if they are generally competitive as to quality. The costs due to poor quality are passed on to customers in the form of higher prices.

Wolf (1983) itemizes how the advantages of improved quality, cost reduction, and improved productivity came about on 10 pilot quality improvement projects. Lossin (1983) discusses some of the side benefits of a quality improvement program.

Fire Fighting versus Improvement. "Improvement" as defined above in the introduction relates to the chronic level of poor quality as shown in Figure 22.1.

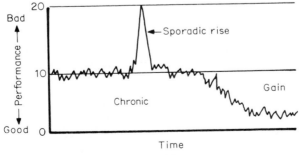

FIG. 22.1   Relation of chronic level improvement.

Figure 22.1 illustrates what is meant by quality improvement. It also brings out the critical distinction between chronic and sporadic quality problems. The figure shows one process for which the defect level regularly runs at about 10 percent. This 10 percent is the area marked "chronic." This chronic defect level goes on and on until some specific action is taken to change it—the action called quality improvement. Thus, quality improvement refers to a change in the *level* of quality.

Figure 22.1 also shows a sporadic departure from the historic level—a "spike" on the chart. This spike is the result of some sudden change in the process. The sudden rise triggers off various alarm signals. In response, the company personnel take "corrective action" to "put out the fire."

In many organizations, the word "improvement" has been considered as synonymous with "corrective action," meaning fire fighting such as getting rid of that sporadic "spike" in Figure 22.1.

EXPERIENCE WITH PRIOR IMPROVEMENT PROGRAMS

A major requirement for a quality improvement program is that it be well received by those impacted—the managers, supervisors, and the work force. This receptivity depends greatly on the history of prior programs of improvement.

Most organizations make use of periodic (annual or so) programs or drives to improve their performance. These programs aim at various targets: quality, productivity, safety, etc. When teams of managers are asked to review and critique the history of a number of such prior programs, they usually arrive at conclusions similar to those set out in Table 22.1. Peters (1983) discusses some of the reasons for success and potential weaknesses in a quality improvement program in a plant manufacturing an automobile component. Holm (1984) presents some "dos" and "don'ts" based on experiences in a quality improvement program at a petroleum equipment manufacturing organization.

The critiques listed in Table 22.1 point to some obstacles to achieving quality improvement.

"Here Comes Another One."   Any new "program," "drive," etc., is suspect. In all companies the personnel have seen a procession of improvement programs come and go. The subject matter has varied (e.g., safety, costs, morale, quality),

TABLE 22.1   Usual Strengths and Weaknesses of Prior Improvement Programs

Strengths	Weaknesses
Upper management was involved at the launching	Upper management did not stay involved
The visibility of the subject matter was raised	More work was demanded of all: attendance at meetings, filling out questionnaires, etc.
Educational materials and training were provided	No provision was made for doing the added work
A coordinator was appointed	The results were not as good as the advocates had promised
Means were provided for recognition	The program did not last. It was pushed aside to make room for the next program

but the features of the programs were alike. Some of the features were positive, but others were negative.

The results fell short of the promises of the advocates, and each program was pushed off center stage by the next program.

These and other negatives create an ever-growing crust of skepticism, so that a new program may be greeted with a cynical "Here comes another one." At the outset the new program is suspected of guilt by association.

Lack of Upper Management Involvement.   Upper managers would like to avoid getting deeply involved into yet another problem. Hence they are tempted to delegate quality improvement to subordinates. However, the subordinate managers are guided more by the actions of upper managers than by their words. If the upper managers do not become actively involved, the subordinates conclude that upper management does not give high priority to quality improvement.

No Organized Approach.   Most companies do not realize that to attain annual quality improvement requires a comprehensive and organized approach. Lacking that knowledge, they conclude that one or another of the roads (see below) constitutes a total solution.

Increased Workload.   To secure annual improvement at a revolutionary pace adds to every participant's workload. The return on investment is remarkable. (It also will in due course reduce the time spent in fire fighting.) However, the investment in added work must precede the return on investment. Persuading upper managers to make that investment has been a serious obstacle.

No Provision for Reward.   All operating managers have long had clear responsibility for meeting *operating* goals, including quality goals but not including quality *improvement* goals. The resulting legitimacy gives those operating goals a first claim on the time of the operating managers. The prevailing reward systems make little or no provision for rewarding efforts devoted to annual quality improvement.

SPORADIC AND CHRONIC PROBLEMS

Basic to the success of a quality improvement program is the distinction between chronic and sporadic quality problems (see Figure 22.1). Most of the time, the quality performance stays within a rather narrow range. However, occasionally the performance departs greatly from the historic level and results in a spike on the chart. These occasional departures from the usual level are "sporadic" quality problems. For example, if the percent defective has been averaging about 10 percent and suddenly jumps to 20 percent, a variety of alarm signals go off. In response, the supervision converges on the scene, investigates, finds out what has changed, and restores performance to the regular 10 percent. The names given to this action are "fire fighting" or "troubleshooting." This activity of restoring the status quo is not the basic kind of improvement to be emphasized in this section. (It will, however, be mentioned later in the section.)

Suppose it is desired to reduce the regular level of 10 percent defective down to 3 percent. This is a "chronic" quality problem because the 10 percent level has existed for a long time. Changing the chronic level of quality *is* the object of this section.

The action taken on the chronic problem is different from that taken on the sporadic. Because the chronic problem has existed for some time, it is often concluded, with reluctance, that the 10 percent level must be lived with and accepted. Several actions may be taken to condone and make this level legitimate: e.g., order an extra 10 percent of material so that despite the 10 percent waste enough good product will be available to meet delivery schedules.

The "regular" continuing 10 percent defect level involves far more money than the amount under the spike. Why is it then that industrial companies do not attack these chronic losses? The reasons are usually because:

1. The chronic losses do not sound any alarms; the alarm signals were disconnected long ago by building waste allowances into cost and other standards.
2. The competitors are usually also enduring the same losses. When such is the case, it is feasible to price the product so as to cover the losses.
3. Managers are unaware that solutions to chronic problems require a special series of managerial actions, each series centered around a specific improvement project. The project approach (discussed below) requires an investment of the time of management and professional personnel. Lacking such an investment, no improvement will happen; the chronic losses will go on and on.

In most companies the response to sporadic quality problems is excellent. Managers and specialists are experienced, effective fire fighters. What is missing is fire prevention—an attack on the chronic levels of waste. These two activities—fire fighting and fire prevention—are remarkably different in their nature. That difference requires a fundamentally different approach to tackle the major opportunity for improvement, i.e., chronic problems.

THE PHASED APPROACH

This "phased approach" describes the sequence of activities (phases) evolved by those companies who have made the most progress toward annual quality improvement.

Awareness.   Awareness is the phase of convincing managers that there is a need to do something different with respect to quality. This conviction is secured by a mixture of:

Citing case examples of loss of sales due to poor quality

Citing case examples in which quality improvement also resulted in cost reduction, improved on-time delivery, higher productivity, etc.

Estimating the cost of poor quality to dramatize the opportunities for further cost reduction

Explaining the opportunities for increasing share of market, or for securing premium prices through quality leadership

Dramatizing the crisis atmosphere resulting from foreign competition

(Further elaboration relative to this phase is provided below under Proof of the Need.)

Setting Goals. The actual goals chosen by companies vary widely. Here are some of the more popular goals:

Quality is number one: There are meanings lurking behind this popular statement. Quite often the number one priority in the company has not been quality; it has been delivery date, or whatever. A major reason behind publicizing "quality is number one" is to announce a change in priority without admitting that it is a change.

Cut the cost of poor quality: This popular goal is sometimes quantified, e.g., "We will cut the cost of poor quality by 50 percent in the next 3 years."

Quality leadership in the marketplace: This is also a frequent goal. It is worded variously. An example from the electronics industry is: "New products may be put on the market only if their reliability is superior to that of competition."

Not limited to manufacture: We are in the early stages of a healthy movement to extend the concept of quality improvement to all the company's functions—not just manufacture. Some of the wordings of goals provide for this extension, e.g., "Quality applies to everything we do—to all of our functions and to every person's job."

No goals: An astonishing number of companies do not set out specific quality goals to be reached. Instead, they adopt some new approach in the hope that it will take them to better results. Most of the time, such hopes are not realized.

Organizing the Overall Program. The project-by-project approach to improvement requires not only the support but the involvement (through hands-on leadership) of upper management. A major form of this involvement is through a "quality improvement council."

Quality Improvement Council. A quality improvement council is a group of upper managers appointed to guide, support, and coordinate the overall program. Such councils may be established at several levels—corporate, division, function, plant. Examples are discussed by Douglas (1984), Noakes (1984), and Woodward (1984). For any level, membership consists of upper managers—the manager in charge plus selected line and staff managers.

Each such council should prepare a mission statement to define its responsibilities. The following list combines extracts from various published mission statements:

Formulate quality policy: For example, quality has top priority; we must improve annually; all must participate; quality will affect merit rating.

Estimate major dimensions: For example, quality versus competition, cost of poor quality, effectiveness of new product launchings, return on investment from prior improvements.

Establish a project system: Solicit nominations; screen; choose projects; appoint project teams. Set responsibilities for carrying out projects: define team charter; assign responsibility for appointing facilitators, team members, and team leaders.

Identify needs for training: For example, in the improvement process, problem solving, team building, group dynamics, participation, others.

Identify the trainees: Facilitators, team leaders, team members, others.

Plan the training: Curricula, course modules, sources of materials, sources of trainers, budget, schedule.

Establish support for teams: Time to work on projects, diagnostic "leg work," staff diagnostic support, facilities for tryouts, facilities for test, help over obstacles.

Provide for coordination: Meetings of facilitators, meetings of team leaders, project progress reports, reviews by higher levels.

Establish new measures: For progress on improvement, product performance, managers' performance.

Revise merit rating for managers to reflect: Quality of operations, improvement in quality.

Design plan for recognition: Establish recognition for assignments carried out, completion of training, service as facilitator, completion of improvement project.

Establish plan for publicity using various media: Bulletin boards, TV, and radio.

Recommended roles for upper management: Recommendations have included some or many of the following:

> Review, approve policy.
>
> Authorize the infrastructure: quality councils, project system, assignment of roles and responsibilities, training program, support for improvement teams, plan for coordination, plan for publicity.
>
> Review and approve revisions in scoreboards on quality and in the merit rating system.
>
> Review progress reports.
>
> Hear final project team reports.
>
> Participate in improvement projects.
>
> Participate in training.

Each company must prepare its own list or lists. (The items on the above list would typically require two or more councils at different levels.)

Upper Management Leadership.   There is unanimous agreement that a company's approach to annual quality improvement is greatly aided if upper management is "involved." Here is a summary of experience with the principal forms of upper management involvement.

Approve the Phased Approach.   All upper managers want the benefits of annual quality improvement. However, not all of them are convinced that this or that road will lead them to those benefits. All can point to past experiences in which equally plausible proposals have ended in failure. The resulting skepticism makes upper managers reluctant to make broad commitments until they are convinced that the proposed road really leads to good results. To provide that conviction prior to proof of good results requires "selling" through means such as were discussed above under the heading Awareness.

Provide Support.   Feedback from companies have made it clear that in approving a broad, phased approach, upper managers are selective in their support for the individual activities. The most ready approval is for those activities which can be carried out without adding people to the payroll. Support for training programs also tends to be positive.

To go fully to annual improvement adds from 5 to 10 percent to the workload of all members of the management team. This means that priorities on other activities must be changed or people must be added to the payroll.

Serve on Councils. In a gratifying number of companies the upper managers do serve on the high-level councils. There should be no hesitancy in proposing to upper managers that they preside over the high-level quality councils. The wide prevalence of this arrangement suggests that most of such proposals meet with a favorable reception.

Serve on the Project Teams. The benefits are:

1. Setting an example for others to follow. A project team consisting of upper managers working on a problem appropriate for their level provides strong evidence of their committment to the improvement process.

2. Enabling upper managers to learn what the realities faced by subordinates are when *they* tackle projects: the added workload; the calendar time required to complete a project (about 4 to 6 months); the ingredients of project completion—persistent analysis and work, not slogans and exhortation.

3. Creating a capacity for solving those projects which cannot be solved without upper management participation. An example is a revision of quality policy on relations with suppliers.

Review Progress. Through such reviews upper management can remain informed as to progress on quality improvement, and can take action as needed. Such reviews also show the rest of the organization that upper management places a high priority on quality.

Revise the Merit Rating System. Merit rating of operating managers has traditionally been keyed to performance against cost and schedule goals. When a company introduces the concept of annual quality improvement, the scoreboards for evaluating managers must be changed to eliminate any doubt about the relative priority on quality.

Training. To go into annual quality improvement is to create a new function in the company. This function assigns new roles to every member of the management team, roles such as member of a quality council; project team chairman, secretary, or member; and facilitator. To carry out these new roles requires training in concepts, skills, and tools such as the quality improvement process, the special tools of quality analysis, team building, etc. See, in this connection, Section 11 under Training for Quality Improvement.

Projects. A structured project approach for pursuing the chronic quality problems is discussed later in this section.

Progress Reports. During the progression of any improvement project it is important to maintain a discipline—a form of neat housekeeping—by preparing regular written progress reports. These reports serve several essential purposes:

To assure that within the project team itself there is really a meeting of the minds as to what has happened and as to the plans for the future

To keep other managers informed—those managers who are not part of the project team but who "have a need to know"; e.g., they are being asked to act on a recommendation, they are in a position to help the project get over an obstacle, etc.

To provide input to the overall evaluation of the company's approach to annual quality improvement, in order to enable the upper managers to judge effectiveness and to make revisions

The project reports are normally drafted by the project team secretary and are reviewed by the project team chair before publication.

Recognition.   Companies have evolved numerous forms of recognition to provide incentives and rewards for activities related to annual quality improvement. For example:

Certificates, placques, etc., are awarded for service as facilitator, completion of training courses, service on project teams.

Project teams present their final report in the office of the ranking local manager.

Project summaries are published in the company news media, along with team pictures.

Dinners are held to honor project teams.

These and other forms of recognition supply "reinforcement" to all.

Communication.   Good communication is another essential aspect of annual quality improvement. The most common subjects of communication used by participating companies include:

Summaries of completed projects: These have a profound impact. Their flavor of reality adds credibility to the training materials and to the associated improvement goals.

Human interest stories: These deal with the individuals behind the projects, their families, their work environment. Photos are welcomed.

News: This covers a wide range: letters from clients, visits from important personages, activities in progress, scoreboards.

The media of communication are varied and include newsletters, bulletin boards, the local press, letters to employee homes, posters, and video cassettes.

Scoreboards.   Scoreboards take several forms:

1. Progress on *individual* improvement projects.

2. Progress on projects *collectively.*

3. *Merit rating of individuals* with respect to quality improvement. There is no debate on the need for revising the merit rating system to include performance on quality improvement. Failure to do so seriously weakens the priority of quality improvement.

Companywide measures on quality performance include in-house technological measures (yield, percent defective), cost of poor quality, field performance of products, quality versus competition, and quality of nonmanufacturing processes. For an elaboration, see Section 6, particularly Table 6.4.

Institutionalizing the Annual Improvement Process.   Many companies have for years conducted annual improvement programs. Examples of such programs are new product development, cost reduction, and productivity improvement.

All of these have featured formal projects, goals, budgets, reviews, and rewards based on the merit rating. This formality has been embodied into business planning. Based on this history, institutionalizing quality improvement requires similar features.

All companies encounter difficulties when they try to institutionalize quality improvement so that it goes on year after year. The main difficulty is that the work needed to make quality improvements interferes with the "regular" job of managers (to meet the current goals for quality, cost, schedule, etc.). The solution is to make quality improvement a part of the regular job of the managers. Various methods have been tested for doing this. The most effective has been to include quality improvement in the annual business plan. Another method is to revise the system of merit rating of managers to put high priority on quality improvement.

A realization of the need to integrate quality improvement into annual business planning is described by a vice-president of manufacturing for an electronics company. Each year, he personally chairs a meeting to discuss next year's cost-reduction program. Potential cost-reduction projects for achieving labor savings are evaluated by discussing both the expected savings and the resources required. By the end of the meeting, he has decided which projects will be pursued, assigned resources to each project, and identified an individual to oversee each project. This is a routine meeting that is part of the overall business planning for the manufacturing function. In contrast, he admitted that no such meeting is held with respect to tackling the chronic quality problems. (It will in the future.)

The foregoing phased approach outlines the broad steps that must be taken to achieve a breakthrough in quality. Fundamental to the approach is the use of projects that are pursued in an organized series of steps (see below under The Universal Sequence for Breakthrough). But first we will consider some alternative approaches to the improvement process.

Alternative Approaches to Improvement.   Companies have been testing out a wide variety of roads to quality improvement.

Quality Circles.   The concept is one of setting up and training voluntary teams of workers to solve problems within their own department (see Section 10 under Quality Circles: Processes, Tools, Administration). Successful circles have done just that and have improved human relations as well. Circles alone cannot possibly solve the company's quality problems, since the major problems are multidepartmental and require the participation of management and professional personnel. (Of course, workers have an essential role in achieving quality objectives. This role includes handling much of the troubleshooting for processes, helping to identify chronic problems, participating in project teams, and reviewing proposed process plans.)

Statistical Quality Control (SQC).   The concept here is to employ the tools of statistics to solve quality problems. A subspecies of SQC—"statistical process control" (SPC)—has been intensely applied in certain industries and clearly has made a significant contribution. (See Section 24, Statistical Process Control.) However, many managers feel that preoccupation with the tools is leading into uneconomic applications and is diverting attention from the major goals. (This actually happened in an earlier wave of SQC during the 1950s and 1960s.)

Exhortation.   Many upper managers have opted for a road which can properly be called "exhortation only." This road consists of using skillful propaganda to arouse awareness among subordinates that quality is important. This is an important first step in a program, but it does not provide organizational machinery to tackle the long-standing complex quality problems. Further, it does not provide a specific answer to the questions "What do you want me to do differently?"

Some upper managers embrace the exhortation approach because of their lack of experience in quality matters. Further, any approach that avoids adding to their own workload is attractive.

Whatever the reasons, the upper managers are generally unaware of how the exhortation approach is perceived by those on the receiving end. Many of those perceptions are not at all flattering. Upper managers are well advised to take soundings on such perceptions before going into the exhortation approach.

Quantify Quality Costs. This concept is one of expanding the company's accounting system so that it regularly quantifies the cost of poor quality, plus other quality-related costs (see Section 4, Quality Costs). To carry out this expansion takes from 1 to 3 years, and a good deal of effort. The final result is a useful aid to problem identification and managerial decision making, but it is not indispensable. It is possible, by estimates, to get adequate information in much shorter time and with much less effort. In any event, the reporting of quality costs is not sufficient. What is also necessary is the machinery to diagnose and find remedies for the problems identified.

Job Self-Analysis. In this approach, employees (in many functions and many levels) undertake to identify their own customers both outside and inside the company. An analysis then determines if the customer needs are being met. The opportunity for problem identification is obvious; the means for remedy is less obvious. In addition, job self-analysis is inherently limited to analysis of intra-departmental problems. Experience with this approach has been insufficient to support any firm conclusions.

Every one of the roads discussed above (and others) can make a useful contribution to quality improvement. The fatal mistake, however, is to assume that one of these alternatives by itself can achieve a major and lasting change in the level of quality. The project-by-project approach to improvement (discussed below) incorporates most of these alternatives (and others) and has shown the most promise. Doran (1985) describes how an electronics manufacturing facility combined the project approach with statistical quality control, quality circles, process analysis, and departmental analysis to achieve a fivefold improvement in output quality over 4 years.

THE UNIVERSAL SEQUENCE FOR BREAKTHROUGH

Study of numerous cases of breakthrough has disclosed that they follow a universal sequence of events:

Proof of the need

Project identification

Organization to guide the projects

Organization for diagnosis—for analysis of projects

Diagnosis—to find the causes

Development of remedies—based on knowledge of the causes

Proof of the remedies—under operating conditions

Dealing with the cultural resistance to change

Control at the new level

TABLE 22.2   Census of Company Practices in Quality Improvement (United States)

Elements of quality improvement	Percent of responses			
	Strong	Adequate	Weak	No opinion
Atmosphere for breakthrough activity	26	41	32	1
Proof of the need	22	48	29	1
Use of the language of management	16	47	35	2
Use of Pareto analysis	16	31	49	4
Establishment of clear priorities for projects	10	39	50	1
Clear responsibility for guiding projects	11	39	49	1
Clear responsibility for diagnosis	7	33	58	2
Use of controllability concept	6	31	56	7
Diagnostic competence	13	48	37	2
Overcoming resistance to change	8	44	47	1
Action on the findings	12	47	40	1
Control at the new level	7	46	42	5

To most people the steps in the breakthrough sequence seem obvious and logical. When they are asked, however, to critically evaluate the adequacy of execution of these steps in their organization, then the effectiveness of various companies is decidedly uneven. Table 22.2 shows the results of censuses taken in the early 1980s during courses on the management of quality control. The responses, from managers in hundreds of companies, are shown as percentages of all responses. For many of these "logical" steps the actual execution is far from satisfactory. Notice that the responses to the first three elements are more positive than the responses to the other elements. (These first three elements are concerned with developing an attitude of awareness; the remaining elements provide the machinery to solve the problems.) This suggests that for many companies, steps have been taken to create *awareness* of the quality problem, but the *machinery* to carry out a program is missing.

PROOF OF THE NEED

This step consists of convincing management that the quality problem is significant enough to require a new approach to improvement.

Experience with quality improvement programs indicates that upper management typically responds well to certain major threats and opportunities.

A Potential or Real Loss in Sales Revenue.   Studies of competition with respect to quality can reveal an actual or impending disaster in the marketplace. Table 22.3 identifies, for four models of product, the suppliers to a major customer. In 1980, manufacturer G was the supplier for two of the models. By 1983,

TABLE 22.3   Suppliers to a Major Customer

Model number	1980	1981	1982	1983
1	G	G	R	R
2	R	R	R	R
3	G	G	G	R
4	T	R	R	R

its position had eroded and a competitor R had gained all of the business with that customer. Manufacturer G *was competitive* on price, delivery schedules, and product features; it was *demonstrably inferior* on quality.

An important input for proof of the need is a marketing research study to determine quality status in the marketplace *relative to competition.* See Section 12 under Competitive Evaluation by Field Studies for examples.

Gold - Savings on maint and logistics

Opportunity for Major Cost Savings.   The costs associated with poor quality are often remarkably high and present an opportunity for major savings along with a reduction in defects sent to customers. To explain this requires talking the language of money.

The Language of Money.   The approach is to use the language of money to bring the chronic quality problems out of their hiding place and convert them into alarm signals that will stimulate action.

Table 22.4 summarizes a study on the costs of poor quality for a process industry plant. Notice how much is disclosed by this study.

TABLE 22.4   Cost of Poor Quality

Category	Amount, $	Percent of total
Internal failures	7,279,000	79.4
External failures	283,000	3.1
Appraisal	1,430,000	15.6
Prevention	170,000	1.9
	9,162,000	100.0

Order of Magnitude.   The size of the quality problem is indicated as $9.2 million per year. For this plant, that sum represented a major opportunity. (For many companies all of these costs have never before been brought together into one overall figure and been expressed on an annual basis. When this is done the result typically is a number much larger than anyone would have expected.)

The Big Chunks.   The table is dominated by the costs of internal failures— 79 percent of the total. Any major reduction in costs requires action on the internal failures.

The Modest Prevention Effort.   The tiny prevention effort (1.9 percent) reveals an opportunity. An investment in additional prevention effort directed at reducing the internal failures can yield a large return on investment in the form of lower internal failure costs.

Use of a Bellwether Project.   An even more effective way to achieve a break-through in the attitude of management is to couple the study on the cost of poor quality with a case example of a successful quality improvement project within the company. This is illustrated in the approach taken by the ABC electronics company.

The order of magnitude of some essential financial data was (in millions) as follows:

Sales	$1000
Profit	100
Stockholder's investment	500
Cost of poor quality	200

A notorious quality problem was scrap for a certain major electronic compo-nent. This scrap ran to about $9 million per year. The principal defect type was defect X, and it was costing about $3 million per year.

The company took on a project to reduce the incidence of defect X. The project was a stunning success. The cost of defect X was cut from $3 million to $1 mil-lion—an annual profit improvement of $2 million.

The investment needed to make this improvement was modest—about $0.25 million (to fine-tune the process and its controls).

Then followed an exciting extrapolation and contrast. It was estimated that extension of the improvement to the entire $200 million (cost of poor quality) could cut the total in two—a profit improvement of $100 million annually. This was 50 times the savings associated with defect X. It was further estimated that this extension would require an investment of about $20 million.

An alternative way to increase profit by $100 million was through increase in sales. This would require added sales of $1000 million, i.e., doubling the size of the company. In turn such a growth in sales would require doubling the size of the investment, i.e., an added $500 million in investment.

The contrast in investment—$500 million versus $20 million—was decisive in securing credibility for the program. The upper management proceeded to give support to expanding the program. They set up an organized approach to carry out, every year, a number of projects similar to the Bellwether Project.

The defect X project proved to the ABC company managers that they could get a big return on investment by improving quality. "It happened right here in our company." This in-house project was more convincing to results-oriented managers than any amount of lectures, books, or success stories about other companies.

Every Company Has a Bellwether Project.   In every company it is possible to identify past projects involving quality improvement and cost reduction. Some of these can serve as bellwether projects. It is also feasible to estimate the "before and after" costs for these projects. It then becomes feasible to extrapolate so as to estimate the improvement potential for the entire company. This potential can then be related to the opportunities available through alternative allocations of assets, e.g., growth in sales. Indeed, such comparisons can show that investing in quality improvement projects is the *best* business to be in.

The Several Languages of Management.   In achieving a breakthrough in attitude to establish proof of the need, we may need to present information in different languages for different levels of management. Consider the pyramid of Figure

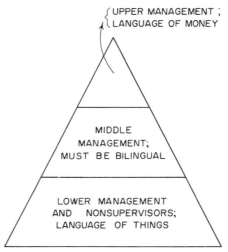

FIG. 22.2 Common languages in the company.

22.2. At the apex is the upper management—usually the general manager and the top management team. At the base are the first-line supervisors and the work force. In between are the middle managers and the specialists.

These segments of the organization use different languages, and the proof of the need must reflect this. The middle managers (and specialists) should of course understand their respective local dialects. But that is not enough. They should, in addition, understand both of the standard languages of things and money. As to these standard languages, the *middle managers should be bilingual.*

Table 22.5 shows examples of statements in money and other languages. In dealing with upper management, useful advice can be obtained from those who regularly meet with upper management on financial matters. For example, in one

TABLE 22.5   Languages of Management

Money (annual cost of poor quality)
24% of sales revenue
15% of manufacturing cost
13 cents per share of common stock
$7.5 million per year for scrap and rework compared to a profit of $1.5 million per year
$176 million per year
40% of the operating cost of a department

Other languages
The equivalent of one plant in the company making 100% defective work all year
32% of engineering resources spent in finding and correcting design weaknesses
25% of manufacturing capacity devoted to correcting quality problems
13% of sales orders canceled
70% of inventory carried attributed to poor quality levels
25% of manufacturing personnel assigned to correcting quality problems

chemical company the controller provided the key. A large part of the cost of poor quality was due to having to rework 40 percent of the batches every year. The controller reasoned as follows: If the rework could be reduced from 40 percent to 10 percent (by means of quality improvement), this would make available production capacity that was no longer needed for rework. This was significant because each year the capital budget included funds to expand the plant production capacity by about 15 percent. With a reduction in rework the controller determined that the capital expenditure for plant capacity could be completely *eliminated for a period of 2 years*. That "language" convinced management to pursue a formal program to reduce rework.

Getting the Cost Figures.   The details of identifying the categories of the cost of poor quality are presented in Section 4, Quality Costs. Collecting the data takes two broad approaches.

By Estimate.   This is the "quick and dirty" approach. It involves only a modest amount of effort. It can, in a few days or weeks, find out enough about quality related costs to tell us:

Whether we have a major cost reduction opportunity or not

Where this opportunity is concentrated

By Enlarging the Accounting System.   This is a more elaborate approach. It requires a lot of effort from various departments, especially Accounting and Quality Control. It also takes a lot of time, running into months and even years.

In the early stages of the breakthrough sequence the estimates are good enough. They certainly involve *less work* and they provide answers in far *less time*. But how about *accuracy?*

The accuracy needed at this stage is that required for a *managerial decision:* Should we or should we not embark on a program of quality improvement and cost reduction? For such a decision the standards of accuracy are fairly loose. To illustrate, recall the process plant figure of $9.2 million of quality-related costs. That figure was an estimate. The real figure might have been as high as $11.0 million or as low as $7.5 million. Had the accuracy of the estimates been challenged, the managers' response would have been: "Every one of those three figures is too high, so let's go after the cost reduction." In other words, even over a wide range of estimate, *the managerial decisions would have been identical.*

An accuracy of ± 20 percent is adequate for such decisions.

Making Presentations to Upper Management.   Experience has evolved some useful dos and don'ts:

1. *Do* summarize the total of the estimated quality costs. This summary makes clear that the total is big enough to command upper management attention.

2. *Do* show the subtotals for the broad major groupings of quality costs, where these are available. A helpful grouping is by the "categories" commonly used in "quality cost accounting" (see Table 22.4).

Note how this table shows the *fallacy of trying to start quality cost reduction by reducing inspection and test.* Typically (as in this case) most of the quality costs are associated with failures, internal and external. The proper sequence is to reduce the failure costs first. Then as the defect levels come down, we can follow through and cut the inspection costs as well.

3. *Do* describe the projects which constitute the heart of the proposed program. For such projects it is important to be bilingual—to use upper management's language of money and also the nonfinancial language of things.

4. *Do* estimate how much is to be saved by the proposed program. This estimate is mainly a buildup of the separate estimates associated with the individual projects. If the company has never before undertaken an organized program to reduce quality-related costs, then *a reasonable goal is to cut these costs in two,* within a space of 5 years.

One of the main figures in estimates of savings is return on investment. Most improvement projects involve little in costly facilities. Their investment is mainly in *analysis.* The resulting return on investment typically runs into hundreds of percent per year!

5. *Do* have the figures reviewed in advance by those people in Finance and elsewhere to whom upper management looks when questions are raised as to the validity of the numbers. It is good practice to bring such people into the estimates from the outset.

There are also some "don'ts" to be observed.

1. *Don't* inflate the present costs by including debatable or borderline items. The risk is that the decisive review meetings will get bogged down in debating the validity of the figures without ever getting to discuss the merits of the proposals for cost reduction.

2. *Don't* imply that the total quality costs can be reduced to zero. Any such implication will likewise attract the wrong kind of attention.

3. *Don't* force the first few projects on managers who are not really sold on them, or on unions that are going to oppose them. Instead, make the climate of receptivity a major parameter in choice of the first projects. It is the results obtained in the first few projects which decide whether the overall program will thrive or die.

Other Forms of Proof of the Need.   Proof of the need may also come from awareness of *new forces* which have an impact on quality. Recent examples have included product liability decisions, the consumerism movement, foreign competition, and legislation of all sorts—product safety, energy conservation, the environment.

Irrespective of the origin of the proof of the need, the approach to solution is the same—through the same universal sequence for breakthrough.

Usually the costs of poor quality *are* shockingly high. Usually something should be done about reducing them and usually it is *not* possible to reduce costs generally; we must be much more specific.

In order to become specific we make use of the project concept—identifying and tackling the specific projects which are to be the subject of the cost reduction. Project identification is the second step in the breakthrough sequence.

THE PROJECT CONCEPT

A *project* is a problem chosen for a solution; it is also a way of managerial life:

An agreed-upon project is also a legitimate project. This legitimacy puts the project on the official priority list. It helps to secure the needed budgets, facilities, and personnel. It also helps those guiding the project to secure attendance at scheduled meetings, to acquire requested data, to secure permission to conduct experiments, etc.

The project provides a forum of converting an atmosphere of defensiveness or blame into one of constructive action.

Participation in a project increases the likelihood that the participant will act on the findings.

All breakthrough is achieved *project by project,* and in no other way.

Reflections after a successful project completion often result in the question, "Why did we not solve this problem 10 years ago?" Experience suggests that the missing ingredients were the machinery for nominating and selecting projects and establishing responsibility for the diagnostic and remedial journeys (for an example, see Nester and Staal, 1986).

The Pareto Principle. As applied to the cost of poor quality, the Pareto principle states that a *few* contributors to the cost are responsible for *the bulk* of the cost. These vital few contributors need to be identified so that quality improvement resources can be concentrated in those areas.

A study of quality-related costs at a paper mill showed a total of $9,070,000 (Table 22.6a). The category called "broke" amounts to $5,560,000 or 61 percent of the quality costs. Clearly there will be no major improvement in these costs unless there is a successful attack on the broke—that is where the money is concentrated. ("Broke" is paper mill dialect for paper so defective that it is returned to the beaters for reprocessing.)

In that paper mill they make 53 types of paper. When the broke is allocated among the various types of paper, the Pareto principle is again in evidence (Table 22.6b). Six of the product types account for $4,480,000, which is 80 percent of the $5,560,000. There will be no major improvement in broke unless there is a successful attack on these six types of paper. Studying 12 percent (6 types out of 53) of the problem results in attacking 80 percent of the broke.

Finally, it is helpful to look at what kinds of defects are being encountered in these six types of paper, and how much are the associated costs for broke. The matrix of Table 22.6c show this analysis. There are numerous defect types, but five of them dominate. In addition, the cost figures in the table also follow the

TABLE 22.6a Pareto Analysis by Accounts—Quality Losses in a Paper Mill

Accounting category	Annual quality loss,* $ Thousands	Percent of total quality loss	
		This category	Cumulative
Broke	5560	61	61
Customer claim	1220	14	75
Odd lot	780	9	84
High material cost	670	7	91
Downtime	370	4	95
Excess inspection	280	3	98
High testing cost	190	2	100
Total	9070		

*Adjusted for estimated inflation since time of original study.

TABLE 22.6b   Pareto Analysis by Products—"Broke" Losses in a Paper Mill

Product type	Annual "broke" loss,* $ Thousands	Percent of "broke" loss	Cumulative percent "broke" loss
A	1320	24	24
B	960	17	41
C	720	13	54
D	680	12	66
E	470	8	74
F	330 (4480)	6	80
47 other types	1080	20	100
Total 53 types	5560	100	

*Adjusted for estimated inflation since time of original study.

TABLE 22.6c   Matrix of Quality Costs*

Type	Trim, $ thousands	Visual defects,† $ thousands	Caliper, $ thousands	Tear, $ thousands	Porosity, $ thousands	All other causes, $ thousands	Total, $ thousands
A	270	94	None‡	162	430	364	1320
B	120	33	None‡	612	58	137	960
C	95	78	380	31	74	62	720
D	82	103	None‡	90	297	108	680
E	54	108	None‡	246	None‡	62	470
F	51	49	39	16	33	142	330
Total	672	465	419	1157	892	875	4480

*Adjusted for estimated inflation since time of original study.
†Slime spots, holes, wrinkles, etc.
‡Not a specified requirement for this type.

Pareto principle. The largest numer is $612,000 for "tear" on paper type B. Then comes $430,000 for "porosity" on paper type A, and so on. It is easy to visualize how this series of analyses would be helpful to a team of managers who are trying to nominate projects for cost reduction.

In a Pareto analysis, there is an endless variety of sources to consider as "contributors." Thus the Pareto breakdown can be by organization (division, plant, etc.), by person (operators), by function (product development, manufacturing, etc.), by type of defect, by process, etc. For example, in the manufacture of an electromechanical detection device, failures can occur at any of five sources (Figure 22.3). About 50 percent of the cost of poor quality occurs at one source, component manufacturing (Betker, 1985a). See also below under Test of Theories of Worker-Controllable Problems for another graphic presentation to dramatize the Pareto principle.

The utter simplicity of the Pareto concept makes it prone to be underestimated as a key tool for quality improvement.

Generally, people hold strong opinions on what are the important areas requiring attention, but these opinions are often not shared by others. The Pareto con-

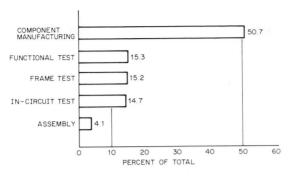

FIG. 22.3 Pareto analysis of percent total annualized failure costs.

cept helps to achieve agreement by collecting facts and summarizing them in a form that shows where most of the problem is concentrated.

The ranking of problem areas using a Pareto analysis of course depends on the criterion used. Tables 22.7a and 22.7b show an example of Pareto ranking using two different criteria (adapted from Selwitchka, 1980). Using "error frequency" and "cost" results in different rankings.

Sometimes it is useful to make Pareto analyses at higher levels as a summary of Pareto analyses made at lower levels. For example, in one large corporation, each plant routinely prepared Pareto analyses of field problems and used the results to direct plant quality improvement programs. In a special study, data from all plants were integrated. A Pareto analysis showed that 3 part types out of 200 accounted for an overwhelming part of the corporate problem. These same three part types were among the vital few at each of the plants. This higher-level Pareto analysis resulted in a corporate-directed effort on the three parts.

Occasionally, a Pareto study fails to reveal vital few contributors. For example, "83 percent of the defects were of a one-of-a-kind nature." In such cases, finding the vital few may require a different form of analysis. Instead of using *type* of defect, try making the analysis by potential *cause* of the defect (material, machine,

TABLE 22.7a Errors Ranked by Frequency of Occurrence

Analysis 1

Type of error	Error frequency	Error proportion, %	Cumulative, Σ%	Rank
A	960	32	32	1
B	870	29	61	2
C	420	14	75	3
D	210	7	82	4
E	180	6	88	5
F	180	6	94	6
G	60	2	96	7
H	60	2	98	8
I	30	1	99	9
J	30	1	100	10

Source: Adapted from Selwitchka, 1980, pp. 3–7.

TABLE 22.7b   Errors Ranked by Cost

Analysis 2

Error type	Error frequency	Add. costs per annum, DM	Costs proportion, %	Proportion cumulative, %	Rank by Frequency	Rank by Cost
C	420	375,000	53.0	53.0	3	1
E	180	124,300	17.6	70.6	5	2
G	60	77,800	11.0	81.6	7	3
D	210	42,000	5.9	87.5	4	4
B	870	28,460	4.0	91.5	2	5
A	960	20,000	2.8	94.3	1	6
H	60	12,125	1.7	96.0	8	7
J	30	9,125	1.4	97.4	10	8
F	180	9,000	1.3	98.7	6	9
I	30	9,000	1.3	100.0	9	10
		706,810				

Source: Adapted from Selwitchka, 1980, pp. 3–7.

specification, etc.) or one of the other sources of contributors previously mentioned.

Nominations for Projects.   Nominations come from several sources:

   1.   The Pareto analysis of the quality-oriented costs.

   2.   The Pareto analysis of field complaints, returns claims, warranty charges, etc.

   3.   Analysis of other field intelligence, e.g., reports from the sales force or actions taken by competitors.

   4.   Emerging developments arising from the impact of product quality on society, e.g., new legislation, extension of government regulation, growth of product liability lawsuits.

   5.   Needs which relate to managerial processes and industrial relations, e.g., organization for quality, training programs, motivation for quality.

   6.   The management hierarchy, i.e., managers, supervisors, professional specialists, project teams.

   7.   Goal-setting processes, e.g., the annual budget, management by objectives.

   8.   The marketplace, as relayed by Sales, Customer Service, Technical Service, and others.

   9.   The work force, through informal ideas presented to supervisors, formal suggestions, ideas from quality circles, and so forth.

One structured approach for obtaining participation of workers is the error cause removed (ECR) system (Halpin, 1966). ECR forms are submitted to the supervisor with a copy to an ECR administrator who has the job of assuring that the proposal is acknowledged, analyzed, and acted upon by the supervisor or referred to other sources. (The administrator is aided by a pledge from top management that ECRs will receive prompt, serious attention.) Some of the problems documented on ECR forms become project nominations for quality improvement teams.

10. "Making the rounds," i.e., visits made by specialists (quality engineers, industrial engineers) to solicit nominations from various departments.

A description of projects from both the manufacturing and nonmanufacturing areas of a wide variety of industries will be found in *The Juran Report,* no. 2, November 1983 (pp. 52–94), *The Juran Report,* no. 2, winter 1985 (pp. 28–45 and 160–179), and *The Juran Report,* no. 6, winter 1986 (pp. 27–40 and 165–180).

An example of a large nonfactory project is cancellation of sales contracts. In one large electronics company it was found that 20 percent of all sales contracts ended up being cancelled. The cancellations were for many reasons: sale for the wrong application, failure to deliver on time, product failed to perform per contract, product not compatible with other elements of the client's system, etc. The numerous reasons followed the Pareto principle—a few of the reasons accounted for most of the cancellations. This led to revisions in the sales procedures and significant reductions in the percent of cancellations.

Screening Nominations and Establishing Priorities. This screening or review process is typically set up at two levels—middle and upper management.

Review by Middle Management. The project nomination should describe (1) the scope and (2) the return on investment. The scope includes the purpose of the project, the activities required to carry it out, personnel and physical facilities required, responsibility (who is to do what), time schedule, and the results expected, tangible and intangible.

Some companies use a standardized form to summarize the facts behind a proposal for a project. McGrath (1985) presents an example of such a form for an electronics company (Figure 22.4).

The explanation of return on investment shows the present costs; the estimated reduction in costs or other benefits; and the estimated investment needed in facilities, salaries, and expenses. These inputs are summarized by calculating the return on investment or, alternatively, the time required to recover the investment.

As managers review the nominations based on the foregoing kinds of information they arrive at priorities by weighing such factors as return on investment, amount of potential improvement, urgency, ease of technological solution, and likely reception of the project.

Some organizations formalize the evaluation of projects. In one approach, 10 criteria are evaluated in terms of yes, no, or uncertain answer. This is illustrated in Figure 22.5 (McGrath, 1985).

Hartman (1983) describes an approach that makes use of a "Pareto priority index" (PPI) to evaluate each project. The index is:

$$PPI = \frac{\text{savings} \times \text{probability of success}}{\text{cost} \times \text{time to completion (years)}}$$

Table 22.8 shows the application of this index to evaluate five potential projects. High PPI values suggest high priority. Note how the ranking of projects A and C is affected when the criterion is changed from savings alone to the index covering the four factors. (Other indices can be created to reflect a different set of factors.)

Obviously, no individual middle manager can supply the facts or make the

Project Title *Parts Handling*
Improvements

Organization _____
Leader/Mgr. *Beth Duffy*

Symptoms: *Parts that don't meet specs. Not fit for use.*

Statement of Problem: *Damage to component parts due to handling. A total impact of $150,000.*

Possible Causes: *Handling & packaging*

Overall Objective(s): *"Receive good parts" – have a 95% improvement.*

Approach/Technique Proposed: *Analyze methods of handling and packaging. Also, analyze incoming parts.*

Project Leader Proposed: _____

Resources Required: *Study Phase*   *Implementation*

Funds   *$1100*   *$42,000*

Time   *60 hours*   *6 months*

Personnel   *Engr. 2 techs*

Product Value/Urgency _____

Productivity Increase From ___*75%*___ to _*95%*_

\# *due to less incoming inspection.*

Reliability Increase From ___*75%*___ to _*95%*_

\# _____

Cost Reduction From ___*$150,000*___ to _____

\# _____

Net Economic Impact Statement *Customer satisfaction*

Estimated Net Saving *$100,000*
($, ROI or Payback)

FIG. 22.4   Quality improvement project.   *(From McGrath, 1984.)*

judgment as to which projects should get the highest priority. Managers from all key departments should participate in choice of the projects. Such a *jury of opinion* reduces the likelihood that the extreme optimism or pessimism of one individual will decide the fate of a project.

The result of the review by middle management is a recommended list of projects. Typically, a responsibility of an upper management quality council is to review the recommendations or create the organizational machinery for review and final approval.

Selection of Initial Projects.   "The first project should be a winner." A successful project is a form of evidence to the project team members that the improvement process does lead to useful results. That same success is also a source of stimulation to do more of the same. The publicity given to the successful project conveys this stimulus to others in the company. In contrast, if the first project fails, the fact of failure is a source of discouragement and of reduced confidence in the com-

```
PROJECT SELECTION LIST                                          YES  NO    ?

   1.  Does the project have a measurable outcome?            ____ ____ ____

   2.  Does the outcome assist in meeting unit targets?       ____ ____ ____

          ...for QUALITY PERFORMANCE INCREASES?              ____ ____ ____
          ...for PRODUCT RELIABILITY INCREASES?              ____ ____ ____
          ...for QUALITY COST REDUCTIONS?                    ____ ____ ____

   3.  Does the proposed approach use an already existing
       technology?                                            ____ ____ ____

   4.  In light of all organizational financial constraints, do we
       presently possess the required resources to implement this
       project...
                                  FUNDS?                      ____ ____ ____
                                  PERSONNEL?                  ____ ____ ____
                                  MATERIALS?                  ____ ____ ____
                                  SPACE?                      ____ ____ ____

   5.  Are  the  estimated  net  cost  savings  substantial? ____ ____ ____

   6.  Can the project be completed or a benchmark met in 90
       days?                                                  ____ ____ ____

   7.  Will this project be readily accepted by other departments? ____ ____ ____

   8.  Can this project be done without extensive cooperation and
       coordination with other units?                         ____ ____ ____

   9.  Will this project be seen as a priority task by the people
       doing the work?                                        ____ ____ ____

  10.  Does top management see the benefits of this specific
       project? Will they suport it fully?                    ____ ____ ____

                                            TOTALS           ==== ==== ====

       ┌─────────────────────────────────────────────┐
       │  Mostly  ? — Need more information            │
       │  Mostly No — May not be a good choice         │
       │  Mostly Yes— Preferred  choice                │
       └─────────────────────────────────────────────┘
```

FIG. 22.5 Selection criteria for quality improvement projects. *(From McGrath, 1985.)*

TABLE 22.8 Ranking by Use of Pareto Priority Index (PPI)

Project	Savings, $ thousands	Probability	Cost, $ thousands	Time, years	PPI
A	100	0.7	10.0	2.0	3.5
B	50	0.7	2.0	1.0	17.5
C	30	0.8	1.6	0.25	60.0
D	10	0.9	0.5	0.50	36.0
E	1.5	0.6	1.0	0.10	9.0

pany's direction. Such discouragement and reduced confidence also become publicized and thereby have an impact outside of the project team directly involved. Ideally:

The project should deal with a *chronic* problem—one which has been awaiting solution for a long time.

The project should be feasible, i.e., have a good likelihood of bringing it to a successful conclusion within a few months.

The project should be *significant*. The end result should be sufficiently useful to merit attention and recognition.

The results should be *measurable* in money as well as in technological terms.

The project should serve as a *learning experience* for the process of problem solving.

The Number of Projects in a Quality Improvement Program.   The number of projects required to achieve a significant improvement in quality is surprisingly large. Means are emerging for estimating the number of projects needed for planned results. The two cardinal figures required for making the estimates are:

1. The average amount of cost reduction achieved per project. A growing data base (Juran, 1985) indicates that for large companies (sales over $1000 million per year), the average annual cost reduction is about $100,000 per project. (Individual project savings range from over $1 million to a loss.)

2. The cost reduction goal to be reached. For example, many companies have a cost of poor quality in excess of 20 percent of sales, of $200 million per year. To reduce this cost by 50 percent would mean a goal of $100 million cost reduction. At an average of $100,000 per project, it would take 1000 projects to reach this goal!

In the above example, if the goal were to make the cost reduction over a 5-year period, the company would need to complete 200 projects per year. That is a number far greater than the actual number of projects carried out by most companies of that size. To assure that a sufficient number of projects are identified and executed requires a methodical approach to organizing.

ORGANIZING FOR PROJECTS

The in-depth investigations needed to solve most chronic quality problems involve two journeys:

1. A journey from symptom to cause (diagnosis)
2. A journey from cause to remedy

Table 22.9 contrasts these two journeys.

The difficult journey is from symptom to cause. Two reasons account for the difficulty: the responsibility for diagnosis is vague, and the needed skills are not always available. These obstacles can be overcome by using a project team.

The Project Team.   The project team consists (usually) of about six to eight persons drawn from multiple company departments. Their job is to bring the project to a successful conclusion.

TABLE 22.9 Contrast of the Diagnostic and Remedial Journeys

	Diagnostic	Remedial
Responsibility	Vague	Clear
Skills needed	Quality disciplines	Technological
Skills present	Sometimes	Usually
Obstacles	Organizational training	Resistance to change

Although there is a "project chairperson" (leader, etc.; see below), the team has no "boss" in a personal sense. Instead there is an impersonal boss—the "charter" given to each project team. The team has two basic responsibilities: (1) Guide the project to a successful conclusion; (2) conduct or oversee the diagnostic work.

A typical charter gives the team the right and duty to:

Analyze the project to understand the symptoms of the problem.

Theorize as to what might be the cause(s) of the symptoms.

Arrange to test the theories to discover the cause(s).

Recommend remedial action to those organizations who are in a position to provide remedies.

Follow up and stimulate remedial action.

Prove the adequacy of the remedies under operating conditions.

Establish controls to hold the gains.

Evaluate and publish the results achieved.

Lounds and Pearson (1985) show a project charter for office automation. Dymtrow (1985) discusses a charter for a service project.

In forming the project teams, several matters must be resolved:

1. *Membership; mandatory or voluntary?* To remain competitive in quality and to reduce the cost of poor quality requires the participation of all members of the management team. Membership on project teams should be mandatory.

2. *Horizontal or vertical?* Project team membership should usually be horizontal, i.e., members are drawn from multiple functions. This approach is compatible with the reality that virtually all major chronic quality problems are multidepartmental in scope.

3. *At what level?* Project teams should be set up at all levels because such is the mixture of projects. Solution of some projects (e.g., reducing the error rate in invoices, or reducing the defect rate in gear cutting) requires team members who understand the details of the respective processes. Such team members are usually first-line supervisors and professional specialists and the work force. (Upper managers should keep out of such projects.) Other projects require extensive experience and training in managerial matters. For such projects, the membership should come from the managerial levels. An example of an upper management project is the reward and recognition process for quality.

4. *The appointment process:* Based on the nature of the project selected, the council (or subcouncil) identifies who are the organization units who should be represented on the project team. It is essential that team membership include the units that are likely to be involved in the remedial changes. The

council then contacts the heads of those organization units to secure their nominations of persons to be team members. Negotiations then take place to reach agreement on the precise makeup of the team.

5. *Team members from nontechnological functions:* Experience has shown that team members from nontechnological functions can be useful members of project teams. They are able to identify and deal with nontechnological matters such as lack of organization for improvement, or suboptimizing, i.e., meeting departmental goals at the expense of company performance. Wolf (1983) shows the constituency of project teams for ten pilot projects.

Project Teams versus Quality Circles. There are important differences between the two types of groups (see Table 22.10).

Principal Roles on Project Teams. The project team consists of the chairperson, secretary, and other team members.

Project Team Chairperson. The project team chairperson (or leader) leads the team in its responsibility of carrying out the project. Successful leadership requires knowledge of the project area and skills in getting cooperation from team members from several functional areas to work as a team. It is often useful that the team chairperson come from the organizational unit most impacted by the problem.

Project Secretary. Each team requires a project secretary to handle documentation: publish agendas, minutes, reports, etc. The secretary is preferably a member of the project team.

Project Team Members. Team membership draws upon all of the skills and knowledge necessary for the project. For chronic problems, the teams are usually cross-functional and consist of middle management, professional, and work force personnel. Surprisingly, some projects are relatively easy and can be handled with a minimum of skills and knowledge. (Such projects are often the result of a previous lack of the project approach.) Other projects are complex and require more depth in team membership, perhaps even supplemented by consulting specialists (see below).

Supplementing the formal team membership may be two additional parties:

Facilitator. Many companies have adopted the concept of using a "facilitator" to help project teams carry out their first project. Although not a member of the

TABLE 22.10 Comparison: Quality Circles and Project Teams

Feature	Quality circles	Project teams
Scope of project	Within a single department	Multidepartmental
Size of project	One of the useful many	One of the vital few
Members come from:	A single department	Multiple departments
Basis of membership	Voluntary	Mandatory
Composition of membership	Work force	Mostly middle management and specialists
Continuity	Circle remains intact, project after project	Team is ad hoc, disbands after project is completed

team, the facilitator can play an important role. The role of the facilitator consists of a selection from the following:

Explaining the company's approach to quality improvement and how it differs from prior efforts at quality improvement

Providing assistance in team building

Assisting in the training of project teams

Assisting the project team leader in solving human relations problems among team members

Helping the team avoid a poor choice of project

Reporting progress of projects to management

The Facilitator: Selection and Training. For the most part, companies use part-time rather than full-time facilitators. These part-time facilitators are usually drawn from the ranks of local managers and supervisors at the various sites.

In the case of full-time facilitators, the most frequent source is the human relations organization. Such individuals typically have a background in the behavioral sciences, enabling them to contribute usefully to training and to team building.

Additional sources of facilitators include former quality circle facilitators, qualified retirees who are recalled on a temporary basis, and experienced project team chairpersons who have demonstrated an aptitude for carrying out the roles of facilitators.

Training for facilitators includes indoctrination in the company's mission with respect to annual quality improvement and the associated role of the facilitator. The indoctrination is then followed by training in the project approach, problem-solving tools, and group dynamics.

A small minority of companies have bypassed the use of facilitators. For example, one large electronics company assigned to each of its general managers the job of leading subordinates through a project. In turn, each subordinate then did the same. The roles of the facilitator were of course still there, but they were carried out by the operating managers.

McGrath (1985) discusses the development of team leaders and facilitators.

Consulting Specialist(s). For some team meetings it may be useful to invite in a specialist who is knowledgeable in specific disciplines required by the project, e.g., metallurgy or computer software reliability engineering.

Responsibility for Diagnosis. Lack of clear responsibility for diagnosis is the main reason for failure to make the journey from symptom to cause. This problem is solved by making the project team responsible for diagnosis.

In some projects the work of diagnosis is not extensive. In such cases the project team personally does the diagnosis.

In other projects the work of diagnosis becomes quite burdensome, due to the need for extensive data collection and analysis. In such cases the team may decide to delegate part of the work of diagnosis. The alternatives for such delegation include:

1. The team secures assistance from line or staff departments. For example: collection of new data may be done by line manufacturing personnel; planning and analysis of special experiments may be done by engineers in Quality Engineering.

2. A full-time diagnostic department is created to do the work associated with data collection and analysis.

Full-Time Diagnosticians: Centralized or Scattered? Full-time diagnosticians can be located on the organization chart in several ways (Figure 22.6.) They can be assigned as follows:

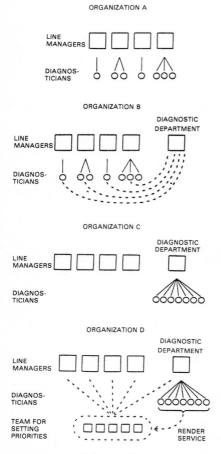

FIG. 22.6 Organizing the diagnostic function.

1. To the various line managers in proportion to the needs of the respective line departments.

This arrangement is preferred by most line managers. In practice, many of these arrangements have ended up with the diagnosticians being assigned to help the line manager in meeting current goals, in fire fighting, etc. Such assignments then take priority over the big, interdepartmental chronic quality problems.

2. To the various line managers [as in (1), above], but with a "dotted line" running to a central diagnostic department (e.g., Quality Engineering).

This arrangement is an improvement from the standpoint of training of diagnosticians, offering them an obvious career road and providing them with consulting assistance. However, the arrangement does not necessarily solve the problem of priorities, i.e., on which projects should the diagnosticians be working.

3. To a central diagnostic department (e.g., Quality Engineering).

This arrangement makes it possible for the diagnosticians to be assigned either to interdepartmental or intradepartmental projects. It also increases the likelihood that interdepartmental projects will have higher priority. In addition, it simplifies the provision of training and consulting assistance for diagnosticians. However, it makes no specific provision for line manager participation in choice of projects or in setting up priorities. Such an omission can be fatal to results.

4. To a central diagnostic department [as in (3), above], but with a structured participation by the line managers.

In effect, a team of line managers chooses the projects and establishes the priorities. The diagnostic department assigns the diagnosticians in response to these priorities. It also provides training, consulting service, and other assistance to the diagnosticians. This arrangement is widely used and has demonstrated its ability to adapt to a wide variety of company situations.

The choice among these (and other) alternatives will depend on many factors which differ from one company to another.

Responsibility for Troubleshooting.   In many companies the diagnosticians who are assigned to quality improvement teams may also be assigned to assist in troubleshooting to solve the sporadic problems. (See Section 17 under Trouble-shooting.) Such multiple assignments complicate the problems of setting priorities and defining responsibilities.

Moehlenbrock (1985) describes how a capacitor manufacturer organized for quality improvement based on the distinction between chronic and sporadic problems. This led to two types of teams: control teams made of local manufacturing personnel to pursue sporadic problems and breakthrough teams made up of interdepartmental personnel to take on the chronic problems.

DIAGNOSIS—GENERAL

Certain key words relating to diagnosis are defined as follows:

A "defect" is any state of unfitness for use, or nonconformance to specification, e.g., oversize, low mean time between failures, illegible invoice. A defect also goes by other names, e.g., error, discrepancy, nonconformance.

A "project" is a problem scheduled for solution.

A "symptom" is an observable phenomenon arising from and accompanying a defect. Sometimes, but not always, the same word is used both as a defect description and as a symptom description, e.g., "open circuit." More usually, a defect will have multiple symptoms; e.g., "insufficient torque" may include the symptoms of vibration, overheating, erratic function, etc.

A "theory" is an unproved assertion as to reasons for the existence of defects and symptoms. Usually, multiple theories are advanced to explain the presence of the observed phenomena.

A "cause" is a proved reason for the existence of the defect. Often there are multiple causes, in which case they follow the Pareto principle; i.e., the vital few causes will dominate all the rest.

A "dominant cause" is a major contributor to the existence of defects and one which must be remedied before there can be an adequate solution.

"Diagnosis" is the process of studying symptoms, theorizing as to causes, testing theories, and discovering causes.

A "remedy" is a change that can successfully eliminate or neutralize a cause of defects.

Two journeys are required for quality improvement: the diagnostic journey from symptom to cause, and the remedial journey from cause to remedy. This distinction is critical. To illustrate, three supervisors were faced with a problem of burrs on screws at final assembly of kitchen stoves. In their haste to act, they skipped the diagnostic journey and concluded that better screws were needed (a remedy). Fortunately, a diagnostician interceded. He pointed out that three separate assembly lines were feeding product into one inspection station, and he suggested that the data be segregated by assembly line. The data revealed that the burrs occurred only on line 3. Further diagnosis based on data led to agreement that the true cause was an improperly trained assembler. Then, the remedy came easily.

Sometimes these two journeys must be repeated before a problem is permanently solved. For an example from a continuous chemical process, see Nester and Staal (1986).

Many managers harbor deep-seated beliefs that most defects are caused during manufacture and specifically are due to worker errors, i.e., that defects are mainly worker-controllable. The facts seldom bear this out, but the belief persists. To deal with such deep-seated beliefs it can be useful to conduct studies to separate defects into broad categories of responsibility. The more frequent of such studies include:

1. A study to determine the origin of the defects in the design, manufacture, etc. Such a study to determine the distribution of causes over functional areas often has some surprising results. In a classic study, Greenridge (1953) examined 850 failures of electronic products supplied by a number of companies. The results showed that 43 percent of the failures were caused by the product design, 30 percent by field operation conditions, 20 percent by manufacturing, and the remaining 7 percent by miscellaneous causes. For products of moderately high technology it is not unusual that about 40 percent of field problems can be traced to the product design.

2. A study to determine whether defects are primarily management-controllable or worker-controllable. ("Management" here includes not only people in supervisory positions but also others who influence quality, e.g., design engineers, process engineers, buyers, etc.) An example of a controllability study is given in Section 17 under Concept of Controllability (see Table 17.2). In general, defects are over 80 percent management-controllable and under 20 percent worker-controllable. Some authors use the term "system-controllable" for "management-controllable."

Such broad studies provide important guidance for improvement.

Diagnosis of Failures in Broad Systems.   It is beneficial to examine a broad approach to diagnosis based on a review of history. In this "historical review" approach, the objective is not to improve the quality of a specific product; the objective is to improve some segment of the systematic approach used to attain quality in the first place. The segment can be a major activity such as product development, manufacturing planning, or supplier relations.

Historical review is based on analysis of a number of past problems; i.e., some skeletons are dissected. Based on interviews, each problem is documented as follows:

1. A brief description of the problem
2. The stage at which the problem was first observed (field, final inspection, prototype test)
3. The earliest stage at which the problem could have been discovered
4. The reasons for not having discovered the problem at that earlier stage
5. What could have been done to have found the problem earlier (or to have avoided the problem altogether)

For example, a historical review of past product development problems reveals that a failure mode, effect, and criticality analysis (see Section 13 under Failure Mode, Effect, and Criticality Analysis) would have identified many of the

Date of problem observed	Symptoms	Damages	Could have been found earlier?	Reasons for not finding earlier
July 9, 1984, 10:00	High readings, all East Coast machines	$2,000 loss	Yes	No incoming inspection
July 15, 1984	Added function to the frame	Lost orders	Yes	No status meetings

FIG. 22.7 Problem log.

problems much earlier. This suggests that the product development system should be changed to require such an analysis for all or selected future products.

Ingram (1984) discusses the historical review technique as applied to specific product problems (see the problem log, Figure 22.7). Kano (1984) describes the application of this concept in new-product development.

In conducting a historical review it is essential to avoid controversy about the causes of the problem. The emphasis must be on discovering potential problems early enough to prevent them from happening.

Another form of historical review is made from established documentation. For example, a sample of 24 engineering change notices were analyzed with the following results:

1. Only one problem was found during development testing; the remaining 23 surfaced later during the production phase.
2. In all 24 cases, the engineers who originally created the design were told of the problem, but the "lessons learned" were not disseminated to other engineers.
3. Of the 24 problems, 11 were associated with performance, reliability, or safety, 8 with "administrative" matters, and 5 with manufacturing.

Many file cabinets are laden with similar collective histories of important knowledge for diagnosis.

From the historical review approach aimed at broad segments of activity, we next discuss diagnosis for specific improvement projects.

Diagnosis for Improvement Projects.   Results come solely from work done on specific improvement projects. This work begins with the diagnostic journey.

The diagnostic journey consists of:

1. Study of the symptoms surrounding the defects to serve as a basis for theorizing about causes
2. Theorizing on the causes of these symptoms
3. Data collection and analysis to test the theories and thereby determine the causes

When the defects can be "switched on or off" at will, the diagnostic journey is over. Table 22.11 lists specific diagnostic techniques and their likely application during the three phases of diagnosis. (Some of these techniques can also be helpful during the remedial journey.)

Nothing is more fundamental to diagnosis than the need to replace conjecture with the authority of fact. The starting point is a clear understanding of symptoms.

TABLE 22.11   Guide to Diagnostic Techniques

Phase of diagnosis	Technique	Reference pages
Study of symptoms	Check sheet	22.35, 22.36
	Autopsies	22.35
	Glossary	22.35
	Pareto analysis	22.19–22.22
Theorizing on causes	Brainstorming	22.36
	Nominal group technique	22.36
	Storyboarding	22.36–22.37
	Tabular arrangement	22.37
	Cause-and-effect diagram	22.37–22.39
	Force field analysis	22.39
	Affinity diagram	22.39
	Structure tree	22.39, 22.40
	Why-why diagram	22.40
	Interrelationship digraph	22.40
	Program decision process chart	22.40
	Matrix	22.40
	Check sheet	22.35, 22.36
	Pareto analysis	22.19–22.22
Data collection and analysis	Historical review	22.32–22.33
	Check sheet	22.35, 22.36
	Pareto analysis	22.19–22.22
	Flow diagram	22.41
	Arrow diagram	22.41
	Process capability analysis	16.14–16.35
	Stream-to-stream analysis	22.41
	Time-to-time analysis	22.41, 22.42
	Cumulative data plots	22.42, 22.44
	Probability paper	23.35–23.42
	Control charts	Section 24
	Piece-to-piece analysis	22.44
	Within piece-to-piece analysis	22.44–22.48
	Multi-Vari diagram	22.45
	Defect concentration diagram	22.45, 22.46
	Interrelation of variables	22.47
	Correlation	22.48
	Ranking	22.48, 22.49
	Matrix	22.49, 22.50
	Measurements at intermediate stages	22.50
	Measurements following noncontrolled operations	22.50
	Measurement of additional properties	22.50, 22.51
	Study of worker methods	22.53–22.59
	Formal experiments	22.51, Section 26
	Other statistical techniques	Section 23
	Measurement for diagnosis	22.52, 22.53

ANALYSIS OF SYMPTOMS

Evidence of defects and errors comes in two forms:

1. The words used in written documentation or oral comments describing the problem
2. The "autopsies" conducted to measure and examine the defects.

Description of Symptoms. Understanding of symptoms is often hindered because some key word or phrase has multiple meanings.

In a plant making rubber products by the latex dip process, the word "tears" was used on the data sheets to describe torn products. One important manager regarded "tears" as worker-controllable and urged a remedy through motivational and disciplinary measures.

Actually there were three species of tears: "strip tears" from a stripping operation, "click tears" from a press operation, and "assembly tears" from an assembly operation.

Only one of these species was worker controllable, and overall extent of worker controllability was only 15 percent. Progress became possible only after the terminology had been made clear and the controllability had been quantified.

In another example, a Pareto analysis of inspection data in a wire mill indicated a high percentage of defects due to "contamination." Various remedies were tried to prevent the contamination. All were unsuccessful. In desperation the investigators spoke with the inspectors to learn more about the contamination. The inspectors explained that there were 12 defect categories on the inspection form. If the observed defect did not fit any of the categories they would report the defect as "contamination."

Imprecise wording also occurs due to use of generic terminology. For example, a software problem is described in a discrepancy report as a "coding error." Such a description is useless for analysis because there are many types of coding errors, e.g., undefined variables, violation of language rules, and violation of programming standards.

A way out of such semantic tangles is to think through the meanings of the words used, reach an agreement, and record the agreement in the form of a *glossary*. Once published, the glossary simplifies the subsequent analysis.

Autopsies. The autopsy determines that the product unit classified as having an "electrical" defect actually exhibits the symptom of open circuit, or short circuit, or dead battery.

Using a wide variety of instruments, today's scientific autopsies furnish extensive objective knowledge about the symptoms, and thereby supplement or override the information contained in the written reports.

Data Recording Methods. Data recording methods range from extremely simple to extremely complex. Figure 22.8 shows a simple data recording device known as a check sheet (G.O.A.L., 1985.) All forms of data recording are designed to test specific theories. For example, a concentration diagram (discussed later in this section) provides excellent input for testing a theory that defects tend to concentrate at one location on a product.

Quantification of Symptoms. The frequency and intensity of symptoms is of great significance in pointing to directions for analysis. The Pareto principle,

Mistake		March		Total
	1	2	3	
Centering	11	111	111	8
Spelling	ⅢⅠ 11	ⅢⅠ ⅢⅠ 1	ⅢⅠ	23
Punctuation	ⅢⅠ ⅢⅠ ⅢⅠ	ⅢⅠ ⅢⅠ	ⅢⅠ ⅢⅠ ⅢⅠ	40
Missed paragraph	11	1	1	4
Wrong numbers	111	1111	111	10
Wrong page numbers	1	1	11	4
Tables	1111	ⅢⅠ	1111	13
Total	34	35	33	102

FIG. 22.8   Checksheet of typing mistakes in Department A.

when applied to records of past performance, can help in quantifying the symptom pattern. (See above under The Pareto Principle.) The Pareto principle applies to several levels of diagnosis: finding the vital few defects, finding the vital few symptoms of a defect, and finding the vital few causes for one symptom.

FORMULATION OF THEORIES

All progress in diagnosis is made theory by theory, i.e., by affirming or denying the validity of the theories about causes. The process consists of three steps: generation of theories, arrangement of theories, and choosing theories to be tested.

Generation of Theories.   Securing the theories is a serious matter and should be done systematically. The best sources of theories are the line managers, the technologists, the line supervisors, and the work force. Normally the list of theories is extensive, 20 or more. If only three or four theories have been proposed, it usually means that the theorizing process has been inadequate.

A systematic way to generate theories is the brainstorming technique. Persons who are potential contributors are assembled for the purpose of generating theories. Creative thinking is encouraged by asking each person, in turn, to propose a theory. No criticism or discussion of ideas is allowed, and all ideas are recorded. The end result is a list of theories which, after the brainstorming session is completed, are critically reviewed.

The nominal group technique is similar to brainstorming. Participants generate their ideas silently, in writing. Each then offers one idea for recording on a chart. After all ideas are recorded, they are discussed. Finally, the group votes to prioritize the ideas.

A useful supplement to the brainstorming technique is "storyboarding." Each theory proposed is recorded on an index card. The cards are appropriately arranged on a board to form a visual display of the theories. Storyboarding provides a visual system for organizing theories and planning subsequent evaluation of these theories. Betker (1986*b*) describes the use of storyboarding in an electronics company.

Theories should include those for systematic causes as well as those for causes which relate to specific products or processes. For example, a manager observes, "In the last 6 weeks we have lost four needed batches of unrelated products due to four different instruments being out of calibration. This shows that we should review our *system* for maintaining the accuracy of our instruments."

Arrangement of Theories.   An orderly arrangement of theories is essential to help all concerned to visualize the interrelation of the theories. In addition, an orderly arrangement is an essential aid to choosing which theories to test. The orderly arrangement can be done in several forms.

Tabular Arrangement.   The brainstorming process provides a helter-skelter list of theories. Brainstorming for theories can have a useful effect on a highly opinionated person. Such a person will list a belief as a theory, and realize it is only a theory. This list is then rearranged to show a logical listing: theories, sub-theories, sub-sub-theories, etc. Table 22.12 is an example as applied to yield of fine powder chemicals.

TABLE 22.12   Orderly Arrangement of Theories

Raw material	Moisture content
Shortage of weight	Charging speed of wet powder
Method of discharge	Dryer, rpm
Catalyzer	Temperature
Types	Steam pressure
Quantity	Steam flow
Quality	Overweight of package
Reaction	Type of balance
Solution and concentration	Accuracy of balance
B solution temperature	Maintenance of balance
Solution and pouring	Method of weighing
speed	Operator
pH	Transporation
Stirrer, rpm	Road
Time	Cover
Crystallization	Spill
Temperature	Container
Time	
Concentration	
Mother crystal	
Weight	
Size	

Cause-and-Effect Diagram.   This diagram (also known as the Ishikawa diagram or the fishbone diagram) was developed in 1950 by Professor Kaoru Ishikawa. To create the diagram, the effect (symptom) is written at the head of the arrow. Potential causes (theories) are then added to complete the diagram. A common set of major categories for causes consists of personnel, work methods, materials, and equipment. Figure 22.9 shows the cause and effect diagram as prepared for the

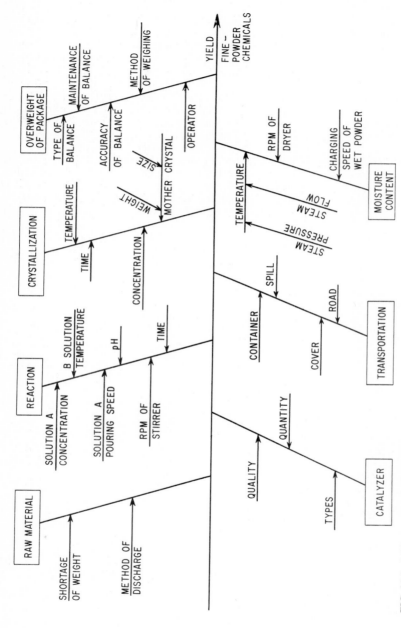

FIG. 22.9 Ishikawa cause-and-effect diagram.

22.38

same list of theories as was arranged in Table 22.12. Note how the diagram aids in identifying possible interrelationships among theories.

Betker (1983) presents both the cause-and-effect diagram and a tabular listing of theories to analyze solder defects on printed circuit board assemblies.

Some organizations use the cause-and-effect diagram to continually collect and display information on the important variables in a process. Section 16 under Initial Planning for Quality describes this simple but effective system.

Cause-and-effect diagrams can also be prepared for broad systems of accomplishing work. In one example, a group of electrical engineers employed the diagram to analyze a weak design review system. Also, see Section 21 under Cause-and-Effect Diagram for examples applied to nonmanufacturing activities.

A cause-and-effect diagram can be combined with a force field analysis (see Stratton, 1987). The team identifies the situations and events that contribute to the problem (these are the "restraining forces"). The actions necessary to counter the restraining forces are then identified (those actions are the "driving forces"). A diagram combining the restraining and driving forces is prepared to assist in diagnosis. The approach is similar to the barriers and aids analysis described below under Resistance to Change.

G.O.A.L. (1985a) describes the use of an affinity diagram for organizing facts, opinions, and issues into natural groupings as an aid to diagnosis on a complex problem. Inputs from knowledgeable people are listed on cards which are then rearranged until useful groups are identified.

Structure Trees. A structure tree is a diagram that starts with the problem, breaks it down into "subproblems," and then theorizes possible causes. An example from Florida Power and Light Company (1984, p. 44) is given in Figure 22.10.

FIG. 22.10 Structure tree example. *(Adapted from Florida Power & Light Co., 1984, p. 44.)*

POTENTIAL ROOT CAUSE	ROOT CAUSE OR SYMPTOM	CAUSES 00% OF PROBLEM	ACTIONABLE (DUG DEEPLY ENOUGH TO LEAD TO CORRECTIVE ACTION) YES/NO	HOW VERIFY	SYSTEM RELATED YES/NO	OTHER
#1	Root Cause	High	Yes	Test	Yes	
#2	Symptom	Low	Yes	Check Procedures	No	
#3	Root Cause	High	Yes	Defect Rate	Yes	
#4	Root Cause	High	No	Analyse New Data	Yes	

FIG. 22.11   Root cause evaluation matrix.

In a similar approach, Bailie (1985) explains how a "why-why diagram" develops a network of reasons for the original problem. End points on the diagram represent root causes for branches of the problem.

G.O.A.L. (1985b) explains how to construct an interrelationship diagraph to help identify key factors for inclusion in a tree diagram. Information is arranged in a diagram to generate ideas and map out logical links among related items. An extension of a tree diagram is the program decision process chart (G.O.A.L., 1986b). For each branch in the tree, the question asked is "What could go wrong at this step?"

Choosing Theories to be Tested.   Priorities must be established for testing the theories. Prioritizing of various theories can be aided by a simple matrix (Figure 22.11). Each potential cause (a theory) is qualitatively evaluated for the five factors listed. These evaluations aid the project team to prioritize these causes for further study.

Gust (1985) describes an example of prioritizing theories based on interviewing people and converting the responses to a quantitative score for each theory.

Whether to test just one theory at a time, one group of interrelated theories at a time, or all theories simultaneously requires a judgment by the improvement team. Usually the experience and creativity of the team clear away much of the fog.

TEST OF THEORIES OF MANAGEMENT-CONTROLLABLE PROBLEMS

Numerous diagnostic methods and tools have been evolved to test theories. Those frequently used are set out and exemplified below. Still other methods abound in the literature. In addition, new situations keep arising, requiring modifications to standard diagnostic tools. Ishikawa (1976) provides additional discussion for many of the diagnostic techniques discussed below.

Product and Process Dissection.   Some products are produced by a "procession" type of process, i.e., a series of sequential operations. At the end of the series the product is found to be defective, but it is not known which operation did the damage. In some of these cases it is feasible to "dissect" the process, i.e., make measurements at intermediate steps in the process to discover at which step the defect appears. Such discovery, if successful, can drastically reduce the subsequent effort in testing theories.

Flow Diagram.   Dissection of a process is aided by constructing a flow diagram showing the various steps in the process. Engle and Ball (1986) explain the role of a flow diagram in reducing the time required for handling special customer orders. A quality improvement team discovered that no one was able to describe the special order process. To understand the process they were trying to improve, the team created a flow diagram. Examples of several types of diagrams for understanding a process are given in Section 16 under Initial Planning for Quality.

An arrow network diagram can be useful in analyzing and replanning the schedule for a complex task that can be divided into subtasks (Riggs, 1981, pp. 206–218). The arrow diagram is a simpler version of the critical path method (CPM) and program evaluation review technique (PERT).

Process Capability Analysis.   One of the theories most widely encountered is: "The process can't hold the tolerances." To test this theory, measurements from the process must be taken and analyzed to determine the amount of variability inherent in the process. This variability is then compared to the specification limits. Those steps are performed in a "process-capability" study. Process capability is discussed in Section 16 under Process Capability. Process capability in administrative and support operations is covered in Section 21 under Process Capability.

Stream-to-Stream Analysis.   In order to meet production volume requirements, several sources of production ("streams") are often necessary. Streams take the form of different machines, operators, shifts, suppliers, etc. Although the streams may seem to be identical, the resulting products may not be. Stream-to-stream analysis consists of recording and examining data separately for each stream. One example was the diagnosis for burrs on kitchen stoves (see above under Diagnosis—General).

Another example (Payne, 1984) comes from a glass tube cutting machine. Glass tubing was cut into small glass rings. The weight of the rings was the critical element in determining the properties of the finished glass product. A sample of data (Figure 22.12a) apparently confirmed a theory that the machine was not capable. However, the machine contained four heads. Data collected separately from each head (stream) revealed that there was nothing wrong with heads 2, 3, or 4—except for the need to recenter their position (Figure 22.12b). There was something wrong with head 1. Ultimately, the remedy was proper maintenance of the machine rather than a redesign of the machine as was originally contemplated based on Figure 22.12a.

Time-to-Time Analysis.   Time-to-time analyses include (1) a simple plot of data on a time scale, (2) analysis of the time between abnormalities or problems, (3) analysis of rate of change, or "drift" of a characteristic, and (4) the use of cumulative data techniques with respect to time. Examples are given below.

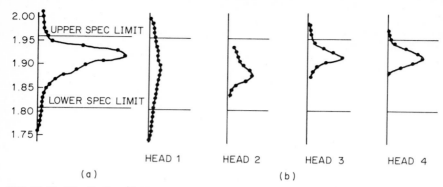

FIG. 22.12   Distribution of glass bead weights. (*a*) Sum of four heads. (*b*) Weight distribution on each of the four heads.   *(Adapted from Payne, 1984, pp. 30–31.)*

In trying to improve the uptime of production equipment, data were recorded on the amount and reasons for downtime for each machine (Payne, 1984). A superficial analysis led to a costly remedy and unsatisfactory results. Next came some real diagnosis. Data were collected for one week by machine and by time of day (Figure 22.13). Analysis of this almanac revealed:

1. Downtime in the morning is twice as much as the afternoon.
2. Much downtime occurs at the beginning of each shift.
3. Some machines perform significantly worse than others.
4. The distribution of fault types is not uniform from machine to machine.

These facts provided a whole new perspective on improving uptime.

In another example, field failures of oil coolers were assumed to be due to manufacturing. A parade of remedies (skipping the journey from symptom to cause) resulted in zero improvement. An engineer decided to plot the frequency of failures by month of the year, and this led to an important discovery. Of 70 failures over a 9-month period, 44 occurred during January, February, and March. These facts shifted the search to other causes such as winter climatic conditions. Subsequent diagnosis revealed the cause to be in design rather than manufacturing.

In analyzing time-to-time variations, the length of time between abnormalities can be a major clue to the cause. In a textile carding operation, there was a cyclic rise and fall of yarn weights, the cycle being about 12 min in length (Figure 22.14). The reaction of the production superintendent was immediate: "The only thing we do every 12 min or so is to stuff that feed box." In like manner, a process for making asbestos roofing shingles was found to produce abnormal weights every 6 min, on a precise timetable. Six minutes was also the interval for dumping a new load of material into the machine.

Within many streams, there is a time-to-time "drift"; e.g., the processing solution gradually becomes more dilute, the tools gradually wear, the worker becomes fatigued. Such drifts can often be quantified to determine the magnitude of the effect.

Cumulative plots of data can help to discover differences that are hidden when the data are in noncumulative form. Figure 22.15 compares a histogram (noncu-

TIME M/C STOPS	1	2	3	NUMBER 16	17	18	TOTAL
0600-0659	x	xxx	x		xxxxx	x	18
0700-0759		xx			xxxx	x	10
0800-0859			x	xx		x	6
0900-0959			x	x	xx	xxx	14
1000-1059	x			x	xx	x	9
1100-1159		xx	x	xx			11
1200-1259	xxx			x	x	xx	15
1300-1359		x	x		x		6
1400-1459	x	x	xx		xx		15
1500-1559					xx		5
1600-1659		x	x	x	x		4
1700-1759	x		x			x	6
1800-1859			x	x	x		5
1900-1959		x		x			4
2000-2059			x	x			5
2100-2159		x					1
Fault Type							
1	x	x	x	x	xx		8
2			x	x	xxx	x	9
3		x	x		xx	xx	10
4	xx	xx	xx	x	xxx	x	21
5	xx	xxx		x		xxx	16
6		x	x	x	x		10
7	x	x	x	xx	xxxxx		17
8	x	x	x		xxx	x	12
9		x	xx		xxxx	x	20
10	x	x	x	x	x	x	11

FIG. 22.13 Matrix for machine stop-time analysis. *(Adapted from Payne, 1984, p. 28.)*

FIG. 22.14 Consecutive weighings of card yarn.

FIG. 22.15 Comparison of histograms and cumulative plots.

mulative) and cumulative plots for data from two separate years. A difference in adjustments for 1970 versus 1969 is apparent from the cumulative plot but is hidden in the histogram.

In investigating lost or diluted brine in a chemical plant, a simple plot of drops in brine concentration over the course of a 24-h production day revealed that only 2 percent differences in concentration were happening during the last 4 h of a shift. This knowledge led to the development of a new theory for test. (See Nester and Staal, 1986.)

Analysis of time-oriented data can often be made more discriminating by plotting the data on probability paper (see Section 23 under The Normal Distribution).

Control charts are a powerful tool of diagnosis. Data are plotted chronologically, and the chart then determines whether the variability from sample to sample is due to chance or assignable causes of variation. Detection of assignable causes of variation can be the link to discovering the cause of a problem. See Section 23, Statistical Process Control.

Piece-to-Piece Analysis.   Products also exhibit piece-to-piece variation, which is quite independent of variations resulting from mixture of streams or from time-to-time drift. Usually, measurement of this variation is done by the familiar techniques such as the frequency distribution. (See Section 23 under Frequency Distribution.)

Beyond conventional statistical analysis, there is room for much creativity in discovering causes of piece-to-piece variation. For example, in a stack casting operation, one theory was that the bottom castings in the stack caused far greater scrap than the remaining castings. When the castings were processed with knowledge of their prior position in the casting stack, the theory was confirmed.

Within-Piece Analysis.   In some cases, what turns out to be decisive is the variation within individual units of product. A useful charting course technique for

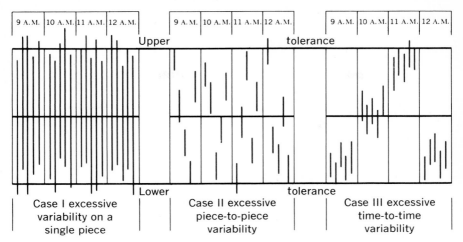

FIG. 22.16   Multi-Vari chart.

comparing within-piece variability to other sources of variability is the Multi-Vari chart.

Multi-Vari Chart.[2]   In this chart, a vertical line depicts the range of variation within a single piece of product. Figure 22.16 depicts three different examples of the relationship of product variation to tolerance limits. The left-hand case is one in which the within-piece variation alone is too great in relation to the tolerance. Hence no solution is possible unless within-piece variation is reduced. The middle example is a case in which within-piece variation is comfortable, occupying only about 20 percent of the tolerance. The problem is piece-to-piece variation. In the right-hand example, the problem is excess time-to-time variability. Traver (1983) presents additional examples of Multi-Vari charts.

Defect Concentration Analysis.   A "defect concentration diagram" plots attribute defect data according to the location on the product. The purpose is to discover whether defects are located in the same physical area.

Figure 22.17 shows a concentration diagram for the location of defects on an office reproduction product. The circled numbers indicate various locations on the equipment; the numbers adjacent to the circles indicate the number of defects found. An accompanying Pareto diagram of all of the locations made it clear that locations number 24 and 2 accounted for about 40 percent of the defects.

Often diagnostic tools must be combined to identify the cause of a problem. In diagnosing the cause of polishing defects on brass pieces, a combination of stream-to-stream analysis and a concentration diagram led to success. The polishing operation was performed by an endless chain of 138 "identical" holding fixtures, each fixture carrying one brass piece past the polishing wheels. A sample of

---

[2]The name "Multi-Vari" was given to this form of analysis by L. A. Seder in his classic paper "Diagnosis with Diagrams," which appeared in *Industrial Quality Control* in January and March 1950. The concept of the basic vertical line (Figure 22.16) had previously been employed by J. M. Juran (and possibly others), who derived it from the method long used by financial editors for showing stock market prices.

FIG. 22.17 Concentration diagram.

pieces selected at random from all fixtures showed defects occurring at different locations on the pieces. Diagnosis commenced by collecting data separately for each fixture—138 streams! Several consecutive pieces were examined from each stream, and the location of the defect was noted for each piece on a concentration diagram. This special collection of data by fixture revealed that pieces from the same fixture had defects concentrated at one location of the piece. The diagrams revealed that the location of the defect was directly related to the wear pattern on the holding fixture involved; the stream-to-stream analysis revealed that the 138 fixtures were not identical and had to be treated as 138 separate machines. Making adjustments unique to each fixture based on the direction given by the concentration diagrams proved to be an effective remedy.

Interrelation of Variables. Variables under study are often multiple in nature and are present in combination form. While they can be studied singly, there are many instances in which the need is to study them in combination. The aim of such studies is to quantify the size of the components of variation and to discover the extent to which they interact with each other. The generalized methods for such combination studies are discussed in Section 26, Design and Analysis of Experiments. However, simplified forms of analysis are available for problems which do not demand the use of sophisticated tools. One such form of analysis is the Multi-Vari chart discussed above. Other forms of such analyses are discussed below.

Simple Vectorial Resolution. Whenever the interaction among variables is negligible, the composite of multiple variations can be expressed by the relationship

$$\sigma_{comp}^2 = \sigma_a^2 + \sigma_b^2 + \sigma_c^2 + \cdots$$

where σ_{comp} = standard deviation of the composite
σ_a = standard deviation of variable a etc.

What is decisive about the size of variables in their contribution to the composite is not the standard deviation, but the square of the standard deviation! The relationship is of great practical value in affirming or denying theories and especially in establishing priorities for mounting an attack on the critical variables.

For example, three of the operations contributing to the thickness variation of optical lenses are blocking, milling, and grinding. On one set of processes the following data were secured:

Operation	σ	σ^2
Block	1.7	2.9
Mill	1.9	3.6
Grind	2.8	7.8
Sum of squares		14.3

The grinding, while seemingly a minor part of the variation when judged by the values of σ, accounts for more than half the sum of the squares.

Even more dramatic is the following synthetic example, which has numerous counterparts in the world of reality.

Six variables exhibit the following values of σ:

Variable	Original σ	Original σ^2	Improved σ	Improved σ^2
A	9	81	6	36
B	5	25	5	25
C	3	9	3	9
D	2	4	2	4
E	1	1	1	1
F	1	1	1	1
Total squares		121		76

Under a state of complete independence, the σ of composite becomes $\sqrt{121}$ = 11.

If the variability of A is now reduced from 9 to 6, the total of the squares will reduce to 76 (right-hand column) and the composite σ will reduce from 11 to 8.7.

If however, the variability of A remains constant and the variability of all the others is reduced to zero, the composite σ will become 9 (the value of A). In this synthetic example, a modest improvement in the variability of the dominant variable does more good than achievement of perfection in all other variables.

SPAN Plan. This is a structured approach to analysis of composite variations, and employs standardized data collection and analysis sheets to permit successive separation of observed total product variability into five recognized stages: lot-to-lot, stream-to-stream, time-to-time, within-piece (or positional), and error of measurement.

The plan is set out in "cookbook" fashion, so that a practitioner can collect the prescribed data, fill in the forms, and get the answer. Being a standardized procedure, the method can be used by the untrained practitioner.

Association Searches. Sometimes diagnosis can be advanced by analyzing data relating symptoms of the problem to some theory of causation pinpointing process, tools, workers, or design. Possible relationships can be examined using various statistical tools such as correlation, ranking, and matrixes.

Correlation. In this approach, data are plotted relating the incidence of symptoms of the problem to values of a potential causal variable. In some cases the analysis can be done with a simple diagram (Figure 22.18); other cases require regression and correlation analysis (see Section 23 under Regression Analysis).

In one case, the symptom was yarn breakage on weaving machines. One theory was "handling damages to the board bobbin." (The spinning mill supplied the yarn reeled into a board bobbin.) A plot of amount of damage against the number of yarn breakages clearly revealed a relationship between reels with heavy damage and subsequent yarn breakage. Further investigation showed that the corregated paper board plates used to protect the bobbins were inadequate. An investment of a few hundred dollars resulted in a cost reduction of $10,000 per year because of the yarn breakages (Bergstrom, 1985).

Ranking. In this technique, data are summarized by ranking the occurrence of the defect according to some source such as product model, machine, or operator. In one case involving 23 types of torque tubes, a ranking procedure showed that the amount of dynamic unbalance ranged form 52.3 percent defective to 12.3

FIG. 22.18 Test of theories by correlation.

percent defective, the average being 22.1 percent. One of the theories advanced that a swaging operation was a dominant cause of dynamic unbalance. A data table (Table 22.13) showed the various types of torque tubes in decreasing order of dynamic unbalance. For each type, the table indicated whether or not a swaging operation was involved. The result was dramatic—the worst seven types were all swaged; the best seven were all unswaged. This led to a closer examination of the swaging process which in turn led to an examination of the specification. There was no requirement in the specification to hold a close coaxial relationship between the swaged and the unswaged diameters and this lack of close relationship is what led to the dynamic unbalance.

Matrix. In this approach, past or current data are collected on two or more variables of a problem and summarized in a table to see if any pattern exists (e.g., see Table 22.13). Additional examples are presented later in this section under

TABLE 22.13 Test of Theories by Ranking

Type	% defective	Swaged (marked ×)	Type	% defective	Swaged (marked ×)
A	52.3	×	M	19.2	×
B	36.7	×	N	18.0	×
C	30.8	×	O	17.3	
D	29.9	×	P	16.9	×
E	25.3	×	Q	15.8	
F	23.3	×	R	15.3	
G	23.1	×	S	14.9	
H	22.5		T	14.7	
I	21.8	×	U	14.2	
J	21.7	×	V	13.5	
K	20.7	×	W	12.3	
L	20.3				

Test of Theories of Worker-Controllable Problems. G.O.A.L. (1986*a*) explains various adaptations of the matrix concept to include two or three sets of interrelated items.

Test of Theories by Collection of New Data ("Cutting New Windows in a Process"). In some cases the discovery of causes requires careful examination of additional stages in the process. This cutting of new windows can take several forms:

1. *Measurements at intermediate stages of a process:* Sometimes the symptom of a quality problem is not observed until after several operations have been performed, i.e., a specification applies to a finished characteristic that requires several manufacturing steps. In diagnosing some quality problems, it is necessary to go back into the previous steps and make observations there in order to evaluate theories.

An example involves the welding of large joints in critical pressure vessels. The weld is made by running a welding "bead" helically around the joint until the welding rod is consumed. A second bead follows the first, then a third, creating layer upon layer of weld material until the joint is completely built up. When the finished joint is x-rayed, any voids are identified.

The project team considered variations from a number of sources: worker, time to time, joint to joint, layer to layer, wtihin layer, and within bead. Prior test data were available to permit analysis of the first three of these theories. The remaining three could not be analyzed, since the x-ray test was performed only when a joint was completely finished. It was necessary to "dissect the process" on some joints by making an x-ray after each bead. This established that the main variable was within bead variation and that the problem was concentrated at the start of the bead.

Cutting new windows is also helpful in the diagnosis of nondissectible characteristics. A characteristic is "dissectible" if it is measurable during the process of manufacutre, e.g., the viscosity of a resinous material as it is processed into a varnish. A characteristic is "nondissectible" if it cannot be measured during such progression, e.g., the tensile strength of a casting. (Many nondissectible characteristics first come into existence at the conclusion of all manufacturing steps.) For diagnosis, it is useful in such cases to measure a related but dissectible property, e.g., hardness of the casting.

An example from a personnel process concerns the time required for hiring new engineers. Measurements taken at six steps in the overall process formed the basis for diagnosis (see Section 21 under Dissection of a Process).

2. *Measurement following noncontrolled operations:* Here, diagnosis includes the collection of additional information at individual steps in a process. Marquez (1985) describes the diagnosis of excessive shutdown time to remove a hot mold from a molding machine. The process of shutdown was divided into 11 steps and measurements taken to estimate the time required for each step. Two of the eleven steps accounted for 62 percent of the shutdown time. This Pareto effect was important in further diagnosis.

An example from a manufacturing area involves the time required to process customer returns and make a claims payment (Gust, 1985). Diagnosis was based on dissection of the overall process into five major steps. This additional information formed a basis for further diagnosis.

3. *Measurement of additional or related properties on the product or process:* Diagnosis sometimes requires measurements on characteristics other than those for which the specification is not being met. Mizell and Strattner (1981) discuss a high incidence of failures in a pressure test on automotive radiators. Effort focused on the heat treating and drying operations which occurred inside a closed assembly line braze oven. To measure accurately what was happening inside the oven, an insulated box—about the size of a radiator—was designed to hold a 10 channel data logger. Thermocouples were mounted on the outside of the box to measure temperature data and feed it to the data logger. The box was placed on the assembly line along with the radiators and sent through the oven on a normal brazing cycle. Data were recorded and transferred to a printer which showed the temperature and time. These data were used to modify the temperature profile inside the oven. Down went the failure rate.

In the manufacture of phonograph records the symptom was a high percent of records with surface defects. Automatic timers controlled the pressing cycle. Diagnosis revealed that the times for various steps should *not* be fixed but should be determined based on additional measurements periodically taken. The remedy was to monitor pressure, temperature, viscosity, and other factors. An on-line computer evaluates these data for each disk, and decides the optimum molding conditions. Only then, and no sooner, does the press create the product.

4. *Study of worker methods:* In some situations there are consistent differences in the defect levels coming from various workers. Month after month, some workers produce more "good" product than others. In such situations, there must be a cause for this consistent difference in observed performance. Diagnosis for problems related to human performance is discussed later in this section.

Diagnosis through Experiment. "Experiment" as used here means mainly creation and processing of trial lots to test the validity of theories about causes of quality deficiencies. The experiment may be conducted either in a laboratory or in the outside world, e.g., the factory, warehouse, or users' premises.

It is easy enough to put down the minimal criteria to be met by an experiment. It should:

Test the theories under study without being confused by extraneous variables

Discover the existence of major causes even if these were not advanced as theories

Be economic in relation to the amounts at stake

Provide reliable answers

To meet these criteria requires inputs from several sources. The *managers* must identify the questions that the experiment should answer; the *technologists* must select and set priorities on the proper variables to be investigated; the *diagnosticians* provide the methods for planning the experimental design and analyzing the resulting data.

Types of Experiments for Diagnosis. Section 26 presents a variety of designs of experiments, from the simple to the complex, that can be useful in diagnosing quality problems. Experimentation for diagnosis is not a matter to be left to the amateur. Although there are many forms of experimental designs, they can be broadly classified into the rifleshot experiment and the unbridled experiment.

The Rifleshot Experiment. In many projects, the analysis of available data may point strongly to only one or two suspect variables. In such cases it is common to avoid elaborate exploratory experiments and instead to conduct narrow experiments to test only the effect of the one or two suspects. Such studies are known as rifleshot experiments.

In its simplest form, the rifleshot experiment identifies, by use of the split-lot technique, which of two suspected variables is the cause. For example, for a batch of homogeneous material, half is sent through process A and the other half through process B. If the material is also a main suspect, two lots of material are split, and each is sent through both processes A and B, creating a two-by-two design of experiment. If three variables are involved, more combinations are needed; but now the technique of design of experiments enters to simplify the procedure.

The Unbridled Experiment. In the absence of strong suspicions as to one or several variables being dominant, the trial-lot approach may take the form of the "unbridled" experiment. In this form, a lot (or lots) of product is followed through the successive processes under a plan which provides for making measurements of many of the suspected variables of the materials and processes. The resulting product characteristics are also measured. The hope is that the subsequent analysis will disclose all significant correlations between causes and effects.

The unbridled experiment is so much in the nature of a fishing expedition that it should be based on a written plan to assure that it is understood and that it represents a meeting of the minds. With careful planning, a well-organized unbridled experiment has a high probability of identifying the dominant causes of variability. The disadvantage is the associated high cost and long time interval to get answers.

Statisticians have developed some remarkably useful tools for getting rid of unwanted variables through "randomizing"; for minimizing the amount of experimentation through skillful use of factorial, blocked, nested, and still other designs; and for reading the meaning out of complex data. See Section 26, Design and Analysis of Experiments.

Measurement for Diagnosis. A roadblock to diagnosis is the use of shop instruments to make the measurements. These instruments were never intended for diagnosis. They were provided for entirely different purposes—i.e., process regulation and product test. There are several principal categories of cases in which measurement for diagnosis must be different from measurement for control. These cases include:

1. *Measurement by variables instead of attributes:* Process capability studies usually demand this type of measurement.

2. *Measurement with a precision superior to that of the shop instruments:* In some cases imprecise shop instruments are the dominant cause of the quality problem.

3. *Measurements at new "windows" cut into the process:* An example is the welding bead case discussed above under Test of Theories by Collection of New Data.

4. *Measurement of properties not in the specification:* The causes of the symptom may often involve a process parameter such as temperature or pressure that is not a product specification or even defined in the manufacturing procedure.

5. *Developing means to summarize sensory test results:* For example, in the optical industry, the extent of scratches on precise components is a major problem affecting process yields and product quality. It is comparatively easy to judge one component for product acceptance purposes. However, for judging process capability, one company developed a "scratch index" which was expressed roughly as the ratio of the scratched area to the total area.

The foregoing paragraphs have described diagnostic techniques for management-controllable problems. Worker-controllable problems can involve additional diagnostic techniques.

TEST OF THEORIES OF WORKER-CONTROLLABLE PROBLEMS

A casual review of errors made by humans can lead to a conclusion that the basic cause is lack of motivation on quality. The facts refute this. Diagnosis of human errors reveals that there are "multiple species" of error and that lack of motivation is only one of the causes. To illustrate these species, Table 22.14 shows the distribution of 80 errors made by six office workers engaged in preparing insurance policy contracts.

TABLE 22.14   Matrix of Errors by Insurance Policy Writers

Error type	Policy writer						Total
	A	B	C	D	E	F	
1	0	0	1	0	2	1	4
2	1	0	0	0	1	0	2
3	0	⑯	1	0	2	0	⑲
4	0	0	0	0	1	0	1
5	2	1	3	1	4	2	⑬
6	0	0	0	0	3	0	3
27							
28							
29							
Total	6	⑳	8	3	㊱	7	80

There were 29 types of errors and they follow the Pareto principle. Notice the data for error type 3. There were 19 of these, and worker B made 16 of the 19. The table also shows the rest of the work done by worker B. Except for error type 3, B makes few errors. There is nothing basically wrong with the job specification or the method, since five workers had little or no trouble with error type 3. There is nothing basically wrong with worker B, except for defect type 3. It follows that worker B and no one else is misinterpreting some instruction, resulting in that cluster of 16 errors of type 3.

Error type 5 is of a different species. There is a cluster of 13 of these, and all the workers make this error, more or less uniformly. This suggests some difference in approach between all the workers on the one hand and the inspector on the other. Such a difference is usually of management-controllable origin, but the realities can soon be established by interviews with the respective employees.

Notice also the column of numbers associated with worker E. The total is 36 errors and is the largest cluster in the table. Worker E made nearly half the errors for the entire team and that worker made them in virtually all error type categories. Why did worker E make so many errors? It might be any of a variety of reasons, e.g., inadequate training, lack the capacity to do such exacting work, etc. Further study is needed, but it might be easier to go from symptom directly to remedy—find a less demanding job for that worker.

Thus, this one table of data shows the presence of multiple species of worker error. The remedy is not as simplistic as "motivate the worker." Understanding these species through diagnosis is important in identifying causes. See also Section 10 under Diagnosing Worker Performance.

Tools of Analysis.   The diagnostic tools include:

1. *The matrix:*   An example is the above case of insurance policy errors. The matrix showed the performance of multiple workers with respect to multiple error types.
2. *The Pareto analysis (see above under Pareto Principle):*   Figure 22.19 shows the distribution of imperfects for 15 weavers in a textile department. Three of the weavers account for 74 percent of the total imperfects.

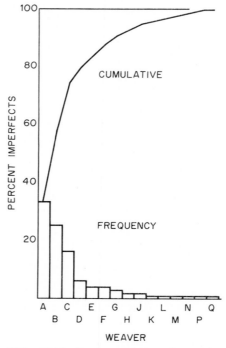

FIG.   22.19 Pareto   analysis   of   weaving imperfects.

3. *The time-to-time analysis:*   An example below (The Gun Assembly Case) shows how such an analysis establishes the presence of "consistency."

By using these tools of analysis, it soon emerges that the great majority of worker errors fall into three species: inadvertent, technique, and conscious. Table

TABLE 22.15 Interrelation among Error Pattern, Likely Subspecies of Worker Error, and Likely Solution

Pattern disclosed by analysis of worker error	Likely subspecies of error causing this pattern	Likely solution
On certain defects, no one is error-prone; defect pattern is random.	Errors are due to inadvertence.	Error-proof the process.
On certain defects, some workers are consistently error-prone while others are consistently "good."	Errors are due to lack of technique (ability, know-how, etc.). Lack of technique may take the form of secret ignorance. Technique may consist of known knack or of secret knowledge.	Discovery and propagation of knack. Discovery and elimination of secret ignorance.
Some workers are consistently error-prone over a wide range of defects.	There are several potential causes: Conscious failure to comply to standards Inherent incapacity to perform this task Lack of training	Solution follows the cause: Motivation Transfer worker Supply training.
On certain defects, all workers are error-prone.	Errors are management controllable.	Meet the criteria for self-control.

22.15 shows the interrelations among the errors pattern, the likely subspecies, and the likely remedies. The three species are examined below.

Inadvertent Errors. Inadvertent errors are those which workers are unable to avoid because of human inability to maintain attention. Centuries of experience have demonstrated that human beings are simply unable to maintain continuing attention. (If the "not paying attention" is deliberate, the resulting errors are conscious rather than inadvertent.)

The usual examples involve a component omitted from an assembly, or a process adjustment that is set incorrectly. Unusual examples also occur. Some stock brokerage companies maintain a special account to cover expenses in connection with errors made in trading stock, e.g., the purchase of the wrong stock because of a similarity in the acronyms used to identify companies. In the athletic arena, a football game is lost because, on a key play near the end of the game, a player mistakenly hears a play called as "green" instead of "three." He misses his defensive assignment and the opposing team scores a touchdown (Anderson, 1982).

Diagnosis to identify errors as inadvertent is aided by understanding their distinguishing features. They are:

Unintentional: The worker does not want to make errors.

Unwitting: At the time of making an error, the worker is unaware of having made it.

Unpredictable: There is nothing systematic as to when an error will be made, what type of error will be made, or which worker will make the error. As a consequence of this unpredictability, the error pattern exhibits *randomness.* Conversely, *a set of data which shows a random pattern of worker error suggests that the errors are inadvertent.* The randomness of the data may apply to the types of error, to the persons who make errors, and to the time when the errors are made.

The evident "cause" of inadvertent defects is inattention. But what causes inattention? The search for an answer leads us into the complexities of psychological (e.g., monotony) and physiological (e.g., fatigue) phenomena—complexities which are not fully understood even by the experts. To explore these complexities in depth means going deeper and deeper into an endless swamp. It is simpler to go around the swamp—to go direct from symptom to remedy.

Remedies for inadvertent errors involve two approaches:

1. Reducing the extent of dependence on human attention. The tools used here are all of the error-proofing type: fail-safe designs, validation of processes, countdowns, redundant verifications, cutoffs, interlocks, alarm signals, automation, robots. Large reduction in errors can result from the use of bar codes to help identify items.

2. Making it easier for the human beings to remain attentive. Reorganization of work to reduce fatigue and monotony, job rotation, sense multipliers, templates, masks, and overlays are examples of remedies.

Technique Errors.   These errors arise because the worker lacks some essential technique, skill, or knowledge needed to prevent the error from happening. Diagnosis to identify errors due to technique is aided by understanding their features. They are:

Unintentional: The worker does not want to make errors.

Specific: Technique errors are unique to certain defect types—those types for which the missing technique is essential.

Consistent: Workers who lack the essential technique consistently make more defects than workers who possess the technique. This consistency is readily evident from data on worker errors.

Unavoidable: The inferior workers are unable to match the performance of the superior workers because they (the inferior workers) do not know "what to do differently."

Discovery of the existence of technique errors makes use of the diagnostic tools for worker errors, as illustrated below in the assembly of shotguns.

The Gun Assembly Case.   Guns were assembled by 22 skilled craft workers, each of whom assembled a complete gun from bits and pieces. After a safety test, about 10 percent of the guns could not be opened up to remove the spent cartridge—a defect known as "open hard after fire." For such defects it was necessary to disassemble the gun and then reassemble, requiring about 2 hours per defective gun— a significant waste.

After an agony of fruitless discussion, it was clear that the missing element was factual information. Data, already in the files, by assembler and time, were collected and arranged in a matrix (Table 22.16). Some helpful information became evident.

1. There was a wide month-to-month *departmental* variation in the defect rate, ranging from a low of 1.8 percent in January to a high of 22.6 percent in Feb-

TABLE 22.16 Matrix Analysis

Assembly operator rank	Nov.	Dec.	Jan.	Feb.	Mar.	Apr.	Total
1	4	1	0	0	0	0	5
2	1	2	0	5	1	0	9
3	3	1	0	3	0	3	10
4	1	1	0	2	2	4	10
5	0	1	0	10	2	1	14
6	2	1	0	2	2	15	22
17	18	8	3	37	9	23	98
18	16	17	0	22	36	11	102
19	27	13	4	62	4	14	124
20	6	5	2	61	22	29	125
21	39	10	2	45	20	14	130
22	26	17	4	75	31	35	188
Total	234	146	34	496	239	241	1390
% defective	10.6	6.6	1.8	22.6	10.9	11.0	10.5
5 best	9	6	0	20	5	8	48
5 worst	114	62	12	265	113	103	669
Ratio	13	10	∞	13	23	13	14

ruary. Since all workers seemed to be affected, this variation had its cause outside of the department. (Subsequent analysis confirmed this.)

2. The ratio of the five best performances to the five worst showed *a stunning consistency.* In each of the 6 months, the five worst performances add up to an error rate which is at least 10 times as great as the sum of the five best performances. There must be a reason for such a consistent difference, and it can be found by studying the work methods—the technique used by the respective workers.

The Knack. The study of work methods showed that the superior performers used a file to cut down one of the dimensions on a complex component; the inferior performers did not file that component. This filing constituted the *"knack"*— a small difference in method which accounts for a large difference in results. (Until the diagnosis was made, the superior assemblers did not realize that the filing greatly reduced the incidence of defects.)

Usually the difference in worker performance is traceable to some superior knack used by the successful performers to benefit the product. In the case of the gun assemblers, the knack consisted of filing that component. In some cases, however, the difference in worker performance is due to unwitting *damage* done to the product (by the inferior performers). For example, the weavers who accounted for most of the imperfects (Figure 22.19) were unwittingly damaging the product—a sort of negative "knack."

There is a useful rule for predicting whether the difference in worker performance is due to a beneficial knack or to a negative knack. Who are in the minority? If the superior performers are in the minority, the difference is probably due to a beneficial knack. If the inferior performers are in the minority, the difference in performance is likely due to a negative knack.

Hiding the Knack. Occasionally, a worker knows the superior knack but chooses to hide the information. Why? Perhaps to avoid admitting that prescribed procedures are not being followed; perhaps to retain a superiority of performance over the other workers. Often the reason is never known.

Sometimes, the causes of technique errors have their origin in a condition that is management-controllable.

1. In reviewing the frequency of damage to crankshafts, an analysis by individual workers showed that only one worker's product was damaged. Observation revealed that the worker sometimes bumped a crankshaft into a nearby conveyor. Why? Because the worker was left-handed and the workplace layout was inconvenient for a left-handed person.

2. In an aircraft assembly operation, data analysis by individual workers revealed that one worker met the production quota consistently while others did not. The worker explained that he had taken his powered screwdriver home and rebuilt the motor. The company replaced all the motors with a resulting increase in productivity and quality.

A Trap for Managers. Cases such as the gun assembly situation make clear the dangers of assuming that some workers are able to do good work and others not, and therefore the remedy is to motivate the inferior workers. Such an assumption has no validity as applied to technique errors. The entire category of technique errors is doomed to go on and on until someone is able to provide the inferior workers with an answer to the question, "What should I do differently than I am doing now?"

How is this question to be answered? Sometimes the workers are able to find the answers by themselves. This is especially true if teams of workers have been trained in problem solving and are given the time to analyze problems. More usually the workers cannot find the answers by themselves. In consequence they will keep on doing what they have been doing and hence will keep on making the same defects. This will go on and on until they get the needed help from management.

Summary for Technique Errors. The sequence of events to identify, analyze, and remedy technique errors is:

1. For the defect types under study, create and collect data which can disclose any significant worker-to-worker differences.

2. Analyze the data on a time-to-time basis to discover whether consistency is present.

3. Identify the consistently best and consistently worst performers.

4. Study the work methods used by the best and worst performers to identify their differences in technique.

5. Study these differences further so as to discover the beneficial knack which produces superior results (or the negative knack which is damaging the product).

6. Bring everyone up to the level of the best through appropriate remedial action such as:

    a. Train inferior performers in use of the knack or in avoidance of damage.

    b. Change the technology so that the process embodies the knack.

    c. Error-proof the process in ways which require use of the knack or which prohibit the technique which is damaging to the product.

Conscious Errors.   Diagnosis to identify errors as conscious is aided by understanding their features. They are:

Witting: At the time of making an error the worker is aware of it.

Intentional: The error is the result of a deliberate intention on the part of the worker.

Persistent: The worker who makes the error usually intends to keep it up.

The outward evidences of conscious errors are likewise unique. Whereas inadvertent errors exhibit randomness, conscious errors exhibit consistency, i.e., some workers consistently make more errors than others. However, whereas technique errors are typically restricted to those defect types which require some special knack, conscious errors tend to cover a wider spectrum of defect types. Knowing these types is helpful in diagnosing errors as conscious.

Management-Initiated Conscious Errors.   Many "conscious" errors are management-initiated. The most common examples arise from the multiple standards which all managers must meet—cost, delivery, productivity, as well as quality. Due to changes in the marketplace, the managers keep shifting their priorities; e.g., in a sellers' market, delivery schedules will prevail over some quality standards. The pressures on the managers are then transmitted to the work force and can similarly result in conscious violation of one standard in order to meet another.

A second major source of management-initiated conscious errors is an atmosphere of blame. In such an atmosphere, workers consciously violate company rules by hiding the scrap, failing to make out the rework tickets, etc.

There are also other examples. As part of a drive to catch up on late deliveries, management posts a new scoreboard to show progress of delivery against schedules. There are no such scoreboards showing performance against quality standards. The work force concludes that mangement is more interested in quantity than quality.

Some well-intentioned actions by management can, instead, have a tragic effect. For example, the managers launch a poster campaign to urge everyone to do better work. However, while the bulk of the defects are management-controllable, the campaign makes no provision to improve quality of purchased materials, process capability, machine maintenance. To the workers it would look like a case of "Do as we say, not as we do."

Worker-Initiated Conscious Errors.   Some conscious errors are worker-initiated. Workers may have real or fancied grievances against the boss or the company. They get their revenge by not meeting standards. A few become rebels against the whole social system and they use sabotage to show their resentment. Some of the instances encountered are so obviously antisocial that no one—not the fellow employees, not the union—will defend the actions.

Some conscious errors *seem* to be worker-initiated but have their origin in inadequate communication by management. For example, three product batches fail to conform to quality characteristic X. In each case the inspector places a hold on the batch. In each case the Material Review Board concludes the batch is fit for use and releases it for delivery. However, neither the production worker nor the inspector is told the reason. Not knowing the reason, these workers may conclude that characteristic X is unimportant. That sets the stage for unauthorized actions.

Complexity of Causes.   Most conscious errors involve complexity: multiple and conflicting standards to be met, foggy communications, shared responsibilities. This complexity has its effect on the journey from symptom to cause. As with the case of inadvertent errors, the journey leads into a swamp. Going into the swamp can be avoided. Even if the causes are unknown, some broad-spectrum remedies for conscious errors are known if the symptoms are understood.

Remedies for Conscious Errors. Generally, the remedies listed here emphasize securing changes in behavior but without special effort to secure a prior change in attitude. Either way, *the approach is oriented primarily to the persons* rather than to the "system"— the managerial or technological aspects of the job.

Depersonalize the Order. In one textile plant, spinners were failing to tie the correct knots ("weaver's knots") when joining two ends of yarn together. The pleas and threats of the supervisor were of no avail. The spinners disliked the supervisor and they resented the company's poor responses to their grievances. The problem was solved when the personnel manager took the informal leader of the spinners *to the weaving department* to show her how the weavers were having trouble because of wrong knots.

The principal involved here is "depersonalizing the order."

One *person* should not give orders to another *person*. Both should take their orders from the "law of the situation" a phrase coined by Mark Parker Follett (see Metcalf and Urwick, 1941.) The situation in the weaving department required that weaver's knots be tied. Hence that situation is binding on the president, the managers, the supervisors, the spinners.

Establish Accountability (Traceability). To illustrate, in one company the final product was packaged in bulky bales which were transported by conventional fork lift trucks. Periodically, a prong of a fork would pierce a bale and do a lot of damage. But there was no way of knowing which trucker moved which bale. When the company introduced a simple means of *identifying which trucker moved which bale,* the amount of damage dropped dramatically.

Provide Balanced Emphasis. The worker discovers the company's priority on multiple standards (quality, productivity, delivery) from the behavior of management. For example, scoreboards on productivity and delivery rates must be supplemented with one on quality to provide evidence of a balanced emphasis.

Conduct Periodic Quality Audits. Systems of continuing traceability or scorekeeping are not always cost-effective. Quality audits can be designed to provide, on a sampling basis, information of an accountability and scorekeeping nature.

Provide Assistance to Workers. Visual reminders to help prevent defects can be useful. For example, a "que" card is a wall poster listing the four or five principal worker-controllable defects for a specific process. Opposite each such defect is a narrative description of the knack which could avoid the defect. Supplemental posters explain the knacks by the use of diagrams.

Improve Communications. Most companies do a good job of communicating essential quality information to workers on matters such as specifications, standards, procedures, methods. But other communication is vital to foster a positive claim for quality. For example, management should:

1. Provide means for workers to communicate their views and ideas
2. Explain to workers those management actions which, on their face, are antagonistic to quality

Assuring that managers do communicate to workers is a problem. A widely prevalent example is the case of nonconforming lots which are sent out as being fit for use, but without telling the workers why they were sent out. Virtually no company makes provision in the "hold" documents to require that managers face the question: "What shall we communicate to the work force?" Lacking such a provision the matter is seldom considered, and hence by default there is no communication.

Communication via Quality Circle Projects. To carry out such projects, workers and managers must communicate on a variety of topics as the project progresses to a conclusion: agreement on which projects to tackle; securing essential data from other departments; securing special tools, instruments, etc., for tryout ideas; securing consulting assistance from company specialists; getting recommendations accepted.

Create Competition, Incentives. These devices have potential value provided they are not misused. Competitions among workers and teams must be designed to be in good humor and on a friendly level, such as prevails among the interdepartmental sport or bridge competitions.

Financial incentives are deceptively attractive. They look good while pay is going up—during the part of the cycle when they are "bonuses" for good work. However, during a spate of poor work, removal of the bonuses converts the "incentives" into "penalties," with all the associated arguments about who is responsible.

Nonfinancial incentives avoid the pitfall of bonuses becoming penalties, but they must be kept above the gimmickry level.

Error-Proof the Operation. The concept of error-proofing has wide application to conscious errors. (See Section 16 under Error-Proofing the Process.)

Reassign the Work. An option usually available to managers is selective assignment, i.e., assign the most demanding work to the workers with the best quality record. Application of this remedy may require redesign of jobs—separation of critical work from the rest so that selective assignment becomes feasible.

Use the Tools of Motivation. This is the eleventh form of remedy for conscious errors. The subject is discussed in Section 10, Managing Human Performance.

The foregoing list of remedies helps to solve most conscious errors, but a study of the symptoms and surrounding circumstances is essential in order to choose the most effective remedy.

Next, we consider the development of remedies in general, for both management-controllable and worker-controllable problems.

DEVELOPMENT OF REMEDIES

Following diagnosis to determine the cause, the next step in the breakthrough process is to choose a remedy. Although remedies must be unquie for each problem, some examples have already been presented for management-controllable problems and for the several subspecies of worker-controllable problems.

Choice of Alternatives. The diagnostic journey may lead to a wide variety of dominant causes of the symptoms: weakness in the design, inadequacy in a production process, lack of precision in a measuring instrument, lack of technique by a worker. Direct remedial action means revising the design, process, instrument, or technique in response to the findings of the diagnosis. An essential criterion is that company costs and customer costs be optimized.

In quantifying company costs the cost impact on a companywide basis (not departmental) should be calculated for each alternative. Included should be the impact on the cost of poor quality, materials usage, facilities usage, productivity, energy consumption, etc. The project team, rather than one department, is best suited to make this evaluation.

Similarly for the customer, the impact on the customers' costs and well-being should be evaluated for each alternative remedy. (Section 3 under Quality and Share of Market discusses the influence of competitive differences on the customer.) Of particular concern is a remedy that results in perfectionism, i.e., adding costs without adding value. Section 3 under Perfectionism discusses perfectionism.)

In order to provide a methodical study of alternatives, a solution selection matrix is helpful (see Figure 22.20 for an example from the Florida Power and Light Company). Such a matrix assures that criteria are defined and applied to each alternative.

Remedial Action. Once the alternatives have been weighed, the project team makes its recommendation to that line department whose responsibilities include taking the type of action recommended. This line department then embarks on the action. It is usual, however, for the project team to keep the topic on its books until the action has been taken and it has been confirmed that the remedy solves the problem. Also of importance is to verify that the remedy does not create a new problem. For example, a ceramic seal ring for a pump had a chronic "pull-out" problem. Changing the firing ridge was confirmed as a remedy for the pull-out problem, but later experience showed that the remedy introduced a new problem in which parts would stick.

Occasionally, remedies can be remarkable. In a plant making chips for integrated circuits, a vibration problem caused by a nearby railroad was solved by constructing a swimming pool between the plant and the railroad. Another problem was caused by cement dust from an adjacent concrete mixing plant. The remedy: buy the plant and destroy it.

Usually remedial actions proceed smoothly once the agreements have been reached. There are, however, some special situations which are discussed below.

Revisions in Systematic Approach. Many remedies are primarily of a technological nature—a change in some design, tool, or instrument. However, many remedies involve changes of a systematic sort—changes in policies, goals, plans, organization, standards, procedures, or emphasis. Such remedies are typically of an

POSSIBLE SOLUTIONS	TEAM CAN IMPLEMENT	COST HIGH/LOW	MANAGEMENT RECEPTIVITY	FIXES SEVERAL ROOT CAUSES	CREATES NEW PROBLEMS	OTHER
#1	Yes	High	High	Yes	No	
#2	No	Low	High	Yes	No	
#3	Yes	Low	Low	No	?	
#4	Yes	High	Low	Yes	Yes	
#5	No	Low	High	No	No	

FIG. 22.20 Solution selection matrix.

interdepartmental character and are often identified by the project team with its broad representation. In addition, such remedies can go well beyond the specific project under study, since policies, plans, procedures, etc., are usually designed to cover wider areas of operations. Examples of the many systematic remedies are formal design review and supplier certification. These and other systematic remedies are discussed in the other sections of this handbook.

Rare but Critical Defects.   Some defects or errors occur in low frequency but have a serious effect when they do occur. These "rare but critical" defects demand special approaches, several of which are discussed below.

Increased Design Margins.   Some product failures are traceable to inadequate margins of safety between the capability of the design and the use to which it is put. This inadequacy can arise in various ways: sale for the wrong application, misuse by the user, cost pressures on the designer, designers' errors, or inadequate testing of models. One potential remedy common to all these causes is to increase the margin of safety.

There are multiple ways to increase the margin of safety: provide more structural material, use more exotic materials, design for misuse rather than intended use, "derate" (specify for use at lower levels of stress), and apply fail-safe and error-proof concepts to the design. Virtually all of these ways involve increase in costs.

Improved Model Testing.   One of the limitations of model construction and test is the small number of model units tested relative to the subsequent large number of product units. If the product failure rates are low, it is unlikely that such failures will be present during model testing at normal conditions of use.

By increasing the severity of test conditions and properly correlating the test results with normal test data, the predictions made by model testing can be significantly improved. However, care must be taken not to increase test severity to a degree which introduces new failure modes—failure modes not encountered in actual practice.

Improved Process Capability.   Some rare but critical defects have their origin in the manufacturing process: the process dispersion is too wide, the process is periodically misdirected, the workers made errors. The needed corrective actions may be in such forms as reducing process variability, improving precision of setup, providing automatic warnings or cutoffs, and error-proofing against human error.

Automated 100 Percent Inspection.   This concept has been widely applied in recent decades, especially with respect to (1) safety-oriented defects and (2) screening of components which would otherwise cause defects in final products. Application of the concept has been supported by a remarkable growth in the associated technology: nondestructive test methods, automated testing devices, and computerized controls.

Redundant 100 Percent Inspection.   Where automated testing is not feasible, human beings must perform the inspection. Particularly when the inspection is monotonous, 100 percent inspection by humans is error-prone; i.e., some defects will be missed. Multiple inspectors can reduce the effect of human errors. Suppose that two inspectors are used and that each finds 80 percent of the defects submitted. The first inspector will find 80 percent and hence will miss 20 percent; the second inspector will find 80 percent of the 20 percent, or 16 percent. A cumulative result of 4 percent of the original defects will be missed.

The Useful Many Defects.   Identification of the vital few defects is an important step in the breakthrough process. The remaining "useful many" defects, however, collectively may still represent a sizable amount of quality deficiency.

Two general approaches are used for the useful many defects:

1. Attack on the useful many *collectively*
2. Attack on the useful many *individually,* on a project-by-project basis

Attacking the useful many *collectively* is feasible by identifying some basis which is common to the numerous "different" product types or defect types. For example, the same chemical process produces many catalog items of paint, each "different" in color. The same electrochemical process is used to produce numerous varieties of semiconducting chips, each "different" in its circuitry.

If defect data on paint is organized by paint catalog number, then the numerous small volume catalog items will likely result in low frequency of defects, and therefore none will qualify for the vital few. If the same data are organized collectively for that one chemical process, then the total defects may be able to compete for a place among the vital few.

To cite another example, in job shop work one of the main sources of product defects is order editing errors. The documents must identify with precision the way in which this order differs from all previous orders. The outward evidence of order editing errors is a long list of many minor product defects. However, the *order-editing process* is common to all of these defects and hence may qualify as one of the vital few projects.

A search for a common basis need not be restricted to a common manufacturing process. Other bases for collective grouping of data include *broader* grouping of data by source of causes, i.e., design, supplier, field conditions, etc. In the other direction, grouping can focus on a *narrower* source of causes, i.e., unanticipated environmental conditions, wrong sequence of manufacturing steps, inadequate maintenance of measuring equipment, etc.

Attacking the useful many *individually,* on a project-by-project basis, is a totally different matter. If any are critical, then the approaches for the "rare but critical defects" apply. For the remainder, the cost of assigning managers and engineers cannot ordinarily be justified by the potential cost reduction. One solution is to tap the great potential of the work force through such means as quality circles (see Section 10 under Quality Circles).

It may also be possible to create a new generic remedy which applies to a wide assortment of error types. For example, office work has long had the annoying problem of misspelled words. Most of these misspellings are inadvertent errors scattered over a wide assortment of different words. Now, some word processing programs include a dictionary in their memory as a means of detecting misspelled words. The planners found a way to deal with numerous error types, each of which is comparatively rare.

Replication of Remedies. A remedy on one project may also apply to the same or similar quality problems throughout an organization. It is useful, therefore, to set up a means of communicating the remedy to others. One method (employed by the Florida Power and Light Company) is to establish a center to track, summarize, and broadcast the remedies. The remedy is entered into a data base that can be easily examined by means of key words, and the information is disseminated to other teams working on similar problems. In addition, those who review proposed remedies on projects are responsible for recommending where else in the organization a remedy could also be helpful.

Reducing the Cost of Inspection.   The obvious benefits of identifying and removing the causes of defects can be supplemented by another benefit: Inspection can be reduced. Several avenues are possible, and these are discussed in Section 18 under Defect Prevention.

PROOF OF THE REMEDIES

Before a remedy is finally adopted, it must be proven effective under operating conditions. In practice, two steps are frequently involved:

1. Preliminary evaluation of the remedy under conditions that imitate the real world ("simulation")
2. Final evaluation under complete conditions of the real world

Examples of a preliminary evaluation of a design change can start with a reliability prediction based on a mathematical model and then proceed to testing of a prototype. The evaluation of a change in a manufacturing process can employ a dry run or a pilot plant.

Preliminary evaluations have limitations. The list is unending: The reliability prediction model is based on assumptions that are never fully met; the prototype test unit is made in the engineering shop rather than the production environment; the testing is done with a small sample size and limited test conditions; the dry run for the revised manufacturing process is conducted by the best workers using the best material and watched over by supervisors and engineers who are determined to make the remedy work, etc.

There is no substitute for the remedies in the real world. If the remedy is a design change on a component, the final evaluation must be a test of the redesigned component operating in the complete system under field conditions; if the remedy is a change in a manufacturing procedure, the new procedure must be tried under typical (not ideal) factory conditions; if the remedy is a change in a maintenance procedure, the effectiveness must be demonstrated in the field environment by personnel with representative skill levels.

The issues involved in proving remedies under typical operating conditions have many similarities to those which arise in the transfer of plans to operations (see Section 6 under Transfer to Operations.)

RESISTANCE TO CHANGE

Once a remedy has been determined, then on the face of it all that remains is to apply that remedy. Not so. Instead, various objections to the remedy are voiced by different parties, e.g., delaying tactics or outright rejection of the remedy by a manager, the work force, the union. "Resistance to change" is the popular name for these obstacles. This step in the universal sequence addresses the issue of making a breakthrough in the cultural resistance to change.

Cultural Patterns.   Change consists of two parts:

1. A *technological* change
2. A *social consequence* of the technological change

The social consequence consists of the impact of the technological change on the "cultural pattern" of the human beings involved, i.e., their beliefs, habits, traditions, practices, status symbols, etc. This social consequence is the root source of the resistance to change. To make matters more complex, those who resist change often state their reasons as technological objections, whereas their real reasons relate to the social consequences. As a result, the attempts to overcome the resistance are thwarted by not knowing the true reason for the resistance.

Illustrations come from all levels:

1. A worker objects to a revised work method claiming that the flow of work will result in less, not more, productivity. Analysis revealed another, but unstated, reason—a desire for recognition. (Under the present method, finished product is stored temporarily at the machine; under the new method, the product is moved out immediately. Hence, front office personnel no longer stop at the machine to admire the superior quality.)

2. Management resists a remedy which involves purchasing new gages externally rather than making them internally. An unstated reason is pride. Management will not admit that an external supplier is a superior gage maker.

3. Some design engineers resist the use of computer-aided design (CAD), claiming that the technology is not as effective as design analysis by a human being. In the case of older designers, the real reasons may include the fear that they will have more difficulty adapting to CAD than their younger rivals.

Analyzing the Impact of Change.   Unfortunately, many advocates of change do not address themselves to a key question: "What threats will this change pose to the cultural pattern of this society?" Many of these advocates are *not even aware of the existence* of the cultural pattern, let alone its detailed makeup. Awareness of the existence, while necessary, is not sufficient. The advocates of change should in addition try to discover precisely what will their proposals threaten—which habits, whose status, what beliefs.

One aid to a study of resistance to change is a *barriers and aids analysis.* With this technique, strategies can be developed to overcome inherent barriers to change and make maximum use of available aids. In applying the technique at a utility organization (Florida Power and Light Co., 1984), five factors are considered: people, environment, hardware, time, and money. The steps in the analysis are:

1. Brainstorm a list of barriers (forces pushing against change).
2. Brainstorm a list of aids (forces pushing for change).
3. Rank all listed items as high, medium, or low.
4. Identify aids which balance or overcome barriers.
5. List matching barriers and aids on a chart.
6. List nonmatching barriers and identify (brainstorm) any offsetting aids.
7. List nonmatching aids and identify any offsetting barriers.
8. Identify items needing team action using the rankings of high, medium, or low.
9. Develop an action plan.

An example of the first two steps is shown in Figure 22.21. A similar technique is "forced field analysis" (see above under Structure Trees; see also Poza, 1983).

Rules of the Road for Introducing Change.   Important among these are:

1. *Provide participation:* This is the single most important rule for introducing change. To do it effectively means that those who are likely to be affected by the change should be members of the project team in order to participate in both diagnosis and remedy. Lack of participation leads to resentment which can harden into a rock of resistance.

Forces pushing against quality improvement	Forces pushing for quality improvement

• Lack of dollars
• People shortage
• Vested interest/old attitude
• Would the team stay together
• Other priorities
   • Time
   • Maintain work flow
   • Complicatd techniques
	• Team
	• Personal commitment
	• Management support
	• Support of line manager
	• Communications
	   • Within team
	   • Outside team
	• New techniques
	• Increasing cost of failure
	• Good planning
	• Specific goals

FIG. 22.21 Barriers and aids.

2. *Provide enough time:* How long does it take the members of a culture to accept a change? They must take enough time to evaluate the impact of the change and find an accommodation with the advocates of the change. Providing enough time takes various forms:

   a. Start small: Conducting a small-scale tryout before going "all out" reduces the risks, for the advocates as well as for the members of the culture.

   b. Avoid surprises: A major benefit of the cultural pattern is its predictability. A surprise is a shock to this predictability and a disturber of the peace.

   c. Choose the right year: There are right and wrong years—even decades— for timing a change.

3. *Keep the proposals free of excess baggage:* Avoid cluttering the proposals with extraneous matters not closely concerned with getting the results. The risk is that the debates will get off the main subject and into side issues.

4. *Work with the recognized leadership of the culture:* The culture is best understood by its members. They have their own leadership and this is often informal. Convincing the leadership is a significant step in getting the change accepted.

5. *Treat the people with dignity:* The classic example is that of the relay assemblers in the "Hawthorne experiments." Their productivity kept rising, under good illumination or poor, because in the "laboratory" they were being treated with dignity. See Section 10 under Process Management and Worker Self-Control.

6. *Reverse the positions:* Ask the question: What position would I take if I were a member of the culture? It is even useful to go into role playing to stimulate understanding of the other person's position.

7. *Deal directly with the resistance:* There are many ways of dealing directly with resistance to change:

   a. Try a program of persuasion.

   b. Offer a quid pro quo—something for something.

   c. Change the proposals to meet specific objections.

   d. Change the social climate in ways which will make the change more acceptable.

   e. Forget it. There are cases in which the correct alternative is to drop the proposal. We simply do not know how to plan so as to be 100 percent successful.

Resolving Differences.   Sometimes the resistance to implementation of a remedy can reach an impasse. To avoid this, a structured process for resolving differences is helpful. Coonley and Agnew (1941) describe such a process and how it was used to establish quality standards on cast iron pipe. The process is based on three conditions which those in disagreement must meet:

1. They must identify their areas of agreement and their areas of disagreement. "That is, they must first agree upon the exact point at which the road began to fork." When this was done it was found that a major point of disagreement concerned the validity of a certain formula.
2. "They must agree on why they disagreed." They concluded that the known facts were inadequate to decide whether the formula was valid or not.
3. "They must decide what they were going to do about it." The decision was to raise a fund to conduct the research needed to establish the necessary facts. "With the facts at hand, the controversies disappeared."

This was essentially the approach taken by the supervisors to resolve disagreements on the causes of the burrs on screws (see the example earlier under Diagnosis—General).

Ackoff (1978) describes a six-step procedure for resolving disagreements. To start, each participant must state the other (opposing) position in a way that is acceptable to the other person. This helps to ensure that the opposing positions are clearly understood. The process continues until the participants can agree on a course of action that has the least serious error associated with it.

Kotter (1985), Argyris (1985), and Kanter (1983) elaborate on resistance to change in the industrial environment. Two classic references by Coch and French (1948) and Lawrence (1969) present the results of research based on industrial examples.

CONTROL AT THE NEW LEVEL

The final step in the breakthrough sequence is holding the gains so that the benefits of the breakthrough will continue on and on. To enable the operating forces to hold the gains requires (1) a successful transfer of the remedy from "laboratory" conditions to operating conditions and (2) a systematic means of holding the gains—the control process. Failure to meet both of these requirements can result in failure to hold the gains.

Transfer from "Laboratory" to Operations.   Three steps are essential:

1. Provide the operating forces with a process capable of holding the gains. Sometimes, this involves minimal change; other times, the process change may be complex. To the extent which is economic, the process changes should be designed to be *irreversible.*

An improvement study in a foundry illustrates two types of remedies. One remedy (irreversible) involved the replacement of old spouts with larger-diameter spouts. The old spouts were destroyed. Another remedy (reversible) required melters to use scales to accurately weigh the amount of metal to be poured. Some melters did not continue to use the scales; they went right back to estimating by eye and feel.

From another industry, changing from hand insertion of components into printed circuit boards to automatic insertion by programmed tape rolls illustrates an irreversible remedy. In wave soldering, requiring a different specific gravity for flux could be reversible because contamination or other factors could result in the previously unacceptable specific gravity.

The test of the revised process is really two tests, at different stages:

a. Under the "laboratory" conditions provided by the remedial department

b. Under operating conditions

The project is not complete until satisfactory results have been produced under operating conditions.

2. Establish operating standards and procedures to serve as a basis for training, control, and audit. Operating standards and procedures tend to be well defined with respect to input materials which are to enter the process; equipment, tools, and measuring instruments; and levels at which to set the critical process variables, e.g., temperature, pressure. In contrast, procedures are often vague or silent on matters such as why the criteria should be met; what can happen if they are not met; standards for esthetic qualities; equipment maintenance; and worker technique. Failure to deal with these latter areas will commonly show up in due course as failures to hold the gains.

3. Train the operating forces to use the procedures and to meet the standards. Changes in standards and procedures clearly require training of the operating forces with respect to the impacts of those changes. The operating forces should be trained to understand: (*a*) Just what has been changed. (*b*) The new product and process standards to be met. (*c*) What new decisions and actions will be required to make the changes effective. (*d*) Who has the responsibility to make these decisions and take these actions. (*e*) How to use the new equipment, tools, and instruments. (*f*) What the techniques are which have been demonstrated to secure the best results. (*g*) What the consequences are of deviating from the specified standards and procedures.

In conducting this training it is well to make use of information collected during diagnosis to help explain the reasons for the changes.

Concept of Control. A good transition enables the operating forces to secure the benefits of the breakthrough. However, these benefits will not be permanent because many forces lie in wait to erode them, including equipment deterioration and breakdown, material shortages and deficiencies, and human backsliding and error. Faced with such future erosion, good managers do not just walk away once the transition has been made. What the managers do is to provide a systematic means for holding the gains—something called control.

Control during operations is done through use of the feedback loop—a cyclical activity involving evaluation of actual performance, comparison with the standard of performance, and action on the difference. Elaboration of the concept of control is discussed in Section 6, under Planning for Control. Section 24, Statistical Process Control, presents a collection of statistical process control techniques for the detection of out-of-control conditions. Section 17, under Audit of Production Quality, describes process audits as a means of verifying that the required process conditions and actions continue in place.

TROUBLESHOOTING

Troubleshooting (fire fighting) is diagnosis and remedial action applied to sporadic troubles (not chronic). Ineffective troubleshooting can result in failure to hold the gains. The same "two journeys" are needed but each is much simpler than for chronic troubles. The sporadic trouble is the result of some adverse change, so the diagnostic journey is one of discovering "What was the adverse change?" The remedial journey removes the discovered adverse change so as to restore the status quo.

Product Comparisons to Discover the Change. As with chronic troubles, there is need to clarify the symptoms, conduct autopsies, theorize, test the theories, etc. To discover what has changed, however, requires some comparisons, mainly:

Comparison of features exhibited by products made prior to the trouble with features of products made since the trouble set in.

Comparison of symptoms exhibited by defective units with features of good units, both having been made since the trouble set in.

Along with these comparisons, a chronology of events is needed.

Reconstructing the Chronology. By definition, a sporadic trouble is the result of some change—an adverse change. During operations, changes are constantly taking place: old material batches are consumed and new material batches come in; the day shift goes out and the night shift comes in; a filling line is cleaned out to make ready for a different size of bottle.

Which of these changes might be related to the sporadic trouble? A time-log chart can be prepared showing the exact time of known changes along with product identification (serial numbers, batch records, etc.) This provides a chronological history of product and process changes. Analysis of this log will then support some theories and will deny others.

Testing the Theories. Because of the intermittent nature of sporadic problems, some theories disappear early. "The new supplier has nothing to do with it. His material came in two days after the trouble started." As these obvious cases are cleared away, the need may arise to create new information, to use stream-to-stream analysis, time-to-time analysis, process dissection, and other tools of diagnosis. Supervisors who will be called upon to do troubleshooting should be trained in use of the necessary tools and techniques.

At company X, an unusual separation into streams helped to solve an outbreak of field complaints on elastic breaking and vinyl cracking in baby pants. Tests on competing products showed them to be free of such problems. Next, opinions focused on inferior raw material from the two suppliers. Both suppliers rejected this belief. One of them said, "What we are sending you is *better* than what we send your competitors." (That implied that the cause was during the processing at X.) To prove the claim, the supplier sent to company X a batch of material being furnished to the competitors and suggested that tests be made to compare that material with material currently in use by company X. Tests were conducted and, to the surprise of the supplier, the results showed that the material going to the competitors was superior, not inferior as claimed. The supplier reacted, "It can't be." Next, both batches of material were carefully inspected and tested. The supplier noticed that some of the "oils" in the elastic sent to company X had dried up; the condition was not present in the sample of material for the competitors. Further investigation unraveled the mystery. A buyer at company X had mistakenly ordered raw material for 2 years, instead of for 1 month. Because the material then sat in storage for many months, the oils dried up and subsequently caused the breaking and cracking problems.

Structured Procedure for Troubleshooting.   Monsanto (undated) describes a step-by-step approach for finding the cause of deviations between expected and actual performance. The approach first describes the deviation, searches for possible causes, and then determines the true cause. Seven steps are involved:

1. State the deviation. Questions are posed to identify a single effect and a single object or group of related objects. What object (or group of related objects) is involved? What's the effect? Does anyone know the cause of this deviation?

2. Specify the deviation. The nature of the deviation is described in terms of *what is involved* with the deviation and *what is not involved.* Questions about the deviation involve what, where, when, and how much?

3. Identify the unique characteristics of the deviation. This is done through use of a matrix (Figure 22.22).

4. Search for changes. The matrix is used and the question is asked, "What, if anything, has changed in, around, or about this unique characteristic?" Answers are listed in the "changes" column.

5. Develop possible causes. For each change the question is asked "How could this change have caused the deviation?"

6. Test the possible causes against the specification. Compare each possible cause to the information in the "is involved" and "is not involved" description and see if the cause is consistent with the information.

7. Verify the cause, attempt to reproduce the deviation using the most probable cause, or eliminate the deviation by correcting the most probable cause.

Operating personnel can be trained to use this type of approach to do their own troubleshooting. An elaboration of this approach is presented by Kepner and Tregoe (1981).

Corrective Action.   Once the cause of the sporadic trouble is known, the worst is over. For the great majority of sporadic troubles the remedy involves going back to what was done before. This is a return to the familiar, not a journey into the unknown (as is often the case when dealing with chronic troubles). The needed technology is usually known to the local people, and they can take the necessary action to restore the status quo. Cultural resistance is minimal.

	Is involved	*Is not involved	Unique characteristics (of "is involved")	Changes
What?				
Where?				
When?				
How much?				

FIG. 22.22   Deviation analysis.

Sometimes the local people can do better than merely restoring the status quo. They can use their ingenuity to find preventive ways to reduce repetition of the sporadic troubles and associated troubleshooting.

REFERENCES

Ackoff, Russell L. (1978). *The Art of Problem Solving.* John Wiley & Sons, New York, pp. 45–47.

Anderson, Dave (1982). "When 3 Meant 6." *New York Times,* Dec. 27, pp. C1, C3.

Argyris, Chris (1985). *Strategy, Change, and Defensive Routines.* Pitman, Boston.

Benedict, Ruth (1946). *Patterns of Culture.* Mentor Books, New American Library of World Literature, New York. Originally published by Houghton Mifflin, Boston, 1934.

Bergstrom, Sigvard (1985). "Quality Improvement by Problem Solving Groups." *Proceedings, EOQC Conference,* vol. 2, pp. 327–333.

Betker, Harry A. (1983). "Quality Improvement Program: Reducing Solder Defects on Printed Circuit Board Assembly." *The Juran Report,* no. 2, November, pp. 53–58.

Betker, Harry A. (1985a). "Quality Improvement Program Project to Identify and Correct All Known Problems on an Electro-Mechanical Detection Device." *The Juran Report,* no. 4, winter, pp. 70–76.

Betker, Harry A. (1985b). "Storyboarding: It's No Mickey Mouse Technique." *The Juran Report,* no. 5, summer, pp. 25–30.

Coch, Lester and French, John R. P., Jr. (1948). "Overcoming Resistance to Change." *Human Relations,* August, pp. 512–532.

Coonley, Howard and Agnew, P. G. (1941). *The Role of Standards in the System of Free Enterprise.* American National Standards Institute, New York.

Doran, P. K. (1985). "A Total Quality Improvement Programme." *International Journal of Quality and Reliability Management,* vol. 2, no. 3, pp. 18–36.

Douglas, R. D. (1983). "Now What Do We Do?" *The Juran Report,* no. 3, November, pp. 100–105.

Dymtrow, Eric D. (1985). "Quality Improvement in Information Processing." *The Juran Report,* no. 4, winter, pp. 134–139.

Florida Power and Light Company (1984). *FPL Quality Improvement Program, Guidebook and Roadmap.* Miami, FL, p. 44.

G.O.A.L., Growth Opportunity Alliance of Greater Lawrence (1985a). *The Memory Jogger.* p. 12.

G.O.A.L. (1985b). "Interrelationship Diagraph." *G.O.A.L. Newsletter,* November–December, pp. 3–4.

G.O.A.L. (1986a). "Matrix Diagram." *G.O.A.L. Newsletter,* March–April, pp. 3–5; May–June, pp. 3–4.

G.O.A.L. (1986b). "Program Decision Process Chart (PDPC)." *G.O.A.L. Newsletter,* July–August, pp. 3–4.

Greenridge, R. M. C. (1953). "The Case of Reliability vs. Defective Components et al." *Electronic Applications Reliability Review,* no. 1, p. 12.

Gust, Lawrence J. (1985). "Non-Manufacturing Quality Improvement." *The Juran Report,* no. 4, winter, pp. 112–120.

Halpin, J. F. (1966). *Zero Defects.* McGraw-Hill, New York.

Hartman, Bob (1983). "Implementing Quality Improvement." *The Juran Report,* no. 2, November, pp. 124–131.

Holm, Robert A. (1985). "Quality Improvement in the Oil Patch." *The Juran Report,* no. 4, winter, pp. 47–51.

Ingram, Gary E. (1984). "Historical Processes for Quality Project Management." *Project Management Institute Proceedings,* Philadelphia, pp. 1–3.

Ishikawa, Kaoru (1976). *Guide to Quality Control.* Asian Productivity Organization. Publication obtainable from the American Society for Quality Control, Milwaukee.

Juran, J. M. (1985). "Charting the Quality Course." *The Juran Report,* no. 5, summer, pp. 10–15.

Kano, Noriaki (1984). "Problem Solving in New Product Development—Application of T-Typed Matrix." *Proceedings, World Quality Congress.* European Organization for Quality Control, Berne, Switzerland, vol. 3, pp. 45–55.

Kanter, R. M. (1983). *The Change Masters.* Simon and Schuster, New York.

Kato, Osamu, Sakai, Yosho, and Sasaki, Katsuo (1981). "Improvement of the Rust Preventive Method for the Body Panel of a Motor Vehicle." *Reports of Statistical Applications and Research,* Japanese Union of Scientists and Engineers, vol. 28, no. 1, March, C section, pp. 40–55.

Kepner, Charles H. and Tregoe, Benjamin B. (1981). *The New Rational Manager.* Princeton Research Press, Princeton, NJ.

Kotter, J. P. (1985). *Power and Influence.* Macmillan Free Press, New York.

Kurland, Leonard T. and Molgaard, Craig A. (1981). "The Patient Record in Epidemiology." *Scientific American,* October, pp. 54–63.

Lawrence, Paul R. (1969). "How to Deal with Resistance to Change." *Harvard Business Review,* January–February, pp. 4–12ff.

Leonard, James F. (1986). "Quality Improvement in Recruiting and Employment." *The Juran Report,* no. 6, pp. 111–118.

Lossin, Richard D. (1983). "Quality Improvement at Westinghouse Furniture Systems." *The Juran Report,* no. 2, November, pp. 31–34.

Lounds, Andrew C. and Pearson, Larry G. (1985). "A Team Project for Improving Office Productivity and Communication." *The Juran Report,* no. 4, winter, pp. 40–45.

Marquez, Manuel (1985). "Quality Improvement at Challenger Caribbean Corporation." *The Juran Report,* no. 4, pp. 52–56.

McGrath, James H. (1985). "Preparation of Improvement Team Leaders and Facilitators." *The Juran Report,* no. 4, winter, pp. 95–101.

Mead, Margaret (ed.) (1955). *Cultural Patterns and Technical Change.* Mentor Books, New American Library of World Literature, New York; also published by UNESCO, Paris, 1951.

Metcalf, Henry C. and Urwick, L. (ed.) (1941). *Dynamic Administration.* Harper and Row, New York.

Mizell, Michael and Strattner, Lawrence (1981). "Diagnostic Measuring in Manufacturing." *Quality,* September, pp. 29–32.

Moehlenbrock, Maxine (1985). "Control Teams Contrasted with Breakthrough Teams." *The Juran Report,* no. 4, winter, pp. 175–179.

Monsanto (undated). *Managerial Analytics Pocket Manual.* Monsanto Company, Corporate Management Development, St. Louis, MO.

Nester, Donald and Staal, Rolf (1986). "The Universal Sequence of Events on the Production Floor of AHC." *The Juran Report,* no. 6, winter, pp. 99–105.

Noakes, Merle E. (1985). "The Three-Level Quality Council." *The Juran Report,* no. 4, winter, pp. 92–94.

Payne, B. J. (1984). "Statistical Techniques in the Management of Quality Improvement." *International Journal of Quality and Reliability Management,* vol. 1, no. 3, pp. 24–35.

Peters, Peter E. (1983). "Axle Plant Jura System and Example of Solving a Non-Quality Problem." *The Juran Report,* no. 2, November, pp. 77–81.

Poza, Ernesto J. (1983). "A Do It Yourself Guide to Group Problem Solving." *Personnel,* March–April, pp. 69–77.

Riggs, James L. (1981). *Production Systems: Planning, Analysis, and Control,* 3rd ed. John Wiley & Sons, New York.

Selwitchka, R. (1980). "The Priority List on Measures for Reducing Quality Related Costs." *EOQC Quality,* vol. 24, no. 5, pp. 3–7.

Stratton, Donald A. (1987). "Force Field Analysis: A Powerful Tool for Facilitators." *The Juran Report,* no. 8, winter, pp. 105–111.

Traver, Robert W. (1983). "Locating the Key Variables." *ASQC Quality Congress Transactions,* Milwaukee, pp. 231–237.

Wachniak, Raymond (1983). "Development and Implementation of a Project Support Review Program." *The Juran Report,* no. 1, pp. 87–90.

Wolf, John D. (1983). "Quality is Management at McDonnell Douglas." *The Juran Report,* no. 2, pp. 116–123.

Woodward, James D. (1985). "Not Just Another Training Program." *The Juran Report,* no. 4, winter, pp. 24–27.

SECTION 23
BASIC STATISTICAL METHODS[1]

Edward J. Dudewicz, Ph.D.

---

[1]In the Third Edition, the section on Basic Statistical Methods was prepared by Frank M. Gryna; the section on Regression Analysis was prepared by John S. Ramberg. Portions of the present text make use of examples and illustrations from the Third Edition.

THE STATISTICAL TOOL KIT

Most decision making in quality control, as in most other areas of modern human endeavor (e.g., evaluation of new medical treatments and scanning machines, planning of scientific polling, and marketing and investment strategies to name a few) rests on a base of statistics—defined narrowly as the collection, analysis, and interpretation of data, or more broadly as "the science of decision making under uncertainty." For the practitioner, "statistics" can be thought of as a kit of tools which helps to solve problems. The statistical tool kit shown in Table 23.1 lists problems to be solved, applicable statistical tools, and where in this handbook the tool is to be found.

Examples of actual practice will be used as extensively as the space allocated to it allows, to provide the reader with both a model for solution and a data set with correct analysis which can be used to verify the accuracy of local computer software. Annotated computer program output from such packages as SAS, BMDP, STATPRO, and LABONE will be used in many of these examples.

In addition to the basic statistical methods discussed in this section, three other sections cover specific areas—Section 24 on Statistical Process Control, Section 25 on Acceptance Sampling, and Section 26 on Design and Analysis of Experiments. Many other sections include additional applications. Also, Appendix III, Selected Quality Standards, Specifications, and Related Documents, includes documents on statistical techniques and procedures.

SOURCES AND SUMMARIZATION OF DATA

The source of a set of data which we desire to analyze to solve a problem is a very important consideration. The two sources we will address and which are the most common are "historical data" and "data from planned experimentation." Investigators using historical data are like blind people probing an elephant, for reasons discussed below under Historical Data, Its Uses, and Caveats, and under Data from Planned Experimentation. Note that all data need careful review, as discussed in Data Screening, below.

Planning for Collection and Analysis of Data. The tools cited in Table 23.1 must be used in an effective manner in order to yield a return appropriate for the cost of using them. To achieve this return, it is not sufficient to plug numbers into formulas. The full process must include careful planning of data collection, analysis of the data to draw statistical conclusions, and making the transition to answer the original technical problem. A checklist of some of the key steps in achieving this is:

1. Collect sufficient background information to translate the engineering problem statement into a specific statement that can be evaluated by statistical methods.
2. Plan the collection of data.
   - *a.* Determine the type of data needed. Variables data (readings on a scale of measurement) may be more expensive than attributes data (go or no-go data), but the information is much more useful.
   - *b.* Determine if any past data are available that are applicable to the present problem; however, bear in mind the hazards of historical data sets.
   - *c.* If the problem requires an evaluation of several alternative decisions, obtain information on the economic consequences of a wrong decision.
   - *d.* If the problem requires the estimation of a parameter, define the precision needed for the estimate.

TABLE 23.1   The Statistical Tool Kit

Problem	Statistical tool	Reference pages or sections
Planning a statistical investigation	Planning and analyzing data for solving specific problems	23.3–23.6
Summarizing data	Frequency distributions, histograms, and indices	23.11–23.21
Predicting future results from a sample	Probability distributions	23.26–23.45
Determining a probability involving several events	Basic theorems of probability	23.21–23.26
Predicting performance without failure (reliability)	Reliability prediction and analysis	23.81–23.91
Determining the significance of difference between two sets of data or between a set of data and a standard value	Tests of hypotheses	23.60–23.81
Determining the sample size required for testing a hypothesis	Sample size determination for hypothesis testing	23.78
Determining the ability of a sample result to estimate a true value	Confidence limits	23.45–23.50
Determining the sample size required to estimate a true value	Sample size determination for estimation	23.50–23.51
Determining tolerance limits on single characteristics	Statistical tolerance limits	23.52–23.56
Determining tolerance limits for interacting dimensions	Tolerance limits for interacting dimensions	23.56–23.59
Incorporating past information in predicting future events	Bayes' theorem	23.25–23.26 23.59–23.60
Incorporating economic consequences in defining decision rules	Statistical decision theory	23.26
Converting data to meet statistical assumptions	Transformations of data	23.91–23.94
Evaluating the relationship between two or more variables by determining an equation to estimate one variable from knowledge of the other variables	Regression analysis	23.96–23.118

TABLE 23.1   The Statistical Tool Kit (*Continued*)

Problem	Statistical tool	Reference pages or sections
Controlling process quality by early detection of process changes:		
1. Using measurements data	Variables control charts	Sec. 24
2. Using go no-go measurements data	Attributes control charts	Sec. 24
Evaluating quality of lots to a previously defined quality level:		
1. Quality measured on a go no-go basis	Attributes sampling plans	Sec. 25
2. Quality measured on a variables basis	Variables sampling plans	Sec. 25
3. Sampling to determine reliability	Reliability sampling plans	Sec. 25
4. Bulk product	Bulk sampling plans	Sec. 25
Planning and analyzing experiments:		
1. Investigating the effect of varying one factor	One-factor experiment	Sec. 26
2. Investigating the effect of varying two or more factors	Designs for two or more factors	Sec. 26
3. Investigating the variability of laboratory measurements	Interlaboratory tests	Sec. 26
4. Experimenting under process conditions to determine optimum settings of variables	Evolutionary operation (EVOP)	Sec. 26
5. Determining the optimum set of values of a group of variables that affect a response variable	Response surface methodology (RSM)	Sec. 26

e. Determine if the error of measurement is large enough to influence the sample size or the method of data analysis; laboratory error can often dwarf experimental variability.

f. Define the assumptions needed to calculate the required sample size.

g. Calculate the required sample size considering the desired precision of the result, statistical risk, variability of the data, measurement error, and other factors.

    h. Define any requirements for preserving the order of measurements when time is a key parameter.

    i. Determine any requirements for collecting data in groups defined so as to reflect the different conditions which are to be evaluated.

    j. Define the method of data analysis and any assumptions required.

    k. Define requirements for any computer programs which will be needed.

3. Collect the data.

    a. Use methods to assure that the sample is selected in a random manner.

    b. Record the data and also all conditions present at the time of each observation.

    c. Examine the sample data to assure that the process shows sufficient stability to make predictions valid for the future.

4. Analyze the data.

    a. Screen the data.

    b. Evaluate the assumptions previously stated for determining the sample size and for analyzing the data. Take corrective steps (including additional observations) if required.

    c. Apply statistical techniques to evaluate the original problem.

    d. Determine if further data and analysis are needed.

    e. Conduct "sensitivity analyses" by varying key sample estimates and other factors in the analysis and noting the effect on final conclusions.

5. Review the conclusions of the data analysis to determine if the original technical problem has been evaluated or if it has been changed to fit the statistical methods.

6. Present the results.

    a. State the conclusions in meaningful form by emphasizing results in terms of the original problem rather than the statistical indices used in the analysis.

    b. Present the results in graphical form where appropriate. Use simple statistical methods in the body of a report and place complicated analyses in an appendix.

7. Determine if the conclusions of the specific problem apply to other problems or if the data and calculations could be a useful input to other problems.

Historical Data, Their Uses, and Caveats. "Historical data" are data which we already have and which may seem to be relevant to a question or problem which has arisen. Such data are also called "existing data sets." Often data are saved during the production process, for example. If a satisfactory process goes out of control after some years of operation, it is often suggested that it would save both time and expense to statistically analyze the historical data, rather than perform a planned experiment to obtain data which could lead to process correction. Thus, we have available data which may consist of measurements Y (such as a process yield, e.g., the strength of a material produced) and associated process variables $x_1, x_2, \ldots, x_k$ (such as x_1 = pressure and x_2 = acid concentration, with $k = 2$).

    This situation is extremely different from that where experiments have been run at each of a number of settings of $x_1, \ldots, x_k$ which were selected in advance by statistical design criteria, and often little can be learned from such data even with the most thorough statistical analysis. Some of the reasons for this are:

The x's may be highly correlated with each other, hence, it may not be possible to separate an effect as due to (for example) x_1 or x_2.

The x's may have been manipulated in order to try to control the output Y of the process (some of them perhaps even in directions which move the output in directions which are not that which is desired); hence, giving spurious indications of directions of effects when analyzed.

The x's may cover a very small part of the possible operating range, so small that any indications of changes in Y attributable to changes in the x's may be overwhelmed by the size of the variability of the process (measured by "standard deviation," discussed below).

Other variables which affect the output of the process (e.g., time of day, atmospheric conditions, operator running the process, etc.) may not have been held constant, and may in fact be the real causes of changes observed in the process (while an analysis conducted based only on the x's may erroneously conclude a model which has no basis in reality).

For these and other reasons, much more information can generally be obtained from a carefully designed experiment than from extensive analysis of historical data sets collected in uncontrolled circumstances. The best one can usually hope for from such historical data set analysis is an indication of the most important variables to include in the designed experiment.

As an example of one of the failings described above, suppose that a historical data set consists of a yield Y at each of the five (x_1, x_2) pairs given in Table 23.2. We see that there is what appears to be a good spread on the x_1 (acid concentration) values, from 80 to 110, and also a good spread on the x_2 (pressure) values, from 105 to 144. However, a plot of the data points (x_1, x_2), as shown in Figure 23.1, shows that in fact all five of the data points lie on a straight line. Thus, there is no hope of any analysis of this data telling us whether any effect we see is due to x_1 or to x_2. The points do not "cover" the space of x_1 between 80 and 110, and x_2 between 105 and 144, well at all. Also, to solve the production problem it may be desirable to explore outside of this space of historical operation, and that is not allowed for in the historical data set.

A problem such as that shown in Figure 23.1 is called "multicollinearity" of the data points, i.e., of the sets of $(x_1, \ldots, x_k)$ which we have available for anal-

TABLE 23.2 Historical Data Set

Data point	x_1 (Acid concentration)	x_2 (Pressure)
1	100	131.0
2	90	118.0
3	105	137.5
4	110	144.0
5	80	105.0

FIG. 23.1 Plot of (x_1, x_2) in a historical data set. Five data points have been plotted, and a straight line has been drawn through them.

ysis. With $k = 2$, such a problem is easy to detect by a graph such as that in Figure 23.1, and such a graph should always be made. With $k = 3$ it may be possible to detect such a situation graphically using computer graphics packages. Often, however, k is much larger than 2 or 3, and then statistical analysis is needed to detect multicollinearity. Near multicollinearity (that is, when the points almost fall on a line when $k = 2$, on a plane when $k = 3$, or on what is called a $k - 1$ dimensional hyperplane when k is larger than 3) is just as much of a problem, and is much harder to detect. For an extensive bibliography and comments on computer routines for this problem, see Hoerl and Kennard (1981).

Data from Planned Experimentation.   Data from planned experimentation are data gathered in an attempt to study the production or other problem which has arisen or is contemplated. Such data are gathered at various settings of the variables felt to be of importance $(x_1, \ldots, x_k)$, while holding constant (if possible, and recording the values of in any case) all other variables which could conceivably have an effect on the output $(x_{k+1}, \ldots, x_m)$—for example, atmospheric pressure may not be able to be controlled in most circumstances, but should be monitored and recorded in every experiment if it is felt beforehand that it might have an effect on the output. (If it is irrelevant, it can be disregarded later; if it is relevant but not recorded, we will not be able to detect that relevance.) Details of designs to use, i.e., how to choose the values of $(x_1, \ldots, x_k)$ for the experiments once the variables to be varied have been chosen, are considered in Section 26, Design and Analysis of Experiments, and in Dudewicz and Karian (1985).

Data Screening. Once the data specified in the above Checklist for Planned Experimentation, step 2, has been collected (step 3), the first step in its analysis (step 4*a*) is to screen the data. We will now discuss the need for this critical (and often omitted) step, some common methods of screening, and a very commonly used method which has some great dangers.

The Need for Data Screening. A data set which contains no instances of incorrectly transcribed values; contains no values which are technically correct but where the experiment went awry for some reason (such as equipment malfunction); and where the basic model does not change its form over the region of experimentation, is called a "clean" data set. Such data sets are commonly expected to be obtained by experimenters who exercise care in their experimental conduct and recording. However, contrary to this expectation of the experimenters, few statisticians have ever seen a clean data set (despite many years of studying many data sets arising in many areas). It follows then that all data sets need, as a first stage of analysis, to be examined for values which may cause invalid inferences to be made if those values are left in the data set. Procedures for performing this examination are called "data screening methods." Among the most powerful such methods are those which are used on the results of a regression analysis (studied later in this section).

There are also a number of methods which can and should be used at the outset, before any regression analyses are performed, with the goal of detecting "outliers," that is, observations (or groups of observations) which deviate markedly from the other available data. Numerous tests are available for detecting outliers (see Sheesley, 1977, for some of these). One simple rule calls an observation an outlier if it lies 2.5, 3, or 4 standard deviations or further from the mean (Draper and Smith, 1981). This is discussed further below.

Methods of Data Screening. One of the most common methods of data screening is to classify observations as outliers if they are outside an interval of L multiples of the standard deviation about the mean. (Standard deviation is discussed below under Sample Characteristics.) The number L is commonly taken to be 2.5, 3, or 4. The larger L is, the less likely it is that outliers will be detected, while the smaller L is, the more good observations one will detect as potential outliers. For example, from Table B in Appendix II, we see that if $L = 3$ then $(100)(.0027) = 0.27$ percent of the observations will be further than 3 standard deviations from the mean even if there are no outliers in the data set; this assumes a normal distribution for the observations. Thus, if one uses $L = 3$, one expects to find about 3 possible outliers in a data set of 1000 data points (since 0.27 percent of 1000 is 2.7, i.e., roughly 3). As the data set being considered becomes larger, the more possible outliers one will identify even if there are no problems with the data (which is quite unlikely). For this reason:

Outliers should be deleted from the analysis only if they can be traced to specific causes (such as recording errors, experimental errors, and the like).

Typically one takes L to depend on the size of the data set to be screened; with $n = 1000$ points, $L = 3$ is reasonable; with $n = 100$, $L = 2.5$ can be used and only (100) (0.0124) = 1.24 outliers will be expected to be found if the data have no problems.

After bad data are deleted or replaced (this is desirable if the experiment can be rerun under comparable conditions to those specified in the experimental plan), the data should be screened again: With the "worst" points removed/corrected, less extreme cases may come to be identified as possible outliers.

Another commonly used method, that of crossplots, is discussed below.

Crossplots and Their Hazards. In crossplots (also called "scatter-plots"), one simply plots each pair of variables in the data set on a set of axes. For example, in the example of Table 23.2, one would plot Y versus x_1, Y versus x_2, and x_1 versus x_2. The last of these plots was given in Figure 23.1 (and showed some problems with the data which have already been discussed). Note that when using this technique, one uses all variables which were measured (and not just the variables which are thought to be of primary interest; see Nelson, 1979, Section 4).

Such plots must be used with great caution. While points which seem odd (away from the majority of the data points, for example) should be subjected to examination to see if there are problems with them, one should not use such plots to conclude relationships of the yield with x_1 and/or x_2. For example, suppose one has the data set of Table 23.3. Then from crossplots of Y versus x_1 and Y

TABLE 23.3   Data Set *A* for Crossplots Example

Data point	x_1	x_2	Y
1	−2	1	10
2	−1	−2	5
3	0	−5	0

versus x_2 (see Figure 23.2), one would be tempted to conclude that Y is a decreasing function of x_1 and an increasing function of x_2 (and so, in attempting to maximize yield, might set x_1 as low as possible, and x_2 as high as possible). However, as can easily be verified, the data in Table 23.3 came exactly from the relationship (model) $Y = 10 + x_1 + 2x_2$. Thus, in fact Y is an increasing function of x_1 (not a decreasing function as the crossplot had suggested). Daniel (1977) has suggested the data set of Table 23.4 may give additional insight here. Crossplots for that data set are given in Figure 23.3. Thus, one sees that even with a strong true relationship (here $Y = 10 + x_1 + 2x_2$ is used again), the crossplots may yield no

 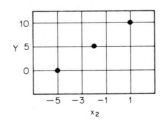

FIG. 23.2   Crossplots of Y versus x_1, and of Y versus x_2, for data set *A* of Table 23.3.

insight at all. Even worse, clearly by choosing the points (x_1, x_2) one may give the Y versus x_1 relationship any slope (negative, as with Table 23.3 and Figure 23.2; zero; or positive), or the relationshp can be smoothly curved in any direction or degree of complexity. (Note that the regression methods given later in this section would not be fooled by the relationships in the data of Table 23.4: They would give the true relationships.) Thus, crossplots are useful for detection of possible outliers; however, they are not a substitute for regression, and can easily be misused.

TABLE 23.4   Data Set B for Crossplots Example

Data point	x_1	x_2	Y
1	-2	1	10
2	-1	-2	5
3	0	0	10
4	1	2	15
5	2	-1	10

Descriptive Statistics for Summarizing Data.   Many of the most practical methods of summarizing data are quite simple in concept. Depending on the goals of the data summarization, sometimes one method will provide a useful and complete summarization. More often, two or more methods will be used to attain the clarity of description which is desired. Several key methods are plots versus time order of data, frequency distributions and histograms, sample characteristics (mean, median, mode, variance, standard deviation, and percentiles), measures of central tendency/location, and measures of dispersion.

Plots versus Time Order of Data.   After a data set has been obtained, it is very instructive in many situations to plot the output Y against the time order in which the experiments were run (which is essentially a crossplot of Y versus time t).

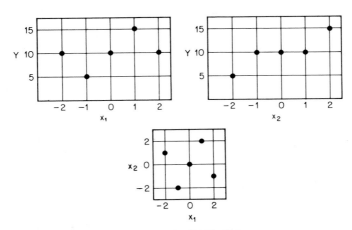

FIG. 23.3   Crossplots for data set B of Table 23.4.

Among the possible phenomena which may come to our attention from such a plot are these:

A few observations, often at the start of the experimentation, are far from the others; this often represents a learning curve of the experimenters with the experimental situation, and those experiments should be repeated if possible.

There are trends within each day (or within each week, etc.); this may represent such phenomena as warming of a machine or process, operator fatigue, or similar time-related trends.

Variability decreases (or, increases) with time; this may be due to a learning curve, or raw material characteristics (as when one lot of material is used up, and the next lot has less or greater heterogeneity).

While the above trends may be apparent even in a plot of the original observations Y versus time, they are often more easily spotted in plots of the residuals of the observations (difference between the observed and predicted value) after a regression analysis. See later in this section under Regression Analysis.

Frequency Histograms. The frequency histogram (or, distribution) is a statistical tool for presenting numerous data in a form which makes clearer the central tendency and the dispersion along the scale of measurement, as well as the relative frequency of occurrence of the various values.

Table 23.5 shows "raw data" representing measurements of electrical resistance of 100 coils. A practitioner scanning these 100 numbers has difficulty in grasping their meaning.

Table 23.6 shows the same data after tabulation. Note how the analyst's tallies in the column "Tabulation" make more evident where the central tendency is and what the dispersion is. The column "Frequency" is merely a recorded count of these same tallies. The column "Cumulative Frequency" shows the number of coils with resistance equal to or greater than the associated resistance value.

Table 23.6 exhibits a range of values from 3.44 to 3.27, or 17 intervals of 0.01 Ω each. When it is desired to reduce the number of such intervals, the data are grouped into "cells." Table 23.7 shows the same data grouped into a frequency distribution of only six cells, each 0.03 ohms wide. Grouping the data into cells simplifies presentation and study of the distribution but loses some of the detail. (However, one can always go back to the original data if necessary.)

The following are the steps taken to construct a frequency distribution:

1. Decide on the number of cells. Table 23.8 provides guidelines which are adequate for most cases encountered. These guidelines are not rigid and should

TABLE 23.5 Resistance (Ohms) of 100 Coils

3.37	3.34	3.38	3.32	3.33	3.28	3.34	3.31	3.33	3.34
3.29	3.36	3.30	3.31	3.33	3.34	3.34	3.36	3.39	3.34
3.35	3.36	3.30	3.32	3.33	3.35	3.35	3.34	3.32	3.38
3.32	3.37	3.34	3.38	3.36	3.37	3.36	3.31	3.33	3.30
3.35	3.33	3.38	3.37	3.44	3.32	3.36	3.32	3.29	3.35
3.38	3.39	3.34	3.32	3.30	3.39	3.36	3.40	3.32	3.33
3.29	3.41	3.27	3.36	3.41	3.37	3.36	3.37	3.33	3.36
3.31	3.33	3.35	3.34	3.35	3.34	3.31	3.36	3.37	3.35
3.40	3.35	3.37	3.32	3.35	3.36	3.38	3.35	3.31	3.34
3.35	3.36	3.39	3.31	3.31	3.30	3.35	3.33	3.35	3.31

TABLE 23.6 Tally of Resistance Values of 100 Coils

Resistance, ohms	Tabulation	Frequency	Cumulative frequency
3.45			
3.44	|	1	1
3.43			
3.42			
3.41	||	2	3
3.40	||	2	5
3.39	||||	4	9
3.38	⊥⊥⊥ |	6	15
3.37	⊥⊥⊥ |||	8	23
3.36	⊥⊥⊥ ⊥⊥⊥ |||	13	36
3.35	⊥⊥⊥ ⊥⊥⊥ ||||	14	50
3.34	⊥⊥⊥ ⊥⊥⊥ ||	12	62
3.33	⊥⊥⊥ ⊥⊥⊥	10	72
3.32	⊥⊥⊥ ||||	9	81
3.31	⊥⊥⊥ ||||	9	90
3.30	⊥⊥⊥	5	95
3.29	|||	3	98
3.28	|	1	99
3.27	|	1	100
3.26			
Total		100	

TABLE 23.7 Frequency Distribution of Resistance Values

Resistance, ohms		Frequency	Cumulative frequency
Boundaries	Midpoints		
3.415–3.445	3.43	1	1
3.385–3.415	3.40	8	9
3.355–3.385	3.37	27	36
3.325–3.355	3.34	36	72
3.295–3.325	3.31	23	95
3.265–3.295	3.28	5	100
		100	

TABLE 23.8 Number of Cells in Frequency Distribution

Number of observations	Recommended number of cells
20–50	6
51–100	7
101–200	8
201–500	9
501–1000	10
Over 1000	11–20

be adjusted when necessary; their aim is not only to provide a clear data summary, but also to reveal any underlying pattern in the data.

2. Calculate the approximate cell interval i. The cell interval equals the largest observation minus the smallest observation divided by the number of cells. Round this result to some convenient number.

3. Construct the cells by listing cell boundaries. As an aid to later calculation:

   a. The cell boundaries should be to one more decimal place than the actual data and should end in a 5.

   b. The cell interval should be constant throughout the entire frequency distribution.

4. Tally each observation into the appropriate cell and then list the total frequency f for each cell.

There are several ways of showing a frequency distribution in graphic form. The most popular is the frequency histogram. Figure 23.4 shows the electrical resistance data of Table 23.7 depicted in histogram form. The diagram is so easy to construct and interpret that it is widely used in elementary analysis of data.

One example of wide, effective use of frequency histograms is comparison of process capabilities with tolerance limits. The histogram of Figure 23.5 shows a process which is inherently capable of holding the tolerances drawn on the same figure. The high degree of defectives being produced is the result of running this process at a setting which does not locate its central tendency near the midpoint of the tolerance range. (See Section 16, under Process Capability Analysis, for other examples.)

Analyses of histograms to draw conclusions beyond the sample data should be based on at least 50 measurements.

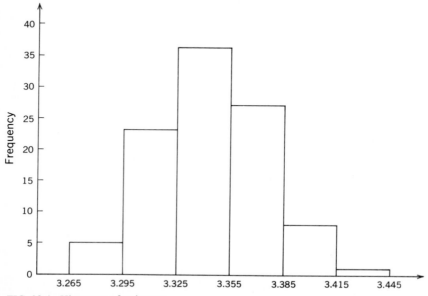

FIG. 23.4   Histogram of resistance.

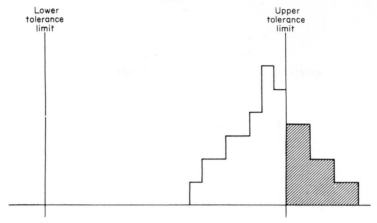

FIG. 23.5 Histogram of a process.

Sample Characteristics: Mean, Median, Mode, Variance, Standard Deviation, Percentiles. Faced with a large data set, *descriptive statistics* furnish a simple method of extracting information from what often seems at first glance to be a mass of numbers without rhyme or reason to it. These characteristics of the data may relate to a "typical (or central) value" (mean, median, mode), a measure of how much variability is present (variance, standard deviation), or a measure of frequency (percentiles). The first two types of characteristics (typical value, and variability) will be discussed below, but first we will present the concept of percentiles.

A percentile curve is a plot of the percentile rank of the data against the data values. For example, for the data of resistance of 100 coils given in Table 23.6, 1 percent are at or below resistance 3.27, 2 percent are at or below 3.28, 5 percent are at or below 3.29, and so on as given in Table 23.9. The percentile rank plot (or percentile curve) for this data is given in Figure 23.6. Note that while the data will result in a "rough" curve (since the percentile curve of the data will jump at each data point, and remain constant between actual data points), a smooth curve drawn through the data will be a better representation of reality; this is the dashed curve drawn in Figure 23.6. (Thus, while values 3.42 and 3.43 did not occur in

TABLE 23.9 Percentile Rank of Resistance Values in Table 23.6

Resistance (x)	3.27	3.28	3.29	3.30	3.31	3.32	3.33	3.34
Percentile rank (y)	1	2	5	10	19	28	38	50
	3.35	3.36	3.37	3.38	3.39	3.40	3.41	3.42
	64	77	85	91	95	97	99	99
	3.43	3.44						
	99	100						

FIG. 23.6   Percentile curve of a data set.

our sample, we expect they would in a larger sample; hence the smooth curve is the one we would utilize to assess their chances of occurring.) Note that no data are discarded (or grouped) in making the percentile curve of a data set; in this sense this is a more precise process than construction of a histogram of the data (as no information is "lost" in the process). Most statistical work uses the percentile curve, under the name *distribution function* of the data. (In early papers, this was called the "cumulative" distribution function.) Since the distribution gives the proportion of the data falling at or below each value, the graph and curve are the same, only the scale on the vertical axis is changed to read from 0 to 1 (since 0 to 100, divided by 100, runs from 0 to 1).

Measures of Central Tendency/Location.   Most frequency distributions exhibit a "central tendency," i.e., a shape such that the bulk of the observations pile up in the area between the two extremes. Central tendency is one of the two most fundamental concepts in all statistical analysis.

There are three principal measures of central tendency: arithmetic mean, median, and mode.

The *arithmetic mean* (the ordinary "average") is used for symmetrical or near symmetrical distributions, or for distributions which lack a clearly dominant single peak.

The arithmetic mean X is the most generally used measure in quality work. It is employed so often to report average size, average yield, average percent of defectives, etc., that control charts have been devised to analyze and keep track of it. Such control charts can give the earliest obtainable warning of significant changes in the central value (see Section 24, Statistical Process Control).

The mean is calculated by adding the observations and dividing by the number of observations. A short method for calculating the mean is given in a subsequent example under Measures of Dispersion.

The *median* (the middle value when the figures are arranged according to size) is used for reducing the effects of extreme values, or for data which can be ranked but are not economically measurable (shades of color, visual appearance, odors) or for special testing situations. If, for example, the average of five parts tested is used to decide whether a life test requirement has been met, then the lifetime of the third part to fail can sometimes serve to predict the average of all five, and thereby the decision of the test can be made much sooner. As shown on Figure 23.6, the median is simply the horizontal scale value where the percentile curve reaches the height 50 percent.

The *mode* (the value which occurs most often in data) is used for severely skewed distributions, describing an irregular situation where two peaks are found, or for eliminating the effects of extreme values.

The statistical "efficiency" of these measures varies. See Dixon and Massey (1969, chap. 9) or Dudewicz (1976, pp. 221–222) for elaboration.

Measures of Dispersion. Extreme value   Data are always scattered around the zone of central tendency, and the extent of this scatter is called dispersion or variation. A measure of dispersion is the second of the two most fundamental measures in all statistical analysis.

There are several measures of dispersion. The simplest is the range, which is the difference between the maximum and minimum values in the data. As the range is based on only two values, it is most useful when the number of observations is small (about 10 or fewer).

The most important measure of variation is the *standard deviation*. The definition of the sample standard deviation is:

$$s = \sqrt{\frac{\Sigma(X - \overline{X})^2}{n - 1}}$$

where s = sample standard deviation
Σ = "sum of"
X = observed values
$\overline{X}$ = arithmetic mean
n = numer of observations

For calculation purposes, an equivalent formula is

$$s = \sqrt{\frac{n\Sigma(X^2) - (\Sigma X)^2}{n(n - 1)}}$$

The square of the standard deviation is called the "variance." There is also a measure called "covariance," which gives information on the relationship between pairs of observations on characteristics X and Y. This is defined as

$$s_{XY} = \frac{\Sigma[(X - \overline{X})(Y - \overline{Y})]}{n - 1}$$

Further discussion of the relationship between two or more variables is given later in this section under Regression and Correlation Analysis.

With data in frequency distribution form, shortcut calculations can simplify

TABLE 23.10   Calculation of Average and Standard Deviation

Midpoint (1)	Frequency f (2)	d' (3)	fd' (4)	$f(d')^2$ (5)
3.43	1	+2	2	4
3.40	8	+1	8	8
3.37	27	0	0	0
3.34	36	−1	−36	36
3.31	23	−2	−46	92
3.28	5	−3	−15	45
	$\Sigma = 100$		$\Sigma = -87$	$\Sigma = 185$

finding the average and the standard deviation. This is illustrated in Table 23.10. To start, an arbitrary origin A is assumed as 3.37.

A zero is arbitrarily placed on this line in the d' column. The other figures in this column indicate how many cells the entry is above or below the arbitrary zero. Minus signs are attached when the entry is smaller than the assumed value, 3.37. The fd' values in column (4) are found by multiplying together the entries in columns (2) and (3). Similarly $f(d')^2$ is found by multiplying the figures in columns (3) and (4). Note that the totals in the last two columns are identified in the formulas as $\Sigma fd'$ and $\Sigma f(d')^2$, respectively, and i is the cell interval. As the multiplications are small enough to be carried out mentally, the complete table can be made quickly.

$$\overline{X} = A + \left(\frac{\Sigma fd'}{n}\right) i = 3.37 + \left(\frac{-87}{100}\right) 0.03 = 3.344$$

$$s = i \sqrt{\frac{n\Sigma f(d')^2 - (\Sigma fd')^2}{n(n-1)}}$$

$$s = 0.03 \sqrt{\frac{100(185) - (-87)^2}{100(99)}} = 0.031$$

For sample sizes of about 10 or fewer observations, the standard deviation can be approximated from the range by calculating R/d_2, where d_2 is a factor in Appendix II, Table A. For example, suppose the first column of values in Table 23.5 represents a sample of 10. The range is $3.40 - 3.29$, or 0.11. From Table A in Appendix II, $d_2 = 3.078$. The estimate of the standard deviation is therefore $0.11/3.078 = 0.036$. This is much simpler than calculating the standard deviation directly. Subsequent topics in this section further illustrate this feature of the range. Dixon and Massey (1969, pp. 136–140) furnish procedures and tables for a variety of applications of the range.

A final measure of variation is the "coefficient of variation." This is defined as the standard deviation divided by the mean and is thus a relative measure of variation. It can be helpful in comparing several sets of similar data that differ in mean value but may have some commonality in *relative* variation.

The methods of summarizing data covered in the previous paragraphs can be performed on a computer, as discussed below. (Also see Section 27 in general for additional information on computer programs for quality control.)

Accurate Calculation of Descriptive Statistics.   Accurate calculation of even simple descriptive statistics is not as easy a task as it might seem at first, as the example in the paragraph on coding of data below shows. In particular:

Calcuation by hand is an error-prone process, especially if there are 10 or more data points.

Construction of computer programs to perform the calculations is a task which requires knowledge of both statistics and numerical analysis as well as computer programming; hence it is inadvisable to "roll your own" in most cases.

Many of the computer software routines which come with computers (especially microcomputers) are not of high quality.

In light of the above, it is recommended that a high-quality package of computer routines for statistics be obtained and used for all such analyses. In particular, the author suggests packages called SAS, BMDP, STATPRO, and LABONE. These are high quality and among them cover a wide variety of computers on which they will run (including IBM and Data General mainframe computers, APPLE and IBM PC microcomputers, and a variety of minicomputers).

For details of SAS, see SAS Institute Inc. (1982). For BMDP, see Dixon (1983). For STATPRO, see Pinsky (1983). For LABONE, see Levy and Dumoulin (1984). In each case, a telephone call will bring current information about which computers the package is available for, as well as licensing information.

Section 27 under Statistical Analysis presents additional information on statistical packages. The graphics available with these packages (such as SAS/GRAPH with SAS) are of such a quality that they would often justify the expenditure for the package to management. The American Society for Quality Control annually publishes a "Directory of Software for Quality Assurance and Quality Control" (see, for example, ASQC, 1987).

Coding of Data.   Suppose that we have five observations $X_1, \ldots, X_5$ as in Table 23.11, and wish to compute the mean and standard deviation. Then on a pocket calculator (such as the Texas Instruments TI-55) or on a mainframe computer, we find

$$\sum_{i=1}^{5} X_1 = 49345 \qquad \sum_{i=1}^{5} X_i^2 = 4.8698581 \times 10^8$$

$$\overline{X} = 9869 \qquad s^2 = 0.985 \qquad s = 0.992$$

The only problem with these answers is that they are *wrong*. For example, 9869 is less than all of the observations; hence it cannot be the mean. And, the standard deviation is a measure of the spread in the data; that spread from largest to smallest is 0.00008; hence 0.992 is much too large. The problem that has led to this

TABLE 23.11   Five Data Points

$X_1 = 9869.00013$
$X_2 = 9869.00007$
$X_3 = 9869.00015$
$X_4 = 9869.00008$
$X_5 = 9869.00009$

inaccuracy is that the computers used keep only about eight decimal places of accuracy, and that results in discarding digits which are needed for accurate calculation. If it can be so troublesome to calculate the mean and standard deviation of five numbers accurately, clearly problems of meaningful size require careful analysis of numerical inaccuracy, as discussed above, and for this reason software should not be trusted without a careful analysis of its capabilities. The four packages suggested are of high quality.

If one must use untested software, it is recommended that one *code* the data; that is, calculate using $Y_1, \ldots, Y_5$ where $Y_i = a(X_i + b)$ for some a and b. For example, if we choose $a = 10^5$ and $b = 9869$, we will have $Y_1 = 13$, $Y_2 = 7$, $Y_3 = 15$, $Y_4 = 8$, and $Y_5 = 9$. For these we calculate (on the same computers)

$$\sum_{i=1}^{5} Y_i = 52 \qquad \sum_{i=1}^{5} Y_i^2 = 588 \qquad \overline{Y} = 10.4 \qquad s_Y^2 = 11.8 \qquad s_Y = 3.4351$$

which are exactly correct. Now it can be shown that the relation between $\overline{X}, s_X^2$ and $\overline{Y}, s_Y^2$ is

$$\overline{X} = \frac{1}{a}\overline{Y} - b \qquad s_X^2 = \frac{1}{a^2}s_Y^2$$

Hence we find (exactly again)

$$\overline{X} = 10.4 \times 10^{-5} + 9869 = 9869.000104$$

$$s_X^2 = 11.8 \times 10^{-10} \text{ (hence } s_X = 0.000034)$$

This method of *coding the data* will preserve accuracy in many other, more complex, statistical calculations (such as regression), and is in fact done internally by many of the high-quality statistical computer packages. Thus, it should be used whenever you are using a package other than one of the high-quality ones listed above. In addition, many absurd results from inaccurate software will be detected early if one observes the cardinal rule of statistics, namely, "look at the data." (It is all too common to have the data gathered and analyzed via computer without a careful look at them with the measures recommended in this section, and that has led to many costly problems for many companies.)

In terms of the choice of a and b for the coding, the best values to use are $a = 1/s_X$ and $b = -\overline{X}$. If those values cannot be calculated in a trustworthy manner by the software, the simple estimates of the next paragraph may be used instead.

Simple Estimates of Location and Dispersion. Simple estimates of the center and the spread of a set of data are often desired (for example, for use in coding of data as discussed above, and also for rapid analysis of a data set under time pressure). Two simple measures for the center are: the median (X); and the midrange, expressed as

$$\frac{\text{Maximum } (X) + \text{ minimum } (X)}{2}$$

A simple measure for the variability is

$$\frac{\text{Maximum } (X) - \text{ minimum } (X)}{4}$$

For the data of Table 23.11, the true value was $\overline{X} = 9860.000104$. The two simple methods yield 9869.00009 and 9869.000110, respectively. Similarly, the true value of the standard deviation was $s_X = 0.000034$, and the simple estimate yields 0.000020. (If we use Table A in Appendix II and take the range divided by d_2 instead of the range divided by 4, we will have a better estimate. With five data points, $d_2 = 2.326$, so our estimate of s_X is then $0.000080/2.326 = 0.000034$.)

PROBABILITY MODELS FOR EXPERIMENTS

A distinction is made between a sample and a population (or "universe"). A "sample" is a limited number of measurements taken from a larger source. A "population" is a large source of measurements from which the sample is taken. (Note that a population may physically exist, such as all stereo sets in a certain lot. It may also be conceptual, as all experiments which might be run.)

A "probability distribution" is a mathematical formula which relates the values of the characteristic with their probability of occurrence in the population. Figure 23.7 summarizes some distributions. When the characteristic being measured can take on any value (subject to the fineness of the measuring process), its probability distribution is called a "continuous" probability distribution. For example, the probability distribution for the resistance data of Table 23.7 is an example of a continuous probability distribution because the resistance could have any value, limited only by the fineness of the measuring instrument. Experience has shown that most continuous characteristics either follow one of several common probability distributions, the "normal" distribution, the "exponential" distribution, and the "Weibull" distribution, or can be fitted with an empirical estimate as discussed later in this section. These distributions find the probabilities associated with occurrences of the actual values of the characteristic. Other continuous distributions (e.g., t, F, and chi square) are important in data analysis but do not provide probabilities of occurrence of actual values.

When the characteristic being measured can take on only certain specific values (e.g., integers 0, 1, 2, 3, etc.), its probability distribution is called a "discrete" probability distribution. For example, the distribution for the number of defectives r in a sample of five items is a discrete probability distribution because r can only be 0, 1, 2, 3, 4, or 5. The common discrete distributions are the Poisson, binomial, negative binomial, and hypergeometric (see Figure 23.7).

The following paragraphs explain how probability distributions can be used with a sample of observations to make predictions about the larger population.

Sample Space. Statistics deals with the *outcomes* of *experiments*. When an experiment is performed, some outcome results; let us denote a typical outcome by the symbol e. Such an outcome is called a "simple event." If we list all of the possible outcomes of the experiment of interest to us, that set is called the "sample space" of the experiment.

As an example, if we perform the experiment of tossing three coins and observing for each coin whether it lands heads (H) or tails (T), the sample space will contain the eight possible outcomes

HHH   HHT   HTH   THH   HTT   THT   TTH   TTT

For simplicity of notation, let us denote these simple outcomes, respectively, by e_1, e_2, e_3, e_4, e_5, e_6, e_7, e_8.

We associate a number called "probability" with each of the simple events. We think of this number as representing the proportion of times each simple event would occur in a very large number of experiments of this type. For exam-

DISTRIBUTION	FORM	PROBABILITY FUNCTION	COMMENTS ON APPLICATION
NORMAL		$y = \dfrac{1}{\sigma\sqrt{2\pi}} e^{-\frac{(X-\mu)^2}{2\sigma^2}}$ μ = Mean σ = Standard deviation	Applicable when there is a concentration of observations about the average and it is equally likely that observations will occur above and below the average. Variation in observations is usually the result of many small causes.
EXPONENTIAL		$y = \dfrac{1}{\mu} e^{-\frac{x}{\mu}}$	Applicable when it is likely that more observations will occur below the average than above.
WEIBULL		$y = \alpha\beta (X-\gamma)^{\beta-1} e^{-\alpha(x-\gamma)^\beta}$ α = Scale parameter β = Shape parameter γ = Location parameter	Applicable in describing a wide variety of patterns of variation, including departures from the normal and exponential.
POISSON*		$y = \dfrac{(np)^r e^{-np}}{r!}$ n = Number of trials r = Number of occurrences p = Probability of occurrence	Same as binomial but particularly applicable when there are many opportunities for occurrence of an event, but a low probability (less than 0.10) on each trial.
BINOMIAL*		$y = \dfrac{n!}{r!(n-r)!} p^r q^{n-r}$ n Number of trials r = Number of occurrences p = Probability of occurrence q = 1-p	Applicable in defining the probability of r occurrences in n trials of an event which has a probability of occurrence of p on each trial.
NEGATIVE BINOMIAL*		$y = \dfrac{(r+s-1)!}{(r-1)!(s!)} p^r q^s$ r = Number of occurrences s = Difference between number of trials and number of occurrences p = probability of occurrence q = 1-p	Applicable in defining the probability that r occurrences will require a total of r+s trials of an event which has a probability of occurrence of p on each trial. (Note that the total number of trials n is r+s.)
HYPERGEOMETRIC*		$y = \dfrac{\binom{d}{r}\binom{N-d}{n-r}}{\binom{N}{n}}$	Applicable in defining the probability of r occurrences in n trials of an event when there are a total of d occurrences in a population of N.

FIG. 23.7 Summary of common univariate probability distributions. (Asterisks indicate that these are discrete distributions, but the curves are shown as continuous for ease of comparison with the continuous distributions.)

ple, the probability of HHH in our experiment of tossing three coins is usually taken to be $\frac{1}{8} = 0.125$ since it typically occurs in about $\frac{1}{8}$th of a large number of experiments where three coins are tossed. We denote the probability of a simple event e by $P(e)$; thus, we usually have $P(\text{HHH}) = \frac{1}{8}$.

Since some outcome occurs in each experiment, when we add up the proportion of times that each e in the sample space occurred, we must obtain a sum of 1. Since probabilities represent what those proportions would be in a large number of experiments, we must also have *probabilities* which *sum to 1 when all outcomes are accounted for.* For example, in our example with three coins

$$P(e_1) + P(e_2) + P(e_3) + P(e_4) + P(e_5) + P(e_6) + P(e_7) + P(e_8) = 1$$

Events. Very often, we are interested not in a simple event, but a combination of them, called a "composite event." For example, the event "more heads than tails" occurs if and only if one of the simple events e_1, e_2, e_3, e_4 (i.e., the simple events HHH, HHT, HTH, THH) occurs in our example of tossing three coins. The frequency with which we find "more heads than tails" will be the sum of the relative frequencies of e_1, e_2, e_3, and e_4. Thus, we say the probability of the event "more heads than tails" is the sum of the probabilities of the simple events which comprise the event "more heads than tails":

$$P\,(\text{more heads than tails}) = P(e_1) + P(e_2) + P(e_3) + P(e_4)$$

To make this simpler to write, we often denote the event of interest by a symbol, such as A for the event "more heads than tails." Then

$$P(A) = P(e_1) + P(e_2) + P(e_3) + P(e_4)$$

Thus, *the probability of a composite event is the sum of the probabilities of all the simple events which comprise it.* Since in the example with three coins we have $P(e_1) = P\,(e_2) = \cdots = P(e_8) = \frac{1}{8}$, we find

$$P(A) = \frac{1}{8} + \frac{1}{8} + \frac{1}{8} + \frac{1}{8} = \frac{1}{2}$$

i.e., we expect to find more heads than tails (when three coins are tossed) in about 50 percent of such experiments.

In the example with three coins, we have *equally likely simple events,* i.e., $P(e_i) = P(e_j) + P(e_j)$ for all i,j. When this is true, it follows that for any composite event A we have

$$P(A) = \frac{\text{number of simple events in } A}{\text{number of points in the sample space}}$$

In the case of the three coins, this yields the same answer obtained before, namely $P(A) = \frac{4}{8} = \frac{1}{2}$.

We say two composite events A_1 and A_2 are *mutually exclusive* if no e_i is in both A_1 and A_2. For example, if A_1 is the event "2 heads" and A_2 is the event "more tails than heads" then A_1 and A_2 are mutually exclusive since $A_1 = \{e_2, e_3, e_4\}$ and $A_2 = \{e_5, e_6, e_7, e_8\}$ have no point in common. We often express the fact that A_1 and A_2 are mutually exclusive in shorthand by writing

$$A_1 A_2 = \phi$$

If A_1 and A_2 are mutually exclusive, then for the event "A_1 or A_2" (which occurs if and only if at least one of A_1, A_2 occurs) we have

$$P(A_1 \text{ or } A_2) = P(A_1) + P(A_2)$$

This follows since $P(A_1 \text{ or } A_2)$ equals the number of e_i in either A_1 or A_2 divided by the total number of simple events; since there are no points in both A_1 and A_2, this is the same as taking the number of points in A_1 and adding to it the number in A_2, then dividing by the total number of simple events. In our example, $P(A_1 \text{ or } A_2) = P(A_1) + P(A_2) = \frac{3}{8} + \frac{4}{8} = \frac{7}{8}$.

In our example so far, we have discussed the events

A: "more heads than tails"

A_1: "2 heads"

A_2: "more tails than heads"

These are shown on the sample space in Figure 23.8. Here A and A_1 are not mutually exclusive, so the simple addition of the probabilities does not hold for them, since $P(A) + P(A_2) = \frac{4}{8} + \frac{3}{8} = \frac{7}{8}$ counts the points e_2, e_3, e_4 twice as to their probabilities. Thus, we see that a correct equation for $P(A \text{ or } A_1)$ will need

FIG. 23.8   Events and sample space, experiment of tossing 3 coins.

to subtract this overcounting part, which is $P(A \text{ and } A_1)$, i.e., the probability that we have an experimental outcome where both A *and* A_1 occur, which is $P(A \text{ and } A_1) = \frac{3}{8}$ in this example. Thus, we have reasoned to the fact that *for any events A and A_1 the Addition Rule is:*

$$P(A \text{ or } A_1) = P(A) + P(A_1) - P(A \text{ and } A_1)$$

For mutually exclusive events the $P(A \text{ and } A_1)$ would be 0, so that this would reduce to 2-additivity in that case.

Rules of Probability, Combinatorics.   Probability theory underlies all decisions which are based on sampling. As we have seen, probability is expressed as a number which lies between 1.0 (certainty that an event will occur) and 0.0 (impossibility of occurrence), and the most intuitive definition of probability is one based on a frequency interpretation. In the simple case when an event A can occur in s cases out of a total of n possible and equally probable cases, then the probability that the event will occur is

$$P(A) = \frac{s}{n} = \frac{\text{number of successful cases}}{\text{total number of possible cases}}$$

Counting s and n can be complex, in which case it is called a problem of "combinatorics."

Example: A lot consists of 100 parts. A single part is selected at random, and thus, each of the 100 parts has an equal chance of being selected. Suppose a lot contains a total of 8 nonconforming parts. Then the probability of drawing a single part that is nonconforming is 8/100, or 0.08.

The following theorems are useful in solving problems involving probability:

Theorem 1: If $P(A)$ is the probability that an event A will occur, then the probability that A will not occur is $1 - P(A)$.

Theorem 2: If A and B are two events, then the probability that either A or B occurs is

$$P(A \text{ or } B) = P(A) + P(B) - P(A \text{ and } B)$$

A special case of this theorem occurs when A and B cannot occur simultaneously (i.e., A and B are "mutually exclusive"). Then the probability that either A or B occurs is

$$P(A \text{ or } B) = P(A) + P(B)$$

Example: The probabilities of r defectives in a sample of six units from a 5 percent defective lot are found below by the binomial. The probability of zero defectives is 0.7351; the probability of one defective is 0.2321. The probability of zero or one defective is then $0.7351 + 0.2321$, or 0.9672.

Theorem 3: If A and B are two events, then the probability of the joint occurrence of both A and B is

$$P(A \text{ and } B) = P(A) \times P(B|A)$$

where $P(B|A) =$ probability that B will occur assuming A has already occurred.
A special case of this theorem occurs when the two events are *independent*, i.e., when the occurrence of one event has no influence on the probability of the other event. If A and B are independent, then the probability of both A and B occurring is

$$P(A \text{ and } B) = P(A) \times P(B)$$

Example: A complex system consists of two major subsystems. The probability of successful performance of the first subsystem is 0.95; the corresponding probability for the second subsystem is 0.90. Both subsystems must operate successfully in order to achieve total system success. The probability of the successful operation of the total system is therefore $0.95 \times 0.90 = 0.855$.
The theorems above have been stated in terms of two events but can be expanded for any number of events.

Conditional Probability; Bayes' Theorem. In "conditional probability" we seek an answer to such questions as "If I know that A_2 has occurred, then on those trials of the experiment where A_2 has occurred, how often does A_1 occur?" We use a special shorthand symbol for this *conditional probability,*

$$P(A_1|A_2)$$

which is read as "the probability of A_1, given that A_2 is known to have occurred" and is calculated from the formula

$$P(A_1|A_2) = \frac{P(A_1 \text{ and } A_2)}{P(A_2)}$$

If $P(A_1|A_2) > P(A_1)$, we say A_2 carries "positive information" about A_1.

If $P(A_1|A_2) < P(A_1)$, we say A_2 carries "negative information" about A_1.

If $P(A_1|A_2) = P(A_1)$, we say A_2 carries no information about A_1, or that A_1 and A_2 are "independent events." In this last case, knowing that A_2 has (or, has not) occurred does not change the chances of A_1 occurring.

The powerful *conditional probability reversal formula*

$$P(A_1|A_2)P(A_2) = P(A_1 \text{ and } A_2) = P(A_2 \text{ and } A_1) = P(A_2|A_1)P(A_1)$$

is the basis of Bayes' theorem. In the simplest setting, this states that

$$P(A_2|A_1) = \frac{P(A_1|A_2)P(A_2)}{P(A_1|A_2)P(A_2) + P(A_1|\text{not } A_2)P(\text{not } A_2)}$$

(Here, "not A_2" is the event that A_2 does not occur.) For worked solutions of problems in probability, see Dudewicz (1980).

The techniques presented under Tests of Hypotheses in this section consist of analyzing a sample of observations and reaching a conclusion (with defined sampling risks) to accept or reject a hypothesis. The experimenter considers the consequences of drawing incorrect conclusions and, to a lesser degree, the likelihood that extreme values of the population parameter will occur. However, this is usually done on a qualitative basis and involves judgment. In practice, a sample size is limited by economics and the experimenter defines the type I error (usually 0.05 or 0.01) in numerical terms and then must accept the type II error that results with the sample size fixed by economics. There is a methodical way of defining the consequences of the type I and type II errors and the likelihood of extreme values. The approach involves Bayes' theorem and statistical decision theory.

Statistical Decision Theory. This concept requires two items of information not formally used in classical analysis:

1. The economic consequences of making type I or type II errors.
2. The probabilities that different values of the population parameter will occur. (The classical approach has no assumption concerning different values of the population parameter.)

Statistical tables and sampling plans based on Bayes' theorem or statistical decision concepts are not common, but the concepts can have a significant effect, and therefore development work seems imminent and worthwhile. Oliver and Springer (1972) give an example of Bayesian acceptance sampling tables. Hadley (1967) provides background material including examples on tests of hypotheses, confidence limits, and acceptance sampling plans. Lenz and Rendtel (1984) compare the performance of MIL-STD-105D, Skip Lot, and Bayesian sampling plans. See also the discussion in Section 25 under Bayesian Procedures.

DISCRETE PROBABILITY DISTRIBUTIONS

Discrete probability distributions are used to model situations where the outcome of interest can take on only a few discrete values (such as 0 or 1 for failure or success, or 0, 1, 2, 3, . . . as a number of occurrences of some event of interest). Below we give the model leading to the most commonly occurring such distributions, consider where one can obtain numerical values of their probabilities, and their uses in quality control.

The Discrete Uniform Distribution.   If each of the values $x_1, \ldots, x_n$ is equally likely to occur as the result of an experiment, then we say the value obtained has the uniform distribution on the set of values $x_1, \ldots, x_n$. In this case the probability of x_i is $1/n$. Since the probabilities are so simple, no special tables are needed.

Model Leading to a Uniform Distribution.   The model leading to a uniform distribution is random selection from a finite population in which each value occurs the same number of times. (This makes values equally likely to occur in the sample.)

Uses of Random Choices.   Random choices are often used in sampling inspection. For example, suppose that a lot of 1000 items is sequentially numbered from 500 through 1499. Then the chance that an item selected at random from the lot will have number i is (for any i between 500 and 1499) $1/1000 = 0.001$. The probability that such an item will have a serial number at least 1400 is $100/1000 = 0.01$.

The Binomial Distribution.   If the probability of occurrence p of an event is constant on each of n independent trials of the event, then the probability of r occurrences in n trials is

$$\frac{n!}{r!(n-r)!}\, p^r q^{n-r}$$

where $q = 1 - p$.

   In practice, the assumption of a constant probability of occurrence is considered reasonable when the population size is at least 10 times the sample size (under this circumstance, the change in probability from one trial to the next due to depletion of the population is negligible). (Note that the binomial has fewer assumptions than the Poisson.)

   Table F in Appendix II provides partial tables for the binomial and gives references for more complete tables. King (1971, chaps. 20 through 22) discusses binomial probability paper.

Model Leading to a Binomial Distribution.   When n independent trials of an experiment each have a constant probability p of occurrence of an event of interest (commonly termed a "success"), then the number of occurrences follows a binomial distribution. The name comes from the fact that the factor

$$\frac{n!}{r!(n-r)!}$$

in the probabilities is called a "binomial coefficient" in mathematics.

Binomial Probabilities and Uses.   A lot of 100 units of product is submitted by a vendor whose past quality has been about 5 percent nonconforming. A random sample of six units is selected from the lot. The probabilities of various sample results are given in Table 23.12.

   In using the formula, note that $0! = 1$. Table F in Appendix II lists binomial probabilities in cumulative form, i.e., the probability of r or fewer occurrences in

TABLE 23.12   Table of Binomial Probabilities

r	P (exactly r defectives in 6) $=$ $[6!/r! \, (6-r)!](0.05)^r(0.95)^{6-r}$
0	0.7351
1	0.2321
2	0.0306
3	0.0021
4	0.0001
5	0.0000
6	0.0000

n trials. For the above example, the probability of 1 or fewer nonconforming items in a sample of 6 can be read from the table as 0.9672. Note that this is the sum of the probabilities for $r = 0$ and $r = 1$, i.e., $0.7351 + 0.2321 = 0.9672$.

The Hypergeometric Distribution.   Occasionally, the assumptions of the Poisson (see below) or binomial cannot be met even approximately. Subject only to the assumption of a random sample, the hypergeometric gives the probability of exactly r occurrences in n trials from a lot of N items having d defectives as

$$\frac{\dbinom{d}{r}\dbinom{N-d}{n-r}}{\dbinom{N}{n}}$$

where $\dbinom{N}{n}$ is the "combinations" of N items taken n at a time and is equal to $N!/$

$[n!(N-n)!]$, where $N! = [N(N-1)\,(N-2)\cdots 1]$ and $0! = 1$. The calculations can be avoided by using tables such as those prepared by Lieberman and Owen (1961). Duncan (1974) compares the results of Poisson, binomial, and hypergeometric distributions.

Model Leading to a Hypergeometric Distribution.   The hypergeometric distribution is appropriate when independent trials are conducted, but the probability of occurrence of the event of interest changes from trial to trial because of depletion of a finite population. Because of their simpler form, in this situation one often uses the binomial or Poisson distributions if their assumptions are approximately met.

Hypergeometric Probabilities and Uses.   A lot of 100 units is submitted by a vendor whose past quality has been about 5 percent nonconforming. A random sample of 20 units is selected from the lot. To calculate the probability of 0 nonconforming in 20, note that the lot has 5 nonconforming items and 95 conforming. Then:

$$P(0 \text{ in } 20) = \frac{\dbinom{5}{0}\dbinom{95}{20}}{\dbinom{100}{20}} = \frac{\left[\dfrac{5!}{0!(5-0)!}\right]\left[\dfrac{95!}{20!(95-20)!}\right]}{\dfrac{100!}{20!(100-20)!}} = 0.319$$

Repeat substitutions into the formula are made to find $P(r$ in 20), where r in this example is 0, 1, 2, 3, 4, and 5.

The Poisson Distribution.   In practice, the most important discrete distribution is the Poisson. It is an approximation to more exact distributions and applies when the sample size is at least 16, the population size is at least 10 times the sample size, and the probability of occurrence p on each trial is less than 0.1. (These conditions are often met.)

Figure 23.7 states the Poisson probability function, but the real work is done by cumulative probability tables.

Model Leading to a Poisson Distribution.   As well as being an approximation to more exact distributions, the Poisson is the exact distribution when certain assumptions are met. These assumptions are: that events occur at random (in time, or in space, or in location for example) with a probability of occurrence roughly proportional to the length of time (or volume of space, or area), and that there is no "clumping." (For details, see Dudewicz, 1976, Section 3.2.) For example, if a target 0.1 mi^2 in size is known to be contained in an area 10 mi^2 in size, and this area is shelled at random (one shell at a time so there will be no clumping), the probability of a hit will be $0.1/10 = 0.01$. The number of hits will follow a Poisson distribution, and the number of shells fired may be set so the probability of eight or more hits on the target will be at least 0.95; this is often done in practice when it is known that eight or more hits will effectively destroy the target and a 95 percent kill probability is desired.

Poisson Probabilities and Uses.   A lot of 300 units of product is submitted by a supplier whose past quality has been about 2 percent nonconforming. A random sample of 40 units is selected from the lot. Table E in Appendix II provides the probability of r or fewer defectives in a sample of n units. (The application of these probabilities is explained in Section 25, under Operating Characteristic, OC, Curve.) Entering the table with a value of np equal to 40 (0.02), or 0.8, gives Table 23.13. Individual probabilities can be found by subtracting cumulative probabilities. Thus, the probability of exactly two defectives is $0.953 - 0.809$, or 0.144.

The Negative Binomial Distribution.   The negative binomial distribution is one of the most commonly occurring distributions in situations where the sample size is not set in advance, but rather is determined as the experiment proceeds.

Model Leading to a Negative Binomial Distribution.   If the probability of occurrence of an event is constant from trial to trial, and we make trials until we find

TABLE 23.13   Table of Poisson
Probabilities

r	Probability of r or fewer in sample
0	0.449
1	0.809
2	0.953
3	0.991
4	0.999
5	1.000

m occurrences, then the probability that r trials will be needed is

$$\frac{(r-1)!}{(m-1)!(r-m)!} p^m (1-p)^{r-m}$$

where r can be m, $m + 1$, $m + 2$, ... This equation is equivalent to the more complex one listed in Figure 23.7. Other situations leading to a negative binomial distribution are discussed in Chapter 5 of Johnson and Kotz (1969). Tables are available in Williamson and Bretherton (1963) in case direct calculation is burdensome; Johnson and Kotz (1969) give references to additional tables.

Negative Binomial Probabilities and Uses.   A large lot is inspected until the first defective ($m = 1$) is found; if that occurs in the first five trials, the lot is rejected. Hence the lot will be accepted if no defective is found in the first five trials (and thus trials 6, 7, ... need not be performed—we will never inspect more than five items with this scheme). If the lot is 10 percent nonconforming, then from Table 23.14 we see that the probability the lot is accepted is $1 - (0.10 + 0.09 + 0.081 + 0.0729 + 0.06561) = 0.59049$.

TABLE 23.14   Table of Negative Binomial Probabilities ($m = 1$, $p = 0.10$)

r	Probability r trials are needed to find $m = 1$ defectives
1	0.10
2	0.09
3	0.081
4	0.0729
5	0.06561
6	0.059049
7	0.053144
8	0.047830

The Multinomial Distribution.   The discrete probability distributions discussed up to this point (the uniform, binomial, hypergeometric, Poisson, and negative binomial) all relate to situations which are "univariate," that is, where the outcome of interest relates to one variable's value (such as the number of defectives in a sample of size n in the binomial case). However, there are important cases where the outcome is "multivariate." One such example is that where in a sample of size n one observes both the number needing rework and the number to be scrapped; since there are two quantities, this is called a "bivariate" situation. The multinomial distribution can be used when there are any number of categories into which the items may be classified.

Model Leading to a Multinomial Distribution.   If exactly one of the events E_1, ..., E_k occurs on each of n independent trials, and the probabilities of occurrence of the events are respectively p_1, ..., p_k (with $p_1 + \cdots + p_k = 1$, so that one of them must occur), then the probability that E_1 occurs x_1 times, and E_2 occurs x_2 times, ..., and E_k occurs x_k times (where $x_1 + x_2 + \cdots + x_k = n$ since there are n trials and one of $E_1, \ldots, E_k$ must occur on each trial) is

$$\frac{n!}{x_1!x_2! \cdots x_k!} \, p_1^{x_1} \, p_2^{x_2} \cdots p_k^{x_k}$$

Tables are not widely available, and calculations are usually done directly from the probability formula, or (if n is large) the multivariate normal distribution (a continuous multivariate distribution discussed later in this section) is used as an approximation.

Multinomial Probabilities and Uses. Suppose that $n = 5$ large assemblies are manufactured and inspected each day. The results of each inspection are either PASS, REWORK, or SCRAP. Past results have shown that 80 percent pass, 15 percent need rework, and 5 percent need to be scrapped. What are the probabilities of the various possible outcomes of one day's output?

In Figure 23.9 we show the probabilities of the outcomes, calculated directly from the basic formula. Note that once the number to be reworked (e.g., 1) and the number to be scrapped (e.g., 0) are specified, the number passed is determined (e.g., $5 - 1 - 0 = 4$). We have had to use the multinomial probability distribu-

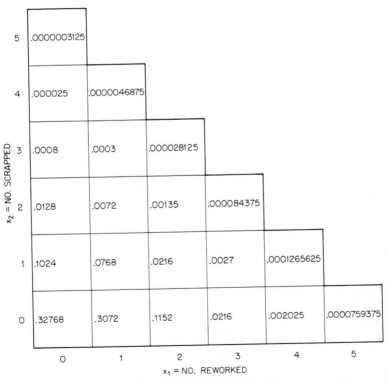

$x_2 = $ NO. SCRAPPED	0	1	2	3	4	5
5	.0000003125					
4	.000025	.0000046875				
3	.0008	.0003	.000028125			
2	.0128	.0072	.00135	.000084375		
1	.1024	.0768	.0216	.0027	.0001265625	
0	.32768	.3072	.1152	.0216	.002025	.0000759375

$x_1 = $ NO. REWORKED

FIG. 23.9 Table of multinomial probabilities, $k = 3$ Categories, $n = 5$, $p_1 = P(\text{Rework}) = 0.15$, $p_2 = P(\text{Scrap}) = 0.05$, $p_3 = P(\text{Pass}) = 0.80$.

tion since the categories are not independent (an item cannot be both passed and scrapped).

Selecting a Discrete Distribution. Selection of which discrete distribution to use is usually made either by knowledge of the underlying sitaution or by fitting a model from relative frequency probability. In either case, a test of the model selected is desirable to check its validity.

Selection from a Model of Reality. In many cases one will know (or assume) that the model which leads to one of the distributions we have discussed underlies the practical situation. For example, if one draws 50 items at random from a large lot with $100p$ percent defective, one will assume the binomial model with $n = 50$ and probability p of a defective on each trial.

(Chi Square) Test of Model Validity. To test the validity of an assumed discrete model, where cell i should occur with probability p_i, one compares the observed cell totals with those predicted by the model using the chi square test discussed later (Test 12b). Such a confirmatory test can be omitted only if one is willing to run the risk of assuming a model which in fact may have little basis in reality. (See Section 9.12 of Dudewicz and Mishra, 1988, and especially Problem 9.12.2 on p. 532.)

Empirical Models via Relative Frequency Probability. If there is little or no reason to lead to the adoption of one of the specific models discussed, a model can be fitted to the data using the relative frequencies observed in the past. For example, if one has observed that in 100 items produced in the past there have been blemishes present in the numbers given in Table 23.15, one would estimate the probability of r blemishes as its relative frequency in the past work, i.e., as in Table 23.16. Such a model should be tested by taking a new sample and performing a chi square test as previously discussed.

TABLE 23.15 Blemishes per Item in Past Work	
No. of blemishes	No. of occurrences
0	50
1	25
2	25

TABLE 23.16 Blemish Probabilities via Relative Frequency Estimation	
No. of blemishes	Probability
0	.50
1	.25
2	.25

CONTINUOUS PROBABILITY DISTRIBUTIONS

Continuous probability distributions are used to model situations where the outcome of interest can take on values in a continuous range (such as all values greater than zero for the failure time of a motor which is run continuously). Below we give the model leading to the most commonly occurring such distributions, consider where one can obtain numerical values of their probabilities, and their uses in quality control.

The Continuous Uniform Distribution.   If all values between a and b $(a < b)$ are possible, and the chances of the value being in a subinterval are proportional to its length, then the uniform distribution is appropriate. The probability function is flat over the interval (a,b), where $y = 1/(b - a)$. Thus, the probability the value is in a subinterval of length c is $c/(b - a)$. Since the probabilities are so simple, no special tables are needed.

Model Leading to a Uniform Distribution.   The model leading to a continuous uniform distribution over the range (a,b) is random selection of a value between a and b. For example, if a valve on a water line is spun at random between pressure 0 lb/in^2 (closed) and 100 lb/in^2 (fully open), then the resulting pressure will be a uniform random variable on $(0,100)$.

Uses of Random Numbers.   Uniform random variables on the range $(0,1)$ are called "random numbers." Such variables are often used to drive digital computer simulation models, and are of great importance in simulation studies of quality systems. Full details on sources of high-quality random numbers may be found in Dudewicz and Ralley (1981). Special considerations for simulation uses on microcomputers are given in Dudewicz, Karian, and Marshall (1985).

The Exponential Distribution.   The exponential probability function is

$$y = \frac{1}{\mu}\, e^{-X/\mu}$$

Figure 23.7 shows the shape of an exponential distribution curve. Note that the normal and exponential distributions have distinctly different shapes. An examination of the tables of areas shows that 50 percent of a normally distributed population occurs above the average value and 50 percent below it. In an exponential population, 36.8 percent are above the average and 63.2 percent below the average. (This refutes the intuitive idea that the average is always the 50 percent point.) The property of a higher percentage below the average sometimes helps to indicate applications of the exponential. For example, the exponential describes the loading pattern for some structural members because smaller loads are more numerous than larger loads. The exponential is also useful in describing the distribution of failure times of certain complex equipment.

Model Leading to an Exponential Distribution.   It can be shown that the exponential distribution of failure times arises when failures occur "at random" (and are not due to wearout, but to such items as random shocks). In fact, the exponential distribution is characterized as the only continuous distribution with the "lack of memory property" that the chances of the item living an additional t_0 time units depend only on the length t_0 and not on how long the item has already been in use (see Dudewicz, 1976, pp. 88, 106, for details).

Predictions with Exponential Distributions.   Predictions based on an exponentially distributed population require only an estimate of the population average. For example, the time between successive failures of a complex piece of equipment is measured and the resulting histogram is found to resemble the exponential probability curve. The results of a sample of measurements indicate that the average time between failures (commonly called MTBF or mean time between failures) is 100 h. What is the probability that the time between two successive failures of this equipment will be at least 20 h?

The problem is one of finding the area under the curve beyond 20 h (Figure 23.10). Table C in Appendix II gives the area under the curve beyond any particular ratio X/μ. In this problem,

$$\frac{X}{\mu} = \frac{20}{100} = 0.20$$

and from Table C in Appendix II the area under the curve beyond 20 h is thus 0.8187. The probability that the time between two successive failures is greater than 20 h is 0.8187; i.e., there is about an 82 percent chance that the equipment will operate without failure continuously for 20 or more hours. Similar calculations would give a probability of 0.9048 for 10 or more hours. Later in this section, this probability is calculated for the specified "mission time" of a product, and the result is called "reliability." These analyses could also be made using exponential probability paper.

The Weibull Distribution.   The Weibull distribution is a family of distributions having the general density function

$$y = \alpha\beta(X - \gamma)^{\beta-1} e^{-\alpha(X-\gamma)^{\beta}}$$

where α = scale parameter, β = shape parameter, and γ = location parameter.

The curve of the function (Figure 23.7) varies greatly depending on the numerical values of the parameters. Most important is the shape parameter β, which reflects the pattern of the curve. Note that when β is 1.0, the Weibull function reduces to the exponential and that when β is about 3.5 (and $\alpha = 1$ and $\gamma = 0$), the Weibull closely approximates the normal distribution. In practice, β varies from about ⅓ to 5. The scale parameter α is related to the peakedness of the curve; i.e., as α changes, the curve becomes flatter or more peaked.

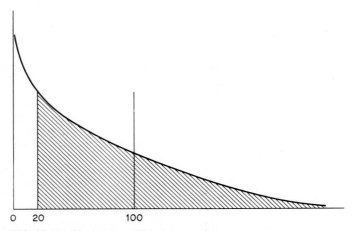

FIG. 23.10   Distribution of time between failures.

The location parameter γ is the smallest possible value of X. This is often assumed to be zero, thereby simplifying the equation. It is often unnecessary to determine the values of these parameters because predictions are made directly from Weibull probability paper. King (1971, pp. 136–140) gives procedures for graphically finding α, β, and γ.

The Weibull covers many shapes of distributions. This makes it popular in practice because it reduces the problem of examining a set of data and deciding which of the common distributions (e.g., normal or exponential) fits best. In particular, both IFR (increasing failure rate) and DFR (decreasing failure rate) cases are included, respectively, with $\beta > 1$ and $\beta < 1$ (see Dudewicz, 1976, pp. 88–89).

Model Leading to a Weibull Distribution   It can be shown that a Weibull distribution arises if an exponential variable is raised to a power, i.e., if Y is exponential then $Y^{1/\beta}$ has a Weibull distribution (Dudewicz, 1976, p. 89).

Predictions with Weibull Distributions   An analytical approach for the Weibull distribution (even with tables) is cumbersome, and the predictions are usually made with Weibull probability paper. For example, five heat-treated shafts were stress-tested until each of them failed. The fatigue life (in terms of number of cycles to failure) is:

10,263
12,187
16,908
18,042
23,271

The problem is to predict the percentage failure of the population for various values of fatigue life. The solution is to plot the data on Weibull paper, observe if the points fall approximately in a straight line, and if so, read the probability predictions (percentage failure) from the graph.

Although Weibull plotting can follow the mean rank procedure of normal probability paper (see below under Predictions with Normal Distributions), much of the literature on Weibull applications uses "median ranks." Table D in Appendix II gives, for various sample sizes, the values of the median rank. (Note that the mean rank procedure does not require a table.) The median ranks necessary for this particular example are based on a sample size of five failures and are as shown in Table 23.17. (The mean rank estimates are shown for comparison.) The

TABLE 23.17   Table of Median and Mean Ranks

Failure number i	Median rank	Mean rank $= \dfrac{i}{5 + 1}$
1	0.1294	0.1667
2	0.3147	0.3333
3	0.5000	0.5000
4	0.6853	0.6667
5	0.8706	0.8333

cycles to failure are now plotted on the Weibull graph paper against the corresponding values of the median rank (see Figure 23.11). These points fall approximately in a straight line (King, 1971, pp. 126–128, describes how to modify a plot to help obtain a straight line), so it is assumed that the Weibull distribution applies. The vertical axis gives the cumulative percent of failures in the population corresponding to the fatigue life shown on the horizontal axis. For example, about 50 percent of the population of shafts will fail in less than 17,000 cycles. About 90 percent of the population will fail in less than 24,000 cycles. By appropriate subtractions, predictions can be made of the percent of failures between any two fatigue life limits.

It is tempting to extrapolate on probability paper, particularly to predict life. For example, suppose the minimum fatigue life were specified as 8000 cycles and the five measurements above were from tests conducted to evaluate the ability of the design to meet 8000 cycles. As all five tests exceeded 8000 cycles, the design seems adequate and therefore should be released for production. However, extrapolation on the Weibull paper predicts that about 8 percent of the *population* of shafts would fail in less than 8000 cycles. This suggests a review of the design before release to production. Thus, the small *sample* (all *within* specifications) gave a deceiving result.

Extrapolation can go in the other direction. Note that a probability plot of life test data does not require that all tests be completed before the plotting starts. As each unit fails, the failure time can be plotted against the median rank. If the early points appear to be following a straight line, then it is tempting to draw in the line *before* all tests are finished. The line can then be extrapolated beyond the actual test data and life predictions can be made without accumulating a large amount of test time. The approach has been applied to predicting, *early in a warranty period,* the "vital few" components of a complex product which will be most trou-

FIG. 23.11   Distribution of fatigue life on Weibull probability paper.

blesome. However, extrapolation has dangers. It requires the judicious melding of statistical theory and engineering experience and judgment.

Moult (1963) describes the use of a Weibull plot in comparing the suitability of two types of steel for use in bearings. The plot is shown in Figure 23.12.

Nelson (1982) discusses Weibull paper. Probability graph paper is available for the normal, exponential, Weibull, and other probability distributions. (A source is TEAM, Technical and Engineering Aids for Management, Box 25, Tamworth, New Hampshire 03886.) Although the mathematical functions and tables provide the same information, the graph paper reveals *relationships* between probabilities and values of X that are not readily apparent from the calculations. For example, the reduction in percent defective in a population as a function of wider and wider tolerance limits can be easily portrayed by the graph paper.

The Normal Distribution. Many engineering characteristics can be approximated by the normal distribution

$$y = \frac{1}{\sigma\sqrt{2\pi}}\, e^{-(X-\mu)^2/2\sigma^2}$$

where $e = 2.718$, $\pi = 3.141$, μ = population average, σ = population standard deviation.

Problems are solved with a table, but note that the distribution requires estimates of only the average μ and standard deviation σ of the population (unless otherwise indicated, Greek symbols will be used for population values and Roman symbols for sample values) in order to make predictions about the population. The curve for the normal probability distribution is related to a frequency distribution and its histogram. As the sample becomes larger and larger, and the width of each cell becomes smaller and smaller, the histogram approaches a smooth curve. If the entire population (in practice, the population is usually considered infinite, e.g., the potential production from a process) were measured, and if it were normally distributed, the result would be as shown in Figure 23.7. Thus,

FIG. 23.12 Composite fatigue endurance—process "C" vacuum degassing versus air cast AISI 8620.

the shape of a histogram of sample data provides some indication of the probability distribution for the population. If the histogram resembles the "bell" shape shown in Figure 23.7, this is a basis for assuming that the population follows a normal probability distribution. (It is not necessary that the sample histogram be perfectly normal—the assumption of normality is applied only to the population, and small deviations from normality are expected in random samples.) Hahn (1971) gives a practical discussion of assuming normality. (The name "normal" distribution dates back to a time when all other distributions were erroneously thought to be abnormal. Today, some prefer the name "Gaussian" distribution.)

Model Leading to a Normal Distribution (Additive Errors, Central Limit Theorem). It can be shown that if a variable Y is the result of adding many other variables, and those variables are not highly dependent on each other, then Y will have approximately a normal distribution. (This result is called the Central Limit Theorem; see Dudewicz, 1976, p. 149.) Statisticians usually recommend that 10 or more terms be added before this result is relied on to produce normality; however, a number of applied studies have shown good results with as few as three terms being added.

Predictions with Normal Distributions.   Predictions require just two estimates and a table. The estimates are:

$$\text{Estimate of } \mu = \overline{X} \quad \text{and} \quad \text{estimate of } \sigma = s$$

The calculations of the sample $\overline{X}$ and s are made by one of the methods previously discussed.

For example, from past experience, a manufacturer concludes that the burnout time of a particular light bulb it manufactures is normally distributed. A sample of 50 bulbs has been tested and the average life found to be 60 days, with a standard deviation of 20 days. How many bulbs in the entire population of light bulbs can be expected to be still working after 100 days of life?

The problem is to find the area under the curve beyond 100 days (see Figure 23.13). The area under a distribution curve between two stated limits represents

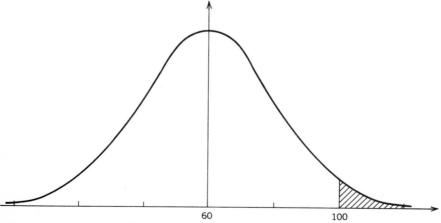

FIG. 23.13   Distribution of light bulb life.

the probability of occurrence. Therefore, the area beyond 100 days is the probability that a bulb will last more than 100 days. To find the area, calculate the difference between a particular value X and the average of the curve in units of standard deviation:

$$K = \frac{X - \mu}{\sigma}$$

In this problem, $K = (100 - 60) \div 20 = + 2.0$. Table B in Appendix II shows, for $K = 2$, a probability of 0.9773. Applied to this problem, the probability that a bulb will last 100 days or less is 0.9773. The normal curve is symmetrical about the average and the total area is 1.000. The probability of a bulb's lasting more than 100 days then is $1.0000 - 0.9773$, or 0.0227, or 2.27 percent of the bulbs in the population will still be working after 100 days.

Similarly, if a characteristic is normally distributed and if estimates of the average and standard deviation of the population are obtained, this method can estimate the total percent of production that will fall within engineering specification limits.

Figure 23.14 shows representative areas under the normal distribution curve (these can be derived from Table B in Appendix II). Thus 68.26 percent of the *population* will fall between the average of the population plus or minus 1 standard deviation of the population, 95.46 percent of the population will fall between the average $\pm 2\sigma$, and finally $\pm 3\sigma$ will include 99.73 percent of the population. The percentage of a *sample* within a set of limits can be quite different from the percentage within the same limits in the population. This important fact is crucial in testing hypotheses (covered later in this section).

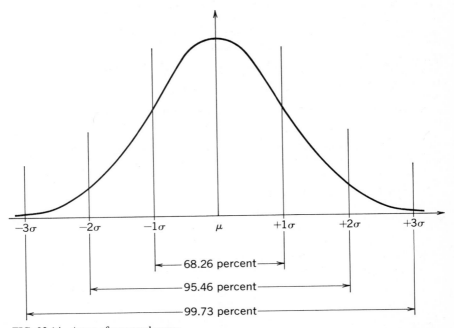

FIG. 23.14   Areas of a normal curve.

Another way of making predictions based on a normal distribution employs probability paper. Probability paper is so constructed that data from a particular kind of distribution plots as a straight line, i.e., a sample of data from a normally distributed population plots approximately as a straight line on normal probability paper. (Small deviations from a straight line are expected because the data represent a *sample* of the population.) The following are the steps taken to plot data on probability paper:

1. Arrange the observations in ascending values. The smallest value is given a rank i of 1 and the largest value a rank of n.

2. For each value, calculate the cumulative frequency.

3. For each value, calculate

$$\frac{\text{Cumulative frequency}}{n + 1} \times 100$$

This provides the mean rank probability estimate, in percent, for plotting the data.

4. Plot the observed values against their mean rank probability estimate.

If the observations are in frequency distribution form, the procedure is the same, except that instead of using the observed values the probability estimates are plotted against the cell boundaries. This is illustrated for the resistance data (see Table 23.18).

The plot is shown in Figure 23.15. Lower cell boundaries are plotted against the last column of Table 23.18 using the upper (Percent Over) scale. The line has been drawn in by eye, and the fit appears reasonable. This line represents an estimate of the population, and predictions like those obtained from the normal probability table can be read directly from the graph. For example, 5 percent of the population of coils will have resistance values greater than about 3.39. Also, 95 percent will have values greater than about 3.29. (Therefore, 95 − 5, or 90 percent, will have values between 3.29 and 3.39.)

Figure 23.16 shows a form which incorporates probability paper plotting with further analysis such as confidence limits and control limits. (This type of form was originally developed by E. F. Taylor.)

King (1971) gives a practical description of probability paper procedures for the normal and other important distributions. While fit is often evaluated by eye when we have clearly good fit (as in Figure 23.15), statistical tests are available and should be used in cases which are not so clearcut; see Iman (1982) for details and graphs on which this analysis can be performed.

TABLE 23.18 Resistance Data

Cell boundaries	Frequency	Cumulative frequency	$\dfrac{\text{Cumulative frequency}}{100 + 1}(100)$
3.415–3.445	1	1	0.99%
3.385–3.415	8	9	8.90
3.355–3.385	27	36	35.60
3.325–3.355	36	72	71.30
3.295–3.325	23	95	94.10
3.265–3.295	5	100	99.00
	100		

FIG. 23.15 Cumulative probability plot of Table 23.18.

The Lognormal Distribution.   If $Y = e^Z$ where Z has a normal distribution, Y is said to have a lognormal distribution (since the logarithm of Y has a normal distribution).

Model Leading to a Lognormal Distribution (Multiplicative or Percentage Effects).   Lognormal variables arise when effects are percentages or multiplicative, which is common in biological and many other applications. For example, if a random percent of a stock of items goes bad each time period, the percentage still good after a large number (10 or more) of time periods will be lognormally distributed. (This result follows from the Central Limit Theorem already discussed when considering the normal distribution, since the logarithm of a product is the sum of the logarithms of the items in the product.)

Predictions with Lognormal Distributions.   As with the normal distribution, predictions require two estimates. For details, see Cohen and Whitten (1981). Note that the lognormal distribution is positively skewed, and is widely employed as a model for distribution of life spans, reaction times, income distributions, and other economic data.

   Often the mean, standard deviation, and probabilities of the lognormal variable Y itself are of basic interest; thus, while one can easily estimate these for Z (the logarithm of $Y = e^Z$), that does not answer the real problem. For example, if Y is the lifetime of some system, one may want to estimate the average life of the system—not the mean of the logarithm of Y. This is why the special methods referred to above have been developed for this distribution.

Mixture Distributions. Y is said to have a mixture distribution if Y results from source i $100p_i$ percent of the time ($i = 1, 2, \ldots$).

Model Leading to a Mixture Distribution.   When output from several sources is mixed (for example, output from several suppliers, several plants, several machines, several workers, and so on), the quality characteristics of the resulting mix have mixture distributions. If each of the components coming into the mix

FIG. 23.16 Normal distribution analysis sheet.

has *exactly* the same distribution, then the mix will also have that distribution. However, if the components coming into the mix have different distributions, then the mix will have a "mixture distribution."

Fitting of Mixtures.   As can be seen from Figure 23.7, the distributions we have considered so far are unimodal (have one peak). When in practice one sees two or more peaks in the histogram, one suspects a mixture underlies the data. In some cases, this itself leads to a study of the items coming into the mix, often to find a problem in one of the streams of what should be homogeneous product.

In other cases, the streams coming into the mix cannot be separated (or it is not desired to separate them), but rather one wishes to fit the density of Y as $p_1 f(Z_1) + p_2 f(Z_2) + \cdots + p_k f(Z_k)$ for some k (2 or more). Here the p_i's add to 1 (100 percent of the mix), and often the Z_i's are known to be normal. To fit the distribution of the Y, one must then select $k - 1$ p's (since they add to 1, the last one is then determined), k means, and k variances. This process requires use of modern computer software such as LABONE. As an example, consider the data of Table 23.19. A histogram of this data (computed as was Figure 23.4 for a similar but different data set) shows that a mixture (of two terms, since there are two peaks) may be involved. The distributions seem to the eye to be normal. Using LABONE Expert Statistical Programs (ESP), we are able to easily fit a mixture of normal distributions.

TABLE 23.19   Data for Mixture Analysis

3.37	3.34	3.48	3.32	3.33	3.38	3.34	3.31	3.43	3.34
3.29	3.46	3.30	3.31	3.43	3.34	3.34	3.46	3.39	3.34
3.45	3.36	3.30	3.42	3.33	3.35	3.45	3.34	3.32	3.48
3.32	3.37	3.44	3.38	3.36	3.47	3.36	3.31	3.43	3.30
3.35	3.43	3.38	3.37	3.54	3.32	3.36	3.42	3.29	3.35
3.48	3.39	3.34	3.42	3.30	3.39	3.46	3.40	3.32	3.43
3.29	3.41	3.37	3.36	3.41	3.47	3.36	3.37	3.43	3.36
3.31	3.43	3.35	3.34	3.45	3.34	3.31	3.46	3.37	3.35
3.50	3.35	3.37	3.42	3.35	3.36	3.48	3.35	3.31	3.44
3.35	3.36	3.49	3.31	3.31	3.40	3.35	3.33	3.45	3.31

The Multinormal Distribution.   The continuous probability distributions discussed up to this point (the uniform, exponential, Weibull, normal, lognormal, and mixture) all relate to situations which are *univariate,* that is, where the outcome of interest has one component (such as lifetime). If there are additional components of interest (such as weight and height), then the outcome is *multivariate* (in this case of three, *trivariate*). The multinormal distribution is appropriate when each of the components has a normal distribution, and is the most widely used continuous multivariate distribution.

Model Leading to a Multinormal Distribution.   The same sort of additive process which leads to a univariate normal distribution, leads to a multivariate normal distribution when more than one component is being measured.

Predictions with Multinormal Distributions.   Predictions with multinormal distributions require computer packages in most cases. The details, with computer code and examples, are discussed by Siotani, Hayakawa, and Fujikoshi (1985).

Selecting a Continuous Distribution. Selection of which continuous distribution to use is usually made by either knowledge of the underlying situation, or by fitting a model to the histogram (often via plots on probability papers of the most usual distributions). In either case a test of the model selected is desirable to check its validity.

Selection from a Model of Reality. In many cases one will know (or assume) that the model which leads to one of the distributions we have discussed underlies the practical situation. For example, if the life distribution of the equipment under study has, in the past, always been adequately fitted by a Weibull model (though with parameters which change from application to application), one will usually start with a Weibull assumption.

Testing Distributional Assumptions (Probability Plotting, Tests for Specific Distributions). In practice, a distribution is assumed by evaluating a sample of data. Often, it is sufficient to evaluate the shape of the histogram or the degree to which a plot on probability paper follows a straight line. These convenient methods do require judgment (e.g., how "straight" must the line be?) because the sample is never a perfect fit; quantitative tests for probability plots should be used (see Iman, 1982). Be suspicious of the data if the fit is "perfect." "Goodness of fit" tests (see Tests of Hypotheses later in this section) evaluate any distribution assumption using quantitative criteria.

Fitting Empirical Probability Distributions. If there is little or no reason to suggest one of the specific models discussed, or if they are rejected (e.g., because of a poor probability paper fit), an alternative is to fit an empirical model. Such models can adapt to a wide range of distributional shapes, including many of those of the specific models discussed above. One of the most widely used empirical families is the *generalized lambda distribution* family *(GLD)*.

As an example, in Table 23.20 we have data (from p. 219 of Hahn and Shapiro, 1967) on the coefficient of friction of a metal in 250 samples. Using procedures and tables given in Ramberg, Dudewicz, Tadikamalla, and Mykytka (1979), a probability function can be developed.

As a check on the goodness of the fit, it is recommended that the probability

TABLE 23.20   Coefficient-of-Friction Data

Range	Frequency
Less than .015	1
0.015–0.020	9
0.020–0.025	30
0.025–0.030	44
0.030–0.035	58
0.035–0.040	45
0.040–0.045	29
0.045–0.050	17
0.050–0.055	9
0.055–0.060	4
More than 0.060	4
Total	250

FIG. 23.17 Coefficient of friction relative frequency histogram and the fitted distribution.

function always be plotted on the same graph as the histogram for a visual assessment of the fit (which can be supplemented by a chi square test if desired). This is done in Figure 23.17, and we see that the fit is excellent (a chi square test comes to the same conclusion).

STATISTICAL ESTIMATION

In statistical estimation, we make inferences about parameters of a population from data on a sample. For example, if we have a random sample of 100 items from a large lot, information on the sample can be used to infer information about the proportion of defectives p in the lot. This inference takes the form of either a single number (a "point estimate") or a pair of numbers (an "interval estimate"); there are several types of interval estimates, depending on our goals. If we found that 15 of the 100 items in the sample were defective, we would estimate p as being $15/100 = 0.15$ (point estimate); a typical interval would be to state that we are 95 percent confident that p is between 0.08 and 0.22 (confidence interval estimate). Thus, a "confidence interval" sets limits on the unknown parameter, here the proportion p. Two other types of intervals often needed are "prediction intervals" and "tolerance intervals." Let X denote the number of defectives in a future sample; a prediction interval sets limits on X, such as

$$P[L_1 \leq X \leq U_1] = 0.95$$

In this example, a "prediction interval" would state that X would be between 5 and 25; these are limits within which one could be 95% sure the number of defectives in a future sample of 100 items would lie. A "tolerance interval" sets limits

(L, U) such that one can be 95 percent sure that at least 99 percent of the population will be included within these limits. In this example, the population is all lots of 100 items drawn from the same process; at least 99 percent of the lots will have a proportion of defectives between $L = 0.05$ and $U = 0.25$. These items are discussed in more detail below.

Point Estimates.   Point estimates are customarily the points at which the interval estimates are centered. In many cases, it is preferable to give an interval estimate, since that estimate tells us how much uncertainty is associated with the estimate. For example, if we observe 15 of 100 items chosen at random from a very large lot are defective, then we will estimate the proportion of defectives in the lot as $15/100 = 0.15$. Similarly if we observe three defectives in a sample of 20 items we will estimate the proportion of defectives as $3/20 = 0.15$. However, in the first case the interval estimate (at 95 percent confidence) will be that p is between 0.08 and 0.22, while in the latter case the interval estimate (at 95 percent confidence) will be that p is between 0.00 and 0.31. In either case, if forced to estimate proportion defective in the lot by a single number, that number would be 0.15; however, the uncertainty in that estimate is much greater with the smaller sample size (where as much as 31 percent of the population might be defective) than with the larger sample size (where as much as 22 percent of the population might be defective).

The typical point estimates are covered below, as the centers of the respective intervals.

Confidence Interval Estimates.   Estimation is the process of analyzing a sample result in order to predict the corresponding value of the population parameter. For example, a sample of 12 insulators has an average impact strength of 0.952 ft·lb (6.7149 N·m). If this is a representative sample from the process, what estimate can be made of the true average impact strength of the entire population of insulators?

1. The "point estimate" is a single value used to estimate the population parameter. For example, 4.952 ft·lb (6.7149 N·m) is the point estimate of the average strength of the population.
2. The "confidence interval" is a range of values which includes (with a preassigned probability called "confidence level") the true value of a population parameter. "Confidence limits" are the upper and lower boundaries of the confidence interval. Confidence level is the probability that an assertion about the value of a population parameter is correct.

Duncan (1974) provides a thorough discussion of confidence limits. The explanation here indicates the concept behind the calculations.

If the population mean is μ, the probability that the sample mean will lie between

$$\mu \pm 1.96 \frac{\sigma}{\sqrt{n}}$$

is equal to 0.95:

$$P\left(\mu - 1.96 \frac{\sigma}{\sqrt{n}} \le \overline{X} \le \mu + 1.96 \frac{\sigma}{\sqrt{n}}\right) = 0.95$$

This is algebraically equivalent to saying that the sample mean plus 1.96 standard deviations of means lies above μ and the sample mean minus 1.96 standard deviations of means lies below μ:

$$P\left(\mu \le \overline{X} + 1.96 \frac{\sigma}{\sqrt{n}} \text{ and } \overline{X} - 1.96 \frac{\sigma}{\sqrt{n}} \le \mu\right) = 0.95$$

or

$$P\left(\overline{X} - 1.96 \frac{\sigma}{\sqrt{n}} \le \mu \le \overline{X} + 1.96 \frac{\sigma}{\sqrt{n}}\right) = 0.95$$

Or the 95 percent confidence interval on μ is $\overline{X} \pm 1.96 \, (\sigma/\sqrt{n})$. This interval has a 0.95 probability of including the population value: 95 percent of the sets of such intervals would include the population value. In practice, this is interpreted to mean that there is a 95 percent "confidence" that the limits based on one sample will include the true value.

For the sample of 12 insulators suppose $\sigma = 0.25$. Then, the 95 percent confidence limits are

$$\overline{X} \pm 1.96 \frac{\sigma}{\sqrt{n}} = 4.952 \pm 1.96 \frac{(0.25)}{\sqrt{12}} = 4.811 \text{ and } 5.093$$

This is interpreted to mean that there is 95 percent confidence that μ is between 4.811 and 5.093. The 95 percent is the confidence level (confidence levels of 90, 95, or 99 percent are usually assumed in practice, and some statisticians call these the "holy" numbers) and 4.811 and 5.093 are the limits of the confidence interval. A confidence level is associated with an assertion based on actual measurements and measures the probability that the assertion is true. Confidence limits are limits which include the true value with a preassigned degree of confidence (the confidence level).

Table 23.21 summarizes confidence limit formulas for common parameters. The following examples illustrate some of these formulas.

Example: Sixty-one specimens of brass have a mean hardness of 54.62 and an estimated standard deviation of 5.34. Determine the 95 percent confidence limits on the mean.

Solution:

$$\text{Confidence limits} = \overline{X} \pm t \frac{s}{\sqrt{n}}$$

$$= 54.62 \pm 2.00 \frac{5.34}{\sqrt{61}}$$

$$= 53.25 \text{ and } 55.99$$

There is 95 percent confidence that the true mean hardness of the brass is between 53.25 and 55.99.

Example: A radar system has been operated for 1200 h, during which time eight failures occurred. What are the 90 percent confidence limits on the mean time between failures for the system?

TABLE 23.21 Summary of Confidence Limit Formulas and Graphs

Parameters	Formulas
1. Mean of a normal population (standard deviation known)	$\overline{X} \pm K_{\alpha/2} \dfrac{\sigma}{\sqrt{n}}$ where $\overline{X}$ = sample average K = normal distribution coefficient (see Appendix II, Table B) σ = standard deviation of population n = sample size
2. Mean of a normal population (standard deviation unknown)	$\overline{X} \pm t_{\alpha/2} \dfrac{s}{\sqrt{n}}$ where t = Student's distribution coefficient (with $n - 1$ degrees of freedom) (see Appendix II, Table G) s = estimated σ
3. Standard deviation of a normal population a. Using sample standard deviation b. Using sample range	Upper confidence limit = $B_U s$ Lower confidence limit = $B_L s$ where B_U and B_L are numerical factors given in Natrella (1963, p. T-34), Dixon and Massey (1969, p. 140)
4. Population fraction defective based on attribute data (fraction defective in sample)	See Appendix II, Chart N
5. Population fraction defective based on variables data ($\overline{X}$ and s in sample)	See Kirkpatrick (1970)
6. Difference between the means of two normal populations (standard deviations σ_1 and σ_2 known)	$(\overline{X}_1 - \overline{X}_2) \pm K_{\alpha/2} \sqrt{\dfrac{\sigma_1^2}{n_1} + \dfrac{\sigma_2^2}{n_2}}$ where K = normal distribution coefficient (see Appendix II, Table B)
7. Difference between the means of two normal populations ($\sigma_1 = \sigma_2$ but unknown)	$(\overline{X}_1 - \overline{X}_2) \pm t_{\alpha/2} \sqrt{\dfrac{1}{n_1} + \dfrac{1}{n_2}}$ $\times \sqrt{\dfrac{\sum (X - \overline{X}_1)^2 + \sum (X - \overline{X}_2)^2}{n_1 + n_2 - 2}}$ where t = Student's distribution coefficient (with degrees of freedom = $n_1 + n_2 - 2$)(see Appendix II, Table G)
8. Difference between the means of two normal populations (σ_1 and σ_2 both unknown)	$(\overline{X}_1 - \overline{X}_2) \pm t^*_{\alpha/2} \sqrt{\dfrac{\sum (X - \overline{X}_1)^2}{n_1(n_1 - 1)} + \dfrac{\sum (X - \overline{X}_2)^2}{n_2(n_2 - 1)}}$ where t^* = Student's distribution coefficient (with the smaller of $n_1 - 1$ and $n_2 - 1$ as degrees of freedom)

TABLE 23.21   Summary of Confidence Limit Formulas and Graphs (*Continued*)

Parameters	Formulas
9. Mean time between failures (based on an exponential population of time between failures)	Upper confidence limit = $2T/\chi^2_{\alpha/2}$, Degrees freedom = $2r$ Lower confidence limit = $2T/\chi^2_{1-\alpha/2}$, Degrees freedom = $2r$ where T = total test time on all units and DF = $2r$, where r is a preassigned number of failures and where χ^2 = chi square distribution coefficient (see Appendix II, Table L)
10. Reliability (based on a Weibull population)	See Thoman, Bain, and Antle (1970)
11. Availability (based on an exponential population of time between failures and log normal population of repair time)	See Gray and Lewis (1967)

Solution:

$$\text{Estimated } m = \frac{1200}{8} = 150 \text{ h}$$

$$\text{Upper confidence limit} = \frac{2(1200)}{7.962} = 301.4$$

$$\text{Lower confidence limit} = \frac{2(1200)}{26.296} = 91.3$$

There is 90 percent confidence that the true mean time between failures is between 91.3 and 301.4 h. (Epstein, 1960, discusses several cases of making estimates from life test data.)

Confusion has arisen on the application of the term "confidence level" to a reliability index such as mean time between failures. Using a different example, suppose the numerical portion of a reliability requirement reads as follows: "The MTBF shall be at least 100 h at the 90 percent confidence level." This means:

1. The minimum MTBF must be 100 h.
2. Actual tests shall be conducted on the product to demonstrate with 90 percent confidence that the 100-h MTBF has been met.
3. The test data shall be analyzed by calculating the observed MTBF and the lower one-sided 90 percent confidence limit on MTBF.
4. The lower one-sided confidence limit must be ≥ 100 h.

The term "confidence level," from a statistical viewpoint, has great implications on a test program. Note that the observed MTBF must be *greater* than 100 if the lower confidence limit is to be ≥ 100. Confidence level means that sufficient tests must be conducted to demonstrate, with statistical validity, that a requirement has been met. Confidence level does *not* refer to the qualitative opinion about meeting a requirement. Also, confidence level does *not* lower a requirement; i.e., a 100-h MTBF at a 90 percent confidence level does not mean that 100 h is desired but that 0.90×100, or 90 h, is acceptable. Such serious misunderstandings have occurred. When the term is used, a clear understanding should be verified and not assumed.

Determination of the Sample Size Required to Achieve a Specified Precision in an Estimate.   Additional tests will increase the precision of the estimates obtained from a test program. The increase in precision usually does not vary linearly with the number of tests—doubling the number of tests usually does not double the precision (even approximately). Further, if the sample is selected randomly and if the sample size is less than 10 percent of the population size, then precision depends primarily on the absolute size of the sample rather than the sample size expressed as a percent of the population size. Thus a sample size which is 1 percent of a population of 100,000 may be more precise than a 10 percent sample from a population of 1000 (see Hahn, 1972).

The cost of additional tests must be evaluated against the value of the additional precision. Confidence limits can help to determine the size of test program required to estimate a product characteristic within a specified precision. Suppose it is desired to estimate the true mean life of a battery. The estimate must be within 2.0 h of the true mean if the estimate is to be of any value. The variability is known as $\sigma = 10.0$. A 95 percent confidence level is desired on the confidence statement. The 2.0 h is the desired confidence interval half-width, so

$$2.0 = \frac{(1.96)(10)}{\sqrt{n}} \qquad n = 96$$

A sample of 96 batteries will provide a mean which is within 2.0 h of the true mean (with 95 percent confidence). Notice the type of information required: (1) desired width of the confidence interval (the precision desired in the estimate), (2) confidence level desired, (3) variability of the characteristic under investigation. The number of tests required cannot be determined until the engineer furnishes these items of information.

Table 23.22 summarizes formulas and graphs useful in determining the sample size required to estimate a population parameter with a specified precision. The following examples illustrate some of the formulas.

Example: A sample must be selected to estimate the population mean length of a part. It appears reasonable to assume that length is normally distributed. An estimate of the standard deviation is not available, but process knowledge suggests that "almost all" production falls between 2.009 and 2.027 in. As a first approximation, the standard deviation is estimated as $(2.027 - 2.009)$ divided by 6, or 0.003 in. It is desired that the estimate of μ be within 0.001 in of the true μ and that the estimation statement be made at the 95 percent confidence level. Referring to Appendix II, Chart S, $E/s = 0.001/0.003 = 0.33$, and the required sample size is about 37. It is instructive to calculate n for other values of E and s (see Table 23.23). Such a "sensitivity analysis" is helpful in evaluating the cost of extra tests against the value of extra precision.

Example: It is desired to estimate the standard deviation σ of a population within 20 percent of the true value at the 95 percent confidence level. Referring to Appendix II, Chart T, the required degrees of freedom is about 46 and, therefore, the sample size is $46 + 1$, or 47.

TABLE 23.22 Summary of Sample Size Formulas and Graphs

Parameters	Formulas
1. Mean of a normal population (σ known)	$n = \dfrac{K_{\alpha/2}^2 \sigma^2}{E^2}$ where K = normal distribution coefficient E = maximum allowable error in estimate (desired precision)
2. Mean of a normal population (σ estimated)	See Appendix II, Chart S
3. Standard deviation of a normal population	See Appendix II, Chart T
4. Fraction defective of a population	$n = p(1 - p)\left(\dfrac{K_{\alpha/2}}{E}\right)^2$ where p = estimate of the population fraction defective. If no estimate of p is available, assume "worst case" of $p = 0.5$

TABLE 23.23 Effect of E and s on n

Maximum error E	Standard deviation s		
	0.002	0.003	0.004
0.0008	27	56	98
0.0010	18	37	64
0.0020	7	12	18

Prediction Intervals. A prediction interval is used when the desire is not an estimate of population characteristics directly, but rather a prediction of what we will find when we take a future item from the population. For example, in the example of $n = 61$ specimens of brass with a mean hardness of 54.62 and an estimated standard deviation of 5.34, we previously found that 95 percent confidence limits on the mean were

$$\overline{X} \pm t\frac{s}{\sqrt{n}} = 53.25 \text{ and } 55.99$$

Now we ask: What limits can we be 95 percent sure the next item sampled will have its hardness within? The appropriate interval here is

$$\overline{X} \pm ts\sqrt{1 + \frac{1}{n}} = 54.62 \pm (2.00)(5.34)(1.0082)$$

$$= 43.85 \text{ and } 65.39$$

For further considerations and tables, see Hahn (1970).

Tolerance Intervals. "Statistical tolerance limits" are similar to "process capability," i.e., they show the practical boundaries of process variability (see Section 16, under Process Capability), and therefore can be a valuable input in the determination of engineering tolerance limits (which specify the allowable limits for product acceptance). Methods for calculating statistical tolerance limits are of two types—those which assume a normal distribution and those which do not require any distributional assumption. Table 23.24 summarizes these methods.

Table 23.25 shows data we will use to illustrate these methods. Five samples of four each were taken and an outside dimension of a cathode pole recorded.

A confidence level of 95 percent and a population percentage of 99 percent have been chosen.

Using method 1 and the standard deviation s, the statistical tolerance limits are

$$\overline{X} \pm Ks = 1.00287 \pm 3.615(0.00034) = 1.00164 \text{ and } 1.00410$$

Using method 2 and the overall range R of the combined data, the limits are

$$\overline{X} \pm K_1R = 1.00287 \pm 1.005(0.00134) = 1.00152 \text{ and } 1.00422$$

Using method 3 and the average of the ranges R, the limits are

$$\overline{X} \pm K_2R = 1.00287 \pm 1.783(0.00078) = 1.00148 \text{ and } 1.00426$$

These methods assume that the characteristic is normally distributed. Method 4 is "distribution-free" and assumes only that the distribution is continuous and the sample is a random one (these assumptions apply to all methods). The statistical tolerance limits by this method are simply the extreme observations in the combined sample, i.e., 1.00231 and 1.00365. Appendix II, Table W indicates that at least 78.4 percent of the population will be included within these limits. (Note that Appendix II, Table X provides the sample size required to include 99 percent of the population; i.e., a sample of 473 is needed to be 95 percent confident that the sample extremes would include 99 percent of the population.)

When it is feasible to assume a normal distribution, method 1 is preferred because it usually provides the narrowest set of limits while recognizing the variation in the sample. Methods 2 and 3 are good approximations. If normality cannot be assumed, then method 4 is appropriate but at the cost of a larger sample size. In practice, a partial sample can first be obtained to evaluate the assumption of normality. If normality can be assumed, the partial sample is then used to determine statistical tolerance limits. Otherwise, the full sample should be taken and the distribution-free approach (method 4) applied to determine the limits.

Tolerance intervals have also been developed for other cases, such as where the distribution is exponential. Ranganathan and Kale (1983) give such intervals which are resistant to the presence of an outlier in the observations. Their Section 5 includes an example with data on reliability of air conditioning on a Boeing 727 jet aircraft.

All the above methods involve two probabilities, i.e., a confidence level γ and the probability P of falling within limits. This is confusing, but these two probabilities are needed to obtain a mathematically correct statement concerning the limits. An approximation uses the sample average $\overline{X}$ and standard deviation s and regards these as highly reliable estimates of μ and σ. If normality is assumed, then 99 percent statistical tolerance limits are calculated as

$$\overline{X} \pm 2.56s$$

TABLE 23.24 Methods for Calculating Statistical Tolerance Limits

Method	Distribution assumption	Formula for limits	Source of factor
1. Measure a sample of n items and calculate the average $\overline{X}$ and standard deviation s	Normal	Two-sided limits: $\overline{X} \pm Ks$ One-sided limit: $\overline{X} + Ks$ or $\overline{X} - Ks$	Appendix II, Table V Appendix II, Table V
2. Measure a sample of n items and calculate the average $\overline{X}$ and range R	Normal	Two-sided limits: $\overline{X} \pm K_1 R$	Appendix II, Table U
3. Measure N samples of n items each and calculate the grand average $\overline{\overline{X}}$ and average range $\overline{R}$	Normal	Two-sided limits: $\overline{\overline{X}} \pm K_2 \overline{R}$	Bingham (1962, p. 37)
4. Define the population percentage P which must be included between the tolerance limits. Measure a sample of n and observe the largest and smallest values	None	Two-sided limits: The probability is γ that at least P % of the population will be between the sample extremes. One-sided limit: The probability is γ that at least P % of the population will be less than the largest value in the sample (or greater than the smallest value).	Appendix II, Table W Natrella (1963, p. T-76)

TABLE 23.25 Data on Cathode Pole Dimension

	Sample 1	Sample 2	Sample 3	Sample 4	Sample 5	
	1.00263	1.00306	1.00293	1.00291	1.00310	
	1.00298	1.00328	1.00343	1.00247	1.00281	$\overline{X} = 1.00287$
	1.00293	1.00274	1.00239	1.00268	1.00256	$s = 0.00034$ (standard deviation of the
	1.00285	1.00303	1.00274	1.00365	1.00231	20 observations about $\overline{X}$)
$\overline{X}$	1.00285	1.00303	1.00287	1.00293	1.00269	$\overline{R} = 0.00078$
R	0.00035	0.00054	0.00104	0.00118	0.00079	$R = 0.00134$

where the value of 2.56 is obtained from the normal distribution table (Appendix II, Table B):

$$\overline{X} \pm 2.56s = 1.00287 \pm 2.56(0.000274)$$

$$= 1.00217 \text{ and } 1.00357$$

These limits are then interpreted to mean that 99 percent of the population is within 1.00217 and 1.00357. Another approach sets the limits at simply $\overline{X} \pm 3s$. At best, these are only approximate because $\overline{X}$ and s are not exactly equal to μ and σ. Bingham (1962) discusses the $X \pm 3s$ approximation. (Confidence limit calculations could indicate the size of the possible error.)

Another approach to simplify the probability statement uses the Chebyshev inequality theorem, which holds for any continuous distribution. The theorem states that the probability of obtaining a value which deviates from μ by more than k standard deviations is less than $1/k^2$. For the limits to include 99 percent,

$$0.01 = \frac{1}{k^2}$$

or

$$k = 10$$

The 99 percent limits would be calculated as $\overline{X} \pm 10s$. These limits are distribution-free and the prediction statement is simple; i.e., at least 99 percent of the population is within $\overline{X} \pm 10s$. However, the multiple of 10 is highly conservative and results in limits much wider than any of the other methods.

For the methods listed in Table 23.24, no provision is made for the division of the remaining $100(1 - P)$ percent between the upper and lower tails of the distribution. Owen and Frawley (1971) give a procedure and tables for setting limits which do provide for controlling the percentage outside each of the two limits.

Statistical tolerance limits are sometimes confused wtih other limits used in engineering and statistics. Table 23.26 summarizes the distinctions among five types of limits. Hahn (1970) gives an excellent discussion with examples and

TABLE 23.26 Distinction among Limits

Name of limits	Meaning
Tolerance limits	Set by the engineering design function to define the minimum and maximum values allowable for the product to work properly.
Statistical tolerance limits	Calculated from process data to define the amount of variation that the process exhibits. These limits will contain a specified proportion of the total population.
Prediction limits	Calculated from process data to define the limits which will contain all of k future observations.
Confidence limits	Calculated from data to define an interval within which a population parameter lies.
Control limits	Calculated from process data to define the limits of chance (random) variation around some central value.

tables to illustrate the differences among several types of limits. Also see Harter (1983) under "Tolerance Limits."

Tolerance Limits for Interacting Dimensions.   Interacting dimensions are those which mate or merge with other dimensions to create a final result. Setting tolerance limits on such dimensions is discussed in the following paragraphs. Setting tolerance limits on noninteracting dimensions makes use of the methods presented under Statistical Tolerance Limits in this section and in Section 13 (see especially Fig. 13.14 and associated discussion).

Conventional Method Relating Tolerances on Interacting Dimensions.   Consider the simple mechanical assembly shown in Figure 23.18. The lengths of components *A, B,* and *C* are interacting dimensions because they determine the overall assembly length.

The conventional method of relating interacting dimensions is simple addition. For the example of Figure 23.18,

Nominal value of the result = nominal value$_A$ + nominal value$_B$
$$+ \text{ nominal value}_C$$

Tolerance T of the result = $T_A + T_B + T_C$

Nominal value of assembly length = $1.000 + 0.500 + 2.000 = 3.500$

Tolerance of assembly length = $0.0010 + 0.0005 + 0.0020 = \pm 0.0035$

This method assumes 100 percent interchangeability of components making up the assembly. If the component tolerances are met, then all assemblies will meet the assembly tolerance determined by the simple arithmetic addition.

The approach of adding component tolerances is mathematically correct, but often too conservative. Suppose that about 1 percent of the pieces of component *A* are expected to be below the lower tolerance limit for component *A* and suppose the same for components *B* and *C*. If a component *A* is selected at random, there is on the average 1 chance in 100 that it will be on the low side, and similarly for components *B* and *C*. They key point is this: If assemblies are made at random and if the components are manufactured independently, then the chance that an assembly will have all three components simultaneously below the lower tolerance limit is

$$\frac{1}{100} \times \frac{1}{100} \times \frac{1}{100} = \frac{1}{1,000,000}$$

There is thus only about one chance in a million that all three components will be too small, resulting in a small assembly. Thus, setting component and assem-

←	Assembly length	→
A	B	C

| 1.000 | 0.500 | 2.000 |
| ±0.001 | ±0.0005 | ±0.002 |

FIG. 23.18   Mechanical assembly.

bly tolerances based on the simple addition formula is conservative in that it fails to recognize the extremely low probability of an assembly containing all low (or all high) components.

Statistical Method of Relating Tolerances on Interacting Dimensions. This method states for the example Figure 23.18:

Nominal value of the result

$$= \text{nominal value}_A + \text{nominal value}_B + \text{nominal value}_C$$

Tolerance of the result $= \sqrt{T_A^2 + T_B^2 + T_C^2}$

Then:

Nominal value of the assembly $= 1.000 + 0.500 + 2.000 = 3.500$

T of the assembly $= \sqrt{(0.001)^2 + (0.0005)^2 + (0.002)^2} = \pm 0.0023$

Practically all (but not 100 percent) of the assemblies will fall within 3.500 ± 0.0023. This is narrower than 3.500 ± 0.0035 (the result by the arithmetic method).

In practice, the problem often is to start with a defined end result (e.g., assembly length specification) and set tolerances on the parts. Suppose the assembly tolerance was desired to be ± 0.0035. Listed in Table 23.27 are two possible sets of component tolerances which when used with the quadratic formula will yield an assembly tolerance equal to ± 0.0035. The tolerance set using the conventional formula is also shown.

TABLE 23.27   Comparison of Statistical and Conventional Methods

Component	Statistical		Conventional
	Alternative 1	Alternative 2	
A	± 0.002	± 0.001	± 0.0010
B	± 0.002	± 0.001	± 0.0005
C	± 0.002	± 0.003	± 0.0020

The advantage of the statistical formula is larger component tolerances. With alternative 1, the tolerance for component A has been doubled, the tolerance for component B has been quadrupled, and the tolerance for component C has been kept the same as the original component based on the simple addition approach. If alternative 2 is chosen, similar significant increases in the component tolerances may be achieved. This formula, then, may result in a larger component tolerance with no change in the manufacturing processes and no change in the assembly tolerance. Note that the *largest single* tolerance has the greatest effect on the overall result.

The disadvantage of the quadratic formula is that it involves several assumptions which, even if met, will still result in a small percent (theoretically 0.27 percent) of results not conforming to the limits set by the formula. The assumptions are:

1. The component dimensions are independent and the components are assembled randomly. This assumption is usually met in practice.

2. Each component dimension should be normally distributed. Some departure from this assumption is permissible.

3. The actual average for each component is equal to the nominal value stated in the specification. For the original assembly example, the actual averages for components *A, B,* and *C* must be 1.000, 0.500, and 2.000, respectively. Otherwise, the nominal value of 3.500 will not be achieved for the assembly, and tolerance limits set about 3.500 will not be realistic. Thus, it is important to control the *average* value for interacting dimensions. This means that process control techniques are needed using variables measurement rather than go, no-go measurement.

A summary of the two methods of tolerance is given in Table 23.28.

The statistical tolerancing formula applies both to assemblies made up of physically separate components and to a chain of several interacting dimensions within one physical item. Further, the result of the interacting dimensions can be an outside dimension (assembly length) or an internal result (clearance between a shaft and hole).

Further Applications of Statistical Tolerancing. It is easy to be deceived into concluding that the statistical method of tolerancing is merely a change from an expression of tolerances in the form of limits on each component to a form of:

1. Upper and lower limits on the average $\overline{X}$ of the mass of components.

2. An upper limit to the scatter σ of the components.

The change is much more profound than mere form of the specification. It affects the entire cycle of manufacturing planning, production, inspection, quality control, service, etc. It is, in effect, *a new philosophy of manufacture.*

The first published example of a *large-scale application* of statistical toleranc-

TABLE 23.28   Comparison of Conventional and Statistical Tolerancing

Factor	Conventional	Statistical
Risk of items not interacting properly	No risk; 100% interchangeability of items	Small percent of final results will fall outside limits (but these can sometimes be corrected with selective assembly)
Utilization of full tolerance range	Method is conservative; tolerances on interacting dimensions are smaller than necessary	Permits larger tolerances on interacting dimensions
Special process control techniques	None	Average of each interacting dimension must be controlled using variables measurement
Statistical assumptions	None	Interacting dimensions must be independent and each must be normally distributed
Lot size for components	Any size	Lot size should be moderately large (to assure balancing effect on extreme interacting dimensions)

ing appears to be that of the L-3 coaxial system (a broad-band transmission system for multiple telephone or television channels). Dodge, Kinsburg, and Kruger (1953) discuss the application.

The general plan was:

1. Discovery of the key quality characteristics of each component element of the system.
2. Determination of the precision of measurement, to separate measurement variability from process and product variability.
3. Collection of data on process capability for the key qualities, to aid in establishing realistic tolerances.

The foregoing were preliminary to:

4. Establishment of tolerances for the key quality characteristics in the dual form of a maximum on the standard deviation σ and limits on the average $\overline{X}$. The limits on X were established as $\pm \frac{1}{8} \sigma$ around the nominal.
5. Establishment of control procedures.

It was recognized that the limits on σ and $\overline{X}$ required further interpretation if the intent of the designers was to be carried out by the manufacturers. To this end, three forms of product acceptance were established.

1. *Control charts:* Shewhart control charts for $\overline{X}$ and σ could be used for product acceptance, provided "eligibility" was established (seven consecutive subgroups, of five pieces each, all met the control limits for X and σ) and provided subsequent statistical control was maintained (based on chart results plus absence of major changes in process).
2. *Batch control:* This was based on examination of a sample of (normally) 50 pieces by variables measurements, with limits on $\overline{X}$ and σ appropriate to the sample size of 50. Each batch stood or fell on its own measurements.
3. *Detailed classification:* Product which did not qualify under 1 or 2 was measured in detail. The resulting conforming units were classified into one of three variable classes. The packaging was then done by selecting classified units in such a way that each package contained an assortment of product which conformed to the intent of the design as to $\overline{X}$ and σ.

Grant and Leavenworth (1980) discuss statistical tolerancing including an application to shafts and holes. The Western Electric Company, Inc. (1982) in its *Statistical Quality Control Handbook* (pp. 122–127) presents examples and discusses the assumptions. Peters (1970) discusses statistical tolerancing, including a method for recognizing cost differences among components. Choksi (1971) discusses the use of computer simulation to determine optimum tolerances.

The concept may be applied to several interacting variables in an engineering relationship. The nature of the relationship need *not* be additive (assembly example) or subtractive (shaft and hole example). The formula can be adapted to predict the variation of results that are the product and/or the division of several variables. Mouradian (1966) discusses these applications.

Bayesian Estimates.   Bayesian estimation can be used when the parameter to be estimated can be considered to be a random variable for which we know the distribution. For example, in sampling inspection, if a manufacturer has a stable production process, then the proportion of defectives p in a lot may be a random variable about which we can fit a distribution by our sampling inspection over time. If so, then in the future that information can be used to provide quality assurance with less sampling; e.g., see Lenz and Rendtel (1984).

When it is not possible to cumulate information about a stable process, some have proposed that we use our "feelings" about the parameter to choose a statistical distribution for it, and then proceed as if the parameter were a random variable with that distribution. This is called the "personal probability" approach, and those who use it are called "Bayesians." Some of the proponents of this approach say it is the only method which any sensible person should use, and this has been cause for bitter debates and ill-will. In our view, while a person in a management position might find this a reasonable way to express his or her insights quantitatively, in most cases this will be an unscientific way of simply incorporating prejudices into the decision process, resulting in costly errors. This approach is of some use in general statistical decision theory (see Chapter 12 of Dudewicz, 1976), but there it is used to generate a set of decision rules which contains all good rules, not just one rule based on one's "feelings." The Bayesian approach should be considered whenever information can be gathered over time on a stable process.

STATISTICAL TESTS OF HYPOTHESES

A statistical hypothesis is an assertion about a population, often about some parameter of a population. Tests of hypotheses (also called "tests of significance") were designed so that experimenters would not ascribe causes to variations in data which were in fact due simply to random variation (and thus did not need a cause to explain them). Thus, statistical hypothesis testing is a modern day version of the medieval Occam's razor principle that "one should not multiply causes without reason." (William of Occam was an English Franciscan philosopher who died about 1349.) For example, if a process has a mean weight of 14.90 lb per item produced, a change is made with a view to increasing the weight per item produced, and a sample of 10 items (taken after the process change) has a mean weight of 15.10 lb, this *does not* necessarily mean that the process mean has been shifted up: It could be that it has remained the same (or has even decreased) and that we are simply seeing the results of the randomness of the process. Making correct inferences in the face of such possibilities is the gist of the area of hypothesis testing.

Basic Concepts, Types of Errors. "Hypothesis" as used here is an assertion made about a population. Usually the assertion concerns the numerical value of some parameter of the population. For example, a hypothesis might state that the mean life of a population of batteries equals 30.0, written as $H: \mu_0 = 30.0$. This assertion may or may not be correct. A "hypothesis test" is a test of the validity of the assertion, and is carried out by analysis of a sample of data.

There are two reasons why sample results must be carefully evaluated. First, there are many other samples which, by chance alone, could be drawn from the population. Second, the numerical results in the sample actually selected can easily be compatible with several different hypotheses. These points are handled by recognizing two types of error which can be made in evaluating a hypothesis:

1. *Reject* the hypothesis when it is *true*. This is called the "type I error"; its probability is called the "level of significance" and is denoted by α.

2. *Accept* the hypothesis when it is *false*. This is called the "type II error"; its probability is usually denoted by β (though some authors call it $1 - \beta$).

These error probabilities can be controlled to desired values.

The type I error is shown graphically in Figure 23.19 for the hypothesis H:μ_0 = 30.0. The area between the vertical lines represents the "acceptance region" for the hypothesis test: If the sample result falls within the acceptance region, the hypothesis is accepted. Otherwise, it is rejected. Notice that there is a small portion of the curve which falls outside the acceptance region. This portion (α) represents the probability of obtaining a sample result outside the acceptance region, even though the hypothesis is correct.

Suppose it has been decided that the type I error must not exceed 5 percent. This is the probability of rejecting the hypothesis when, in truth, the true average life is 30.0. The acceptance region can be obtained by locating values of average life which have only a 5 percent chance of being exceeded when the true average life is 30.0. Further, suppose a sample n of four measurements is taken and $\sigma = 10.0$.

Remember that the curve represents a population of sample averages because the decision will be made on the basis of a sample average. Sample averages vary less than individual measurements according to the relationship $\sigma_{\bar{x}} = \sigma/\sqrt{n}$.

Further, the distribution of sample averages is approximately normal even if the distribution of the individual measurements (going into the averages) is not normal (see Grant and Leavenworth, 1972, pp. 69–71). The approximation holds best for large values of n but is adequate for n as low as 4.

Table B in Appendix II shows that a 2.5 percent area in each tail is at a limit which is 1.96 standard deviations from 30.0. Then under the hypothesis that μ_0 = 30.0, 95 percent of sample averages will fall within $\pm 1.96\sigma_{\bar{x}}$ of 30.0, or

$$\text{Upper limit} = 30.0 + 1.96 \frac{10}{\sqrt{4}} = 39.8$$

$$\text{Lower limit} = 30.0 - 1.96 \frac{10}{\sqrt{4}} = 20.2$$

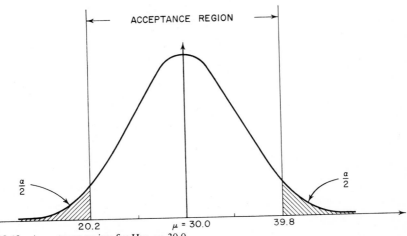

FIG. 23.19 Acceptance region for H:μ_0 = 30.0.

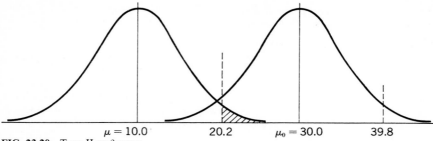

$\mu = 10.0$ 20.2 $\mu_0 = 30.0$ 39.8

FIG. 23.20 Type II or β error.

The acceptance region is thereby defined as 20.2 to 39.8. If the average of a random sample of four batteries is within this acceptance region, the hypothesis is accepted. If the average falls outside the acceptance region, the hypothesis is rejected. This decision rule provides a type I error of 0.05.

The type II or β error, the probability of accepting a hypothesis when it is false, is shown in Figure 23.20 as the shaded area. Notice it is possible to obtain a sample result within the acceptance region, even though the population has a true average which is not equal to the average stated in the hypothesis. The numerical value of β depends on the true value of the population average (and also on n, σ, and α). This is depicted by an "operating characteristic" (OC) curve.

The problem now is to construct an operating characteristic curve to assess the magnitude of the type II (β) error. As β is the probability of *accepting* the original hypothesis ($\mu_0 = 30.0$) when it is *false,* the probability that a sample average will fall between 20.2 and 39.8 must be found when the true average of the population is something other than 30.0. This has been done for many values of the true average, and the result is shown in Figure 23.21. [This curve should not be confused with that of a normal distribution of measurements. In some cases the shape is similar, but the meanings of an OC curve and a distribution curve are entirely different; Juran and Gryna (1980, pp. 410–412) give the detailed calculations; also

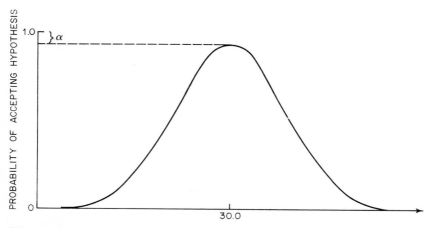

FIG. 23.21 Operating characteristic curve.

see Dudewicz, 1976, pp. 272–275.] Thus, the OC curve is a plot of the probability of accepting the original hypothesis as a function of the true value of the population parameter (and the given values of n, σ, and α).

Use of the Operating Characteristic Curve in Selecting an Acceptance Region.

The acceptance region was determined by dividing the 5 percent allowable α error into equal parts (see Figure 23.19). This is called a "two-tailed test." The entire 5 percent could also be placed at either the left or the right tail of the distribution curve (Figure 23.22). These are "one-tailed tests."

Operating characteristic curves for tests having these one-tailed acceptance regions can be developed following the approach used for the two-tailed region. Although the α error is the same, the β error varies for the three tests. (See Figure 9.2-2 on p. 275 of Dudewicz, 1976.)

In some problems, knowledge is available to indicate that if the true average of the population is *not* equal to the hypothesis value, then it is on one side of the hypothesis value. For example, a new material of supposedly higher average strength will have an average equal to or *greater than* that of the present material. Such information will help select a one-tailed or two-tailed test to make the β

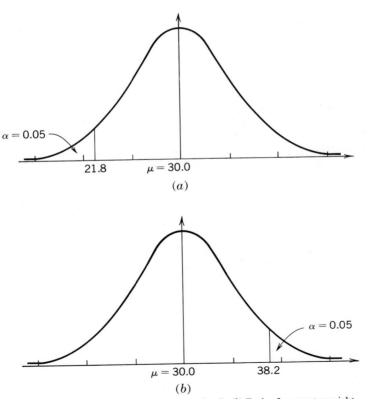

FIG. 23.22. (*a*) Entire 5 percent error on left tail. (*b*) Entire 5 percent on right tail.

error as small as possible. The following guidelines are based on the analysis of OC curves:

Use a one-tailed test with the entire α risk on the right tail if (1) it is known that (if μ_0 is not true) the true mean is $> \mu_0$ or (2) values of the population mean $< \mu_0$ are acceptable and we are interested only in detecting a population mean $> \mu_0$.

Use a two-tailed test if (1) there is no prior knowledge on the location of the true population mean or (2) we are interested in detecting a true population mean $<$ or $>$ the μ_0 stated in the original hypothesis. (With a two-tailed test, the hypothesis is sometimes stated as the original hypothesis $H_0:\mu_0 = 30.0$ against the alternative hypothesis $H_1:\mu_0 \neq 30.0$. With a one-tailed test, $H_0:\mu_0 = 30.0$ against the alternative $H_1:\mu_1 < 30.0$ if α is placed in the left tail or $H_1:\mu_1 > 30.0$ if α is placed in the right tail.)

Every test of hypothesis has an OC curve. Duncan (1974) and Natrella (1963) are good sources of OC curves. [Some references present "power" curves, but power is simply $1 -$ (the probability of acceptance) $= 1 - \beta$.]

With this background, our discussion now proceeds to the steps for testing a hypothesis.

Testing a Hypothesis When the Sample Size is Fixed in Advance.   Ideally, desired values for the type I and type II errors are defined in advance and the required sample size determined (see later discussion on Determining the Sample Size Required for Testing a Hypothesis). If the sample size is fixed in advance because of cost or time limitations, then usually the desired type I error is defined and the following procedure is followed:

1. State the hypothesis.
2. Choose the type I error. Common values are 0.01, 0.05, or 0.10.
3. Choose the test statistic for testing the hypothesis.
4. Determine the acceptance region for the test, i.e., the range of values of the test statistic which result in a decision to accept the hypothesis.
5. Obtain the sample of observations, compute the test statistic, and compare the value to the acceptance region to make a decision to accept or reject the hypothesis.
6. Draw an engineering conclusion.

Table 23.29 summarizes some common tests of hypotheses. (These are tests commonly mentioned in the literature and used in practice. A number of them assume a normal distribution. Harter and Dubey, 1967, define tests for the mean and variance but assuming a Weibull distribution—which really covers a family of distributions.) The procedure is illustrated through the following examples. Further examples and elaboration of the procedure are provided in Dixon and Massey (1969), Johnson and Leone (1964), Duncan (1974), Dudewicz (1976), and Natrella (1963). Table 23.29 lists a few unique or additional references for certain tests. For nonparametric tests, see especially Gibbons (1985).

Example.   Tests on eight units of an experimental engine showed that they operated, respectively, for 28, 26, 31, 29, 25, 27, 28, and 27 min with 1 liter of a certain kind of fuel. A proposed specification states that the engine must operate for an average of at least 30 min. Does the engine meet the requirement? Assume a 5 percent significance level.

TABLE 23.29 Summary Table of Tests of Hypotheses

Test statistic and its distribution	Assumptions	Remarks
Test 1. The mean of a population is equal to μ_0 ($H; \mu = \mu_0$).		
(a) $U = \dfrac{\overline{X} - \mu_0}{\sigma/\sqrt{n}}$ Normal distribution (Appendix II, Table B)	X is distribution-free but should be continuous and have only one mode.	Standard deviation of population is known.
(b) $t = \dfrac{\overline{X} - \mu_0}{s/\sqrt{n}}$ t distribution with DF $= n - 1$ (Appendix II, Table G)	X is normally distributed.	Standard deviation of population is estimated by sample s.
(c) $\tau_1 = \dfrac{\overline{X} - \mu_0}{R}$ τ_1 distribution (Appendix II, Table H)	X is normally distributed.	Dispersion of the population is estimated from sample range.
(d) r = number of occurrences of less frequent sign for a two-tail test (or number of positive or negative signs for a one-tail test) Distribution of r (Appendix II, Table I)	Distribution-free but population should be continuous and symmetrical.	Data are analyzed by evaluating signs of $(X_i - \mu_0)$. (This is a "sign" test; see Gibbons, 1985, p. 106.)

23.65

TABLE 23.29 Summary Table of Tests of Hypotheses (*Continued*)

Test statistic and its distribution	Assumptions	Remarks
Test 2. The means of two populations are equal ($H: \mu_1 = \mu_2$).		
(a) $U = \dfrac{\overline{X}_1 - \overline{X}_2}{\sqrt{\sigma_1^2/n_1 + \sigma_2^2/n_2}}$ Normal distribution (Appendix II, Table B)	X_1 and X_2 are distribution-free but should be continuous and have only one mode. If the populations are not normally distributed, sample sizes n_1 and n_2 should be large so that sampling distribution of U is approximately normal.	Standard deviations of populations are known.
(b) $t = \dfrac{\overline{X}_1 - \overline{X}_2}{\sqrt{\dfrac{1}{n_1} + \dfrac{1}{n_2}}\sqrt{\dfrac{[(n_1 - 1)s_1^2 + (n_2 - 1)s_2^2]}{n_1 + n_2 - 2}}}$ t distribution with DF = $n_1 + n_2 - 2$ (Appendix II, Table G)	$\sigma_1 = \sigma_2$. X_1 and X_2 are normally distributed.	Standard deviations of populations are estimated by sample s_1 and s_2.
(c) $\tau_d = \dfrac{\overline{X}_1 - \overline{X}_2}{0.5(R_1 + R_2)}$ Distribution of τ_d (Appendix II, Table J)	X_1 and X_2 are normally distributed.	Dispersions of populations are estimated by sample ranges.

23.66

Test	Assumptions	Conditions
(d) $$t' = \frac{\bar{X}_1 - \bar{X}_2}{\sqrt{s_1^2/n_1 + s_2^2/n_2}}$$ t distribution with DF = $\min(n_1 - 1, n_2 - 1)$ (Appendix II, Table G)	X_1 and X_2 are normally distributed.	Standard deviations of populations are estimated by sample s_1 and s_2 (no assumption that $\sigma_1 = \sigma_2$).
(e) $$t = \frac{\bar{d}}{s_d/\sqrt{n}}$$ t distribution with DF = number of pairs − 1 (Appendix II, Table G)	Populations are normally distributed.	Data are taken in n pairs, and difference d within each pair is calculated.
(f) r = number of occurrences of less frequent sign for a two-tail test (or number of positive or negative signs for a one-tail test) Distribution of r (Appendix II, Table I)	n_1 and n_2 each ≥ 6. Populations must be continuous and symmetrical; each of the two observations in a pair has been obtained under similar conditions.	Data are analyzed by evaluating signs of $(X_1 - X_2)$. (This is a "sign" test.) Distribution of r (Appendix II, Table I)

Test 3. Two characteristics on one product have specified population means (H:$\mu_X = \mu_{X0}$ and $\mu_Y = \mu_{Y0}$) (Johnson and Leone, 1964).

Test	Assumptions	Conditions
$$T^2 = \frac{s_Y^2}{s_X^2 s_Y^2 - s_{XY}}(X - \mu_{X0})^2 - \frac{2s_{XY}}{s_X^2 s_Y^2 - s_{XY}} s_{XY}$$ $$(X - \mu_{X0})(Y - \mu_{Y0}) + \frac{s_X^2}{s_X^2 s_Y^2 - s_{XY}}(Y - \mu_{Y0})^2$$ where $s_{XY} = \dfrac{n\Sigma(XY) - \Sigma X \Sigma Y}{n(n - 1)}$ where critical value for $T^2 = \dfrac{2(n - 1)F}{n - 2}$ and where the F distribution has $DF_1 = 2$; $DF_2 = n - 2$ (Appendix II, Table K)	Bivariate normal distribution.	Population standard deviations are estimated by s_X and s_Y (T^2 is called Hotelling's T^2).

TABLE 23.29 Summary Table of Tests of Hypotheses (*Continued*)

Test statistic and its distribution	Assumptions	Remarks

Test 4. The standard deviation of a population is equal to σ_0 (H:$\sigma = \sigma_0$).

$\chi^2 = \dfrac{(n-1)s^2}{\sigma_0^2}$ Chi-square distribution with DF $= n - 1$ (Appendix II, Table L)	Population is normally distributed.	Standard deviation of population is estimated by sample s.

Test 5. The standard deviations of two populations are equal (H:$\sigma_1^2 = \sigma_2^2$).

(*a*) $F = \dfrac{s_1^2}{s_2^2}$ F distribution with $DF_1 = n_1 - 1$ and $DF_2 = n_2 - 1$ (Appendix II, Table K)	Populations are normally distributed.	Standard deviations of populations are estimated by sample s_1 and s_2.
(*b*) $F' = \dfrac{R_1}{R_2}$ Distribution of F' (Appendix II, Table M)	Distribution-free but X_1 and X_2 should be continuous.	Dispersions of populations are estimated by sample ranges.

Test 6. The proportion of a population exhibiting a certain characteristic is p_0 (H:$p = p_0$).

(*a*) $U = \dfrac{X - np_0}{\sqrt{np_0(1 - p_0)}}$ Normal distribution (Appendix II, Table B)	$n \geq 100$. Only for large sample sizes.	Proportion of population is estimated by sample proportion.
(*b*) Determine confidence limits (Appendix II, Table N) and observe if p_0 falls within the limits		Proportion of population is estimated by sample proportion (useful when $n < 100$).

Test 7. The proportions in two populations are equal (H:$p_1 = p_2$).

$U = \dfrac{X_1/n_1 - X_2/n_2}{\sqrt{\hat{p}(1-\hat{p})(1/n_1 + 1/n_2)}}$ where $\hat{p} = \dfrac{X_1 + X_2}{n_1 + n_2}$ Normal distribution (Appendix II, Table B)	$np > 5$ for each population. Sample sizes n_1 and n_2 must be large so that sampling distribution of U is approximately normal.	Proportions in populations are estimated by sample proportions.

Test 8. Proportion of correct decisions on a sensory evaluation is p_0 (H:$p = p_0$).

(a) $U = \dfrac{X/n - 0.50}{\sqrt{0.25/n}}$ Normal distribution (Appendix II, Table B)	$p = 0.5$, n should be > 30.	Judge is asked to identify which of two specimens is the same as a control specimen originally given to him or her. (This is a "duo-trio" test.)
(b) $U = \dfrac{X/n - 0.33}{\sqrt{0.22/n}}$ Normal distribution (Appendix II, Table B)	$p = 0.33$, n should be > 30.	Judge is asked to identify which of three specimens is different from the other two. (This is a "triangle" test.)

23.69

TABLE 23.29 Summary Table of Tests of Hypotheses (*Continued*)

Test statistic and its distribution	Assumptions	Remarks
Test 9. Samples are from identically distributed populations [H:$F(X_1) = F(X_2)$ where $F(X)$ = distribution function] [Johnson and Leone, 1964].		
(*a*) For evaluation of means T' = sum of ranks in smaller sample Distribution of T' (Appendix II, Table O)	Distribution-free; if $n_1 >$ 8 and $n_2 > 8$, the distribution of statistic T' can be closely approximated by normal.	Data are evaluated by ranking the combined observations from the two samples (1 for the smallest, 2 for the next smallest, etc.). Then calculate the sum of the ranks in the smaller sample. A rejected hypothesis leads to the conclusion that the means are different. (This is a "rank sum" test.)
(*b*) For evaluation of standard deviations T' = sum of ranks in smaller sample Distribution of T' (Appendix II, Table O)	Distribution-free; if $n_1 >$ 8, and $n_2 > 8$, the distribution of statistic T' can be closely approximated by normal.	Data are evaluated by ranking the combined observations but ranking assigns 1 to smallest observation, 2 to largest observation, 3 to next smallest, etc. The sum of the ranks for the smaller sample is calculated. A rejected hypothesis means that the standard deviations are different. (This is a "rank sum" test.)

23.70

Test 10. The observations in a sample have been randomly drawn from a single population (Bennett and Franklin, 1954, and Dixon and Massey, 1969).

(a) u = number of runs Distribution of runs (Appendix II, Table P)	$n_1 \geq 10$, $n_2 \geq 10$.	Data are evaluated in terms of number of sequences or "runs" above and below the median. (This is a "runs" test.)
(b) $M = \dfrac{\sum\limits_{i=1}^{n-1}(X_{i+1} - \overline{X}_i)^2}{\Sigma(X_i - \overline{X})^2}$ $U = \dfrac{1 - M/2}{\sqrt{(n-2)/[(n-1)(n+1)]}}$ Normal distribution (Appendix II, Table B)	1. $n \geq 4$. 2. Normal population.	Data are evaluated in terms of differences between successive observations in a sequence $(X_{i+1} - X_i)$. (This is the "mean square successive difference, M, test.")

Test 11. An observation does belong to the same population as the other observations in a sample (Dixon and Massey, 1969; Grubbs, 1969).

Both X_1 and X_2 are to be evaluated if extreme observations in either direction are undesirable.	X is normally distributed. Population mean and standard deviation are unknown.	Data are evaluated by arranging data in order of magnitude and comparing the distance of one extreme observation from other observations with a measure of variability.

n	r
$3 \leq n \leq 7$	$r_{10} = \dfrac{X_2 - X_1}{X_n - X_1}$
$8 \leq n \leq 10$	$r_{11} = \dfrac{X_2 - X_1}{X_{n-1} - X_1}$
$11 \leq n \leq 13$	$r_{21} = \dfrac{X_3 - X_1}{X_{n-1} - X_1}$
$14 \leq n \leq 25$	$r_{22} = \dfrac{X_3 - X_1}{X_{n-2} - X_1}$

Distribution of r (Appendix II, Table Q)

TABLE 23.29 Summary Table of Tests of Hypotheses (*Continued*)

Test statistic and its distribution	Assumptions	Remarks

Test 12. A sample of data comes from a population with the specified probability function.

Test statistic and its distribution	Assumptions	Remarks
(*a*) D = largest deviation of actual % cumulative frequency from theoretical % cumulative frequency. Distribution of D (Miller and Freund, 1965, p. 409; or Gibbons, 1985, Table C)	Distribution should be continuous.	Data are evaluated by first plotting on probability paper. The largest deviation of a plotted point from a straight line is then evaluated. This test applies particularly where $n < 30$. (This is the "Kolmogorov-Smirnov test.")
(*b*) $\chi^2 = \Sigma \dfrac{(f_a - f_e)^2}{f_e}$	$n > 30$ and preferably > 100.	Data are evaluated by first constructing a frequency distribution. Theoretical frequencies (based on the distribution assumption) are calculated for each cell. The actual (f_a) and theoretical (f_e) frequencies are then compared. This test can be used for continuous and discrete distributions. If any theoretical frequency is less than 5, the cell involved should be combined with one or more adjacent cells.

Distribution	DF
Normal	Number of cells minus 3
Exponential	Number of cells minus 2
Weibull	Number of cells minus 4
Poisson	Number of cells minus 2
Binomial	Number of cells minus 2

Test statistics for all distributions follow the chi square distribution (Appendix II, Table L)

Solution: Using Test 1*b* of Table 23.29,

$$H:\mu_0 = 30.0$$

Test statistic:

$$\tau_1 = \frac{\overline{X} - \mu_0}{R}$$

Acceptance region:

$$\text{Degrees of freedom DF} = 8 - 1 = 7$$

$$t \geq -1.895$$

A mathematical derivation of "degrees of freedom" is beyond the scope of this handbook, but the underlying concept can be stated. "Degrees of freedom" is a measure of the assurance involved when a sample standard deviation is used to estimate the true standard deviation of a universe. When the true standard deviation is known, DF = ∞. More generally, DF equals the number of measurements used to determine the sample standard deviation minus the number of constants estimated from the data in order to compute the standard deviation. In this example, it was necessary to establish only one constant (the sample average) in order to compute the standard deviation, therefore DF = 8 − 1.

Analysis:

$$\overline{X} = 27.6 \qquad s = 1.86$$

$$t = \frac{27.6 - 30.0}{\frac{1.86}{\sqrt{8}}} = -3.68$$

Conclusion: Reject the hypothesis. There is sufficient evidence to conclude that the engine does not meet the requirement.

Example: Solve the previous example using the range instead of the standard deviation.

Solution: Using Test 1*c* of Table 23.29,

$$H:\mu_0 = 30.0$$

Test statistic:

$$\tau_1 = \frac{\overline{X} - \mu_0}{R}$$

Acceptance region:

$$\tau_1 \geq -0.388$$

Analysis:

$$\tau_1 = \frac{27.6 - 30.0}{6} = -0.40$$

Conclusion: Reject the hypothesis. There is sufficient evidence to conclude that the engine does not meet the requirement.

Example: Solve the previous example using the sign test.

Solution: Using Test 1*d* of Table 23.29,

$$H:\mu_0 = 30$$

Test statistic: Number of positive signs *r*.
Acceptance region:

$$r = 1 \text{ (one-tailed test)}$$

Analysis:

X	$X - \mu_0$	
28	−	
26	−	
31	+	
29	−	$r = 1$
25	−	
27	−	
28	−	
27	−	

Conclusion: Reject the hypothesis. There is sufficient evidence to conclude that the engine does not meet the requirement.

Example: Five batches of rubber were made by each of two recipes and tested for tensile strength with the following results:

Recipe 1	Recipe 2
3067	3200
2730	2777
2840	2623
2913	3044
2789	2834

Test the hypothesis that average strength is the same for the two recipes. Assume a 5 percent significance level.

Solution: First, Test 5*a* of Table 23.29 tests the assumption of equal variances. The outcome of this is used to decide whether to use Test 2*b* or 2*d* to evaluate the question about average strength.

$$H:\sigma_1^2 = \sigma_2^2$$

Test statistic:

$$DF_1 = 5 - 1 = 4, \qquad DF_2 = 5 - 1 = 4$$

$$F = \frac{(s_1)^2}{(s_2)^2}$$

Acceptance region:

$$\frac{1}{9.60} \leq F \leq 9.60$$

Analysis:

$$s_1^2 = 16,923.7$$

$$s_2^2 = 51,713.3$$

$$F = \frac{16,923.7}{51,713.3} = 0.33$$

Conclusion: Accept the hypothesis. This is used to satisfy the assumption of equal variances in the following test of hypothesis. Now, using Test 2b,

$$H: \mu_1 = \mu_2$$

Test statistic:

$$t = \frac{\overline{X}_1 - \overline{X}_2}{\sqrt{\frac{1}{n_1} + \frac{1}{n_2}} \sqrt{\frac{[(n_1-1)s_1^2 + (n_2-1)s_2^2]}{n_1 + n_2 - 2}}}$$

Acceptance region:

$$DF = 5 + 5 - 2 = 8$$

$$-2.306 \leq t \leq +2.306$$

Analysis:

$$t = \frac{2867.8 - 2895.6}{\sqrt{\frac{1}{5} + \frac{1}{5}} \sqrt{\frac{(5-1)16,923.7 + (5-1)51,713.3}{5 + 5 - 2}}}$$

Conclusion: Accept the hypothesis. There is insufficient evidence to conclude that the recipes differ in average strength.

Example: Solve the previous example using ranges instead of standard deviations.

Solution: First, Test 5b of Table 23.29 tests the assumption of equal variances.

$$H: \sigma_1^2 = \sigma_2^2$$

Test statistic:

$$F' = \frac{R_1}{R_2}$$

Acceptance region:

$$0.32 < F' < 3.2$$

Analysis:

$$R_1 = 3067 - 2730 = 337$$

$$R_2 = 3200 = 2623 = 577$$

$$F' = \frac{337}{577} = 0.58$$

Conclusion: Accept the hypothesis. This is used to satisfy the assumption of equal variances in the following test of hypothesis. Now, using Test 2c,

$$H{:}\mu_1 = \mu_2$$

Test statistic:

$$\tau_d = \frac{\overline{X}_1 - \overline{X}_2}{0.5(R_1 + R_2)}$$

Acceptance region:

$$-0.493 \leq \tau_d \leq +0.493$$

$$R_1 = 3{,}067 - 2{,}730 = 337$$

$$R_2 = 3{,}200 - 2{,}623 = 577$$

Analysis:

$$\tau_d = \frac{2867.8 - 2895.6}{0.5(337 + 577)} = -0.061$$

Conclusion: Accept the hypothesis. There is insufficient evidence to conclude that the recipes differ in average strength.

Drawing Conclusions from Tests of Hypotheses. The payoff for these tests of hypotheses comes from reaching useful conclusions. The meaning of "Reject the hypothesis" or "Accept the hypothesis" is shown in Table 23.30 along with some analogies to explain subtleties of the meanings.

When a hypothesis is rejected, the practical conclusion is "the parameter value specified in the hypothesis is wrong." This conclusion is made with strong conviction—roughly speaking at a confidence level of $100 (1 - \alpha)$ percent. The key question then is: Just what is a good estimate of the value of the parameter for the population? Help can be provided on this question by calculating the "confidence limits" for the parameter discussed under Statistical Estimation: Confidence Interval Estimates.

When a hypothesis is accepted, the numerical value of the parameter stated in the hypothesis has not been proved, but it has not been disproved. It is *not* correct to say that the hypothesis has been proved as correct at the $100 (1 - \alpha)$ percent confidence level. Many other hypotheses could be accepted for the given sample of observations and yet only one hypothesis can be true. Therefore, an acceptance does *not* mean a high probability of proof that a specific hypothesis is correct. (All other factors being equal, the smaller the sample size, the more likely it is that the hypothesis will be accepted. Less evidence certainly does not imply proof.) For this reason often today the wording used is "the hypothesis was not rejected at level of significance α" rather than "the hypothesis was accepted at level α."

TABLE 23.30   The Meaning of a Conclusion from Tests of Hypotheses

	If hypothesis is rejected	If hypothesis is accepted
Adequacy of evidence in the sample of observations	Sufficient to conclude that hypothesis is false	Not sufficient to conclude that hypothesis is false; hypothesis is a reasonable one but has *not* been proved to be true
Difference between sample result (e.g., $\overline{X}$) and hypothesis value (e.g., μ_0)	Unlikely that difference was due to chance (sampling) variation	Difference could easily have been due to chance (sampling) variation
Analogy of guilt or innocence in a court of law	Guilt has been established beyond a reasonable doubt	Have not established guilt beyond a reasonable doubt
Analogy of a batting average in baseball	If player got 300 base hits out of 1000 times at bat, this is sufficient to conclude that the overall batting average is about 0.300	If player got 3 hits in 10 times, this is not sufficient to conclude that the overall average is about 0.300

With an acceptance of a hypothesis, a key question then is: What conclusion, if any, can be drawn about the parameter value in the hypothesis? Two approaches are suggested:

1. Calculate confidence limits on the sample result (see the previous topic of Statistical Estimation). These confidence limits define an interval within which the true population parameter lies. If this interval is small, then an acceptance decision on the test of hypothesis means that the true population value is either equal to or close to the value stated in the hypothesis. Then, it is reasonable to act as if the parameter value specified in the hypothesis is in fact correct. If the confidence interval is relatively wide, then this is a stern warning that the value stated in the hypothesis has not been proved and that the true value of the population might be far different from that specified in the hypothesis.

2. Construct and review the operating characteristic curve for the test of hypothesis. This defines the probability that other possible values of the population parameter could have been accepted by the test. Knowing these probabilities for values relatively close to the original hypothesis can help draw further conclusions about the acceptance of the original hypothesis. For example, Figure 23.21 shows the OC curve for a hypothesis which specified that the population mean is 30.0. Note that the probability of accepting the hypothesis when the population mean μ is 30.0 is 0.95 (or $1 - \alpha$). But also note that if μ really is 35.0, then the probability of accepting $\mu = 30.0$ is still high (about 0.83). If μ really is 42.0, the probability of accepting $\mu = 30.0$ is only about 0.33.

Care must always be taken in drawing engineering conclusions from the statistical conclusions, particularly when a hypothesis is accepted. (Rutherford, 1971, discusses a procedure for drawing conclusions which requires that a choice be made between two policies for drawing conclusions, i.e., conservative and liberal.)

Determining the Sample Size Required for Testing a Hypothesis. The previous sections assumed that the sample size was fixed by nonstatistical reasons and that the type I error only was predefined for the test. The ideal procedure is to predefine the desired type I and type II errors and calculate the sample size required to cover both types of errors.

The sample size required will depend on (1) the sampling risks desired (α and β), (2) the size of the smallest true difference that is to be detected, and (3) the variation in the characteristic being measured. The sample size can be determined by using the "operating characteristic" curve for the test. Table 23.31 summarizes methods useful in determining the sample size required for two-sided tests of certain hypotheses. (Further sources of OC curves are Duncan, 1974, and Natrella, 1963.)

Suppose it were important to detect the fact that the average life of the batteries cited previously was 35.0. Specifically, be 80 percent sure of detecting this change ($\beta = 0.2$). Further, if the true average was 30.0 (as stated in the hypothesis), there should be only a 5 percent risk of rejecting the hypothesis ($\alpha = 0.05$). In using Appendix II, Chart R, d is defined as

$$ d = \frac{\mu - \mu_0}{\sigma} = \frac{35.0 - 30.0}{10} = 0.5 $$

Entering with $d = 0.5$ and $P_a = 0.2$ (the β risk), the curves indicate that a sample size of about 30 is required.

Duncan (1974) discusses the calculation of the sample size required to meet the type I and II errors. In practice, however, one is often not sure of desired values of these errors. Reviewing the operating characteristic curves for various sample sizes can help to arrive at a decision on the sample size required to reflect the relative importance of both risks. It is especially important to consider β as well as α, lest meaningless results be obtained. (Note that randomizing so as to reject H_0 100α percent of the time yields a test with level of significance α. That in itself, without consideration of β, is trivial.)

Relation to Confidence Intervals. Confidence limits provide a set of limits within which a population parameter lies (with specified probability). Tests of hypotheses evaluate a specific statement about a population parameter. These procedures are related, and most hypothesis tests can also be made using confidence limit calculations.

TABLE 23.31 Summary of Sample Size Graphs and Tables

Hypothesis	Graph or table
1. Mean of a population $= \mu_0$ (σ known)	Appendix II, Chart R
2. Mean of a population $= \mu_0$ (σ estimated by s)	Duncan (1974, p. 539)
3. Means of two populations are equal (σ_1 and σ_2 known)	Natrella (1963, pp. T-16, T-17)
4. Means of two populations are equal ($\sigma_1 = \sigma_2$ but estimated by s_1 and s_2)	Natrella (1963, pp. T-16, T-17)
5. Standard deviation of a population $= \sigma_0$	Duncan (1974, p. 324)
6. Standard deviations of two populations are equal	Duncan (1974, p. 572)

Example: A sample of 12 insulators has an average strength of 4.95 ft·lb (6.7149 N·M). The standard deviation of the population is known to be 0.25 ft·lb (0.34 N·M). It is desired to test the hypothesis that the population mean is 5.15 ft·lb (6.9834 N·M).

Solution using tests of hypotheses: Table 23.29 defines the test statistic 1*a* as $U = (\overline{X} - \mu_0)/(\sigma/\sqrt{n})$, and U is normally distributed. If $\alpha = 0.05$, the acceptance region is a U between $\pm$ 1.96.

Then

$$H{:}\mu = \mu_0 = 5.15$$

$$U = \frac{4.95 - 5.15}{0.25/\sqrt{12}} = -2.75$$

As the sample index is outside the acceptance region, the hypothesis is rejected. The procedure using confidence limits is:

1. State the hypothesis concerning the value of a population parameter.
2. Obtain a sample of data and calculate confidence limits for the population parameter.
3. If the hypothesis value falls within the confidence limits, accept the hypothesis. If the hypothesis value falls outside the confidence limits, reject the hypothesis.

Solution using confidence limits:

$$H{:}\mu = \mu_0 = 5.15$$

From Table 23.21, parameter 1, the confidence limits are

$$\overline{X} \pm K_{\alpha/2} \frac{\sigma}{\sqrt{n}}$$

The 95 percent confidence limits are 4.95 $\pm$ 1.96 (0.25/$\sqrt{12}$) = 4.81 and 5.09. As the hypothesis value falls outside the confidence limits, the hypothesis is rejected. This is the same conclusion reached by using the hypothesis testing procedure.

Confidence limit concepts and tests of hypotheses are therefore alternative approaches to evaluating a hypothesis. [For certain hypotheses, these two approaches will result in slightly different type I errors (see Barr, 1969).] As discussed under Drawing Conclusions from Tests of Hypotheses, confidence limits are a valuable supplement to the test of hypothesis procedure. For example, in the above example, not only do confidence limits tell us that μ is not 5.15, they also tell us that μ is between 4.81 and 5.09.

Standard Cases.   Some of the most important practical cases have been covered in Table 23.29, namely:

Binomial proportion	Tests 6, 8
Two binomial proportions	Test 7
Normal mean	Test 1
Two means	Test 2
Bivariate normal mean	Test 3
One normal standard deviation	Test 4

Two standard deviations	Test 5
Two distributions are equal	Test 9
Random order of observations	Test 10
Test for outliers	Test 11

Many of these problems can also be solved using sequential tests. There, the sample size is not set in advance, but based on the data we decide how many observations are needed. For example, if one decided to inspect a fixed number of items such as 100 items, and reject the lot if 15 or more defectives were found, clearly one could stop sampling as soon as the fifteenth defective were found. Similar ideas allow savings in numbers of observations in most of the standard cases listed above, and are especially important when sampling is costly or time-consuming. For details, see Govindarajulu (1981).

Paired versus Unpaired Data. In Test 2*e* of Table 23.29, a test is given which is appropriate when data are taken in pairs and the difference within each pair is used as the basic data. This procedure is often used in order to "wash out" the effects of variables which are believed to have effects, but whose effects we do not wish to study.

For example, suppose that there is an effect of the operator of the machine, and we wish to compare two types of operation on that machine—but do not wish to evaluate the size of the operator effect. Then by letting each operator perform each operation and taking the difference, we wash out the effect of the operator. (Whereas, if one operator performed all of one procedure, and another operator performed all of the other procedure, differences observed might be due not to the procedures, but to the operators.)

As another example, in testing of mailing lists to evaluate competing advertising copy, for example, often an "A/B split" is used. That is, one type of copy goes to names 1, 3, 5, 7, . . . on the list, while the other type goes to names 2, 4, 6, ... Since (on zip-code-ordered lists) adjacent listings may be expected to be more similar than entries far apart, this is an appropriate pairing.

This technique of pairing is *not* used when there is no advance pairing of the data. For example, it is an error to pair items by their sequence in a data listing (where often they may be sorted by some other characteristic).

Statistical Significance versus Practical Significance. Suppose we are using Test 1*a* of Table 23.29 to test the hypothesis that the mean is 30, and wish a two-tailed test with level of significance 0.05. Then we will reject H if U is outside the interval $(-1.96, 1.96)$. If we find $U = 3.15$, one way of reporting the result of the test is to state that H was rejected at level 0.05.

Another way of reporting is to find for which level of significance the acceptance interval would be $(-3.15, 3.15)$. From Table B in Appendix II we see that level is (2) (0.00082) = 0.00164. This is called the "significance probability" of the test we have conducted. It is the smallest level of significance at which we would reject H for the data we observed.

One advantage of the significance probability is that if we use it, then we can report the significance probability as 0.00164 without choosing a level of significance. Anyone reading our report can use the level of significance he or she believes is appropriate: If theirs is less than 0.00164 they do not reject, while if theirs is equal to or greater than 0.00164 they do reject the hypothesis.

One disadvantage of the significance probability is that it can be very small (indicating, one would think, a "very significant" result) even when the true mean is close to 30. For example, $U = 3.15$ when $\overline{X} = 33.15$ and $\sigma/\sqrt{n} = 1.00$; $U = 3.15$ also when $\overline{X} = 30.0315$ and $\sigma/\sqrt{n} = 0.01$. In each case the significance probability is 0.00164 (i.e., 0.164 percent). In the first case, the confidence interval on the mean at 95 percent confidence runs over (31.19,35.11), while in the second the interval runs over (30.0119,30.0511). In terms of *practical significance,* the latter is much more likely to be a trivial difference to the practitioner than is the former. However, there is no way to tell these two situations apart by using the significance probability. For this reason, it is recommended that this concept not be used, but that instead confidence intervals be computed and presented in all cases.

RELIABILITY

The term "reliability" is used in a general sense to express a degree of confidence that a part or system will successfully function in a certain environment during a specified time period. It is also used specifically to mean the probability of failure-free operation for a time period at least a specified t_0, in which case it is denoted $R(t_0)$.

Basic Concepts. The most basic concepts of reliability are those of reliability $R(t_0)$ as a function of time already defined, failure rate, time between failures (TBF), and average (or mean) time between failures (MTBF), which are discussed below.

Failure Rate. Complex products often follow a familiar pattern of failure. Consider the data in Table 23.32. Assume that one unit was started on test and the time when it failed was recorded. The unit was repaired, again placed on test, and the time of the next failure recorded. The "failure rate" for the unit can be calculated for equal time intervals as the number of failures per unit time. (Some applications require the use of a "hazard rate" instead of "failure rate." See Section 25, under Reliability Sampling.) When the failure rate is plotted against a continuous time scale, the resulting chart (Figure 23.23), known as the "bathtub curve," exhibits three distinct periods or zones. These zones differ from each other in frequency of failure and in the failure causation pattern as follows:

1. *The infant mortality period:* This is characterized by high failure rates which show up early in usage. Commonly these failures are the result of blunders in design, manufacture, or usage or of misapplication and other identifiable causes. Sometimes it is possible to "debug" the product by simulated use test or by overstressing (in electronics this is known as "burn-in"). The weak units still fail, but the failure takes place in the test rig rather than in service.

2. *The constant failure rate period:* Here the failures result from the limitations inherent in the design plus accidents caused by usage or poor maintenance. The latter can be held down by good control on operating and maintenance procedures. However, a reduction in the basic failure rate requires a basic redesign.

3. *The wear-out period:* These are failures due to old age; e.g., the metal becomes embrittled or the insulation dries out. A reduction in failure rates requires preventive replacement of these dying components before they result in catastrophic failure.

TABLE 23.32 Failure History for a Unit of Electronic Ground Support Equipment

Time of failure, infant mortality period		Time of failure, constant failure rate period		Time of failure, wear-out period	
1	7.2	28.1	60.2	100.8	125.8
1.2	7.9	28.2	63.7	102.6	126.6
1.3	8.3	29.0	64.6	103.2	127.7
2.0	8.7	29.9	65.3	104.0	128.4
2.4	9.2	30.6	66.2	104.3	129.2
2.9	9.8	32.4	70.1	105.0	
3.0	10.2	33.0	71.0	105.8	
3.1	10.4	35.3	75.1	106.5	
3.3	11.9	36.1	75.6	110.7	
3.5	13.8	40.1	78.4	112.6	
3.8	14.4	42.8	79.2	113.5	
4.3	15.6	43.7	84.1	114.8	
4.6	16.2	44.5	86.0	115.1	
4.7	17.0	50.4	87.9	117.4	
4.8	17.5	51.2	88.4	118.3	
5.2	19.2	52.0	89.9	119.7	
5.4		53.3	90.8	120.6	
5.9		54.2	91.1	121.0	
6.4		55.6	91.5	122.9	
6.8		56.4	92.1	123.3	
6.9		58.3	97.9	124.5	

The top portion of Figure 23.23 shows the corresponding Weibull plot when a $\gamma = 2.6$ was applied to the original data. The values of the shape parameter β were approximately 0.5, 1.0, and 6.0, respectively. A shape parameter of less than 1.0 indicates a decreasing failure rate, a value of 1.0 a constant failure rate, and a value greater than 1.0 an increasing failure rate (see Figure 23.23).

The Distribution of "Time Between Failures." Users are concerned with the length of time that a product will run without failure. For repairable products, this means that the "time between failures," or TBF, is a critical characteristic. The corresponding characteristic for nonrepairable products is usually called the "time to failure." The variation in time between failures can be studied statistically (Figure 23.24).

When the failure rate is constant, the distribution of time between failures is distributed exponentially. Consider the 42 failure times in the constant failure rate portion of Table 23.32. The time between failures for successive failures can be tallied, and the 41 resulting TBFs can then be formed into the frequncy distribution shown in Figure 23.24. The distribution is roughly exponential in shape, indicating that when the failure rate is constant the distribution of time between failures (not mean time between failures) is exponential. This is the basis of the exponential formula for reliability.

The Exponential Formula for Reliability. The distribution of time between failures indicates the chance of failure-free operation for the specified time period. The chance of obtaining failure-free operation for a specified time period or longer

FIG. 23.23 Failure rate versus time.

can be shown by changing the TBF distribution to a distribution showing the number of intervals equal to or greater than a specified time length (Figure 23.24). If the frequencies are expressed as relative frequencies, they become estimates of the probability of survival. When the failure rate is constant, the probability of survival (or reliability) is

$$P_s = R = e^{-t/\mu} = e^{-t\lambda}$$

where P_s = R = probability of failure-free operation for a time period equal to or greater than t
e = 2.718
t = a specified period of failure-free operation

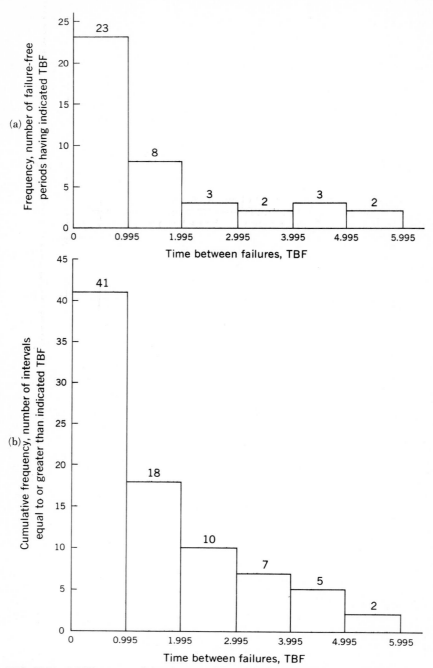

FIG. 23.24 (*a*) Histogram of time between failures. (*b*) Cumulative histogram of time between failures.

μ = mean time between failures, or MTBF (the mean of the TBF distribution)

λ = failure rate (the reciprocal of μ)

Note that this formula is simply the exponential probability distribution rewritten in terms of reliability.

Example: Previous experience shows that the mean time between failures of a radar set is 240 h. Assuming a constant failure rate, what is the chance of running the set for 24 h without failure?

$$R = e^{-t/\mu}$$

$$R = e^{-24/240} = 0.90$$

There is a 90 percent chance of obtaining 24 h or more of failure-free operation.

The assumption of a constant failure rate is rightly questioned. However, experience suggests that the assumption is often a fair one to make. (More fundamental than arguing the validity of the assumption is the need to take design actions to yield a constant failure rate. For example, the careful determination of burn-in periods and replacement periods for both parts and systems is good design practice that will help achieve a constant failure rate.)

The Meaning of "Mean Time between Failures." Confusion surrounds the meaning of "mean time between failures" (MTBF). Further explanation is warranted.

1. The MTBF is the mean (or average) time between successive failures of a product. This definition assumes that the product in question can be repaired and placed back in operation after each failure. These conditions are not always met. Furthermore, the MTBF is not always the most appropriate index for a product. For example, some other index such as percent uptime (uptime is equivalent to percent operative, as contrasted with downtime) is more pertinent when a product operates continuously as compared with the product needed for specific mission times (e.g., petroleum refinery equipment versus a guidance system for a missile).

2. If the failure rate is constant, the probability that a product will operate without failure for a time equal to or greater than its MTBF is only 37 percent. (R is equal to 0.37 when t is equal to the MTBF.) This is contrary to the intuitive feeling that there is a 50–50 chance of exceeding an MTBF.

3. MTBF is not the same as "operating life," "service life," or other indices which generally connote overhaul or replacement time. In Figure 23.23, "life" is the *length* of the constant failure rate period while MTBF is the reciprocal of the failure rate (*height* of the bathtub curve).

4. An increase in an MTBF does not result in a proportional increase in reliability (the probability of survival). If $t = 1$ h, the following table shows the mean time between failures required in order to obtain various reliabilities:

MTBF, h	R, %
5	0.82
10	0.90
20	0.95
100	0.99

A fivefold increase in MTBF from 20 to 100 h is necessary to increase the reliability by 4 percentage points as compared with a doubling of the MTBF from 5 to 10 h to get 8 percentage points increase in reliability. This is important because MTBF is often used as the criterion for making important decisions affecting reliability, whereas the probability of survival for a specified time t may be the more important index to the user.

Alternative methods (also see Section 13, Table 13.5) of denoting reliability are sometimes used to avoid the serious consequences of misinterpreting the meaning of MTBF. One alternative is the reciprocal of MTBF, i.e., the *failure rate*. This eliminates the confusion with "service life" or "operating life." Another recognizes that MTBF is really just a substitute for the reliability percent R and its associated time t. Reliability is then stated as (1) the percent reliability required and (2) the mission time, instead of condensing these two numbers into one number (MTBF).

Predicting Reliability Based on the Exponential Distributiion. Section 13, under Reliability Analysis and Prediction, presents a procedure for reliability prediction based on the exponential distribution. The extensive use of the exponential reliability function warrants further discussion.

The mechanism underlying the exponential is that of random or chance failures which are independent of accumulated life and consequently are individually unpredictable. The justification of this type of "failure law" involves several conditions.

1. Many forces can act upon the product and produce failure. For example, various deterioration mechanisms, part failure rates, and environmental conditions often result in stress-strength combinations that produce failures randomly in time.

2. A constant failure rate often occurs for the total product regardless of the failure pattern of individual parts. This is a result of the mixing of ages of parts by replacement or repair of parts. (This concept is called the "approach to a stable state.")

3. Many parts have multiple failure modes. For example, a resistor may open or a lead may break off; a transistor may go outside tolerance limits or it may abort. For some parts, the failure modes representing random catastrophic failures are likely to occur before wear-out characteristics become evident. For other parts, catastrophic failures are not likely. However, tolerance failures—which are usually associated with wear-out—can be induced both by time and by environmental conditions. The question then is whether a tolerance failure is more likely to result from wear-out or from environmental peaks. The latter case often leads to a constant failure rate.

Because of the simplicity of the exponential function, it has been used extensively in reliability work. However, the assumption is valid only if supported [for testing the assumption with data, see Test 12*b* (Table 23.29) under the previous discussion of Tests of Hypotheses] by the failure data collected. For noncomplex products when the principal failure mechanism is wear-out, the exponential assumption is not valid.

Predicting Reliability during Design Based on the Weibull Distribution. Prediction of overall reliability based on the simple addition of component failure rates is valid only if the failure rate is constant. When this assumption cannot be made, an alternative approach, based on the Weibull distribution, can be used.

1. Graphically or analytically use the Weibull distribution to predict the reliability R for the time period specified. Do this for each component.
2. Combine the component reliabilities using the product rule and/or redundancy formulas to obtain the prediction of system reliability.

Rich, Smith, and Korte (1967) give an example of predicting the reliability of a tractor pump for a 500-h period and a 1500-h period (see Table 23.33). The first analysis was on a proposed design. Note how the prediction highlights the "vital few" parts such as the oil seal and control valve. The analysis after some design changes on these parts shows a significant increase in reliability and decrease in failure cost per tractor. (Table 23.33 lists data for important items only and then summarizes reliability and cost for the complete assembly of 68 parts.)

Reliability as a Function of Applied Stress and Strength. In some situations, an individual component is satisfactory if its strength is greater than the stress applied to it. For the same design, strength will vary from component to component. The applied stress will also vary. The variation in each of the two parameters is depicted in Figure 23.25. Consider the difference between strength and applied stress in a given instance. The probability of successful performance ("reliability") is the probability that this difference is greater than zero. Figure 23.26 shows a distribution of the difference between strength and stress. Assuming independence of strength and stress:

$$\mu_{\text{difference}} = \mu_{\text{strength}} - \mu_{\text{stress}}$$

$$\sigma_{\text{difference}} = \sqrt{\sigma_{\text{strength}}^2 + \sigma_{\text{stress}}^2}$$

If normality is assumed, the probability of a difference greater than 0 can be estimated by finding the area under the curve.

TABLE 23.33 Reliability Prediction for a 1.38-in^3/revolution Variable Displacement Pump

Part name (only parts with significant percent failure are listed)	First analysis			Analysis after changes		
	% failure at		$/tractor at 500 h	% failure at		$/tractor at 500 h
	500 h	1500 h		500 h	1500 h	
Pump drive coupling special screws	0.6	3.0	0.21	0.2	1.0	0.07
Pump drive coupling	0.07	0.8	0.01	0.07	0.8	0.01
Hydraulic pump shaft	0.02	0.06	0.01	0.02	0.06	0.01
Pump shaft oil seal	3.7	20.0	0.41	1.0	5.0	0.10
Pump shaft bushing	0.75	2.25	0.30	0.25	0.75	0.10
O-ring packings (11) (evaluated separately)	0.63	2.10	0.08	0.63	2.10	0.08
Stroke control valve	13.0	38.0	0.77	0.05	0.15	0.02
Assembly reliability (68 parts):						
At 500 h		80%			97.3%	
At 1500 h		49%			92.0%	
Cost at 500 h			2.18			0.77

Example: Suppose the following estimates apply to a part:

	Strength, lb/in²	Applied stress, lb/in²
Average	60,000	46,000
Standard deviation	3,000	5,500

Then average difference $= 60,000 - 46,000 = 14,000$, and

$$\sigma_{\text{difference}} = \sqrt{(3000)^2 + (5500)^2} = 6260$$

$$Z = K = \frac{0 - 14,000}{6260} = -2.24$$

$$Z = \frac{Strength - Stress}{\sqrt{(Std\ Dev\ Strength)^2 + (Std\ Dev\ Stress)^2}}$$

From Table B in Appendix II, the area greater than zero is 0.9875; i.e., the reliability is 98.75 percent.

This discussion has been simplified in order to stress a basic concept. The key point is that *variation* in addition to average value must be considered in design. Designers have always recognized the existence of variation by using a "safety factor" in design. However, safety factor is often defined as the ratio of average strength to the worst stress expected. (Kececioglu and Cormier, 1964, discuss various definitions.)

Lusser (1958) proposed the use of safety margins in specifications for critical products such as guided missiles (Figure 23.27). He suggested safety margins for strength and stress. Specifically, the reliability boundary (maximum stress) was to be defined as 6 standard deviations (of stress) above the average stress. The aver-

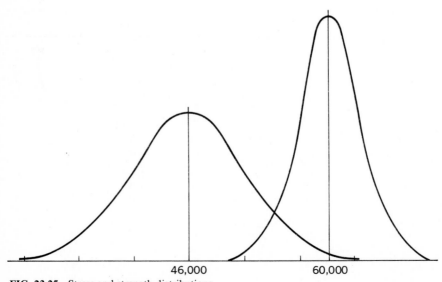

FIG. 23.25 Stress and strength distributions.

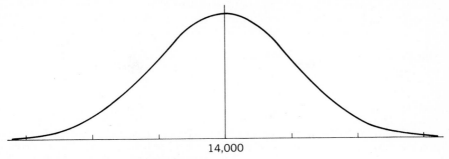

FIG. 23.26 Distribution of (strength-stress).

FIG. 23.27 Illustrating how scatterbands of stresses and strengths shall be separated by a reliability boundary.

age strength would have to be at least 5 standard deviations (of strength) above the reliability boundary. These minimum values of safety margin were suggested for products requiring extremely high reliability.

The Relationship between Part and System Reliability. It is often assumed that system reliability (i.e., probability of survival P_s) is the product of the individual reliabilities of the n parts within the system: $P_s = P_1 P_2 \cdots P_n$. This is known as the "product rule." The formula assumes (1) that the failures of any part will cause failure of the system and (2) that the reliabilities of the parts are independent of each other, i.e., that the reliability of one part is not dependent on the reliability of another part. (Evans, 1966, gives a good discussion of this and other assumptions in reliability calculations.) A set of lights in series on a Christmas tree demonstrates the product rule. These assumptions are usually not 100 percent correct. However, the formula is a convenient approximation that should be refined as information becomes available on the interrelationships of parts and their relationship to the system. [The redundancy formula (see below under Redundancy) is an example of this.] The following illustrates the product rule:

Example: The following reliability requirements have been set on the subsystems of a communications system:

Subsystem	Reliability (for a 4-h period), %
Receiver	0.970
Control system	0.989
Power supply	0.995
Antenna	0.996

What is the expected reliability of the overall system if the above requirements are met?

$$P_s = (0.970)(0.989)(0.995)(0.996) = 0.951$$

The chance that the overall system will perform its function without failure for a 4-h period is 95 percent.

If it can be assumed that each part follows the exponential distribution, then

$$P_s = e^{-t_1 \lambda_1} e^{-t_2 \lambda_2} \cdots e^{-t_n \lambda_n}$$

Further, if t is the same for each part,

$$P_s = e^{-t \Sigma \lambda}$$

Thus, when the failure rate is constant (and therefore the exponential distribution applies), a "reliability prediction" of a system can be made based on the addition of the part failure rates. This is illustrated in Section 13 under Reliability.

Redundancy. A number of system designs have been devised which attempt to increase system reliability by introducing redundancy. The simplest such system is the *parallel system,* which operates if at least one of its components operates.

If each component has reliability $R(t_0)$, then the parallel system consisting of m components has reliability equal to (see Dudewicz, 1976, p. 39):

$$1 - [1 - R(t_0)]^m$$

which is greater than $R(t_0)$.

Many other designs have been introduced, with a view both to reliability and cost, such as the k-out-of-n systems. For details on these and other aspects of reliability, see Zacks (1983), Ireson (1982), and Lloyd and Lipow (1982).

ADDITIONAL STATISTICAL TOOLS

Today, a large number of statistical tools are used in quality control. The statistical tool kit (see Table 23.1) stresses the statistical base of collection, analysis, and interpretation of data. "Transformations," discussed below, are a method often used to assure that data will meet the assumptions of statistical procedures, while "Monte Carlo sampling methods" and "clustering and discrimination procedures" are powerful methods whose use in quality control is now growing. They allow analysis with minimal assumptions, and analysis of multivariate characteristics, respectively.

Transformations of Data. Most of the statistical methodology presented in this section assumes that the quality characteristic follows a known probability distribution. The analysis and conclusions that result are, of course, valid only to the extent that the distribution assumption is correct. Under Tests of Hypotheses, a "goodness of fit" test was presented for quantitatively evaluating a set of data to judge the validity of a distributional asumption. Moderate deviations of a sample of observations from a theoretical population assumption are to be expected because of sampling variation. The goodness-of-fit test determines whether the deviation of the sample from a theoretical assumption is likely to have been due to sampling variation. If it turns out as unlikely, then it is concluded that the assumption is wrong.

Sometimes a set of data does not fit one of the standard distributions such as the normal distribution. One approach uses "distribution-free" statistical methods for further analysis. Some of these were listed under Tests of Hypotheses, and Natrella (1963) and Gibbons (1985) present further material. However, these methods often require larger sample sizes than conventional methods for equivalent statistical risks. Some other approaches to analysis are:

1. Examine the data to see if there is a nonstatistical explanation for the unusual distributional pattern. For example, the output of each of several supposedly identical machines may be normally distributed. If the machines have different means or standard deviations, then the combined output probably has an unusual distribution pattern such as the mixture distribution already discussed in this section. In this case, separate analyses could be made for each machine.

2. Analyze the data in terms of averages instead of individual values. As stated under the Two Types of Sampling Error, sample averages closely follow a normal probability distribution even if the population of individual values from which the sample averages came is not normally distributed. If it is sufficient to draw a final conclusion on a characteristic in terms of the average value, the normal distribution assumption can be applied. However, the conclusions apply only to the average value and not to the individual values in the population. (Predicting the percent of a population falling outside engineering limits illustrates the situation where analysis in terms of the average would not be sufficient because engineering limits refer to individual values rather than averages.)

3. Use the Weibull probability distribution. The Weibull distribution is really a group of many continuous distributions with each distribution uniquely defined by numerical values of the parameters of the Weibull probability function (e.g., a beta value of 1.0 indicates an exponential distribution). If a set of data yields an approximate straight-line plot on Weibull paper, the straight line then directly provides estimates of the probabilities for the population. Whether the exact form of the probability distribution is normal, or exponential, or another distribution, becomes somewhat secondary because the straight-line plot provides the needed probability estimates.

4. Make a transformation of the original characteristic to a new characteristic that is normally distributed. Figure 23.28 summarizes several of these mathematical transformations. These transformations are useful for (a) achieving normality of measured results, (b) satisfying the assumption of equal population variances required in certain tests, and (c) satisfying the assumption of additivity of effects required in certain tests. Natrella (1963) discusses transformations for all these uses.

The most common transformations for achieving normality are

$$\xi_1(X_1) = \sqrt{X_1 - a}$$

$$\xi_2(X_1) = X_1^{1/3}$$

$$\xi_3(X_1) = \log_{10}(X_1)$$

$$\xi_4(X_1) = \arcsin \sqrt{X_1}$$

$$\xi_5(X_1) = \sinh^{-1} \sqrt{X_1}$$

If one of these, say $\xi(X_1)$, is normally distributed, the mean and variance of $Y_i = \xi(X_i)$ may be estimated by

$$\overline{Y} = \sum_{j=1}^{n} \frac{Y_j}{n} \qquad s_Y^2 = \sum_{j=1}^{n} \frac{(Y_j - \overline{Y})^2}{(n - 1)}$$

However, interest in many cases is not in the expected value $E\xi(X_1)$, and the variance, $\mathrm{Var}\, \xi(X_1)$, but in the original problem units, EX_1 and $\mathrm{Var}(X_1)$. Simply using the inverse transformation—for example to estimate EX_1 by $\overline{Y}^2 + a$ in the case of ξ_1—results in a biased estimate. Good estimators for the mean of the X's are given in Table 23.34. Good estimators of the variance of the X's allows us to find approximate 95 percent confidence intervals for the mean of the X's; such estimates are given in Table 23.35. For example, when using $\sqrt{X_1 - a}$, a 95 percent confidence interval for the mean of the X's is

$$\overline{Y}^2 + a + \left(1 - \frac{1}{n}\right) s_Y^2 \pm 2\sqrt{\lambda}$$

where

$$\lambda = \frac{4}{n} s_Y^2 \overline{Y}^2 + s_Y^4 \left\{ \left(1 - \frac{1}{n}\right)^2 - \frac{n-1}{n+1}\left[1 - 2\left(1 - \frac{1}{n}\right)^2 + 3\left(1 - \frac{1}{n}\right)^4\right]\right\}$$

FIG. 23.28 Summary of some transformations.

TABLE 23.34 Transformations and
Estimators of $E(X_1)$†

$\xi(X_1)$	Estimator of $E(X_1)$
$\sqrt{X_1 - a}$	$\overline{Y}^2 + a + \left(1 - \dfrac{1}{n}\right)s_Y^2$

†For estimators in the cases $\log_{10}(X_1)$, arcsin
$\sqrt{X_1}$, and $\sinh^{-1}\sqrt{X_1}$, see Dudewicz (1983).

TABLE 23.35 Estimators of Variances of Estimators of $E(X_1)$†

$\xi(X_1)$	Estimator of variance of estimator of $E(X_1)$
$\sqrt{X_1 - a}$	$\dfrac{4}{n}s_Y^2\,\overline{Y}^2 + s_Y^4\left\{\left(1 - \dfrac{1}{n}\right)^2 - \dfrac{n-1}{n+1}\left[1 - 2\left(1 - \dfrac{1}{n}\right)^2 + 3\left(1 - \dfrac{1}{n}\right)^4\right]\right\}$

†For estimators in the cases $\log_{10}(X_1)$, arcsin $\sqrt{X_1}$, and $\sinh^{-1}\sqrt{X_1}$, see Dudewicz (1983).

Full references are given by Dudewicz (1983), which also covers procedures for dealing with cases where variances are unequal and data is normal. It is standard to recommend that equality of variability should be investigated, even when data is normal; for example, see Section 26 under General Remarks on Analysis of Data. Procedures for dealing with variance inequality when it is found had not been available until recent years. Recently, Dudewicz and Dalal (1983) showed how to compare several new processes with a standard process in this setting; their paper also includes consideration of nonnormality and a data set (their Section 5) with numerical details and normal probability plots for an example arising with solvents.

Monte Carlo Sampling Methods. Monte Carlo sampling methods are finding increasing and important uses in quality control. For example, Gutt and Gruska (1977) use it to predict quality problems which may result from variation in manufacturing and assembly operations. This method is based on fitting distributions to data (such as the GLD distribution discussed above under Continuous Probability Distributions), and sampling from it using random numbers (also discussed previously), using the resulting data to assess the performance of the simulated system (which allows optimization of the system before it is built or modified). Other uses occur in optimization (Golden, Assad, and Zanakis, 1984).

Clustering and Discrimination. *Clustering and discrimination* methods are a part of the area of statistics called *multivariate analysis* (Siotani, Hayakawa, and Fujikoshi, 1985). A typical type of problem where these methods are used in quality control is when several different kinds of malfunctions within a production facility cause product to fall outside of engineering limits. It is often difficult to determine the causes of the malfunction in any one case. Then, clustering a number of cases may reveal causal links via common factors over the clusters. (That is, this method allows one to ask, "What do the cases with malfunctions of each type have in common?")

As an example of the power of the "discrimination" method, Fisher (1936)

TABLE 23.36 Two Length (L_1, L_2) and Two Width (W_1, W_2) Measurements on 150 Individuals (50 from Each of Types $T = 1, 2, 3$), in 0.01-cm. Units*

L_1	W_1	L_2	W_2	T
50	33	14	02	1
64	28	56	22	3
65	28	46	15	2
67	31	56	24	3
63	28	51	15	3
46	34	14	03	1
69	31	51	23	3
62	22	45	15	2
59	32	48	18	2
46	36	10	02	1
61	30	46	14	2
60	27	51	16	2
65	30	52	20	3
56	25	39	11	2
65	30	55	18	3
⋮	⋮	⋮	⋮	⋮

*To save space, only the first 15 individuals' measurements are shown.

gave the data excerpted in Table 23.36. (A convenient source of the full data set is Dixon, 1983, p. 520.) This consists of two length and two width measurements on each of three distinct varieties which might be found in the same location. We wish to know: How well can the varieties (which can be classified by a more involved analysis without error) be classified by just use of the two length and two width measurements? After these data are entered into a computer, program 7M of the BMDP set of programs (Dixon, 1983) may be used to answer this question. The program code is given in Figure 23.29. From the resulting output, of key interest are the so-called *canonical variables,* which are the linear combinations of L_1, L_2, W_1, and W_2 which best discriminate among the three groups. In this example, these turn out to be

$$V_1 = 2.10510 + 0.82938L_1 + 1.53447W_1 - 2.20121L_2 - 2.81046W_2$$

$$V_2 = -6.66147 + 0.02410L_1 + 2.16452W_1 - 0.93192L_2 + 2.83919W_2$$

```
//   EXEC    BIMED, PROG =BMDP7M
/problem title is 'fisher data'.
/input variables are 5. format is '(4f3.1, f3.0)'.
/variable names are L1, w1, L2, w2, t.
grouping is t.
/group codes(5) are 1 to 3.
names(5) are set, ver, vir.
/end
```

FIG. 23.29 BMDP 7M program for dataset analysis.

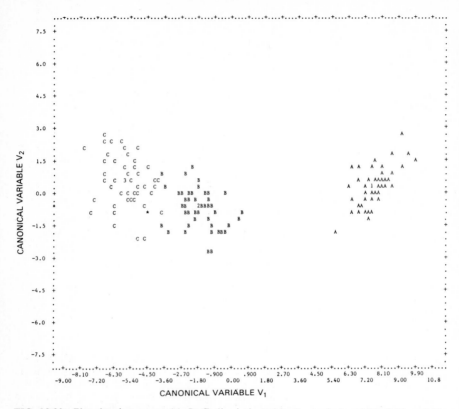

FIG. 23.30 Plot showing groups (*A, B, C*) discriminated by "canonical variables" V_1 and V_2. Overlap of different groups is indicated by *.

A plot of the (V_1, V_2) values for the 150 data points is given in Figure 23.30, with $T = 1, 2, 3$ cases labeled *A, B, C*, respectively, and shows the excellent results obtained. These results are deemed excellent since they allow us to classify a future observation into the correct group with high probability of being correct. For example, if we find $V_1 = 7.20$ and $V_2 = 1.00$, we are virtually certain group *A* is involved. (This plot is produced by program 7M.)

REGRESSION AND CORRELATION ANALYSIS

Many quality control problems require estimation of the relationship between two or more variables. Often interest centers on finding an equation relating one particular variable to a set of one or more variables. For example, how does the life of a tool vary with cutting speed? Or how does the octane number of a gasoline vary with its percentage purity?

Regression analysis is a statistical technique for estimating the parameters of an equation relating a particular variable to a set of variables. (Some authors refer

TABLE 23.37   Tool Life (Y in Minutes) versus Cutting Speed (X in Feet per Minute)

Y	X
41	90
43	90
35	90
32	90
22	100
35	100
29	100
18	100
21	105
13	105
18	105
20	105
15	110
11	110
6	110
10	110

FIG. 23.31   Tool life Y versus cutting speed X.

to this as "least squares" or "curve" fitting.) The resulting equation is called a "regression equation."

Some experimental data for the tool life example are given in Table 23.37 (from Johnson and Leone, 1964, p. 380) and plotted in Figure 23.31. Tool life is the "response variable" (also called the "dependent variable" or the "predictand") and cutting speed is the "independent variable" (also called the "predictor variable"). In this case, the independent variable is controllable; i.e., it is fixed by the experimenter or the operator of the machine. In the second example, both the octane number and the percentage purity are random. The data for this example (from Volk, 1956) are given in Table 23.38 and plotted in Figure 23.32. Since the goal is to predict the octane number, it is regarded as the dependent variable, and the percentage purity is considered as the independent variable. (In many problems there are a number of independent variables, and in some cases this set of independent variables includes both random and controllable variables.)

The computations for two-variable regression problems can be done quite easily on a desk calculator, but when there are many variables, the number of com-

TABLE 23.38   Octane Number Y versus Percentage Purity X

Y	X
88.6	99.8
86.4	99.7
87.2	99.6
88.4	99.5
87.2	99.4
86.8	99.3
86.1	99.2
87.3	99.1
86.4	99.0
86.6	98.9
87.1	98.8

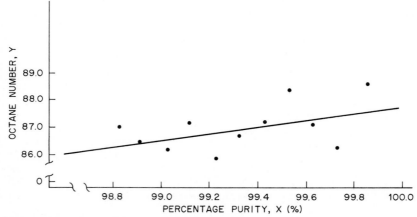

FIG. 23.32   Octane number versus percentage purity.

putations becomes overwhelming. (Even in the two-variable case, many of the computer programs available fail to provide numerically accurate calculations. It is strongly recommended that one *not* write one's own regression program, and that only major tested software packages such as SAS, BMDP, and the like be utilized.) With modern digital computer multiple regression programs, the number of variables is not a restriction. To understand and interpret the results of multidimensional problems, a thorough knowledge of the two and three variable cases is necessary.

There are many reasons for constructing regression equations. Although the motives do not affect the calculations, they do affect the interpretation of the results. In some cases, regression analysis is used to describe the nature of a relationship in a quantitative manner. Often, the *goals* are more specific. In the first example, where the cutting speed is controllable, the objective might be to find the particular value of cutting speed which minimizes tool wear or some cost function based on tool wear. Least squares regression can also be used to determine the important independent variables in a process, e.g., whether process variables such as moisture, pressure, or temperature affect a quality characteristic of the product such as strength.

In other problems, where the independent variable is not controllable, the goal may be to predict the value of the dependent or response variable. This might be done because the independent variable is easier to measure than the dependent variable. Or the independent variable may be available before the dependent variable, and hence it would be desirable to forecast the value of the dependent variable before it occurs. In still other cases it might allow a destructive test to be replaced by a nondestructive test.

The following list includes a number of *uses of regression equations:*

1. Forecasting and prediction
2. Quantitatively describing the relationship between a particular variable and another set of variables
3. Interpolating between values of a function
4. Determining the important independent variables
5. Locating the optimum operating conditions
6. Discriminating between alternative models
7. Estimating particular regression coefficients

For any of the goals stated above, the *basic steps in a regression study* are those of the Checklist for Planned Experimentation given at the beginning of this section. A summary, specifically relating the steps to regression, is:

1. Obtain a clear statement of the objectives of the study. Determine which variable is to be the response variable and which variables can be included as independent variables. In addition, obtain some measure of the precision of the results required—not necessarily in statistical terminology. (It is important to have a thorough understanding of what use will be made of the regression equation, since this may preclude the use of certain variables in the equation and will also help to give an understanding as to how much effort and money should be devoted to the project.)

2., 3. Specify collection procedures for the data. Collect the data. (The end results can only be as good as the data upon which they are based. Careful planning at this stage is of considerable importance and can also simplify the analysis of the data.)

4. Prepare crossplots (plots of one variable versus another) of the data to obtain information about the relationships between the variables; screen the data; calculate the regression equation; and evaluate how well it fits the data (including looking at transformations of variables for a better fit, or the removal of variables from an equation if they do not improve the prediction). Give measures of the precision of the equation and any procedure for using the equation. Also specify procedures for updating the equation and checks to determine whether it is still applicable, including control charts for the residuals (observed value–predicted value). (Section 24, Statistical Process Control, discusses control charts.)

5., 6., 7. As in the Checklist for Planned Experimentation.

A number of texts have been written on regression, including Daniel and Wood (1971) and Draper and Smith (1981). These include computer programs and output. Dudewicz and Karian (1985) also discuss design questions in detail. In addition to regression, other techniques have been devised for the analysis of multivariate data; see Kramer and Jensen (1969, 1970) and Siotani (1985) for details. (One of these techniques is discriminant and cluster analysis, already discussed in this section.)

Our discussion of regression begins with a single predictor problem, then proceeds to problems with more than one predictor variable and a discussion of computer programs and outputs, with their interpretation. While many texts emphasize advanced mathematical aspects of regression, this is not needed for a practical understanding now that high-quality software is available; hence we find no need for such mathematics. This makes this important subject accessible to most quality practitioners.

Simple Linear Regression.   Many problems involve only a single predictor variable X. (The dependent variable Y is often related to other predictor variables, which have either been held constant during the experiment or their effects judged to be much smaller than that of X.) These problems are often referred to as ones of "simple linear regression."

Graphing the Data.   A first step in any study of relationships between variables is to plot a graph of the data (often called a "scatter diagram"). The convention is to plot the response variable on the vertical axis and the independent variable on the horizontal axis. A graph can provide a great deal of information concerning the relationship between variables and often suggests possible models for the data. The data plotted in Figure 23.31 suggests that Y is linearly related to X over the range of this experiment. (If this were not the case, various transformations of the data as well as curvilinear relationships could also be considered. Often the relationship can be "linearized" by taking the logarithm of one or both of the variables.)

A graph can also indicate whether any of the observations are outliers, i.e., observations which deviate substantially from the rest of the data. (Outliers may be due to measurement errors or recording errors, in which case they should be corrected or deleted. They may be due to process changes or other causes, and the investigation of these changes or causes may provide more information than the analysis of the rest of the data.) No outliers are apparent in Figure 23.31.

A closer inspection of the graph can give an indication of the variability of Y for fixed X. In addition, it may show that this variability remains constant over all X or that it changes with X. In the latter case the method of weighted least squares (see Draper and Smith, 1981) may be preferred to the standard least squares technique discussed here.

The Model.   After graphing the data, we want to obtain an equation relating Y to X. To do this, a model for the data must be postulated. (We emphasize that the proposed model may be modified during the course of the study and is just a starting point.)

A possible model for the data in Figure 23.31 is

$$Y = \beta_0 + \beta_1 X + \epsilon$$

where β_0 and β_1 are the unknown intercept and slope, respectively, of the regression line. The model assumes that Y is a linear function of X plus a random error term, denoted by ϵ. This random error may be due to errors in the measurement of Y and/or to the effects of variables not included in the model, which is called

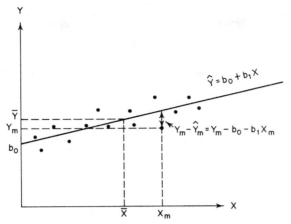

FIG. 23.33 Least squares.

"equation error." The X's are assumed to be measured with negligible error. For the data in Figure 23.31, the X's are fixed; however the same model can be used when the X's are random as in Figure 23.32.

Estimating the Prediction Equation.   The objective is to find estimates (b_0, b_1) of the unknown parameters (β_0, β_1) and thus obtain a prediction equation

$$\hat{Y} = b_0 + b_1 X$$

where $\hat{Y}$ is the predicted value of Y for a given value of X.

Least squares provides a method for finding estimates of these parameters from a set of N observations $(Y_1, X_1), \ldots, (Y_N, X_N)$. The estimates are called "least squares estimates" because they minimize the sum of the squared deviations between the observed and predicted values of the response variable $\Sigma(Y_m - \hat{Y}_m)^2 = \Sigma(Y_m - b_0 - b_1 X_m)^2$. These ideas are illustrated in Figure 23.33. (For a mathematical derivation of the estimates, see any of the texts mentioned in the introduction.)

If (1) the observations are independent, (2) the variance of the errors is constant over these observations, and (3) the linear model postulated is correct, the least squares estimates are the "best linear unbiased estimates": In the class of linear unbiased estimates of the parameters, the least squares estimates have the smallest variance. (Even if these conditions are not satisfied, the least squares technique can be used, although modifications or other methods may provide better estimates.) Note that no assumption has been made concerning the distribution of the random error, and in particular a normal distribution is not assumed: No assumption on this error term will be required until confidence intervals and tests of hypotheses are constructed.

The least squares estimates for the parameters of the linear model $Y = \beta_0 + \beta_1 X + \epsilon$ are

$$b_1 = \frac{\Sigma(X_m - \overline{X})(Y_m - \overline{Y})}{\Sigma(X_m - \overline{X})^2}$$

$$b_0 = \overline{Y} - b_1 \overline{X}$$

where $\overline{X} = \Sigma X_m/N$ and $\overline{Y} = \Sigma Y_m/N$ are sample averages. All these summations range from $m = 1$ to $m = N$. (Except where needed, the additional notation will be omitted for typographical simplicity.)

As can be seen, b_1 is related to the sample correlation coefficient

$$r = \frac{\Sigma(X_m - \overline{X})(Y_m - \overline{Y})}{\sqrt{\Sigma(X_m - \overline{X})^2 \Sigma(Y_m - \overline{Y})^2}}$$

by

$$b_1 = r\sqrt{\frac{\Sigma(Y_m - \overline{Y})^2}{\Sigma(X_m - \overline{X})^2}}$$

However, the concept of correlation is meaningful only when both the variables are random, whereas b_1, the least squares estimate of the rate of change of Y per unit change in X has meaning for both the case of random X and controllable or fixed X.

The sums, sums of squares, and sum of cross-products for the data ($N = 16$) given in Table 23.37 are

$$\Sigma X_m = 90 + 90 + \cdots + 110 = 1620$$

$$\Sigma Y_m = 41 + 43 + \cdots + 10 = 369$$

$$\Sigma X_m^2 = 8100 + 8100 + \cdots + 12{,}000 = 164{,}900$$

$$\Sigma Y_m^2 = 1681 + 1849 + \cdots + 100 = 10{,}469$$

$$\Sigma X_m Y_m = 3690 + 3870 + \cdots + 1100 = 36{,}170$$

(Note that calculations for regression are very susceptible to both human and numerical error because of their complexity. Hence good software should be used. The numerical examples in this section can be used both to test one's understanding of that software and to test its accuracy.)

The summary statistics are computed using the following computational formulas:

$$\overline{X} = \frac{\Sigma X_m}{N} = 101.25 \qquad \overline{Y} = \frac{\Sigma Y_m}{N} = 23.06$$

$$\Sigma(X_m - \overline{X})^2 = \Sigma X_m^2 - \frac{(\Sigma X_m^2)^2}{N} = 164{,}900 - \frac{(1{,}620)^2}{16} = 875.00$$

$$\Sigma(Y_m - \overline{Y})^2 = \Sigma Y_m^2 - \frac{(\Sigma Y_m)^2}{N} = 10{,}469 - \frac{(369)^2}{16} = 1958.94$$

$$\Sigma(X_m - \overline{X})(Y_m - \overline{Y}) = \Sigma X_m Y_m - \frac{\Sigma X_m \Sigma Y_m}{N}$$

$$= 36{,}170 - \frac{(1620)(369)}{16}$$

$$= -1191.25$$

From these results the least squares estimates can be calculated as

$$b_1 = \frac{-1191.25}{875} = -1.3614$$

$$b_0 = 23.06 - (-1.3614)(101.25) = 160.9018$$

and hence the prediction equation is

$$\hat{Y} = 160.90 - 1.3614X$$

The prediction equation is sometimes written in terms of deviations from averages, i.e., $\hat{Y} = \overline{Y} + b_1(X - \overline{X})$, which for this example becomes

$$\hat{Y} = 23.06 - 1.3614(X - 101.25)$$

Examining the Prediction Equation. After estimating the coefficients of the prediction equation, the equation should be plotted over the data to check for gross calculation errors. Roughly half the data points should be above the line and half below it. In addition, the equation should pass exactly through the point $(\overline{X}, \overline{Y})$

A number of criteria exist for judging the adequacy of the prediction equation. One common measure of the adequacy of the prediction equation is the proportion of variation R^2 explained. To compute R^2, the sum of the squared deviations of the Y_m about $\overline{Y}$ is partitioned into two parts, the sum of squares due to regression and the residual sum of squares:

$$\Sigma(Y_m - \overline{Y})^2 = SS(REG) + SS(RES)$$

$$= \Sigma(\hat{Y}_m - \overline{Y})^2 + \Sigma(Y_m - \hat{Y}_m)^2$$

$$= b_1\Sigma(X_m - \overline{X})(Y_m - \overline{Y}) + \Sigma(Y_m - \hat{Y}_m)^2$$

From this, the proportion of the variation $\Sigma(Y_m - \overline{Y})^2$ explained by the regression is computed as

$$R^2 = \frac{SS(REG)}{\Sigma(Y_m - \overline{Y})^2}$$

$$= \frac{b_1\Sigma(X_m - \overline{X})(Y_m - \overline{Y})}{\Sigma(Y_m - \overline{Y})^2}$$

$$= \frac{(-1.3614)(-1191.25)}{1958.94} = 0.828$$

Thus, in this example the prediction equation explains 82.8 percent of the variation of the tool life.

Another interpretation of R^2 (when both the independent and the dependent variables are random) is as the square of the sample multiple correlation coefficient. When there is only one independent variable, this reduces to the square of the sample correlation coefficient r defined earlier.

Although R^2 is a useful measure of the adequacy of the prediction equation,, an estimate of the variability of the Y's about the regression equation is usually more important. Either the sample variance s^2 or its square root s, called the "standard error of the estimate," can be used. The latter is often preferred, because it is measured in the same units as Y. Both of these, as well as other results, can be obtained from the analysis of variance (ANOVA) given in Table 23.39.

The corrected total sum of squares (some authors include the total sum of squares, uncorrected, in the ANOVA table, partitioning it into two parts—the corrected sum of squares and the sum of squares due to $\overline{Y}$ (or b_0); see Draper and Smith, 1981) and the regression sum of squares are calculated from the summary statistics and the estimate of the regression coefficient. Although the residual sum of squares can be calculated directly, it is more easily obtained as the difference between the corrected total sum of squares and the sum of squares due to regression. Each of these sums of squares has an associated degrees of freedom (see Testing a Hypothesis When the Sample Size is Fixed in Advance). The corrected total sum of squares has $N - 1$ degrees of freedom, since one degree of freedom is used in estimating the mean. For this *one* variable model, there is *one* degree of freedom associated with the regression sum of squares, leaving $(N - 1) - 1 = N - 2$ degrees of freedom associated with the residual sum of squares. The mean squares (MS) are calculated by dividing the sum of squares by their associated degrees of freedom. The estimate of the variance of Y about the regression line is $s^2 = $ MS(RES); hence the standard error of the estimate is $s = \sqrt{\text{MS(RES)}}$.

From the mean squares an F statistic can be calculated as

$$F_{\text{CALC}} = \frac{\text{MS(REG)}}{\text{MS(RES)}}$$

If (1) the ϵ's in the original model are normally distributed with a common variance, (2) the observations are independent, and (3) the postulated linear model is correct, then the regression can be tested for significance, i.e., the statistical hypothesis

$$H_0 : \beta_1 = 0$$

can be tested against the alternative hypothesis

$$H_1 : \beta_1 \neq 0$$

by comparing F_{CALC} with the tabulated F at an appropriate level of significance α. If $F_{\text{CALC}} > F_{\text{TAB}}$, we conclude that the regression is significant and that the prediction equation is a better predictor of Y than $\overline{Y}$. Although it is difficult to

TABLE 23.39 ANOVA Table (Linear Model)

Source	Sum of squares	Degrees of freedom	Mean square
1. Due to regression (b_1)	$b_1 \Sigma(X_m - \overline{X})(Y_m - \overline{Y})$	1	MS (REG) = SS(REG)/1
2. Residual	$\Sigma(Y_m - \hat{Y}_m)^2$†	$N - 2$	MS (RES) = SS(RES)/($N - 2$)
3. Total corrected for the mean	$\Sigma(Y_m - \overline{Y})^2$	$N - 1$	

†Obtained by subtracting (1) from (3).

TABLE 23.40 ANOVA Example

Source	Sum of squares	Degrees of freedom	Mean square	F_{CALC}
1. Due to regression	1621.80	1	1621.80	67.35
2. Residual	337.14	14	24.08	
3. Total corrected for the mean	1958.94	15		

check the assumptions stated above, the test is not extremely sensitive to departures in the distribution of ϵ from normality if the number of observations is relatively large. If the X's are random, this test must be interpreted in a conditional sense, i.e., given the values of the X's.

For the example, the analysis of variance (ANOVA) table is given in Table 23.40. (See Section 26, under Completely Randomized Design—A Simple One Factor Experiment.) The regression is significant at an $\alpha = 0.01$ level ($F_{TAB} = 8.86$) and $s = \sqrt{24.08} = 4.91$.

It is important to note that even when the regression is significant, the unexplained variability can still be large, and the prediction equation may not be of any value.

Residuals, Outliers, Confidence and Prediction Bands, Extrapolation; Lack of Fit—Replicated Observations. If it is feasible to replicate, i.e., take more than one observation on Y at one or more values of X, the adequacy of the model can also be tested. (An estimate of the pure error may sometimes be available from sources outside the immediate experiment.) In this case the SS(RES) can be partitioned into two parts—that due to pure error, SS(PE), and that due to lack of fit, SS(LF).

Suppose that there are N_m readings $Y_{m1}, Y_{m2}, \ldots, Y_{mN_m}$ at x_m, where $m = 1, 2, \ldots, k$. The contribution to the sum of squares due to pure error for X_m is

$$\sum_{j=1}^{Nm} (\hat{Y}_{mj} - \overline{Y}_m)^2 = \sum_{j=1}^{Nm} Y_{mj}^2 - \frac{\left(\sum_{j=1}^{Nm} Y_{mj} \right)^2}{N_m}$$

and the associated degrees of freedom is $N_m = 1$. The SS(PE) is just the sum of these k contributions and the associated degrees of freedom (DF) is

$$\sum_{m=1}^{k} (N_m - 1) = \sum_{m=1}^{k} N_m - k$$

For the example given in Table 23.37:

X_m		SS(PE)	DF
90	$41^2 + 43^2 + 35^2 + 32^2 - (151)^2/4 =$	78.75	3
100	$22^2 + 35^2 + 29^2 + 18^2 - (104)^2/4 =$	170.00	3
105	$21^2 + 13^2 + 18^2 + 20^2 - (72)^2/4 =$	38.00	3
110	$15^2 + 16^2 + 6^2 + 10^2 - (42)^2/4 =$	41.00	3
	Total	327.75	12

The SS(LF) is found by subtraction as

$$SS(LF) = SS(RES) - SS(PE) = 337.14 - 327.75 = 9.39$$

and the lack of fit degrees of freedom is obtained in a similar manner as $14 - 12 = 2$. The mean squares are then found by dividing the sum of squares by the appropriate degrees of freedom and

$$F_{CALC} = \frac{MS(LF)}{MS(PE)}$$

If the F_{CALC} is greater than the tabled F, the lack of fit is "significant" and a better or more complete model is needed (e.g., $Y = \beta_0 + \beta_1 X + \beta_2 X^2$). Plots of the residuals $(Y_m - \hat{Y}_m)$ versus X_m are particularly helpful in suggesting alternative models. Some examples are given in Figure 23.34. (Daniel and Wood, 1971, pp. 19–24, present graphs of a number of nonlinear functions and give transformations which "linearize" them.) In each case the model $Y = \beta_0 + \beta_1 X$ was postulated and the plots are of the resulting residuals.

FIG. 23.34   Residuals and lack of fit.

If F_{CALC} is less than the tabled F, the model is accepted. This does not mean that other variables should not be considered in the model, but only that the form of X in the model is adequate.

The calculations for our example are summarized in Table 23.41. The lack of fit is judged not significant at an α level of 0.05 ($F_{TAB} = 3.89$). Hence, the pos-

TABLE 23.41   ANOVA Lack of Fit Example

Source	Sum of squares	Degrees of freedom	Mean square	F_{CALC}
Lack of fit	9.39*	2	4.695	0.172
Pure error	327.75	12	27.3125	

*Obtained by subtracting SS(PE) and SS(RES).

tulated model is accepted and the residual mean square is used as the estimate of the variance.

If replication is not possible, e.g., X is random rather than controllable, the Y values corresponding to X values which are close together can be used to obtain an estimate of the variability and hence judge the lack of fit. (See pp. 123–125 of Daniel and Wood, 1971.)

Confidence Intervals.   Both R^2 and s^2 provide measures of the reliability or adequacy of a prediction equation. Confidence intervals provide another measure of the reliability of the various estimates. All these confidence intervals are based on the square root of the residual mean square. A $(1 - \alpha)$ two-sided confidence interval for the slope β_1 is given by

$$b_1 \pm \frac{ts}{\sqrt{\Sigma(X_m - \overline{X})^2}}$$

where the value t is obtained from Appendix II, Table G, with $N - 2$ degrees of freedom. The term in the denominator plays the role that $n^{1/2}$ plays in confidence intervals on population means. For the example, the 0.95 confidence interval on β_1 is

$$-1.36 \pm \frac{(2.145)(4.91)}{\sqrt{875}} = -1.36 \pm 0.356$$

The term $s/\sqrt{\Sigma(X_m - \overline{X})^2}$ is often called the standard error of the regression coefficient.

In addition to the confidence interval on β_1, more importantly *confidence intervals* can also be constructed *for the mean of Y at a given value of X.* The $(1 - \alpha)$ confidence interval on the mean of Y at X (or equivalently on $\beta_0 + \beta_1 X$) is

$$b_0 + b_1 X \pm ts \sqrt{\frac{1}{N} + \frac{(X - \overline{X})^2}{\Sigma(X_m - \overline{X})^2}}$$

where X is the value at which the confidence interval is being constructed and t again has $N - 2$ degrees of freedom. (By letting $X = 0$, a confidence level for β_0 is obtained.)

In addition to the assumptions previously stated, these confidence intervals also require (1) that the independent variable is fixed rather than random and (2) that the errors are normally distributed. However, if the X's are random, confidence intervals can still be calculated, but they must be interpreted in a conditional sense. Confidence intervals are not sensitive to departures from normality if the sample size is reasonably large. This is not the case for the following interval, which is very sensitive to the normality assumption. *Least absolute value* (LAV) and *Chebyshev estimation* are two possible alternatives to least squares estimation, which are less sensitive to model departures than is least squares. For sources of efficient computer algorithms, with a detailed numerical example, see Dielman and Pfaffenberger (1984).

In addition to a confidence interval on the expected value of Y at a given X, there may be a need for *an interval estimate for a future individual observation on Y at X.* (A more complete discussion of confidence intervals is given in Draper and Smith, 1981. See Daniel and Wood, 1971, for a confidence interval which simultaneously includes the whole line. See Dudewicz, 1976, p. 427, for a plot of the interval for all X, called a *prediction band,* and its uses.) In this case the interval must also take into account the variability of Y about $\beta_0 + \beta_1 X$, and the result is

$$b_0 + b_1 X \pm ts \sqrt{1 + \frac{1}{N} + \frac{(X - \overline{X})^2}{\Sigma(X_m - \overline{X})^2}}$$

where t has $N - 2$ degrees of freedom. Computations of these intervals for various values of X are given in Table 23.42.

Multiple Regression. Although there are many problems involving single predictor variables, more often there are many predictor variables. A generalization of the least squares technique, previously discussed, can be used to estimate the coefficients of the multivariable prediction equation. This problem is called multiple regression.

The General Model. For a problem with k predictor variables, the model can be written as

$$Y = \beta_0 + \beta_1 X_1 + \cdots + \beta_k X_k + \epsilon$$

where the β's are unknown parameters and ϵ is the random error. These variables may be transformations of the original data. For example, in predicting gasoline yields from data on the specific gravity and vapor pressure of crude oil, Y may be the log of the gasoline yield, X_1 the crude oil specific gravity, X_2 the crude oil vapor pressure, and X_3 the product of the crude oil specific gravity with its vapor pressure.

The general model includes polynomial models in one or more variables, such as

$$Y = \beta_0 + \beta_1 X_1 + \beta_2 X_2 + \beta_3 X_1^2 + \beta_4 X_2^2 + \beta_5 X_1 X_2 + \epsilon$$

(which is called the *full quadratic model* of Y on X_1 and X_2, and is of great use in designed experiments; see Dudewicz and Karian, 1985). This is still a linear model, since the term "linear model" means that the model is linear in the β's. (See Draper and Smith, 1981, for a discussion of models which are nonlinear.)

Estimating the Prediction Equation. The objective now is to find the least squares estimates $(b_0, b_1, \ldots, b_k)$ of the unknown parameters $(\beta_0, \beta_1, \ldots, \beta_k)$ and obtain a prediction equation

$$\hat{Y} = b_0 + b_1 X_1 + \cdots + b_k X_k$$

where $\hat{Y}$ is the predicted value of Y for the given values of $X_1, \ldots, X_k$. Letting $x_i = X_i - \overline{X}_i$ and using the fact that

$$b_0 = \overline{Y} - b_1 \overline{X}_1 - \cdots - b_k \overline{X}_k$$

this prediction equation can be expressed in the alternative form:

$$\hat{Y} = \overline{Y} + b_1 x_1 + \cdots + b_k x_k$$

To simplify the formulas, the observations can also be expressed as deviations from their sample averages; i.e., for the mth observation $x_{im} = X_{im} - \overline{X}_i$ and $y_m = Y_m - \overline{Y}$. Then the least squares estimates of the $k + 1$ parameters of the

TABLE 23.42 Computation of Confidence Limits

X (1)	$b_0 + b_1X$ (2)	$\dfrac{(X - \overline{X})^2}{\Sigma(\overline{X}_m - \overline{X})^2}$ (3)	$\sqrt{\dfrac{1}{N} + (3)}$ (4)	$ts \times (4)$ (5)	90% confidence limits on the mean of Y at X		$\sqrt{1 + \dfrac{1}{N} + (3)}$ (8)	$ts \times (8)$ (9)	90% prediction limits on Y at X	
					Lower (2) − (5) (6)	Upper (2) + (5) (7)			Lower (2) − (9) (10)	Upper (2) + (9) (11)
90	38.37	0.14464	0.4551	3.94	34.43	42.31	1.0987	9.50	28.87	47.87
100	24.76	0.00179	0.2535	2.20	22.56	26.96	1.0316	8.92	15.84	33.68
($\overline{X}$) 101.5	($\overline{Y}$) 23.06	0.0	0.2550	2.17	20.89	25.23	1.0308	8.91	14.15	31.97
110	11.15	0.08750	0.3870	3.36	7.79	14.51	1.0724	9.27	1.88	20.42

Note: Numbers in parentheses are column numbers. $t_{14,0.95} = 1.761$.

multivariable linear model $Y = \beta_0 + \beta_1 X_1 + \cdots + \beta_k X_k + \epsilon$ can be obtained by solving the set of $k + 1$ linear equations:

$$b_1 \Sigma x_{1m}^2 + b_2 \Sigma x_{1m} x_{2m} + \cdots + b_k \Sigma x_{1m} x_{km} = \Sigma x_{1m} y_m$$

$$b_1 \Sigma x_{1m} x_{2m} + b_2 \Sigma x_{2m}^2 + \cdots + b_k \Sigma x_{2m} x_{km} = \Sigma x_{2m} y_m$$

$$\vdots \qquad\qquad \vdots$$

$$b_1 \Sigma x_{1m} x_{km} + b_2 \Sigma x_{2m} x_{km} + \cdots + b_k \Sigma x_{km}^2 = \Sigma x_{km} y_m$$

$$b_0 = \overline{Y} - b_1 \overline{X}_1 - b_2 \overline{X}_2 - \cdots - b_k \overline{X}_k$$

(All the above summations are on m and range from 1 to N.)

Solving these "reduced normal" equations simultaneously can be tedious, is error prone, and involves matrix algebra. Many reference works emphasize how to perform these calculations accurately. To the user of modern accurate statistical software, these calculations are of no direct importance: That user can trust they are being done accurately, and concentrate on statistical aspects of model adequacy, interpretation, and use.

Examining the Prediction Equation. After obtaining $(b_0, b_1, \ldots, b_k)$, an ANOVA table can be constructed and the adequacy of the prediction equation evaluated by a number of criteria. The ANOVA table, which is a generalization of that derived for the single predictor variable, is given in Table 23.43. The third row in Table 23.43 is the same as in Table 23.39. Note that the expressions in the first row reduce to those in the first row of Table 23.39 when $k = 1$.

Since there are k variables in the model, the sum of squares due to regression has k degrees of freedom associated with it. In addition since k coefficients and one intercept have been estimated, the residual sum of squares has $N - (k + 1) = N - k - 1$ degrees of freedom associated with it. The F statistic is calculated as before—i.e., $F = \text{MS(REG)}/\text{MS(RES)}$—and $s = \sqrt{\text{SS(RES)}/(N - k - 1)}$. In this case the F statistic can be used to test the statistical hypothesis

$$H_0: \beta_i = 0 \qquad (i = 1, 2, \ldots, k)$$

TABLE 23.43 ANOVA Table (Linear Model)

Source	Sum of squares	Degrees of freedom	Mean square
1. Due to regression	$b'a$†	k	$\text{MS(REG)} = \text{SS(REG)}/k$
2. Residual	$\Sigma(\overline{Y}_m - \hat{Y}_m)^2$‡	$N - k - 1$	$\text{MS(RES)} = \text{SS(RES)}/(N - k - 1)$
3. Total corrected for the mean	$\Sigma(Y_m - \overline{Y}_m)^2$	$N - 1$	

†The sum of squares due to regression can be written as $b'a = b_1 \Sigma x_{1m} y_m + b_2 \Sigma x_{2m} y_m + \cdots + b_k \Sigma x_{km} y_m$. [Note that b' is the transpose of the b vector, i.e., $b' = (b_1 \ b_2 \ \cdots \ b_k)$. Those not familiar with vector notation can regard $b'a$ as a shorthand for the sum given in this footnote. Since computations are usually done with computer software, details of vector notation are not given and will not be needed by most readers.]
‡Obtained by subtracting (1) from (3).

against the alternative statistical hypothesis

$$H_1: \text{Some } \beta_i \neq 0 \qquad (i = 1, 2, \ldots, k)$$

The only change is in the degrees of freedom used to look up the F_{TAB} ($k, n - k - 1$ versus $1, n - 2$).

The proportion of variation explained by the equation (R^2) can be obtained from the ANOVA table. Note that R^2 does not depend on the number of variables in the equation, but s^2 does. In fact, if a new variable is added to the model (and the least squares estimates and ANOVA table are recomputed), the value of R^2 *cannot decrease*. However, s^2 can either increase or decrease, since it depends on the residual degrees of freedom in addition to the residual sum of squares, which decreases by one when a new variable is added.

Confidence Intervals. Confidence intervals for individual β's can be developed, as

$$b_i \pm ts \sqrt{c_{ii}}$$

where t has ($N - k - 1$) degrees of freedom, and c_{ii} is defined below. However, since the b_i ($i = 1, \ldots, k$) have a joint distribution and are in general not uncorrelated, care must be taken in the interpretation of sets of these confidence intervals (see, for example, Draper and Smith, 1981).

More usefully, a confidence interval on the regression equation at a point $x = (x_1, \ldots, x_k)$ where $x_i = X_i - \overline{X}_i$ is given by

$$\overline{Y} + b_1 x_1 + \cdots + b_k x_k \pm ts \left(\frac{1}{N} + x'Cx \right)^{1/2}$$

where t has $N - k - 1$ degrees of freedom and $x'Cx$ is a quadratic form which takes into account the covariances and variances of the b's. (Here C is as defined in the next paragraph.)

In a similar manner an interval for a future Y at X is given by

$$\overline{Y} + b_1 x_1 + \cdots + b_k x_k \pm ts \left(1 + \frac{1}{N} + x'Cx \right)^{1/2}$$

where t has $N - k - 1$ degrees of freedom. (Here $C = S^{-1}$, where S is the $k \times k$ matrix whose entry in row i and column j is $\Sigma x_{im} x_{jm}$. In practice, as we will see, these matrix calculations are done by the computer and the user need not bother with them—or even understand the concept of a "matrix" and its "inverse.")

An example: The methods discussed can now be illustrated by an example furnished by Mason E. Wescott (example 5 from *Mimeo Notes*, Mason E. Wescott, Rochester Institute of Technology, Rochester, NY) with $k = 2$ predictor variables. The problem is to relate the green strength (flexural strength before baking) of electric circuit breaker arc chutes to the hydraulic pressure used in forming them and the acid concentration. The data are given in Table 23.44, with hydraulic pressure and green strength given in units of 10 lb/in^2 and the acid concentration given as a percent of the nominal rate for 20 observations. Two-variable plots of the data are given in Figures 23.35, 23.36, and 23.37. Summary statistics including sums, sums of squares, and cross products, both raw and corrected, as well as the sample means, are given in Table 23.45.

TABLE 23.44 Arc Chute Data

Green strength Y in units of 10 lb/in²	Hydraulic pressure X_1 in units of 10 lb/in²	Acid concentration X_2, as % of nominal rate
665	110	116
618	119	104
620	138	94
578	130	86
682	143	110
594	133	87
722	147	114
700	142	106
681	125	107
695	135	106
664	152	98
548	118	86
620	155	87
595	128	96
740	146	120
670	132	108
640	130	104
590	112	91
570	113	92
640	120	100

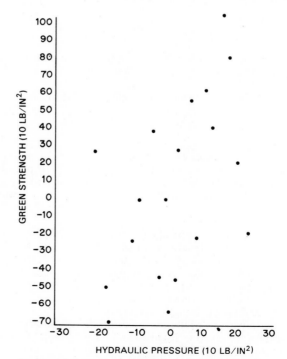

FIG. 23.35 Green strength versus hydraulic pressure (deviations from averages).

23.112

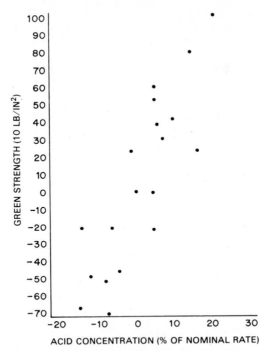

FIG. 23.36 Green strength versus acid concentration (deviations from averages).

FIG. 23.37 Acid concentration versus hydraulic pressure (deviations from averages). Rectangles indicate points at which confidence intervals have been calculated.

23.113

TABLE 23.45   Summary Statistics

$N = 20$		
$\Sigma Y_m = 12{,}832$	$\Sigma X_{1m} = 2628$	$\Sigma X_{2m} = 2012$
$\Sigma Y_m^2 = 8{,}286{,}988$	$\Sigma X_{1m}^2 = 348{,}756$	$\Sigma X_{2m}^2 = 204{,}500$
$\Sigma X_{1m} Y_m = 1{,}693{,}226$	$\Sigma X_{2m} Y_m = 1{,}300{,}253$	$\Sigma X_{1m} X_{2m} = 264{,}785$
$\overline{Y} = 641.6$	$\overline{X}_1 = 131.4$	$\overline{X}_2 = 100.6$

S		a
$s_{11} = 3436.8$	$s_{12} = \quad 408.2*$	$a_1 = 7{,}101.2\dagger$
$s_{21} = \quad 408.2$	$s_{22} = 2092.8$	$a_2 = 9{,}353.8$

$*s_{12} = \Sigma x_{1m} x_{2m} = \Sigma X_{1m} X_{2m} - (\Sigma X_{1m}\Sigma X_{2m}/N) = 264{,}785 - [(2628)(2012)/20] = 408.2.$
$\dagger a_1 = \Sigma x_{1m} y_m = \Sigma X_{1m} Y_m - (\Sigma X_{1m}\Sigma Y_m/N) = 1{,}693{,}226 - [(2628)(12{,}832)/20] = 7101.2.$

The estimates are:

$$b_2 = 4.162940$$

$$b_1 = 1.571779$$

$$b_0 = \overline{Y} - b_1\overline{X}_1 - b_2\overline{X}_2 = 16.27475$$

The C matrix is:

$$c_{22} = 0.00048916$$

$$c_{12}(= c_{21}) = -0.000058099$$

$$c_{11} = 0.00029787$$

and hence

$$C = \begin{vmatrix} 297.869 & -58.099 \\ -58.099 & 489.160 \end{vmatrix} \times 10^{-6}$$

The prediction equations can be calculated as

$$\hat{Y} = 16.277 + 1.572X_1 + 4.163X_2$$

$$\hat{Y} = 641.600 + 1.572(X_1 - 131.400) + 4.163(X_2 - 100.600)$$

(The latter form will be used in the remaining computations.)

The ANOVA table (Table 23.46) for the example follows directly from the summary statistics of Table 23.45 and from Table 23.43. The residual mean square error is 228.0, and hence the standard deviation s is 15.100.

The 95 percent confidence intervals on β_1 and β_2 are obtained as

$$1.572 \pm 2.110 \times 15.100 \times \sqrt{297.869} \times 10^{-3}$$

$$= 1.572 \pm 0.550 = 1.02 \text{ and } 2.12$$

and

$$4.163 \pm 2.110 \times 15.0997 \times \sqrt{489.16} \times 10^{-3}$$

$$= 4.163 \pm 0.705 = 3.46 \text{ and } 4.87$$

TABLE 23.46   ANOVA Example

Source	Sum of squares	Degrees of freedom	Mean square
1. Due to regression	50,100.8*	2	25,050.40
2. Residual	3,876.0†	17	228.0
3. Total corrected for the mean	53,976.8	19	

*(1.571779)(7101.2) + (4.16294)(9353.8) = 50,100.825.
†By subtraction.

Confidence intervals for $\beta_0 + \beta_1 X_1 + \beta_2 X_2$ and for a future observation of Y, at five combinations of X_1 and X_2, are given in Table 23.47. (The five points at which the confidence intervals are computed are also indicated in Figure 23.37.)

Computer Programs.   Because of the widespread popularity of regression, almost every computer facility has at least one and most have many regression programs. These programs may have been locally written, or they may have been obtained from other sources. In the latter case, the program usually has been modified in some manner, so that it can be run on the local computer system and satisfy the needs of the local users.

Studies by Longley (1967) and Wampler (1970) indicate that the user should *strongly* prefer software such as that of SAS and BMDP. One should not presume that the program has been checked, just because a sample data problem is given in the program manual. Unfortunately a number of the algorithms used in these programs are often taken directly from desk calculator instructions. These algorithms are often not good, and can produce numerically inaccurate results, even in double precision. For example, Longley found that many of the programs computed the squared deviations of a variable about its mean by the computational formula $\Sigma X_m^2 - (\Sigma X_m)^2/N$, rather than by $\Sigma (X_m - \overline{X})^2$. Since these quantities are the base for most of the regression calculations, numerical errors may be present in all the results.

Since the user may not be able (or simply does not want to invest the time) to check a program, a few simple checks for this purpose are given below. These can be used to gain some idea of the limitations of a program; however, we again strongly recommend against "rolling your own" when SAS, BMDP, and (perhaps) other excellent software is available at reasonable prices, and is kept up to date with advances in statistics.

1. Add the residuals about the regression line. They should sum to zero, within rounding error.
2. If the residuals sum to zero, make additional runs of the problem after adding 10, 100, 1000, 10,000 etc., to each variable. The coefficients will begin to change at a point where round-off error occurs.
3. As a check on the accuracy of the inversion routine, run a problem with two variables X_1 and X_2. Then make another run with the same response variable but two new independent variables $X_1^* = X_1 + X_2$ and $X_2^* = X_1 - X_2$. The following results should hold: $b_1 = b_1^* + b_2^*$ and $b_2 = b_1^* - b_2^*$.

Longley (1967) gives some additional checks, and Wampler (1970) lists results on many regression programs.

TABLE 23.47 Computation of Confidence Intervals

X_1 (1)	X_2 (2)	$\hat{Y}$ (3)	$(x'Cx)$ (4)	$\sqrt{\frac{1}{N}+(4)}$ (5)	$ts\times(5)$† (6)	95% confidence limits on the mean of Y at X_1,X_2 Lower (3) − (6) (7)	Upper (3) + (6) (8)	$\sqrt{1+\frac{1}{N}+(4)}$ (9)	$ts\times(9)$ (10)	95% prediction limits on Y at X_1,X_2 Lower (3) − (10) (11)	Upper (3) + (10) (12)
111.4	90.6	568.53	0.1457*	0.4424	14.10	554.43	582.63	1.0935	34.84	533.69	603.37
111.4	110.6	651.79	0.1922	0.4921	15.68	636.11	667.47	1.1145	35.51	616.28	687.30
131.4	100.6	641.60	0.0	0.2236	7.12	634.48	648.72	1.0247	32.65	608.95	674.25
151.4	90.6	631.41	0.1922	0.4921	15.68	615.73	647.09	1.1145	35.51	595.90	666.92
151.4	110.6	714.67	0.1457	0.4424	14.10	700.57	728.77	1.0935	34.85	679.82	749.52

Note: Numbers in parentheses are column numbers.

*Since $x' = (111.4 - 131.4, 90.6 - 100.6) = (-20, -10)$, then

$$x'Cx = (-20,-10)\begin{vmatrix} 297.869 & -58.099 \\ -58.099 & 498.160 \end{vmatrix} \times 10^{-6}\begin{vmatrix} -20 \\ -10 \end{vmatrix} = (-5,376.39, -3,819.62)\times10^{-6}\begin{vmatrix} -20 \\ -10 \end{vmatrix} = 0.1457.$$

†t_{TAB} with 17 degrees of freedom is 2.110, $s = 15.100$.

A write-up is usually available with regression programs; it should include a complete discussion of the *input* required and an explanation of the *output* and *options* available, as well as a complete statement of the calculation formulas and a sample problem. (Although documenting a program is a difficult task, poorly written documentation is often a warning of a poorly or improperly written computer program.)

While the input formats of regression programs vary, most programs have an option which allows the user to specify a variety of transformations of the data, such as logs, powers, and cross products. Typical regression outputs include ANOVA tables, residuals plots, and other statistics, in addition to the estimates of the regression coefficients. Although often omitted, an "echo-check," i.e., a printout of the original and transformed data, is essential. Often "strange" regression results can be traced to a misplaced decimal point in an observation, the wrong variables being read in, or incorrect use of the transformation option. (If this is not available in a program, ask the computer center to modify the program so that it is automatically printed out unless the user deletes it.)

R^2 and C_p Criteria for Model Choice.

In many situations there are a large number of possible variables for a model and the problem is to select the "vital few" from these "useful many," instead of obtaining the complete regression equation. There are many reasons for not using all the variables. For example, a subset of variables can provide a better prediction equation than the full set, even though the full set has a higher R, since the full set will also include more variability. In addition, equations with fewer variables are easier to understand, and hence more likely to gain acceptance and be used.

Unless the data come from a properly designed experiment, there is no simple test for significant variables. Since there are $2^k - 1$ possible prediction equations to evaluate, for large k it is obvious that a brute force approach is not feasible (for example, if $k = 20$, then $2^k - 1 = 1,048,575$).

"Stepwise regression" is a heuristic technique for avoiding this computational problem. It begins by selecting the single independent variable which is the "best" predictor in the sense that it maximizes R^2. Then it adds variables to the equation in a sequential manner, in order of importance. At each step the variable added is the one which increases the sum of squares (and hence R^2) or equivalently reduces the residual sum of squares by the largest amount. This procedure not only selects variables, but deletes variables previously selected, if at some point they no longer appear important.

Stepwise regression does not guarantee that the "best" set of variables will be included in the final equation. However, it does provide an efficient method for reducing the number of variables k to a manageable size; e.g., if $k = 100$ then stepwise regression can be used to select the best 25 or fewer for more exhaustive study. Stepwise regression programs are widely available; see Draper and Smith (1981).

In addition to stepwise regression, numerous other techniques have been developed. One which seems to have great potential was developed by Hocking and Leslie (1967) and improved by LaMotte and Hocking (1970). Their algorithm finds the "best" subset of variables of size $1, 2, \ldots, k$ where k is the total number of variables submitted. Although the computations require more time than the stepwise procedure, this procedure guarantees the best subset in the R^2 sense and in addition gives a number of the "contending" subsets. (Of course, if the number of variables is small, we could compute all regressions.) These "best" regression algorithms are available in BMDP, and can handle k up to 20 or 25 without computer time problems.

The set of possible variables should be selected on the basis of preliminary investigations of the factors which influence the response variables. The indiscriminate use of regression analysis to "find" relationships, where no facts suggest the existence of a relationship, often leads to nonsensical results. Unfortunately, this is usually discovered after the prediction equation fails miserably in predicting future observations.

If a large amount of data is available, one portion of it can be used for selecting variables and estimating coefficients, saving the remainder of the data for testing the derived equations. In any case, the equation should be periodically reviewed as new data become available.

A powerful tool in modern regression analysis is the C_p statistic (see, e.g., Dudewicz and Karian, 1985, pp. 236, 413). While R^2 measures the goodness of the regression equation in predicting the data points in the data set one is using to develop a model, C_p estimates the variance of future predictions made using the model. While adding a variable will increase the R^2 (even if that variable is totally unrelated to what we are trying to predict), C_p typically decreases as variables are added to the model, then increases. Thus, searching for the minimal C_p statistic in all possible regressions is a reasonable approach—though if a large gain in R^2 can be obtained with a modest increase in C_p, it should be taken.

REFERENCES

ASQC (1987). "QA/QC Software Directory." *Quality Progress,* March, pp. 33–66.

Barr, Donald R. (1969). "Using Confidence Intervals to Test Hypotheses." *Journal of Quality Technology,* vol. 1, no. 4, pp. 256–258.

Bennett, Carl A. and Franklin, Norman L. (1954). *Statistical Analysis in Chemistry and the Chemical Industry.* John Wiley & Sons, New York, chap. 11.

Bingham, R. S., Jr. (1962). "Tolerance Limits and Process Capability Studies." *Industrial Quality Control,* vol. XIX, no. 1, pp. 36–40.

Choksi, Suresh (1971). "Computer Can Optimize Manufacturing Tolerances for an Economical Design." *ASQC Technical Conference Transactions,* Milwaukee, pp. 323–330.

Cohen, A. Clifford and Whitten, Betty Jones (1981). "Estimation of Lognormal Distributions." *American Journal of Mathematical and Management Sciences,* vol. 1, no. 2, pp. 139–153.

Daniel, Cuthbert (1977). Personal Communication. August.

———— and Wood, Fred S. (1971). *Fitting Equations to Data.* John Wiley & Sons, New York.

Dielman, Terry E. and Pfaffenberger, Roger C. (1984). "Computational Algorithms for Calculating Least Absolute Value and Chebyshev Estimates for Multiple Regression." *American Journal of Mathematical and Management Sciences,* vol. 4, nos. 1 and 2, pp. 169–197.

Dixon, W. J. (1983). *BMDP Statistical Software, 1983 Printing with Additions.* University of California Press, Berkeley, CA.

———— and Massey, Frank J., Jr. (1969). *Introduction to Statistical Analysis,* 3rd ed., McGraw-Hill, New York.

Dodge, H. F., Kinsburg, B. J., and Kruger, M. K. (1953). "The L3 Coaxial System—Quality Control Requirements." *Bell System Technical Journal,* vol. 32, pp. 943–1005.

Draper, N. R. and Smith, H. (1981). *Applied Regression Analysis,* 2nd ed., John Wiley & Sons, New York.

Dudewicz, Edward J. (1976). *Introduction to Statistics and Probability.* Holt, Rinehart and Winston, New York. (Currently published by American Sciences Press, Columbus, OH. Address: P.O. Box 21161, Columbus 43221-0161.)

————— (1980). *Solutions in Statistics and Probability,* American Sciences Press, Columbus, OH.

————— (1983). "Heteroscedasticity." In N. L. Johnson, S. Kotz, and C. B. Read (eds.), *Encyclopedia of Statistical Sciences, Volume 3.* John Wiley & Sons, New York, pp. 611–619.

————— and Dalal, Siddhartha R. (1983). "Multiple-Comparisons with a Control when Variances Are Unknown and Unequal." *American Journal of Mathematical and Management Sciences,* vol. 3, no. 4, pp. 275–295.

————— and Karian, Zaven A. (1985). *Modern Design and Analysis of Discrete-Event Computer Simulations.* IEEE Computer Society Press, Los Angeles, CA. (Address is P.O. Box 80452, Worldway Postal Center, Los Angeles 90080; Order No. CN597.)

————— and Mishra, S. N. (1988). *Modern Mathematical Statistics.* John Wiley, New York.

————— and Ralley, Thomas G. (1981). *The Handbook of Random Number Generation and Testing with TESTRAND Computer Code,* American Sciences Press, Columbus, OH.

————— Karian, Zaven A. and Marshall, Rudolph James III (1985). "Random Number Generation on Microcomputers." *Proceedings of the Conference on Simulation on Microcomputers.* The Society for Computer Simulation (Simulation Councils, Inc.), La Jolla, CA. (Address: P.O. Box 2228, La Jolla, 92038.)

Duncan, Acheson J. (1974). *Quality Control and Industrial Statistics,* 4th ed., Richard D. Irwin, Homewood, IL.

Epstein, Benjamin (1960). "Estimation from Life Test Data." *Technometrics,* vol. 2, no. 4, pp. 447–454.

Evans, Ralph A. (1966). "Problems in Probability." *Proceedings of the Annual Symposium on Reliability,* IEEE, New York, pp. 347–353.

Fisher, R. A. (1936). "The Use of Multiple Measurements in Taxonomic Problems." *Annals of Eugenics,* vol. 7, pp. 179–188.

Gibbons, Jean Dickinson (1985). *Nonparametric Methods for Quantitative Analysis,* 2nd ed. American Sciences Press, Columbus, OH.

Golden, Bruce, L., Assad, Arjang A. and Zanakis, Stelios H. (eds.) (1984). *Statistics and Optimization: The Interface.* American Sciences Press, Columbus, OH.

Govindarajulu, Z. (1981). *The Sequential Statistical Analysis of Hypothesis Testing, Point and Interval Estimation, and Decision Theory.* American Sciences Press, Columbus, OH.

Grant, E. L. and Leavenworth, R. S. (1980). *Statistical Quality Control,* 5th ed., McGraw-Hill, New York.

Gray, H. L. and Lewis, Truman (1967). "A Confidence Interval for the Availability Ratio." *Technometrics,* vol. 9, no. 3, pp. 465–471.

Grubbs, Frank E. (1969). "Procedures for Detecting Outlying Observations in Samples." *Technometrics,* vol. 11, no. 1, pp. 1–21.

Gutt, J. D. and Gruska, G. F. (1977). "Variation Simulation." *ASQC Technical Conference Transactions,* Milwaukee, pp. 557–563.

Hadley, G. (1967). *Introduction to Probability and Statistical Decision Theory.* Holden-Day, San Francisco.

Hahn, G. J. (1970*a*). "Additional Factors for Calculating Prediction Intervals for Samples from a Normal Distribution." *Journal of the American Statistical Association,* vol. 65, no. 332, pp. 1668–1676.

————— (1970*b*). "Statistical Intervals for a Normal Population, Part I, Tables, Examples and Applications; Part II, Formulas, Assumptions, Some Derivations." *Journal of Quality Technology,* vol. 2, no. 3, pp. 115–125; vol. 2, no. 4, pp. 195–206.

————— (1971). "How Abnormal is Normality?" *Journal of Quality Technology,* vol. 3, no. 1, pp. 18–22.

————— (1972). "The Absolute Sample Size is What Counts." *Quality Progress,* vol. V, no. 5, pp. 18–19.

————— and Shapiro, S. S. (1967). *Statistical Models in Engineering.* John Wiley & Sons, New York.

Harter, H. Leon (1983). *The Chronological Annotated Bibliography of Order Statistics, Volume II: 1950–1959.* American Sciences Press, Columbus, OH.

———— and Dubey, Satya D. (1967). *Theory and Tables for Tests of Hypotheses concerning the Mean and the Variance of a Weibull Population.* Document AD 653593, Clearinghouse for Federal Scientific and Technical Information, U.S. Department of Commerce, Washington, DC.

Hocking, R. R. and Leslie, R. N. (1967). "Selection of the Best Subset in Regression Analysis." *Technometrics,* vol. 9, no. 4, pp. 531–540.

Hoerl, Arthur E. and Kennard, Robert W. (1981). "Ridge Regression—1980, Advances, Algorithms, and Applications." *American Journal of Mathematical and Management Sciences,* vol. 1, no. 1, pp. 5–83.

Iman, Ronald L. (1982). "Graphs for Use with the Lillefors Test for Normal and Exponential Distributions." *The American Statistician,* vol. 36, no. 2, pp. 109–112.

Ireson, W. Grant (ed.) (1982). *Reliability Handbook.* McGraw-Hill, New York.

Johnson, Norman L. and Kotz, Samuel (1969). *Discrete Distributions.* Houghton Mifflin, Boston.

Johnson, Norman L. and Leone, Fred C. (1964). *Statistics and Experimental Design, Vol. I.* John Wiley & Sons, New York.

Juran, J. M. and Gryna, Frank M., Jr. (1980). *Quality Planning and Analysis,* 2nd ed. McGraw-Hill, New York.

Kececioglu, D. and Cormier, D. (1964). "Designing a Specified Reliability into a Component." *Proceedings of the Third Annual Aerospace Reliability and Maintainability Conference.* Society of Automotive Engineers, Washington, DC, p. 546.

King, James R. (1971). *Probability Charts for Decision Making.* The Industrial Press, New York.

Kirkpatrick, R. L. (1970). "Confidence Limits on a Percent Defective Characterized by Two Specification Limits." *Journal of Quality Technology,* vol. 2, no. 3, pp. 150–155.

Kramer, C. Y. and Jensen, D. R. (1969, 1970). "Fundamentals of Multivariate Analysis." *Journal of Quality Technology,* vol. 1, no. 2, pp. 120–133, no. 3, pp. 189–204, no. 4, pp. 264–276; vol. 2, no. 1, pp. 32–40.

LaMotte, L. R. and Hocking, R. R. (1970). "Computational Efficiency in the Selection of Regression Variables." *Technometrics,* vol. 12, no. 1, pp. 83–93.

Lenz, H.-J. and Rendtel, U. (1984). "Performance Evaluation of the MIL-STD-105 D, Skip-Lot Sampling Plans, and Bayesian Single Sampling Plans." In Lenz, H.-J., Wetherill, G. B., and Wilrich, P.-Th. (eds.), *Frontiers in Statistical Quality Control 2.* Physica-Verlag, Rudolf Liebing GmbH & Co., Würzburg, W. Germany, pp. 92–106.

Levy, George C. and Dumoulin, Charles L. (1984). *The LAB ONE NMR1 Spectroscopic Data Analysis Software System, Revision 2.00 User's Manual.* Department of Chemistry, Syracuse University, Syracuse, NY. (Address: Dept. of Chemistry, Browne Hall, Syracuse University, Syracuse 13244.)

Lieberman, G. J. and Owen, D. B. (1961). *Tables of the Hypergeometric Probability Distribution.* Stanford University Press, Stanford, CA.

Lloyd, David K. and Lipow, Myron (1982). *Reliability: Management, Methods and Mathematics,* 2nd ed. Prentice-Hall, Englewood Cliffs, NJ.

Longley, J. W. (1967). "An appraisal of Least Squares Programs for the Electronic Computer from the Point of View of the User." *Journal of the American Statistical Association,* vol. 62, no. 319, pp. 819–841.

Lusser, R. (1958). *Reliability through Safety Margins.* United States Army Ordnance Missile Command, Redstone Arsenal, AL.

Martin Marietta Corp. (1966). *Reliability for the Engineer, Book 5: Testing for Reliability.* Martin Marietta, Orlando, FL, pp. 29–31.

Moult, John F. (1963). "Critical Agents in Bearing Fatigue Testing." *Lubrication Engineering,* December, pp. 503–511.

Mouradian, G. (1966). "Tolerance Limits for Assemblies and Engineering Relationships." *ASQC Technical Conference Transactions,* Milwaukee, pp. 598–606.

Natrella, Mary G. (1963). *Experimental Statistics, National Bureau of Standards Handbook 91.* Government Printing Office, Washington, DC.

Nelson, Wayne (1979). *How to Analyze Data with Simple Plots.* Volume 1 of Dudewicz, E. J. (ed.), *The ASQC Basic References in Quality Control: Statistical Techniques.* American Society for Quality Control, Milwaukee.

———— (1982). *Applied Life Data Analysis.* John Wiley & Sons, New York.

Oliver, Larry R. and Springer, Melvin D. (1972). "A General Set of Bayesian Attribute Acceptance Sampling Plans." *Technical Papers of the 1972 Conference, American Institute of Industrial Engineers,* pp. 443–455.

Owen, D. B. and Frawley, W. H. (1971). "Factors for Tolerance Limits which Control Both Tails of the Normal Distribution." *Journal of Quality Technology,* vol. 3, no. 2, pp. 69–79. See also Frawley, W. H., Kapadia, C. H., Rao, J. N. K., and Owen, D. B. (1971). "Tolerance Limits Based on Range and Mean Range." *Technometrics,* vol. 13, no. 3, pp. 651–656.

Peters, J. (1970). "Tolerancing the Components of an Assembly for Minimum Cost." ASME Paper 70-Prod.-9, *Transactions of the ASME Journal of Engineering for Industry,* American Society of Mechanical Engineers, New York.

Pinsky, Paul D. (1983). *Statpro, The Statistics and Graphics Database Workstation, Statistics User's Guide.* Wadsworth Electronic Publishing Company, Boston. (Address: Statler Office Building, 20 Park Plaza, Boston 02116.)

Ramberg, John S., Dudewicz, Edward J., Tadikamalla, Pandu R., and Mykytka, Edward F. (1979). "A Probability Distribution and its Uses in Fitting Data." *Technometrics,* vol. 21, no. 2, pp. 201–214.

Ranganathan, J. and Kale, B. K. (1983). "Outlier-Resistant Tolerance Intervals for Exponential Distributions." *American Journal of Mathematical and Management Sciences,* vol. 3, no. 1, pp. 5–25.

Rich, Barrett G., Smith, O. A., and Korte, Lee (1967). *Experience with a Formal Reliability Program.* SAE Paper 670731, Farm, Construction and Industrial Machinery Meeting, Society of Automotive Engineers, Warrendale, PA.

Rutherford, John R. (1971). "A Logic Structure for Experimental Development Programs." *Chemical Technology,* March, pp. 159–164.

SAS Institute Inc. (1982). *SAS User's Guide: Basics, 1982 Edition.* SAS Institute, Cary, NC. (Address: P.O. Box 8000, Cary 27511.)

Sheesley, J. H. (1977). "Tests for Outlying Observations." *Journal of Quality Technology,* vol. 9, no. 1, pp. 38–41.

Siotani, Minoru, Hayakawa, T., and Fujikoshi, Y. (1985). *Modern Multivariate Statistical Analysis: A Graduate Course and Handbook.* American Sciences Press, Columbus, OH.

Thoman, D. R., Bain, L. J., and Antle, C. E. (1970). "Maximum Likelihood Estimation, Exact Confidence Intervals for Reliability and Tolerance Limits in the Weibull Distribution." *Technometrics,* vol. 12, no. 2, pp. 363–371.

Volk, William (1956). "Industrial Statistics." *Chemical Engineering,* March, pp. 165–190.

Wampler, R. H. (1970). "On the Accuracy of Least Squares Computer Programs." *Journal of the American Statistical Association,* vol. 65, no. 330, pp. 549–565.

Wescott, M. E. *Mimeo Notes.* Rochester Institute of Technology, Rochester, NY.

Western Electric Company, Inc. (1982). *Statistical Quality Control Handbook.* American Society for Quality Control, Milwaukee.

Williamson, E. and Bretherton, M. H. (1963). *Tables of the Negative Binomial Probability Distribution.* John Wiley & Sons, New York.

Zacks, Shelemyahu (1983). *Workshop on Statistical Methods of Reliability Analysis for Engineers.* Center for Statistics, Quality Control, and Design, State University of New York, Binghamton, NY.

SECTION 24

STATISTICAL PROCESS CONTROL[1]

Dorian Shainin, CMC
Peter D. Shainin, PE

[1]In the Third Edition, the section on Process Control by Statistical Methods was prepared by C. A. Bicking and Frank M. Gryna.

This section of the handbook is concerned with those statistical tools which have been evolved to quantify the elements of the feedback loop and to put process controls on a quantified basis. Other aspects of process control are discussed elsewhere in the handbook, and include:

Topic	Discussed in
Management universals of the feed-back loop	Section 6 under The Feedback Loop
Ability of process to meet standards	Section 16 under Process Capability
Control system for dominant process variables	Section 16 under Planning Process Controls
Product acceptance	Section 25, Acceptance Sampling
Attainment of Optimum Process Conditions	Section 26 under Evolutionary Operations and Response Surface Methodology
Role of process control personnel in closing the loop	Section 17 under Concept of Self-Control

Appendix III, Selected Quality Standards, Specifications, and Related Documents, includes documents on control charts.

We start with some definitions and notation.

DEFINITIONS

Process: Any specific combination of machines, tools, methods, materials and/or people employed to attain specific qualitites in a product or service. A change in any one of these constituents results in a *new* process. These qualities (a dimension, material property, appearance, etc.) will be called "quality characteristics" to avoid confusion with levels of quality. Some processes are manufacturing processes; some are service processes; still others are support operations common to both manufacturing and service industries.

Control: The control process is a feedback loop through which we measure actual performance, compare it with standard, and act on the difference. The quicker the response to deviation from the standard, the more uniform the produced quality.

Statistical process control (SPC): The application of statistical techniques for measuring and analyzing the variation in processes.

Statistical quality control (SQC): The application of statistical techniques for measuring and improving the quality of processes. SQC includes SPC, diagnostic tools, sampling plans, and other statistical techniques.

NOTATION

In mathematics, causes are traditionally x's, and effects, y's. We will refer to the features which affect customer enthusiasm as y's and the specific quality characteristics which cause them to vary as x's. The variables which control the x's will be A's, B's, C's, etc. Cutting oil temperature on a lathe, variable A, will affect the diameter of a pump shaft cut on that lathe, quality characteristic x_1, which in turn affects the hydraulic leakage past a shaft seal, feature y_1.

Observed data are samples coming from unknown populations. In keeping with the convention of ANSI/ASQC (1985), population parameters will be represented by Greek letters and sample data by Roman letters. An overbar represents an average. A double overbar represents an average of averages (see Appendix I, Glossary of Symbols).

SPC THEORY

Control Charts. Dr. Walter A. Shewhart, of Bell Telephone Laboratories, developed a theory of statistical quality control in the second half of the 1920s. He analyzed many different processes and concluded: All manufacturing processes display variation. He identified two components: a steady component which appeared to be inherent in the process, and an intermittent component. Shewhart attributed inherent variation, currently called *random*[2] variation, to chance and undiscoverable causes, and intermittent variation to *assignable* causes. He concluded that assignable causes could be economically discovered and removed with a tenacious diagnostic program, but that random causes could not be economically discovered and could not be removed without making basic changes in the process.

The variation of any particular quality characteristic can be quantified by sampling the output of the process and estimating the parameters of its statistical distribution. Changes in the distribution can be revealed by plotting these parameters versus time. Samples usually consist of more than one individual measurement, and so are called "subgroups." Charts for variables are usually based on a subgroup size of 4 to 10 individuals, charts for attributes on a minimum of 50 and often several hundred individuals. Twenty-five subgroups are measured. For $\overline{X}$ and R charts, the most common type, the quality characteristic, X, is measured for each individual. The average, $\overline{X}$, and range, R, are calculated for each subgroup and plotted *in order of production* on separate charts. A central line is drawn on each chart at the grand average, $\overline{\overline{X}}$ and at the average range, $\overline{R}$. Control limits are established at the average ± 3 standard deviations. These are the upper control limit (UCL) and lower control limit (LCL). An example is shown in Figure 24.1 (Kukunaris, 1985).

The band between the control limits defines the random variation in the process. Points outside of the control limits indicate one or more assignable causes of variation. A process with only random causes present is said to be in "statistical control." Its output is considered to be as uniform as economically feasible.

After an assignable cause of variation is discovered and removed, new control limits calculated from 25 new subgroup averages and ranges often give a substantially narrower process capability. Under control chart theory this new process capability becomes the economic limit to improvement.

---

[2]*Random* in this sense means of unknown and insignificant cause, as distinguished from the mathematical definition of random—without cause. For a complete discussion, see Wadsworth and Bryan (1974), p. 40.

FIG. 24.1   Control chart for linewidth—proximity print photoresist process.

Shewhart organized his research material for a course at Bell Telephone Laboratories, then presented his theory to the outside world in a series of lectures at Stevens Institute of Technology. This lecture material became his well-known book, *Economic Control of Quality of Manufactured Product* (1931).

Shewhart's charts came into wide use in the 1940s as a result of war production efforts. Those who used them realized substantial gains in quality and productivity but also had difficulties in performing the required calculations and interpreting the charts. In the late 1940s and early 1950s there were many attempts to simplify the calculations and broaden the applicability of Shewhart's methods. In 1953 a team[3] from Rath & Strong, Inc., Management Consultants of Boston, MA, under contract to Jones & Lamson Machine Co. of Springfield, VT, developed PRE-Control. It was first published in 1954 and its first extensive production use was by J & L's customer, IBM, at Endicott, NY, in 1954.

PRE-Control.   PRE-Control is a simple algorithm which gives the worker direct control of his or her process. The tolerance band is divided into three zones, a target zone bounded by two cautionary zones. The worker measures a pair of individuals periodically. If both fall in the cautionary zones or either falls outside the tolerance, the operator adjusts the process immediately. Otherwise, the process is left alone. The subgroup of two does not attempt to estimate the distribution parameters, only to sense whether the distribution is safely within the tolerance or has either moved toward a tolerance limit or grown wider than the tolerance.

---

[3]The team consisted of Warren R. Purcell, Franklin E. Satterthwaite, C. W. (Bill) Carter, and Dorian Shainin.

This rapid warning allows the worker to adjust before nonconforming work is produced; thus, the name "PRE-Control."

Both $\overline{X}$ and R charts and PRE-Control enjoy wide usage today. Many of the calculation and charting difficulties associated with $\overline{X}$ and R charts have been overcome with computers. PRE-Control requires no calculations or charting. A later portion of this section presents procedures for using PRE-Control.

New Developments in Diagnostic Techniques. Since the introduction of Shewhart's theory, great strides have been made in statistics and their applications to quality control. Sir Ronald Fisher developed factorial experiments and his principles of replication, randomization, and balance (Fisher, 1935). Dr. Frank Yates (1937) published his algorithm for analyzing factorial experiments (see Section 26 under Factorial Experiments with k Factors). Leonard Seder developed Multi-Vari (see Section 22 under Diagnosis of Management-Controllable Problems), an effective charting method for analyzing variation in a process (Seder, 1950); and J. M. Juran generalized Pareto's principle: Most of the trouble comes from a few of the causes (Juran, 1950; see Section 22 under Pareto Concept). These techniques, used together, have proved to be very powerful. With them we can economically reduce variation to levels well below those of Shewhart's time. There is still a minimum level; but as our tools get better, that level gets lower. An optimist would conclude that in the next 60 years we will be able to reduce variation to levels that are inconceivable today.

Random Cause, Pareto, and the Red X. The variation described by the statistical distribution of a quality characteristic has many separate causes. The Pareto principle tells us that a few of these causes will have a major effect on the total variation. A few more will have a somewhat lesser effect. Most will have a very small effect.

Figure 24.2 illustrates the relative magnitude of effect of each of the many causes of variation. But each cause itself varies and can be described as a statistical distribution. This is illustrated in Figure 24.3.

FIG. 24.2 Pareto curve.   **FIG. 24.3** Distribution of causes.

Some x's are causing the quality characteristic y to move in one direction while others are causing it to move in the opposite direction and by different amounts at each different point in time. The dispersion of each of these distributions is measured by its standard deviation σ. Independent standard deviations add by the square root of the sum of the squares rule. The total variation of a quality characteristic, $\Delta x = (x_1^2 + x_2^2 + x_3^2 + x_4^2 + \cdots + x_n^2)^{1/2}$. If $x_1 = 5$ and $x_4 = 1$, then $x_1^2 = 25$ while $x_4^2 = 1$. The total effect of x_1 on variation will be 25 times the effect of x_4 even though it is only 5 times larger! This largest cause is called the "red X." The second largest is a "pink X." The shade becomes lighter as the cause becomes more minor.

Normal distributions are the result of many approximately equal causes of variation. The Pareto principle would lead us to expect that most distributions of quality characteristics would not be quite normal. Both Shewhart's and the authors' experience confirm this.

A red X will cause a distribution of *individuals* to be nonnormal, but a subgroup size of four is large enough to cause the distribution of *averages* to be very close to normal. Thus, virtually all of the averages will fall within the ± 3 standard deviation control limits. A large, steady red X will increase the dispersion of subgroup averages and/or change the location of the overall average, but it will not usually show up as an assignable cause. Assignable causes result from one or more transient red X's.

If 25 subgroups are taken to establish control limits for a new process and the process is affected by one or more transient causes during the sample period, the distribution of subgroup averages which is estimated by these 25 subgroups is an average of the different distributions of subgroup averages which existed at each different time that subgroups were taken. Subgroup averages outside of these control limits indicate that the distribution which existed at the time of the out-of-limit subgroups was taken is probably different from the "average" distribution for which the control limits were calculated.

Shewhart's assignable cause was a transient red X. His random causes were the minor X's. As each minor X was found and eliminated, it made hardly any difference at all in the process output. No wonder Shewhart thought it was not economically feasible to reduce variation below this "random" level. Unfortunately, a consistent red X will appear on a control chart as part of the random variation, and a consistent red X is the rule rather than the exception in the authors' experience. With the diagnostic techniques mentioned above, we can usually find that red X.

When Shewhart developed his theory, the concept of statistically analyzing the variation of a process in order to improve quality was unheard of. His work was truly pioneering. He intended his book as a prospectus of the future in quality control. The preface states, "This book constitutes a record of progress and an indication of the direction in which future developments may be expected to take place" (p. vii). Unfortunately, as is often the case in such matters, Shewhart's prospectus has become orthodoxy for many of today's quality control practitioners.

The concepts of improving a process by analyzing its variation and of a continuous and tenacious program to attack variation, as given to us by Shewhart, remain central to modern statistical quality control methods. The concept of dividing the causes of variation into assignable and chance catagories is of less practical use today. Processes which are running within correctly determined tolerances should be left alone. Processes which are displaying excessive variation (not running within tolerance all the time) should be investigated and improved using Multi-Vari and Factorial experiments. There are circumstances in which product uniformity around a target value is more important than the percent of product that meets specifications. See Section 16 under Process Capability; the Concept. See also Section 17 under Ability to Regulate (particularly Table 17.6) for a discussion of action to be taken considering both statistical control limits and product tolerances.

Marketing people must determine which features are important to customers and the range of each required to evoke enthusiasm. The engineering people must determine which quality characteristic(s) causes each feature and the critical range of each. This quality characteristic range becomes the manufacturing tolerance.

Many manuals on control charts suggest that if a process capability is wider than a tolerance, consideration should be given to expanding the tolerance. If the tolerance was set by an engineering guess, a common occurrence, process capability might be as good a reason as any to change it. But if the tolerance was set correctly, the tolerance must stay where it is and the process capability must be improved. If one does not find the red X, but a competitor does, one's market will be gone before one knows it.

CONTROL CHARTS

Uses of Control Charts.   Control charts are commonly used to:

1. Attain a state of statistical control (all subgroup averages and ranges within control limits; therefore, no assignable causes of variation present).
2. Monitor a process.
3. Determine process capability. *After* the process is in control, the limits of process variation can be determined. Since the control limits are established for averages, they must be multiplied by $\sqrt{n}$ (n = subgroup size) before they can be compared to tolerances. (See Section 16 under Process Capability Measurement for further discussion.)

A surprising number of companies try to use $\overline{X}$ and R for product acceptance purposes. They form subgroups by taking individuals at random from the entire lot. This is an incorrect procedure. Subgroups must be formed in production sequence.

Control charts can have an important role in product acceptance. Processes that are capable of meeting specifications and are in statistical control are prime candidates for auditing by acceptance sampling. Statistical control verifies the stability of the process and homogeneity of the product. Then a variety of sampling procedures (or no sampling at all) can be effectively applied. One of those procedures makes use of subgroups and simple statistical limits (see Section 25 under Variables Sampling; Lot Plot).

Attaining a State of Control.   Construct a control chart to attain a state of statistical control by:

1. Take 25 subgroups. The subgroup size will depend on the type of chart. Charts for variables data typically use four or five measurements; charts for attributes data employ subgroup sizes that depend on the specific type of chart.
2. Keep a log of any process changes (material, worker, tool, etc.) during the collection of these data.
3. Compute trial control limits from these data (see specific chart type for instructions).
4. Chart the data for each subgroup on their respective charts. If all points are within the control limits, the process is in statistical control. If any points fall outside the control limits, the process is not in statistical control. Find the assignable cause of this excessive variation and eliminate it. Retest as above to ensure that no assignable causes remain.

Most industrial processes are not in control when first analyzed; many points outside of control limits are common. The reasons for these assignable causes can be discovered and removed (Section 22 under Diagnosis). Mark explanations found for points out of control right on the chart. As remedies are made to the process, new data should be collected, control limits recalculated, and the new data plotted against the revised limits. Control is often attained by degrees. Removing assignable cause and recalculating control limits can be an iterative process. For an example, see Juran and Gryna (1980).

When it is difficult to collect new data, it is common practice to remove the out-of-control subgroups and recalculate the limits from the remaining data. But if new data are not taken, there is no way to be sure all assignable causes have been removed. Control limits and central lines calculated with new data will often be different than those calculated by modifying original data.

Control limits calculated from 10 rather than 25 subgroups are common practice, especially where production runs are short. Unfortunately, their proper location is known with considerably less precision.

Even if no process changes have consciously been made, it is a good idea to recalculate central lines for every 25 subgroups. In practice the old and new central lines are usually compared without any formal test. The procedures in Section 23 under Tests of Hypotheses could also be used.

Monitoring a Process. Control charts can monitor the aim and variability and thereby continually check the *stability* of the process. This check of stability in turn helps to assure that the statistical distribution of the product characteristic is consistent with quality requirements. For parts per million defect levels, tight process control procedures are the key answer to the high sample sizes that would be necessary with acceptance sampling procedures.

Basic Concepts of Control Charts

Estimating the Mean, μ. Shewhart investigated both the subgroup median and the subgroup mean as estimators of μ. He concluded that the mean, $\overline{X}$, was a more sensitive estimator. The mean of a subgroup is the sum of all of the individual points in that subgroup divided by the number of points in that subgroup. $\overline{X} = \Sigma X_i/n$.

Estimating the Standard Deviation σ. Subgroup range R is commonly used to estimate the standard deviation of the distribution of X's, σ_X. For subgroup size n of 2, R is as efficient an estimator of σ_X as the standard deviation of the subgroups s. Both statistics use all of the available data. For $n = 3$, s becomes a more efficient statistic. s uses all three of the data points in each subgroup. R uses only the two end points and thus ignores the information contained in the center point. For hand calculation and small n's, the ease of use and reduced possibility of error make R a better choice than s. Tippet (1950) recommends R for $n \leq 20$. ANSI/ASQC (1985) recommends R for manual calculation and $n \leq 10$.

$$\sigma_X \backsimeq \overline{R}/d_2 \backsimeq \bar{s}/c_2 \qquad s_X = \sqrt{\Sigma(X - \overline{X})^2/(n - 1)}$$

$$R = X_{\text{LARGEST}} - X_{\text{SMALLEST}} \qquad \overline{R} = \frac{\Sigma R}{N}$$

d_2 and c_2 are functions of subgroup size and may be found in Table A, Appendix II. Both R and s are valid estimators of σ_X only if the subgroups are taken at random from a stable population (Tippett, 1950, pp. 9–10). Since it is common practice to take subgroups periodically rather than at random, there is a risk that the frequency of sampling will align with the action of some unknown variable and produce a range or standard deviation out of proportion to σ_X.

Control Limits.   Control limits based on the statistical variation of the process can be established at the mean ± 3 standard deviations of the parameter. If the parameter being charted is distributed normally, about 99.73 percent of all values will fall within the control limits. Therefore, if a point falls outside the control limits, there are only 27 chances in 10,000 that the distribution has not changed. A red X probably caused the distribution to shift, grow wider, or both. The chance of a false out-of-control signal for control limits set at other multiples of σ_X can be found in a table of areas under the normal curve (Table B, Appendix II). The distribution of $\overline{X}$ will always be very close to normal for $n \geq 4$. The distribution of X may or may not be normal. See the specific chart types below for the formulas and factors used to calculate control limits.

The control limits for R will be too wide if the distribution of X's is skewed or leptokurtic (more pointed top and longer, thinner tails than normal); too narrow if the distribution of X's is platykurtic (flatter top than normal). If the value of $\overline{X}$ changes within the subgroups while the subgroups for setting control limits are being taken, the control limits for R will be too wide. Trending factors such as tool wear or temperature increase are a common cause of this malady. Subgroups taken too far apart will make this situation worse. Too small a number of subgroups can give an inaccurate $\overline{R}$ and thus incorrect control limits for both $\overline{X}$ and R. If the control limits for $\overline{X}$ and R are too wide, the risk of missing a signal for action (β risk) increases. If the control limits for R are too narrow, the risk of getting a false out-of-control signal (α risk) increases.

Control limits can also be calculated to include a preassigned percentage (e.g., 99.0 percent) of the charted values when the process is in statistical control. For formulas and factors, see ANSI/ASQC (1985).

A note of caution: A state of "statistical control" merely means that only random causes are present. It does not necessarily mean that the product meets specifications. Conversely, a process which is not in statistical control may still be producing product which conforms to specification. Action on such a process should have a much lower priority than action on processes which are producing nonconforming product.

Subgroup Size, n.   Since $\sigma_{\overline{X}} = \sigma_X / \sqrt{n}$, the larger the subgroup size, n, the smaller the standard deviation of the distribution of averages, $\sigma_{\overline{X}}$, the tighter the 3σ control limits, and the more sensitive the chart for $\overline{X}$. However, as n gets larger, the time required to obtain and plot the data gets longer. Transient red X's can do substantial damage before they are discovered. The sensitivity of a chart for detecting process changes with different subgroup sizes can be defined by an operating characteristic curve. An example is given below. Subgroups are normally of equal size. Grant and Leavenworth (1980) give procedures for unequal subgroups. Four and five are common subgroup sizes for variable data.

See Control Charts for Fraction Nonconforming, below, for a discussion of subgroup size when charting attribute data.

Rational Subgrouping.   Each subgroup must come from a single distinct population. A subgroup of consecutively produced individuals taken from the same die cavity of a multiple-cavity mold is appropriate.

Improper or irrational choice of subgroups can be visually detected on a plotted $\overline{X}$ and R chart. Two examples are:

1. The $\overline{X}$ points clustered close to the $\overline{\overline{X}}$ line, not filling out the space between the upper and lower control limits

2. The $\overline{X}$ points beyond both control limits most of the time

In both cases the range points nicely fill out the space between their control limits.

The first condition is caused by using items from different die cavities on a multicavity mold in the same subgroup. R is a function of cavity-to-cavity differences rather than of the time-to-time differences on which the charts are based. $\Delta \overline{X}$ is a function of time-to-time differences. Since time-to-time differences are usually much smaller than cavity-to-cavity differences, R and the resulting control limits are inflated relative to $\overline{X}$.

The second condition is caused by taking all of the individuals in one subgroup from the same die cavity but taking successive subgroups from different die cavities. Now R is smaller but $\overline{X}$ is inflated by the cavity-to-cavity differences. In this case R is a function of time but $\Delta\overline{X}$ is a function of cavity geometry.

As a general rule, a separate die cavity must be treated as a separate machine and plotted on a separate set of charts. The same logic holds for any multiple-position machine.

Some authorities recommend taking successive subgroups from different die cavities when monitoring a process that has already been shown to be in control. This would seem to allow one set of charts to do the work of several. If the die cavity numbers are noted with the subgroup average on the chart, cavity-to-cavity variation will be revealed. This is similar to Multi-Vari, but the use of averages makes it less informative.

Why Use Averages? Averages are more sensitive to change than individuals (Figure 24.4). Consider a process in which σ for individual items is 50 and the average of individuals is 1000. The 3σ range of individuals is 150; therefore, the limit lines will be $1000 + 150 = 1150$ and $1000 - 150 = 850$. A change in process from 1000 to 1100 will change the 3σ limit lines to 1250 and 950. The chance of an individual from the changed process falling outside the first limit lines is about 16 in 100. Detecting the change with a certainty of 99 in 100 will require, on the average, 27 subgroups of one individual each.

If subgroups of four are used, the limit lines will be $1000 \pm 3\sigma/\sqrt{n} = 1000 \pm (3 \times 50)/2$, 1075 and 925. For the same change in average, from 1000 to 1100, the chance of the average of the subgroup of four falling outside the first limit lines is about 84 in 100. Now to detect the change with a certainty of 99 in 100 will require, on the average, only *two* or *three* subgroups. The risk of not detecting the change is $(0.16)^2 = 0.026$ for two subgroups and $(0.16)^3 = 0.004$ for three subgroups.

Operating Characteristics Curve for a Control Chart. The operating characteristic (OC) curve is a plot of the true value of a process parameter, e.g., the average, against the probability that a single sample will fall within the control limits. It shows the ability of the chart to detect process changes. Figure 24.5 is an OC curve for an $\overline{X}$ control chart with a true average $\mu_X = 45.8$, standard deviation $\sigma_X = 2.9$, and subgroup size $n = 4$. This curve should not be confused with a normal distribution of measurements. In some cases the shape is similar but the meanings are entirely different.

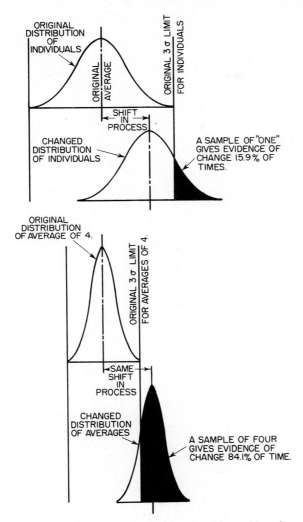

FIG. 24.4 How averages are more sensitive to detecting change than individuals.

If μ_X shifts from 45.8 to 40.0, the probability that a single subgroup average $\overline{X}$ will fall within control limits is about 0.16; there is only a 16 percent chance that a change of this magnitude will be undetected. If the process average shifted only to 43.0, the probability that a single $\overline{X}$ will fall within control limits is about 0.84. It is unlikely this shift would go undetected very long. The probability that it will be undetected after five subgroups is $(0.84)^5 = 0.418$.

The OC curve is a function of the subgroup size n, width of control limits $t\sigma$ (e.g., 1.5σ, 2σ, 3σ), and standard deviation σ. By evaluating the OC curves for various subgroup sizes and control limits, a chart can be designed for unique problems with the best compromise between n and t. Duncan (1974) has excellent discussions on the methods of constructing OC curves for $\overline{X}$, R, p, and c control charts and on the conclusions which can be drawn from these curves. Krishnamoorthi (1985) discusses sensitivity of control charts and presents the concept of customizing a chart to be most economical for the process.

FIG. 24.5 Operating characteristic curve for a control chart.

Steps in Setting Up Control Charts

1. Choose the characteristic to be charted. This is a matter of judgment, but use the following guides:

    a. Give high priority to characteristics that are running defective and where adjustment controls are available to the worker. A Pareto analysis (see Section 22 under The Project Concept) can establish priorities.

    b. Identify the process variables and conditions contributing to end product characteristics. For example, pH, salt concentration, and temperature of plating solution are process variables which could contribute to plating smoothness. A word of warning: The selection of such variables is usually subjective and quite opinionated. Objectivity is needed. A useful step is to make a scatter plot of data on suspected variables versus the end product characteristic for at least 30 items produced at different times.

    c. Choose characteristics which will provide the kind of data needed for diagnosis of problems. Attribute data (e.g., percent defective) provide summary information but may need to be supplemented by variables data (e.g., numerical diameter of individual pieces) to diagnose causes and determine action.

    d. Determine the earliest point in the production process at which testing can be done to get information on assignable causes so that the chart can serve as an effective early warning device to prevent nonconformities.

2. Choose the type of control chart. Table 24.1 compares several basic control charts. The objective is to make items which conform to specifications. The proper use of p, np, u, and c charts should lead to their extinction.

3. Decide the central line to be used and the basis of calculating the control limits. The central line may be the average of past data, or may be a desired average (i.e., a standard value). The limits are usually set at $\pm 3\sigma$, but other multiples may be chosen for different statistical risks. $\pm 3\sigma$ limits involve a very small risk of looking for trouble that does not exist (α or type I risk), but a larger risk of failing to detect trouble when it does exist (β or type II risk). See Section 23 under Statistical Tests of Hypotheses. When the control plan incorporates a statistically determined frequency of taking subgroups, the two types of risk can be balanced. Limits set at $\pm 2\sigma$ would have a large α risk but a smaller β risk. These risks depend on the sample size and other factors. A study by Duncan (1974) found that charts using 2σ or even 1.5σ limits are more economical than charts using the conventional 3σ limits. This is true if it is possible to

TABLE 24.1 Guide to Control Charts Discussed in Section 24

Data type	Parameters plotted	Typical use	Advantages	Disadvantages	Comments
Variables					
$\overline{X}$ and R/s	Subgroup average and range or standard deviation	Machine-dominant processes	A good window into the statistical variation of a process.	Complex calculations; slow response; indirect relationship between control limits and tolerance.	Select subgroup size, frequency and number of subgroups used to set and reset control limits carefully.
X and R	Individual and subgroup range	Where only one observation per lot is available	Quicker, easier to plot and explain. Compares directly to tolerance.	Not as sensitive as $\overline{X}$ and R chart.	
CumSum	Cumulative sum of deviation of subgroup averages from a reference value	High cost product or test where 0.5σ to 2σ shift is common	Faster response to an abrupt shift in mean than $\overline{X}$ and R chart.	Complex, hard to explain.	PRE-Control is faster and simpler.
Attributes					
p np u c	Fraction nonconforming Number nonconforming Nonconformities per unit Number of nonconformities	Only attribute data available or to monitor quality of a complex unit with more than one characteristic of interest	Data is usually easier to obtain than variable data. Calculations are easier than $\overline{X}$ charts.	Attribute data is not as useful for diagnostic work as variable data.	As quality gets better, subgroups get bigger. Eventually, all attribute charts should make themselves obsolete.

decide very quickly and inexpensively that nothing is wrong with the process when a point (just by chance) happens to fall outside the control limits; i.e., when the cost of looking for trouble when none exists is low. Contrariwise, it will be more economical to use charts with 3.5σ to 4σ limits if the cost of looking for trouble is very high.

4. Choose the rational subgroup (see Rational Subgrouping, above).

5. Choose the frequency of subgroups (individuals within a subgroup should be consecutive if possible). The rate of change in the process (tool wear or deterioration of a chemical solution) will determine the maximum time to allow between subgroups. Sample a new process frequently until the data indicate the frequency can be reduced.

6. Choose the subgroup size (see Subgroup Size, above).

7. Provide the system for collecting data. If the control chart is to serve as a day-to-day shop tool, it must be made simple and convenient to use. A shop awash with cutting oil won't do well with ordinary pencil and paper. Special covers, paper, and crayons can help. Measurement must be kept simple and error-free. Instruments must give prompt reliable readings. Direct recording instruments are best. If control charts are being used to monitor a process, data must be plotted and the results given to the worker immediately. Any delay, such as waiting until the end of the day to plot the date, will negate the value of the charts.

8. Calculate the control limits and provide specific instructions on interpretation of results and action to be taken. Ford Motor Company (1984) has prepared a useful guide giving detailed procedures and forms for applying the basic types of control charts. Vance (1983) provides an extensive bibliography of articles classified by type of control chart technique.

TYPES OF CONTROL CHARTS

Variables versus Attributes Data. Charts for variables data require measurements on a continuous scale such as length, weight, pH, or resistance. Charts for attributes data require only a count of discrete measurements such as good or bad. Variables data include more information than attributes data, thus are preferred for SPC and essential for diagnosis.

Charts for attributes will be useful provided the defective rate is high enough to show on the chart with a reasonable subgroup size. Current competitive quality requirements in many industries are so high that attributes charts are not useful.

Variables Data

Control Chart for Average and Range, $\overline{X}$ and R.   This chart is particularly helpful for machine-dominant processes. Take 25 subgroups of four or five individuals each. Calculate the average, $\overline{X}$, and range, R, of each subgroup. Calculate the average of all subgroups, $\overline{\overline{X}}$, and the average range $\overline{R}$. Calculate the 3σ control limits using:

$$\text{Central line} = \overline{\overline{X}}$$

$$\text{Upper control limit for } \overline{X} = \overline{\overline{X}} + A_2\overline{R}$$

$$\text{Lower control limit for } \overline{X} = \overline{\overline{X}} - A_2\overline{R}$$

$$\text{Central line} = \overline{R}$$

$$\text{Upper control limit for } R = D_4\overline{R}$$

$$\text{Lower control limit for } R = D_3\overline{R}$$

For subgroup size, $n > 10$, use standard deviation σ instead of range (see above under Subgroup Size). Calculate the 3σ control limits using:

$$\text{Central line} = \overline{\overline{X}}$$

$$\text{Upper control limit for } \overline{X} = \overline{\overline{X}} + A_1\overline{s}$$

$$\text{Lower control limit for } \overline{X} = \overline{\overline{X}} - A_1\overline{s}$$

$$\text{Central line} = \overline{s}$$

$$\text{Upper control limit for } s = B_4\overline{s}$$

$$\text{Lower control limit for } s = B_3\overline{s}$$

The values of the A, B, and D factors depend on subgroup size, n, and are given in Table A, Appendix II. Draw the control limits, the $\overline{\overline{X}}$ and $\overline{R}$ or $\overline{s}$ lines, and plot $\overline{X}$ and R or s on their respective charts.

The control chart factors assume a normal population of individuals; moderate deviations are acceptable. Examples of a data sheet and control chart for $\overline{X}$ and R are shown in Figures 24.6 and 24.7.

Interpretation of Charts. Place the charts for $\overline{X}$ and R (or s) one above the other so the average and range for any one subgroup are on the same vertical line. Observe whether either or both indicate lack of control for that subgroup.

$\overline{X}$'s outside the control limits are evidence of a general change affecting all pieces after the first subgroup out of limits. Study the log kept during data collection, the operation of the process, and the worker's experience attempting to discover a variable which could have caused the out-of-control subgroups. Typical causes are a change in material, personnel, machine setting, tool wear, temperature, or vibration.

R's outside control limits are evidence that the uniformity of the process has changed. Typical causes are a change in personnel, increased variability of material, or excessive wear in the process machinery. In one case a sudden increase in R warned of an impending machine accident.

A single R out of control can be caused by a shift in the process which occurred while the subgroup was being taken.

Look for unusual patterns, nonrandomness. Nelson (1984 and 1985) provides eight tests to detect such patterns on control charts using 3σ control limits (Figure 24.8). Each of the zones shown is 1σ wide. (Note that test 2 in Figure 24.8 requires nine points in a row; other authors suggest seven or eight points in a row; see Nelson, 1985, for elaboration.) AT&T (1984) is another excellent reference for control chart patterns.

Compare the process data with specification limits. See Section 16 under Process Capability Measurement.

	6/8			6/9				6/10				6/11				6/12				6/15				6/16	
TIME	8	10	12	2	8	10	12	2	8	10	12	2	8	10	12	2	8	10	12	2	8	10	12	2	8
R 1	.65	.75	.75	.60	.70	.60	.75	.60	.65	.60	.80	.85	.70	.65	.90	.75	.75	.75	.65	.60	.50	.60	.80	.65	.65
E 2	.70	.85	.80	.70	.75	.75	.80	.70	.80	.70	.75	.75	.70	.70	.80	.80	.70	.70	.65	.60	.55	.80	.65	.60	.70
A 3	.65	.75	.80	.70	.65	.85	.65	.80	.85	.60	.90	.85	.75	.85	.80	.75	.85	.60	.85	.65	.65	.65	.75	.65	.70
D 4	.65	.85	.70	.75	.85	.85	.75	.75	.85	.80	.50	.65	.75	.75	.75	.80	.70	.70	.65	.60	.80	.65	.65	.60	.60
S 5	.85	.65	.75	.65	.80	.70	.70	.75	.75	.65	.80	.70	.70	.60	.85	.65	.80	.60	.70	.65	.80	.75	.65	.70	.65
SUM	3.50	3.85	3.80	3.40	3.75	3.65	3.65	3.60	3.90	3.35	3.75	3.80	3.60	3.55	4.10	3.75	3.80	3.35	3.50	3.10	3.30	3.45	3.50	3.20	3.30
X̄ = SUM / NO. OF READINGS	.70	.77	.76	.68	.75	.73	.73	.72	.78	.67	.75	.76	.72	.71	.82	.75	.76	.67	.70	.62	.66	.69	.70	.64	.66
R = HIGHEST / LOWEST	.20	.20	.10	.15	.20	.25	.15	.20	.20	.20	.40	.20	.05	.25	.15	.15	.15	.15	.20	.05	.30	.20	.15	.10	.10

FIG. 24.6 Data sheet for $\overline{X}$ and R control chart.

CONTROL CHARTS — APPLYING TO WEIGHT OF EXPLOSIVE CHARGE in Grains

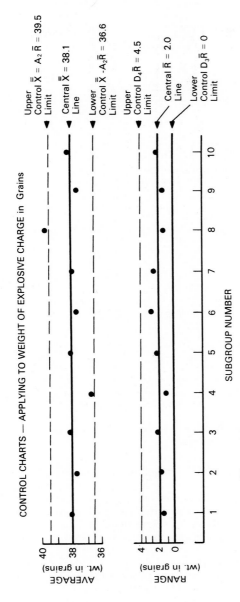

FIG. 24.7 Example of $\overline{X}$ and R control chart

Upper Control $\overline{\overline{X}} = A_2\overline{R} = 39.5$ Limit

Central $\overline{\overline{X}} = 38.1$ Line

Lower Control $\overline{\overline{X}} - A_2\overline{R} = 36.6$ Limit

Upper Control $D_4\overline{R} = 4.5$ Limit

Central $\overline{R} = 2.0$ Line

Lower Control $D_3\overline{R} = 0$ Limit

AVERAGE (wt. in grains)

RANGE (wt. in grains)

SUBGROUP NUMBER

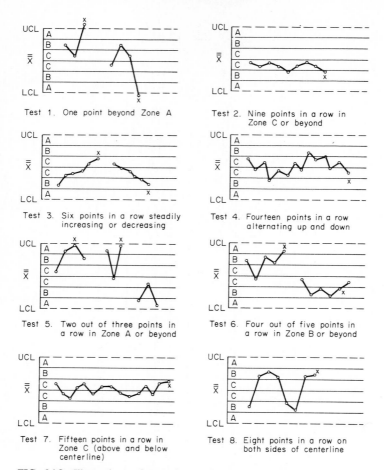

FIG. 24.8 Illustrations of tests for special causes applied to $\overline{X}$ control charts. *(From Nelson, 1984.)*

To illustrate the technical investigations that accompany a control chart, Flynn and Bolcar (1984) present a variety of examples and the lessons learned from each. Ott (1975) presents an extensive collection of cases with innovative statistical analysis conducted after the initial control charts. For an example showing how basic diagnostic tools such as Pareto analysis and the cause and effect diagram are used in conjunction with control charts, see Corbi, Nay, and Belt (1986).

Control Chart for Individuals X, and Range R.   This is a plot of individual observations and is useful when only one observation per lot or batch is available. It is not as sensitive as the $\overline{X}$ chart (see Why Use Averages? above). For this reason 2σ control limits are often used. Unlike control limits for averages, control limits for individuals can be directly compared to tolerance limits.

Take a minimum of 30 individuals in subgroups of at least 2. Calculate the average of all 30 individuals, $\overline{X}$, the range of each subgroup, R, and the average of the ranges, $\overline{R}$. Calculate the 3σ control limits using:

$$\text{Central line} = \overline{X}$$

$$\text{Upper control limit for } X = \overline{X} + E_2\overline{R}$$

$$\text{Lower control limit for } X = \overline{X} - E_2\overline{R}$$

$$\text{Central line} = \overline{R}$$

$$\text{Upper control limit for } R = D_4\overline{R}$$

$$\text{Lower control limit for } R = D_3\overline{R}$$

2σ control limits are calculated by using two-thirds of the 3σ band:

$$\text{Upper control limit for } X = \overline{X} + \tfrac{2}{3} E_2\overline{R}$$

$$\text{Lower control limit for } X = \overline{X} - \tfrac{2}{3} E_2\overline{R}$$

The values of the E_2 and D factors depend on subgroup size n, and are given in Tables Y and A, respectively, Appendix II. Draw the control limits, the $\overline{X}$ and $\overline{R}$ lines, and plot X and R on their respective charts.

The control chart factors assume a normal population of individuals; moderate deviations are acceptable.

Example of a Control Chart for X and R. A batch-type manufacturing process is controlled by measurements of the flow point. Two batches are made per day, so that a daily subgroup of two is a rational one. It is desirable to examine the results for possible corrective action batch by batch. A control chart for individual batches is indicated. Data are given in Table 24.2.

TABLE 24.2 Flow Point of Resin

Subgroup	Measurements X_1	Measurements X_2	Range R
1	133.5	117.5	16.0
2	124.0	126.5	2.5
3	132.5	130.5	2.0
4	118.0	126.5	8.5
5	127.5	133.5	6.0
6	131.5	128.5	3.0
7	124.0	124.0	0
8	137.0	143.5	6.5
9	132.5	133.5	1.0
10	133.0	126.5	6.5
11	126.0	135.5	9.5
12	121.5	131.0	9.5
13	135.5	131.5	4.0
14	136.0	128.0	8.0
15	127.5	126.0	1.5
16	125.0	123.5	1.5
17	130.0	130.0	0
Totals		4391.0	86.0
Averages		129.15	5.06

For the X chart:

$$\text{Central line} = \overline{X} = 129.15$$

$$\text{Control limits} = \overline{X} \pm E_2\overline{R} = 129.15 \pm 2.660 \times 5.06$$

$$= 142.61 \text{ and } 115.69$$

For the R chart:

$$\text{Central line} = \overline{R} = 5.06$$

$$\text{Control limits} = D_4\overline{R} \text{ and } D_3\overline{R} = 3.27 \times 5.06 \text{ and } 0 \times 5.06$$

$$= 16.6 \text{ and } 0$$

These limits are drawn on the charts for X and R, and individual batch results and ranges are plotted. The charts are not shown, but we can see from Table 24.2 that the second batch on the eighth day is out of control. All ranges are in control. The reason for the out-of-control points should be investigated and discovered.

Unfortunately, this information came to light too late. We did not have 30 individual points on which to base the control limits until the end of day 15 which was 7 days after the out-of-control point. PRE-Control would have avoided this delay (see PRE-Control, below).

Attributes Data

Control Charts for Fraction Nonconforming. Fraction nonconforming, p, is the ratio of nonconforming items to the total number of items in a subgroup. It may describe a single quality characteristic or two or more characteristics considered collectively. A distinction is made between a nonconformity (e.g., a defect) and a nonconforming unit (e.g., a defective). A *nonconformity* is a single instance of nonconformance to some requirement; a *nonconforming unit* is a single item containing one or more nonconformities. Set up separate charts for each characteristic, if possible. Grouping nonconformities resulting from several different causes can make meaningful interpretation of the chart very difficult.

Subgroup size n is a function of the nonconformity rate. The better the quality, the larger the subgroup size needed to detect lack of control. ANSI/ASQC (1985) recommends at least one nonconforming item per subgroup. Ford (1985) recommends $n\overline{p} > 5$. n is almost always greater than 50 and $n = 400$ to 600 is not uncommon. Small subgroup sizes will give wide control limits and cause a poor process to be in control. As the nonconformity rate gets smaller and subgroup size gets larger, the time required to obtain each point gets longer and the chart's response time increases. With continuous use, all charts for attributes should make themselves obsolete for control purposes.

Subgroups should be of equal size if possible. If individual subgroups do not vary from the average subgroup size $\overline{n}$ by more than 25 percent use $\overline{n}$ rather than n to calculate the control limits. Individual subgroups varying from the average by more than 25 percent require their own separate set of control limits, calculated for each subgroup, using its particular size n. Varying control limits can be difficult to explain to both operators and management.

Take 25 subgroups. Calculate each subgroup's fraction nonconforming, p, and the average fraction nonconforming of all subgroups, $\overline{p}$. Calculate the 3σ control limits using:

$$\text{Central line} = \bar{p}$$

$$\text{Upper control limit for } p = \bar{p} + 3\sqrt{\bar{p}(1 - \bar{p})/n}$$

$$\text{Lower control limit for } p = \bar{p} - 3\sqrt{\bar{p}(1 - \bar{p})/n}$$

(For $\bar{p} < 0.10$, the control limit formula may be simplified to $\bar{p} \pm 3\sqrt{\bar{p}/n}$.) Draw the central line and the upper and lower control limits. Plot the fraction nonconforming, p, for each subgroup.

Example of Control Chart for p.   Table 24.3 shows the results of final testing and inspection, during a period of 5 months, of certain permanent magnets used in electrical relays. The total number of magnets tested was 14,091: The total number found to be nonconforming was 1030. The average sample size was

$$\bar{n} = \frac{14{,}091}{19} = 741.6$$

The average fraction nonconforming was

$$\bar{p} = \frac{1{,}030}{14{,}091} = 0.073$$

TABLE 24.3   *p* Chart Data

Subgroup: Production during week. Inspected at: Final assembly and test				
Week no.	Week ending	No. magnets inspected	No. nonconforming magnets	Fraction nonconforming, p
1	12/3	724	48	0.067
2	12/10	763	83	0.109
3	12/17	748	70	0.094
4	12/31	748	85	0.114
5	1/7	724	45	0.062
6	1/14	727	56	0.077
7	1/21	726	48	0.066
8	1/28	719	67	0.093
9	2/4	759	37	0.049
10	2/11	745	52	0.070
11	2/18	736	47	0.064
12	2/25	739	50	0.068
13	3/4	723	47	0.065
14	3/11	748	57	0.076
15	3/18	770	51	0.066
16	3/25	756	71	0.094
17	4/1	719	53	0.074
18	4/8	757	34	0.045
19	4/15	760	29	0.038
Totals		14,091	1030	
Averages		741.6	54.2	0.073

Calculate

Control limits for the chart were placed at

$$\bar{p} \pm 3\sigma_p = \boxed{\bar{p} \pm 3\sqrt{\frac{\bar{p}(1 - \bar{p})}{n}}} = 0.073 \pm 3\sqrt{\frac{0.073(1 - 0.073)}{741.6}}$$

$$= 0.073 \pm 0.0287 = 0.102 \text{ and } 0.044$$

The value 0.0287 is found either by direct calculation or by referring to Chart Z (in Appendix II). To use the graph, find the sample size on the lower scale, move upward to the intersection with the solid diagonal line at $\bar{p}$ (interpolate to find 0.073). Then move to the left-hand scale to obtain the value of $3\sigma_p$, which is given there as 0.029. The upper limit for p is thus $\text{UCL}_p = 0.073 + 0.029 = 0.102$, and the lower limit is $\text{LCL}_p = 0.073 - 0.029 = 0.044$. The resulting control chart is shown in Figure 24.9. Note that the last sample is below the lower control limit, indicating a significantly low fraction nonconforming. Although this might mean that there is some assignable cause resulting in better quality, such points can also be due to an inspector's accepting some nonconforming units in error.

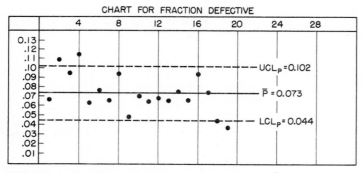

FIG. 24.9 p chart for permanent magnets.

The lower p may have began during week 9. The 3σ control limits can have a large β risk, thus failing to detect a change when it does exist. Grant and Leavenworth (1980) give additional examples.

Control Charts for Number Nonconforming, np. np is a direct count of the number of nonconforming in a subgroup. The directions and cautions for an np chart are the same as those for a p chart except all subgroup sizes must be the same.

Take 25 subgroups. Count the number nonconforming, np, in each subgroup. Calculate the average number nonconforming of all subgroups, $n\bar{p}$. Calculate the 3σ control limits using:

$$\text{Central line} = n\bar{p}$$

$$\text{Upper control limit for } p = n\bar{p} + 3\sqrt{n\bar{p}(1 - \bar{p})}$$

$$\text{Lower control limit for } p = n\bar{p} - 3\sqrt{n\bar{p}(1 - \bar{p})}$$

(For $\bar{p} < 0.10$, the control limit formula may be simplified to $n\bar{p} \pm 3\sqrt{n\bar{p}}$.) Draw the central line and the upper and lower control limits. Plot the number nonconforming, np, for each subgroup.

Example of Control Chart for np.   For the example in Table 24.3:

$$\text{Center line} = n\bar{p} = 54.2$$

$$\text{Control limits} = n\bar{p} \pm 3\sqrt{n\bar{p}} = 54.2 \pm 3\sqrt{54.2}$$

$$= 54.2 \pm 22.1 = 76.3 \text{ and } 32.1$$

The simplified formula is used because $\bar{p}$ is less than 0.10. The same subgroups are out of control on this basis as in the control chart for p (Figure 24.9). The charts are identical except for the vertical scale; so the np chart has not been reproduced. The sample sizes in this example vary slightly but are sufficiently similar to be treated as equal.

Control Chart for Nonconformities per Unit u.   The control chart for u is most useful when several independent nonconformities (they must be independent) may occur in one unit of product. This is likely to happen in complex assemblies.
The control chart lines for sample size n are:

$$\text{Central line} = \bar{u}$$

$$\text{Upper control limit} = \bar{u} + 3\sqrt{\bar{u}/n}$$

$$\text{Lower control limit} = \bar{u} - 3\sqrt{\bar{u}/n}$$

where $\bar{u}$ is the total number of nonconformities in all samples divided by the total number of units in all samples, that is, the nonconformities per unit in the complete set of test results. For samples of unequal size, control limits are computed for each size separately, using a pooled value of $\bar{u}$.
  Example of Control Chart for u.   Table 24.4 gives inspection results for 25 consecutive lots of a product. The lot size was essentially constant; so a constant sample size ($n = 10$) was used. All nonconformities were counted because two or more nonconformities of the same or different kinds could occur on each item. The nonconformities per unit are found by dividing the number of nonconformities found by the sample size.
  Then, for the control chart for u,

$$\text{Central line} = \bar{u} = \frac{37.5}{25} = 1.5$$

$$\text{Control limits} = \bar{u} \pm 3\sqrt{\frac{\bar{u}}{n}} = 1.50 \pm 3\sqrt{\frac{1.50}{10}}$$

$$= 1.50 \pm 1.16 = 2.66 \text{ and } 0.34$$

The control chart is given in Figure 24.10. The ninth sample is out of control. An investigation is in order. Grant and Leavenworth (1980) provide additional examples.

Control Chart for Number of Nonconformities c.   A control chart for number of nonconformities in a sample is the equivalent of the control chart for u. It is a practical alternative when all samples are of the same size n. It is particularly effective when the number of nonconformities *possible* on a unit is large but the percentage for any single nonconformity is small. Examples are physical nonconformities such as surface irregularities, flaws, or pinholes on continuous or exten-

TABLE 24.4 Number of Nonconformities

Sample no.	Total nonconformities in sample c	Nonconformities per unit u
1	17	1.7
2	14	1.4
3	6	0.6
4	23	2.3
5	5	0.5
6	7	0.7
7	10	1.0
8	19	1.9
9	29	2.9
10	18	1.8
11	25	2.5
12	5	0.5
13	8	0.8
14	11	1.1
15	18	1.8
16	13	1.3
17	22	2.2
18	6	0.6
19	23	2.3
20	22	2.2
21	9	0.9
22	15	1.5
23	20	2.0
24	6	0.6
25	24	2.4
Total	375	37.5

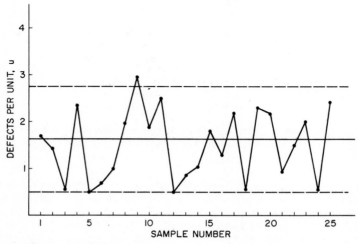

FIG. 24.10 Control chart for u.

sive products such as yarn, wire, paper, textiles, or other sheeted materials. The chance of a nonconformity occurring at any one spot may be small, but the overall opportunity for nonconformities may be great.

The chart for c makes direct use of the count of defects. See the column headed "Total Nonconformities in Sample c" in Table 24.4.

Formulas for control chart lines are

$$\text{Central line} = \bar{c}$$

$$\text{Upper control limit} = \bar{c} + 3\sqrt{\bar{c}}$$

$$\text{Lower control limit} = \bar{c} - 3\sqrt{\bar{c}}$$

where $\bar{c}$ is the total number of nonconformities in all samples divided by the number of samples, that is, the average number of nonconformities per sample.

Examples of Control Charts for c.   For the examples in Table 24.4,

$$\text{Central line} = \bar{c} = \frac{375}{25} = 15.0$$

$$\text{Control limits} = \bar{c} \pm 3\sqrt{\bar{c}} = 15.0 \pm 3\sqrt{15.0}$$

$$= 15.0 \pm 11.6 = 26.6 \text{ and } 3.4$$

The same sample, no. 9, is out of control on this chart as in the control chart for u. The charts are identical except for the vertical scale; so the c chart has not been reproduced.

An example of the control chart for c to control nonconformities of a sheeted material follows. Table 24.5 shows the results of a series of pinhole tests of paper intended to be impervious to oils. Specimen sheets 11×17 in in size were taken from production at intervals, and colored ink was applied to one side of the sheet. Each individual inkblot which appeared on the other side of the sheet within 5 min was counted as a nonconformity.

The center line of the chart is located at $\bar{c} = 200/25 = 8.0$ nonconformities per sheet. Control limits, which are at $8.0 \pm 3\sqrt{8.0}$, may be computed directly or

TABLE 24.5   *c* Chart Data

Sheet no.	No. of pinholes	Sheet no.	No. of pinholes
1	8	14	6
2	9	15	14
3	5	16	6
4	8	17	4
5	5	18	11
6	9	19	7
7	9	20	8
8	11	21	18
9	8	22	6
10	7	23	9
11	6	24	10
12	4	25	5
13	7		
		Total	200

found from Chart AA (in Appendix II). The average value, 8.0, is located at either the upper or lower edge of this chart. The points at which the vertical line through 8.0 crosses the solid curves are noted. The corresponding limits are found at the side of the chart. In this case, the upper 3σ limit is found at 16.5 and the lower 3σ limit at zero. The resulting c chart is pictured in Figure 24.11. Grant and Leavenworth (1980) provide additional examples.

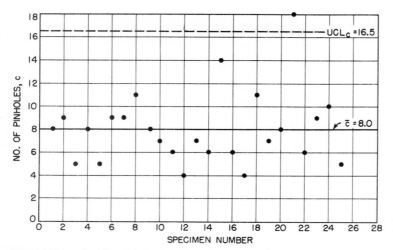

FIG. 24.11 c chart for pinholes in paper.

Cumulative Sum Control Charts.   A plot of the cumulative sum of deviations of subgroup averages from a reference value is particularly good at detecting abrupt shifts of the mean ($0.5\sigma_{\overline{X}}$ to $2.0\sigma_{\overline{X}}$) which remain with the process for at least five subgroups. Each point contains information from all observations up to and including itself. Usually, each point equals the preceding point plus the value of a statistic computed from the last subgroup.

Cumulative sum control charts (CSCC), like the other control charts discussed here, are interpreted by comparing the plotted values to critical limits. But the critical limits for a CSCC are neither parallel nor fixed. A mask in the shape of a V is usually constructed. It is laid over the chart with its origin over the last plotted point. Points covered by the mask are an indication that the process has shifted.

To Plot a CSCC

1. Obtain an estimate of $\sigma_{\overline{X}}$. (From $\overline{X}$ and R data, the estimate is $(\overline{R}/d_2)/\sqrt{n}$.)
2. Determine the least amount of change D in the average that it is desired to detect, and calculate $\delta = D/\sigma_{\overline{X}}$.
3. Determine the probability level at which decisions are to be made. For limits equivalent to standard control limits, $\alpha = 0.00135$.
4. Define k as the scale factor which is the *numerical* change in the value of the variable (vertical scale) per one unit change in *distance* (between two tick marks) in the horizontal scale. (The horizontal scale represents the subgroup

sample number.) Ewan (1963) recommends that k be chosen to be between $1\sigma_{\overline{X}}$ and $2\sigma_{\overline{X}}$, but preferably closer to $2\sigma_{\overline{X}}$.

5. To obtain the lead distance d, enter Table BB of Appendix II with $\delta = D/\sigma_{\overline{X}}$.

6. To obtain the mask angle θ, calculate D/k (recall that k is the scaling factor from step 4). Substituting D/k for δ, enter Table BB and read (or interpolate for) θ at the "δ" row corresponding to D/k.

7. Using d and θ construct the mask to define the control limits.

Subgroup Number. The guidelines for $\overline{X}$ and R charts apply, but for best results Ewan (1963) suggests:

$$n = \frac{2.25s^2}{D}$$

(where s is an estimate of the population standard deviation) and an interval between subgroups of $T/6$ where T is the permissible average time before the shift of D is detected.

Some Common Patterns of Plots. The mask is placed over the last point plotted. If any of the previous points are covered by the mask, a process shift has occurred (the process is "out of control"). Points covered by the top of the mask means a decrease in the average; the bottom of the mask detects an increase. The first point covered by the mask indicates the time at which the shift in average started. If all the points are exposed by the mask, the process is considered in control.

Some Cautions:

1. Periodically check with an R chart to see if the standard deviation is constant before drawing conclusions on the average.

2. Watch for *gradual* changes in the process average or changes that enter and leave the process (say in less than five sampling intervals). These conditions are not as apparent on a cumulative sum chart as on an $\overline{X}$ chart.

Statistical Distribution Assumption. The population of individual measurements is distributed normally.

Example of a CSCC. The data in Table 24.6 summarizes measurements from 20 subgroups of four each on the percent of water absorption in common building brick. The reference value R_0 was 10.0. To illustrate the CSCC, the original data were modified to introduce a decrease in the overall average of 2.0 percent starting with subgroup 11.

1. $\sigma_{\overline{X}}$ is estimated by $\overline{R}/d_2\sqrt{n} = 8.08/2.059\sqrt{4} = 1.96$.

2. We wish to detect a shift $D = 1\sigma_{\overline{X}}$; therefore $\partial = 1.96/1.96 = 1.0$.

3. We will use $\alpha = 0.00135$, the value for a standard $\overline{X}$ chart.

4. The scale factor $k = 2\sigma_{\overline{X}} = 2 \times 1.96 = 3.92 \approx 4$.

5. From Table BB, Appendix II, the lead distance of the mask, $d = 13.2$.

6. Substituting $D/k \approx 2/4 \approx 0.5$ for a "δ" value in Table BB of Appendix II, $\theta = 14°$.

Figure 24.12 shows the CSCC with the mask located at subgroup 17. The mask was moved from left to right with the zero point on the mask placed over each

TABLE 24.6 Data on Percent Water Absorption

Subgroup no.	$\overline{X}$	$\overline{X} - 10.0$	$\Sigma(\overline{X} - 10.0)$
1	15.1	5.1	5.1
2	12.3	2.3	7.4
3	7.4	−2.6	4.8
4	8.7	−1.3	3.5
5	8.8	−1.2	2.3
6	11.7	1.7	4.0
7	10.2	0.2	4.2
8	11.5	1.5	5.7
9	11.2	1.2	6.9
10	10.2	0.2	7.1
11	7.6	−2.4	4.7
12	6.2	−3.8	0.9
13	8.2	−1.8	−0.9
14	7.8	−2.2	−3.1
15	6.8	−3.2	−6.3
16	6.1	−3.9	−10.2
17	4.3	−5.7	−15.9
18	8.5	−1.5	−17.4
19	7.7	−2.3	−19.7
20	9.7	−0.3	−20.0

Note: $\overline{R} = 8.08$.

plotted point. For the first 16 points, the mask did not cover any of the plotted points. This meant no shift in process level. At point 17, the mask detected the shift and indicated that the shift started at about the time subgroup 10 was taken (it really started at subgroup 11).

Figure 24.12 also shows the standard $\overline{X}$ chart. It would not have detected the shift on the basis of an $\overline{X}$ beyond the $\pm 3\sigma_{\overline{X}}$ control limits. However, note that by subgroup 17 the shift would be detected by four out of five successive points in zone B or beyond (Figure 24.8, Test 6).

A comparison of the cumulative sum chart and the standard $\overline{X}$ chart involves the concept of average run length (ARL).[4] The ARL is the average number of sample points plotted at a specified quality level before the chart detects a shift from a previous level. Ewan (1963) compares the ARL for the two charts for various amounts of shift in a process average. For shifts between about $0.5\sigma_{\overline{X}}$ and $2\sigma_{\overline{X}}$, the cumulative sum chart detects the shift with roughly half the number of subgroups as the standard $\overline{X}$ chart,[5] limiting the delay for action to that number of periods. The standard $\overline{X}$ chart works better for shifts on both sides of this range.

Johnson and Leone (1964, pp. 320–340) provide a thorough discussion and procedures (including scale values, lead distance, and mask angle) for applying CSCC to sample ranges, variances, number of defectives, fraction defective, and

---

[4]The procedure for determining d and θ can reflect desired values of the average run length. See Ewan (1963) and Bowker and Lieberman (1972), pp. 495–478.

[5]The comparison gets involved because there are modifications to the standard $\overline{X}$ chart that are pertinent (Ewan, 1963). Also the cumulative sum chart is superior only for certain significance levels (Johnson and Leone, 1964, pp. 340–342).

FIG. 24.12 Comparison of cumulative sum and $\overline{X}$ and R charts.

number of defects. Lucas (1985) discusses cumulative sum schemes for counts (attributes).

Constructing a Control Chart for Maintaining Control in the Future (Control with Standard Given). As a process is brought into control, data become available as to what is the expected level of the process and what is the expected dispersion. From these data it is possible to establish the expected range of variation for the process. This expected range of variation then becomes the standard against which subsequent samples are compared to detect the entry of significant causes of variation.

Use of the expected range of variation as a standard will detect significant changes in the process. Whether these changes would cause defects or not is quite another matter and depends on the relation of the product specification limits to the control limits.

The data from the process are the actual average values and are so designated, as

$$\text{Grand average} = \overline{\overline{X}}$$

$$\text{Average fraction nonconforming} = \overline{p}$$

$$\text{Average number of nonconformities} = \overline{c}$$

$$\text{etc.}$$

If these factors are used to specify the expected future values from the process, then the same quantities are simply redesignated, as "standard" values, by substituting the subscript "$_0$" symbol for the bar, so that

$$\text{Expected or "standard" average} = \overline{X}_0$$

$$\text{Expected or standard fraction nonconforming} = p_0$$

$$\text{Expected or standard number of nonconformities} = c_0$$

If the past data are not precisely the same as the desired standard, control limits based on the desired standard can still be set up, but only if there is evidence or real reason to believe the standard value can be achieved.

These standard values are for the entire volume of material to be manufactured; i.e., they are desired population values. Since the range theoretically expected in a normal population is infinitely wide, it is necessary to adopt some other measure as the standard for dispersion. The measure σ_0, which is equal to $\overline{R}/d_2$ or $\overline{s}/c_2$, is customarily used.

Control limits are calculated as follows:

Averages:

$$\text{Central line} = \overline{X}_0$$

$$\text{Upper control limit} = \overline{X}_0 + A\sigma_0 \text{ or } \overline{X}_0 + A_2R_0$$

$$\text{Lower control limit} = \overline{X}_0 - A\sigma_0 \text{ or } \overline{X}_0 - A_2R_0$$

Ranges:

$$\text{Central line} = R_0 \text{ or } d_2\sigma_0$$

$$\text{Upper control limit} = D_2\sigma_0$$

$$\text{Lower control limit} = D_1\sigma_0$$

Standard deviation:

$$\text{Central line} = s_0 \text{ or } c_2\sigma_0$$

$$\text{Upper control limit} = B_6\sigma_0$$

$$\text{Lower control limit} = B_5\sigma_0$$

Fraction nonconforming:

$$\text{Central line} = p_0$$

$$\text{Upper control limit} = p_0 + 3\sqrt{p_0(1 - p_0)/n}$$

$$\text{Lower control limit} = p_0 - 3\sqrt{p_0(1 - p_0)/n}$$

Number of nonconforming units:

$$\text{Central line} = np_0$$

$$\text{Upper control limit} = np_0 + 3\sqrt{np_0(1 - p_0)}$$

$$\text{Lower control limit} = np_0 - 3\sqrt{np_0(1 - p_0)}$$

Number of nonconformities per unit:

$$\text{Central line} = u_0$$

$$\text{Upper control limit} = u_0 + 3\sqrt{u_0/n}$$

$$\text{Lower control limit} = u_0 - 3\sqrt{u_0/n}$$

Values of the numerical factors are given in Appendix II, Table A. See ANSI/ASQC Z1.3 (1985) for further discussion.

Standard values may also be calculated from some criteria unrelated to the actual statistical variation of the process such as tolerance limits. The nominal may be used for $\overline{X}_0$. Upper and lower control limits will be the extreme tolerance minus the nominal all divided by $\sqrt{n}$. For a subgroup size of four the distance between the upper and lower control limits will be half the tolerance. Terms such as "modified control limits," "reject limits," and "narrow limit gaging" are associated with this approach. For an example, see Yu and Case (1984).

Control limits set without regard to the actual statistical variation of the specific group of raw materials, machines, and people employed to manufacture the product may bear little relationship to that variation. A process can be within such control limits but actually be operating out of *statistical* control. The presence of an assignable cause does not have to result in rejected work. On the other hand, a process operating in statistical control will produce a large quantity of rejects if the process capability, adjusted for sample size, is appreciably wider than the tolerance.

Correct tolerances are set by their ability to create customer enthusiasm. Customers have little interest in the statistical variation experienced by a manufacturer. It makes more sense to base limits for monitoring a process on the tolerance than on the $\pm 3\sigma$ limits of random variation of the process.

Special Control Charts. Some of the standard control charts assume normality. When measurements are distributed nonnormally, they can sometimes be "transformed" mathematically, and the transformed measurements can then be treated by standard control limit formulas. See Section 23 under Additional Statistical Tools. Be particularly careful of special types of data such as ranks or ratios of two characteristics. Rank data are usually nonnormal. Ratios are sometimes normal but must be carefully analyzed from the viewpoint of statistical control because of possible interacting conditions between the two characteristics comprising the ratio.

Table 24.7 summarizes some special control charts not discussed above and gives references to detailed instructions for their construction and use.

PRE-CONTROL

PRE-Control Theory. PRE-Control is a simple algorithm for controlling a process based on the tolerances. It assumes the process is producing product with a measurable and adjustable quality characteristic which varies according to some distribution. It makes no assumptions concerning the actual shape and stability of the distribution. Cautionary zones are designated just inside each tolerance extreme.

A new process (new setup, raw material, worker, etc.) is qualified by taking consecutive samples of individuals until five in a row fall within the central (non-

TABLE 24.7   Special Control Charts not Discussed in Section 24

Name of chart	Feature	Reference
Median	No arithmetic computations when subgroup size is odd	Grant and Leavenworth (1980), pp. 287–289
Moving average and moving range	Has smoothing effect to emphasize trends: new average plotted with each individual measurement	Grant and Leavenworth (1980), pp. 293–298
Geometric moving average: exponentially smoothed average	Combines successive measurements: effective in detecting small process shifts	Wortham and Heinrich (1972)
Demerits	Permits weighting of defects by degree of seriousness	Grant and Leavenworth (1980), pp. 269–271; see also Section 8 under Product Auditing
Adaptive	Evaluates process data against predicted value and quantifies adjustment needed	Section 28, under Adaptive Control
τ^2	One chart evaluates two or more related variables that have a joint effect on a quality characteristic	Montgomery and Wadsworth (1972); Hunter (1984)

cautionary) zone before two in a row fall in the cautionary zones. This ensures that the distribution is narrow enough and close enough to center to produce product within the tolerance limits. This is not statistical control; it is capability control; the process is now known to be capable of producing product within tolerance. If the process can not be qualified, diagnostic work to identify and control the red X must begin immediately.

Once the process is qualified, it is monitored by taking periodic samples consisting of two individuals each (called an A,B pair). This small subgroup size and the immediate information it provides directly to the process worker constitutes a very tight, quick feedback loop. Action is taken only if both A and B are in the cautionary zone. (For a reprint of a classic paper on adjusting processes, see Grubbs, 1983.)

The statistical power of PRE-Control resides in the rule of the product of independent probabilities: $P(A,B) = P(A) \times P(B)$. Thus the risk of a false signal is dramatically reduced by using a sample size of two. The actual probabilities are a function of the width of the cautionary zones. See α Risk, below. The probability of missing out-of-tolerance work is controlled by the size of the cautionary zones and frequency of taking samples. See β Risk, below.

The rules concerning setup, sample size, and frequency of sampling have been developed both mathematically and through operating experience (Shainin, 1984). Because the PRE-Control rules are so simple, users often conclude they are arbitrary and change them in an effort to improve PRE-Control. The sample size (two) is a compromise between lowering the risk of a false signal and waiting too long to take action. The width of the cautionary zones is a compromise between sensitivity and hunting. With the cautionary zones set as shown below, hunting is a sign that the actual distribution is wider than the tolerance. The process must be repaired. The frequency of sampling is a compromise between the cost and effort of more frequent samples and the risk of producing out-of-tolerance work. The original PRE-Control calculations indicated a frequency of 25 *A,B* pairs between typical process adjustments would ensure an average of 1 percent or less, out-of-tolerance production. Most processes require periodic adjustments to remain within specifications. Subsequent experience has shown that the currently recommended frequency of six *A,B* pairs between adjustments is sufficient to provide virtually no out-of-tolerance work. See β Risk, below. Brown (1966) reports on an application where 30,000,000 pieces were produced without a single reject. Changing the already optimized zone and subgroup size rules will result in less effective process control.

Requirements for Use. PRE-Control is effective for *any* process where the worker can measure a quality characteristic of interest (dimension, color, strength, etc.) and can adjust the process to change that characteristic, and where the process has either a continuous output (i.e., paper) or a discrete output (i.e., machine parts) with a total production run of three or more pieces.

Although PRE-Control requires a minimum of five items to qualify a setup, it is actually controlling the process while those five items are being produced. If the first two items are yellow, adjust the process *before* making the third! The qualifying count must start over, but we have already prevented possible nonconforming product. If the total production run is only three items, PRE-Control can provide valuable information before the third item is produced.

There are *no* additional requirements and *no* underlying assumptions concerning process capability or the frequency distribution of the quality characteristic. (The population of individuals need not be normal and the process need not be in statistical control.)

Setting Up PRE-Control

Two-Sided Tolerance. Place reference lines at nominal $+\frac{1}{4}$ tolerance range and nominal $-\frac{1}{4}$ tolerance range. Color the areas: between the reference lines (half the total tolerance) green, between each reference line and the adjacent tolerance limit yellow, and outside the tolerance limits red. See Figure 24.13.

One-Sided Tolerance, Total Indicator Reading (Flatness or Concentricity). Place one reference line at half the tolerance from the maximum limit toward zero. Color the areas: between zero and the reference green, between the reference and the maximum limit yellow, and above the maximum red. See Figure 24.14

FIG. 24.13 PRE-Control lines for two-sided tolerance.

FIG. 24.14 PRE-Control lines for a one-sided tolerance, total indicator reading.

One-Sided Tolerance, Minimum or Maximum (Yield Strength). Place one reference line a quarter of the way from the tolerance limit toward the best sample produced during past operations. Color the areas: from the reference line to beyond the best piece green, from the reference line to the tolerance limit yellow, and beyond the tolerance limit red. See Figure 24.15

FIG. 24.15 PRE-Control lines for a one-sided tolerance, minimum and maximum.

Provide the process operator with means of measuring the characteristic, and color the instrument face green (good), yellow (caution), and red (stop) according to the rules given above.

Using PRE-Control

Qualify the Setup. Measure every piece produced until you obtain five greens in a row. If one yellow is encountered, restart the count. If two yellows in a row or any reds are encountered, adjust the process and restart the count. This step replaces first piece inspection.

Run. Measure two consecutive pieces periodically (called an *A,B* pair). If both are yellow on the same side, adjust. If yellow on opposite sides, call for help (this condition usually requires a more sophisticated correction). If either are red, adjust. In the case of two yellows, the adjustment must be made immediately to prevent nonconforming work. In the case of red, stop; nonconforming work is already being produced! Do not put the red piece in with previous parts.

Frequency of Measuring. Measure six *A,B* pairs on average between each required process adjustment. Since there are 60 min in an hour, this rule conveniently reduces to: time between measurements in minutes = time between adjustments in hours × 10:

Time between adjustments, h	Time between measurements, min
1	10
2	20
3	30
4	40
etc.	

For an instructive case history on the use of PRE-Control and results obtained, see Brown (1966).

Risk. All techniques for analyzing process variation involve two risks. Section 23 under Statistical Tests of Hypotheses discusses these risks as the type I (or α) risk and the type II (or β) risk. These risks also apply to PRE-Control.

α *Risk.* The risk of a false alarm at a specific operating condition. The risk of a double yellow signal when the process should not be adjusted.

β *Risk.* The risk of a miss at a specific operating condition. The risk of producing out-of-tolerance work and not getting a double yellow or red signal.

The worst practical operating condition for α risk is a normal frequency distribution of the quality characteristic with its mean μ at the nominal (center of the tolerance) and $\pm 3\sigma$ right on the upper and lower tolerance limits, respectively (Figure 24.16). Reference to a table of areas under the normal curve (Appendix II, Table B) will show that the green zone ($\pm 1.5\sigma$) contains 86 percent of the area, leaving 7 percent for each of the yellow tails. There are nine possible permutations of A,B pairs (see Fig. 24.16). Since the probability of each is the product of the probabilities of its component events, the probability of obtaining any permutation of A and B is the proportion of area under the normal curve which will give a particular A times the proportion of area which will give a particular B. There are four permutations of A and B which will constitute a false alarm (see under "Help" and "Adjust" in Figure 24.16). The probability of each permutation is $\frac{1}{14} \times \frac{1}{14} = \frac{1}{196}$. The probability of all four permutations is therefore $\frac{4}{196} \approx 2$ percent.

In the worst likely case, an worker using PRE-Control will get a signal to adjust the process when it should not be adjusted 2 percent of the time. When the worker adjusts the process and tries to requalify the setup, probably two consecutive yellows will occur before five greens. This second double yellow signals to adjust the

FIG. 24.16 PRE-control α risk calculation.

process back toward its original position. The result of this false signal is a sequence of two unnecessary adjustments—one as a result of the false signal and one to correct it. It does not result in the production of any nonconforming product.

The worst practical operating condition for β risk is the same normal distribution with $\pm 3\sigma$ equal to the full tolerance used above, but with its mean μ displaced from the nominal by 0.85σ. In this case the out-of-tolerance work produced will not exceed an average of 1 percent. The calculation is somewhat more complex than that for α risk. For a complete discussion of PRE-Control β risk, see Shainin (1984).

Implementation. PRE-Control was designed to be used by the production worker as an integral part of the production process. Implementation requires his or her cooperation. Let PRE-Control sell itself. Ask for a volunteer to conduct a 2-week experiment. Explain PRE-Control and provide the volunteer with colored gages and a written set of PRE-Control rules. The faces may be colored with nail polish for this initial "experiment." Check periodically for the first couple of days to answer any questions. At the end of the 2 weeks, tell the worker the experiment is over, and offer to take the gages away. The authors' experience is that the worker will not want the gages removed. The word will already have been passed to the rest of the shop about how much more control the worker has with PRE-Control. It is not uncommon for other workers to request PRE-Control before the initial 2-week experiment is completed. Implement PRE-Control on each operation as the worker on that operation requests it. It may take 6 months before the whole shop is using it, but they will be using it effectively.

Do not provide special inspectors to measure the samples from each process and do not ask the workers to make charts or tally sheets of their measuring results. The purpose of PRE-Control, like the purpose of the shop, is to make good product, not charts or any other kind of record. PRE-Control's effectiveness can be audited with an appropriate sampling inspection plan (see Section 25, Acceptance Sampling).

Comparison of $\overline{X}$, R Charts and PRE-Control. A comparison of $\overline{X}$ and R charts with PRE-Control is given in Table 24.8. Sinbaldi (1985) describes simulations run to compare the two techniques.

STATISTICAL CONTROL OF AUTOMATED PROCESSES

Section 16, under Automated Manufacturing, defines some of the basic approaches used in automating manufacturing processes. Section 27, Computers and Quality, discusses the role of computers in both automated and nonautomated processes.

From the viewpoint of data analysis in process control, the march toward automation has sparked some innovations:

1. Continuous reading instrumentation which yields large amounts of data on process variables and quality characteristics.

2. Automation of statistical analysis (e.g., calculation of means, standard deviation, control limits). This is discussed below under Software for Statistical Process Control.

TABLE 24.8 Comparison of $\overline{X}$ and R Control Charts and PRE-Control

Item	$\overline{X}$ and R charts	PRE-Control
Purpose	Discover amount of variation caused by "random" and assignable causes Detect time of assignable cause Provide record of SPC	Prevent manufacture of defects
Decision rules	Subgroup $\overline{X}$ beyond control limit 9 subgroup $\overline{X}$'s on same side of $\overline{\overline{X}}$ Subgroup R beyond control limit	2 consecutive yellows on same side of target zone 2 consecutive yellows on opposite sides of target zone
Subgroup size	≥ 2, usually 4 or 5	Always 2
Effect of x's distribution shape	For subgroup size ≥ 4, not significant	Not significant; controls by the size of the cautionary zones, not by the target zone
To improve statistical sensitivity	Increase subgroup size	Optimized by setting the sum of the cautionary zones equal to half the tolerance
To reduce detection time	Decrease subgroup size More frequent subgroups Speed up calculations	Take more A,B pairs between typical process adjustments
To qualify a process	Take 25 subgroups, compute control limits, demonstrate state of statistical control Common practice to take 10 subgroups and disregard 1 or 2 out-of-control points or to use old control limits after eliminating an assignable cause	Run of 5 greens in a row before 2 yellows in a row
Effect of process capability greater than tolerance	None, unless $\overline{X}$ control limits are compared with tolerance (control limit $\times$ square root of subgroup size is comparable to tolerance)	2 yellows will occur on opposite sides of target zone before a run of 5 greens, or 2 yellows on one side of target zone will switch to the other side with only a small process adjustment; therefore, stop!
Effect of one out-of-tolerance individual in a subgroup	None, as long as $\overline{X}$ is within the control limits; theory says the process cannot be economically improved, i.e., zero defects are not economically possible	Out-of-tolerance is red, therefore stop!

TABLE 24.8 Comparison of $\overline{X}$ and R Control Charts and PRE-Control (*Continued*)

Item	$\overline{X}$ and R charts	PRE-Control
α Risk, (probability of hunting)	For control limits @ $\pm 3\sigma$ = 0.0027; for control limits @ $\pm 2\sigma$ = 0.05	0.00 to 0.02
β Risk (probability of missing out-of-tolerance work)	Not usually considered but often very large (depends on frequency of subgroups and relationship between tolerance and control limits); out-of-tolerance rates of 2% not uncommon; irrational subgrouping and failure to calculate new control limits after changing the process can make this rate much worse	Depends on frequency of sampling; out-of-tolerance work theoretically will not exceed 1% for six pairs between typical adjustments; actual experience indicates rate is 0%

3. Comparison of process results with preset numerical standards. This comparison may result in

   a. The generation of a document or other form of alert giving pertinent information on a nonstandard condition.

   b. The generation of an error signal that automatically makes a process adjustment. The authors have been impressed with the improvement in recent years of "size control" devices. While an item is being ground, a measuring pair of contacts monitors the change in size and electronically instructs the grinding wheel to prepare to stop removing material as the desired size is being approached.

Software for Statistical Process Control. Many mini and personal computer programs are available for statistical analysis of data including virtually all types of control charts. Gages with direct digital outputs can be plugged into hand-held data collection devices. These devices will store the gage readings collected on the shop floor and will download them to a personal computer in the office. As an alternative, gage readings may be entered into the collection device with its keyboard.

The software will calculate the sample parameters, initial control limits, and the control chart. Of course, control limits may be easily recalculated periodically, and $\pm 2\sigma$ limits can be calculated as an additional guide. Most software will provide additional summaries and analyses such as listings of the raw data, out-of-specification values, histograms, checks for runs and other patterns within control limits, tests for normality, process capability calculations, Pareto analyses, and trend analyses.

The relatively low cost of personal computers and the availability of software have contributed substantially to the renewed interest in $\overline{X}$ and R charts. This computer-software combination has also made it practical to collect large quantities of data and subject it to various and complex forms of analysis. However, process improvement still requires the identification of the vital few and often unexpected variables causing excess variation. Computer analysis is no substitute for such tools as Multi-Vari (Section 22 under Test of Theories of Management-Controllable Problems) or factorial experiments (Section 26 under Factorial Experiments). Computers are most helpful when the diagnostician has created a template for a spreadsheet program and least helpful when a prepackaged statistical analysis program is used. Users are rarely familiar with the detailed logic of the prepackaged programs and can be led to erroneous conclusions.

The American Society for Quality Control annually publishes a directory of software for process control and other areas of quality assurance (ASQC, 1986). In addition, the *Journal of Quality Technology* (ASQC) and *Quality* (Hitchcock Publishing Co.) have computer columns describing programs for process control.

REFERENCES

American Telephone and Telegraph (AT&T) (1984). *Statistical Quality Control Handbook,* 2nd ed., 10th printing. Delmar Printing Company, Charlotte, NC.

ANSI/ASQC (1985). Z1.1, *Guide for Quality Control Charts;* Z1.2, *Control Chart Method for Analyzing Data;* and Z1.3, *Control Chart Method of Controlling Quality during Production.* American Society for Quality Control, Milwaukee.

ASQC (1987). "QA/QC Software Director." *Quality Progress,* March, pp. 33–66.

Bowker, Albert H. and Lieberman, Gerald J. (1972). *Engineering Statistics,* 2nd ed. Prentice-Hall, Englewood Cliffs, N.J.

Brown, N. Raymond, Jr. (1966). "Zero Defects the Easy Way with Target Area Control." *Modern Machine Shop,* July.

Corbi, Jean-Claude, Nay, Michael J., and Belt, Philip Brown (1986). "Statistical Quality Control in the Bleach Plant." *TAPPI Journal,* February, pp. 60–66.

Duncan, Acheson J. (1974). *Quality Control and Industrial Statistics,* 4th ed. Richard D. Irwin, Homewood, IL.

Ewan, W. D. (1963). "When and How to Use Cu-Sum Charts." *Technometrics,* February, pp. 1–22.

Fisher, Ronald A. (1935). *The Design of Experiments.* Oliver and Boyd, London.

Flynn, Michael F. and Bolcar, John A. (1984). "The Road to Hell." *ASQC Quality Congress Transactions,* Milwaukee, pp. 192–196.

Ford Motor Company (1984). *Continuing Process Control and Process Capability Improvement.* Ford Motor Company, Statistical Methods Publications, P.O. Box 1000, Plymouth, MI 48170.

Grant, E. L. and Leavenworth, R. S. (1980). *Statistical Quality Control,* 5th ed. McGraw-Hill, New York.

Grubbs, Frank E. (1983). "An Optimum Procedure for Setting Machines or Adjusting Processes." *Journal of Quality Technology,* October, pp. 186–189.

Hunter, J. S. (1984). "The Status of U.S. Quality." *Quality,* January, p. 52.

Johnson, Norman L. and Leone, Fred C. (1964). *Statistics and Experimental Design,* vol. 1. John Wiley & Sons, New York.

Juran, J. M. (1951). *Quality Control Handbook,* 1st ed. McGraw-Hill, New York.

Juran, J. M. and Gryna, Frank M., Jr. (1980). *Quality Planning and Analysis,* 2nd ed. McGraw-Hill, New York.

Krishnamoorthi, K. S. (1985). *Why the Control Chart Ticks?* Paper 8515-001, Metals/Material Technology Series, American Society for Metals, Metals Park, OH 44073.

Lucas, James M. (1985). "Cumulative Sum (Cusum) Control Schemes." *ASQC Quality Congress Transactions,* Milwaukee, pp. 367–372.

Montgomery, Douglas C. and Wadsworth, Harrison M., Jr. (1972). "Some Techniques for Multivariate Quality Control Applications." *ASQC Technical Conference Transactions,* Milwaukee, pp. 427–435.

Nelson, Loyd S. (1984). "The Shewhart Control Chart—Tests for Special Causes." *Journal of Quality Technology,* vol. 16, no. 4, October, pp. 237–239.

Nelson, Loyd S. (1985). "Interpreting Shewhart $\overline{X}$ Control Charts." *Journal of Quality Technology,* vol. 17, no. 2, April, pp. 114–116.

Ott, Ellis R. (1975). *Process Quality Control.* McGraw-Hill, New York.

Seder, Leonard A. (1950). "Diagnosis with Diagrams." *Industrial Quality Control,* January.

Shainin, Dorian (1984). "Better than Good Old $\overline{X}$ and R Charts Asked by Vendees." *ASQC Quality Congress Transactions,* Milwaukee, pp. 302–307.

Shewhart, Walter A. (1931). *Economic Control of Quality of Manufactured Product.* D. Van Nostrand, New York.

Sinbaldi, Frank J. (1985). "PRE-Control; Does It Really Work with Non-Normality?" *ASQC Quality Congress Transactions,* Milwaukee, pp. 428–433.

Tippett, L. H. C. (1950). *Technological Applications of Statistics.* John Wiley & Sons, New York.

Vance, Lonnie C. (1983). "A Bibliography of Statistical Quality Control Chart Techniques, 1970–1980." *Journal of Quality Technology,* vol. 15, no. 2, April, pp. 59–62.

Wadsworth, G. P. and Bryan, J. G. (1974). *Applications of Probability and Random Variables.* McGraw-Hill, New York.

Wortham, A. W. and Heinrich, G. F. (1972). "Control Charts Using Exponential Smoothing Techniques." *ASQC Technical Conference Transactions,* Milwaukee, pp. 451–458.

Yates, Frank (1937). *The Design and Analysis of Factorial Experiments.* Technical Communication 35, Imperial Bureau of Soil Science, Rothamsted, Harpenden, UK.

Yu, Shawn S. and Case, Kenneth E. (1984). "An Updated Look at NLG for Process Control." *ASQC Quality Congress Transactions,* Milwaukee, pp. 308–314.

SECTION 25
ACCEPTANCE SAMPLING[1]

Edward G. Schilling
Dan J. Sommers

---

[1]In the Third Edition, material on sampling was prepared by several authors: attributes sampling by J. M. Wiesen, variables sampling by Edward G. Schilling, and bulk sampling by Acheson J. Duncan.

INTRODUCTION

Acceptance Sampling—General. The disposition of a lot can be determined by inspecting every unit ("100 percent inspection") or by inspecting a sample or portion of the lot. Economy is the key advantage of acceptance sampling as compared with 100 percent inspection. However, sampling has additional advantages:

1. Economy due to inspecting only part of the product
2. Less handling damage during inspection
3. Fewer inspectors, thereby simplifying the recruiting and training problem

4. Upgrading the inspection job from monotonous piece-by-piece decisions to lot-by-lot decisions
5. Applicability to destructive testing, with a quantified level of assurance of lot quality
6. Rejections on suppliers or shop departments of entire lots rather than mere return of the defectives, thereby providing stronger motivation for improvement

Sampling also has some inherent disadvantages:

1. There are risks of accepting "bad" lots and of rejecting "good" lots.
2. There is added planning and documentation.
3. The sample usually provides less information about the product than does 100 percent inspection.

Why is Sampling Valid?   The broad scheme of use of sampling is shown in Fig. 25.1*a*. It is universally realized that inspection of a sample gives information then and there about the quality of the pieces in the lot. But that is only the beginning. Beyond this, a vast area of knowledge is unfolded because *the product can tell on the process.*

FIG. 25.1a   Measurement of sample tells (1) whether the pieces in the sample are good or bad; (2) whether the process, at the time the samples were made, was doing good work or bad; (3) whether the uninspected pieces made at the same time by the same process are good or bad (principle of sampling inspection); (4) whether the process is stable; (5) whether the unmanufactured pieces are going to be good or bad (control inspection).

The sample, being the result of the variables present in the process at the time of manufacture, can give evidence as to those variables. Thereby it is possible to draw conclusions as to whether the process was doing good work or bad at the time it produced the samples.

From these conclusions about the process, it is then possible to reverse the reasoning, so that the known *process now can tell on the product.* We already know about the inspected product, but the knowledge of the process gives information about the uninspected pieces. In this way acceptance sampling of a lot is valid not only because the uninspected pieces are neighbors of the inspected pieces; acceptance sampling is also valid because the uninspected pieces may be derived from the same process which the inspected pieces have labeled as "good."

When we go a step further, and examine a series of samples, we learn whether the process is stable or not. Once the series of samples tells on the process by certifying stability, we can use this knowledge of stability to predict the quality of unmanufactured product.

Cowden (1957) has summarized the characteristics of a good acceptance plan. It will:

1. Protect the producer against having lots rejected when the product is in a state of control, and satisfactory as to level and uniformity
2. Protect the consumer against the acceptance of bad lots
3. Provide long-run protection to the consumer
4. Encourage the producer to keep the process in control
5. Minimize sampling costs, inspection, and administration
6. Provide information concerning product quality

Types of Sampling. Any acceptance sampling application must distinguish whether the purpose is to accumulate information on the immediate *product* being sampled or on the *process* which produced the immediate lot at hand. Accordingly, two types of sampling have been distinguished:

Type A: Sampling to accept or reject the immediate lot of product at hand

Type B: Sampling to determine if the process which produced the product at hand was within acceptable limits

The type of sampling will determine the appropriate probability distribution to be used in characterizing the performance of the plan. In addition, the type of data generated will also play a role. In acceptance sampling, data can be of these types:

Attributes—go no-go information

Defectives—usually measured in proportion or percent defective. This refers to the acceptability of units of product for a wide range of characteristics.

Defects—usually measured by actual count or as a ratio of defects per unit. This refers to number of defects found in the units inspected, and hence can be more than the number of units inspected.

Variables—measurement information

Variables—usually measured by the mean and standard deviation. This refers to the distribution of a specific measurable characteristic of the product inspected.

Terminology of Acceptance Sampling. The terminology of acceptance sampling has evolved over the years into a precise and well-directed set of terms defining various properties of acceptance sampling plans and procedures. These are clearly described in the national standard ANSI/ASQC A2 (1987), *Terms, Symbols and Definitions for Acceptance Sampling.*

It is important to distinguish between product which is not fit for use and product which does not meet specification requirements. This is done in ANSI/ASQC A2 (1978), which uses the term "defect" in relation to the former and "nonconformity" in relation to the latter. These are defined as:

Defect. A departure of a quality characteristic from its intended level or state that occurs with a severity sufficient to cause an associated product not to satisfy intended normal, or reasonably foreseeable, usage requirements.

Nonconformity.   A departure of a quality characteristic from its intended level or state that occurs with a severity sufficient to cause an associated product or service not to meet a specification requirement.

Clearly, a unit of product containing one or more defects or nonconformities is a "defective" or a "nonconforming unit."

Since acceptance sampling plans usually relate to requirements imposed by the customer (internal or external), the terms "defect" and "defective" will be generally used here. Furthermore, in referring to the literature of acceptance sampling, the terms "defect" and "defective" will be commonly found. However, in appropriate instances in this section such as variables sampling plans which compare measurements to specifications, the terms "nonconformity" and "nonconforming unit" will be used.

Acceptance Sampling Procedures

Forms of Sampling.   Sampling plans can be classified in two categories: attributes plans and variables plans.

Attributes Plans.   In these plans, a sample is taken from the lot and each unit classified as conforming or nonconforming. The number nonconforming is then compared with the acceptance number stated in the plan and a decision is made to accept or reject the lot. Attributes plans can further be classified by one of the two basic criteria:

1. Plans which meet specified sampling risks provide protection on a lot-by-lot basis. Such risks are:

   a. A specified quality level for each lot (in terms of percent defective) having a selected risk (say 0.10) of being accepted by the consumer. The specified quality level is known as the lot tolerance percent defective (p_2); the selected risk is known as the consumer's risk (β).

   b. A specified quality level for each lot such that the sampling plan will accept a stated percentage (say 95 percent) of submitted lots having this quality level. This specified quality level is termed the acceptable quality level (AQL). The risk of rejecting a lot of AQL quality (p_1) is known as the producer's risk (α).

2. Plans which provide a limiting average percentage of defective items for the long run. This is known as the average outgoing quality level (AOQL).

Variables Plans.   In these plans, a sample is taken and a measurement of a specified quality characteristic is made on each unit. These measurements are then summarized into a simple statistic (e.g., sample mean) and the observed value compared with an allowable value defined in the plan. A decision is then made to accept or reject the lot. When applicable, variables plans provide the same degree of consumer protection as attributes plans while using considerably smaller samples.

Attributes plans are generally applied on a percent defective basis. That is, the plan is instituted to control the proportion of accepted product which is defective or out of specification. Variables plans for percent defective are also used in this way. Such plans provide a sensitivity greater than attributes but require that the shape of the distribution of individual measurements must be known and stable. The shape of the distribution is used to translate the proportion defective into specific values of process parameters (mean, standard deviation) which are then controlled.

Variables plans can also be used to control process parameters to given levels when specifications are directed toward the process average or process variability and not specifically to percent defective. These variables plans for process parameter do not necessarily require detailed knowledge of the shape of the underlying distribution of individual measurements.

Sampling plans used in reliability and in the sampling of bulk product are generally of this type. Published plans in the reliability area, however, usually require detailed knowledge of the shape of the distribution of lifetimes. Some of the important features of attributes and variables plans for percent defective are compared in Table 25.1.

The principal advantage of variables plans for percent defective over corresponding attributes plans is a reduction in the sample size needed to obtain a given degree of protection. Table 25.2 shows a comparison of variables sample sizes necessary to achieve the same protection as the attributes plan: $n = 125$, $c = 3$ (sample size of 125 units, allowable number of defectives of 3).

Probably the most important consideration in the application of variables sampling plans is the requirement that the shape of the underlying distribution of

TABLE 25.1 Comparison of Attributes and Variables Sampling Plans for Percent Defective

Feature	Attributes	Variables
Inspection	Each item classified as defective or nondefective. Go no-go gages may be employed.	Each item measured. Inspection more sophisticated. Higher inspection and clerical cost.
Distribution of individual measurements	Need not be known.	*Must* be known (normal usually assumed).
Type of defect	Any number of defect types can be assessed by one plan.	Separate plan required for each type of defect.
Sample size	Depends on protection required.	Smaller sample size for same protection as attributes (at least 30% smaller*).
Process information	Percent defective.	Percent defective plus valuable information on process average and variability for corrective action.
Severity	Weights all defectives of a given kind equally.	Weights each unit inspected by its proximity to specifications.
Evidence to supplier	Defectives available as evidence.	Possible for lot to be rejected on sample containing no defectives.
Measurement errors	Measurements not recorded.	Measurements available for review.
Screened lots	No effect on performance of plan.	Screened lots may be rejected in error even though they contain no defectives.

*Bowker and Goode (1952), pp. 32–33. Assumes single sample of one characteristic.

TABLE 25.2 Comparison of Variables and Attributes
Sample Sizes*

$p_1 = 0.0109; \alpha = 0.05; p_2 = 0.0535; \beta = 0.10$

Plan	Sample size
Single-sampling attributes	125
Variables:	
σ known	19
σ unknown (s)	52
σ unknown ($\overline{R}$ of groups of 5)	75
Sequential sampling, σ known (ASN at p_1)	10.3

*Specifications assumed to be $> 6\sigma$ apart if two-sided.
Source: MIL-STD-105D, Code K, 1% AQL.

measurements to which the plan is to be applied must be known. For example, if the diameters of individual units of product are to be inspected, those diameters must be distributed in a known pattern. This means that statistical tests on past data must show that the distribution of the measurements involved is actually that assumed by the plan. Control chart evidence is also desirable to indicate process stability. This point cannot be overemphasized since a principal use of the distributional assumption in variables acceptance sampling for percent defective is with regard to individual units and not sample means, which can usually be assumed to be normally distributed. While it has been argued that variables plans may be roughly correct when applied to distributions other than the distribution assumed, judicious application requires confirmation that the underlying distribution of the process to which the plan is applied is actually that assumed by the plan.

Since some fundamental knowledge of the process producing the product is required for proper application of variables sampling plans for percent defective, a natural area of application of such plans is to in-house inspection, e.g., process control or final inspection. Use of these plans in incoming inspection should be restricted to product from known and trusted suppliers with a confirmed history of a reasonably stable process steadily producing product with a known shape of distribution. Process history should be initially developed under an attributes sampling plan. A switch to variables may be considered after a plot on probability paper or a goodness-of-fit test (see Section 23 under Selecting a Continuous Distribution) indicates that the distribution of product is as assumed. A control chart for at least 20 lots is useful to confirm process stability. There are times when the inspection situation demands the use of fewer lots. In such situations, appropriate limits for a 10-lot control chart have been developed by Hillier (1969). Variables plans are inappropriate for inspection of single lots unless the sample size is large enough to allow for meaningful goodness-of-fit tests to confirm that the shape of the underlying distribution of measurements is as assumed.

Variables plans for process parameter may be used whenever specifications are stated in terms of process mean or standard deviation. While control charts assess the consistency of process levels, acceptance sampling plans should be used to determine conformance to specifications. This is important, since both consumer and producer risks should be considered in acceptance sampling, while conventional Shewhart control charts consider only the producer's risk at one specified level ($\alpha = 0.003$).

In applying variables plans, it is advantageous to use a "known standard deviation" plan whenever possible. This usually requires a control chart, in control, with about 20 or more samples plotted to assure a stable level of standard deviation. The chart is maintained as long as the known standard deviation plan is being used. In the absence of such a chart, unknown standard deviation plans may be used, although knowledge of the shape of the distribution is still required for variables plans for percent defective. The construction and use of control charts are discussed in Section 24, Statistical Process Control.

Types of Sampling Plans. In single-sampling plans, the decision to accept or reject a lot is based on the results of inspection of a single group of units drawn from the lot. In double-sampling plans, a smaller initial sample is usually drawn, and a decision to accept or reject is reached on the basis of this smaller first sample if the number of defectives is either quite large or quite small. A second sample is taken if the results of the first are not decisive. Since it is necessary to draw and inspect the second sample only in borderline cases, the average number of pieces inspected per lot is generally smaller with double sampling. In multiple-sampling plans, one, or two, or several still smaller samples of n individual items are taken (usually truncated after some number of samples) until a decision to accept or reject is obtained. The term "sequential-sampling plan" is generally used when a decision is possible after each individual unit has been inspected.

Sampling Schemes and Systems. While simple sampling plans are often employed solely in sentencing individual lots, sampling schemes and systems are generally used in acceptance control applications involving a steady flow of product from the producer. The ANSI/ASQC Standard A2 (1987) defines a sampling plan as "a specific plan that states the sample size or sizes to be used, and the associated acceptance and nonacceptance criteria," and a sampling scheme as "a specific set of procedures which usually consists of acceptance sampling plans in which lot sizes, sample sizes, and acceptance criteria, or the amount of 100 percent inspection and sampling are related." The Definitions and Nomenclature Subcommittee of the ANSI Z-1 Committee on Quality Assurance defined a sampling system as a "unified collection of one or more sampling schemes." Thus, $n = 134$, $c = 3$ is a sampling plan; Code J, 1.0 percent AQL is a sampling scheme; and MIL-STD-105D, or its civilian version ANSI/ASQC Z1.4, is a sampling system.

The selection of a given sampling procedure depends upon the extent and nature of quality history. Thus, with a supplier having average quality history, it may be well to start with a single sampling plan and switch to an AQL scheme after moderate quality history has been obtained and then to skip-lot, supplier certification, or control chart procedures when extensive excellent history has been generated.

Published Tables and Procedures. From the point of view of ease of negotiation between the producer and the consumer, it is usually best to use published procedures and standards. This avoids problems of credibility created when one party or the other generates its own sampling plan. Also, the legal implications of using plans which appear in the litrature (such as Dodge-Romig plans) or have been subjected to national consensus review (such as ANSI/ASQC Z1.4, 1981) are obvious. Unique plans, specifically generated for a given application are probably best used internally.

Acceptance Control and Acceptance Sampling. Acceptance sampling refers to the application of specific sampling plans to a designated lot or sequence of lots. Acceptance sampling procedures can, however, be used in a program of *acceptance control* to achieve better quality at lower cost, improved control, and increased productivity. This involves the selection of sampling procedures to continually match operating conditions in terms of quality history and sampling results. In this way the plans and procedures of acceptance sampling can be used in an evolutionary manner to supplement each other in a continuing program of acceptance control for quality improvement with reduced inspection. It is the objective of acceptance control in any application to eventually phase out acceptance sampling in favor of supplier certification and process control. After explaining a variety of specific sampling procedures, this section concludes with suggestions on how and when to progress from sampling inspection toward reliance on process control and check inspection and eventually to no inspection at all, depending on the stage of the life cycle of the product and the state of control.

SAMPLING RISKS AND PARAMETERS

Risks. When acceptance sampling is conducted, the real parties of interest are the producer (supplier or Production Department) and the consumer, i.e., the company which buys from the supplier or the department which is to use the product. Since sampling carries the risk of rejecting "good" lots and of accepting "bad" lots, with associated serious consequences, producers and consumers have gone far to standardize the concepts of what constitutes good and bad lots, and to standardize also the risks associated with sampling. These risks are stated in conjunction with one or more parameters, i.e., quality indices for the plan. These indices are as follows.

Producer's Risk. The producer's risk α is the probability that a "good" lot will be rejected by the sampling plan. In some plans, this risk is fixed at 0.05; in other plans, it varies from about 0.01 to 0.10. The risk is stated in conjunction with a numerical definition of the maximum quality level that may pass through the plan, often called the acceptable quality level.

Acceptable Quality Level. As defined by MIL-STD-105D (1963), the acceptable quality level (AQL) is the maximum percent defective (or maximum number of defects per hundred units) that, for the purpose of sampling inspection, can be considered satisfactory as a process average. A sampling plan should have a low producer's risk for quality which is equal to or better than the AQL.

Consumer's Risk. The consumer's risk β is the probability that a "bad" lot will be accepted by the sampling plan. The risk is stated in conjunction with a numerical definition of rejectable quality such as a lot tolerance percent defective.

Lot Tolerance Percent Defective. The lot tolerance percent defective (LTPD) is the level of quality that is unsatisfactory and therefore should be rejected by the sampling plan. A consumer's risk of 0.10 is common and LTPD has been defined as the lot quality for which the probability of acceptance is 0.10; i.e., only 10 percent of such lots will be accepted. (LTPD is a special case of the concept of limiting quality, LQ, or rejectable quality level, RQL. The latter terms are used in tables that provide plans for several values of the consumer's risk as contrasted to a value of 0.10 for the LTPD.)

A third type of quality index, average outgoing quality limit, is used with 100 percent inspection of rejected lots and will be discussed later in this section.

The producer's and consumer's risks and associated AQL and LTPD are summarized graphically by an operating characteristic curve.

Operating Characteristic Curve. The Operating Characteristic (OC) curve is a graph of lot fraction defective versus the probability that the sampling plan will accept the lot.

Figure 25.1b shows an ideal OC curve for a case where it is desired to accept all lots 3 percent defective or less and reject all lots having a quality level greater than 3 percent defective. Note that all lots less than 3 percent defective have a probability of acceptance of 1.0 (certainty); all lots greater than 3 percent defective have a probability of acceptance of zero. Actually, however, no sampling plan exists that can discriminate perfectly; there always remains some risk that a "good" lot will be rejected or that a "bad" lot will be accepted. The best that can be achieved in practice is to control these risks.

Figure 25.1c shows the curve of behavior that would be obtained if an inspector were instructed to take a sample of 150 pieces from a large lot and to accept the lot if no more than four defective pieces were found. Such curves can be constructed from the appropriate probability distribution. For example, using the Poisson table (Appendix II, Table E), we find that for a sample size of 150 ($n = 150$) and 2 percent defective ($p = 0.02$) we would expect $np = 3.0$ defectives in the sample. The table shows for $r = 4$ and $np = 3.0$, the probability of acceptance (for four or fewer defectives) is 0.815.

It is seen from this curve that a lot 3 percent defective has one chance in two of being accepted. However, a lot 3.5 percent defective, though technically a "bad" lot, has 39 chances in 100 of being accepted. In like manner, a lot 2.5 percent defective, though technically a good lot, has 34 chances in 100 of not being accepted.

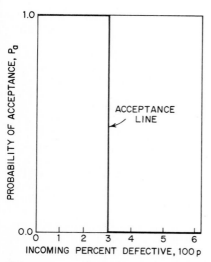

FIG. 25.1b An ideal sampling plan performance.

FIG. 25.1c An actual sampling plan performance.

Actually the lack of a sharp distinction may not be too serious. Economically, it may be a matter of indifference whether a lot 3 percent defective is accepted or sorted. In the case of lots 2.5 or 3.5 percent defective it makes a difference, but the difference may not be great in relation to the cost of trying for greater precision, and in view of the imponderables which are still present in computing break-even points.

The effect of parameters of the sampling plan on the shape of the OC curve is demonstrated in Figure 25.2, where the curve for perfect discrimination is given along with the curves for three particular acceptance sampling plans. The following statements summarize the effects:

1. When the sample size approaches the lot size or, in fact, approaches a large percentage of the lot size, and the acceptance number is chosen appropriately, the OC curve approaches the perfect OC curve (the rectangle at p_1).
2. When the acceptance number is zero, the OC curve is exponential in shape, concave upward (see curves 2 and 3).

FIG. 25.2 Shape of the OC curve.

3. As the acceptance number increases, the OC curve is pushed up, so to speak, for low values of p, and the probability of acceptance for these quality levels is increased, with a point of inflection at some larger value of p (see curve 1).

4. Increasing the sample size and the acceptance number together gives the closest approach to the perfect discrimination OC curve (see curve 1).

It is sometimes useful to distinguish between type A and type B OC curves (see Dodge and Romig, 1959, pp. 56–59). Type A curves give the probability of acceptance for an individual lot that comes from finite production conditions that cannot be assumed to continue in the future. Type B curves assume that each lot is one of an infinite number of lots produced under essentially the same production conditions. In practice, most OC curves are viewed as type B. With the few exceptions noted, this section assumes type B OC curves.

Average Sample Number Curve.   The average sample number (ASN) is the average number of units inspected per lot in sampling inspection ignoring any 100 percent inspection of rejected lots. In single-sampling inspection the ASN is equal to n, the sample size. However, in double- and multiple-sampling plans the probability of not reaching a decision on the initial sample, and consequently being forced to inspect a second, third, etc., sample must be considered. For a double-sampling plan with sample sizes n_1 and n_2, the average sample number, ASN is simply

$$\text{ASN} = n_1 + (1 - P_{a_1}) \, n_2$$

where P_{a_1}, is the probability of acceptance on the first sample. The ASN for multiple sampling is more complicated to calculate; see Schilling (1982).

A comparison of ASN for some specific plans is shown in Figure 25.3. (The calculations assume that all samples selected are completely inspected.) As indicated, double and multiple sampling generally lead to economies over single sampling when quality is either very good or very poor.

Average Outgoing Quality Limit.   The acceptable quality level (AQL) and lot tolerance percent defective (LTPD) have been cited as two common quality indices for sampling plans. A third commonly used index is the average outgoing quality limit (AOQL). The AOQL is the upper limit of average quality of outgoing product from accepted lots and from rejected lots which have been screened.

The AOQL concept stems from the relationship between the fraction defective before inspection (incoming quality) and the fraction defective after inspection (outgoing quality) when inspection is nondestructive and rejected lots are screened. When incoming quality is perfect, outgoing quality must likewise be perfect. However, when incoming quality is very bad, outgoing quality will also be near perfect, because the sampling plan will cause most lots to be rejected and 100 percent inspected. Thus, at either extreme—incoming quality very good or very bad—the outgoing quality will tend to be very good. It follows that between these extremes is the point at which the percent defective in the outgoing material will reach its maximum. This point is known as the AOQL.

If p is incoming quality, P_r is the probability of lot rejection, and all rejected lots are screened and made free of defects (i.e., 0 percent), then

$$\text{AOQ} = (p)P_a + (0)P_r = (p)P_a$$

FIG. 25.3 Average sample number vs. fraction defective.

This calculation is approximate in that it does not account for the small effect of 100 percent inspection of the units in the samples from accepted lots. Taking this into account:

$$\text{AOQ} = pP_a \left(1 - \frac{n}{N} \right)$$

for sample size n and lot size N.

Average Outgoing Quality Curve. An example of the calculation for the AOQL and a plot of the average outgoing quality (AOQ) curve is shown in Table 25.3 and Figure 25.4. Schilling (1982) has indicated that for acceptance numbers of five or less

$$\text{AOQL} \simeq \frac{0.4}{n} (1.25c + 1)$$

Average Total Inspection. The average total inspection (ATI) takes into account the likelihood of 100 percent inspection of rejected lots when this is possible; i.e., inspection is nondestructive. The lot size N must now be taken into account. Again with single-sampling plans with sample size n, lot size N, probability of acceptance P_a, and probability of rejection P_r,

$$\text{ATI} = P_a n + P_r N$$

TABLE 25.3 Computations for Average Outgoing Quality Limit (AOQL); for this Example, $n = 78$, $c = 1$

Incoming quality fraction defective $= p$	np	Probability of acceptance $= P_a$	Average outgoing quality (AOQ) $= p \times P_a$
0.005	0.39	0.940	0.00470
0.010	0.78	0.820	0.00820
0.015	1.17	0.680	0.01020
0.020	1.56	0.550	0.01100*
0.025	1.95	0.430	0.01075
0.030	2.34	0.330	0.00990
0.035	2.73	0.250	0.00875
0.040	3.12	0.190	0.00760
0.045	3.51	0.140	0.00630
0.050	3.90	0.100	0.00500
0.055	4.29	0.075	0.00402
0.060	4.68	0.050	0.00300

*AOQL $\cong$ maximum AOQ $\cong 0.01100 = 1.1\%$.

FIG. 25.4 AOQ curve and AOQL for a typical sampling plan.

An extension to double sampling is simply

$$\text{ATI} = n_1 + (1 - P_{a1})n_2 + (N - n_1 - n_2)(1 - P_a)$$

where P_{a1} is the probability of acceptance on the first sample. Extension to multiple-sampling plans of k levels is straightforward and will not be derived here. See Schilling (1982).

Minimum Total Inspection.   Minimum inspection per lot, for a given type of protection, can be illustrated by the following example.

Assume that a consumer establishes acceptance criteria as an LTPD of 5 percent. A great many sampling plans meet this criterion. Some of these plans are:

Take from each lot a sample n of	Accept the lot if the number of defectives does not exceed the maximum acceptance number c
46	0
78	1
106	2
134	3
160	4

Figure 25.5 shows the corresponding operating characteristic curves. Each plan has an LTPD of 5 percent; i.e., the probability of acceptance of a submitted inspection lot with fraction defective of 0.05 is 0.10. Which plan should be used? One logical basis for choosing among these plans is to use that one which gives the least inspection per lot.

The total number of units inspected consists of (1) the sample which is inspected for each lot and (2) the remaining units which must be inspected in those lots which are rejected by the sampling inspection. The number of lots

FIG. 25.5 Family of sampling plans each having LTPD = 0.05.

rejected in turn depends on the normal level of defectives in the product so that minimum inspection is a function of incoming quality.

A sample computation of minimum inspection per lot is shown in Table 25.4. It is assumed that rejected lots are detail (100 percent) inspected. For small acceptance numbers the total inspection is high because many lots need to be detailed. For large acceptance numbers the total is again high, this time because of the large size of samples. The minimum sum occurs at a point between these extremes.

From the foregoing it is seen that for any specified conditions of

Lot tolerance percent defective

Consumer's risk

Lot size

Process average

it becomes possible to derive the values of

n = sample size

to obtain c = allowable number of defectives in the sample

I_m = minimum inspection per lot

Similar reasoning may be applied in making a selection from a group of sampling plans designed to give the same average outgoing quality limit (AOQL).

Complete tables for sampling have been derived for minimum inspection per lot for a variety of $\bar{p}$, LTPD, and AOQL values (e.g., Dodge and Romig, 1959). These will be described later.

Selection of a Numerical Value of the Quality Index.   There are three alternatives for evaluating lots: no inspection, inspect a sample, 100 percent inspection (or more). An economic evaluation of these alternatives requires a comparison of *total* costs under each of the alternatives.

TABLE 25.4   Computation of Minimum Inspection per Lot for 5 Alternative n-c Combinations Appropriate to Lots of N = 1000 Articles

All plans have the same lot tolerance percent defective. Incoming material has a process average percent defective, $\bar{p}$ = 0.5%.

				Average no. pieces inspected		
Sample size n	Allowable number of defects c	Probability of acceptance by sampling P_a	Probability of inspecting residue of lot $1 - P_a$	In sample* n	In rest of lot† $(N - n) \times (1 - P_a)$	Total inspected per lot
46	0	0.795	0.205	46	196	242
78	1	0.940	0.060	78	55	133
106	2	0.983	0.017	106	15	121‡
134	3	0.995	0.005	134	4	138
160	4	0.998	0.002	160	2	162

*The sample size indicates the number inspected from each lot.
†The size of the uninspected residue of the lot, multiplied by the probability that it will have to be inspected because of rejection of the sample.
‡This is the minimum sought.

Enell (1954) has suggested that a break-even point be used in the selection of a quality index:

$$p_b = \frac{I}{A}$$

where I = inspection cost per item
A = damage cost incurred if a defective slips through inspection

If it is thought that the lot quality p is less than p_b, the total cost will be lowest with sampling inspection or no inspection. If p is greater than p_b, 100 percent inspection is best. If p is unknown, it may be best to sample using an appropriate sampling plan such as an AOQL scheme.

For example, a microcomputer device costs $0.50 per unit to inspect. A damage cost of $10.00 is incurred if a defective device is installed in the larger system. Therefore,

$$p_b = \frac{0.50}{10.00} = 0.05 = 5.0 \text{ percent}$$

If it is expected that the percent defective will be greater than 5 percent, then 100 percent inspection should be used. Otherwise, use sampling or no inspection.

The formula assumes that the sample size is small compared to the lot size, the cost to replace a defective found in inspection is borne by the producer or is small compared to the damage or inconvenience caused by a defective, and no inspection errors occur.

As a 5 percent defective quality level is the break-even point between sorting and sampling, the appropriate sampling plan should provide for a lot to have a 50 percent probability of being sorted or sampled; i.e., the probability of acceptance for the plan should be 0.50 at a 5 percent defective quality level. The operating characteristic curves in a set of sampling tables such as MIL-STD-105D can now be examined to determine an AQL. For example, suppose that the device is inspected in lots of 3000 pieces. The operating characteristic curves for this case (code letter K) are shown in MIL-STD-105D. The plan closest to having a P_a of 0.50 for a 5 percent level is the plan for an AQL of 1.5 percent. Therefore, this is the plan to adopt.

Some plans (for example, MIL-STD-105D) include a classification of defects to help determine the numerical value of the AQL. Defects are first classified as critical, major, or minor, according to definitions provided in the standard. Different AQLs may be designated for groups of defects considered collectively, or for individual defects. Critical defects may have a 0 percent AQL while major defects might be assigned a low AQL, say 1 percent, and minor defects a higher AQL, say 4 percent. Some manufacturers of complex products specify quality in terms of number of defects per million parts.

The variability in quality from lot to lot is important. If past history shows that the quality level is much better than the break-even point and is stable from lot to lot, little if any inspection may be needed. If the level is much worse than the break-even point, and consistently so, it will usually be cheaper to use 100 percent inspection (or change suppliers) rather than sample. If the quality is at neither of these extremes, a detailed economic comparison of no inspection, sampling, and 100 percent inspection should be made. Sampling is usually best when the product is a mixture of high-quality lots and low-quality lots, or when the producer's process is not in a state of statistical control.

The high costs associated with component failures in complex electronic equipment coupled with the development of automatic testing equipment for components has resulted in the economic justification of 100 percent inspection for some electronic components. The cost of finding and correcting a defective can increase by a ratio of 10 for each major stage that the product moves from production to the customer; i.e., if it costs $1 at incoming inspection the cost increases to $10 at the printed circuit board stage, $100 at the system level, and $1000 in the field (Wescom, 1978).

In practice, the quantification of the quality index is a matter of judgment based on the following factors:

1. Past performance on quality
2. Effect of nonconforming product on later production steps
3. Effect of nonconforming product on fitness for use
4. Urgency of delivery requirements
5. Cost to achieve the specified quality level

IMPLEMENTATION OF AN ACCEPTANCE SAMPLING PROCEDURE

Assumptions Made in Sampling Plans

Inspection Error. In implementing acceptance sampling plans, it is commonly assumed that:

1. The inspectors follow the prescribed sampling plan.
2. The inspection is made without error; i.e., no human or equipment mistakes are made in measurement or in judging conformance.

In practice, these assumptions are not fully valid. See Section 18, under Inspector Errors.

Units of Product. These may consist of (1) discrete pieces or (2) specimens from bulk material. The criteria used for judging the conformance of a single unit of product to standard are somewhat different for these two categories. The criteria used for judging lot conformance differ even more widely.

Seriousness Classification of Defects. Many sampling plans set up their criteria for judging lot conformance in terms of an allowable number of defects in the sample. Since defects differ greatly in seriousness, the sampling plans must somehow take these differences into account.

Where there exists a formal plan for seriousness classification of defects, the sampling plans may be structured so that:

1. A separate sampling plan is used for each seriousness class, e.g., large sample sizes for critical defects, small sample sizes for minor defects.
2. A common sampling plan is used, but the allowable number of defects varies for each class; e.g., no critical defects are allowed, but some minor defects are allowed.
3. The criteria may be established in terms of defects per hundred units, the allowable number being different for each class.

4. The criteria may be based on demerits per unit; i.e., all defects found are converted to a scale of demerits based on the classification system.

In the absence of a formal system of seriousness classification, all defects are considered equally important during the sampling inspection. However, when nonconforming lots are subsequently reviewed to judge fitness for use, the review board gives consideration to the seriousness of the defects.

Lot Formation. The general approach to lot formation is discussed in Section 18, under the Nature of Lots of Product. While most acceptance sampling plans can be validly applied regardless of how lots are formed (skip-lot plans are an exception), the economics of inspection and the quality of the accepted product are greatly influenced by the manner of lot formation.

The interrelation of lot formation to economics of inspection is discussed in Section 18, under How Much Inspection? and will not be elaborated here. The interrelation of lot formation to quality of accepted product can be seen from a single example.

Ten machines are producing the same product. Nine of these produce perfect product. The tenth machine produces 100 percent defectives. If lots consist of product from single machines, the defective product from the tenth machine will always be detected by sampling. If, however, the lots are formed by mixing up the work from all machines, then it is inevitable that some defects will get through the sampling plan.

The fact that lot formation so strongly influences outgoing quality and inspection economics has led to some guidelines for lot formation:

1. Do not mix product from different sources (processes, production shifts, input materials, etc.) unless there is evidence that the lot-to-lot variation is small enough to be ignored.

2. Do not accumulate product over extensive periods of time (for lot formation).

3. Do make use of extraneous information (process capability, prior inspections, etc.) in lot formation. Such extraneous information is especially useful when product is submitted in isolated lots, or in very small lots. In such cases the extraneous information may provide better knowledge on which to base an acceptance decision than the sampling data.

4. Do make lots as large as possible consistent with the above to take advantage of low proportionate sampling costs. (Sample sizes do not increase greatly despite large increases in lot sizes.)

When production is continuous (e.g., the assembly line) so that the "lot" is necessarily arbitrary, the sampling plans used are themselves designed to be of a "continuous" nature. These continuous sampling plans are discussed later in this section.

Lot-by-Lot Inspection. When product is submitted in a series of lots (termed "lot-by-lot"), the acceptance sampling plans are defined in terms of

N = lot size
n = sample size
c = acceptance number, i.e., the allowable number of defects in the sample
r = rejection number

When more than one sample per lot is specified, the successive sample sizes are designated as n_1, n_2, n_3, etc. The successive acceptance numbers are c_1, c_2, c_3, etc. The successive rejection numbers are r_1, r_2, r_3, etc.

Selecting the Sample. The results of sampling are greatly influenced by the method of selecting the sample. In acceptance sampling, the sample should be representative of the lot. In those cases where the inspector has knowledge of how the lot was formed, this knowledge can be used in selecting the sample by stratification (see below). Lacking this knowledge, the correct approach is to use random sampling.

Random Sampling. All published sampling tables are prepared on the assumption that samples are drawn at random; i.e., at any one time each of the remaining uninspected units of product has an equal chance of being the next unit selected for the sample. To conduct random sampling requires that (1) random numbers be generated and (2) these random numbers be applied to the product at hand.

Random numbers are available in prefabricated form in tables of random numbers (Appendix II, Table CC). One uses such a table by entering it at random (without "looking") and then proceeding in some chosen direction (up, down, right, left, etc.) to obtain random numbers for use. Numbers which cannot be applied to the product arrangement are discarded.

Random numbers may also be generated by various devices. These include:

1. *Calculators or computers:* Many calculators are available with random-number routines built in. Computers are, of course, an excellent source of random numbers. Statistical software often has random numbers built in.

2. *A bowl of numbered chips or marbles:* After mixing, one is withdrawn and its number recorded. It is then replaced and the bowl is again mixed before the next number is withdrawn.

3. *Random number dice:* One form is the icosahedron (20-sided) dice. There are three of these, each of a different color, one for units, one for tens, and one for hundreds. (Each die has the numbers from 0 to 9 appearing twice.) Hence one throw of the three dice displays a random number within 000 to 999.

Once the random numbers are available, they must be adapted to the form in which the product is submitted. For systematically packed material, the container system can be numbered to correspond to the system of random numbers. For example, a lot might be submitted in 8 trays, each of which has 10 rows and 7 columns. In such a case, the trays might be numbered from 0 to 7, the rows from 0 to 9, and the columns from 0 to 6. Then, using three-digit random numbers, the digits are assigned to trays, rows, and columns, respectively.

For bulk packed materials, other practical procedures may be used. In the case of small parts, they may be strewn onto a flat surface which is marked with grid lines in a 10×10 arrangement. Based on two-digit random numbers, the cell at the intersection of these digits is identified. Within the cell, further positional identity can be determined with a third digit.

For fluid or well-mixed bulk products, the fluidity obviates the need for random numbers, and the samples may be taken from "here and there."

Stratified Sampling. When the "lots" are known to come from different machines, production shifts, operators, etc., the product is actually multiple lots which have been arbitrarily combined. In such cases, the sampling is deliberately stratified; i.e., an attempt is made to draw the sample proportionately from each true lot. However, within each lot, randomness is still the appropriate basis for sampling.

A further departure from randomness may be due to the economics of opening containers, i.e., whether to open few containers and examine a few pieces from each.

Sampling Bias.   Unless rigorous procedures are set up for sampling at random and/or by stratification, the sampling can deteriorate into a variety of biases which are detrimental to good decision making. The more usual biases consist of:

1. Sampling from the same location in all containers, racks, or bins
2. Previewing the product and selecting only those units which appear to be defective (or nondefective)
3. Ignoring those portions of the lot which are inconvenient to sample
4. Deciding on a pattern of stratification in the absence of knowledge of how the lot was made up

Sampling by Attributes.   The classical example is the legendary inspector who always took samples from the four corners and center of each tray and the legendary production worker who very carefully filled these same spots with perfect product.

Because the structured sampling plans do assume randomness, and because some forms of sampling bias can significantly distort the product acceptance decisions, all concerned should be alert to plan the sampling to minimize these biases. Thereafter, supervision and auditing should be alert to assure that the actual sampling conforms to these plans.

ATTRIBUTES SAMPLING

Overview of Single, Double, Multiple, and Sequential Plans.   In general, all four sampling plans can be planned to give lots of specified qualities nearly the same chance of being accepted; i.e., the operating-characteristic curves can be made quite similar (matched) if desired. However, the best type of plan for one producer or product is not necessarily best for another. The suitability of a plan can be judged by considering the following factors:

1. Average number of parts inspected
2. Cost of administration
3. Information obtained as to lot quality
4. Acceptability of plan to producers

The advantages and disadvantages of the four forms of sampling plans are tabulated in Table 25.5. The average number of parts that need to be inspected to arrive at a decision varies according to the plan and the quality of the material submitted. In cases where the cost of inspection of each piece is substantial, the reduction in number of pieces inspected may justify use of sequential sampling despite its greater complexity and higher administrative costs. On the other hand, where it is not practicable to hold the entire lot of parts while sampling and inspection are going on, it becomes necessary to set aside the full number of items that may need to be inspected before inspection even begins. In these circum-

TABLE 25.5 Comparative Advantages and Disadvantages of Single, Double, and Multiple Sampling

Feature	Single sampling	Double sampling	Multiple sampling	Sequential
Acceptability to producer	Psychologically poor to give only one chance of passing the lot	Psychologically adequate	Psychologically open to criticism as being indecisive	Psychologically open to criticism as being more indecisive than multiple
Number of pieces inspected per lot*	Generally greatest	Usually (but not always) 10 to 50% less than single sampling	Generally (but not always) less than double sampling by amounts of the order of 30%	Minimum over all attributes plans
Administration cost in training, personnel, records, drawing and identifying samples, etc.	Lowest	Greater than single sample	Greater	Greatest
Information about prevailing level of quality in each lot	Most	Less than single sample	Less than double	Least

*This is not to be confused with total cost of inspection, which includes administration cost of the plan.

stances single sampling may be preferable if the cost of selecting, unpacking, and handling parts is appreciable. It is of course simplest to train personnel, set up records, and administer a single-sampling plan. A crew of inspectors hastily thrown together cannot easily be taught all the intricacies of the more elaborate plans. However, double-sampling plans have been demonstrated to be simple to use in a wide variety of conditions, economical in total cost, and acceptable psychologically to both producer and consumer.

Selecting Sampling Plans. Sampling plans are often specified by choosing two points on the OC curve: the AQL denoted by p_1 and the LTPD symbolized by p_2. Tables have been developed to facilitate the selection process by using unity (np) values from the Poisson distribution. See Cameron (1952), Duncan (1974), and Schilling and Johnson (1980). Such tables use the operating ratio, $R = p_2/p_1$, in conjunction with the unity value of (np_1) or (np_2) to obtain the sample size and acceptance number(s) for the plan whose OC curve passes through the points specified. Often other unity values are provided which assess other properties of the plan. Such tables are illustrated below by the Schilling-Johnson (1980) table, reproduced in part as Table 25.6, which uses producer risk $\alpha = 0.05$ and consumer risk $\beta = 0.10$ with equal sample sizes at each stage of a double or multiple sampling plan. The table provides matched sets of single, double, and multiple sampling plans, such that their OC curves are roughly equivalent. For example, if $p_1 = 0.012$ and $p_2 = 0.053$ then $R = 4.4$. The closest value given under the column for R is 4.058, corresponding to an acceptance number of 4. The sample size is then found to be $n = 7.994 \div 0.053 = 150.8$, which would usually be taken to be 150. The operating characteristic curve for the plan can be seen in Figure 25.1c.

Single Sampling. In single sampling by attributes, the decision to accept or reject the lot is based on the results of inspection of a single sample selected from the lot. The operation of a single-sampling plan by attributes is given in Figure 25.6. The characteristics of an attributes sampling plan are given in Table 25.7.

Double Sampling. In double sampling by attributes, an initial sample is taken, and a decision to accept or reject the lot is reached on the basis of this first sample if the number of nonconforming units is either quite small or quite large. A second sample is taken if the results of the first sample are not decisive. The operation of an attributes double-sampling plan is given in Figure 25.7. The characteristics of an attributes double-sampling plan are given in Table 25.8.

Multiple Sampling. In multiple sampling by attributes, more than two samples can be taken in order to reach a decision to accept or reject the lot. The chief advantage of multiple sampling plans is a reduction in sample size for the same protection. The operation of multiple sampling by attributes is given in Figure 25.8. The characteristics of a multiple sampling plan are given in Table 25.9.

Sequential Sampling. In sequential sampling, each item is treated as a sample of size one, and a determination to accept, reject, or continue sampling is made after inspection of each item. The major advantage of sequential sampling plans is that these plans offer the opportunity for achieving the minimum sample size for a given protection. The operation of sequential sampling by attributes is given in Figure 25.9. The characteristics of a sequential sampling plan are given in Table 25.10.

TABLE 25.6 Unity Values for Construction and Evaluation of Single, Double, and Multiple Sampling Plans

($n_1 = n_2 = \cdots = n_k$; # indicates acceptance not allowed at a given stage)

Plan	Acceptance numbers	$R=p_2/p_1$	np_2		.99	.95	.90	.75	.50	.25	.10	.05	.01	.005	.001	.0005	.0001
											Probability of acceptance						
0S	Ac = 0 Re = 1	44.893	2.303	np ASN n_1	.0101 1	.0513 1	.105 1	.288 1	.693 1	1.386 1	2.303 1	2.996 1	4.605 1	5.298 1	6.908 1	7.601 1	9.206 1
1S	Ac = 1 Re = 2	10.958	3.890	np ASN n_1	.149 1	.355 1	.532 1	.961 1	1.678 1	2.693 1	3.890 1	4.744 1	6.638 1	7.430 1	9.234 1	10.000 1	11.759 1
1D	Ac = 0 1 Re = 2 2	12.029	2.490	np ASN n_1	.0860 1.079	.207 1.168	.310 1.228	.566 1.321	1.006 1.368	1.661 1.316	2.490 1.206	3.124 1.137	4.649 1.045	5.324 1.026	6.914 1.007	7.604 1.004	9.209 1.001
1M	Ac = # # 0 0 1 1 2 Re = 2 2 2 3 3 3 3	8.903	.917	np ASN n_1	.0459 3.254	.103 3.501	.148 3.637	.252 3.774	.416 3.640	.643 3.169	.917 2.601	1.121 2.270	1.602 1.761	1.815 1.618	2.325 1.388	2.549 1.319	3.075 1.205
2S	Ac = 2 Re = 3	6.506	5.322	np ASN n_1	.436 1	.818 1	1.102 1	1.727 1	2.674 1	3.920 1	5.322 1	6.296 1	8.406 1	9.274 1	11.230 1	12.053 1	13.934 1
2D	Ac = 0 3 Re = 3 4	5.357	3.402	np ASN n_1	.363 1.298	.635 1.443	.827 1.511	1.231 1.581	1.816 1.564	2.566 1.450	3.402 1.306	3.986 1.222	5.290 1.097	5.852 1.066	7.201 1.025	7.810 1.016	9.295 1.005
2M	Ac = # 0 0 1 2 3 4 Re = 2 3 3 4 4 5 5	6.244	1.355	np ASN n_1	.111 2.432	.217 2.789	.293 2.983	.451 3.207	.683 3.165	.988 2.776	1.355 2.261	1.635 1.950	2.343 1.470	2.671 1.344	3.458 1.167	3.803 1.122	4.602 1.060

Plan	Ac	Re	R	np*	np / ASN												
3S	3	4	4.891	6.681	np	.823	1.366	1.745	2.535	3.672	5.109	6.681	7.754	10.045	10.978	13.062	13.935	15.922
					ASN	1	1	1	1	1	1	1	1	1	1	1	1	1
3D	1 4	4 5	4.398	4.398	np	.635	1.000	1.246	1.750	2.465	3.373	4.398	5.130	6.808	7.542	9.270	10.019	11.757
					ASN	1.130	1.245	1.316	1.421	1.470	1.414	1.293	1.211	1.084	1.053	1.017	1.010	1.003
					n_1													
3M	# 0 1 2 3 4 6	3 3 4 5 6 6 7	4.672	1.626	np	.200	.348	.446	.642	.910	1.246	1.626	1.901	2.553	2.848	3.566	3.887	4.650
					ASN	2.461	2.820	3.026	3.286	3.288	2.935	2.450	2.156	1.693	1.559	1.340	1.274	1.163
					n_1													
4S	4	5	4.058	7.994	np	1.279	1.970	2.433	3.369	4.671	6.274	7.994	9.154	11.605	12.594	14.795	15.711	17.792
					ASN	1	1	1	1	1	1	1	1	1	1	1	1	1
4D	3 5	6 6	4.102	6.699	np	1.099	1.633	1.992	2.728	3.789	5.162	6.699	7.762	10.047	10.978	13.062	13.933	15.909
					ASN	1.025	1.077	1.125	1.233	1.341	1.345	1.242	1.164	1.055	1.033	1.009	1.005	1.001
					n_1													
4M	# 1 2 3 4 5 6	3 4 4 6 6 7 7	4.814	2.118	np	.266	.440	.558	.798	1.141	1.591	2.118	2.502	3.385	3.763	4.640	5.016	5.884
					ASN	2.128	2.300	2.417	2.590	2.618	2.384	2.021	1.792	1.427	1.326	1.174	1.132	1.070
					n_1													
5S	5	6	3.550	9.275	np	1.785	2.613	3.152	4.219	5.670	7.423	9.275	10.513	13.109	14.150	16.455	17.411	19.578
					ASN	1	1	1	1	1	1	1	1	1	1	1	1	1
5D	2 6	5 7	3.547	5.781	np	1.116	1.630	1.959	2.607	3.490	4.579	5.781	6.627	8.537	9.357	11.253	12.066	13.928
					ASN	1.097	1.199	1.263	1.360	1.405	1.352	1.243	1.171	1.064	1.039	1.012	1.007	1.002
					n_1													
5M	# 1 2 3 5 7 9 10	4 5 6 7 8 9 10	3.243	2.270	np	.490	.700	.830	1.079	1.410	1.814	2.270	2.604	3.411	3.776	4.642	5.017	5.884
					ASN	2.496	2.906	3.143	3.459	3.516	3.188	2.677	2.347	1.791	1.628	1.367	1.292	1.171
					n_1													

Source: Schilling and Johnson, 1980, p. 221.

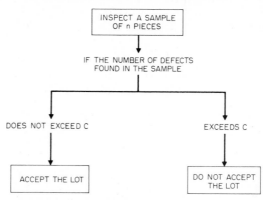

SCHEMATIC OPERATION OF SINGLE SAMPLING

FIG. 25.6 Schematic operation of single sampling. In practice, the lot not to be accepted may be repaired, junked, etc. Sampling tables usually assume that the lot is detail-inspected and the defective pieces all repaired or replaced by good pieces.

Rectification Schemes.   Rectification schemes are used when it is desired to ensure that the average outgoing quality level of a series of lots will not exceed specified levels. Such schemes employ 100 percent inspection (screening), with nonconforming items replaced by conforming items.

There are two basic types of rectification schemes: LTPD schemes and AOQL schemes. LTPD schemes ensure consumer quality level protection for each lot, while AOQL schemes ensure AOQL protection for a series of lots. Both types of schemes minimize ATI at the projected process average percent nonconforming. See Dodge and Romig (1959).

TABLE 25.7   Single Sampling by Attributes

Example: Determine a plan which will have AQL $= 100\,p_1 = 1.0\%$ with producer risk $\alpha = 0.05$ and LTPD $= 100p_2 = 5.0\%$ with consumer risk $\beta = 0.10$. Suppose a sample is taken from a lot of $N = 500$ and four nonconforming units are found.

Summary of plan	Calculations
I. Restrictions: Random sample of dichotomous data	

II. Necessary information
    A. Producer quality level, p_1
    B. Producer risk, α
    C. Consumer quality level, p_2
    D. Consumer risk, β
	II.
	    A. $p_1 = 0.01$
	    B. $\alpha = 0.05$
	    C. $p_2 = 0.05$
	    D. $\beta = 0.10$

III. Selection of plan (using Table 25.6)
    A. Calculate operating ratio
 	
        $R = p_2\,/\,p_1$
	III.
	    A. $R = 0.05/0.01$
	        $= 5$

TABLE 25.7 Single Sampling by Attributes (*Continued*)

Summary of plan	Calculations
B. Choose single sampling plan (*S*) from Table 25.6 which shows $R \leq$ the value calculated	*B.* Choose Plan 3S since R shown is 4.891
C. Acceptance and rejection numbers are given	*C.* Ac = 3 Re = 4
D. Determine sample size from value of (np_2) shown for the plan as $n = (np_2)/p_2$; round up	*D.* $n = \dfrac{6.681}{0.05}$

IV. Elements
  A. Sample size: See III above
  B. Statistic: d = number nonconforming in sample
  C. Decision criteria:
    1. Accept if $d \leq c$
    2. Reject if $d > c$
	IV.
	
	  A. n = 134
	  B. d = 4
	
	  C. 4 > 3, reject

V. Action: Dispose of lot as indicated by decision rules.	V. Reject

VI. Measures (using Table 25.6)
  A. Probability of acceptance (OC curve)
    1. Under each value of probability of acceptance listed across top of table, there corresponds a value of np shown for the plan
    2. Divide the values of np by sample size n to get p
 	
    3. Draw OC curve from corresponding values of p and P_a
  B. Average sample number (ASN curve)
    1. Calculate p from P_a as above
 	
    2. Under the value np from which p was calculated is listed a value of ASN/n_1
    3. Multiply ASN/n_1 by n to obtain ASN corresponding to p
    4. Draw ASN curve from corresponding values of p and P_a
  C. Average outgoing quality
    1. Use formula
$$\text{AOQ} \simeq p\,P_a$$
  D. Average outgoing quality limit
$$\text{AOQL} \simeq \frac{0.4}{n}(1.25c + 1) \text{ for } c \leq 5$$
  E. Average total inspection
$$\text{ATI} = n\,P_a + N(1 - P_a)$$
	VI.
	  A.
	    1. P_a = 0.50 corresponds to np = 3.672
	
	    2. $p = \dfrac{3.672}{134}$
	       = 0.027
	    3. p = 0.027
	       P_a = 0.50
	  B.
	    1. P_a = 0.50
	       p = 0.027
	    2. ASN/n_1 = 1
	
	    3. (1)(134) = 134
	
	    4. p = 0.027
	       ASN = 134
	  C.
	    1. at p = 0.027,
	       AOQ = 0.027 (0.50)
	           = 0.014
	  D.
	    1. AOQL $\simeq$
	$$\frac{0.4}{134}[1.25(3)+1] \simeq 0.019$$
	  E. at p = 0.027
	       ATI = 134(0.5) + 500(0.5)
	           = 317

SCHEMATIC OPERATION OF DOUBLE SAMPLING

FIG. 25.7   Schematic operation of double sampling. In regard to the lot not to be accepted, inspect the remainder of the pieces, replacing or repairing those defective.

Continuous Sampling.   Some production processes deliver product in a continuous stream rather than on a lot-by-lot basis. Separate plans have been developed for such continuous production based on the AOQL concept. These plans generally start with 100 percent inspection until some consecutive number of units free of defects is found and then provide for inspection on a sampling basis until a specified number of defective units is found. One hundred percent inspection is then instituted again until a specified number of consecutive good pieces is found, at which time sampling is reinstituted. Continuous sampling plans have been proposed by Harold F. Dodge and modifications developed by Dodge and Torrey (1951). Dodge (1970) recounts these and other developments in the evolution of continuous sampling plans. MIL-STD-1235 B (1981) provides a tabulation of continuous sampling plans.

The following are prerequisites for application of the single-level continuous sampling plans:

1. The inspection must involve "moving product," i.e., product which is flowing past the inspection station, e.g., on a conveyor belt.
2. Rapid 100 percent inspection must be feasible.

TABLE 25.8 Double Sampling by Attributes

Example: Determine a double sampling plan which will have $AQL = 100p_1 = 1.0\%$ with producer risk $\alpha = 0.05$ and $LTPD = 100p_2 = 5.0\%$ with consumer risk $\beta = 0.10$. Suppose a sample is taken from a lot of $N = 500$ and four nonconforming units are found.

Summary of plan	Calculations
I. Restrictions: Random sample of dichotomous data	
II. Necessary information *A.* Producer quality level, p_1 *B.* Producer risk, α *C.* Consumer quality level, p_2 *D.* Consumer risk, β	II. *A.* $p_1 = 0.01$ *B.* $\alpha = 0.05$ *C.* $p_2 = 0.05$ *D.* $\beta = 0.10$
III. Selection of plan (using Table 25.6) *A.* Calculate operating ratio $$R = p_2 / p_1$$ *B.* Choose double sampling plan (*D*) from Table 25.6 which shows $R \leq$ the value calculated *C.* Acceptance (*a*) and rejection (*r*) numbers are given as Ac and Re *D.* Determine first sample size from value of (np_2) shown for the plan as $n = (np_2)/p_2$ This is sample size of each of the double samples	III. *A.* $R = 0.05/0.01$ $\quad = 5$ *B.* Choose plan 3D since R shown is 4.398 *C.* First sample $\quad a_1 = 1, r_1 = 4$ Second sample $\quad a_2 = 4, r_2 = 5$ *D.* $n = 4.398/0.05$ $\quad = 88$
IV. Elements *A.* Sample size: See III above *B.* Statistic: d_1 = number nonconforming in first sample; d_2 = number nonconforming in second sample *C.* Decision criteria 　1. Accept on first sample if $d_1 \leq a_1$ 　2. Reject on first sample if $d_1 \geq r_1$ 　3. Take a second sample if $a_1 < d_1 < r_1$ 　4. Accept on second sample if $d_1 + d_2 \leq a_2$ 　5. Reject on second sample if $d_1 + d_2 \geq r_2$	IV. *A.* $n_1 = 88$ $\quad n_2 = 88$ *B.* $d_1 = 4$ *C.* 　1. 4 not ≤ 1 　2. $4 \geq 4$, reject
V. Action: Dispose of lot as indicated by decision rules.	V. Reject
VI. Measures (using Table 25.6) *A.* Probability of acceptance (OC curve) 　1. Under each value of probability of acceptance listed across the top of table, there corresponds a value of np shown for the plan 　2. Divide the values of np by sample size n to get p	VI. *A.* 　1. $P_a = 0.50$ corresponds to $np = 2.465$ 　2. $p = \dfrac{2.465}{88}$ $\quad = 0.028$

25.29

TABLE 25.8 Double Sampling by Attributes (*Continued*)

Summary of plan	Calculations

3. Draw OC curve from corresponding values of p and P_a
B. Average sample number (ASN curve)
  1. Calculate p from P_a as above
 	
  2. Under the value np from which p was calculated is listed a value of ASN/n_1
  3. Multiply ASN/n_1 by n_1 to obtain ASN corresponding to p
  4. Draw ASN curve from corresponding values of p and P_a
C. Average outgoing quality
  1. Use formula
$$AOQ \simeq p\,P_a$$
 	
D. Average outgoing quality limit
  1. AOQL = maximum of AOQ curve
 	
E. Average total inspection $ATI = n_1 + n_2(1 - P_{a_1}) + (N - n_1 - n_2)(1 - P_a)$ where P_{a_1} is probability of acceptance on first sample
	3. p = 0.028
	   P_a = 0.50
	B.
	  1. P_a = 0.50
	     p = 0.028
	  2. ASN/n_1 = 1.470
	
	  3. 1.470(88)
	        = 129.4
	  4. p = 0.028
	      ASN = 129.4
	C.
	  1. at p = 0.028
	     AOQ = 0.028(.5)
	        = 0.014
	D.
	  1. AOQL = 0.0151 at
	       p = 0.022
	E. P_{a_1} = probability no more than one defective in 88
	
	P_{a_1} = 0.29
	ATI = 88 + 88 (0.71) + 324(0.50)
	     = 312.5

3. The inspection must be relatively easy.

4. The product must be homogeneous.

CSP-1 Plans. CSP-1 plans use 100 percent inspection at the start. When i successive units are found to be acceptable and when there is assurance that the process is producing homogeneous product, 100 percent inspection is discontinued and sampling is instituted to the extent of a fraction f of the units. The sampling is continued until a defective unit is found. One hundred percent inspection is then reinstated and the procedure is repeated. Dodge (1943) has provided graphs which can be used to select such plans based on the AOQL desired. See also Schilling (1982).

For example, consider the plan $i = 35, f = \frac{1}{10}$. One hundred percent inspection is used until 35 successive units are found nondefective. Sampling, at the rate of 1 unit in 10, is then instituted. If a defective is found, 100 percent inspection is reinstituted and continued until 35 successive units are found nondefective, at which time sampling is reinstituted.

CSP-2 Plans. CSP-2 plans were developed to permit sampling to continue even if a single defective is found. Again, 100 percent inspection is used at the start until i successive units are found free of defects. When sampling is in effect and a defective is found, 100 percent inspection is instituted only if a second defective occurs in the next i or fewer sample units inspected. Details on the selection of such plans will be found in Dodge and Torrey (1951) or in Schilling (1982).

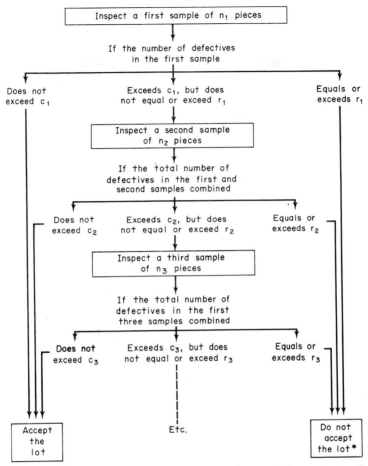

FIG. 25.8 Schematic operation of multiple sampling. Asterisk means some of these plans continue to the "bitter end," i.e., the taking of samples continues if necessary until the lot is fully inspected, unless the plan has meanwhile "made up its mind." Other plans, described as "truncated," are designed to force a decision after a certain number of inconclusive samples have been examined.

Stopping Rules. Murphy (1959) has investigated four different "stopping rules" for use with CSP-1 plans. He concludes that a useful rule is to stop when a specified number of defectives is found during any one sequence of 100 percent inspection.

Multilevel Continuous Sampling. Continuous sampling plans have been developed by Lieberman and Solomon (1955) and others which reduce the sampling rate beyond that of other continuous plans when the quality level is better than a defined AOQL. In addition, sudden changes in the amount of inspection are avoided by providing for several "levels" of inspection. Figure 25.10 outlines the procedure for using the plan. The procedure provides for reducing the sampling

TABLE 25.9 Multiple Sampling by Attributes

Example: Determine a multiple sampling plan which will have AQL $= 100p_1$ $= 1.0\%$ with producer risk $\alpha = 0.05$ and LTPD $= 100p_2 = 5.0\%$ with consumer risk $\beta = 0.10$. Suppose a sample is taken from a lot of $N = 500$ and four nonconforming units are found.

Summary of plan	Calculations
I. Restrictions: Random sample from dichotomous population	

II. Necessary information
   A. Producer quality level, p_1
   B. Producer risk, α
   C. Consumer quality level, p_2
   D. Consumer risk, β
	II.
	   A. $p_1 = 0.01$
	   B. $\alpha = 0.05$
	   C. $p_2 = 0.05$
	   D. $\beta = 0.10$

III. Selection of plan (Table 25.6)
 	
   A. Calculate operating ratio
         $R = p_2/p_1$
   B. Choose multiple sampling plan (M) from Table 25.6 which shows $R \leq$ the value calculated
   C. Acceptance (a) and rejection (r) numbers are given as Ac and Re; note # indicates acceptance is not possible at that sample
   D. Determine first sample size from value of (np_2) shown for the plan as
         $n = (np_2)/p_2$
This is sample size of each of the multiple samples
	III.
	
	   A. $R = 0.05/0.01 = 5$
	
	   B. Choose plan 3M since R shows 4.672
	
	   C.
	     Ac = #, 0, 1, 2, 3, 4, 6
	     Re = 3, 3, 4, 5, 6, 6, 7
	
	   D. $n = 1.626/0.05$
	       $= 33$

IV. Elements
   A. Sample size: See III above
   B. Statistic: $\sum_{i=1}^{k} d_i = $ total number nonconforming up to kth sample
   C. Decision Criteria
     1. Accept on kth sample if
          $\sum_{i=1}^{k} d_i \leq a_k$
     2. Reject on kth sample if
          $\sum_{i=1}^{k} d_i \geq r_k$
     3. Continue sampling if
          $a_k < \sum_{i=1}^{k} d_i < r_k$
	IV.
	   A. $n = 33$
	   B. $\sum_{i=1}^{1} d_i = 4$
	
	   C.
	     1. # indicates cannot accept
	
	     2. $4 \geq 3$, reject on first sample

V. Action Dispose of lot as indicated by decision rules	V. Reject

VI. Measures (using Table 25.6)
   A. Probability of acceptance (OC curve)
     1. Under each value of probability of acceptance listed across the top of the table, there corresponds a value of np shown for the plan
	VI.
	   A.
	     1. $P_a = 0.50$ corresponds to $np = 0.910$

TABLE 25.9   Multiple Sampling by Attributes (*Continued*)

Summary of plan	Calculations
2. Divide the values of np by sample size n to get p	2. $p = \dfrac{0.910}{33} = 0.028$
3. Draw OC curve from corresponding values of p and P_a	3. $p = 0.028$ $P_a = 0.50$

B. Average sample number (ASN curve)
   1. Calculate p from P_a as above
	B.
	   1. $P_a = 0.50$
	     $p = 0.028$

2. Under the value np from which p was calculated is listed a value of ASN/n_1	2. $\mathrm{ASN}/n_1 = 3.288$
3. Multiply ASN/n_1 by n to obtain ASN corresponding to p	3. $\mathrm{ASN} = 3.288(33)$ $= 108.5$
4. Draw ASN curve from corresponding values of p and P_a	4. $p = 0.028$ $\mathrm{ASN} = 108.5$

C. Average outgoing quality
   1. Use formula $\mathrm{AOQ} \simeq p\,P_a$
	C.
	   1. at $p = 0.028$
	      $\mathrm{AOQ} \simeq 0.028(.5)$
	           $= 0.014$

D. Average outgoing quality limit
   $\mathrm{AOQL} = $ maximum of AOQ curve
	D.
	   $\mathrm{AOQL} = 0.0148$ at
	      $p = 0.022$

E. Average total inspection (approximate)
   $\mathrm{ATI} \approx \mathrm{ASN}\,(P_a) + N(1 - P_a)$
	E.
	   $\mathrm{ATI} \simeq 108.5(0.5) + 500(0.5)$
	        $\simeq 304$

rate each time i successive units are found to be free of defects. The first sampling rate after leaving 100 percent inspection is f, and each succeeding sampling rate is f raised to one larger power. The number of sampling levels is k. Thus, if $f = \tfrac{1}{2}$ and $k = 3$, the successive sampling rates are $\tfrac{1}{2}$, $\tfrac{1}{4}$, and $\tfrac{1}{8}$.

Notice that all the continuous plans discussed so far are based on the AOQL concept, i.e., requiring periods of 100 percent inspection during which only non-defective product is accepted. This action controls the average defective-ness of accepted product at some pre-determined level. In all these cases, inspection must be nondestructive to employ the AOQL principle.

Additional detail on continuous sampling plans will be found in Stephens (1979).

Skip-Lot Schemes. Skip-lot sampling plans are used when there is a strong desire to reduce the total amount of inspection. The approach is to require some initial criterion be satisfied, such as 10 or so consecutively accepted lots, and then determine what

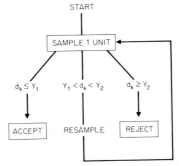

FIG. 25.9   Schematic operation of sequential sampling. *(From Schilling, 1982, p. 156.)*

TABLE 25.10 Sequential Sampling by Attributes

Example: Determine a sequential sampling plan which will have AQL $= 100p_1$ $= 1\%$ with producer risk $\alpha = 0.05$ and LTPD $= 100p_2 = 5\%$ with consumer risk $\beta = 0.10$. Suppose all the samples taken from a lot of 500 are defective.

Summary of plan	Calculations

I. Restrictions
   Random sample of dichotomous data

II. Necessary information
     A. Producer quality level, p_1
     B. Producer risk, α
     C. Consumer quality level, p_2
     D. Consumer risk, β

II.
     A. $p_1 = 0.01$
     B. $\alpha = 0.05$
     C. $p_2 = 0.05$
     D. $\beta = 0.10$

III. Selection of plan
     A. Parameters
       1. $h_1 = \log{[(1 - \alpha)/\beta]} / \{\log{(p_2/p_1)} + \log{[(1 - p_1)/(1 - p_2)]}\}$
       2. $h_2 = \log{[(1 - \beta)/\alpha]} / \{\log{(p_2/p_1)} + \log{[(1 - p_1)/(1 - p_2)]}\}$
       3. $s = \log{[(1 - p_1)/(1 - p_2)]} / \{\log{(p_2/p_1)} + \log{[(1 - p_1)/(1 - p_2)]}\}$
     B. Acceptance criteria
       1. Acceptance line
         $y_1 = sk - h_1$
       2. Rejection line
         $y_2 = sk + h_2$

       3. k = number of samples taken

III.
     A.
       1. $h_1 = 1.3639$

       2. $h_2 = 1.7510$

       3. $s = 0.02499$

     B.
       1. $y_1 = 0.02499k - 1.3639$
       2. $y_2 = 0.02499k + 1.7510$

       3. Take $k = 2$

IV. Elements
     A. Sample size
       Not definite since samples are taken one at a time
     B. Statistic
       d_k = cumulative number nonconforming by the kth sample
     C. Decision criteria
       1. Accept if $d_k \leq y_1 = sk - h_1$

       2. Reject if $d_k \geq y_2 = sk + h_2$
       3. Continue sampling if $y_1 < d_k < y_2$

IV.
     A.

     B. At $k = 2$
       $d_2 = 2$

     C.
       1. 2 not ≤ -1.31, cannot accept
       2. $2 \geq 1.8$, reject
       3. Discontinue sampling

V. Action: Dispose of lot as indicated by the decision rule

V. Reject

VI. Measures
     A. Probability of acceptance (OC curve)
       1. Pick arbitrary value of h
       2. Then
   $$p = \frac{1 - [(1 - p_2)/(1 - p_1)]^h}{(p_2/p_1)^h - [(1 - p_2)/(1 - p_1)]^h}$$
   and
   $$P_a = \frac{[(1 - \beta)/\alpha]^h - 1}{[(1 - \beta)/\alpha]^h - [\beta/(1 - \alpha)]^h}$$

VI.
     A.
       1. $h = 1$
       2. $p = 0.01$
       $P_a = 0.95$

TABLE 25.10 Sequential Sampling by Attributes (*Continued*)

Summary of plan	Calculations

B. Average sample number (ASN curve)
  1. Calculate p and P_a as above
 	
  2. Then
	B.
	  1. $p = 0.01$
	     $P_a = 0.95$
	  2. ASN $= 81$

$$ASN = \frac{\left\{ \begin{array}{l} P_a \log \left[(\beta/(1 - \alpha)) \right] + \\ (1 - P_a) \log \left[(1 - \beta)/\alpha \right] \end{array} \right\}}{\left\{ \begin{array}{l} p \log (p_2/p_1) + (1 - p) \\ \log \left[(1 - p_2)/(1 - p_1) \right] \end{array} \right\}}$$

Summary of plan	Calculations

C. Average outgoing quality (AOQ curve)
  1. Use approximate formula
  $$AOQ \simeq p\, P_a$$
 	
D. Average outgoing quality limit
  AOQL $=$ maximum of AOQ curve
E. Average total inspection (approximate)
  ATI $\approx$ ASN $(P_a) + N(1 - P_a)$
	C.
	  1. At $p = 0.01$
	     AOQ $\simeq 0.01(0.95)$
	       $= 0.0095$
	D. AOQL $= 0.0145$ at
	     $p = 0.021$
	E. At $p = 0.01$
	  ATI $\approx 81(.95) + 500$
	     (0.05)
	     $\simeq 102$

fraction of lots will be inspected. Given this fraction, the lots to be inspected are chosen using some random selection procedure. The assumptions on which the use of skip-lot plans are based are much like those for chain-sampling plans (see below). OC curves for the entire skip-lot sampling scheme can be derived, and an AOQL concept does apply. Strong dependence is made on the constancy of production and consistency of process quality as well as faith in the producer and inspector. The skip-lot sampling scheme was devised by Dodge (1955a) and is, in essence, an extension of continuous sampling acceptance plans with parameters i and f. He designated the initial scheme as SkSP-1.

Here, a single determination of acceptability was made from a sample of size $n = 1$ from each lot. Lots found defective under sampling were 100 percent inspected or replaced with good lots. The AOQL then was in terms of the long term average proportion of defective *lots* that would reach the customer. This is called AOQL-2. Later, Dodge and Perry (1971) incorporated the use of a "reference" sampling plan to determine whether a lot is acceptable or rejectable. Such skip-lot plans are designated SkSP-2 and require 100 percent inspection of rejected lots. The resulting AOQL is in terms of the long-term average proportion of individual product *units* that would reach the customer. This is called AOQL-1.

The application of skip-lot sampling should be confined to those instances where a continuous supply of product is obtained from a reasonably stable and continuous process.

The parameters of the SkSP-2 plan (in terms of continuous sampling) are:

$i =$ number of successive lots to be found conforming to qualify for skipping lots either at the start or after detecting a nonconforming lot

$f =$ fraction of lots to be inspected after the initial criteria have been satisfied

FIG. 25.10 Procedure for multilevel continuous sampling.

n = sample size per inspected lot

c = acceptance number for each inspected lot

For example, if $i = 15, f = \frac{1}{3}, n = 10, c = 0$, the plan is to inspect 10 units from each lot submitted until 15 consecutive lots are found conforming, i.e., have no defective in the sample. Then one-third of the submitted lots are chosen at random for inspection and inspected to the same n and c. As long as all lots are found to be conforming, the f-rate applies. When a nonconforming lot is identified, reversion to inspection of all lots occurs until again 15 consecutive lots are found to be conforming, and then skipping is permissible again.

Many values of f and i are possible. For SkSP-1 these may be obtained from the Basic Curves for Plan CSP-1. See Dodge (1955a.) In using SkSP-2, unity values for selection of a plan having a designated operating ratio will be found in Dodge and Perry (1971). See also Schilling (1982).

One further consideration is whether to apply the skip-lot procedure to only one characteristic of a product, to all characteristics simultaneously, or just to some. The plan is obvious and straightforward when applied only to one product characteristic, perhaps a particularly expensive one in time or dollars. If applied to several characteristics, it might be best to inspect the f fraction for these characteristics on each lot. For example, if 6 characteristics are candidates for skip-lot sampling and $f = \frac{1}{3}$, perhaps 2 of these would be examined on one lot, two on another, and two on the third, again in some random fashion, so that all lots receive some inspection. Of course, if the most expensive part of the sampling scheme were forming the lot, sampling from it, and keeping records, the choice might be to inspect all characteristics on the same sample units. This argument may be extended to the case where all inspection characteristics are on a skip-lot basis; but if inspection is very complex, this is difficult to visualize.

Perry (1973) has extended skip-lot plans in many ways including the incorporation of multi-level plans. See Perry (1973a). Skip-lot plans are described in detail by Stephens (1982).

Chain-Sampling. Chain-sampling plans utilize information over a series of lots. The original plans by Dodge (1955), called ChSP-1, utilized single sampling on an attributes basis with n small and $c = 0$. The distinguishing feature is that the current lot under inspection can also be accepted if one defective unit is observed in the sample provided that no other defective units were found in the samples from the immediately preceding i lots, i.e., the chain. Dodge and Stephens (1965, 1966) derived some two-stage chain-sampling plans which make use of cumulative inspection results from several samples and are generalizations and extensions of ChSP-1. Conversely, ChSP-1 is a subset of the new plans, and the discussion here will be in terms of the two-stage plans.

Before discussing the details of the plans, the general characteristics of chain sampling are described. Chain-sampling plans, in comparison with single-sampling plans, have the characteristic of "bowing up" the OC curve for small fractions defective while having little effect on the end of the curve associated with higher fractions defective. The effectiveness of chain-sampling plans strongly depends upon the assumptions on which the plans are based, namely:

1. Production is steady, as a continuing process.

2. Lot submittal is in the order of production.

3. Attributes sampling is done where the fraction defective p is binomially distributed.

4. A fixed sample size from each lot is assumed.

5. There is confidence in the supplier to the extent that lots are expected to be of essentially the same quality.

Chain-sampling plans are particularly useful where inspection is costly and sample sizes are relatively small. However, they may also be found useful with large sample sizes. The advantage over double-sampling plans is the fixed sample size. The disadvantage is that moderate changes in quality are not easily detected. However, major changes in quality are detected as easily with chain-sampling plans having much smaller sample sizes as with single-sampling with the same AQL.

The two-stage chain-sampling plans have acceptance based on cumulation of defectives in each stage separately and are defined by the parameters and designators:

n = sample size, constant over all samples
k_1 = maximum number of samples for cumulation of defectives in the first stage
k_2 = maximum number of samples for cumulation of defectives in the second stage and in the "normal" period following the second stage
C_1 = allowable number of defectives in the cumulative results of k_1 or fewer samples in the first stage
C_2 = allowable number of defectives in the cumulative results of $k_1 + 1$ to k_2 or fewer samples, or the last k_2 samples
d = number of defectives in a sample
d_i = number of defective units in the ith sample
D = cumulative number of defectives in a series of samples
D_i = cumulative number of defective units at the ith sample with cumulation performed according to the plan

The acceptance criterion is a cumulative results criterion (CRC). At the start (initial application of the plan) and at a restart, the CRC for k_1 must be satisfied. To establish the normal acceptance period, the CRC for k_2 must be satisfied, and the normal period continues as long as the CRC is satisfied for the last k_2 lots. Restart occurs whenever the CRC is not satisfied. The flow chart for the plan, reproduced from Dodge and Stephens (1966), is given in Figure 25.11.

Dodge and Stephens adopt the designation ChSP-0, 2, e.g, to designate a two-stage sampling plan with $C_1 = 0$, $C_2 = 2$, and n, k_1, k_2 as unspecified or open parameters. A plan with $n = 10$, $k_1 = 1$, $k_2 = 3$, $C_1 = 0$, $C_2 = 2$ would be a particular plan in ChSP-0, 2. Additional sets of plans would then be designated by ChSP-0, 1; CHSP-1, 2; etc.

The original ChSP-1 plans had $k_1 = k_2 - 1$ and k_1 was designated as i. The plan is to inspect a sample of n units from a lot, accept the lot if zero defectives were found in the n units, or accept the lot if one defective were found in the sample and no defectives were found in the samples from the immediately preceding i lots. Thus for ChSP-1 comparison with ChSP-0, 1; $n = n$, $k_1 = k_2 - 1 = i$, $k_2 = i + 1$, $C_1 = 0$, $C_2 = 1$, and ChSP-1 is a subset of the two-stage plans.

Formulas for the OC curves for ChSP-0, 1; ChSp-0, 2 and several OC curves for various values of n, k_1, and k_2 are given by Dodge and Stephens (1965, 1966). All are based on the type B sampling situation. Soundararajan (1978) has prepared tables of unity values for selection of chain-sampling plans from various criteria. Stephens (1982) provides additional detail on implementing chain plans.

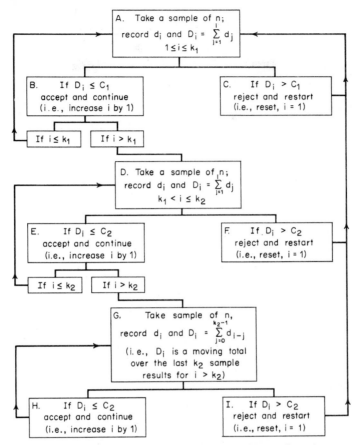

FIG. 25.11 Flow chart of operations, two-stage chain-sampling scheme.

Cumultive Sum Sampling Plans. A scheme has been devised by Beattie (1962) whereby the continuous inspection approach may be employed when inspection is destructive. Acceptance or rejection of the continuously produced product is based on the cumulation of the observed number of defectives. In addition, it is possible to discriminate between two levels of quality, an acceptable quality level (AQL) and rejectable quality level (RQL).

Prior to the development of continuous and cumulative sum plans, the following situation frequently occurred when inspection was destructive. Since production was continuous, usually there was no technically rational procedure for defining lots. A common procedure was to accumulate product until a lot was formed, but then the time delay in making a decision on the product was often too long, and a few short periods of bad production could cause a large quantity of good product to be rejected. Various approaches to lessening this jeopardy were used, all with some logical or practical drawback.

The procedure of Beattie (1962) establishes two zones, an accept zone and a reject zone, and product is accepted or rejected according to the cumulative sum

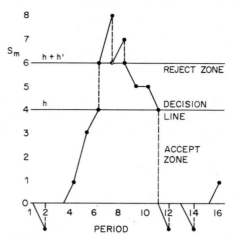

FIG. 25.12 Form of chart for acceptance under cumulative sum sampling plans.

of defectives observed. Figure 25.12 illustrates the plan. To implement the procedure, a sample of size n is chosen at regular intervals from production. The units are inspected and the number of defective units d_i in the ith sample recorded. Then,

$$S_m = \sum_{i=1}^{m} (d_i - k)$$

is accumulated, where k is a parameter of the scheme and S_m is computed and plotted according to the following rules:

1. Start the cumulation, S_m, at zero.
2. Accept product as long as $S_m < h$, where h is a second parameter of the scheme. When $S_m < 0$, return the cumulation to zero.
3. When h is crossed or reached from below, reject product and restart the cumulation at $h + h'$ (h' is a third parameter of the plan).
4. Continue rejecting product as long as $S_m > h$. When $S_m > h + h'$, return calculation to $h + h'$ and continue rejecting product until $S_m < h$.
5. When h is crossed or reached from above, accept product and restart cumulation at zero.

The discriminatory capability of the plans is controlled through the choice of k, h, and h' and their combinations. In familiar terms, k is akin to an acceptance number and h defines how far one is willing to deviate from this number over a long run and still accept product. The quantity h' is essentially how much evidence is required to be assured the process has been corrected.

The protection offered by this type of plan, which is similar to a type B acceptance situation, is defined by an OC curve which is determined by the ratio of the average run length (ARL) in the accept zone to the sum of the ARL in the accept and reject zones. An example, taken from Prarie and Zimmer (1973), follows.

A production situation exists where thermal batteries are produced at the rate of 50 per day. Testing is destructive, and a suitable number for testing is five per day. Based upon the reliability requirements of the system for which the battery is a component, a sampling plan with $P_a \approx 0.95$ at $p_1 = 0.025$ (AQL = 2.5 percent) and $P_a \approx 0.10$ at $P_2 = 0.15$ (LTPD = 15 percent) was appropriate.

On the basis of the desired AQL and LTPD, two comparable plans were suggested: (1) a conventional single-sampling plan with $n = 35$, $c = 2$, and (2) a cumulative sum plan with $n = 10$, $h = 1$, $h' = 2$, $k = 1$. The OC curves of these two plans coincide.

The two plans were compared during a period of 70 days production of 50 batteries per day. For Plan 1, a sample was generated by taking five batteries per day for 7 days, and from this sample the total number of defective batteries was recorded. If there were two or fewer observed defective batteries, the 7 day's production was accepted; otherwise it was rejected.

For Plan 2, a sample was formed by taking five batteries per day for 2 days, and from this sample the total number of defective batteries was recorded. The cumulative sum $\Sigma (d - 1)$, since $k = 1$, was then plotted for each 2-day period, and the decision to reject or accept these periods of production was based on the value of $\Sigma (d - 1)$.

The results of the comparison showed that 21 days' production with three observed defectives was accepted by the single-sampling plan and 30 days' production with four observed defectives was accepted by the cumulative sum plan. Thus, the cumulative sum plan provided a 42 percent greater yield of batteries with the same protection and approximately the same (0.027 versus 0.028) estimated quality of accepted product.

The above example points up the weakness of using a conventional single-sampling plan when the quality is spotty where just a few isolated days of bad product can cause several days' production to be rejected. Conversely, the cumulative sum procedure was able to adapt to the sporadic quality and appears to be well suited for such a process.

Published Tables and Procedures. Table 25.11 summarizes the principal published attributes sampling tables showing, for each, its area of application, main features, and quality index.

The published plans cover three quality indices: AQL, LTPD, and AOQL.

AQL Plans. Sampling schemes indexed by AQL are designed to give high assurance for type B situations (that is, sampling from a process) and give high assurance of lot acceptance when process quality is equal to or better than the specified AQL; i.e., the process fraction defective is less than or equal to that AQL. These plans are devised for producer's protection or to keep the producer's risk small. Consideration is given to what might be called the other end of the plan, the consumer's risk through the switching rules. If there is interest in controlling both producer's risk and consumer's risk with the use of schemes indexed by AQL values, the best approach is to study the scheme OC curves and choose the plan which provides adequate protection against both types of risks. See Schilling and Sheesley (1978); also Schilling and Johnson (1980).

MIL-STD-105D is the best-known sampling scheme indexed by AQL. The AQLs presented in this standard form a sequence which is evident in the standard. The sequence chosen, while arbitrary, does provide a sensible grouping and indexing of plans for use.

LTPD Plans. Sampling schemes indexed by LTPD or other values of limiting quality (LQ) are designed for type A situations and are essentially the mirror

TABLE 25.11 Summary of Published Attributes Sampling Plans for Lot-by-Lot Inspection

Name of plan	Type of sampling	Type of application	Key features
MIL-STD-105D and ANSI/ ASQC Z1.4 (1981)	Single, double and multiple	General application whether or not rejected lots can be 100% inspected	Maintains average quality at a specified level or better. Aims to minimize rejection of good lots. Also provides single-sampling plans for fixed consumer risks and average quality levels in the long run. Tables and mechanics of operation are simplified to minimize training required to use plan.
Dodge-Romig	Single and double	General application where rejected lots can be 100% inspected	One type of plan has a consumer's risk of 0.10 of accepting bad quality. A second type of plan limits the average quality level in the long run. Protection is provided with minimum inspection per lot.
Chain sampling	Single- and two-stage	Particularly useful when inspection involves destructive or costly tests	Aims to minimize sample sizes without a large risk of rejection of good lots. Occurrence of a single defective does not necessarily cause rejection of lot.
Bayesian plans	Generally single	General application where probability of occurrence of defective lots can be estimated a priori	Smaller sample size required as compared with standard attribute schemes.
Skip-lot sampling plans	Single	Particularly useful when indicated quality level is high and inspection involves costly or destructive tests	Aims to minimize inspection with adequate protection against major degradation in quality.
MIL-STD-1235B	Continuous	General application when production is truly continuous and inspection is nondestructive	Although plans are indexed by AQL, plans actually limit the average quality in the long run.

TABLE 25.11 Summary of Published Attributes Sampling Plans for Lot-by-Lot Inspection (*Continued*)

Name of plan	Type of sampling	Type of application	Key features
Cumulative sum	Continuous	General application when production is truly continuous and no restriction on the nature of inspection	Plans limit the average quality in the long run but in sense different from above.

image of plans indexed by AQL. That is, the plans are chosen such that the consumer's risk of accepting a submitted lot of product with quality equal to or worse than the LQ is equal to or less than some specified value. Specifically, LTPD plans provide a 10 percent probability of accepting lots of the listed LTPD quality. The Dodge-Romig sampling scheme is the best-known set of plans indexed by LTPD. MIL-STD-105D also provides some LQ plans. Schilling (1978) has developed a set of lot sensitive plans with $c = 0$ which are selected directly from the lot size and the LTPD using a simple table.

AOQL Plans. Sampling schemes indexed by AOQL are derived to provide assurance that the long-run average of accepted quality, given screening of rejected lots, will be no worse than the indexed AOQL value. The Dodge-Romig (1959) plans provide the best available tables of sampling plans indexed by AOQL.

The steps to be applied in any lot-by-lot sampling acceptance procedure are summarized in Table 25.12.

TABLE 25.12 Summary of Lot-by-Lot Sampling Procedure

Establishment of standards (by inspection executive):
    Decide what shall be a unit of product.
    Classify the quality characteristics for seriousness.
    Fix an acceptable quality level for each class.
    Fix an inspection level for the product.
Installation of procedure (by inspection supervisor):
    Arrange for formation of inspection lots.
    Decide what type of sampling shall be used (single, double, multiple).
    Choose sampling plan from tables.
Operation of procedure (by line inspector):
    Draw sample units from each inspection lot.
    Inspect each sample unit.
    Determine whether to accept or reject the inspection lot (if sampling for acceptance) or whether to urge action on the process (if sampling for control).
Review of past results (by inspection supervisor):
    Maintain a record of lot acceptance experience and cumulative defects by successive lots.
    Determine whether to tighten or reduce inspection on future lots.

MIL-STD-105D Sampling Tables. MIL-STD-105 was first issued in 1950 as MIL-STD-105A with the current issue, MIL-STD-105D (1963), published April 29, 1963. The current issue includes many important improvements over previous issues and will be the only one discussed here. Pabst (1963) describes the theoretical aspects and characteristics of issue D. The reader interested in these matters, as well as comparison of issue D with important aspects of previous issues, should study that reference.

The quality index in MIL-STD-105D and its civilian version ANSI/ASQC Z1.4 (1981) is the acceptable quality level (AQL). *corresponds to MTBF*

- A choice of 26 AQL values is available ranging from 0.010 to 1000.0. (Values of 10.0 or less may be interpreted as percent defective or defects per hundred units. Values above 10.0 must be interpreted as defects per hundred units.)
- The probability of accepting at AQL quality varies from 89 to 99.5 percent.
- Defects are classified as critical, major, or minor.
- The purchaser may, at its option, specify separate AQLs for each class or specify an AQL for each kind of defect which a product may show.

The purchaser also specifies the relative amount of inspection or inspection level to be used. For general applications there are three levels, and level II is regarded as normal. The three levels involve inspection in amounts roughly in the ratio of 1 to 2.5 to 4. Level II is generally used unless factors such as the simplicity and cost of the item, inspection cost, destructiveness of inspection, quality, consistency between lots, or other factors make it appropriate to use another level. The standard also contains special procedures for "small-sample inspection" where small sample sizes are either desirable or necessitated by some aspects of inspection. Four additional inspection levels (S1 through S4) are provided in these special procedures.

The procedure for choice of plan from the tables is outlined below.

1. The following information must be known:
   a. Acceptable quality level.
   b. Lot size.
   c. Type of sampling (single, double, or multiple).
   d. Inspection level (usually level II).
2. Knowing the lot size and inspection level, obtain a code letter from Table 25.13.
3. Knowing the code letter, AQL, and type of sampling, read the sampling plan from one of the nine master tables (Table 25.14 is for single-sampling normal inspection; the standard also provides tables for double and multiple sampling).

For example, suppose that a purchasing agency has contracted for a 1 percent AQL for a certain characteristic. Suppose also that the parts are bought in lots of 1500 pieces. From the table of sample size code letters (Table 25.13), it is found that letter K plans are required for inspection level II, the one normally used. Then the plan to be used initially with normal inspection would be found in Table 25.14 in row K. The sample size is 125. For AQL = 1.0, the acceptance number is given as 3 and the rejection number as 4. This means that the entire lot of 1500 units may be accepted if 3 or fewer defective units are found in the sample of 125,

TABLE 25.13   Sample Size Code Letters*

Lot or batch size		General inspection levels		
		I	II	III
2 to	8	A	A	B
9 to	15	A	B	C
16 to	25	B	C	D
26 to	50	C	D	E
51 to	90	C	E	F
91 to	150	D	F	G
151 to	280	E	G	H
281 to	500	F	H	J
501 to	1,200	G	J	K
1,201 to	3,200	H	K	L
3,201 to	10,000	J	L	M
10,001 to	35,000	K	M	N
35,001 to	150,000	L	N	P
150,001 to	500,000	M	P	Q
500,001 and over		N	Q	R

*Sample size code letters given in body of table are applicable when the indicated inspection levels are to be used. The Standard includes an added table of code letters for small-sample inspection.

but must be rejected if 4 or more are found. Where an AQL is expressed in terms of "defects per hundred units," this term may be substituted for "defective articles" throughout. Corresponding tables are provided in the standard for tightened and reduced inspection.

The system for choosing the initial sampling plan takes account of the quality of product actually submitted only in the limited sense that the AQL is thought to be attainable. When the material later submitted is of generally high quality, the functions of inspection emphasized are somewhat different from those when submitted material is of generally poor quality. If the average quality is high, sampling gives information on the prevailing quality level and provides some assurance that any sudden deterioration in quality will be detected and the resulting low-quality lots rejected. The functions of sorting good lots from bad and of applying pressure to cause the supplier to improve quality are less important. Moreover, poor or borderline material is seldom submitted for inspection (because it is usually detected by the producer in the inspection), so a relatively small amount of inspection is all that is economically justified.

If the quality of product submitted is consistently poor, most lots will be rejected. Also, it is unfortunate but true that the few inspection lots accepted in these circumstances will not be appreciably better than those rejected. If the AQL were properly chosen and is one that can or has been met by this or other suppliers, it becomes necessary to apply greater pressure to bring the supplier's quality into line. In addition, the sampling inspection has greater need for sharp discrimination between good and bad material in order to reduce the consumer's risk. Accordingly, the standard provides two variations in sampling severity from that chosen as normal, the choice of reduced or tightened inspection.

TABLE 25.14 MIL-STD-105D Master Table for Normal Inspection (Single Sampling)

Acceptable Quality Levels (normal inspection)

Sample size code letter	Sample size	0.010		0.015		0.025		0.040		0.065		0.10		0.15		0.25		0.40		0.65		1.0		1.5		2.5		4.0		6.5		10		15		25		40		65		100		150		250		400		650		1000	
		Ac	Re	Ac	Re	Ac	Re	Ac	Re	Ac	Re	Ac	Re	Ac	Re	Ac	Re	Ac	Re	Ac	Re	Ac	Re	Ac	Re	Ac	Re	Ac	Re	Ac	Re	Ac	Re	Ac	Re	Ac	Re	Ac	Re	Ac	Re	Ac	Re	Ac	Re	Ac	Re	Ac	Re	Ac	Re	Ac	Re
A	2	↓		↓		↓		↓		↓		↓		↓		↓		↓		↓		↓		↓		↓		↓		↓		↓		0	1	1	2	2	3	3	4	5	6	7	8	10	11	14	15	21	22	30	31
B	3	↓		↓		↓		↓		↓		↓		↓		↓		↓		↓		↓		↓		↓		↓		↓		0	1	1	2	2	3	3	4	5	6	7	8	10	11	14	15	21	22	30	31	44	45
C	5	↓		↓		↓		↓		↓		↓		↓		↓		↓		↓		↓		↓		↓		↓		0	1	1	2	2	3	3	4	5	6	7	8	10	11	14	15	21	22	30	31	44	45	↑	
D	8	↓		↓		↓		↓		↓		↓		↓		↓		↓		↓		↓		↓		↓		0	1	1	2	2	3	3	4	5	6	7	8	10	11	14	15	21	22	30	31	44	45	↑		↑	
E	13	↓		↓		↓		↓		↓		↓		↓		↓		↓		↓		↓		↓		0	1	1	2	2	3	3	4	5	6	7	8	10	11	14	15	21	22	30	31	44	45	↑		↑		↑	
F	20	↓		↓		↓		↓		↓		↓		↓		↓		↓		↓		↓		0	1	1	2	2	3	3	4	5	6	7	8	10	11	14	15	21	22	30	31	44	45	↑		↑		↑		↑	
G	32	↓		↓		↓		↓		↓		↓		↓		↓		↓		↓		0	1	1	2	2	3	3	4	5	6	7	8	10	11	14	15	21	22	30	31	44	45	↑		↑		↑		↑		↑	
H	50	↓		↓		↓		↓		↓		↓		↓		↓		↓		0	1	1	2	2	3	3	4	5	6	7	8	10	11	14	15	21	22	30	31	44	45	↑		↑		↑		↑		↑		↑	
J	80	↓		↓		↓		↓		↓		↓		↓		↓		0	1	1	2	2	3	3	4	5	6	7	8	10	11	14	15	21	22	30	31	44	45	↑		↑		↑		↑		↑		↑		↑	
K	125	↓		↓		↓		↓		↓		↓		↓		0	1	1	2	2	3	3	4	5	6	7	8	10	11	14	15	21	22	30	31	44	45	↑		↑		↑		↑		↑		↑		↑		↑	
L	200	↓		↓		↓		↓		↓		↓		0	1	1	2	2	3	3	4	5	6	7	8	10	11	14	15	21	22	30	31	44	45	↑		↑		↑		↑		↑		↑		↑		↑		↑	
M	315	↓		↓		↓		↓		↓		0	1	1	2	2	3	3	4	5	6	7	8	10	11	14	15	21	22	30	31	44	45	↑		↑		↑		↑		↑		↑		↑		↑		↑		↑	
N	500	↓		↓		↓		↓		0	1	1	2	2	3	3	4	5	6	7	8	10	11	14	15	21	22	30	31	44	45	↑		↑		↑		↑		↑		↑		↑		↑		↑		↑		↑	
P	800	↓		↓		↓		0	1	1	2	2	3	3	4	5	6	7	8	10	11	14	15	21	22	30	31	44	45	↑		↑		↑		↑		↑		↑		↑		↑		↑		↑		↑		↑	
Q	1250	↓		↓		0	1	1	2	2	3	3	4	5	6	7	8	10	11	14	15	21	22	30	31	44	45	↑		↑		↑		↑		↑		↑		↑		↑		↑		↑		↑		↑		↑	
R	2000	↓		0	1	1	2	2	3	3	4	5	6	7	8	10	11	14	15	21	22	30	31	44	45	↑		↑		↑		↑		↑		↑		↑		↑		↑		↑		↑		↑		↑		↑	

⇩ = Use first sampling plan below arrow. If sample size equals, or exceeds, lot or batch size, do 100 percent inspection.

⇧ = Use first sampling plan above arrow.

Ac = Acceptance number.

Re = Rejection number.

Inspection Severity—Definitions and General Rules for Changing Levels. The commonly used attributes acceptance sampling plans make provision for shifting the amount of inspection and/or the acceptance number as experience indicates. If many consecutive lots of submitted product are accepted by an existing sampling plan, the quality of submitted product must exceed that specified as necessary for acceptance. This makes it desirable to reduce the amount and cost of inspection (with a subsequent higher risk of accepting an occasional lot of lesser quality) simply because the quality level is good. On the other hand, if more than an occasional lot is rejected by the existing sampling plan, the quality level is either consistently lower than desired or the quality level fluctuates excessively among submitted lots. In either case it is desirable to increase the sampling rate and/or reduce the acceptance number to provide greater discrimination between lots of adequate and inadequate quality.

Three severities of inspection are provided: normal, tightened, and reduced. All changes between severities are governed by rules associated with the sampling scheme. Normal inspection is adopted at the beginning of a sampling procedure and continued until evidence of either lower or higher quality than that specified exists. Schematically, the rules for switching severities specified in MIL-STD-105D and ANSI/ASQC Z1.4 (1981) are given in Figure 25.13.

From the schematic it can be seen that the criteria for change from normal to tightened and back to normal are simple and straightforward. (This is a vast improvement over past issues of MIL-STD-105.) Again, the change from reduced to normal is straightforward and occurs with the first indication that quality has slipped. Considerably more evidence is required to change from normal to reduced.

In using schemes like MIL-STD-105D or ANSI/ASQC Z1.4 (1981), the customer assumes that the changes from normal to tightened and reduced to normal are a necessary part of the scheme. (Recall that such AQL plans provide primarily producer's assurance that quality at the AQL level will be accepted.) The change from normal to tightened or reduced to normal occurs when evidence exists that quality level has deteriorated. In this way the consumer's protection is maintained.

On the other hand, the supplier is interested in keeping inspection costs as low as possible consistent with the demands placed upon it. Certainly it is desirable to change from tightened to normal inspection when conditions warrant. Generally it would be economic to change from normal to reduced except in those cases where record-keeping costs or bother exceed the saving in reduced sampling effort. The initiative for these types of change generally rests with the supplier; only in those instances where an economic advantage exists would a customer insist on reduced inspection. This might occur, e.g., when the customer is using these sampling plans, where inspection is destructive or degrading, or when the psychological impact on the supplier makes reduced inspection a motivational force.

The case could arise where a complex item is being inspected for many characteristics, some of which are classified as critical, some major, and some minor. A different sampling plan could be in effect for each class. It is also possible on this same product to have reached the situation where, for example, reduced inspection could be in effect for critical defects, tightened inspection for major defects, and normal inspection for minor defects. The bookkeeping involved with complete flexibility of sampling plan choice by classification of characteristic and inspection severity can be enormous. On the other hand, the savings involved with lower inspection rates, especially with destructive inspection, could be sizable. Inspection cost and convenience, along with the consequences of the error of

FIG. 25.13   Rules for switching inspection severity, MIL-STD-105D.

applying an improper sampling plan, are the main determinants in any decision to use anything but the highest sampling rate associated with all defect classifications and whether to take advantage of reduced inspection for one or more defect classes when allowed. Of course, when tightened inspection is dictated by sampling experience, there is no recourse but to adopt it for at least that classificaton or characteristic, other than to discontinue acceptance inspection of submitted product.

The standard also provides limiting quality (LQ) single-sampling plans with a consumer's risk of 10 percent (LTPD) and 5 percent for use in isolated lot acceptance inspection. If other levels of LQ are desired, the individual OC curves can be examined to adopt an appropriate plan.

Finally, a table of AOQL values is provided for each of the single-sampling plans for normal and tightened inspection. These may also be used as rough guides for corresponding double- and multiple-sampling plans.

The sampling plans in MIL-STD-105D and ANSI/ASQC Z1.4 are sufficiently varied in type (single, double, multiple), amount of inspection, etc., to be useful in a great number of situations. The inclusion of operating characteristic curves and average sample size curves for most of the plans is a noteworthy advantage of the standard. The reader is also referred to the excellent supplementary publication, H-53 (1965), which discusses and provides recommendations on many of the practical problems that arise during the day-to-day application of the standard.

Dodge-Romig Sampling Tables. Dodge and Romig (1959) provide four different sets of tables:

1. Single-sampling lot tolerance tables (SL)
2. Double-sampling lot tolerance tables (DL)
3. Single-sampling AOQL tables (SA)
4. Double-sampling AOQL tables (DA)

All four types of plans were constructed to give minimum total inspection for product of a given process average. All lots rejected are assumed to be screened, and both the sampling and the expected amount of 100 percent inspection were considered in deriving the plan which would give minimum inspection per lot. This is a particularly appropriate approach for a manufacturer's inspection of its own product as when the product of one department is examined prior to use in another. Practically, it may be reasonable to use the same theory even when the sampling is done by the purchasing company and the detailing of rejected material is done by the supplying company, since in the long run all the supplier's costs to provide material of a specified quality are reflected in the price.

The first and second sets of tables are classified according to lot tolerance percent defective at a constant consumer's risk of 0.10. Available lot tolerance plans range from 0.5 to 10.0 percent defective. In contrast, the third and fourth sets of tables are classified according to the average outgoing quality limit (AOQL) which they assure. Available AOQL values range from 0.1 to 10.0 percent. Lot tolerance plans emphasize a constant low consumer's risk (with varying AOQLs). In other words, they are intended to give considerable assurance that individual lots of poor material will seldom be accepted. The AOQL plans emphasize the limit on poor quality in the long run, but do not attempt to offer uniform assurance that individual lots of low quality will not get through. The relative importance of these two objectives will guide the choice of types.

Table 25.15 shows a representative Dodge-Romig table for single sampling on the lot tolerance basis. All the plans listed in this table have the same risk (0.10) of accepting submitted lots that contain exactly 5 percent of defective units. The table has six columns. Each of these lists a set of plans appropriate to a specified average value of incoming quality. For example, if the estimated process average percent defective is between 2.01 and 2.50 percent, the last column at the right gives the plans that will provide the minimum inspection per lot. However, the assurance that a lot of quality 5 percent defective will be rejected is the same for all columns, so an initial incorrect estimate of the process average would have little effect except to increase somewhat the total number of pieces inspected per lot. The selection of a plan from this table thus requires only two items of information: the size of the lot to be sampled and the prevailing average quality of the supplier for the product in question. If the process average is unknown, the table is entered at the highest value of process average shown.

TABLE 25.15 Dodge-Romig Table* for Lot Tolerance Single Sampling

Lot tolerance percent defective = 5.0%

Process average %	0–0.5			0.06–0.50			0.51–1.00			1.01–1.50			1.51–2.00			2.01–2.50		
Lot size	n*	c*	AOQL* %	n	c	AOQL %	n	c	AOQL %	n	c	AOQL %	n	c	AOQL %	n	c	AOQL %
1–30	All	0	0	All	0	0	All	0	0	All	0	0	All	0	0	All	0	0
31–50	30	0	0.49	30	0	0.49	30	0	0.49	30	0	0.49	30	0	0.49	30	0	0.49
51–100	37	0	0.63	37	0	0.63	37	0	0.63	37	0	0.63	37	0	0.63	37	0	0.63
101–200	40	0	0.74	40	0	0.74	40	0	0.74	40	0	0.74	40	0	0.74	40	0	0.74
201–300	43	0	0.74	43	0	0.74	70	1	0.92	70	1	0.92	95	2	0.99	95	2	0.99
301–400	44	0	0.74	44	0	0.74	70	1	0.99	100	2	1.0	120	3	1.1	145	4	1.1
401–500	45	0	0.75	75	1	0.95	100	2	1.1	100	2	1.1	125	3	1.2	150	4	1.2
501–600	45	0	0.76	75	1	0.98	100	2	1.1	125	3	1.2	150	4	1.3	175	5	1.3
601–800	45	0	0.77	75	1	1.0	100	2	1.2	130	3	1.2	175	5	1.4	200	6	1.4
801–1,000	45	0	0.78	75	1	1.0	105	2	1.2	155	4	1.4	180	5	1.4	225	7	1.5
1,001–2,000	45	0	0.80	75	1	1.0	130	3	1.4	180	5	1.6	230	7	1.7	280	9	1.8
2,001–3,000	75	1	1.1	105	2	1.3	135	3	1.4	210	6	1.7	280	9	1.9	370	13	2.1
3,001–4,000	75	1	1.1	105	2	1.3	160	4	1.5	210	6	1.7	305	10	2.0	420	15	2.2
4,001–5,000	75	1	1.1	105	2	1.3	160	4	1.5	235	7	1.8	330	11	2.0	440	16	2.2
5,001–7,000	75	1	1.1	105	2	1.3	185	5	1.7	260	8	1.9	350	12	2.2	490	18	2.4
7,001–10,000	75	1	1.1	105	2	1.3	185	5	1.7	260	8	1.9	380	13	2.2	535	20	2.5
10,001–20,000	75	1	1.1	135	3	1.4	210	6	1.8	285	9	2.0	425	15	2.3	610	23	2.6
20,001–50,000	75	1	1.1	135	3	1.4	235	7	1.9	305	10	2.1	470	17	2.4	700	27	2.7
50,001–100,000	75	1	1.1	160	4	1.6	235	7	1.9	355	12	2.2	515	19	2.5	770	30	2.8

*Note: n = size of sample; entry of "All" indicates that each piece in lot is to be inspected.

  c = allowable defect number for sample.

  AOQL = average outgoing quality limit.

Source: Reproduced from Dodge and Romig (1959) by permission of the publisher and of Bell Telephone Laboratories, Inc.

Process average is determined from control charts and past records, modified by any supplemental knowledge useful for predicting the expected level of defects. The following are suggested as useful rules for determining process average:

1. Compute from the first samples[2] taken on about 25 lots, the total inspected, the total defects found, and the resultant average fraction defective $\bar{p}$.
2. Eliminate any samples from "abnormal" lots. This is done by plotting a control chart to find any instances in which the fraction defective for one sample exceeds the average fraction defective $\bar{p}$ by any amount greater than $3\sqrt{\bar{p}(1-\bar{p})/n}$, where n is the size of the sample for the lot under suspicion. (Dodge and Romig (1959) recommend that these abnormal samples be not eliminated but rather corrected through equating them to $\bar{p} \pm 2\sqrt{\bar{p}(1-\bar{p})/n}$ depending on the direction of the abnormality.)
3. Recompute $\bar{p}$ with the abnormal cases eliminated (or corrected by the Dodge-Romig method). The new value of $\bar{p}$ is to be used as process average $\bar{p}$.

VARIABLES SAMPLING

Overview. In using variables plans, a sample is taken and a measurement of a specified quality characteristic is made on each unit. These measurements are then summarized into a simple statistic (e.g., sample mean) and the observed value is compared with an allowable value defined in the plan. A decision is then made to accept or reject the lot. When applicable, variables plans provide the same degree of consumer protection as attributes plans while using considerably smaller samples.

Table 25.16 summarizes various types of variables plans showing, for each, the assumed distribution, the criteria specified, and special features.

Sampling for Percent Nonconforming. When interest is centered on the proportion of product outside measurement specifications, and when the underlying distribution of individual measurements is known, variables plans for percent nonconforming may be used. These plans relate the proportion of individual units outside specification limits to the population mean through appropriate probability theory. The sample mean, usually converted to a test statistic, is then used to test for the position of the population mean.

Assume the distribution of individual measurements is known to be normal and a plan is desired such that the OC curve will pass through the two points $(p_1, 1 - \alpha)$ and (p_2, β) where

$$p_1 = \text{acceptable quality level}$$
$$1 - \alpha = \text{probability of acceptance at } p_1$$
$$p_2 = \text{rejectable quality level}$$
$$\beta = \text{probability of acceptance at } p_2$$

The OC curve should appear as indicated in Figure 25.14. Some important plans of this type are described below.

---

[2] If this computation is made from all samples in double sampling, the results will be biased, since second samples are taken only from lots of borderline quality.

TABLE 25.16 Summary of Variables Sampling Plans

Type of plan	Plan	Assumed distribution	Criteria specified	Features
	Single-sampling variables plan	Normal	Acceptable and rejectable percent nonconforming	Formulas for determining sample size and acceptance criteria to meet defined risks.
	Double-sampling variables plan	Normal	Acceptable and rejectable percent nonconforming	Tables for determining sample size and acceptance criteria to meet defined risks.
Percent nonconforming	Narrow-limit gauging	Normal	Acceptable and rejectable percent nonconforming	Tables for determining sample size and acceptance criteria to meet defined risks.
	Lot plot	None	Allowable percent nonconforming	Requires 50 measurements. Simple calculations and graphical procedure used to evaluate lot.

Test of hypothesis	Appropriate for test	Mean or standard deviation	Formulas for determining sample size and acceptance criteria to meet defined risks.
Lot or process parameter—general			
Acceptance control chart	Appropriate for determining acceptable and rejectable values of mean	Mean	Graphical procedure to determine if mean falls within defined limits.
Sequential sampling	Normal	Mean or standard deviation	Procedures for evaluating one measurement at a time to determine if mean falls within defined limits. Complex but total sample size lower than with other plans.
Published plans for percent nonconforming			
MIL-STD-414	Normal	Acceptable quality level (percent defective)	Tables and procedures for lot evaluation to a specified AQL. Requires tightened and reduced inspection. OC curves given. Includes mixed plans for use when lots have been screened before submission to sampling inspection.
Lot or process parameter—bulk sampling			
Specific bulk sampling models	Appropriate for test	Mean	Formulas for determining sample size to estimate mean with specified confidence interval. Applicable for gaseous, liquid, or solid products which occur in nondiscrete units.

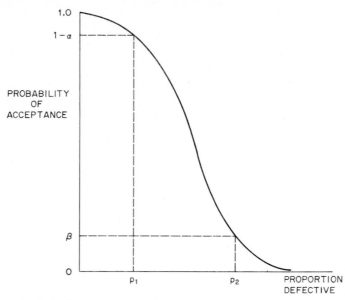

FIG. 25.14   Operating characteristic curve.

Single Sampling.   The rationale for variables sampling plans for percent non-conforming is illustrated in Figure 25.15, which assumes the underlying distribution of measurements to be normal with standard deviation σ known.

Suppose the following sampling plan is used to test against an upper specification limit U:

1. Sample n items from the lot and determine the sample mean $\overline{X}$.

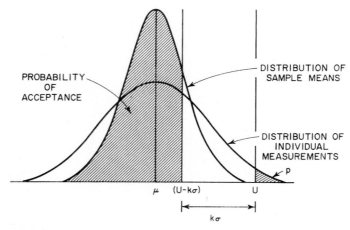

FIG. 25.15 $(U - k\sigma)$ method.

2. Test against an acceptance limit $(U - k\sigma)$, k standard deviation units inside the specification.

3. If $\overline{X} \leq (U - k\sigma)$, accept the product; otherwise reject the product.

If the distribution of individual measurements is normal, as shown, a proportion p of the product above the specification limit U implies the mean of the distribution must be fixed at the position indicated by μ. Means of samples of size n are, then, distributed about μ, as shown; so the probability of obtaining an $\overline{X}$ not greater than $(U - k\sigma)$ is indicated by the shaded area of the distribution of sample means. This shaded area is the probability of acceptance when the fraction nonconforming in the process is p. Note that the normal shape supplies the necessary connection between the distribution of the sample means and the proportion of product nonconforming. While, for reasonable sample sizes, the distribution of sample means will be normal, regardless of the shape of the underlying distribution of individual measurements, it is the underlying distribution of measurements itself that determines the relationship of μ and p. Hence, the plan will be quite sensitive to departures from normality.

Since $\overline{X} \leq U - k\sigma$ is equivalent to $\overline{X} + k\sigma \leq U$, the above sampling plan may be expressed as follows:

1. Sample n items from the lot and determine the sample mean $\overline{X}$.

2. If $\overline{X} + k\sigma \leq U$, accept the product; otherwise reject the product.

This is the method used to specify variables sampling plans in MIL-STD-414 (1957) and its civilian version ANSI/ASQC Z1.9 (1980). Diagrammatically, this second method of specifying a sampling plan is indicated in Figure 25.16. Adding $k\sigma$ to each $\overline{X}$ moves the distribution of the sample means to the right a distance $k\sigma$, so that the upper specification limit U plays the role of the acceptance limit. This can be seen by comparing Figure 25.15 with Figure 25.16.

Using Figure 25.15 or Figure 25.16 and normal probability theory, it is possible to calculate the probability of acceptance P_a for various possible values of p, the proportion defective. A graph of P_a versus p traces the operating characteristic curve of the acceptance sampling plan. Figure 25.17 shows the operating charac-

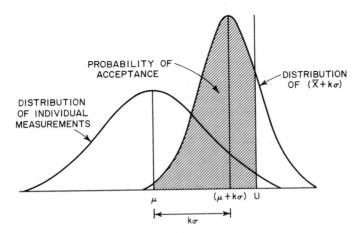

FIG. 25.16 $(\overline{X} + k\sigma)$ method.

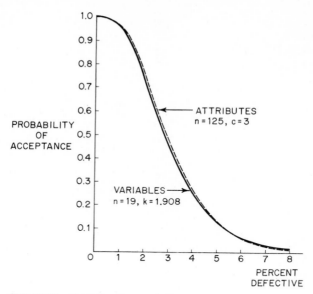

FIG. 25.17   Operating characteristic curve.

teristic curve of the variables plan $n = 19$, $k = 1.908$, testing against a single-sided specification limit with known standard deviation. For comparative purposes, the OC curve of the attributes plan $n = 125$, $c = 3$ is also given. Note that the OC curves intersect at about $p = 0.01$ and $p = 0.05$, indicating roughly equivalent protection at these fractions defective.

Probability theory appropriate to other methods of specifying variables plans (e.g., standard deviation unknown, double specification limits) can be used to give the OC curves and other properties of these procedures. Formulas for determining plans to meet specific prescribed conditions can also be derived. Note that the OC curves of variables plans are generally considered to be type B. That is, they are regarded as sampling from the process producing the items inspected, rather than the immediate lot of material involved.

Two-Point Variables Plans for Percent Nonconforming.   Two-point single-sampling plans for variables inspection can be readily obtained using an approximation derived by Wallis. For example, a two-point plan testing against a single specification limit, incorporating producer's quality level p_1 and consumer's quality level p_2 with producer's and consumer's risks fixed at $\alpha = 0.05$ and $\beta = 0.10$ may be found using

$$k = 0.438Z_1 + 0.562Z_2$$

$$n_\sigma = \frac{8.567}{(Z_1 - Z_2)^2}$$

or

$$n_s = \left(1 + \frac{k^2}{2}\right) n_\sigma$$

Here Z_1 is the standard normal deviate corresponding to an upper tail area of p_1, and Z_2 is the standard normal deviate corresponding to an upper tail area of p_2. Use n_σ or n_s depending on whether the standard deviation is known or unknown. For other risks or double specification limits more detailed procedures are necessary. See Duncan (1974).

As an example of the use of the procedure, consider $p_1 = 0.01$, $p_2 = 0.05$, $\alpha = 0.05$, $\beta = 0.10$. Application of the formulas with $Z_1 = 2.326$ and $Z_2 = 1.645$ gives $k = 1.94$, $n_\sigma = 18.5 \sim 19$ and $n_s = 53.3 \sim 54$. This plan matches the attributes plan $n = 131$, $c = 3$.

A procedure for applying double-sampling variables plans was first presented by Bowker and Goode (1952). Tables to expedite the selection and application of these plans are given by Sommers (1981). Double sampling by variables can account for about a 20 percent reduction in average sample numbers from single sampling. For example, the plan matching the single-sampling plan derived above would have average sample size 14.9 for the known standard deviation plan and 41.5 when the standard deviation is unknown. The application of double-sampling by variables is analogous to double sampling by attributes.

The relative efficiency of two-point variables plans over the matched variables plans varies with k. Hamaker (1979) has shown that

$$\frac{n_a}{n_\sigma} = 2\pi p_k (1 - p_k) e^{k^2}$$

where p_k is the upper tail normal area corresponding to the standard normal deviate $Z = k$ and n_a is the attributes sample size. For the example above, $k = 1.94$ so $p_k = .0262$ and $n_a/n_\sigma = 6.9$ and we observe that $131/19 = 6.9$.

Narrow-Limit Gaging for Percent Nonconforming. Narrow- (or compressed-) limit gaging plans bridge the gap between variables and attributes inspection by combining the ease of attributes inspection with the power of variables inspection to reduce sample size. An artificial specification limit is set inside the specification limit. Samples are selected and gaged against this artificial "narrow limit." The narrow limit is set using the properties of the normal distribution, to which the product is assumed to conform. A standard attributes sampling plan is applied to the results of gaging to the narrow limit and the lot is sentenced accordingly.

The criteria for the narrow-limit gaging plan are, then, as follows

n = sample size
c = acceptance number
t = number of standard deviation units the narrow-limit gage is set inside the specification limit

The standard deviation σ is assumed to be known.

A set of two-point plans having minimum sample size for selected values of producer's and consumer's quality levels with $\alpha = 0.05$ and $\beta = 0.10$ has been given by Schilling and Sommers (1981). They have also compiled a complete set of narrow-limit plans matching MIL-STD-105D.

Consider the plan having producer's and consumer's quality levels $p_1 = .01$ and $p_2 = 0.05$ with $\alpha = 0.05$ and $\beta = 0.10$. The appropriate plan given in the Schilling-Sommers tables is $n = 28$, $c = 14$, $t = 1.99$. A narrow-limit gage is set 1.99σ inside the specification limit. A sample of 28 is taken and gaged against the limit. If 15 or more units fail the narrow limit, the lot is rejected. Otherwise, it is accepted.

A good approximation to the optimum narrow limit plan can be constructed from the corresponding known standard deviation variables plan (n_σ, k) as follows:

$$n = \frac{3n_\sigma}{2}$$

$$t = k$$

$$c = \frac{3n_\sigma}{4} - \frac{2}{3}$$

For the example, we have seen that $n_\sigma = 18.5$ and $k = 1.94$

$$n = 27.8 \sim 28$$

$$t = 1.94$$

$$c = 13.2 \sim 14$$

Narrow-limit plans have had many successful applications and are readily accepted by inspectors because of the ease with which they can be applied.

Lot Plot.   Probably no variables acceptance sampling plan matches the natural inclination of the inspector better than the lot plot method developed by Dorian Shainin (1950) at the Hamilton Standard Division of United Aircraft Co. The procedure employs a histogram and rough estimates of the extremes of the distribution of product to determine lot acceptance or rejection. A standard sample size of 50 observations is maintained.

The method is useful as a tool for acceptance sampling in situations where more sophisticated methods may be inappropriate or not well received by the parties involved. The lot plot plan is especially useful in introducing statistical methods. The subjective aspects of the plan (classification of frequency distributions, their construction, etc.) and its fixed sample size suggest the use of more objective procedures in critical applications. The wide initial acceptance of Shainin's (1952) work attests to its appeal to inspection personnel. The lot plot method is outlined in Table 25.17. See Grant and Leavenworth (1979) for details. For a critical review, see Moses (1956).

A special lot plot card is helpful in simplifying some of the calculations. Figure 25.18 shows the form filled out for the example given in Table 25.17.

Grand Lot Schemes.   Acceptance inspection and compliance testing often require levels of protection for both the consumer and the producer that make for large sample size relative to lot size. A given sample size can, however, be made to apply to several lots jointly if the lots can be shown to be homogeneous. This reduces the economic impact of a necessarily large sample size. Grand lot schemes, as introduced by L. E. Simon (1941), can be used to effect such a reduction. Application of the grand lot scheme has been greatly simplified by incorporating graphical analysis of means procedures in verifying the homogeneity of a grand lot. In this way individual sublots are subjected to control chart analysis for uniformity in level and variation before they are combined into a grand lot. The resulting approach can be applied to attributes or variables data, is easy to use, provides high levels of protection economically, and can reduce sample size by as much as 80 percent. It may be applied to unique "one-off" lots, isolated lots

TABLE 25.17 Variables Plans for Percent Defective Lot Plot

Example: A lot plot is to be used in inspecting the width of caps. A sample of 50 is taken in 10 subgroups of 5 with the following results:

1	2	3	4	5	6	7	8	9	10
0.2538	0.2581	0.2556	0.2531	0.2501	0.2521	0.2541	0.2555	0.2489	0.2529
0.2519	0.2571	0.2542	0.2566	0.2506	0.2557	0.2499	0.2569	0.2557	0.2579
0.2508	0.2521	0.2521	0.2534	0.2534	0.2569	0.2514	0.2553	0.2542	0.2565
0.2537	0.2545	0.2521	0.2557	0.2516	0.2541	0.2536	0.2496	0.2529	0.2577
0.2529	0.2563	0.2518	0.2519	0.2559	0.2524	0.2492	0.2512	0.2546	0.2541

These data are shown analyzed in Fig. 25.18. Should the lot be accepted?

Summary of plan	Calculations

I. Restrictions: None.

II. Necessary information: Specification limits.

III. Selection of plan.
    A. Plan is constant lot to lot.
    B. A special form (Fig. 25.18) is used to apply plan.

IV. Elements
    A. Sample size: A random sample of 50 pieces is taken from the lot in 10 subsamples of 5 each. Subsample identification is maintained.
    B. Statistic (for symmetric distribution).
        1. Statistic is $\overline{\overline{X}} \pm 3\hat{\sigma}$ calculated as follows:
          a. Construct cells for frequency distribution on chart.
            (1) Determine mean $\overline{X}_1$ and range R_1 for the first subgroup
            (2) Position $\overline{X}_1$ at line number 0 on lot plot form
            (3) Set cell width w so that $w \simeq R_1/4$
            (4) Fill in lot plot form with cell midpoints
          b. Tally measurements for frequency distribution using subsample number as tally mark. Tally marks form a histogram.
          c. Record range of each subsample on form in terms of number of cells between lowest and highest tally mark for each subgroup.
          d. Calculate grand mean $\overline{\overline{X}}$ from frequency distribution in terms of line numbers above (+) and below (−) arbitrary origin taken as the zero cell.

B.
    1*a.* $\overline{X}_1 = 0.2526$, $R_1 = 0.003$

        $\overline{X}_1 \sim 0.253$ at 0

        $w \simeq \dfrac{0.003}{4} = 0.00075$

        take $w = 0.001$

    1*b.* See Fig. 25.18

    1*c.* See Fig. 25.18 under "range" on right side

    1*d.* Zero cell shown as arrow in Fig. 25.18 $\overline{\overline{X}} = +0.14$

Table 25.17 Variables Plans for Percent Defective Lot Plot (*Continued*)

Summary of plan	Calculations
e. Draw $\overline{\overline{X}}$ on chart in terms of line numbers.	1*e.* $\overline{\overline{X}}$ drawn 0.14 cell widths above middle of zero cell
f. Estimate 3σ of line numbers from average of subsample ranges $3\hat{\sigma} = 3\overline{R}/d_2 = 1.29\,\overline{R}$	1*f.* $3\hat{\sigma} = 1.29\left(\dfrac{51}{10}\right) = 6.6$

g. Label $\overline{\overline{X}} \pm 3\sigma$ in terms of line numbers as
  (1) ULL = Upper Lot Limit ($\overline{\overline{X}} + 3\hat{\sigma}$)
  (2) LLL = Lower Lot Limit ($\overline{\overline{X}} - 3\hat{\sigma}$)
	1*g.* See Fig. 25.18 marked ULL and LLL

h. Draw specification limits on chart.	1*h.* See Fig. 25.18 marked SPEC

C. Decision criteria.
  1. Acceptance criterion.
    a. Symmetric distribution well within specification limits—accept automatically.
    b. Symmetric distribution other than above:
      (1) Lot limits within specification—accept.
      (2) Lot limits outside specification—estimate proportion of product outside specification with special technique using code strip. If less than allowable value—accept. See reference below.
    c. Nonsymmetric, bimodal distributions, etc. Special technique provided for estimating proportion out of specification using code strip. See reference below. If less than allowable value—accept.
  2. Rejection criterion: Reject otherwise.	

V. Action: Dispose of lot as indicated. The Lot plot form provides a useful communication device with vendor.	V. Reject the lot
VI. Characteristics: See source reference below.	
VII. Reference: Shainin, 1950.	

from a continuing series, an isolated sequence of lots, or to a continuing series of lots. The procedure has been described in depth by Schilling (1979).

Sampling for Process Parameter. When process parameters are specified, sampling plans can be developed from analogous tests of significance with cor-

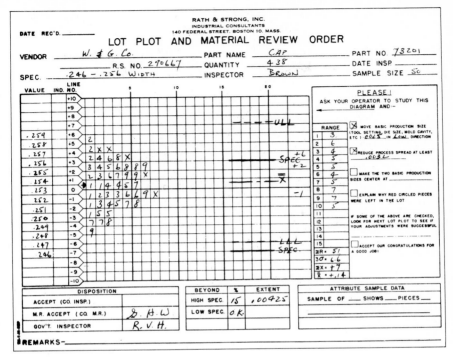

FIG. 25.18 Illustration of lot plot method.

responding OC curves. These plans do not require percent nonconforming to be related to the process mean, since the specifications to which they are applied are not in terms of percent nonconforming. This means that assumptions of process distribution may not need to be as rigorously held as in variables plans for percent nonconforming.

With specifications stated in terms of process location or variability, as measured by specific values of the mean μ or the process standard deviation σ, interest is centered not on fraction defective, but rather on controlling the parameters of the distribution of product to specified levels. From specifications of this type, it is usually possible to distinguish two process levels which may be used as bench marks as conceived by Freund (1957):

1. APL = acceptable process level—a process level which is acceptable and should be accepted most of the time by the plan.

2. RPL = rejectable process level—a process level which is rejectable and should be rejected most of the time by the plan.

The probability of acceptance for each of these process levels is usually specified as:

$$1 - \alpha = \text{probability of acceptance at the APL}$$

$$\beta = \text{probability of acceptance at the RPL}$$

where α = producer's risk, β = consumer's risk.

Variables plans appropriate for this type of specification can be derived from the operating characteristic curves of appropriate tests of hypotheses. This is the case for single-sampling plans for process parameter which are, simply, appropriately constructed tests of hypotheses, e.g., testing the hypotheses that μ equals a specific value, against a one- or two-sided alternative. Thus, the statistical tests presented in Section 23 under Statistical Tests of Hypotheses can be used for this type of acceptance sampling plan.

Sequential sampling procedures have been developed which are particularly useful when levels of process parameter are specified. They usually offer a substantial decrease in sample size over competing procedures, although they may be difficult to administer. To use sequential sampling:

1. Take a sample of one measurement at a time.
2. Plot the cumulative sum T of an appropriate statistic against the sample number n.
3. Draw two lines

$$T = h_2 + sn$$

$$T = -h_1 + sn$$

where the intercepts h_1 and h_2 are values associated with the plan used and the symbol s is not a standard deviaton but is a constant computed from the values of the acceptable process level (APL) and the rejectable process level (RPL). The use of s here corresponds to its use in the literature of sequential sampling plans.

4. Continue to sample if the cumulative sum lies between these lines, and take the appropriate action indicated if the plot moves outside the lines.

Procedures for constructing such plans and determining appropriate values of h_1, h_2, and s are given in detail in Duncan (1974).

Acceptance control charts offer a unique answer to the problem of sampling for process parameter and can be used to implement such plans when an acceptable process level and rejectable process level are defined in terms of the mean value. They satisfy the natural desire of inspection personnel to observe quality trends and to look upon sampling as a continuing process.

These charts incorporate predetermined values of consumer and producer risk in the limits and so provide the balanced protection for the interested parties that is often lacking in the use of a conventional control chart for product acceptance.

It is not necessary that the population of individual measurements be normally distributed. The distribution must be known so that acceptable and rejectable values of the mean can be calculated. The procedure then uses the normal distribution in the analysis of the sample mean because the distribution of sample means of samples of reasonable size may be regarded as normal for any distribution of individual measurements.

The procedure for implementing this technique is shown in Table 25.18. The acceptance control chart concept is shown in Figure 25.19, and an acceptance control chart example is shown in Figure 25.20. See Freund (1957) for additional details.

Published Tables and Procedures.   There is often much more involved in acceptance sampling than simple tests of hypotheses. Sampling plans applied individually to guard against an occasional discrepant lot can be reduced to

TABLE 25.18 Variables Plans for Process Parameter—Acceptance Control Charts

Example: The specification limits for electrical resistance are 620 and 680, the AQL 2.5%, and the standard deviation 13. Assuming a normal distribution of individual measurements, the mean may be as low as $620 + 1.96$ (13), or 646, or as high as $680 - 1.96$ (13), or 654. This pair of values represents the range of the acceptable process level (APL). It was decided that the rejectable process level would occur when 14% was beyond a specification limit. Thus, the range of RPL was $620 + 1.08$ (13) and $680 - 1.08$ (13), or 634 and 666. Should the lot be accepted if $\overline{X} = 647$?

Summary of plan	Calculations
I. Restrictions: None	
II. Necessary information (single-sided specification)	II.
A. σ = known standard deviation	*A.* $\sigma = 13$
B. μ_1 = APL (acceptable process level) with $P_a = 1 - a$	*B.* $\mu_1 = 654$, $P_a = 0.95$
C. μ_2 = RPL (rejectable process level) with $P_a = \beta$	*C.* $\mu_2 = 666$, $P_a = 0.10$
III. Selection of plan: See below	
IV. Elements	IV.
A. Sample size $$n = \left[\frac{(z\alpha + z\beta)\,\sigma}{\mu_2 - \mu_1} \right]^2$$ where z_p cuts off upper tail area of p in standard normal curve	*A.* $n =$ $$\left[\frac{(1.645 + 1.282)\,(13)}{12} \right]^2$$ $n = 10.06 \sim 10$
B. Statistic: $\overline{X}$ = mean of sample of n	*B.* $\overline{X} = 647$
C. Decision criteria	*C.* $d =$
1. Compute: $$d = \frac{z\alpha}{z\alpha + z\beta} |\,\mu_2 - \mu_1\,|$$ and set the acceptance control limit, ACL, a distance d from APL in the direction of the RPL. Sign of $|\mu_2 - \mu_1|$ ignored.	$\left(\dfrac{1.645}{1.645 + 1.282} \right) (12)$ $= 6.74$ Upper ACL $= 654 + 6.74$ $= 660.74$ By symmetry Lower ACL $= 646 - 6.74$ $= 639.26$
2. Construct an acceptance control chart (Fig. 25.19) and accept if $\overline{X}$ falls within acceptance control limits; reject otherwise. Double-sided specification chart shown (see remarks below). Use appropriate half of chart for single-sided specification.	Plot as in Fig. 25.20
V. Action: Single lot disposed of as indicated by chart	V. Accept the lot
VI. Characteristics: Two points originally specified give indication of OC curve	

TABLE 25.18 Variables Plans for Process Parameter—Acceptance Control Charts (*Continued*)

Summary of plan	Calculations
VII. Reference:	Freund, 1957.
VIII. Remarks	VIII.
A. Above formulas are for single upper or single lower process limits, or for both if (Upper ACL − Lower ACL) $\geq k\sigma / \sqrt{n}$ where:	*A.* Can use both upper and lower limits since $(660.74 - 639.26) >$ $\dfrac{(5)(13)}{\sqrt{10}}$ $21.48 > 20.56$

α	k
0.05	5
0.01	6
0.001	7

        If (Upper ACL − Lower ACL) $< k\sigma / \sqrt{n}$, see above reference for appropriate factors

    B. If standard deviation is estimated from control chart, see reference above for appropriate limits

    C. Advisable to run range chart with acceptance control chart to ensure stability of variation

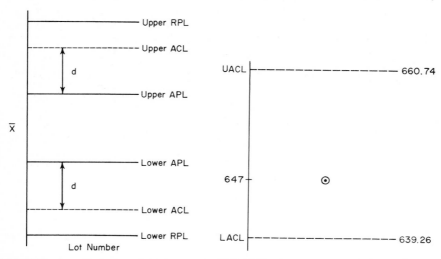

FIG. 25.19 Acceptance control chart concept. **FIG. 25.20** Acceptance control chart example.

hypothesis tests. Sampling plans, however, may be combined into sampling schemes, intended to achieve a predetermined objective. Sampling schemes, as overall strategies using one or more sampling plans, have their own measures such as AOQ (average outgoing quality) or ATI (average total inspection), not to be found in hypothesis testing. Thus, MIL-STD-105D (1963) and its civilian version ANSI/ASQC Z1.4 (1981) together with their variables counterpart MIL-STD-414 (1957) and its modified civilian version ANSI/ASQC Z1.9 (1980) are sampling schemes which specify the use of various sampling plans under well-defined rules.

Military Standard 414 (1957) and the modernized version ANSI/ASQC Z1.9 (1980) are AQL-type sampling schemes which assume the individual measurements to which they are applied to be normally distributed.

These standards allow for the use of three alternative measures of variability: known standard deviation σ, estimated standard deviation s, or average range ($\overline{R}$). If the variability of the process producing the product is known and stable as verified by a control chart, it is profitable to use σ. The choice between s and $\overline{R}$, when σ is unknown, is an economic one. The range requires larger sample sizes but is easier to compute. The operating characteristic curves given in the standards are based on the use of s, the σ and $\overline{R}$ plans having been matched, as closely as possible, to those using s.

MIL-STD-414 and ANSI/ASQC Z1.9 (1980) offer two alternative procedures. In addition to the method using an acceptance constant k, each standard also presents a procedure for estimating the proportion defective in the lot from the variables evidence. The former method is called Form 1; the latter is called Form 2. Form 2 is the preferred procedure in MIL-STD-414 since the switching rules for reduced and tightened inspection cannot be applied unless the fraction defective of each lot is estimated from the sample. The switching rules of ANSI/ASQC Z1.9 are patterned after MIL-STD-105D and can be used with Form 1 or Form 2.

These two forms can be compared with equivalent forms of attributes sampling. One possibility is to compare the number of defectives found in the sample d with an acceptance number c. Alternatively, the proportion defective in the population could be estimated from the proportion defective in the sample, and that estimate then compared with some acceptance limit (M). These possibilities are compared with their variables counterparts in Figure 25.21.

Attributes	Variables
Form 1 ..... $d \leq c$	$z = \dfrac{U - \overline{X}}{s} \geq k$
Form 2 ..... $p = \dfrac{d}{n} \leq \dfrac{c}{n} = M$	$Q = \dfrac{U - \overline{X}}{s}$ is used to estimate p
	$p \leq M$

FIG. 25.21 Criteria for acceptance (sample of n).

The standards are composed of sections indexed by measure of variability, type of specification (single or double), and form of the acceptance procedure. Only Form 2 is officially available for the case of double specification limits; however, factors are provided for application of Form 1 if desired. The structure of these standards is shown in Figure 25.22. Table 25.19 contrasts MIL-STD-414 and ANSI/ASQC Z1.9.

Application of these variables schemes follows the pattern of MIL-STD-105D, which is also an AQL sampling scheme. Sample sizes are determined from lot size, and after choosing the measure of variability to be used and the Form of the acceptance procedure, appropriate acceptance limits are obtained from the standard. As in MIL-STD-105D, operating characteristic curves are included in MIL-

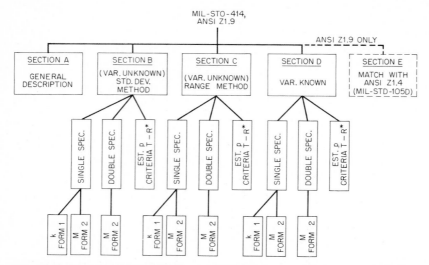

FIG. 25.22   Structure of MIL-STD-414 and ANSI/ASQC Z1.9-1980.   *(From E. G. Schilling (1981). "ANSI/ASQC Z1.9(1980)—A Modernization of MIL-STD-414." Quality Progress, March, p. 28.)*

TABLE 25.19   Comparison of ANSI Z1.9-1980 and MIL-STD-414

	ANSI Z1.9-1980	MIL-STD-414
Switching rules	Same as MIL-STD-105D; Figure 25.13	Unique; Figure 25.23
Inspection levels and sample size code letters	Same as MIL-STD-105D; Table 25.13	Unique; Table 25.21
Plans	Matched to MIL-STD-105D	Unique

STD-414 and ANSI/ASQC Z1.9. These should be consulted before a specific plan is instituted. Note that the plans contained in MIL-STD-414 and MIL-STD-105D do not match; however, the plans in ANSI Z1.9 are matched to MIL-STD-105D and ANSI/ASQC Z1.4.

Since it is an AQL scheme, MIL-STD-414 and its civilian counterpart are based on an overall strategy which incorporates switching rules to move from normal to tightened or reduced inspection and return depending on the quality observed in the previous 10 lots. These switching rules are indicated in Figure 25.23 for MIL-STD-414 and should be used if the standard is to be properly applied. The switching rules for ANSI/ASQC Z1.9 (1980) are the same as those of MIL-STD-105D and ANSI/ASQC Z1.4 (1981) except that the limit numbers for reduced inspection have been eliminated. This allows these standards to be readily interchanged.

A check sequence for application of MIL-STD-414 and ANSI/ASQC Z1.9 (1980) is given in Figure 25.24. Tables 25.20 to 25.25 show the specific steps involved in application of the two forms using the sample standard deviation as a measure of variability. Although the procedures of ANSI/ASQC Z1.9 (1980) are

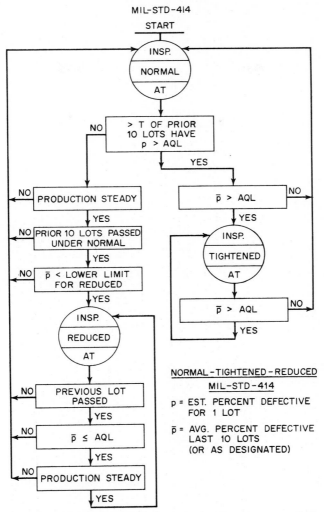

MIL-STD-414

START

INSP. NORMAL AT

> T OF PRIOR 10 LOTS HAVE p > AQL — NO

YES

PRODUCTION STEADY — NO

$\bar{p}$ > AQL — NO

YES

PRIOR 10 LOTS PASSED UNDER NORMAL — NO

YES

INSP. TIGHTENED AT

$\bar{p}$ < LOWER LIMIT FOR REDUCED — NO

YES

$\bar{p}$ > AQL — NO

YES

INSP. REDUCED AT

PREVIOUS LOT PASSED — NO

YES

$\bar{p}$ ≤ AQL — NO

YES

PRODUCTION STEADY — NO

YES

NORMAL - TIGHTENED - REDUCED
MIL-STD-414

p = EST. PERCENT DEFECTIVE FOR 1 LOT

$\bar{p}$ = AVG. PERCENT DEFECTIVE LAST 10 LOTS (OR AS DESIGNATED)

FIG. 25.23 Switching rules for MIL-STD-414 only. *(From Schilling, 1970.)*

analogous, it should be noted that the ranges, inspection levels, and tables of plans are different in the two standards, since Z1.9 has been revised to match MIL-STD-105D and ANSI/ASQC Z1.4 (1981). Procedures for upper, lower, and double specification limits are indicated in these tables together with appropriate references to the standard and an illustrative example. Modifications to the procedure, necessary when variability is measured by average range or a known standard deviation, are described. Table 25.26 shows the relationship of the statistics and procedures used under the various measures of variability allowed, for each of the forms.

FIG. 25.24   Check sequence for MIL-STD-414 and ANSI/ASQC Z1.9-1980.

MIL-STD-414 has a liberal supply of excellent examples. The reader is referred to the standard for more detailed examples of its applications.

Mixed Plans.   One disadvantage of variables plans is the fact that screened lots may at times be rejected by a sample $\overline{X}$ or s indicating percent defective to be high when, actually, the discrepant material has been eliminated. To prevent rejection of screened lots, double-sampling plans have been developed which use a variables criterion on the first sample and attributes on the second sample. Lots are accepted if they pass variables inspection; however, if they do not pass, a second sample is taken and the results are judged by an attributes criterion. In this way screened lots will not be rejected, since rejections are made only under the attributes part of the plan. This type of plan was proposed by Dodge (1932). The procedure has been discussed in some detail by Bowker and Goode (1952), Gregory and Resnikoff (1955), and Schilling and Dodge (1969). MIL-STD-414 and ANSI/ASQC Z1.9 (1980) allow for the use of such procedures, although only ANSI/ASQC Z1.9 (1980) is properly matched to MIL-STD-105D or ANSI/ASQC Z1.4 (1981) to allow for proper use of mixed plans. The steps involved are shown in Table 25.27.

RELIABILITY SAMPLING

Overview.   Sampling plans for life and reliability testing are similar in concept and operation to the variables plans previously described. They differ to the

TABLE 25.20 MIL-STD-414 (1957) and ANSI/ASQC Z1.9 (1980), Variability Unknown, Standard Deviation Method, Form 1

Example: The specification for electrical resistance of a certain component is 620 to 680 ohms. A lot of 100 is submitted for inspection, inspection level IV, normal inspection, with AQL = 2.5 percent. Should the lot be accepted if $\overline{X}$ = 647 and s = 17.22?

Summary of plan	Calculations
1. Restrictions: Individual measurements normally distributed	
II. Necessary information	II.
A. Lot size	*A.* Lot size = 100
B. AQL	*B.* AQL = 2.5%
C. Severity of inspection: normal, tightened, reduced	*C.* Normal inspection
III. Selection of plan	III.
A. Determine code letter (Table 25.21 for MIL-STD-414 only) from lot size and inspection level [normally, inspection level IV is used in MIL-STD-414 and inspection level II in ANSI/ASQC Z1.9 (1980)]	*A.* Code F
B. From code letter and AQL, determine (Table 25.22 for MIL-STD-414 only)	*B.*
1. Sample size = n	$n = 10$
2. Acceptance constant = k	$k = 1.41$
C. Double specification limits: obtain MSD = $F(U - L)$, where F is obtained from appropriate table in the Standard	*C.* MSD = 0.298(680 − 620) = 17.88
IV. Elements	IV.
A. Sample size: See above	*A.* $n = 10$
B. Statistic	*B.* $T_U = (680 - 647)/$
1. Upper specification: $T_U = (U - \overline{X})/s$	$17.22 = 1.92$
2. Lower specification: $T_L = (\overline{X} - L)/s$	
3. Double specification: T_U and T_L	
C. Decision Criteria	*C.*
1. Acceptance criterion	
a. Upper specification: $T_U \geq k$	1.92 > 1.41
b. Lower specification: $T_L \geq k$	1.57 > 1.41
c. Double specification: $T_U \geq k$, $T_L \geq k$, and $s \leq$ MSD	17.22 < 17.88
2. Rejection criterion: Reject otherwise	
V. Action: Dispose of lot as indicated and refer to switching rules for next lot; see Figure 25.23	V. Accept the lot
VI. Characteristics: OC curves given	
VII. Reference: 1957 version of MIL-STD-414 and ANSI/ASQC Z1.9 (1980).	
VIII. Remarks (use appropriate tables from Standard)	
A. Range method	
1. Use $\overline{R}$ of subsamples of 5 if $n \geq 10$; use $\overline{R}$ if $n < 10$	
2. Substitute $\overline{R}$ for s in statistics	
3. Double specifications—use values of f (for MAR) in place of F (for MSD), where MAR is the maximum allowable range	
B. Variability known: Substitute σ for s in statistics	

TABLE 25.21   MIL-STD-105D Sample Size Code Letters*

Lot size	\multicolumn{5}{c}{Inspection levels}
	I	II	III	IV	V
3–8	B	B	B	B	C
9–15	B	B	B	B	D
16–25	B	B	B	C	E
26–40	B	B	B	D	F
41–65	B	B	C	E	G
66–110	B	B	D	F	H
111–180	B	C	E	G	I
181–300	B	D	F	H	J
301–500	C	E	G	I	K
501–800	D	F	H	J	L
801–1,300	E	G	I	K	L
1,301–3,200	F	H	J	L	M
3,201–8,000	G	I	L	M	N
8,001–22,000	H	J	M	N	O
22,001–110,000	I	K	N	O	P
110,001–550,000	I	K	O	P	Q
550,001 and over	I	K	P	Q	Q

*Sample size code letters given in body of table are applicable when the indicated inspection levels are to be used.

extent that, when units are not all run to failure, the length of the test becomes an important parameter determining the characteristics of the procedure. Further, time to failure tends to conform naturally to skewed distributions such as the exponential or as approximated by the Weibull. Accordingly, many life test plans are based on these distributions. When time to failure is normally distributed and all units tested are run to failure, the variables plans assuming normality, discussed above, apply; attributes plans such as MIL-STD-105D may also be used.

Life tests, terminated before all units have failed, may be:

1. Failure terminated—a given sample size n is tested until the rth failure occurs. The test is then terminated.
2. Time terminated—a given sample size n is tested until a preassigned termination time T is reached. The test is then terminated.

Furthermore, these tests may be based upon specifications written in terms of one of the following characteristics:

1. Mean life—the mean life of the product
2. Hazard rate—instantaneous failure rate at some specified time t
3. Reliable life—the life beyond which some specified proportion of items in the lot or population will survive
4. Failure rate (FR or λ)—the percentage of failures per unit time (say 1000 hours of test)

Several sets of plans are available for the testing of life and reliability. Table 25.28 summarizes some of these plans. Nelson (1983) provides considerable insight into the analysis of reliability data.

TABLE 25.22 — MIL-STD-414 Master Table for Normal and Tightened Inspection for Plans Based on Variability Unknown, Standard Deviation Method

(Single specification limit, form 1)

Sample size code letter	Sample size	Acceptable quality levels (normal inspection)													
		0.04	0.065	0.10	0.15	0.25	0.40	0.65	1.00	1.50	2.50	4.00	6.50	10.00	15.00
		k	k	k	k	k	k	k	k	k	k	k	k	k	k
B	3	→	→	→	→	→	→	→	↓	↓	1.12	0.958	0.765	0.566	0.341
C	4	→	→	→	→	→	→	→	1.45	1.34	1.17	1.01	0.814	0.617	0.393
D	5	→	→	→	→	→	→	1.65	1.53	1.40	1.24	1.07	0.874	0.675	0.455
E	7	→	→	→	→	2.00	1.88	1.75	1.62	1.50	1.33	1.15	0.955	0.755	0.536
F	10	→	→	→	2.24	2.11	1.98	1.84	1.72	1.58	1.41	1.23	1.03	0.828	0.611
G	15	2.64	2.53	2.42	2.32	2.20	2.06	1.91	1.79	1.65	1.47	1.30	1.09	0.886	0.664
H	20	2.69	2.58	2.47	2.36	2.24	2.11	1.96	1.82	1.69	1.51	1.33	1.12	0.917	0.695
I	25	2.72	2.61	2.50	2.40	2.26	2.14	1.98	1.85	1.72	1.53	1.35	1.14	0.936	0.712
J	30	2.73	2.61	2.51	2.41	2.28	2.15	2.00	1.86	1.73	1.55	1.36	1.15	0.946	0.723
K	35	2.77	2.65	2.54	2.45	2.31	2.18	2.03	1.89	1.76	1.57	1.39	1.18	0.969	0.745
L	40	2.77	2.66	2.55	2.44	2.31	2.18	2.03	1.89	1.76	1.58	1.39	1.18	0.971	0.746
M	50	2.83	2.71	2.60	2.50	2.35	2.22	2.08	1.93	1.80	1.61	1.42	1.21	1.00	0.774
N	75	2.90	2.77	2.66	2.55	2.41	2.27	2.12	1.98	1.84	1.65	1.46	1.24	1.03	0.804
O	100	2.92	2.80	2.69	2.58	2.43	2.29	2.14	2.00	1.86	1.67	1.48	1.26	1.05	0.819
P	150	2.96	2.84	2.73	2.61	2.47	2.33	2.18	2.03	1.89	1.70	1.51	1.29	1.07	0.841
Q	200	2.97	2.85	2.73	2.62	2.47	2.33	2.18	2.04	1.89	1.70	1.51	1.29	1.07	0.845
		0.065	0.10	0.15	0.25	0.40	0.65	1.00	1.50	2.50	4.00	6.50	10.00	15.00	
		Acceptable quality levels (tightened inspection)													

Note: All AQL values are in percent defective.

→ Use first sampling plan below arrow, that is, both sample size as well as *k* value. When sample size equals or exceeds lot size, every item in the lot must be inspected.

Source: 1957 version of MIL-STD-414.

25.71

TABLE 25.23 MIL-STD-414 and ANSI/ASQC Z1.9 (1980), Variability Unknown, Standard Deviation Method, Form 2

Example: The specification for electrical resistance of a certain electrical component is 620 to 680 ohms. A lot of 100 is submitted for inspection, inspection level IV, normal inspection, with AQL = 2.5 percent. Should the lot be accepted if $\overline{X}$ = 647 and s = 17.22?

Summary of plan	Calculations
I. Restrictions: Individual measurements normally distributed	
II. Necessary information	II.
A. Lot size	A. Lot size = 100
B. AQL	B. AQL = 2.5%
C. Severity of inspection: normal, tightened, reduced	C. Normal inspection
III. Selection of plan	III.
A. Determine (Table 25.21 for MIL-STD-414 only) code letter from lot size and inspection level (usually, inspection Level IV is used in MIL-STD-414 and inspection Level II in ANSI/ASQC Z1.9)	A. Code F
B. From code letter and AQL, determine (Table 25.24 for MIL-STD-414 only)	B.
1. Sample size = n	n = 10
2. Value of M	M = 7.29
IV. Elements	IV.
A. Sample size: See above	A. n = 10
B. Statistic	B.
1. Upper specification: $Q_U = (U - \overline{X})/s$	Q_U = (680 − 647)/17.22 = 1.92
2. Lower specification: $Q_L = (\overline{X} - L)/s$	Q_L = (6.47 − 620)/17.22 = 1.57
3. Double specification: Q_U and Q_L	
C. Estimate Percent Defective from Table 25.25	C.
1. Upper specification: estimate p_U (%) from Q_U and n	p_U (%) = 1.68
2. Lower specification: estimate p_L (%) from Q_L and n	p_L(%) = 4.92
3. Double specification: estimate p (%) = p_U (%) + p_L(%)	p(%) = 6.60
D. Decision criteria	D.
1. Acceptance criterion	
a. Upper specification: p_U (%) < M	
b. Lower specification: p_L(%) < M	
c. Double specification: p(%) < M	6.60 < 7.29
Note: if AQLs not equal on upper and lower specifications, obtain M for each and apply a, b, c, above, using larger of two M values in c	

TABLE 25.23 MIL-STD-414 and ANSI/ASQC Z1.9 (1980), Variability Unknown, Standard Deviation Method, Form 2 (*Continued*)

Summary of plan	Calculations
2. Rejection criterion: Reject otherwise	
V. Action: Dispose of lot as indicated and refer to switching rules for next lot; see Figure 25.23	V. Accept the lot
VI. Characteristics: OC curves given	
VII. Reference: 1957 version of MIL-STD-414 and ANSI/ASQC Z1.9 (1980).	

VII. Remarks (use appropriate tables from Standard)
   A. Range method—similar except:
     1. Use $\overline{R}$ of subsamples of 5 if $n \geq 10$; use R if $n < 10$
     2. Substitute $\overline{R}/c$ for s in statistics, where c is a scale factor given with n and M in the Standard
   B. Variability known—similar except:
     1. Substitute σ/v for s in statistics, where v factor is given with n and M in the Standard	

Relation of Life Characteristics. Specification and test of various life characteristics are intimately related. Tables 25.29 and 25.30 will be found useful in converting life test characteristics. Formulas for various characteristics are shown in terms of mean life μ. Thus, using the tables, it will be found that a specification of mean life $\mu = 1000$ hours for a Weibull distribution with $\beta = 2$ is equivalent to a hazard rate of 0.000157 at 100 hours or to a reliable life of 99.22 percent surviving at 100 hours.

Exponential Distribution: H108. *Quality Control and Reliability Handbook,* H108 (1960), presents a set of life test and reliability plans based on the exponential model for time to failure. The plans contained therein are intended for use when mean time to failure β is specified[3] in terms of acceptable mean life β_0 and unacceptable mean life β_1. Testing may be conducted:

With replacement: Units replaced when failure occurs. Test time continues to be accumulated on replacement unit.

Without replacement: Units not replaced upon failure.

The handbook contains three types of plans:

1. *Life tests terminated upon occurrence of a preassigned number of failures:* Here, n units are tested until r failures occur. The average life is calculated and compared with an acceptable value defined by the plan, and a decision is made.

---

[3]Note that elsewhere in this handbook the mean value is described by the symbol μ.

TABLE 25.24 MIL-STD-414, Master Table for Normal and Tightened Inspection for Plans Based on Variability Unknown, Standard Deviation Method

(Double specification limit and form 2, single specification limit)

Sample size code letter	Sample size	\ \ Acceptable quality levels (normal inspection) \ \													
		0.04	0.065	0.10	0.15	0.25	0.40	0.65	1.00	1.50	2.50	4.00	6.50	10.00	15.00
		M	M	M	M	M	M	M	M	M	M	M	M	M	M
B	3	↓						→	↓	↓	7.59	18.86	26.94	33.69	40.47
C	4								1.53	5.50	10.92	16.45	22.86	29.45	36.90
D	5					→	→	1.33	3.32	5.83	9.80	14.39	20.19	26.56	33.99
E	7				→	0.422	1.06	2.14	3.55	5.35	8.40	12.20	17.35	23.29	30.50
F	10			→	0.349	0.716	1.30	2.17	3.26	4.77	7.29	10.54	15.17	20.74	27.57
G	15	0.099	0.186	0.312	0.503	0.818	1.31	2.11	3.05	4.31	6.56	9.46	13.71	18.94	25.61
H	20	0.135	0.228	0.365	0.544	0.846	1.29	2.05	2.95	4.09	6.17	8.92	12.99	18.03	24.53
I	25	0.155	0.250	0.380	0.551	0.877	1.29	2.00	2.86	3.97	5.97	8.63	12.57	17.51	23.97
J	30	0.179	0.280	0.413	0.581	0.879	1.29	1.98	2.83	3.91	5.86	8.47	12.36	17.24	23.58
K	35	0.170	0.264	0.388	0.535	0.847	1.23	1.87	2.68	3.70	5.57	8.10	11.87	16.65	22.91
L	40	0.179	0.275	0.401	0.566	0.873	1.26	1.88	2.71	3.72	5.58	8.09	11.85	16.61	22.86
M	50	0.163	0.250	0.363	0.503	0.789	1.17	1.71	2.49	3.45	5.20	7.61	11.23	15.87	22.00
N	75	0.147	0.228	0.330	0.467	0.720	1.07	1.60	2.29	3.20	4.87	7.15	10.63	15.13	21.11
O	100	0.145	0.220	0.317	0.447	0.689	1.02	1.53	2.20	3.07	4.69	6.91	10.32	14.75	20.66
P	150	0.134	0.203	0.293	0.413	0.638	0.949	1.43	2.05	2.89	4.43	6.57	9.88	14.20	20.02
Q	200	0.135	0.204	0.294	0.414	0.637	0.945	1.42	2.04	2.87	4.40	6.53	9.81	14.12	19.92
		0.065	0.10	0.15	0.25	0.40	0.65	1.00	1.50	2.50	4.00	6.50	10.00	15.00	
		\ \ Acceptable quality levels (tightened inspection) \ \													

Note: All AQL and table values are in percent defective.

↓ Use first sampling plan below arrow, that is, both sample size as well as *M* value. When sample size equals or exceeds lot size, every item in the lot must be inspected.

Source: 1957 version of MIL–STD–414.

25.74

TABLE 25.25 Table for Estimating the Lot Percent Defective Using Standard Deviation Method

Q_U or Q_L	Sample sizes															
	3	4	5	7	10	15	20	25	30	35	40	50	75	100	150	200
0.1	47.2	46.7	46.4	46.3	46.2	46.1	46.1	46.1	46.0	46.0	46.0	46.0	46.0	46.0	46.0	46.0
0.2	44.5	43.3	42.9	42.5	42.4	42.2	42.2	42.2	42.2	42.1	42.1	42.1	42.1	42.1	42.1	42.1
0.3	41.6	40.0	39.4	38.9	38.6	38.4	38.4	38.3	38.3	38.3	38.3	38.3	38.2	38.2	38.2	38.2
0.4	38.7	36.7	35.9	35.3	34.9	34.7	34.6	34.6	34.6	34.6	34.5	34.5	34.5	34.5	34.5	34.5
0.5	38.8	33.3	32.4	31.7	31.4	31.2	31.1	31.0	31.0	31.0	31.0	30.9	30.9	30.9	30.9	30.9
0.6	32.6	30.0	29.0	28.3	27.9	27.7	27.6	27.6	27.6	27.5	27.5	27.5	27.5	27.5	27.4	27.4
0.7	29.3	26.7	25.7	25.0	24.7	24.5	24.4	24.3	24.3	24.3	24.3	24.3	24.2	24.2	24.2	24.2
0.8	25.6	23.3	22.5	21.9	21.6	21.4	21.3	21.3	21.3	21.3	21.2	21.2	21.2	21.2	21.2	21.2
0.9	21.6	20.0	19.4	18.9	18.7	18.5	18.5	18.5	18.5	18.4	18.4	18.4	18.4	18.4	18.4	18.4
1.0	16.7	16.7	16.4	16.1	16.0	15.9	15.9	15.9	15.9	15.9	15.9	15.9	15.9	15.9	15.9	15.9
1.1	9.8	13.3	13.5	13.5	13.5	13.5	13.5	13.5	13.5	13.5	13.5	13.5	13.6	13.6	13.6	13.6
1.2	0	10.0	10.8	11.1	11.2	11.3	11.4	11.4	11.4	11.4	11.4	11.5	11.5	11.5	11.5	11.5
1.3	0	6.7	8.2	8.9	9.2	9.4	9.5	9.5	9.6	9.6	9.6	9.6	9.6	9.6	9.6	9.7
1.4	0	3.3	5.9	7.0	7.4	7.7	7.8	7.9	7.9	7.9	7.9	8.0	8.0	8.0	8.0	8.0
1.5	0	0	3.8	5.3	5.9	6.2	6.3	6.4	6.5	6.5	6.5	6.6	6.6	6.6	6.6	6.6

TABLE 25.25 Table for Estimating the Lot Percent Defective Using Standard Deviation Method (*Continued*)

Q_U or Q_L	Sample sizes															
	3	4	5	7	10	15	20	25	30	35	40	50	75	100	150	200
1.6	0	0	2.0	3.8	4.5	4.9	5.1	5.2	5.2	5.3	5.3	5.3	5.4	5.4	5.4	5.4
1.7	0	0	0.7	2.6	3.4	3.8	4.0	4.1	4.2	4.2	4.2	4.3	4.4	4.4	4.4	4.4
1.8	0	0	0	1.6	2.5	2.9	3.1	3.2	3.3	3.4	3.4	3.4	3.5	3.5	3.5	3.6
1.9	0	0	0	0.9	1.8	2.2	2.4	2.5	2.6	2.6	2.6	2.7	2.8	2.8	2.8	2.8
2.0	0	0	0	0.4	1.2	1.6	1.8	1.9	2.0	2.0	2.1	2.1	2.2	2.2	2.2	2.2
2.1	0	0	0	0.1	0.7	1.2	1.3	1.4	1.5	1.5	1.6	1.6	1.7	1.7	1.7	1.8
2.2	0	0	0	0	0.4	0.8	1.0	1.1	1.1	1.2	1.2	1.2	1.3	1.3	1.3	1.4
2.4	0	0	0	0	0.1	0.3	0.5	0.5	0.6	0.6	0.7	0.7	0.7	0.8	0.8	0.7
2.6	0	0	0	0	0	0.1	0.2	0.3	0.3	0.3	0.3	0.4	0.4	0.4	0.4	0.4
2.8	0	0	0	0	0	0	0.1	0.1	0.1	0.1	0.2	0.2	0.2	0.2	0.2	0.2
3.0	0	0	0	0	0	0	0	0	0.1	0.2	0.1	0.1	0.1	0.1	0.1	0.1

Source: 1957 version of MIL-STD-414.

TABLE 25.26 Application of MIL-STD-414 and ANSI/ASQC Z1.9 (1980)

Step	Section	Form 1	Form 2
Preparatory		Obtain k and n from appropriate tables	Obtain M and n from appropriate tables
Determine criteria	Section B (s)	$T_U = \dfrac{U - \overline{X}}{s}$ $T_L = \dfrac{\overline{X} - L}{s}$	$Q_U = \dfrac{U - \overline{X}}{s}$ $Q_L = \dfrac{\overline{X} - L}{s}$
	Section C $(\overline{R})$	$T_U = \dfrac{U - \overline{X}}{\overline{R}}$ $T_L = \dfrac{\overline{X} - L}{\overline{R}}$	$Q_U = \dfrac{(U - \overline{X})c}{\overline{R}}$ $Q_L = \dfrac{(\overline{X} - L)c}{\overline{R}}$
	Section D (σ)	$T_U = \dfrac{U - \overline{X}}{\sigma}$ $T_L = \dfrac{\overline{X} - L}{\sigma}$	$Q_U = \dfrac{(U - \overline{X})v}{\sigma}$ $Q_L = \dfrac{(\overline{X} - L)v}{\sigma}$
Estimation			Enter table with n and Q_U or Q_L to get p_U or p_L
Action	Single specification	Accept if $T_U \geq k$ or $T_L \geq k$	Accept if $p_U \leq M$ or $p_L \leq M$
	Double specification	Accept if* $T_U \geq k$, $T_L \geq k$ and $s <$ MSD or $\overline{R} <$ MAR	Accept if $p_U + p_L \leq M$

Note:

c = scale factor

$$v = \sqrt{\frac{n}{n-1}}$$

*Not official procedure.
Source: Schilling, 1970, p. 175.

2. *Life tests terminated at a preassigned time:* Here, n units are tested for a specified length of time T. If T is reached before r failures occur, the test is stopped and the lot accepted. If r failures occur before T is reached, the test is stopped and the lot rejected.

3. *Sequential life testing plans:* Here n units are placed on test and time, and failures are recorded until sufficient data are accumulated to reach a decision at specified risk levels. Periodically throughout the test, the time accumulated on all units is calculated and compared with the acceptable amount of time for the total number of failures accumulated up to the time of observation. If the total time exceeds the limit for acceptance, the lot is accepted; if the total time

TABLE 25.27 Variables Plans for Percent Defective, Mixed Variables—Attributes, ANSI/ASQC Z1.9 (1980)

Example: The specification for electrical resistance of a certain component is 620 to 680 ohms. A lot of 100 is submitted for inspection, inspection level IV, normal inspection, with AQL = 2.5 percent. Should the lot be accepted if $\overline{X}$ = 647 and s = 17.22?

Summary of plan	Calculations
I. Restrictions: Measurements normally distributed	

II. Necessary information
   A. Lot size
   B. AQL
	II.
	   A. Lot size = 100
	   B. AQL = 2.5%

III. Selection of plan
   A. Using AQL and Lot Size, select appropriate variables plan from ANSI/ASQC Z1.9—1980, Normal Inspection
   B. Using AQL and Lot Size, select single-sampling attributes plan from MIL-STD-105 or ANSI/ASQC Z1.4—1981 using Tightened Inspection
	III.
	   A. n = 10
	      M = 7.29
	
	   B. MIL-STD-105D gives Code *F*
	      n = 32
	      c = 1

IV. Elements
   A. Sample size: See above; use items drawn in first sample as part of second sample
 	
   B. Statistic: Use appropriate statistics from ANSI/ASQC Z1.9 (1980) and MIL-STD-105 or ANSI/ASQC Z1.4 (1981) as indicated in each standard
   C. Decision criteria
      1. Apply ANSI/ASQC Z1.9 (1980) plan
         a. Accept lot if plan accepts
         b. Otherwise, apply MIL-STD-105 or ANSI/ASQC Z1.4 (1981) plan, taking additional samples to satisfy sample size requirements
      2. Apply MIL-STD-105 or ANSI/ASQC Z1.4 (1981) plan if necessary
         a. Accept lot if plan accepts
         b. Otherwise reject lot
	IV.
	   A. First sample: n = 10
	      Second sample:
	      n = (32 − 10)
	      n = 22
	
	   C. Table 25.23 indicates ANSI/ASQC Z1.9 (1980) plan accepts; if the plan rejected the lot, an additional 22 samples would be drawn and the MIL-STD-105D or ANSI/ASQC Z1.4 (1981) plan applied to the number of defectives in the combined sample of 32

V. Action
   A. Dispose of lot as indicated
   B. Switching rules not applicable to mixed variables-attributes inspection
	V. Accept the lot

TABLE 25.27 Variables Plans for Percent Defective, Mixed Variables—Attributes, ANSI/ASQC Z1.9 (1980) (*Continued*)

Summary of plan	Calculations

VI. Characteristics
    A. Since the procedure outlined in MIL-STD-414 is a "dependent" mixed plan, see the following references:
      1. σ known: Schilling and Dodge (1969)
      2. σ unknown: Gregory and Resnikoff (1955)
      3. Approximation for σ unknown: Bowker and Goode (1952)	

Source: ANSI/ASQC Z1.9 (1980).

exceeds the limit for rejection, the lot is rejected. If the total time falls between the two limits, the test is continued.

Plans are given for various values of the consumer and producer risks, and operating characteristic curves are provided for life tests terminated at a preassigned number of failures or preassigned time. Special tables are also included showing the expected saving in test time by increasing the sample size or by testing with replacement of failed units.

Exponential Distribution: Other Plans (MIL-STD-690B, MIL-STD-781C).
MIL-STD-690B (1960) is a military standard concerned primarily with "process qualification," i.e., an explicit decision on the process rather than the lot. The standard provides plans that evaluate the ability of the process to produce electronic parts that meet a specified failure rate requirement. It presents three sets of plans (Tables I, II, and IV of the standard), based on failure rate (FR) levels expressed in percent failures per 1000 hours of operation (%/1000 hours). The standard is intended as a tool for the assessment of:

1. Qualification of the process at the initial FR level

2. Extension of qualification to lower FR levels

3. Maintenance of FR level qualification

4. Lot conformance FR inspection

Operating characteristic curves for the qualifying plans are provided, and confidence levels are also specified. The plans involved are similar in operation to the time terminated sampling plans of H108, which are presented in that handbook in terms of mean life (ML). Note that

$$\text{ML} = \frac{1{,}000{,}000}{\%/1000 \text{ h}} = \frac{100{,}000}{\text{FR}}$$

An excellent discussion of MIL-STD-690B is given by Grubman, Martin, and Pabst (1969).

MIL-STD-781C (1977) provides a standard set of acceptance testing plans for both preproduction reliability qualification and reliability acceptance testing in production. This standard was developed for electronic equipment as contrasted

TABLE 25.28 Summary of Some Life Testing and Reliability Plans

Document*	Basic distribution and type of plan	Plans in terms of					Type of test		
		Mean life	Hazard rate	Reliable life	Failure rate (FR)		Failure terminated	Time terminated	Sequential
MIL-HDBK 108	Exponential, Lot by Lot	X			X		X	X	X
MIL-STD 690B	Exponential, Lot by Lot				X			X	
MIL-STD-781B	Exponential, Sampling Scheme	X						X	X
TR-3	Weibull, Lot by Lot	X						X	
TR-4	Weibull, Lot by Lot		X					X	
TR-6	Weibull, Lot by Lot			X				X	
TR-7	Weibull, (Lot by Lot, converts MIL-STD-105D)	X	X	X				X	

*See References for this section for complete publication information on documents cited.

TABLE 25.29 Life Characteristics for Two Failure Distributions

$$Exponential\ f(t) = \frac{1}{\mu} e^{-t/\mu}$$

$$Weibull^* f(t) = \frac{\beta t^{\beta-1}}{\eta^\beta} e^{-(t/\eta)^\beta}\ where\ \mu = \eta\Gamma\left(1 + \frac{1}{\beta}\right)$$

Life characteristic	Exponential	Weibull
Proportion $F(t)$ failing before time t	$F(t) = 1 - e^{-t/\mu}$	$F(t) = 1 - e^{-g(t/\mu)^\beta}$
Proportion $R(t)$ of population surviving to time t	$R(t) = e^{-t/\mu}$	$R(t) = e^{-g(t/\mu)^\beta}$
Mean life, ML or mean time between failures	μ	μ
Hazard rate, $Z(t)$, instantaneous failure rate at time t	$Z(t) = \frac{1}{\mu}$	$Z(t) = \frac{\beta g t^{\beta-1}}{\mu^\beta}$
Cumulative hazard rate $M(t)$ for period 0 to t	$M(t) = \frac{t}{\mu}$	$M(t) = \frac{g t^\beta}{\mu^\beta}$
Failure rate λ or average hazard rate period 0 to t, $m(t)$	$\lambda = \frac{1}{\mu}$	$m(t) = \frac{g t^{\beta-1}}{\mu^\beta}$

*Weibull parameters explained in discussion of TR-3. The formulas given here are those of H108 (exponential) and TR-3 (Weibull).

to MIL-STD-690B developed for electronic parts. Much of the standard is devoted to test conditions and procedural considerations. The sampling plans given are expressed in terms of mean time between failures (MTBF). Appendix C of the standard presents the following plans:

1. Fixed-length test plans
2. Probability ratio sequential tests (PRST)

TABLE 25.30 Values of $g = [\Gamma(1 + 1/\beta)]^\beta$ for Weibull Distribution*

β	0.0	0.1	0.2	0.3	0.4	0.5	0.6	0.7	0.8	0.9
0.0	· · ·	4.5287	2.6052	1.9498	1.6167	1.4142	1.2778	1.1794	1.1051	1.0468
1.0	1.0000	0.9615	0.9292	0.9018	0.8782	0.8577	0.8397	0.8238	0.8096	0.7969
2.0	0.7854	0.7750	0.7655	0.7568	0.7489	0.7415	0.7348	0.7285	0.7226	0.7172
3.0	0.7121	0.7073	0.7028	0.6986	0.6947	0.6909	0.6874	0.6840	0.6809	0.6778

β	0.33	0.67	1.33	1.67	3.33	4.00	5.00
g	1.8171	1.2090	0.8936	0.8289	0.6973	0.6750	0.6525

*The columns of this table are subdivisions of the rows. Thus when $\beta = 1.2$, the value of g is 0.9292.

3. Short-run, high-risk PRST plans

4. All-equipment reliability test

Expected test time (ETT) curves are given for the PRST plans.

The sequential tests operate in a manner analogous to those presented in H108. The fixed length tests are also similar to the time terminated tests of H108; however, no specific sample size is set, much in the manner of the failure terminated plans of H108. Note that MTBF in MIL-STD-781C is analogous to ML in H108. The plans given in MIL-STD-781C are indexed by producer's risk α, consumer's risk β, and discrimination ratio θ_0/θ_1. OC curves are given for the sequential tests, all-equipment, and fixed-length tests. Methods for construction of confidence intervals on MTBF are also provided for application after a fixed-length test. Schmee (1980) describes MIL-STD-781C and shows how appropriate confidence intervals can be constructed for the PRST plans.

Weibull Distribution: TR-3, TR-4, TR-6. Defense Department quality control and reliability technical reports TR-3 (1961), TR-4 (1962), TR-6 (1963) present sampling plans based on an underlying Weibull distribution of individual measurement t. The cumulative probability distribution function at time t_0 is

$$F(t_0) = p' = P(t \leq t_0) = 1 - \exp\left[-\left(\frac{t_0 - \gamma}{\eta}\right)^\beta \right]$$

with density function

$$f(t) = \frac{\beta(t - \gamma)^{\beta - 1}}{\eta^\beta} \exp\left[-\left(\frac{t - \gamma}{\eta}\right)^\beta \right] \qquad t \geq \gamma$$

The symbol p' is used for cumulative probability in the technical reports. The three reports provide plans for reliability criteria developed from the following relationships:

$$\mu = \gamma + \eta\Gamma\left(1 + \frac{1}{\beta}\right)$$

where Γ is the gamma function. A table giving values of gamma will be found in Burrington and May (1970).

$$Z(t) = \frac{\beta}{\eta}\left(\frac{t - \gamma}{\eta}\right)^\beta - 1$$

$$P_r = \gamma + \eta(-\ln r)^{1/\beta}$$

where γ = location (or threshold) parameter
  β = shape parameter
  η = scale parameter (characteristic life)
  μ = mean life
  $Z(t)$ = hazard rate—instantaneous failure rate
  P_r = reliable life—life beyond which some specified proportion r of the items will survive

In general the location parameter γ is taken to be zero. If it is not zero, say $\gamma = \gamma_0$, then the observations t are adjusted to $t' = t - \gamma_0$; so accordingly $\mu' = \mu -$

γ_0, and the analysis proceeds in terms of t' and μ'. Then the final results are reported in terms of t and μ by reversing the process, so that

$$t = t' + \gamma_0$$

$$\mu = \mu' + \gamma_0$$

for final results t' and μ'.

Plots on probability paper or goodness-of-fit tests must be used to assure that individual measurements are distributed according to the Weibull model. When this distribution is found to be an appropriate approximation to the failure distribution, methods are available to characterize a product or a process in terms of the three parameters of the Weibull distribution (see Section 23 under The Weibull Distribution). These include probability plots and also point and interval estimates. Sampling plans are available for use with the Weibull approximation, which assumes β and γ to be known. The plans are given in the technical reports mentioned above and are based on the following criteria:

1. Mean life criterion (TR-3)
2. Hazard rate criterion (TR-4)
3. Reliable life criterion (TR-6)

The tables cover a wide range of the family of Weibull distributions by providing plans for shape parameter β from ⅓ to 5. The technical reports abound in excellent examples and detailed descriptions of the methods involved.

Technical report TR-3 provides plans and procedures for developing and applying Weibull plans using mean life μ as the criterion for acceptance. The dimensionless ratio t/μ is related to the cumulative probability p'. Values of t or μ can easily be determined for either of the constituents of the ratio t/μ once the other is specified. Since p' is the proportion of product failing before time t, it can be used in the role of "percent defective" in any attributes plan. The relationship of p' to t/μ then, ties the "percent defective" to specified values of test time t and mean life μ. Seven tables, using this relationship, present factors and classifications useful in designing life test plans when the underlying distribution is Weibull. Each is indexed by various values of the shape parameter β. The tables included in TR-3 are:

Table 1: Values of $(t/\mu) \times 100$ indexed by p' (%)

Table 2: Values of p' (%) indexed by $(t/\mu) \times 100$

Table 3: Values of sample size n and $(t/\mu) \times 100$ for which $P_a \geq 0.95$ (shown in parentheses) indexed by acceptance number c and $(t/\mu) \times 100$ for which $P_a \leq 0.10$

Table 4: Values of the discrimination ratio $\mu_{0.95}/\mu_{0.10}$ indexed by acceptance number c

Table 5: Conversions of MIL-STD-105B to Weibull life test; values of $(t/\mu) \times 100$ for which $P_a \leq 0.10$ indexed by AQL and related $(t/\mu) \times 100$ and also by sample size code letter

Table 6: Values of $(t/\mu) \times 100$ indexed by related AQL values

Table 7: Single-sampling acceptance criteria for MIL-STD-105B (1958)

Tables 1 and 2 allow the direct conversion of any attributes plan to a Weibull life test. Tables 5 and 7 give factors to convert MIL-STD-105B. Tables 3 and 4 provide for the construction of Weibull life tests on the basis of the discrimination ratio $\mu_{0.95}/\mu_{0.10}$.

TR-4 is patterned after TR-3, using the product $tZ(t) \times 100$ in place of the dimensionless ratio $(t/\mu) \times 100$. Note that the value of t given is the termination time of the test. If hazard rates are specified for other times, tables are provided which convert the hazard rate specified into a corresponding hazard rate at the termination time of the test. The cumulative probability p' is related to $tZ(t) \times 100$. Resulting values and classifications useful in converting any attributes plan to a Weibull life test, where hazard rate is specified, are presented in seven tables, each indexed by various values of the shape parameter β. These tables are analogous to those found in TR-3. The use of Tables 3 and 4 in TR-4 corresponds to Tables 3 and 4 in TR-3.

Technical report TR-6 is also patterned somewhat after its predecessors, TR-3 and TR-4, but uses the reliable life (p) criterion. It uses the dimensionless quantity $(t/p) \times 100$ in the manner of $(t/\mu) \times 100$ and $tZ(t) \times 100$ in the previous reports. The cumulative probability p' is related to $(t/p) \times 100$, and resulting values and classifications useful in converting any attributes plan to a Weibull life test where reliable life is specified are presented in six tables, each indexed by various values of the shape parameter β. Plans are provided for values of reliable life of 0.50, 0.90, and 0.99. These tables are similar to those given in the previous two technical reports.

Technical report TR-7 (1965) provides factors and procedures for adapting MIL-STD-105D plans to life and reliability testing when a Weibull distribution of failure times can be assumed. Tables of the appropriate conversion factors are provided for the following criteria:

Table	Criterion	Conversion factor
1	Mean life	$(t/\mu) \times 100$
2	Hazard rate	$tZ(t) \times 100$
3	Reliable life ($r = 0.90$)	$(t/p) \times 100$
4.	Reliable life ($r = 0.99$)	$(t/p) \times 100$

Each table is presented in three parts, each of which is indexed by 10 values of $\beta(\beta = \frac{1}{3}, \frac{1}{2}, \frac{2}{3}, 1, 1\frac{1}{3}, 1\frac{2}{3}, 2, 2\frac{1}{2}, 3\frac{1}{3}, 4)$. TR-7 is used in a manner analogous to the three technical reports.

BULK SAMPLING [4]

Bulk material may be of gaseous, liquid, or solid form. Usually it is sampled by taking increments of the material, blending these increments into a single composite sample, and then, if necessary, reducing this gross sample to a size suitable for laboratory testing.

If bulk material is packaged or comes in clearly demarked segments, if it is for all practical purposes uniform within the packages, but varying between packages,

---

[4]This section is condensed from Section 25A of the third edition of this handbook, prepared by Acheson J. Duncan.

and if the quality of each package in the sample is measured, then the sampling theory developed for discrete units may be employed.

A special theoretical discussion is necessary for the sampling of bulk material:

1. If the packages are uniform but the increments from individual packages are not tested separately; instead they are physically composited, in part at least, to form one or more composite samples that are tested separately
2. If the contents of the packages are not uniform so that the question of sampling error arises with respect to the increments taken from the packages
3. If the bulk material is not packaged and sample increments have to be taken from a pile, a truck, a railroad car, or a conveyor belt

In the above circumstances, the special aspects that make bulk sampling different from the sampling of discrete indivisible units are:

1. The possibility of physical compositing and the subsequent physical reduction (or subsampling) that is generally necessary.
2. The need in many cases to use a mechanical sampling device to attain the increments that are taken into the sample. In this case the increments are likely to be "created" by the use of the sampling device and cannot be viewed as preexisting.

Objectives of Bulk Sampling. In most cases the objective of sampling bulk material is to determine its mean quality. This may be for the purpose of pricing the material or for levying custom duties or other taxes, or for controlling a manufacturing process in which the bulk material may be used. It is conceivable that interest in bulk material may also at times center on the variability of the material; or, if it is packaged, on the percent defective; or on the extreme value attained by a segment or package, as described in ASTM (1968). In view of the limited space that is available, the discussion will be restricted to estimation of the mean quality of a material.

Special Terms and Concepts. A number of special terms and concepts are used in the sampling of bulk material. These are:

1. *Lot:* The mass of bulk material the quality of which is under study—not to be confused with a statistical population.
2. *Segment:* Any specifically demarked portion of the lot, actual or hypothetical.
3. *Strata:* Segments of the lot that are likely to be differentiated with respect to the quality characteristic under study.
4. *Increment:* Any portion of the lot, generally smaller than a segment.
5. *Sample increments:* Those portions of the lot initially taken into the sample.
6. *Gross sample:* The totality of sample increments taken from the lot.
7. *Composite sample:* A mixture of two or more sample increments.
8. *Laboratory sample:* That part of a larger sample which is sent to the laboratory for test.
9. *Reduction:* The process by which the laboratory sample is obtained from a composite sample. It is a method of sampling the composite sample. It may take the form of hand-quartering or riffling or the like.

10. *Test-unit:* That quantity of the material which is of just sufficient size to make a measurement of the given quality characteristic.

11. *Quality of a test-unit:* The expected value of the hypothetically infinite number of given measurements that might be made on the test-unit. Any single measurement is a random sample of one from this infinite set. The analytical variance is the variance of such measurements on the infinite set.

12. *Mean of a lot:* If a lot is exhaustively divided into a set of M test-units, the mean of the qualities of these M test-units is designated the mean of the lot. It is postulated that this mean will be the same no matter how the M test-units are obtained. This assumes that there is no physical interaction between the quality of test-units and the method of division. See item 16 below.

13. *Mean of a segment (stratum, increment, composite sample, or laboratory sample):* Defined in a manner similar to that used to define the mean of a lot. It is assumed that the segment is so large relative to the size of a test-unit that any excess over the integral number of test-units contained in the segment can be theoretically ignored. If this is not true, then the quality of the fraction of a test-unit remaining is arbitrarily taken to be the quality of the mean of the segment minus this fraction.

14. *Uniformity:* A segment of bulk material will be said to be uniform if there is no variation in the segment. If, for example, every cubic centimeter of a material contains exactly the same number of "foreign particles," the density of these particles would be said to be uniform throughout the segment. See the note under item 15, however.

15. *Homogeneous:* A segment of bulk material will be said to be homogeneous with respect to a given quality characteristic if that characteristic is randomly distributed throughout the segment.

    Note: The character of being uniform or homogeneous is not independent of the size of the units considered. The number of foreign particles may be the same for every cubic meter of a material, and with respect to this size unit the material will be said to be uniform. For units of size 1 cubic centimeter, however, there may be considerable variation in the number of foreign particles, and for this size of unit the material would not be judged to be uniform. The same considerations are involved in the definition of homogeneity. The number of foreign particles per cubic meter could vary randomly from one cubic meter to the next, but within each cubic meter there might be considerable (intraclass) correlation between the number of foreign particles in the cubic centimeters that make up the cubic meter.

16. *Systematic physical bias:* If the property of the material is physically affected by the sampling device or method of sampling employed, the results will have a systematic bias. A boring or cutting device, for example, might generate sufficient heat to cause loss of moisture.

17. *Physical selection bias:* If a bulk material is a mixture of particles of different size, the sampling device may tend to select more of one size particle than another. This means that if a segment was exhaustively sampled by such a device, early samples would tend to have relatively more of certain size particles than later samples.

18. *Statistical bias:* A function of the observations that is used to estimate a characteristic of a lot, e.g., its mean, is termed a "statistic." A statistic is statistically biased if in many samples its mean value is not equal to the lot characteristic it is used to estimate.

Determination of the Amount of Sampling. Since the variance of a sample mean $\sigma_{\overline{X}}^2$ is a function of the amount of sampling, say the number of increments taken, then once a model has been adopted and a formula obtained for $\sigma_{\overline{X}}^2$, it becomes possible to determine the amount of sampling required to attain a confidence interval of a given width or to attain a specified probability of making a correct decision.

A similar approach is involved in determining the amount of sampling to get a desired set of risks for lot acceptance and rejection.

Models and Their Use. Sampling plans for discrete product have been cataloged in a number of tables. This has not yet been possible for bulk sampling, and instead, a "sampling model" must be created for each type of bulk material and the model used to determine the sample size and acceptance criteria for specific applications.

A bulk sampling model consists of a set of assumptions regarding the statistical properties of the material to be sampled plus a prescribed procedure for carrying out the sampling. A very simple model, for example, would be one in which it is assumed that the quality characteristics of the test-units in a lot are normally distributed and simple random sampling is used.

With the establishment of a model, a formula can generally be derived for the sampling variance of an estimate of the mean of a given lot. This must be uniquely derived based on the type of product, lot formation, and other factors. The reader is urged to consult the references for specific formulas (see especially Duncan, 1962). From an estimate of this sampling variance, confidence limits can be established for the lot mean, and/or a decision with given risk can be made about the acceptability of the lot.

Let the variance of a sample mean be denoted as $\sigma_{\overline{X}}^2$ and its estimate as $s_{\overline{X}}^2$. Then "0.95 confidence limits" for the mean of the lot will be given by

$$0.95 \text{ confidence limits for } \mu = \overline{X} \pm t_{0.025} s_{\overline{X}}$$

where μ is the mean of the lot, $\overline{X}$ is the sample mean, and $t_{0.025}$ is the 0.025 point of a t-distribution for the degrees of freedom involved in the determination of $s_{\overline{X}}^2$.

If a decision is to be made on the acceptability of a lot, a criterion for acceptability will take some such form as

$$\text{Accept if } t = \frac{\overline{X} - L}{s_{\overline{X}}} \text{ is positive or if it has a}$$

negative value numerically less than $t_{0.025}$

where L is the lower specification limit on the product and $t_{0.025}$ is the 0.025 point of a t-distribution for the degrees of freedom involved in the determination of $s_{\overline{X}}^2$. See Grubbs and Coon (1954).

Models for Distinctly Segmented Bulk Material ("Within and Between" Models). Much bulk material comes in distinctly segmented form. It may be packaged in bags, bales, or cans, for example, or may come in carloads or truckloads.

For distinctly segmented material it can be established that the overall variance of individual test-units is, for a large number of segments each with a large number of test-units, approximately equal to the sum of the variance between segments and the average variance within segments. In what follows, the variance within segments is assumed the same for all segments.

Model 1A. Isolated Lots, Nonstratified Segments.   For an isolated lot of distinctly segmented material, the sampling procedure will be to take an increment of *m* test-units from each of *n* segments, reduce each increment to a laboratory sample, and measure its quality *X*. The mean of the *n* test-units is taken as an estimate of the mean of the lot.

Model 1B. One of a Series of Lots.   Suppose the current lot is one of a series of lots of distinctly segmented material and that estimates of the between and within variances have been made in a pilot study, together with estimates of the reduction variance and test variance. It will be assumed that the reduction variance yielded by the pilot study is valid for larger amounts than that used in the study.

   With the given prior information, an estimate of the sampling variance for the current sample estimate of mean lot quality can be based on the pilot study, and there is need only for a current check on the continued validity of this study. Consequently, composite samples can be used requiring only a few measurements, and the cost of inspection of the current lot may be considerably curtailed.

   The "Within and Between" Models: Stratified Segments.   In some situations the quality characteristic of the bulk material may be stratified in that in each segment it may vary from layer to layer and is not randomly distributed throughout the segment. Difficulties in formulating a model for stratified segments of this kind can be overcome if the strata are reasonably parallel and if the increments taken from the sample segments are taken perpendicular to the strata and penetrate all strata. In taking a sample from a bale of wool, for example, a thief could cut a sample running vertically from top to bottom of the bale.

Models for Bulk Material Moving in a Stream.   In many instances the bulk material to be sampled is moving in a stream, say on a conveyer belt. In such instances it is the common practice to take increments systematically from the stream, the increment being taken across the full width of the stream.

Isolated Lots.   If increments are taken at random from the stream, we would have a simple random sample from the lot, and we could proceed much as indicated for isolated lots of distinctly segmented material.

Model 2A. A Stream of Lots: A Segregation Model.   When a stream of bulk material persists for some time, with possible interruptions, determinations of quality and/or action decisions may have to be made for a number of lots. Here, a pilot study might be profitable.

   The kind of pilot study needed will depend on the assumptions about the statistical properties of the material in the stream. If the quality of the material varies randomly in the stream, then a pilot study based on a number of randomly or systematically taken increments would be sufficient to determine the variance of the material, and this could be used to set up confidence limits for the means of subsequent lots or make decisions as to their acceptability, even though in each of these lots a single composite sample was taken.

Obtaining the Test-Units.   Three factors are important in obtaining the test-units.

1. *The models discussed above assume random sampling:* Either the increments are picked at random (using, preferably, random numbers if the units can be identified) or the increments are selected systematically from material that is itself random. Random sampling may have to be undertaken while the material is in motion or being moved. If random sampling cannot be used, special efforts should be made to get a representative picture of a lot, noting strata and the like. Some element of randomness must be present in a sampling procedure to yield a formula for sampling variance.

2. *Grinding and mixing:* In the processing of bulk material and in the formation of composite samples, grinding and/or mixing may be employed in an attempt to attain homogeneity or at least to reduce the variability of the material.

If a material can be made homogeneous for the size increment that is to be used in subsequent sampling, then an increment of that size can be viewed as a random sample of the material. The attainment of homogeneity of bulk material in bags, cartons, barrels, etc., is thus a worthy objective when the contents of these containers are to be sampled by a thief or other sampling instruments. However, random sampling does not guarantee minimum sampling variation, and grinding and mixing may lead to a reduction in overall sampling variation without attaining homogeneity. See Cochran (1977).

Although grinding and mixing are aimed at reducing variability, these operations may in some circumstances cause segregation and thus increase variability.

3. *Reduction of a sample to test-units:* Measurements often may be made directly on the sample itself. However, sometimes a portion of the sample must be carefully reduced in either particle size or physical quantity to facilitate laboratory testing. The unreduced portion of the sample may be retained for subsequent reference for legal purposes or verification of results. An example of a technique is coning and quartering. The material is first crushed and placed in a conical pile, which is then flattened. The material is then separated into quarters and opposite quarters selected for further quartering or as the final test-units.

Bicking (1967) and Bicking, Donovan, Sosnowski, and Bicking (1967) provide unique details on obtaining test-units for a large variety of specific bulk products.

Tests of Homogeneity. The homogeneity of bulk material may be tested by $\overline{X}$-charts and c-charts. For mixtures of particles that can be identified, local homogeneity may be tested by running a χ^2 short-distance test. See Shinner and Naor (1961).

BAYESIAN PROCEDURES

The concept that experience or analytical studies can yield prior frequency distributions of the quality of submitted lots and that these "prior" distributions can in turn be used to derive lot-by-lot sampling plans has gained some popularity in recent years. This is generally termed the "Bayesian approach." Bayes' theorem and the Bayesian decision theory concept are discussed in Section 23, Basic Statistical Methods. The general concept of the use of prior information is discussed in Section 18, under How Much Inspection?

Considerable literature exists on Bayesian sampling. However, a very limited number of sampling tables based on particular prior distributions of lot quality are available. Calvin (1984) provides procedures and tables for implementing

Bayesian plans. Another example is the set of tables by Oliver and Springer (1972), which are based on the assumption of a Beta prior distribution with specific posterior risk to achieve minimum sample size. This avoids the problem of estimating cost parameters. It is generally true that a Bayesian plan requires a smaller sample size than does a conventional sampling plan with the same consumer's and producer's risk. Among others, Schafer (1967) discusses single sampling plans by attributes using three prior distributions of lot quality. Given specified risks α and β, sampling plans which satisfied these risks and which minimized sample size were determined. For example, with a particular prior distribution, $n = 6$ and $c = 0$ gave protection equivalent to a conventional sampling plan with $n = 34$, $c = 0$.

Advantages similar to those quoted above are usually cited. However, one prime factor is frequently ignored: How good is the assumption on the prior distribution? Hald (1960) gives an extensive account of sampling plans based on discrete prior distributions of product quality. Hald also employs a simple economic model along with the discrete prior distribution and the hypergeometric sampling distribution to answer a number of basic questions on costs, relationship between sample size and lot size, etc. Schafer (1964) also considers the Bayesian operating characteristic curve. Hald (1981) has also provided an excellent comparison of classical and Bayesian theory and methodology for attributes acceptance sampling. The Bayesian approach to sequential and nonsequential acceptance sampling has been described by Grimlin and Breipohl (1972). Most such plans incorporate cost data reflecting losses involved in the decision making process to which the plan is to be applied. An excellent review of Bayesian and non-Bayesian plans has been given by Wetherill and Chin (1975).

While the explicit specification of a prior distribution is characteristic of the classical Bayes approach, procedures have been developed to incorporate much of the philosophy and approach of Bayes without explicit specification of a prior distribution. These methods are based on the incorporation of past data into an empirical estimate of the prior, and hence the approach is called "empirical Bayes." An excellent description of this method of estimation has been presented by Krutchkoff (1972). Application of the empirical Bayes methodology to attributes sampling has been given by Martz (1975). Craig and Bland (1981) show how it can be used in variables sampling.

These ideas have been further extended by the application of shrinkage estimators to the empirical Bayes problem as described by Morris (1983). One outstanding application of such procedures is in the so-called "universal sampling plan" utilized in the quality measurement plan (QMP) of American Telephone and Telegraph. Audit sample sizes are based on historical process control, economics, quality standards, and the heterogeneity of audit clusters as described by Hoadley (1981). Strictly speaking, the weights for the Stein shrinkage estimators utilized in the procedure are developed through a classical Bayes approach, and so this application is more properly viewed as Bayes empirical Bayes methodology.

Application of Bayesian methods has been hindered by the difficulty involved in correct assessment of the necessary prior distributions and in collecting and keeping current the required cost information. Clearly, greater reliance on prior empirical information and the potential of the computer for generating cost information should be helpful in this regard. Pitfalls in the selection of a prior distribution have been pointed out by Case and Keats (1982).

While studies have indicated that Bayesian schemes may be quite robust to errors in the prior distributions and loss functions, they nevertheless assume the prior to be stationary in the long-term sense (i.e. a process in control). Classical methods do not make this assumption. Bayesian plans are, in fact, quite application-specific, requiring extensive information and update for proper application, and like variables sampling, they are applied one characteristic at a time. Nevertheless, where appropriate, they provide yet another tool for economic sampling.

HOW TO SELECT THE PROPER SAMPLING PROCEDURES

The methods of acceptance sampling are many and varied. It is essential to select a sampling procedure appropriate to the acceptance sampling situation to which it is to be applied. This will depend upon the nature of the application itself, on quality history, and the extent of knowledge of the process and the producer. Indeed, according to Dodge (1950, p. 8):

> A product with a history of consistently good quality requires less inspection than one with no history or a history of erratic quality. Accordingly, it is good practice to include in inspection procedures provisions for reducing or increasing the amount of inspection, depending on the character and quantity of evidence at hand regarding the level of quality and the degree of control shown.

This will be discussed further in the Conclusion, below.

The steps involved in the selection and application of a sampling procedure are shown in Figure 25.25 taken from Schilling (1982). Emphasis here is on the feedback of information necessary for the proper application, modification, and evolution of sampling. As Ott (1975, pp. 181–182) has pointed out:

> There are two standard procedures that, though often good in themselves, can serve to postpone careful analysis of the production process:
>
> 1. On-line inspection stations (100% screening). These can become a way of life.
>
> 2. On-line acceptance sampling plans which prevent excessively defective lots from proceeding on down the production line, but have no feedback procedure included.
>
> These procedures become bad when they allow or encourage carelessness in production. It gets easy for production to shrug off responsibility for quality and criticize inspection for letting bad quality proceed.

It is therefore necessary for sampling to be constantly subject to modification in a system of acceptance control. Each plan has a specific purpose for which it is to be applied. Table 25.31 shows the relation of plan and purpose for some of the plans which have been discussed. Those not discussed here will be found described in detail in Schilling (1982). These plans then are the elements involved in a system of acceptance control. Their effective use in a continuing effort to provide protection while reducing inspection and moving to process control is a function of the ingenuity, integrity, and industry of the user.

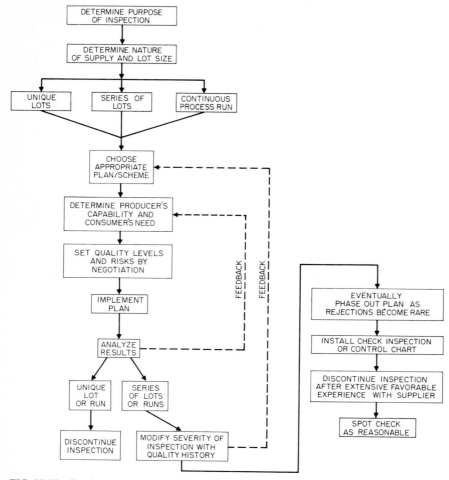

FIG. 25.25   Check sequence for implementation of sampling procedure.

COMPUTER PROGRAMS FOR ACCEPTANCE SAMPLING

A variety of computer programs have become available for application of specific sampling plans. Some of these are listed in Table 25.32. They will become increasingly important, particularly in the application of selected plans and in the development of plans for specific applications. It should be noted, however, that it is unlikely that these programs will ever replace hard copy procedures and standards which play a vital role in the negotiations between producer and consumer and which are immediately available for in-plant meetings and discussions at any location.

TABLE 25.31 Selection of Plan

Purpose	Supply	Attributes	Variables
Simple guarantee of producer's and consumer's quality levels at stated risks	Unique lot	Two-point plan (type A)	Two-point plan (type B)
	Series of lots	Dodge-Romig LTPD Two-point plan (type B)	Two-point plan (type B)
Maintain level of submitted quality at AQL or better	Series of lots	MIL-STD-105D QSS plan	MIL-STD-414 No calc. plan
Rectification guaranteeing AOQL to consumer	Series of lots	Dodge-Romig AOQL Anscombe plan	Romig variables plans
	Flow of individual units	CSP-1, 2, 3 Multilevel plan MIL-STD-1235A	Use measurements as go–no go
	Flow of segments of production	Wald-Wolfowitz Girschik	Use measurements as go–no go
Reduced inspection after good history	Series of lots	Skip-lot Chain Deferred sentencing	Lot plot Mixed variables-attributes Narrow-limit gaging

TABLE 25.31 Selection of Plan (*Continued*)

Purpose	Supply	Attributes	Variables
Check Inspection	Series of lots	Demerit rating	Acceptance control chart
Compliance to mandatory standards	Unique lot	Lot-sensitive plan	Mixed variables-attributes with $c = 0$
	Series of lots	TNT plan	Simon grand lot plan
Reliability sampling	Unique lot	Two-point plan (type B)	MIL-HDBK-108 TR 7
	Series of lots	LTPD plan QSS system CRC plan	TR-7 using MIL-STD-105D switching rules
Check accuracy of inspection	Series of lots	MIL-HDBK-109	Use measurements as go–no go

Source: Schilling, 1982, p. 569.

TABLE 25.32 Computer Programs for Acceptance Sampling (Optional Input/Output in Brackets)

Purpose	Input	Output	Reference
Single sampling—derivation	p_1, p_2, α, β, (lot size, p)	Plan (ATI at p, AOQL)	Snyder and Storer, 1972
Double sampling—derivation	AQL, LTPD (lot size) (assumes α = 0.05, β = 0.10)	Plans for n_2, = n_1 and n_2 = $2n_1$ with AOQL (p, P_a, AOQ, ATI, ASN)	Chow, Dickinson, and Hughes, 1973 and 1975
Multiple sampling—derivation	AQL, LTPD (lot size) (assumes α = 0.05, β = 0.10)	Plans for equal n with AOQL (p, P_a, AOQ, ATI, ASN)	Hughes, Dickinson, and Chow, 1973
Single, double, multiple sampling—evaluation (P_a given p or p given P_a) (hypergeometric, binomial Poisson, normal)	Distribution, sample sizes, acceptance/rejection numbers, fractions defective to be evaluated, probabilities of acceptance to be determined (lot size)	Plan control table, p, P_a, ASM, AOQ, ATI	Schilling, Sheesley, and Nelson, 1978

TABLE 25.32 Computer Programs for Acceptance Sampling (Optional Input/Output in Brackets) (*Continued*)

Purpose	Input	Output	Reference
Dodge continuous sampling—evaluation CSP-1, 2, 3	Fractions defective, index of plan (1, 2, 3), f, i, k	$p, F, P_a,$ AOQ	Sheesley, 1975
MIL-STD-414—implementation acceptance/rejection Decision given data	Number lots, type inspection (T, N, R), measure of variability, lot size, specification limits, AQL, data	Plan $\hat{p}, M,$ accept or reject	Nelson, 1977

Snyder, D. C. and Storer, R. F. (1972). "Single Sampling Plans Given an AQL, LTPD, Producer and Consumer Risks." *Journal of Quality Technology*, vol. 4, no. 3, July 1972, pp. 168–171.

Chow, B., Dickinson, P. C., and Hughes, H. (1973). "A Computer Program for the Solution of Double Sampling Plans." *Journal of Quality Technology*, vol. 4, no. 4, October 1973, pp. 205–209; also, *Journal of Quality Technology*, vol. 5, no. 4, October 1975, p. 166.

Hughes, H., Dickinson, P. C., and Chow, B. (1973). "A Computer Program for the Solutions of Multiple Sampling Plans." *Journal of Quality Technology*, vol. 5, no. 1, January 1973, pp. 39–42.

Schilling, E. G., Sheesley, J. H., and Nelson, P. R. (1978). "GRASP: A General Routine for Attribute Sampling Plan Evaluation." *Journal of Quality Technology*, vol. 10, no. 3, July 1978, pp. 125–130.

Sheesley, J. H. (1975). "A Computer Program to Evaluate Dodge's Continuous Sampling Plans." *Journal of Quality Technology*, vol. 7, no. 1, January 1975, pp. 43–45.

Nelson, P. R. (1977). "A Computer Program for Military Standard 414: Sampling Procedures and Inspection by Variables for Percent Defective." *Journal of Quality Technology*. vol. 9, no. 2, April 1977, pp. 82–86.
Source: Schilling, 1982, p. 587.

CONCLUSION—MOVING FROM ACCEPTANCE SAMPLING TO ACCEPTANCE CONTROL

There is little control of quality in the application of a sampling plan to an individual lot. Such an occurrence is static, whereas control implies movement and direction. When used in a system of *acceptance control,* over the life of the product, however, the plan can provide:

Protection for the consumer

Protection for the producer

Accumulation of quality history

Feedback for process control

Pressure on the producer to improve the process

Acceptance control involves adjusting the acceptance sampling procedure to match existing conditions with the objective of eventually phasing out the inspection altogether. This is much as the old-time inspector varied the inspection depending on quality history. Thus, acceptance control is "a continuing strategy of selection, application and modification of acceptance sampling procedures to a changing inspection environment" (see Schilling, 1982, p. 564). This involves a progression of sampling procedures applied as shown in Table 25.33.

These procedures are applied as appropriate over the lifetime of the product in a manner consistent with the improvement of quality and the reduction and elimination of inspection. This can be seen in Table 25.34.

Modern manufacturing is not static. It involves the development, manufacture, and marketing of new products as well as an atmosphere of continuing cost reduction, process modification, and other forms of quality improvement. Changes are continually introduced into the production process which are delib-

TABLE 25.33 Progression of Attribute Sampling Procedures

Past results	Quality history			Criterion
	Little	Moderate	Extensive	
Excellent	AQL plan	Cumulative results plan	Demerit rating or remove inspection	Almost no (<1%) lots rejected
Average	Rectification or LTPD plan	AQL plan	Cumulative results plan	Few (<10%) lots rejected
Poor	100% inspection	Rectification or LTPD plan with cumulative results criterion	Discontinue acceptance	Many (≥10%) lots rejected
Amount	Fewer than 10 lots	10–50 lots	More than 50 lots	

Source: Schilling, 1982, p. 565.

TABLE 25.34   Life Cycle of Acceptance Control Application

Stage	Step	Method
Preparatory	Choose plan appropriate to purpose	Analysis of quality system to define the exact need for the procedure
	Determine producer capability	Process performance evaluation using control charts
	Determine consumer needs	Process capability study using control charts
	Set quality levels and risks	Economic analysis and negotiation
	Determine plan	Standard procedures if possible
Initiation	Train inspector	Include plan, procedure, records, and action
	Apply plan properly	Ensure random sampling
	Analyze results	Keep records and control charts
Operational	Assess protection	Periodically check quality history and OC curves
	Adjust plan	When possible change severity to reflect quality history and cost
	Decrease sample size if warranted	Modify to use appropriate sampling plans taking advantage of credibility of supplier with cumulative results
Phase out	Eliminate inspection effort where possible	Use demerit rating or check inspection procedures when quality is consistently good Keep control charts
Elimination	Spot check only	Remove all inspection when warranted by extensive favorable history

Source: Schilling, 1982, p. 566.

erate, or unexpected from an unknown source. When this happens, acceptance sampling is necessary to provide protection for the producer and the consumer until the process can be brought into control. This may take days, months, or years. Under these circumstances, the inspection involved should be systematically reduced in a system of acceptance control which will reduce inspection reciprocally with the increase of the learning curve in the specific application. This can provide the protection necessary for the implementation of proper process control in a manner protrayed roughly in Figure 25.26. Acceptance control and process control are synergistic in the sense that one supports proper use of the other. As Dodge (1969, p. 156) has pointed out:

The "acceptance quality control system" . . . encompassed the concept of protecting the consumer from getting unacceptable defective material and encouraging

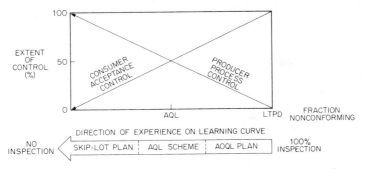

FIG. 25.26 Synergy between Acceptance Control and Process Control. *(From Schilling, 1982, p. 570.)*

the producer in the use of process quality control by: varying the quantity and severity of acceptance inspections in direct relation to the importance of the characteristics inspected, and in inverse relation to the goodness of the quality level as indicated by these inspections.

It is in this sense that acceptance control is an essential part of the quality system.

REFERENCES

ANSI/ASQC A2 (1987). *Terms, Symbols and Definitions for Acceptance Sampling.* American Society for Quality Control, Milwaukee.

ANSI/ASQC Z1.9 (1980). *Sampling Procedures and Tables for Inspection by Variables for Percent Nonconforming.* American Society for Quality Control, Milwaukee.

ANSI/ASQC Z1.4 (1981). *Sampling Procedures and Tables for Inspection by Attributes.* American Society for Quality Control, Milwaukee.

ASTM (1968). *Standard Methods of Test for Sampling Coal* (D2234-68). American Society for Testing and Materials, Philadelphia.

ASTM (1981). *Recommended Practice for Sampling Industrial Chemicals* (E 300-73). American Society for Testing and Materials, Philadelphia.

Beattie, D. W. (1962). "Continuous Acceptance Sampling Procedure Based upon a Cumulative Sum Chart for the Number of Defectives." *Applied Statistics,* vol. 11, no. 3, November, pp. 137–147.

Bicking, C. A. (1967). "The Sampling of Bulk Materials." *Materials Research and Standards,* March, pp. 95–116.

Bicking, C. A., Donovan, T. A., Sosnowski, T. S., and Bicking, C. M. (1967). *Bibliography on Precision Bulk Sampling and Related Applications of Statistics—Supplement.* CA Report 10, Technical Association of the Pulp and Paper Industry.

Bowker, A. H. and Goode, H. P. (1952). *Sampling Inspection by Variables.* McGraw-Hill, New York.

Burington, R. S. and May, D. C. (1970). *Handbook of Probability and Statistics with Tables,* 2nd ed. McGraw-Hill, New York.

Calvin, T. W. (1984). *How and When to Perform Bayesian Acceptance Sampling.* American Society for Quality Control, Milwaukee.

Cameron, J. M. (1952). "Tables for Constructing and for Computing the Operating Characteristics of Single Sampling Plans." *Industrial Quality Control,* vol. 9, no. 1, July, pp. 37–39.

Case, K., and Keats, J. B. (1982). "On the Selection of a Prior Distribution in Bayesian Acceptance Sampling." *Journal of Quality Technology,* vol. 14, no. 1, January, pp. 10–18.

Cochran, W. G. (1977). *Sampling Techniques,* 3rd ed. John Wiley & Sons, New York.

Cowden, D. J. (1957). *Statistical Methods in Quality Control.* Prentice-Hall, Englewood Cliffs, NJ, pp. 489–490.

Craig, J. A., Jr. and Bland, R. P. (1981). "An Empirical Bayes Approach to a Variables Acceptance Sampling Plan Problem." *Communication in Statistics—Theory, Methods,* vol. A10, no. 23, pp. 2399–2410.

Dodge, H. F. (1932). "Statistical Control on Sampling Inspection." *American Machinist,* October, pp. 1085–1088.

Dodge, H. F. (1943). "A Sampling Plan for Continuous Production." *Annals of Mathematical Statistics,* vol. 14, no. 3, pp. 264–279.

Dodge, H. F. (1950). "Inspection for Quality Assurance." *Industrial Quality Control,* vol. 7, no. 1, June, p. 8.

Dodge, H. F. (1955). "Chain Sampling Inspection Plan." *Industrial Quality Control,* vol. 11, no. 4, January, pp. 10–13.

Dodge, H. F. (1955a). "Skip-lot Sampling Plans." *Industrial Quality Control,* vol. 11, no. 5, February, pp. 3–5.

Dodge, H. F. (1969). "Notes on the Evolution of Acceptance Sampling Plans, Part II." *Journal of Quality Technology,* vol. 1, no. 3, July, p. 156.

Dodge, H. F. (1970). "Notes on the Evolution of Acceptance Sampling Plans, Part IV." *Journal of Quality Technology,* vol. 2, no. 1, January, pp. 1–8.

Dodge, H. F. and Perry, R. L. (1971). "A System of Skip-Lot Plans for Lot-by-Lot Inspection." *ASQC Technical Conference Transactions,* Milwaukee, pp. 469–477.

Dodge, H. F. and Romig, H. G. (1959). *Sampling Inspection Tables,* 2nd ed. John Wiley & Sons, New York.

Dodge, H. F. and Stephens, K. S. (1965). "Some New Chain Sampling Inspection Plans." *ASQC Technical Conference Transactions,* Milwaukee, pp. 8–17.

Dodge, H. F. and Stephens, K. S. (1966). "Some New Chain Sampling Inspection Plans." *Industrial Quality Control,* vol. 23, no. 2, August, pp. 61–67.

Dodge, H. F. and Torrey, M. N. (1951). "Additional Continuous Sampling Inspection Plans." *Industrial Quality Control,* vol. 7, no. 5, March, pp. 7–12.

Duncan, A. J. (1962). "Bulk Sampling Problems and Lines of Attack." *Technometrics,* vol. 4, no. 3, August, pp. 319–344.

Duncan, A. J. (1974). *Quality Control and Industrial Statistics.* Richard D. Irwin, Homewood, IL.

Enell, J. W. (1954). "What Sampling Plan Shall I Choose?" *Industrial Quality Control,* vol. 10, no. 6, May, pp. 96–100.

Freund, R. A. (1957). "Acceptance Control Charts." *Industrial Quality Control,* vol. 14, no. 4. October, pp. 13–23.

Grant, E. L. and Leavenworth, R. S. (1979). *Statistical Quality Control,* 5th ed. McGraw-Hill, New York.

Gregory, G. and Resnikoff, G. J. (1955). *Some Notes on Mixed Variables and Attributes Sampling Plans.* Technical Report 10, Applied Mathematics and Statistics Laboratory, Stanford University, Stanford, CA.

Grimlin, D. R. and Breipohl, A. M. (1972). "Bayesian Acceptance Sampling." *IEEE Transactions on Reliability,* vol. R-21, no. 3, August pp. 176–180.

Grubbs, F. E. and Coon, H. J. (1954). "On Setting Testing Limits Relative to Specification Limits." *Industrial Quality Control,* vol. 10, no. 5, March, pp. 15–20.

Grubman, S., Martin, C. A., and Pabst, W. R., Jr. (1969). "MIL-STD-690B Failure Rate Sampling Plans and Procedures." *Journal of Quality Technology,* vol. 1, no. 3, July, pp. 205–216.

MIL-HDBK-53 (1965). *Guide for Sampling Inspection.* Government Printing Office, Washington, DC, June 30.

MIL-HDBK-108 (1960). *Sampling Procedures and Tables for Life and Reliability Testing (Based on Exponential Distribution).* Quality Control and Reliability Handbook, U.S. Department of Defense, Government Printing Office, Washington, D.C.

Hald, A. (1960). "The Compound Hypergeometric Distribution and a System of Single Sampling Inspection Plans Based on Prior Distributions and Costs." *Technometrics,* vol. 2, no. 3, August, pp. 275–340.

Hald, A. (1981). *Statistical Theory of Sampling Inspection by Attributes.* Academic Press, New York, pp. 532.

Hamaker, H. C. (1979). "Acceptance Sampling for Percent Defective by Variables and by Attributes." *Journal of Quality Technology,* vol. 11, no. 3, July, pp. 139–148.

Hillier, F. S. (1969). "$\overline{X}$ and R—Chart Control Limits Based on a Small Number of Subgroups." *Journal of Quality Technology,* vol. 1, no. 1, January, pp. 17–26.

Hoadley, B. (1981). "The Universal Sampling Plan." *ASQC Quality Congress Transactions,* Milwaukee, pp. 80–87.

Krutchkoff, R. G. (1972). "Empirical Bayes Estimation." *The American Statistician,* vol. 26, no. 5, December, pp. 14–16.

Lieberman, G. J. and Solomon, H. (1955). "Multi-Level Continuous Sampling Plans." *Annals of Mathematical Statistics,* vol. 26, no. 4, pp. 686–704.

Martz, H. F. (1975). "Empirical Bayes Single Sampling Plans for Specified Posterior Consumer and Producer Risks." *Naval Research Logistic Quarterly,* vol. 22, no. 4, December, pp. 651–665.

MIL-STD-105B (1958). *Sampling Procedures and Tables for Inspection by Attributes.* Government Printing Office, Washington, DC.

MIL-STD-105D (1964). *Sampling Procedures and Tables for Inspection by Attributes.* Government Printing Office, Washington, DC.

MIL-STD-414 (1968). *Sampling Procedures and Tables for Inspection by Variables for Percent Defective.* Military Standard, U.S. Department of Defense, Government Printing Office, Washington, DC.

MIL-STD-690B (1960). *Failure Rate Sampling Plans and Procedures,* Military Standard, U.S. Department of Defense, Government Printing Office, Washington, DC.

MIL-STD-781C (1977). *Reliability Tests: Exponential Distribution.* Military Standard, U.S. Department of Defense, Government Printing Office, Washington, DC.

MIL-STD-1235B (1981). *Continuous Sampling Procedures and Tables for Inspection by Attributes.* Government Printing Office, Washington, DC.

Morris, C. N. (1983). "Parametric Empirical Bayes Inference: Theory and Applications." *Journal of the American Statistical Association,* vol. 78, no. 131, March, pp. 47–55.

Moses, L. E. (1956). "Some Theoretical Aspects of the Lot Plot Sampling Inspection Plan." *Journal of the American Statistical Association,* vol. 51, no. 273, pp. 84–107.

Murphy, R. B. (1959). "Stopping Rules with CSP-1 Sampling Inspection Plans in Continuous Production." *Industrial Quality Control,* vol. 16, no. 5, November, pp. 10–16.

Nelson, W. (1983). *How to Analyze Reliability Data.* American Society for Quality Control, Milwaukee.

Oliver, L. R. and Springer, M. D. (1972). *A General Set of Bayesian Attribute Acceptance Plans.* American Institute of Industrial Engineers, Norcross, GA.

Ott, E. R. (1975). *Process Quality Control,* McGraw-Hill, New York, pp. 181–182.

Pabst, W. R., Jr. (1963). "MIL-STD-105D." *Industrial Quality Control,* vol. 20, no. 5, November, pp. 4–9.

Perry, R. L. (1973). "Skip-Lot Sampling Plans." *Journal of Quality Technology,* vol. 5, no. 3, July, pp. 123–130.

Perry, R. L. (1973a). "Two-Level Skip-Lot Sampling Plans—Operating Characteristic Properties." *Journal of Quality Technology,* vol. 5, no. 4, October, pp. 160–166.

Prairie, R. R. and Zimmer, W. J. (1973). "Graphs, Tables, and Discussion to Aid in the

Design and Evaluation of an Acceptance Sampling Procedure Based on Cumulative Sums." *Journal of Quality Technology,* vol. 5, no. 2, April, pp. 58–66.

Schafer, R. E. (1964). "Bayesian Operating Characteristic Curves for Reliability and Quality Sampling Plans." *Industrial Quality Control,* vol. 21, no. 3, September, pp. 118–122.

Schafer, R. E. (1967). "Bayes Single Sampling Plans by Attributes Based on the Posterior Risk." *Naval Research Logistics Quarterly,* vol. A, no. 1, March, pp. 81–88.

Schilling, E. G. (1970). "Variables Sampling and MIL-STD-414." *Transactions of 26th Quality Control Conference of the Rochester Society for Quality Control,* March 30, pp. 175–188.

Schilling, E. G. (1978). "A Lot Sensitive Sampling Plan for Compliance Testing and Acceptance Inspection." *Journal of Quality Technology,* vol. 10, no. 2, April, pp. 47–51.

Schilling, E. G. (1979). "A Simplified Graphical Grand Lot Acceptance Sampling Procedure." *Journal of Quality Technology,* vol. 11, no. 3, July, pp. 116–127.

Schilling, E. G. (1982). *Acceptance Sampling in Quality Control.* Marcel Dekker, New York and Basel.

Schilling, E. G. and Dodge, H. F. (1969). "Procedures and Tables for Evaluating Dependent Mixed Acceptance Sampling Plans." *Technometrics,* vol. 11, no. 2, May, pp. 341–372.

Schilling, E. G. and Johnson, L. I. (1980). "Tables for the Construction of Matched Single, Double and Multiple Sampling Plans with Application to MIL-STD-105D." *Journal of Quality Technology,* vol. 12, no. 4, October, pp. 220–229.

Schilling, E. G. and Sheesley, J. H. (1978). "The Performance of MIL-STD-105D under the Switching Rules." *Journal of Quality Technology,* Part 1: vol. 10, no. 2, April, pp. 76–83; Part 2: vol. 10, no. 3, July, pp. 104–124.

Schilling, E. G. and Sommers D. J. (1981). "Two-Point Optimal Narrow Limit Plans with Applications to MIL-STD-105D." *Journal of Quality Technology,* vol. 13, no. 2, April, pp. 83–92.

Schmee, J. (1980). "MIL-STD-781C and Confidence Intervals." *Journal of Quality Technology,* vol. 12, no. 3, April, pp. 98–105.

Shainin, D. (1950). "The Hamilton Standard Lot Plot Method of Acceptance Sampling by Variables." *Industrial Quality Control,* vol. 7, no. 1, July, pp. 15–34.

Shainin, D. (1952). "Recent Lot Plot Experiences around the Country." *Industrial Quality Control,* vol. 8, no. 5, March, pp. 20–29.

Shinner R. and Naor, P. (1961). "A Test of Randomness for Solid-Solid Mixtures." *Chemical Engineering Science,* vol. 15, no. 3/4, pp. 220–229.

Simon, L. E. (1941). *An Engineer's Manual of Statistical Methods.* John Wiley & Sons, New York.

Sommers, D. J. (1981). "Two-Point Double Variables Sampling Plans." *Journal of Quality Technology,* vol. 13, no. 1, January, pp. 25–30.

Soundararajan, V. (1978). "Procedures and Tables for Construction and Selection of Chain Sampling Plans (ChSP-1)." *Journal of Quality Technology,* Part 1: vol. 10, no. 2, April, pp. 56–60; Part 2: vol. 10, no. 3, July, pp. 99–103.

Stephens, K. S. (1979). *How to Perform Continuous Sampling (CSP).* American Society for Quality Control, Milwaukee.

Stephens, K. S. (1982). *How to Perform Skip-Lot and Chain Sampling.* American Society for Quality Control, Milwaukee.

TR-3 (1961). *Sampling Procedures and Tables for Life and Reliability Testing Based on the Weibull Distribution (Mean Life Criterion).* Quality Control and Reliability Technical Report, U.S. Department of Defense, Government Printing Office, Washington, DC.

TR-4 (1962). *Sampling Procedures and Tables for Life and Reliability Testing Based on the Weibull Distribution (Hazard Rate Criterion).* Quality Control and Reliability Technical Report, U.S. Department of Defense, Government Printing Office, Washington, DC.

TR-6 (1963). *Sampling Procedures and Tables for Life and Reliability Testing Based on the Weibull Distribution (Reliable Life Criterion).* Quality Control and Reliability Technical Report, U.S. Department of Defense, Government Printing Office, Washington, DC.

TR-7 (1965). *Factors and Procedures for Applying MIL-STD-105D Sampling Plans to Life and Reliability Testing.* Quality Control and Reliability Technical Report, U.S. Department of Defense, Government Printing Office, Washington, DC.

"Wescom, Inc.—A Study in Telecommunications Quality." (1978). *Quality,* August, p. 30.

Wetherill, G. B. and Chin, W. K. (1975). "A Review of Acceptance Sampling Schemes with Emphasis on the Economic Input." *International Statistical Review,* vol. 43, no. 2, pp. 191–209.

SECTION 26

DESIGN AND ANALYSIS OF EXPERIMENTS[1]

J. Stuart Hunter

with Mary G. Natrella, E. Harvey Barnett, William G. Hunter, and Truman L. Koehler

---

[1]This section borrows extensively from the Third Edition, in which Mary Natrella prepared the section on design and analysis of experiments; E. Harvey Barnett prepared the section on evolutionary operation; and William G. Hunter and Truman L. Koehler prepared the section on response surface methodology. The present author, J. Stuart Hunter, gratefully acknowledges this earlier work and takes full responsibility for all changes in organization and emphasis.

INTRODUCTION

An experiment has been defined, in the most general sense, as a "considered course of action aimed at answering one or more carefully framed questions." This section discusses a more restricted kind of experiment, in which the experimenter chooses certain factors for study, deliberately varies those factors in a controlled fashion, and then observes the effect of such action. In addition, this section discusses how to design such experiments and how to interpret the resulting data.

The section is organized into three subdivisions:

1. An introduction, which provides those basic definitions that are essential to the understanding of problems in experimental design and analysis. Other definitions are provided later as needed.

2. A series of typical problems in design and analysis of experiments, starting with the simplest and increasing in complexity. For each of these problems the method of structuring the experiment and analyzing the resulting data is presented. General comments on each design are also presented.

3. A discussion of the size of the experiment, assumptions, and other matters pertinent to all designs, plus reference to other works.

Basic Definitions.   Several fundamental terms are widely used throughout this section. They may be defined as follows:

Factor.   A "factor" is one of the controlled or uncontrolled variables whose influence upon a response is being studied in the experiment. A factor may be quantitative, e.g., temperature in degrees, time in seconds. A factor may also be qualitative, e.g., different machines, different operators, switch on or off.

Level (Version).   The "levels" ("versions") of a factor are the values of the factor being examined in the experiment. For quantitative factors, each chosen value becomes a level, e.g., if the experiment is to be conducted at four different temperatures, then the factor "temperature" has four "levels." In the case of qualitative factors, "switch on or off" becomes two levels (versions) for the switch factor; if six machines are run by three operators, the factor "machine" has six levels (versions) while the factor "operator" has three levels (versions).

Treatment.   A "treatment" is a single level (version) assigned to a single factor during an experimental run, e.g., temperature at 800 degrees. A "treatment combination" is the set of levels for all factors in a given experimental run. For example, an experimental run using an 800-degree temperature, machine 3, operator A, and switch off would constitute one treatment combination.

Experimental Units.   The "experimental units" consist of the objects, materials, or units to which treatments are being applied. They may be biological entities, natural materials, fabricated products, etc.

Experimental Environment.   The "experimental environment" comprises the surrounding conditions that may influence the results of the experiment in known or unknown ways.

Block.   A factor in an experimental program that has influence as a source of variability is called a "block." The word is derived from early agricultural usage, in which blocks of land were the sources of variability. A block is a portion of the experimental material or of the experimental environment that is likely to be more homogeneous within itself than between different portions. For example, specimens from a single batch of material are likely to be more uniform than specimens from different batches. A group of specimens from such a single batch would be regarded as a block. Observations taken within a day are likely to be more homogeneous (to have smaller variance) than observations taken across days. "Days" then becomes a block factor.

Experimental Design.   The formal plan for conducting the experiment is called the "experimental design" (also the "experimental pattern"). It includes the choice of the responses, factors, levels, blocks, and treatments and the use of certain tools called planned grouping, randomization, and replication.

Some Tools for Good Experimentation. Good experimentation is an art and depends heavily upon the prior knowledge and abilities of the experimenter. Some tools of experimentation of importance in the statistical aspects of experimental planning and design follow.

Planned Grouping or Blocking. Beyond the factors selected for study, there are other "background" variables that may affect the outcome of the experiment. When the experimenter is aware of these variables, it is often possible to plan the experiment so that:

1. Possible influences due to background variables do not affect information obtained about the factors of primary interest.
2. Some information about the effects of the background variables can be obtained.

In designing experiments wide use is made of the uniformity within blocks in order to minimize the effect of unwanted variables and to accentuate the effect of the factors under study. Designs that make use of this uniformity within blocks are called "block designs," and the process is called "planned grouping."

Randomization. The sequence of experiments and/or the assignment of specimens to various treatment combinations in a purely chance manner is called "randomization." Such assignment increases the likelihood that the effect of uncontrolled variables will balance out. It also improves the validity of estimates of experimental error variance and makes possible the application of statistical tests of significance and the construction of confidence intervals. Whenever possible, randomization is part of the experimental program.

Replication. "Replication" is the repetition of an observation or measurement in order to increase precision or to provide the means for measuring precision. A single replicate consists of a single observation or experimental run. Replication provides an opportunity for the effects of uncontrolled factors or factors unknown to the experimenter to balance out and thus, with randomization, acts as a bias-decreasing tool. Replication also helps to detect gross errors in the measurements. In replications of groups of experiments, different randomizations should apply to each group.

Table 26.1 lists some requisites for sound experimentation and shows the way in which these tools contribute to meeting the requisites. A checklist that should be helpful in all phases of an experiment is given in Table 26.2; see Bicking, 1954.

TABLE 26.1 Some Requisites and Tools for Sound Experimentation

Requisites	Tools

1. The experiment should have carefully defined objectives. See Table 26.2.	1. The definition of objectives requires all the specialized subject matter knowledge of the experimenter, and involves such things as:
	   a. Choice of factors, including their range
	   b. Choice of experimental materials, procedures, and equipment
	   c. Choice of the metric for the factors (e.g., temperature or log

TABLE 26.1   Some Requisites and Tools for Sound Experimentation (*Continued*)

Requisites	Tools
	temperature) and method of measurement
2. As far as possible, effects of factors should not be obscured by other variables.	2. The use of an appropriate experimental pattern helps to free the comparisons of interest from the effects of uncontrolled variables and simplifies the analysis of results.
3. As far as possible, the experiment should be free from bias, conscious or unconscious.	3. Some variables may be taken into account by planned grouping. Use randomization. Replication helps randomization to do a better job.
4. Experiments should provide a measure of experimental error variance (precision).	4. Replication provides the measure of variance and randomization ensures its validity.
5. Precision of experiment should be sufficient to meet objectives set forth in requisite 1.	5. Greater precision may be achieved by: refinements of measurement and experimental technique, experimental pattern (including planned grouping), replication.

TABLE 26.2   Checklist for Planning Test Programs

A. Obtain a clear statement of the problem.
   1. Identify the problem area in quantitative terms.
   2. Identify the response(s) to be measured, the factors that may be varied, the factors to be held constant, and the factors that cannot be controlled.
   3. Identify the ranges or limitations of the measurements and of the experimental factors.
B. Collect available background information.
   1. Investigate all available sources of information.
   2. Tabulate data pertinent to planning the experimental program.
   3. Be quantitative.
C. Design the experimental program.
   1. Hold a conference of all parties concerned.
      a. State the propositions to be explored.
      b. Agree on magnitude of differences in the response considered worthwhile.
      c. Outline possible alternative outcomes.
      d. Choose the factors to be studied.
      e. Determine practical range of factors and specify levels.
      f. Choose the measurements and methods of measurement.
      g. Consider the effect of sampling variability and of precision of the measurement methods.
      h. Consider possible interrelationships (interactions) of the factors.
      j. Determine influences of time, cost, materials, manpower, instrumentation, and other facilities and of extraneous conditions such as weather.
      k. Consider personnel and human relations requirements of the program.
   2. Design the experimental program in preliminary form.
      a. Prepare a systematic and inclusive schedule, which includes the randomization pattern.
      b. Provide for stepwise performance or adaptation of schedule if necessary.

TABLE 26.2　Checklist for Planning Test Programs　(*Continued*)

---

　　　c. Eliminate effect of variables not under study by controlling, balancing, or randomization.
　　　d. Minimize the number of experimental runs consistent with objectives.
　　　e. Choose the method of statistical analysis.
　　　f. Arrange for orderly accumulation of data.
　　3. Review the experimental design program with all concerned.
　　　a. Adjust the program as required.
　　　b. Spell out the steps to be followed in unmistakable terms.
D. Plan and carry out the experimental work.
　　1. Develop methods, materials, and equipment.
　　2. Carry out the experimental design in some random order.
　　3. Record ancillary data.
　　4. Record any modifications of the experimental design.
　　5. Take precautions in the collection and recording of data, especially data from extra experiments and missing experiments.
　　6. Record progress of the program by date, run number, and other ancillary data.
E. Analyze the data.
　　1. Review the data with attention to recording errors, omissions, etc.
　　2. Use graphics: plot the data, plot averages, plot simple graphs.
　　3. Apply appropriate statistical techniques.
F. Interpret the results.
　　1. Consider all the observed data.
　　2. Confine initial conclusions to strict deductions from the experimental evidence at hand.
　　3. Elucidate the analysis in both graphical and numerical terms.
　　4. State results in terms of verifiable probabilities.
　　5. Arrive at conclusions as to the technical meaning of results as well as their statistical significance.
　　6. Point out implications of the findings for application and for further work.
　　7. Account for any limitations imposed by the data or by the methods of analysis used.
G. Prepare the report.
　　1. Describe work clearly, giving background, pertinence of problems, meaning of results.
　　2. Use tabular and graphic methods of presenting data, and consider their possible future use.
　　3. Supply sufficient information to permit readers to verify results and to draw their own conclusions.
　　4. Limit conclusions to objective summary of evidence.

CLASSIFICATION OF EXPERIMENTAL DESIGNS

Statisticians by themselves do not design experiments, but they have developed a number of structured schedules called "experimental designs," which they recommend for the taking of measurements. These designs have certain rational relationships to the purposes, needs, and physical limitations of experiments. Designs also offer certain advantages in economy of experimentation and provide straightforward estimates of experimental effects and valid estimates of variance. There are a number of ways in which experiment designs might be classified, for example, the following:

1. By the number of experimental factors to be investigated (e.g., single-factor versus multifactor designs)

2. By the structure of the experimental design (e.g., blocked, factorial, nested, or response-surface design)
3. By the kind of information the experiment is primarily intended to provide (e.g., estimates of effects, estimates of variance, or empirical mappings)

Some of the common statistical experimental designs are summarized in Table 26.3. Basic features of the designs are summarized in terms of these criteria of classification and the details of design and analysis are given under the topics that follow. The analysis for observed responses is always based on a statistical model unique to the specific design.

TABLE 26.3 Classification of Designs

Design	Type of application	Structure	Information sought
Completely randomized	Appropriate when only one experimental factor is being investigated.	Basic: One factor is investigated by allocating experimental units at random to treatments (levels of the factor). Blocking: none.	1. Estimate and compare treatment effects. 2. Estimate variance.
Factorial	Appropriate when several factors are to be investigated at two or more levels and interaction of factors may be important.	Basic: Several factors are investigated at several levels by running all combinations of factors and levels. Blocking: none.	1. Estimate and compare effects of several factors. 2. Estimate possible interaction effects. 3. Estimate variance.
Blocked factorial	Appropriate when number of runs required for factorial is too large to be carried out under homogeneous conditions.	Basic: Full set of combinations of factors and levels is divided into subsets so that some high-order interactions are equated to blocks. Each subset constitutes a block. All blocks are run. Blocking: Blocks are usually units in space or time. Estimates of certain interactions are sacrificed to provide blocking.	1. Same as factorial except that certain high-order interactions cannot be estimated.

TABLE 26.3 Classification of Designs *(Continued)*

Design	Type of application	Structure	Information sought
Fractional factorial	Appropriate when there are many factors and levels and it is impractical to run all combinations.	Basic: Several factors are investigated at several levels but only a subset of the full factorial is run. Blocking: Sometimes possible.	1. Estimate and compare effects of several factors. 2. Estimate certain interaction effects (some may not be estimable). 3. Certain small fractional factorial designs may not provide sufficient information for estimating the variance.
Randomized block	Appropriate when one factor is being investigated and experimental material or environment can be divided into blocks or homogeneous groups.	Basic: Each treatment or level of factor is run in each block. Blocking: Usually with respect to only one variable.	1. Estimate and compare effects of treatments free of block effects. 2. Estimate block effects. 3. Estimate variance.
Balanced incomplete block	Appropriate when all the treatments cannot be accommodated in a block.	Basic: Prescribed assignments of treatments to blocks are made. Every pair of treatments will appear at least once in the experimental design, but each block will contain only a subset of pairs.	1. Same as randomized block design. All treatment effects are estimated with equal precision. Treatment averages must be adjusted for blocks.
Partially balanced incomplete block	Appropriate if a balanced incomplete block requires a larger number of blocks than is practical.	Basic: Prescribed assignments of treatments to blocks are made.	1. Same as randomized block design but all treatments are not estimated with equal precision.

TABLE 26.3 Classification of Designs *(Continued)*

Design	Type of application	Structure	Information sought
Latin square	Appropriate when one primary factor is under investigation and results may be affected by two other experimental variables or by two sources of nonhomogeneity. It is assumed that no interactions exist.	Basic: Two cross groupings of the experimental units are made corresponding to the columns and rows of a square. Each treatment occurs once in every row and once in every column. Number of treatments must equal number of rows and number of columns Blocking: With respect to two other variables in a two-way layout.	1. Estimate and compare treatment effects, free of effects of the two blocked variables. 2. Estimate and compare effects of the two blocked variables. 3. Estimate variance.
Youden square	Same as Latin square but number of rows, columns, and treatments need not be the same.	Basic: Each treatment occurs once in every row. Number of treatments must equal number of columns. Blocking: With respect to other variables in a two-way layout.	1. Same as Latin square.
Nested	Appropriate when objective is to study relative variability instead of mean effect of sources of variation (e.g., variance of tests on the same sample and variance of different samples).	Basic: Factors are strata in some hierarchical structure; units are tested from each stratum.	1. Relative variation in various strata, components of variance.

26.9

TABLE 26.3   Classification of Designs (*Continued*)

Design	Type of application	Structure	Information sought
Response surface	Objective is to provide empirical maps (contour diagrams) illustrative of how factors under the experimenter's control influence the response.	Factor settings are viewed as defining points in the factor space (may be multidimensional) at which the response will be recorded	Maps illustrating the nature of the response surface
Mixture designs	Same as factorial designs.	Many unique arrays. Factor settings are constrained. Factor levels are often percentages that must sum to 100%. Other factor level constraints are possible.	Same as factorial

COMPLETELY RANDOMIZED DESIGN—A ONE-FACTOR EXPERIMENT

The completely randomized design is appropriate when a total of N experimental units are available for the experiment and there are k treatments (or levels of the factor) to be investigated. Of the total number N, it is usual to assign *randomly* an equal number n to each of the k treatments.

Example.   A study was made to investigate the effect of three different conditioning methods on the breaking strength T (in pounds per square inch) of cement briquettes. Fifteen briquettes were available from one batch and were assigned at random to the three methods. The results are summarized in Table 26.4. The purpose of the experiment was to investigate the effect of conditioning methods on breaking strength, and the analysis was designed to answer the question: Do the mean breaking strengths differ for the different conditioning methods?

This is an example of a randomized one-factor experiment. Only one experimental factor (method of conditioning) is under study. There are three methods, i.e., the number of treatments k equals 3. The number of units n assigned at random to each treatment is 5. The total number of experimental units N is 15.

Analysis.   The analysis of these data begins with a plot of the three treatment averages, as shown in Figure 26.1. The reference distribution plotted above the averages will be explained later. The average responses are obviously different. The key question is whether the observed differences between the averages is due

TABLE 26.4 Breaking Strength T of Cement Briquettes, lb/in^2

	Method 1	Method 2	Method 3
	553	553	492
	550	599	530
	568	579	528
	541	545	510
	537	540	571
Total T	2749	2816	2631
n	5	5	5
Average $\bar{y}$	549.8	563.2	526.2
Estimate of variance s^2	145.7	626.2	864.2
Degrees of freedom	4	4	4

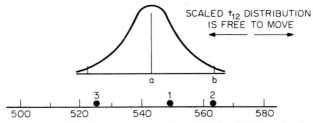

SCALED t_{12} DISTRIBUTION IS FREE TO MOVE

FIG. 26.1 Plot of treatment averages and their reference t-distribution. (Distance from a to b = $t_{\nu,\ \alpha/2}\sqrt{s^2/n}$ = $t_{12,\ 0.025}\sqrt{s^2/n}$ = $2.179\sqrt{545.4/5}$ = 22.8.)

solely to the inherent variability of the observations or is caused by this variability plus real differences between the treatment means. (In this section on experimental design the word "mean" is used to connote the *expected value* of an average, that is, the value an average would take if an infinite number of observations were made.) The analysis of variance (ANOVA) is a basic statistical technique in the analysis of such data and is illustrated for the data in Table 26.5.

Analysis of Variance. Referring to Table 26.4, the total T is:

$$T = 8196 \qquad N = 15 \qquad n_i = 5 \qquad i = 1,2,3$$

TABLE 26.5 Analysis of Variance for a One-Factor Experiment

Source of variation	Sum of squares	Degrees of freedom	Mean square
Between treatments	SSB = 3,509.2	$(k - 1) = 2$	MSB = SSB/$(k - 1)$ MSB = 3509.2/2 = 1754.6
Within treatments	SSW = 6,544.4	$k(n - 1) = 12$	MSW = SSW/$k(n - 1)$ MSW = 6544.4/12 = 545.4
Total	TSS = 10,053.6	$(N - 1) = 14$	

Calculate the following:

The *uncorrected* total sum of squares Σy^2 = 4,488,348

$$C = \text{correction factor (a special constant)} = \frac{T^2}{N} = \frac{(8196)^2}{15} = 4,478,294.4$$

TSS = *corrected* total sum of squares $\sum y^2 - C$

$$= 4,488,348 - 4,478,294.4 = 10,053.6$$

$$\text{SSB} = \text{between-treatments sum of squares} = \sum_i \frac{T_i^2}{n} - C = \frac{22,409,018}{5} - C$$

$$= 4,481,803.6 - 4,478,294.4 = 3509.2$$

SSW = within-treatments sum of squares = TSS − SSB

$$= 10,053.6 - 3,509.2 = 6,544.4$$

(SSW is here obtained by subtraction. It may be obtained directly for the special case of the completely randomized design by calculating $\Sigma y^2 - [(\Sigma y)^2/n]$ for each treatment and summing for all treatments.)

The corrected total sum of squares TSS has $N - 1$ degrees of freedom (DF), the between-treatments sum of squares SSB has $(k - 1)$ degress of freedom, and the within-treatments sum of squares SSW has $(N - k)$ degrees of freedom.

The mean-square column in the table is computed as follows:

$$\text{Mean square between treatments MSB} = \frac{\text{SSB}}{k - 1}$$

$$\text{Mean square within treatments MSW} = \frac{\text{SSW}}{N - k}$$

These calculated quantities are inserted in Table 26.5.

Calculate $F = \text{MSB/MSW} = 1754.6/545.5 = 3.22$. Choose α, the significance level of the test. If the calculated F exceeds $F_{1-\alpha}$ from Appendix II, Table K, for $(k - 1)$ and $k (n - 1)$ degrees of freedom, conclude that there are differences among treatment means. For example, $\alpha = 0.05$ level, $F_{0.95}$ for (2,12) degrees of freedom = 3.89; the calculated F does not exceed this value, and we may conclude that the mean breaking strength is not different for the different conditioning methods. The differences between the treatment averages are thus assumed to be due to the error variance. Had the hypothesis that there are no treatment effects been rejected by the F test, then one could conclude that at least one of the mean breaking strengths differs from the others. The formal issue of comparing treatment means, the problem of "multiple comparisons," is discussed in Montgomery (1976).

In this example the n_i are all equal. Designs that have an equal number of observations in each treatment are generally to be preferred. Such designs provide each treatment with an equal opportunity for comparison against all other treatments. On rare occasions, as when one of the treatments is a standard against which all other treatments are to be compared, more observations are placed in the standard treatment than in the alternatives. When the n_i are not all equal, use the following formula for the between-treatments sum of squares:

$$\text{SSB} = \frac{T_1^2}{n_1} + \frac{T_2^2}{n_2} + \cdots + \frac{T_k^2}{n_k} - C$$

Here SSW = TSS $-$ SSB and MSW = SSW/$(N - k)$ as before. The MSW (the overall estimate of variance) can also be obtained by estimating the variance within each treatment and pooling these estimates. The pooled estimate has $N - k$ degrees of freedom.

Graphical Analysis.   An approximate graphical analysis of these data is provided by sketching an appropriate "reference" distribution for the average, as illustrated in Figure 26.1. When σ^2 (the population variance) or, equivalently, σ (the population standard deviation) is known, averages may be referred to a normal distribution with standard error $\sigma/\sqrt{n}$. Here σ^2 is unknown, and its estimate s^2 must be determined from the data. Averages must be referred to a student's t-distribution, suitably scaled by $s/\sqrt{n}$. The number of degrees of freedom in t is equal to the number of degrees of freedom in s^2. The estimate of σ^2 is obtained from the analysis of variance table (s^2 = MSW) or by pooling the separate estimates of variance obtained from within each treatment classification. The pooled estimate of variance is given by the weighted average of the individual estimates, the weights being their degrees of freedom. Thus

$$s^2 = \sum_i \frac{(n_i - 1)s_i^2}{N - k}$$

$$= \frac{4(145.7) + 4(626.2) + 4(864.2)}{16} = 545.5$$

$$s = 23.34 \text{ with 12 degrees of freedom}$$

A sketch of the appropriately scaled t distribution appears in Figure 26.1. The distance from the center of the distribution to each extremal point equals $t_{12,\,0.025}s/\sqrt{n} = 2.18(23.35)/\sqrt{5} = 22.8$, and 95 percent of the distribution falls within the range $2(22.8) = 45.6$. The distribution is easily sketched; there is no need for great precision in its shape save that it look reasonably normal. The distribution can be moved back and forth, and has been located in this instance so that it just fits over the three averages. Thus, based upon this graphical evidence, the suggestion that all three averages could have come from the same parent distribution and hence could be estimates of the identical mean seems reasonable.

This graphical interpretation is verified by using the F test in the analysis of variance table; that is, the computed F ratio was not statistically significant. When averages do not fit reasonably under the distribution, the graphical analysis suggests that the differences between the treatment averages reflect real differences between the treatment means. Such graphical evidence could, of course, be verified by an F test. The scaled reference distribution can be of great value in interpreting treatment averages. Often, although it is technically possible to place the reference distribution over all the averages and simultaneously to obtain a nonsignificant F test, interesting differences between groups of the averages may become clear. The F test does not consider patterns among the averages, a factor that can be of great importance to the analyst (see Box, Hunter, and Hunter,

1978). Alternative approximate analysis techniques, in particular those based upon the use of the range statistic in place of the estimated standard deviation, are available (see the papers by Kurtz et al., 1965, and by Sheesley, 1980).

GENERAL COMMENTS ON A COMPLETELY RANDOMIZED DESIGN

The completely randomized design is simple to organize and analyze and may be the best choice when the experimental material is homogeneous and when background conditions can be well controlled during the experiment.

The advantages of the design are:

1. Complete flexibility in terms of number of treatments and number of units assigned to a treatment
2. Simple analysis
3. No difficulty with lost or missing data

In planning the experiment, n units are assigned at random to each of the k treatments. When the data have been taken, the results are set out as in Table 26.6.

Displayed this way, the results of experiments are indistinguishable from a situation in which there has been no design and no allocation at all but in which several different samples have been tested from each of several different sources of material or several observations have been made under each of several different conditions. Whether the observations come from units randomly allocated to several different treatments or from units obtained from several different sources, the data table looks the same, and in fact the analysis will be essentially the same.

This simple one-factor design is called "completely randomized" to distinguish it from other experiment designs in which either randomization is constrained or the principle of "blocking," or planned grouping, has been made part of the structure.

One-Way Analysis of Variance—Models. The results of an experiment run according to a completely randomized design are summarized in a one-way table such as Table 26.6. The completely randomized design is called a "one-way" clas-

TABLE 26.6 Completely Randomized Design

Observations within treatments*	Treatments				
	1	2	3	$\cdots$	k
1	y_{11}	y_{12}	y_{13}	$\cdots$	y_{1k}
2	y_{21}	y_{22}	y_{23}	$\cdots$	y_{1k}
3	y_{31}	y_{32}	y_{33}	$\cdots$	y_{3k}
.	.	.	.		.
.	.	.	.		.
.	.	.	.		.
n	y_{n1}	y_{n2}	y_{n3}	$\cdots$	y_{nk}

*The entire nk observations are recorded in random order *without* regard to the treatment classifications.

sification of data, whether or not the data came from a designed experiment. To discuss the associated analysis of variance, statisticians require "models" for the data. In the case of a one-way classification analysis of variance, the most appropriate model is determined by answering the question: Do the several groups (into which the data are classified) represent unique groups of interest to the experimenter? If they do, the model is called "Model I," the "Fixed Effects Model." If, on the other hand, the groups are considered to be a random sample from some population made up of many such groups, the model is called "Model II," the "Random Effects Model." For example, suppose that the data in Table 26.4 were not from a completely randomized design in which 15 briquettes were allocated at random to three unique conditioning treatments of interest to the experimenter. Suppose instead the column headings were "Batch 1," "Batch 2," "Batch 3," where the "batches" represented some convenient grouping of briquettes so that five briquettes were tested per batch. In the original experimental program, in which the three conditioning treatments of the designed experiment were the unique treatments of interest to the experimenter, the data may be represented by the Fixed Effects Model (Model I), whereas in the second program the three batches presumably were a random sample of batches, and hence these data are represented by the Random Effects Model (Model II).

For both Model I and Model II, the experimenter is trying to determine whether the three groups are different in mean value. For Model II the experimenter may also be interested in knowing about the "components of variance"; that is, the variance between samples from the same batch and the variance existing between batches. Knowledge of the variability of different samples within a batch and between different batches is helpful in planning how many samples to test in future experiments.

Data obtained from a designed experiment, as described for this completely randomized design, are usually considered to be represented by Model I, since presumably the experimenter includes the treatments of interest. If the data correspond to Model II, the analysis of variance table and F test are used with one extra step, which requires adding an extra column labeled "Expected Mean Square," to Table 26.5.

	Expected mean square
Between groups	$\sigma_w^2 + n\sigma_b^2$
Within groups	σ_w^2

For the data in Table 26.5, we have:

	Mean square	Expected mean square
Between groups	MSB = 1754.6	$\sigma_w^2 + 5\sigma_b^2$
Within groups	MSW = 545.4	σ_w^2

The quantity σ_b^2 is called the "between component of variance," and σ_w^2 is called the "within component of variance"; MSB is an estimate of the "Expected Between-Groups Mean Square"; and MSW is an estimate of the "Expected

Within-Groups Mean Square." Estimates of s_b^2 and s_w^2 or σ_b^2 and σ_w^2 can be obtained as follows:

MSB is set equal to $s_w^2 + ns_b^2$ and MSW is set equal to s_w^2:

$$s_w^2 = 545.4$$

$$s_b^2 = \frac{1754.6 - 545.4}{5} = \frac{1209.2}{5} = 241.8$$

The total variance assignable to a single observation from one randomly chosen batch and a single briquette is estimated as:

$$s^2 = s_b^2 + s_w^2$$

FACTORIAL EXPERIMENTS—GENERAL

Factorial designs are most frequently employed in engineering and manufacturing experiments. In a factorial experiment several factors are controlled, and their effects upon some response are investigated at each of two or more levels. The experimental plan consists of taking an observation at each of all possible combinations of levels that can be formed from the different factors. Each different combination of factor levels is called a "treatment combination."

Suppose that an experimenter is interested in investigating the effect of the two factors amperage (current) level and force upon the response y, which equals the measured resistivity of silicon wafers. In the past, one common experimental approach has been the so-called "one-factor-at-a-time" approach. This experimental strategy studies the effect of first varying amperage levels at some constant force and then applying different force levels at some constant level of amperage. The two factors would thus be varied one at a time with all other conceivable factors held as constant as possible. The results of such an experiment are fragmentary in the sense that we learn about the effect of different amperage levels only at one force level and the effect of different force levels at only one amperage level. The effects of one factor are conditional on the chosen level of the second factor. The measured resistivity of the wafer at different current levels may, of course, be different when a different force level has been chosen. Similarly, any observed relation of resistivity to force level might be quite different at other amperage levels. In statistical language, there may be an "interaction effect" between the two factors over the range of interest, and the one-at-a-time procedure does not enable the experimenter to detect the interaction.

In a factorial experiment, the levels of each factor are chosen, and a measurement is made at each of all possible combinations of levels of the factors. Suppose that five levels of amperage and four levels of force are chosen. There would thus be 20 possible combinations of amperage and force, and the factorial experiment would consist of 20 trials. In this example, the term "level" is used in connection with quantitative factors, but the same term is also used when the factors are qualitative.

In the analysis of factorial experiments, one speaks of "main effects" and "interaction effects" (or simply "interactions"). Estimated main effects of a given factor are always functions of the average yield response at the various levels of the factor. When a factor has two levels, the estimated main effect is the difference between the average responses at the two levels, i.e., the averages computed over all levels of the other factors. In the case in which the factor has more than two levels, there are several main effect components (linear, quadratic, cubic, etc.), the number of estimable main effect components being one less than the number of levels.

When the factors are qualitative, other comparisons, called treatment "contrasts," are possible. If the difference in the expected response between two levels of factor A remains constant over the levels of factor B (except for experimental error), there is no interaction between A and B; that is, the AB interaction is zero. Figure 26.2 shows two examples of response, or yield, curves; one example shows the presence of an interaction and the other shows no interaction. If there are two levels each of the factors A and B, then the AB interaction (neglecting experimental error) is the difference in the average yields of A at the second level of B minus the difference in the average yields of A at the first level of B. If there are more than two levels of either A or B, then the AB interaction can be composed of more than one component. If we have a levels of the factor A and b levels of the factor B, then the AB interaction has $(a - 1)(b - 1)$ independent components. A two-factor interaction (e.g., AB) is also called a "second-order" effect or "coupled" effect.

For factorial experiments with three or more factors, interactions can also be defined. For example, the ABC interaction is the interaction between the factor C and the AB interaction (or, equivalently, between the factor B and the AC interaction or between A and the BC interaction). A three-factor interaction (e.g., ABC) is a "third-order" effect.

EXAMPLE OF A FACTORIAL EXPERIMENT WITH TWO FACTORS

A two-factor experiment is the simplest kind of multifactor experiment, i.e., all possible combinations of the levels of the two factors are run. For example, mea-

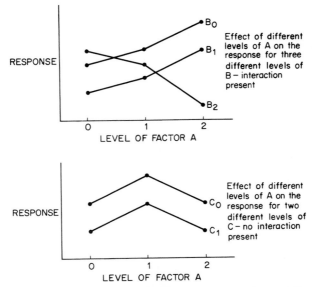

FIG. 26.2 Response curves showing presence or absence of interaction.

surements of the response resistivity of a silicon wafer are usually made at a standard amperage level while using 150 g of force. Let us consider an investigation in progress to see what happens when other values of force and amperage are employed. Four values of force are to be investigated (25, 50, 100, 150 g), along with five levels of amperage (levels 1, 2, 3, 4, and 5, where level 3 is the standard level). An experimental trial is made at each of the $4 \times 5 = 20$ possible combinations. The data can be displayed in a two-way array, as in Table 26.7. This is an unreplicated two-factor multilevel factorial experiment. Some textbooks will describe it as having two "crossed" factors.

Analysis. The first stage of the analysis is to compute, plot, and review both the column and row averages shown in Table 26.8.

Plots of the response versus the factor levels are always useful; in this case they would point up the noticeably higher resistivity values at amperage level 5 and the apparent changes in the resistivity with increasing force, particularly at the outer values of amperage. When the factors are quantitative and the levels equally spaced, there are simple methods to check on various types of trends (linear, quadratic, etc.) in the response measurements as a function of varying levels of a factor (see Hicks, 1982).

The analysis of variance can be used to test two hypotheses: (1) the mean resistivity at all levels of force is the same; and (2) the mean resistivity at all levels of amperage is the same.

The construction of the analysis of variance table would proceed as follows:

$$r = \text{number of rows} = 4$$

$$c = \text{number of columns} = 5$$

$$T = \text{grand total} = \sum_j C_j = \sum_i R_i = 236.77$$

$$N = \text{total number of observations} = r \times c = 20$$

$$C = \text{the correction factor} = \frac{T^2}{N} = 2803.001645$$

$$\text{SSR} = \text{row sum of squares} = \frac{\sum_i R_i^2}{r} - C = 0.014855$$

$$\text{SSC} = \text{column sum of squares} = \frac{\sum_j C_j^2}{r} - C = 0.021430$$

$$\text{TSS} = \text{total corrected sum of squares}$$

$$= (\text{all observations squared}) - C$$

$$= 2803.043500 - 2803.001645 = 0.041855$$

$$\text{SSE} = \text{error (or residual) sum of squares}$$

$$= \text{TSS} - \text{SSR} - \text{SSC} = 0.005570$$

The analysis of variance table for this (unreplicated) two-factor crossed factorial is shown in Table 26.9. Tests of hypotheses that no treatment effects exist are now possible. For rows conclude that statistically significant effects exist between rows

TABLE 26.7 Resistivity Measurements

Force, g	Current level					Row totals R_i
	1	2	3	4	5	
25	11.84	11.83	11.84	11.81	11.96	$R_1 = 59.28$
50	11.84	11.88	11.88	11.87	11.90	$R_2 = 59.37$
100	11.77	11.80	11.80	11.81	11.88	$R_3 = 59.06$
150	11.79	11.80	11.80	11.80	11.87	$R_4 = 59.06$
Column totals C_j	$C_1 = 47.24$	$C_2 = 47.31$	$C_3 = 47.32$	$C_4 = 47.29$	$C_5 = 47.61$	$T = 236.77$

TABLE 26.8 Table of Averages and Effects

Row number	Row average	Row effect
1	11.8560	0.0175
2	11.8740	0.0355
3	11.8120	−0.0265
4	11.8120	−0.0265

Column number	Column average	Column effect
1	11.8100	−0.0285
2	11.8275	−0.0110
3	11.8300	−0.0085
4	11.8225	−0.0160
5	11.9025	0.0640

TABLE 26.9 Analysis of Variance of Resistivity Measurements given in Table 26.7

Source of variation	Sum of squares (SS)	Degrees of freedom (DF)	Mean square = SS/DF	F*
Rows (force)	0.014855	$(r-1) = 3$	0.004952	10.67†
Columns (current)	0.021430	$(c-1) = 4$	0.005358	11.54†
Error	0.005570	$(r-1)(c-1) = 12$	0.000464	
Total	0.041855	$(rc-1) = 19$		

*F = mean square (source)/mean square (error).
†Significant at the 1% level.

TABLE 26.10 Residuals, Row and Column Effects, Grand Average

Force, g	Amperage, A					Force effects
	Level 1	Level 2	Level 3	Level 4	Level 5	
25	0.0125	−0.0150	−0.0075	−0.0300	0.0400	0.0175
50	−0.0055	0.0170	0.0145	0.0120	−0.0380	0.0355
100	−0.0135	−0.0010	−0.0035	0.0140	0.0040	−0.0265
150	0.0065	−0.0010	−0.0035	0.0040	−0.0060	−0.0265
Current effects	−0.0285	−0.0110	−0.0085	−0.0160	0.0640	$11.8385 = \bar{y}$

TABLE 26.11 Analysis of Variance Table for Two-Factor Factorial (k Replicates per Cell)

Source of variation	Sum of squares	Degrees of freedom	Mean square	F
Rows	SSR	$r-1$	$SSR/(r-1) = MSR$	MSR/MSE
Columns	SSC	$c-1$	$SSR/(c-1) = MSC$	MSC/MSE
Interaction	SSI	$(r-1)(c-1)$	$SSI/(r-1)(c-1) = MSI$	MSI/MSE
Error	SSE	$rc(k-1)$	$SSE/rc(k-1) = MSE$	
Total	SST	$krc-1$		

if F = (row mean square)/(error mean square) is greater than $F_{1-\alpha}$ for $(r - 1)$ and $(r - 1)(c - 1)$ degrees of freedom (from Appendix II, Table K). Similarly, for columns conclude that statistically significant effects exist if F = (column mean square)/(error mean square) is greater than the tabulated value of F for $(c - 1)$ and $(r - 1)(c - 1)$ degrees of freedom. In this example both F tests reject the hypothesis that no effects exist.

The analysis of variance table and its associated tests of hypotheses are only one part of the analysis of data from a factorial design. The model postulated for the data assumes that the force and amperage factor effects are additive. Thus there can be no interactions; that is, the effects of force upon resistivity remain unchanged whatever the levels of the second factor. One way to check this assumption is to compute Tukey's one-degree-of-freedom test for nonadditivity (see Snedecor and Cochran, 1967, or Box, Hunter, and Hunter, 1978). The test for nonadditivity here proved to be nonsignificant.

Table 26.8 has been extended to include the estimated row and column *effects* (the estimated row effect is the row average minus the grand average; the estimated column effect is the column average minus grand average). The row and column effects can then be used to make a two-way table of "residuals," in which the residual for the cell in the ith row and jth column is equal to the observation in that cell minus the sum of the grand average, the ith row effect, and the jth column effect. The table of residuals, Table 26.10, is examined for individual large values (indicating a possibly erroneous observation) and for unusual patterns in sign and size (indicating possible interaction effects). The residuals should be plotted in the time order in which the treatment combinations were run; any indication of trends indicative of other factors disturbs the response. The residuals can also be plotted on normal probability paper as a check on the normality assumption.

The discussion thus far assumes that only one determination per cell was made. To obtain a truly valid estimate of the error variance from this experiment, the cell's observations must be replicated. When experiments are replicated (ideally with each cell containing the same number of observations), it is useful to have a table similar to Table 26.7, where now in each cell both the average and the estimate of variance are recorded. Homogeniety of variance tests may be made (see Snedecor and Cochran, 1967, or Duncan, 1974), although it is well to remember that such tests require near exact normality if they are to be useful. The analysis of variance assumes these variance estimates to be homogeneous and pools them.

A plot of each cell average versus cell estimate of variance (or standard deviation) is often revealing. Individual outlying points or a pattern of dependence of variability on average value should be looked for. (In the latter case, the need for a transformation of the data should be considered; see Box, Hunter, and Hunter, 1978.)

In this experiment replicate measurements were made in each cell of the table since the investigator was interested in finding out about possible interactions and whether the variance of the resistivity measurements would be constant at the extreme values of the factors. In this original experiment, no significant interactions were found, nor was the variance nonhomogeneous.

The analysis of variance of a replicated two-factor crossed factorial design experiment is easily modified from that of the unreplicated one. The procedure is to calculate the following quantities and insert them in Table 26.11:

$$r = \text{number of rows}$$

$$c = \text{number of columns}$$

k = number of determinations per cell

N = total number of observations = krc

T = grand total

$C = T^2/N$

$$\text{SSR} = \text{row sum of squares} = \frac{\sum_i R_i^2}{kc} - C$$

$$\text{SSC} = \text{column sum of squares} = \frac{\sum_j C_j^2}{kr} - C$$

SSI = Interaction sum of squares

$$= \frac{(\text{cell}_{ij}\ \text{total})^2}{k} - \text{SSR} - \text{SSC} - C$$

$$\text{TSS} = \text{total sum of squares} = \Sigma y^2 - C$$

SSE = error sum of squares = TSS − SSR − SSC − SSI

The foregoing instructions will fill in all the cells in the "Sum of squares" column of the analysis of variance table (Table 26.11), but the similarities to Table 26.5 should be noted. The value of the mean square error (MSE) in Table 26.11 can also be obtained by pooling the $(r \times c)$ estimates of the within-cell variances.

FACTORIAL EXPERIMENTS WITH k FACTORS (EACH FACTOR AT TWO LEVELS)

The 2^k factorial designs have widespread industrial applicability. The designs permit the separate estimation of the individual effects and the interaction effects of the k factors in an experimental program in which all k factors are varied simultaneously in a carefully organized pattern of trials.

Symbols. A factorial experiment with k factors, each at two levels, is known as a 2^k factorial experiment. The experiment consists of 2^k trials, one trial at each combination of levels of the factors. To identify the individual trials, different notations are used, as illustrated in Table 26.12. One convention is to label each factor by a letter (or numeral) and then to denote the two levels (versions) of each factor by a plus (+) and a minus (−) sign. Commonly the minus sign refers to the lower level, the standard condition, or the absence of the factor. Thus, if there are three factors labeled A, B, and C, the eight trials comprising the 2^3 factorial design are as shown in Table 26.12. The (+, −) notation is sometimes referred to as "geometric." For example, the eight $(\pm, \pm, \pm)$ factor settings for the 2^3 design may be interpreted as giving the $(\pm 1, \pm 1, \pm 1)$ coordinates of the eight vertices of a cube. Alternative notations are to employ 0 and 1, respectively, or, following the Japanese tradition earlier established by Taguchi, 1 and 2 for the two versions of each factor. The classical convention is to denote the two versions of each lettered factor by the presence and absence of its corresponding lowercase

TABLE 26.12 Different Notations for the 2^3 Factorial Design

Run no.	Geometric notation			Alternative notation			Japanese notation			Classical notation		
	A	B	C	A	B	C	A	B	C	A	B	C
1	−	−	−	0	0	0	1	1	1	1		
2	+	−	−	1	0	0	2	1	1	a		
3	−	+	−	0	1	0	1	2	1	b		
4	+	+	−	1	1	0	2	2	1	ab		
5	−	−	+	0	0	1	1	1	2	c		
6	+	−	+	1	0	1	2	1	2	ac		
7	−	+	+	0	1	1	1	2	2	bc		
8	+	+	+	1	1	1	2	2	2	abc		

letter, as is also illustrated in Table 26.12. Here the trial in which all factors are at their "low" level is denoted by a 1. The sequence of trials in Table 26.12 is written in standard or "Yates" order. The trials would, of course, be run in random order.

Example.   The data in Table 26.13 are taken from a larger experiment on fire-retardant treatments for fabrics. The excerpted data are intended only to provide an example for demonstrating the technique of analysis. The experiment has four

TABLE 26.13 Results of Flame Test of Fire-Retardant Treatments (a 2^4 Factorial Experiment)

Treatment combinations					
Geometric notation				Classical notation	Response yield, inches burned
A	B	C	D		
−	−	−	−	1	4.2
+	−	−	−	a	3.1
−	+	−	−	b	4.5
+	+	−	−	ab	2.9
−	−	+	−	c	3.9
+	−	+	−	ac	2.8
−	+	+	−	bc	4.6
+	+	+	−	abc	3.2
−	−	−	+	d	4.0
+	−	−	+	ad	3.0
−	+	−	+	bd	5.0
+	+	−	+	abd	2.5
−	−	+	+	cd	4.0
+	−	+	+	acd	2.5
−	+	+	+	bcd	5.0
+	+	+	+	$abcd$	2.3

factors, each at two levels, i.e., it is a 2^4 factorial. Note that all factors are qualitative in this experiment. The experimental factors and levels (versions) are:

Factors	Levels
A—Fabric	− Sateen
	+ Monk's Cloth
B—Treatment	− Treatment x
	+ Treatment y
C—Laundering	− Before laundering
	+ After one laundering
D—Direction	− Warp
	+ Fill

The observations reported in Table 26.13 are inches burned, measured on a standard-sized sample after a flame test. For convenience, alternative design notations representing the treatment combinations appear beside the resulting observation.

Estimation of Main Effects and Interactions. The 2^k factorial designs permit the estimation of all k main effects (first-order effects), all $k(k-1)/2$ two-factor interactions, all $k(k-1)(k-2)/3!$ three-factor interactions, etc. Each estimated effect is a statistic of the form $\overline{y}_+ - \overline{y}_-$, that is, it is expressed by the difference between two averages, each containing 2^{k-1} observations. For a 2^k design the analyst would thus be able to estimate, in addition to the grand average, four main effects, six two-factor interactions, four three-factor interactions, and a single four-factor interaction, giving a total of 16 statistics. Remarkably, all these statistics are "clear" (orthogonal) of one another, that is, the magnitudes and signs of each statistic are in no manner influenced by the magnitude and sign of any other.

The question as to which observations go into which average for each estimated effect is determined from the k columns of + and − signs that together form the experimental design (the design column "vectors"). Additional column vectors of + and − signs are then constructed for each interaction, as illustrated in Table 26.14. For example, the vector of signs labeled AB is obtained by algebraically multiplying, for each row, the + or − sign found in column A by the + or − sign found in column B.

Table 26.14 also contains the column of observations. To estimate the AB interaction effect, all the observations carrying a + sign in the AB column are placed in $\overline{y}_+$ and those with a minus sign in $\overline{y}_-$. The estimated AB interaction effect $(\overline{y}_+ - \overline{y}_-)$ is therefore:

$$\frac{4.2 + 2.9 + \cdots + 2.3}{8} - \frac{3.1 + 4.5 + \cdots + 5.0}{8}$$

$$= \frac{27.0}{8} - \frac{30.5}{8} = \frac{-3.5}{8} = -0.4375$$

Yates' Algorithm. An alternative and more rapid method for obtaining estimates of main effects and interactions for two-level factorials, called "Yates' algorithm," applies to all two-level factorials and fractional factorials. The first step

TABLE 26.14 Table of Signs for Calculating Effects for a 2^4 Factorial

A	B	C	D	AB	AC	AD	BC	BD	CD	ABC	ABD	ACD	BCD	ABCD	Obs.*
−	−	−	−	+	+	+	+	+	+	−	−	−	−	+	4.2
+	−	−	−	−	−	−	+	+	+	+	+	+	−	−	3.1
−	+	−	−	−	+	+	−	−	+	+	+	−	+	−	4.5
+	+	−	−	+	−	−	−	−	+	−	−	+	+	+	2.9
−	−	+	−	+	−	+	−	+	−	+	−	+	+	−	3.9
+	−	+	−	−	+	−	−	+	−	−	+	−	+	+	2.8
−	+	+	−	−	−	+	+	−	−	−	+	+	−	+	4.6
+	+	+	−	+	+	−	+	−	−	+	−	−	−	−	3.2
−	−	−	+	+	+	−	+	−	−	−	+	+	+	−	4.0
+	−	−	+	−	−	+	+	−	−	+	−	−	+	+	3.0
−	+	−	+	−	+	−	−	+	−	+	−	+	−	+	5.0
+	+	−	+	+	−	+	−	+	−	−	+	−	−	−	2.5
−	−	+	+	+	−	−	−	−	+	+	+	−	−	+	4.0
+	−	+	+	−	+	+	−	−	+	−	−	+	−	−	2.5
−	+	+	+	−	−	−	+	+	+	−	−	−	+	−	5.0
+	+	+	+	+	+	+	+	+	+	+	+	+	+	+	2.3

*Obs. = observations.

26.25

in Yates' algorithm is to list the observed data in Yates order, as illustrated in Table 26.15. The generation of the values in Table 26.15 proceeds as follows:

1. A two-level factorial with r replicates contains $N = r2^k$ runs. The associated Yates' algorithm table will have $k + 2$ columns, the first of which contains the experimental design, i.e., the 2^k treatment combinations in standard (Yates) order.

2. In column 2 enter the observed yield corresponding to each treatment combination listed in column 1. If the design is replicated, enter the total for each treatment combination.

3. In the top half of column 3 enter, in order, the sums of consecutive *pairs* of entries in column 2, i.e., the first plus the second, the third plus the fourth, and so on. In the bottom half of column 3 enter, in order, the differences between the same consecutive pairs of entries, i.e., second entry minus first entry, fourth entry minus third entry, etc. Change the sign of the top (first of the pair) and algebraically add.

4. Obtain columns 4, 5, . . . , $k + 2$, in the same manner as column 3, i.e., by obtaining in each case the sums and differences of the pairs in the preceding column in the manner described in step 3.

5. The entries in the last column (column $k + 2$) are labeled $g(T)$, $g(A)$, $g(B)$, $g(AB)$, etc. The letters in the parentheses correspond to the $+$ signs in the geometric notation. The first value $g(T)$ is divided by N to give the grand average. Estimates of the remaining main effects and interactions are obtained by dividing each $g(\cdot \cdot \cdot)$ by $N/2$. (*Note:* The remaining steps of this procedure are checks on the computations.)

6. The sum of all the individual responses (column 2) should equal the total given in the first entry of column 6, i.e., $g(T)$ must equal the grand total.

TABLE 26.15 Yates' Method of Analysis Using Data of Table 26.13

A B C D	2	3	4	5	6		Estimated effects	
− − − −	4.2	7.3	14.7	29.2	57.5 =	$g(T)$	Average =	3.5938
+ − − −	3.1	7.4	14.5	28.3	−12.9 =	$g(A)$	A =	−1.6125
− + − −	4.5	6.7	14.5	−5.2	2.5 =	$g(B)$	B =	0.3125
+ + − −	2.9	7.8	13.8	−7.7	− 3.5 =	$g(AB)$	AB =	−0.4375
− − + −	3.9	7.0	−2.7	1.2	− 0.9 =	$g(C)$	C =	−0.1125
+ − + −	2.8	7.5	−2.5	1.3	− 0.5 =	$g(AC)$	AC =	−0.0625
− + + −	4.6	6.5	−3.5	−0.8	1.3 =	$g(BC)$	BC =	0.1625
+ + + −	3.2	7.3	−4.2	−2.7	0.5 =	$g(ABC)$	ABC =	0.0625
− − − +	4.0	−1.1	0.1	−0.2	− 0.9 =	$g(D)$	D =	−0.1125
+ − − +	3.0	−1.6	1.1	−0.7	− 2.5 =	$g(AD)$	AD =	−0.3125
− + − +	5.0	−1.1	0.5	0.2	0.1 =	$g(BD)$	BD =	0.0125
+ + − +	2.5	−1.4	0.8	−0.7	− 1.9 =	$g(ABD)$	ABD =	−0.2375
− − + +	4.0	−1.0	−0.5	1.0	− 0.5 =	$g(CD)$	CD =	−0.0625
+ − + +	2.5	−2.5	−0.3	0.3	− 0.9 =	$g(ACD)$	ACD =	−0.1125
− + + +	5.0	−1.5	−1.5	0.2	− 0.7 =	$g(BCD)$	BCD =	−0.0875
+ + + +	2.3	−2.7	−1.2	0.3	0.1 =	$g(ABCD)$	$ABCD$ =	0.0125
Total	57.5							

Sum of squares 219.15   3506.40

7. The sum of the squares of the quantities in column 2 should equal the sum of the squares of the entries in column $(k + 2)$ divided by 2^k.

8. Each $g(\cdot \cdot \cdot)$ in the last column equals the sum of observations carrying a $+$ sign minus the sum of observations carrying a $-$ sign when the columns of signs displayed in Table 26.14 are employed. The corresponding estimated effects are given by $g(\cdot \cdot \cdot)/(N/2)$. The algorithm is best explained with an example.

Example: The example shown in Table 26.13 has 2^4 runs. Thus the associated Yates algorithm will have six columns, as shown in Table 26.15. The grand average is $\bar{y} = 57.5/16 = 3.5938$. The next entry in column 6 is $g(A) = -12.9$. The estimated main effect of factor A is then:

$$A \text{ effect} = \frac{-12.9}{8} = -1.6125$$

The estimate of the main effect of A can be checked by taking the average of the responses recorded on the high $(+)$ side of the factor A and subtracting the average response on the low $(-)$ side to give $\bar{y}_+ - \bar{y}_- = 22.3/8 - 35.2/8 = -12.9/8 = -1.6125$.

The remaining effects are similarly computed. Thus the estimated AD interaction effect $= -2.5/8 = -0.3125$.

The following steps are checks on the computations in Table 26.15:

6. The sum of column 2 equals $g(T)$.

7. The sum of squares of the entries in column 2 equals 219.5. The sum of squares in column 6 divided by $2^4 = 3506.4/16 = 219.5$.

Testing Main Effects and Interactions.   The following steps are used for testing the statistical significance of main effects and interactions.

1. Choose α, the level of significance.

2. If there is no available estimate of the variance due to experimental error, one way to proceed is to use the sum of squares associated with interactions of three or more factors. The sum of squares with one degree of freedom associated with a two-level factorial effect is given by:

$$\frac{N(\text{effect})^2}{4}$$

for all replicated or nonreplicated two-level factorial and fractional factorial designs; N is always the total number of observations.

3. To obtain s^2, divide the total of the sum of squares obtained in step 2 by e, where e is the number of interaction effects contributing to the total. In a 2^k factorial, the number of third- and higher-order interactions will be $2^k - (k^2 + k + 2)/2$. If an independent estimate of error variance is available, use this s^2.

4. Look up $t_{\alpha/2}$ for e degrees of freedom in Appendix II, Table G. If an independent estimate s^2 is used, e equals the degrees of freedom associated with this estimate.

5. The standard error (SE) for each estimated effect is given by:

$$\text{SE(estimated effect)} = \text{SE}(\bar{y}_+ - \bar{y}_-) = \frac{2s}{\sqrt{N}}$$

and the $100(1 - \alpha)$ percent confidence limits by:

$$\text{Effect} \pm t_{\alpha/2}[\text{ SE(effect)}]$$

6. For any estimated main effect or interaction, if the absolute value of an estimated effect is greater than the $t \cdot \text{SE(effect)}$, conclude that the difference of true effect from zero is statistically significant.

Example:

1. Let $\alpha = 0.05$

2. Using Table 26.15, the sum of squares equals:

$$\frac{16[(ABC)^2 + (ABD)^2 + \cdots + (ABCD)^2]}{4}$$

$$= \frac{16[(0.0625)^2 + (-0.2375)^2 + \cdots + (0.0125)^2]}{4} = 0.3231$$

3. We have

$$e = 5 \text{ DF}$$

$$s^2 = \frac{0.3231}{5} = 0.0646 \quad \text{and} \quad s = 0.254$$

4. We also have

$$t_{1-\alpha/2} \text{ for 5 DF} = 2.571$$

5. Then

$$\text{Standard error (effect)} = \frac{2(0.254)}{\sqrt{16}} = 0.1270$$

$$\text{Effect 95\% confidence limits} = \pm 2.571(0.1270) = \pm 0.3265$$

6. Only the main effect of A and the AB interaction are greater than 0.3265; therefore, the main effect of A and the interaction effect AB are declared to be statistically significant.

TABLE 26.16   Collapsed 2^4 Giving a Replicated 2^3

A B D	Responses	Difference	
− − −	4.2, 3.9	0.3	
+ − −	3.1, 2.8	0.3	
− + −	4.5, 4.6	−0.1	
+ + −	2.9, 3.2	−0.3	$s^2 = \Sigma d^2 / 2 n_d$
− − +	4.0, 4.0	0	
+ − +	3.0, 2.5	0.5	$s^2 = 0.57/2(8)$
− + +	5.0, 5.0	0	$= 0.03560$
+ + +	2.5, 2.3	0.2	

Collapsing 2^k Factorials. An alternative method for obtaining an estimate of variance from an unreplicated 2^k factorial (or 2^{k-p} fractional factorial) requires the analyst to identify the largest estimated effects without regard to sign and then to note whether any of the k studied factors are absent. In this example, the largest estimated effects are, in order, A, AB, B, and AD. Factor C appears to have no great influence upon the response. If the analyst now assumes that factor C has no effect or effects so small as to be readily shrouded by error, then the 2^4 design collapses into a replicated 2^3 design in the effective factors A, B, and D. The collapsed design is displayed in Table 26.16.

The estimated effects for factors A, B, and D remain unchanged. An estimate of variance can now be obtained from the repeated runs. When there are pairs of observations, a shortcut computation for s^2 is given by:

$$s^2 = \frac{\sum_i d_i^2}{2n_d}$$

where the d_i are the differences between the $i = 1, 2, \ldots, d$ pairs of observations and n_d is the number of differences. This estimate of variance has $e = n_d$ degrees of freedom. Thus, for this example:

$$s^2 = \frac{0.57}{(2)(8)} = 0.0356$$

with $e = 8$ degrees of freedom and $s = 0.1887$. The standard error of each effect (excluding all those carrying the label C, of course), is

$$SE(effect) \frac{2s}{\sqrt{N}} = \frac{2(0.1887)}{\sqrt{16}} = 0.0943$$

Using t with $e = 8$ degrees of freedom, the 95 percent confidence limits for the estimated effects are given by

$$(t_{\alpha/2})SE(effect) = \pm 2.306(0.0943) = \pm 0.2175$$

Half-Normal Plots. Daniel (1959) proposed a simple and effective technique for use in the interpretation of data from factorial experiments with all factors at two levels. This technique, called "half-normal plots," helps one to study the magnitude of the effects, identify which main effects and interactions can reasonably be assumed to be zero, and detect wild observations. It may also give evidence that the conditions of the actual experiment have inadvertently departed from the assumptions usually made in the analysis.

Detection of "Wild Values." Half-normal plots can be used to detect an aberrant value. Hunter (1966) proposed a method which reverses the procedure of Yates' algorithm, using significant coefficients only, to obtain predicted values for each treatment combination. Residuals (differences between observed values and predicted values) are then obtained and examined. Large residuals may indicate aberrant observations and should be investigated.

EVOP: EVOLUTIONARY OPERATION

An important application of experimental design in the production environment was proposed by Box (1957). Essentially, a simple experimental design, run repeatedly, provides a routine of small systematic changes in a production process. The objective is to force the process to produce information about itself while simultaneously producing product to standards. Only small changes in the process factors are allowed, and the consequences of these changes must be detected in the presence of the many natural variabilities that surround the process. The repetition of an experimental design, commonly a 2^2 factorial with center point, permits the blocking of many of the disturbances that commonly influence production. Through the process of replication, the design provides steadily improving estimates of the main effects and interactions of the studied factors.

Response Surface.   A response surface is the mathematical or graphical representation of the connection between important independent variables, controlled factors, and a dependent variable. (An independent variable is a factor that is, or conceivably could be, controlled. Examples are flow rate and temperature. The value of a dependent variable is the result of the settings of one or more independent variables.) Most processes have several dependent variables, such as yield, impurities, and pounds per hour of a byproduct. These responses are usually smooth and may be graduated approximately by simple contours such as a family of circles or of parabolas. We ordinarily work on processes that have unknown response surfaces—if they were known, the work would not be necessary.

A response surface for a process might look like the one in Figure 26.3, which shows the yield of a catalytic oxidation as a function of temperature and feed rate of hydrocarbon. If this information were known, the pounds per hour of product could be determined and better operating conditions selected for any desired production rate. The response surface is initially unknown, but improvement can be made if we only find out which way is up. Multiple regression can be used to approximate the response contours (see Section 23, under Multiple Regression).

EVOP Technique.   The problem, then, is to increase profit in an operating plant with minimum work and risk and without upsetting the plant. These are the steps:

1. Survey company reports and open literature on the process. Study cost, yield, and production records.

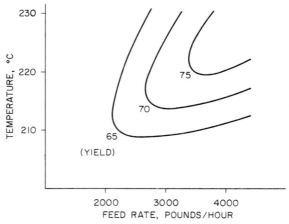

FIG. 26.3 Typical response surface: yield as a function of feed rate and temperature for a catalytic reactor.

2. Study this section on EVOP and preferably the definitive text (Box and Draper, 1969).
3. Obtain agreement and support from production management. Hold training sessions.
4. Select two or three controllable factors that are likely to influence the most important response.
5. Change these factors in small steps according to a plan.
6. After the second repetition of the plan (Cycle 2) and each succeeding cycle, estimate the effects.
7. When one or more of the effects is significant, move to the indicated better operating conditions and start a new EVOP program, perhaps with new ranges or new factors.
8. After eight cycles, if no factor has been shown to be effective, change the ranges or select new variables (Box and Draper, 1967).
9. Continue moving the midpoint of the EVOP plan and adjust the ranges as necessary.
10. When a maximum has been obtained, or the rate of gain is too slow, drop the current factors from the plan and run a new plan with different factors.

The following topics explain these steps in detail.

Literature Search.   Sources of information include the process instructions, company reports, manufacturers' literature, patents, textbooks, and encyclopedias of technology. Do not neglect people. Company personnel, consultants, and operators can all contribute. Search for information on:

1. Important independent variables
2. Test methods for intermediate and final results
3. Recommended procedures
4. Records of good and bad results and their causes
5. Long-term history of results; plant production rate and yield by week or month and similar data; effect of past changes in equipment and conditions

When information is contradictory, an EVOP program is an ideal strategy for resolving the conflict.
   Always consider the physical and chemical principles that apply.

The EVOP Design.   EVOP uses planned runs that are repeated over and over (replicated). One plan in wide use is the two-level complete factorial. There are important reasons to maintain observations on a known set of conditions, called a "reference point." For simplicity in the present discussion, let this point be the center of the square formed by the vertices of the factorial.

Example: This example shows coded data from an actual EVOP program (Barnett, 1960). The problem involved a batch organic reaction, and after the steps above were followed, the two factors and their ranges were selected as shown in Figure 26.4. The response Y is a coded yield in pounds per batch and should be maximized. In this diagram, the reference run (batch) was made at 130°C for 3½ h. The next batch was made at 120°C for 3 h, and so on. The first *cycle* contains five runs, one at each of the conditions. Samples were taken from each batch and analyses were obtained.

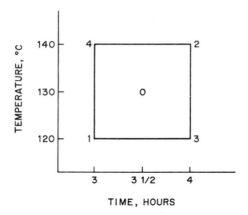

FIG. 26.4 An EVOP plan. Numbers are in run order; 0 is the reference run.

If the process were continuous, it would be allowed to stabilize after each change of conditions, perhaps by waiting for three residence times or preferably by determining the actual time to equilibrium by a test. (Residence time is volume of the vessel divided by the flow rate in appropriate units.)

Warning: It is not unusual to have difficulty in obtaining a representative sample. Procedures and tests are discussed in Sections 23 and 25.

Effects can be estimated at the end of Cycle 1, but in the absence of repeated trials, no estimate of error variance is available. At the conclusion of Cycle 2 both estimated effects and error variance are possible. The estimated effects and their confidence intervals may be computed on a form such as Figure 26.5, which shows this example. The form helps reduce the work and minimizes mistakes. Instructions should be printed on the reverse side (see Figure 26.6).

Here, the error term that puts the magnitude of effects into perspective is obtained from the range by use of factor K first derived by Box and Hunter (1959). The uncertainty in estimating the effects is stated as a confidence interval and the Change-in-mean effect (CIM) is calculated by comparing the results at the outer four corners with the result in the center. The use of this last information is discussed below.

A "phase" is defined as all the cycles that use the same settings of the same factors. The phase average shows the general level of the response and can be used to compare different phases.

The left part of the form is used to record data and estimate effects. It also has the scaled diagram of the phase. The right third is used to determine the error limits of effects and corner averages. The error limits are called "2 S.E." for "two standard errors." The estimated effect ± 2 S.E. covers the usual 95 percent confidence region. Caution should be exercised in claiming statistical significance until after two or three cycles.

For the present example, at the end of Cycle 2 the A effect (time) is estimated as 66 ± 166; it lies somewhere between -100 and $+232$. Thus, the true value of this effect could be negative, positive, or nil. The B (temperature) effect, however, is estimated to be 174 ± 166, or in the range $+8$ to 340. Technically, it is likely to be a positive real effect. The interaction AB is small, and so is the change in mean. Since the confidence region for B is so close to zero and following the

J–227–x

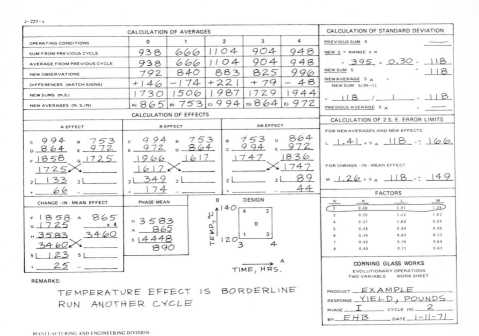

FIG. 26.5 Calculation form at the end of Cycle 2. *(Modified from Barnett, 1960.)*

Differences	Subtract new observations from old averages. Note the algebraic sign of the difference. (938 − 792 = 146)
New Sums	Add the new observations to the old sums. (938 + 792 = 1,730)
New Averages	Divide the new sums by N, the number of the cycle. (1730/2 = 865)
Calculation of Effects	(For example, the A effect)
	Write the new averages for operating conditions 2 and 3 opposite (C) and (D). Add these two to get the number in space (F). Carry out corresponding operations to get the number for space (G).
	The next operation is subtraction. If (F) is larger than (G), recopy (G) under (F) and subtract (G) from (F). If (G) is larger than (F), recopy (F) under (G) and subtract (F) from (G). In either case divide by 2 and the sign of quotient is shown on the form. (The A effect is +66.)
Change-in-mean effect	Copy (F) and (G) as shown and add these two. (A) is multiplied by 4. The next operation is subtraction as above. Divide by 5. (The Change-in-mean effect is +25.)
Average phase	Copy (H) and (A) from Change-in-mean box, add them, and divide by 5. (The phase mean is 890.)
Calculation of Standard Deviation	Range. The range is the algebraic difference between the most positive and most negative differences. The range is always positive. (The range of +146, −174, +221, +79, and −48 is 395.) The standard deviation is estimated by taking the range times K.
Constants	Read K, L, and M factors from the table.
Note:	The numerical illustrations apply to the data of Fig. 26.5.

FIG. 26.6 Instructions for EVOP form.

26.33

J-227-x'

CALCULATION OF AVERAGES	0	1	2	3	4
OPERATING CONDITIONS	0	1	2	3	4
SUM FROM PREVIOUS CYCLE	1730	1506	1987	1729	1944
AVERAGE FROM PREVIOUS CYCLE	865	753	994	864	972
NEW OBSERVATIONS	934	853	1066	852	953
DIFFERENCES (WATCH SIGNS)	-69	-100	-72	+12	+19
NEW SUMS (N.S.)	2664	2359	3053	2581	2897
NEW AVERAGES (N. S./N)	A) 888	B) 786	C) 1018	D) 860	E) 966

CALCULATION OF STANDARD DEVIATION

PREVIOUS SUM S 118
NEW S = RANGE x K = 119 x 0.35 = 42
NEW SUM S = 160
NEW AVERAGE S_A = NEW SUM S/(N-1) = 160 / 2 = 80
PREVIOUS AVERAGE S_A = 118

CALCULATION OF EFFECTS

A EFFECT
```
C 1018    B  786
D  860    E  966
F 1878    G 1752
  1752
2  126  2
+   63
```

B EFFECT
```
C 1018    B  786
E  966    D  860
  1984      1646
  1646
2  338  2
+  169
```

AB EFFECT
```
B  786    D  860
C 1018    E  966
  1804      1826
            1804
2    22
+    11
```

CALCULATION OF 2 S. E. ERROR LIMITS

FOR NEW AVERAGES AND NEW EFFECTS
L 1.15 x S_A 80 = ± 92

FOR CHANGE - IN - MEAN EFFECT
M 1.03 x S_A 80 = ± 82

CHANGE - IN - MEAN EFFECT
```
F 1878    A  888
G 1752       x 4
H 3630     3552
  3552
5   78  5
+   16
```

PHASE MEAN
```
H 3630
A  888
5 4518
   904
```

B DESIGN (diagram): TEMP, °C — 140, 120; TIME, HRS. — A

FACTORS

N	K	L	M
2	0.30	1.41	1.26
3	0.35	1.15	1.03
4	0.37	1.00	0.89
5	0.38	0.89	0.80
6	0.39	0.82	0.73
7	0.40	0.76	0.68
8	0.40	0.71	0.63

CORNING GLASS WORKS
EVOLUTIONARY OPERATIONS
TWO VARIABLE WORK SHEET

PRODUCT — EXAMPLE
RESPONSE — YIELD, POUNDS
PHASE — I   CYCLE (N) — 3
BY — EHB   DATE — 1-12-71

REMARKS:

TEMPERATURE EFFECT IS +77 → +261
INCREASE TEMPERATURE & START PHASE II

MANUFACTURING AND ENGINEERING DIVISION

FIG. 26.7 Calculation form after Cycle 3.

advice above to be cautious at Cycle 2, another cycle is run. Its results are shown in Figure 26.7.

After Cycle 3, the B effect (temperature) was declared statistically significant, since its likely values fall in the range of 169 ± 92, or +77 to +261. It does not appear that data from more cycles would change the conclusion that temperature should be increased to increase the response y.

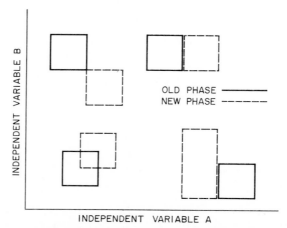

INDEPENDENT VARIABLE B

INDEPENDENT VARIABLE A

OLD PHASE ————
NEW PHASE - - - - -

FIG. 26.8 Possible relations of old phase and new phase.

When statistical significance is found for one factor but not for the other, *move* the plan in the desirable direction for the "discovered" important factor and increase the range for the second (nonsignificant) one. Possible old and new phases of an EVOP program are shown in Figure 26.8. When significance is found for both variables, the center of the plan is moved in both directions in proportion to the size of the effects. This is the direction of steepest ascent (see below, under Determine Direction of Steepest Ascent). Whenever the plan is changed, a new *phase* is started. During the second and later phases, the previous estimate of standard deviation is often used since it was obtained under the current operating method.

Moves.   To be conservative, as EVOP should be, moves are contiguous; i.e., one or more of the points in the old phase and new phase coincide. This limits the moves to those types shown in Figure 26.8.

There is nothing "magic" about drawing these plans as squares—1 h does not equal 20°C anyway. A particularly strong signal may justify a move to a plan that does not adjoin the previous one.

Change-in-Mean.   The Change-in-mean effect is the difference between the results at the center point and the average of the other four peripheral points. It is therefore a signal of curvature as shown in Figure 26.9. It is used in conjunction with the effects to indicate when a maximum (or a minimum) has been reached and to indicate the sensitivity of the response to changes in the independent factors. In rare cases it may happen that the first phase is located symmetrically about the maximum with respect to the two independent factors chosen. In this case the factors should be nonsignificant but the Change-in-mean may be significant.

Blocking.   A process response ordinarily changes slightly with time, reflecting changes in sources of raw material, changes in air temperature from day to night, and so on.

Runs made close together in time are expected to be more nearly alike than those over a longer interval. Blocking is used to minimize the trouble caused by

FIG. 26.9   Cross section through a response surface. CIM indicates curvature.

temporal changes of this type. For the EVOP calculations shown here, a block is one cycle. Changes in average level that occur between cycles are completely eliminated from the estimated effects, as can be seen by adding a constant to the five runs of Cycle 3 and recalculating the effects. (The phase average is changed, of course.)

Multiple Dependent Responses.   So far the explanation has been in terms of a single dependent response. This is rather unrealistic, except for the profit variable. Most processes have several dependent responses that must be measured or calculated, such as yield, production rate, percent impurity, or pounds of by-product. A calculation sheet is made for each dependent response, and statistical significance may be noted on one dependent sheet but not on others. In this case, it may be well to run another cycle or two to get more information on the other dependent responses before a move is made.

The most troublesome case occurs when the indicated directions for improvement of two responses (say production rate and percent impurity) do not agree. The EVOP program has brought information from the production process. Decisions as to what to do next now rest upon information supplied by the EVOP program coupled with information to be supplied by the subject matter experts.

BLOCKING THE 2^k FACTORIALS

Experimenters often find difficulty in maintaining a homogeneous experimental environment for all the experiments required in a 2^k factorial. For example, an experimenter might need 2 days to run the eight trials required in a 2^3 factorial. The question is how to choose the trials to be run each day so as not to disturb the estimates of the major effects of the three factors, i.e., how to best "block" the design into two blocks of four runs each. Here blocking is accomplished by sacrificing the interaction estimate of least concern, i.e., the three-factor interaction. The procedure to be followed is illustrated in Table 26.17, part *a*, for a 2^3 factorial. First, the plus and minus signs of the 2^3 design are written down. Next, the columns of plus and minus signs commonly used to estimate the *ABC* interaction is constructed and labeled the block "generator." Those runs carrying a plus sign in the block generator column form the first block; those carrying a minus sign form the second block.

When this design is employed, the estimate of the three-factor interaction (abbreviated 3fi) cannot be distinguished from the block effect; the block effect and 3fi effect are "confounded." All other estimated effects are clear of the block effect.

To partition the design into four blocks of two runs each, the proper block generators are provided by the two columns of plus and minus signs associated with the interactions *AB* and *BC* as illustrated in Table 26.17, part *b*. Note that the generators produce four combinations of minus and plus signs, each combination identifying a block of two runs. In this particular design all 2fi (two-factor interactions) are confounded with blocks.

The block generators must be carefully chosen. The blocking arrangements for the 2^3, 2^4, and 2^5 designs appear in Table 26.18. A more complete table and description of factorial design blocking appears in Box, Hunter, and Hunter (1978).

TABLE 26.17 Partitioning the 2^3 Factorial Design

a. Partitioning the 2^3 into two blocks of four runs

2^3			ABC = block generator	2^3 in two blocks		
				(+) Block		(−) Block
A	B	C		A B C		A B C
−	−	−	−	+ − −		− − −
+	−	−	+	− + −		+ + −
−	+	−	+	− − +		+ − +
+	+	−	−	+ + +		− + +
−	−	+	+			
+	−	+	−			
−	+	+	−			
+	+	+	+			

b. Partitioning the 2^3 into four blocks of two runs

2^3			Block generators	
A	B	C	AB	BC
−	−	−	+	+
+	−	−	−	+
−	+	−	−	−
+	+	−	+	−
−	−	+	+	−
+	−	+	−	−
−	+	+	−	+
+	+	+	+	+

+ + Block	− + Block	+ − block	− − Block
A B C	A B C	A B C	A B C
− − −	+ − −	+ + −	− + −
+ + +	− + +	− − +	+ − +

TABLE 26.18 Blocking Arrangements for the 2^k Factorials

k = number of factors	Block size	Block generators	Interactions confounded with blocks
3	4	ABC	ABC
	2	AB,BC	AB,BC, AC
4	8	$ABCD$	$ABCD$
	4	ABC, ACD	ABC, ACD,BD
	2	AB,BC,CD	all 2fi and 4fi
5	16	$ABCDE$	$ABCDE$
	8	ABC,CDE	$ABC,CDE, ABDE$
	4	ABC,BCD,CDE	$ABC,BCD,CDE, AD, ABDE, BE, ACE$
	2	AB,BC,CD,DE	all 2fi and 4fi

FRACTIONAL FACTORIAL EXPERIMENTS (EACH FACTOR AT TWO LEVELS)

If there are many factors, a complete factorial experiment, requiring all possible combinations of the levels of the factors, involves a large number of tests—even when only two levels of each factor are being investigated. In these cases, it is useful to have a plan that requires fewer tests than the complete factorial experiment. The fraction is a carefully prescribed subset of all possible combinations. The analysis of fractional factorials is relatively straightforward, and the use of a fractional factorial does not preclude the possibility of later completion of the full factorial experiment.

Confounding (Aliasing, Biasing). In a complete factorial experiment we have 2^k experimental trials. In the analysis of a complete factorial, we have the grand average, k main effects, $2^k - k - 1$ interaction effects. The 2^k experiments can be used to give independent estimates of all 2^k effects. In a fractional factorial (say the fraction $1/2^p$) there will be only 2^{k-p} experiments, and therefore only 2^{k-p} independent estimates are possible. In designing the fractional plans (i.e., in selecting an optimum subset of the 2^k total combinations), the goal is to keep each of the 2^{k-p} estimates as unbiased or "clear" as possible, i.e., to keep the estimates of main effects and if possible second-order interactions mutually unbiased, or nearly so.

To explain, consider the following 2^{3-1} fractional:

A B C	Observed
− − +	$y_1 = 8$
+ − −	$y_2 = 11$
− + −	$y_3 = 9$
+ + +	$y_4 = 14$

The main effects are given by the statistics $\bar{y}_+ - \bar{y}_-$, where once again the plus and minus subscripts of each letter in the design identify the observations entering each average. Thus, the main effect of A is estimated to be $(11 + 14)/2 - (8 + 9)/2 = 4.0$. The main effects of B and C are, respectively, $(9 + 14)/2 - (8 + 11)/2 = 2$ and $(8 + 14)/2 - (11 + 9)/2 = 1.0$. Now consider the estimate of the two-factor interaction AB. The analyst will find that the signs required to estimate the AB interaction are identical to those already employed to estimate the main effect of C. The main effect of C and the two-factor interaction AB are confounded. Said another way, the statistic $\bar{y}_+ - \bar{y}_- = 1.0$ has an "alias" structure, that is, the statistic may be identified as either C or AB. In fact, the expected value of the statistic equals $C + AB$, the sum of the two effects, and in the absence of clear information on the main effect of C, we cannot tell whether the AB effect is plus, minus, large, or small. The reader will note that estimate A is confounded with BC, as is B with AC.

When some or all main effects are confounded with two-factor interactions, the fractional factorial design is said to be of "Resolution III." When one or more of the main effects are confounded with (at least) three-factor interactions, the fractional is said to be a "Resolution IV" design. Fractionals with main effects